EVALUATION GUIDE FOR CHEMISTRY: A MODERN COURSE

Chemistry: A Modern Course presents an up-to-date approach to teaching chemistry. Chemical concepts and principles are developed in a logical yet flexible order to make the study of chemistry interesting and challenging for students. Many features have been included to strengthen the presentation with the intent of increasing students' understanding and interest in chemistry.

To examine the features of *Chemistry: A Modern Course,* please turn to the following pages:

p. 2 — A **color photo** and **thought-provoking paragraph** introduce each chapter.

p. 17 — **Goal** statements at the beginning of each chapter establish a purpose for study.

pp. 42-43 — **New terms** are presented in boldface type and defined in context.

pp. 98-99 — **Student notes** placed in the margin emphasize important information and aid students' review of the text material.

pp. 116-117 — Important **laws** and **points of emphasis** are printed in italic type.

pp. 120–121 — Accurate **diagrams,** along with **photographs,** and **line drawings** help students visualize ideas presented in the text.

pp. 190-191 — **Tables** appear within the context of related material.

pp. 374-375 — **Example problems,** using the factor-label method, guide students through the mathematical concepts needed for chemical calculations.

p. 414 — **Biographies** are included of scientists who have contributed to the principles discussed in each chapter.

pp. 480-481 — **Chemical Career** and **Technology** features present additional relevant material related to the chapter.

pp. 574-577 — A **Summary** of main ideas, a listing of boldfaced **Vocabulary** terms, comprehensive **Problems** and **questions, Review problems** and **questions** covering preceding chapters, **One More Step questions** and **projects,** as well as suggested **Readings** appear at the end of each chapter.

pp. 626-642 — The **Appendices** include supplementary information on careers and logarithms as well as numerous tables for general reference.

pp. 643-655 — The **Glossary** includes all important terms used in the text.

pp. 656-664 — **Index.**

CHEMISTRY
A MODERN COURSE

TEACHER ANNOTATED EDITION

ROBERT C. SMOOT

Rollins Fellow in Science
McDonogh School
McDonogh, Maryland

JACK PRICE

Superintendent
Palos Verdes Peninsula Unified School District
Palos Verdes, California

RICHARD G. SMITH

Chairman, Science Department
Bexley High School
Bexley, Ohio

MERRILL PUBLISHING CO.
A BELL & HOWELL COMPANY
COLUMBUS, OHIO
TORONTO • LONDON • SYDNEY

PREFACE

The Teacher Annotated Edition for the seventh edition of *Chemistry: A Modern Course* is an integral part of the Merrill Chemistry Program. In one book, you have at your fingertips all of these important features: detailed solutions to all problems in the text, a planning guide, suggested teaching aids, demonstrations, and teaching strategies and techniques for presenting text material.

This *Annotated Edition* eliminates the need to carry with you a variety of easily misplaced supplementary books. All of the materials you will need are in this annotated text. Thus you eliminate the time-consuming, frustrating, and often fruitless search for usable supplementary materials.

The comments, notes, and suggestions are concise and written with an awareness of the classroom situation. *The Teacher Annotated Edition* is designed to make your teaching of chemistry effective.

The Teacher Annotated Edition is divided into two parts:

Annotated Student Pages. The annotations are concise statements overprinted in red on the Student text. Each annotation is directly applicable to the section or problem where it is located. Demonstrations are used to introduce chapters and sections where appropriate. Answers are provided for most problems (where space allows) for your convenience.

Teacher Guide. The *Teacher Guide* appears at the front of the *Teacher Annotated Edition*. These pages have gray edges to set them off from the Student text. The *Teacher Guide* is a compilation of the complete problem solutions together with explanations and comments arranged in consecutive order as they appear within the text. The introductory section of the *Teacher Guide* provides you with some insight into our philosophy of teaching chemistry, the features of the text, and other components of the Merrill Chemistry Program. The *Teacher Guide* is organized to allow you to locate material quickly and check assignments. Performance objectives are included for each chapter. The introductory materials also include a discussion on using performance objectives, audiovisual aids, and literature references.

A questionnaire is included on the last page of the *Teacher Guide*. We hope that you will take the time to complete it after you have reviewed this text thoroughly. It is our goal to consistently provide a text to meet your teaching needs.

The Authors

ISBN 0-675-06402-3

PUBLISHED BY

MERRILL PUBLISHING CO.
A BELL & HOWELL COMPANY
COLUMBUS, OHIO 43216

CONTENTS

Includes: Teaching Techniques, Demonstration Information,
Detailed Solutions to all Questions and Problems

PHILOSOPHY

Chemistry: A Modern Course is organized around a central theme: the properties of matter are a consequence of its structure. We feel that before beginning a detailed study of structure, it is necessary to establish communication between students and teacher by developing a working chemistry vocabulary. This vocabulary is established in the first six chapters of the text. The organization of the early chapters allows you to begin quantitative lab work early in the course. Students get the motivational benefits of hands-on activity while studying the more concrete aspects of chemistry. Chapter 1 discusses the function of chemistry in society. Chapter 2 reviews basic measurement principles and mathematical techniques that are important in problem solving and laboratory work. In addition, the factor-label method of problem solving is introduced here. Note that the International System of measurement is used throughout the text after its introduction in Chapter 2. Students should learn these units because they are the proper foundation for communication among scientists all over the world. Chapter 3 outlines the basic classification system for matter. Chemical symbols and formulas are presented in Chapter 4. Chapter 5 begins an elementary study of the stoichiometry of compounds with an emphasis on the mole as the chemist's basic counting unit. Chapter 6 introduces the chemical equation as a shorthand representation of chemical change, and covers the mass and energy relationships associated with chemical change. Thus, with the first six chapters as a framework, students can move on to more abstract concepts.

The study of structure begins with Chapters 7-11, which concern the atom. In Chapter 7, atomic theory, subatomic particles, and basic ideas about the structure of atoms are discussed. A more detailed look at the theory and behavior of electrons in atoms is the subject of Chapter 8. Atoms are classified on the basis of their structure into the periodic system in Chapter 9. Properties of some elements as a consequence of their atomic structure comprise the subject matter of Chapters 10 and 11.

The combining of atoms into compounds is covered in Chapters 12-14. Chapter 12 discusses the underlying principles of chemical bond formation, while Chapter 13 concerns the bonds themselves and their geometric arrangement in molecular structures. Properties of polar molecules as a consequence of their structure are discussed in Chapter 14.

Chapters 15-19 consider groups of molecules and ions. The discussion begins with their kinetic behavior.

Chapter 15 presents the physical states of matter as a consequence of their thermal behavior. Chapters 16-19 introduce the basic principles of the three common physical states as a consequence of their structure. The solid state is presented first because it is the most familiar state. The gaseous state is covered last because its characteristics are less easily observed. The mole is reintroduced in Chapter 19 in connection with Avogadro's principle in developing the ideal gas equation.

Chapter 20 brings together various concepts of energy and disorder which have been introduced at appropriate points earlier in the text. These ideas are organized into a formal presentation of elementary thermodynamics.

Chapters 21-27 consider aggregates of molecules and ions of different kinds. Nonreacting homogeneous mixtures are presented in Chapter 21. The properties of solutions and colloids are discussed on the basis of their structure in Chapter 22. Chapter 23 describes chemical reactions on the basis of rate and establishing equilibrium. Acids and bases are discussed in Chapter 24, with emphasis on their behavior in water solution. Chapter 25 discusses salts and their behavior in water. Chapter 26 presents reactions in which electron transfer takes place. Chapter 27 builds on the topics of salt solutions and electron transfer in discussing electrochemistry.

Chapter 28 introduces the specialized area of nuclear chemistry. This vital area of our present economy is a high interest subject for students. The nomenclature and structure of the simplest classes of organic compounds are covered in Chapter 29. The reactions of organic compounds with emphasis on petroleum products, synthetic materials, and biochemical systems concludes the text in Chapter 30.

Throughout this text, we have used the basic learning principle of proceeding from familiar or known information to the unknown. As you can see from the sequence of chapters, we recognize that a certain amount of repetition is a necessary part of the learning process. Thus, principles of structure, matter-energy relationships, the mole concept, thermodynamics, and chemical equilibrium are presented several times throughout the text with varying degrees of emphasis. We believe students will develop a sense of confidence when they recognize familiar concepts presented later in greater depth. Minimum emphasis has been placed on memorization of fact. Instead, our purpose is to foster understanding and the ability to predict the behavior of substances under various conditions.

CHEMISTRY A MODERN COURSE

Gives students a working knowledge of chemistry

A logical sequence builds understanding of basic principles.

Written by experienced educators in science and mathematics, *CHEMISTRY: A MODERN COURSE* reflects the preferences of science educators throughout the country.

Students need a chemistry course that prepares them for future science courses. CHEMISTRY: A MODERN COURSE gives students a comprehensive course in chemistry with a balanced combination of theories, practical applications, and problem solving.

The suggested *chapter sequence* helps students understand chemical principles without the tedious memorization of equations and facts.

Topics in the program cover a wide range. Chapters 1 through 6 introduce the vocabulary used throughout the course including the mole theory. Chapters 7 through 27 cover:

* atomic structure
* bonding
* kinetic theory
* physical states
* solutions
* energy
* equilibrium systems
* redox
* analytical techniques

Chapters 28 through 30 are devoted to basic information on nuclear and organic chemistry, and biochemistry.

2T

iv

A study of the solid state is the study of the structure and properties of cystalline substances. When we think of a solid, we imagine an orderly arrangement of particles. However, as the photograph shows most crystals are not perfectly ordered structures. There are advantages to having defective arrangements in crystals. What are the types of crystal defects? Why are defects added purposely to some crystals? How do these defects affect the properties of the crystal?

SOLIDS

16

Chapter 16 introduces crystals through a study of unit cells. The relationship between packing arrangement and properties is covered for various substances. The distinction between crystalline solids and amorphous materials is emphasized.

DEMONSTRATION: Place a shallow glass dish on the overhead projector. Add 10 cm³ of H_2O and 10–15 drops of liquid dishwashing detergent to the dish. Gently blow bubbles with a straw or glass tube. The bubbles will arrange themselves like the unit cells in a crystal. Emphasize the definition of a crystal as having particles arranged in a repeating fashion. See Teacher Guide.

Have you ever examined table salt under a magnifying glass? If so, you would have seen that the crystals appear to be little cubes. The lengths of the edges may vary, but the angles between the surfaces are always exactly 90°.

The systematic study of crystals began with Nicolaus Steno, in 1669. He observed that corresponding angles between faces on different crystals of the same substance were always the same. This fact was true regardless of the size or source of the crystals.

Steno's observation has been extended to all intensive properties (density, refractive index, face angles, and other similar properties). For example, a single crystal of the mineral beryl, $Be_3Al_2Si_6O_{18}$, with a mass of more than 40 tons was unearthed in New Hampshire. This huge crystal was found to be identical in intensive properties to all other beryl crystals. The size or mass of the crystal is not important. It can now be stated that *the extensive properties of crystals vary while the intensive properties remain the same.* (See Section 3:4 to refresh your memory on the difference between intensive and extensive properties.)

16:1 CRYSTALS

The study of the solid state is really a study of crystals. All true solid substances are crystalline. Apparent exceptions to this statement can be explained in either of two ways. In some cases, substances we think of as solids are not solids at all. In other cases, the crystals are so small that the solid does not appear crystalline to the unaided eye. The relationship of properties to structure is important to chemists in the study of crystals as in other aspects of chemistry. Once the relationship is established, the chemist can use that knowledge to predict properties of new substances.

GOALS:
• You will gain an understanding of crystal structure.
• You will use the concepts of bonding to explain melting point of crystals.
• You will study crystal aberrations such as defects, transistors, liquid crystals, hydrated crystals, and amorphous solids.

SUGGESTION: Wooden models of the various crystal structures are available and can be helpful in the study of this chapter. It is also possible to have one or more students construct such models from foam spheres.

All crystals of the same substance have the same angles between faces.

Extensive properties of crystals of the same substance may vary, but intensive properties remain the same.

No exceptions have been found to Steno's Law.
A study of crystals is a study of the solid state.

SUGGESTION: Obtain a microscope and allow students to observe salt crystals under low power, or use a microprojector.

299

CHEMISTRY A MODERN COURSE

Reading and study aids ensure learning.

Important points are emphasized in the student margin notes that are printed in blue. Key phrases and sentences appear in italic type within the narrative.

Goal statements at the beginning of each chapter identify the major objectives for each chapter.

Numbered sections provide students with a ready outline of the chapter to help students see the relationships among concepts.

New terms are highlighted in boldface type. They are used repeatedly to help students become familiar with the meaning and use of each term. Every new term is listed at the end of the chapter and clearly defined in the Glossary.

KINETIC THEORY 15

GOALS:
• You will gain an understanding of kinetic theory.
• You will use the kinetic theory to describe the effects of energy and pressure on matter.
• You will differentiate among the four states of matter.

The **kinetic theory** explains the effect of temperature and pressure on matter. First, let us consider some basic assumptions of the theory. *All matter is composed of small particles* (atoms, ions, or molecules). *These small particles are in constant motion.* Finally, *all collisions between particles are perfectly elastic.* Perfectly elastic means that there is no change in the total kinetic energy of two particles before and after their collision. It may be difficult to imagine that all particles in a great structure such as the Golden Gate Bridge are in constant motion. However, as we shall see, many of the properties of matter are the result of such motion. As early as the mid-seventeenth century, the English inventor Robert Hooke proposed a kinetic theory. He predicted that there were particles in nature that were in constant motion. In order to have some concept of size for the quantities involved, we will first discuss oxygen.

The kinetic theory is based on three assumptions.
1. All matter is composed of particles.
2. The particles of matter are in constant motion.
3. All collisions are perfectly elastic.

15:1 OXYGEN MOLECULES IN MOTION

At room temperature (25°C), the average speed of an oxygen molecule is 443 m/s. This speed is equivalent to just over 1700 kilometers per hour. At this speed, the molecules collide with each other frequently. We can determine the average number of collisions a molecule undergoes in a unit of time. We do so by finding the average distance a molecule travels before colliding with another molecule. This distance is called the **mean free path** of the molecule. For oxygen at 25°C, the mean free path is 106 nm. The diameter of the oxygen molecule is about 0.339 nm. Thus, an oxygen molecule at 25°C will travel, on the average, about 314 times its own diameter before colliding with another molecule.

Even at room temperature molecules are moving extremely fast.

The mean free path of a molecule is the average distance a molecule travels between collisions.

285

Problem solving builds a working knowledge of chemistry.

EXAMPLE: Making a Solution

How would you make 5.00×10^2 cm^3 of a 0.133M solution of MnSeO$_4$, manganese(II) selenate?

Solving Process:
First, use the given quantity of solution, 5.00×10^2 cm^3, to find the part of a dm^3 desired. Then use the molarity to convert from solution to moles of substance. Finally, convert the moles of substance to grams.

$$\frac{5.00 \times 10^2 \text{ cm}^3}{} \left| \frac{1 \text{ dm}^3}{1000 \text{ cm}^3} \right| \frac{0.133 \text{ mol MnSeO}_4}{1 \text{ dm}^3} \left| \frac{198 \text{ g MnSeO}_4}{1 \text{ mol MnSeO}_4} \right| = 13.2 \text{ g MnSeO}_4$$

To make the solution, then, you would dissolve 13.2 g MnSeO$_4$ in sufficient water to make 5.00×10^2 cm^3 of solution.

PROBLEMS

Compute the molarity of the following solutions.
11. 89.7 g (NH$_4$)$_2$C$_4$H$_4$O$_6$ in 5.00×10^2 cm^3 of solution
12. 9.94 g CoSO$_4$ in 2.50×10^2 cm^3 of solution
13. 5.23 g Fe(NO$_3$)$_2$ in 100.0 cm^3 of solution
14. 44.3 g Pb(ClO$_4$)$_2$ in 200.0 cm^3 of solution
15. 8.55 g MnSiF$_6$ in 50.0 cm^3 of solution

Describe the preparation of the following solutions.
16. 1.000×10^3 cm^3 of 3.00M NiCl$_2$
17. 2.50×10^2 cm^3 of 4.00M RbOH
18. 5.00×10^2 cm^3 of 1.50M AgF
19. 2.50×10^2 cm^3 of 0.500M SrSiF$_6$
20. 2.50×10^2 cm^3 of 0.002 00M Tl$_2$CO$_3$

5:5 PERCENTAGE COMPOSITION

A chemist often compares the percentage composition of an unknown compound with the percentage composition calculated from an assumed formula. If the percentages agree it will help confirm the identity of the unknown. *The percentage of the total mass of a compound contributed by an element is the percentage of that element in the compound.* Consider the percentage composition of the following substances: copper, sodium chloride, and ethanol. For copper, the percentage composition is 100 percent Cu because it is composed of a single element. Salt is composed of two elements, sodium and chlorine. We know they are always present in the same ratio by mass. The ratio in which they are present is the ratio of their atomic masses. Therefore, the percentage of

---

Examples are used throughout the text as models to which students can refer when solving chemistry problems.

Practice problems throughout each chapter enable students to review material immediately. Answers are provided for some problems so that students can check their work.

SI units are used to provide students with the proper base for communicating in science. This measurement system is simple for students to learn and uses fewer units than other systems of measurement.

---

11. 0.975M
12. 0.257M

16. Dissolve 390 g NiCl$_2$ in enough water to make 1000 cm^3 of solution.
17. Dissolve 103 g RbOH in enough H$_2$O to make 250 cm^3 of solution.

Percentage composition may be used in the identification of some compounds.

Total percent of all elements in a compound equals 100%.

CHEMISTRY A MODERN COURSE

Outstanding illustrations clarify ideas at a glance.

Tables organize text information and quantitative data. The use of a tabular format helps students quickly see relationships among ideas and data.

Illustrations provide understandable visual models of abstract topics such as bonding, atomic and molecular structure, and large-scale industrial processes.

Graphs show relationships between measured quantities.

Photographs directly illustrate text information or present additional applications or analogies to help students understand difficult concepts. The captions reinforce the text or provide additional relevant information.

---

170   Periodic Table

Lanthanides add electrons to the 4f sublevels.

Table 9-7

Z	Element	1 s	2 s	2 p	3 s	3 p	3 d	4 s	4 p	4 d	4 f	5 s	5 p	5 d	6 s
57	La	2	2	6	2	6	10	2	6	10		2	6	1	2
58	Ce	2	2	6	2	6	10	2	6	10	1	2	6	1	2
59	Pr	2	2	6	2	6	10	2	6	10	3	2	6		2
60	Nd	2	2	6	2	6	10	2	6	10	4	2	6		2
61	Pm	2	2	6	2	6	10	2	6	10	5	2	6		2
62	Sm	2	2	6	2	6	10	2	6	10	6	2	6		2
63	Eu	2	2	6	2	6	10	2	6	10	7	2	6		2
64	Gd	2	2	6	2	6	10	2	6	10	7	2	6	1	2
65	Tb	2	2	6	2	6	10	2	6	10	9	2	6		2
66	Dy	2	2	6	2	6	10	2	6	10	10	2	6		2
67	Ho	2	2	6	2	6	10	2	6	10	11	2	6		2
68	Er	2	2	6	2	6	10	2	6	10	12	2	6		2
69	Tm	2	2	6	2	6	10	2	6	10	13	2	6		2
70	Yb	2	2	6	2	6	10	2	6	10	14	2	6		2

Header groupings: Lanthanide Series — columns 1, 2, 3, 4, 5, 6.

Actinides add electrons to the 5f sublevels.

8:6   Wave-Mechanical View of the Hydrogen Atom   145

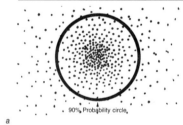

a   90% Probability circle.

b   Radial distribution (probability) vs. Distance from the nucleus — 0.053 nm

FIGURE 8-4. Probability plots for a hydrogen electron are shown in (a). Note the area represented by 90% probability. The point of highest probability for a hydrogen electron occurs at about 0.053 nm from the nucleus (b).

exist. It is something we use in our minds to help locate the most probable position of the electron.

There is another way of looking at probability. The electron moves about the nucleus in such a way as to pass through the points of high probability more often than through any other points. The electron is traveling at a high rate of speed. If the electron were visible to the eye, its rapid motion would cause it to appear as a cloud. Think of an electric fan as shown in Figure 8-5. When the fan is turning, it appears to fill the complete circle through which it turns. We cannot place an object between the blades while the fan is turning. If we do, the result will show that the fan is effectively filling the entire circle. So it is with the electron. It effectively fills all the space. At any given time, it is more likely to be somewhere on the surface of the shape described by the points of highest probability. The probability of finding the blade outside its volume is

An electron effectively occupies all the space around a nucleus.

FIGURE 8-5. The fan blades (a) appear to occupy the total volume through which they turn. An electron occupies a 3-dimensional volume to form a cloud of negative charge (b).

a

b   Electron cloud

SUMMARY

1. Avogadro's principle: *At equal temperatures and pressures, equal volumes of gases contain equal numbers of molecules.* **19:1**
2. The molar volume of a gas is the volume occupied by 1 mole of the gas; at STP, its value is 22.4 dm^3 for all gases. **19:2**
3. The ideal gas equation is $PV = nRT$, where P = pressure, V = volume, n = number of moles, R = a constant, and T = kelvin temperature. **19:3**
4. The molecular mass of a gas may be determined by using a modified form of the ideal gas equation. **19:4**
5. A limiting reactant is a reactant that is completely consumed in a reaction and thereby limits the amount of product. Any remaining reactants are said to be in excess. **19:8**
6. In solving problems involving gas volumes, consideration must be given to the change of gas volume with change in pressure and temperature. **19:9**
7. A gas that expands or is compressed does work or has work done on it. **19:10**

VOCABULARY

Avogadro's principle **19:1**	limiting reactant **19:8**
molar volume **19:2**	excess reactant **19:8**
ideal gas equation **19:3**	isothermal **19:10**

PROBLEMS

11. In Problem 10, if the gas were collected at 27°C and 104.5 kPa pressure, what volume would it occupy?
12. What would be the density of the CO_2 gas collected under the conditions stated in Problem 11?
13. At 17°C and 61.2 kPa, 0.316 mol of gas expands from 11.3 dm^3 to 22.1 dm^3. What work does the gas do on the surroundings?
14. A gas expands by an adiabatic reversible change. The heat capacity of the gas is 20.8 J/mol·K. This change causes a temperature change of 91.1 K. What work is done by the gas?

REVIEW

1. If a sample of gas occupies 642 cm^3 at 93.9 kPa, what volume will it occupy at 109.0 kPa if the temperature remains constant?
2. If a sample of gas collected over water at 50°C occupies 62.5 cm^3 at a total pressure of 114.9 kPa, what volume will the dry gas occupy at 50°C and 97.8 kPa?
3. If a sample of gas occupies 286 cm^3 at 98.1 kPa and 42°C, what volume will it occupy at 42.2 kPa and 60.0°C?
4. Compute the relative rates of diffusion for oxygen and argon at the same temperature.
5. What is the density of a gas at STP if 1.34 g of the gas occupy 343 cm^3 at 24°C and 99.9 kPa?
6. Define an ideal gas.
7. If 60.0 dm^3 of gas at 7°C is heated to 312°C, what is the new volume of the gas (pressure is constant)?

ONE MORE STEP

1. Investigate Cannizzaro's role in gaining acceptance for Avogadro's principle.
2. Molecular masses of materials are often found today by using a mass spectrograph, which we have already discussed (Chapter 8). Find out how a "time-of-flight" spectrometer works.
3. How would knowledge of chemistry help an iron foundry?
4. If a student performs an experiment to determine the molecular mass of a gaseous compound using the modified ideal gas equation, $M = mRT/PV$, and forgets to correct for the fact that the gas was collected over water, would the results be high or low?
5. How much work is done by a gas that expands against zero external pressure?

READINGS

Hakala, Reino W., "The Value of the Critical Compressability Factor for the Redlich-Kwong Equation of State of Gases," *Journal of Chemical Education*, Vol. 62, No. 2(February 1985), pp. 110-111.

Complete chapter-end materials reinforce and extend every chapter.

Summary lists the major points presented in the chapter. The section in which each statement appears is noted to enable students to refer to the chapter.

Vocabulary lists boldfaced terms from the chapter and the sections in which they appear.

Problems includes questions and practice problems to help students check their understanding of the chapter before a test. The questions range from simple recall to the application of previously studied material to new situations.

Review includes questions and practice problems on material from previous chapters to help students constantly build on what they have already learned.

One More Step includes questions and activities that take students beyond the material in the chapter. These items are ideal for individualized study or extra credit work.

Readings is a list of suggested references and high-interest articles that allow students to explore chapter concepts in more depth.

CHEMISTRY A MODERN COURSE

Added features complete a balanced study of chemistry.

Appendices include comprehensive reference tables as well as supplementary information on logarithms, careers, and using calculators.

Careers and Chemistry features are overviews of a variety of career choices requiring some knowledge of chemistry.

Biographies are brief insights into the lives and discoveries of men and women who have made significant contributions to chemistry.

Technology and Chemistry articles discuss supplemental material or current research topics involving practical applications of chemistry concepts.

APPENDIX C

CALCULATOR OPERATION

There are two basic types of hand-held calculators: algebraic (e.g., Texas Instruments, Casio, Sharp)

CAREERS AND CHEMISTRY

4:7   Scientific Writing and Illustrating

The decisions that we must make as voters and consumers require us to have an understanding of science and technology. Only when a society understands the facts and issues can it make intelligent choices. Communicating the facts and issues is the function of the science journalist.

There are many people who have a strong interest in science and

---

fusion reactions to occur, the reactants must be held in the temperature range of 10^8 to 10^9°C for a suitable time. The energy requirements to achieve these temperatures are quite high. The length of time required depends upon how closely packed the particles are during that time. At these high temperatures, matter is in the form of plasma. One major problem in designing a fusion reactor is containing the fuel at that temperature. Containers made from usual materials cannot be used. The plasma would lose energy to them so rapidly that fusion temperatures would never be reached. Since plasmas are charged particles, they are affected by magnetic fields. By properly shaping a magnetic field, a plasma may be contained. As fusion occurs and the temperature rises, the pressure of a plasma causes it to expand. With charged particles in the plasma moving around at tremendous velocities, the plasma itself generates electric currents. Both of these effects make leakage from the magnetic "bottle" a difficult problem to solve. All of these problems are topics of present research. Who can predict what role developments in this fascinating field will play in shaping our future!

Matter must be in the form of plasma (10^8°C) for a fusion reaction to occur.

Fusion reactions can be contained in "magnetic bottles."

BIOGRAPHY   Shirley Ann Jackson (1946-   )

Shirley Jackson has a history of being first at a number of accomplishments. She was first in her high school graduating class and eventually became the first black woman to earn a doctorate degree at Massachusetts Institute of Technology. Following graduation from MIT, she did research at the Fermi National Accelerator Laboratory and at CERN in Geneva, Switzerland.

Although her interest was high energy physics, Dr. Jackson now works with microscopic solid state physics in the development of miniature physical systems such as electronic chips and microtransistors. Although she is currently employed by Bell Laboratories, she retains her tie to MIT through membership on the board of trustees.

TECHNOLOGY AND CHEMISTRY

28:14   Stellar Nucleosynthesis

In addition to the moon, stars, and planets we see in the sky, there are great clouds of gas and dust. About 75% of the matter in the universe is hydrogen and almost 25% is helium. All other elements make about 1% of the matter in the universe.

Ancillary materials provide for hands-on learning, development of math skills, and evaluation of student progress.

LABORATORY PROGRAM

Chemical concepts often appear abstract to students. *LABORATORY CHEMISTRY* provides students with an opportunity to investigate many of the concepts covered in *CHEMISTRY: A MODERN COURSE*. A teaching approach that combines lecture and textbook materials with practical laboratory experiences will enhance students' ability to comprehend new and difficult material.

The focus of *LABORATORY CHEMISTRY* is on a logical approach to investigating and analyzing problems. A wide variety of laboratory techniques that stress safety are presented. Accurate reporting of experimental data in a well organized laboratory report is emphasized. Students are then required to interpret their results in terms of the concepts being investigated.

LABORATORY CHEMISTRY is designed to be flexible for a variety of teaching needs. When time or cost is a prohibitive factor, teachers are encouraged to use experiments for class demonstrations. The Planning Guide on pages 14T-15T contains a suggested laboratory sequence which correlates the experiments with the text material.

COMPUTER-ASSISTED DATA-CHECKING PROGRAMS are designed for use with 19 of the experiments in *LABORATORY CHEMISTRY*. The data-checking programs are easy to use and require a minimal amount of computer time.

PROBLEM SOLVING

Students often encounter difficulty in applying their mathematical skills to chemical calculations. *SOLVING PROBLEMS IN CHEMISTRY* is designed to develop problem solving skills through the use of *Example* and practice problems. The factor-label method is used as in the text *CHEMISTRY: A MODERN COURSE*. Each Example problem has a carefully explained step-by-step solving process. Emphasis has been placed on the practical applications of problem solving in chemistry. Industrial and everyday uses of chemicals are discussed within the problems.

SOLVING PROBLEMS IN CHEMISTRY is an excellent source of supplementary problems and exercises for developing problem-solving skills. It follows the same chapter sequencing as *CHEMISTRY: A MODERN COURSE*. This feature enhances the usefulness of the problem book.

TEACHER RESOURCES

CHEMISTRY: A MODERN COURSE, TEACHER RESOURCE BOOK is a unique, time-saving, teacher aid designed to assist you in all phases of your chemistry instruction. It provides effective tools for scheduling and planning, teaching content, reinforcing basic skills, and enriching lessons.

The loose-leaf binder format of the *TEACHER RESOURCE BOOK* offers flexibility and convenient access to all material. The introductory section of the book includes resources designed to help you plan and implement your total chemistry program. Also included in this section is information on chemical storage. The introductory section concludes with a series of Skills Masters.

Following the introductory material, the *TEACHER RESOURCE BOOK* is organized and tabbed to follow the text on a chapter-by-chapter basis. Each chapter in the *TEACHER RESOURCE BOOK* includes individual chapter planning guides and performance objectives, teaching masters for making overhead transparencies, review masters for providing additional drill on selected text topics, masters for one or two brief investigations, enrichment masters, and reduced pages. The appendix contains reference tables that are suitable for use as reproducible masters.

EVALUATION OF STUDENT PROGRESS

The *EVALUATION PROGRAM FOR CHEMISTRY: A MODERN COURSE* is designed to be used as a learning tool as well as an instrument in evaluating student progress. The book consists of a four-part test for each of the 30 chapters in *CHEMISTRY: A MODERN COURSE*. The four sections of each chapter test include:

Understanding Vocabulary—A set of completion items using the chemical terms from the textbook.

Discovering Concepts—A set of multiple choice questions.

Interpreting Concepts—A set of completion and matching items.

Using Concepts—A set of problems and/or essay questions.

The major focus of each test is to help students improve their knowledge of chemistry. Using these tests as a diagnostic tool you can decide what supplemental materials may be needed.

USING CHEMISTRY: A MODERN COURSE

ORGANIZATION AND SEQUENCE

The **TEACHER ANNOTATED EDITION OF CHEM-ISTRY: A MODERN COURSE** is divided into two sections—the Teacher Guide having grey edges along the pages and the red overprinted Student text.

The Student text is divided into 30 chapters. Each chapter is further divided into numbered sections. The numbering and headings of the sections aid students in locating specific topics and assist you in arranging class and homework assignments.

CHEMISTRY: A MODERN COURSE follows a logical, sequential development of major chemistry principles. The text begins with the "mechanics" of chemistry, the mole concept, and the structure of matter. The text then deals with the behavior of matter in terms of acidity, oxidation-reduction, and electric potential. It also includes descriptive material in nuclear, organic, biochemistry, and analytical chemistry.

TEACHER GUIDE

Overview

This section provides you with a short synopsis of the major themes of the chapter. You are also given an insight as to how the chapter material fits into the overall sequence.

Demonstrations

Good teacher demonstrations are important in helping students visualize abstract concepts and allow for the development of observational skills and proper lab techniques. Use the demonstrations in the text to emphasize safety rules and procedures. The approach you use in presenting a demonstration can be one of the following: either begin with a clearly defined problem or perform the demonstration silently with a goal of developing students' ability to observe and draw conclusions. These skills will be critical to their success in the laboratory portion of the course. Good demonstrations allow students to recognize and verbalize relationships based on their level of experience. The demonstration as a teaching technique allows you to present a maximum amount of text material in a concrete and visual manner. You will find numerous demonstrations printed in red

throughout the Student's text. Any additional preparation and teaching strategies will be covered in the Teacher Guide section for that chapter.

Performance Objectives

The Goals of the chapter are followed by a list of specific objectives. Thus, you are aware of the points to emphasize in covering the chapter. When designing your chapter tests or course of study for beginning chemistry use these objectives as a framework. The *Evaluation Program,* which is part of the Merrill Chemistry Program, is written based on the chapter objectives. A thorough explanation on how to use performance objectives is found on pages 22T-24T. The performance objectives for each chapter are included as reproducible masters in the *Teacher Resource Book.*

Teaching Techniques

Section teaching techniques are provided when appropriate. These strategies include information concerning the authors' approach to a particular topic, additional science background, and suggestions as to how to achieve a better level of success in presenting a section to students.

Problem Solutions

Answers to most problems are found in red overprinted on the Student's page for convenience. However, note that some answers would not fit in the existing space on a page. The Teacher Guide contains full solutions for all questions and problems in the Student's text.

Teacher Annotations

The red Teacher Annotations consist of answers to problems, demonstrations, science background, points of emphasis, teaching suggestions, and strategies. The annotations are highlighted with the headings DEMONSTRATION, BACKGROUND, and SUGGESTION. They are conveniently located with the appropriate text material.

STUDENT TEXT

Readability

Readability plays a major role in determining the success of a textbook in the classroom. A text that can be comprehended by the majority of students promotes their interest and involvement in the subject area. This feature promotes teachability and helps facilitate classroom management.

In controlling reading level, careful attention has been given to vocabulary, sentence construction, paragraph structure, chapter organization, illustrations, and text format.

The vocabulary in the text is consistent with the developmental level of average high school students. Words with a large number of syllables have been avoided whenever possible. In addition, important science terms are printed in boldface or italic type when first presented. Some terms are followed by their phonetic spellings. Each term is then clearly defined and used repeatedly throughout the discussion to reinforce its meaning.

The open format is the result of appropriate spacing between sections, problems, and illustrations. The typeface and size in which the text is set is another aspect that enhances readability. The margin is used for supplemental information in the form of margin notes, captions, and annotations. Thus, the flow of ideas in the main body of the text is not disrupted. Highlighting and organizing important information using boldface type, student notes, tables, and Summary statements also enhances readability.

Photographs and Illustrations

We maintain that a visual presentation not only motivates students but certainly adds to their level of understanding. The use of material that provides students with visual links between chemistry principles and real-world happenings is a vital part of the learning process. Each chapter opening consists of a color photograph and a thought-provoking paragraph designed to stimulate student interest in the material to be presented in the chapter. In addition over 550 color photographs, illustrations, and graphs are included throughout the text to reinforce and clarify concepts presented in adjacent paragraphs. Use these graphics as part of your presentation as much as possible so students learn to think of them as an active part of the text.

Example Problems

Example problems are used extensively to present the mathematical concepts needed in studying chemistry. The factor-label method of problem solving is used and unit cancellation lines are printed in blue to aid students in setting-up problems. The Example problems provide students with clear, logical models they can use to achieve an answer. Each Example problem is titled and set-off from the body of the text for quick reference. Take the time in your presentation of a section to thoroughly review each Example with students.

Student Notes

Student notes are placed in the margin to aid in review. Using the section titles as a framework, these notes can be used to provide students with a ready outline of the concepts discussed within the chapter. They are also an excellent reading aid in providing students with a concise statement of a paragraph or concept. CAREER notes describing chemistry-related careers are included where appropriate.

Careers and Chemistry

These features are designed to give students an awareness of the many fields that draw on a knowledge of chemistry. These features should be used to emphasize the importance of this subject in students' overall education. Use the features as a starting point for students to do additional research into the many career options available. Emphasize that a doctorate in chemistry is not necessary to pursue a chemistry-related career. A basic chemistry course is adequate background for many jobs.

Technology and Chemistry

These features present supplemental discussions of chapter concepts and insights into current research problems. These pages should be used to motivate students to seek additional information concerning timely issues such as the use of scarce resources, energy alternatives, progress, and the environment. Some features highlight an additional application of some topic within the chapter. Thus, students are aware of how our knowledge of topics such as crystal structure and ion activity was formulated.

Biographies

Each chapter includes a short biography of a scientist whose work has contributed to the principles presented in that chapter. The Biographies are designed to bring out the human aspects of scientists in general and to relate their work to the relevant problems of their times. In using the Biographies be sure to emphasize that many great scientists had to overcome numerous obstacles in the pursuit of their work.

Section- and Chapter-End Materials

Questions and problems follow many sections of the text. They are designed for students to check their understanding of the previously covered material. Answers are provided in blue for some questions and problems within a chapter to allow students to gain confidence in the mastery of new material.

The chapter-end materials begin with a *Summary* that concisely reviews the major concepts and principles in the chapter. Each Summary statement is numbered and keyed back to the chapter by a blue student note. You can begin the chapter using the Summary to determine how much your students know about a topic from previous science courses. The Summary is an excellent reading aid in that it helps students discern the important points in the chapter. It also gives you an insight as to the points the authors feel should be emphasized in presenting a chapter.

The *Vocabulary* section lists all boldface terms in the chapter. The vocabulary terms are keyed to the section where they are defined. These terms are tested in Part A of the Evaluation Program.

The *Problems* section provides questions and problems to review the major concepts of the chapter. Students' success depends greatly on their being given the opportunity to develop math skills and apply their chemical knowledge to new situations. Having students answer these items and then thoroughly reviewing each with them should be adequate preparation for a chapter test.

The *Review* section provides questions and problems where students recall the important principles and concepts from previous chapters. Since many topics in this text build on the knowledge gained in a previous chapter, this section provides an excellent way of unifying information. It also gives students additional practice in problem solving and applying concepts.

The *One More Step* section presents questions and activities to lead students beyond the material covered in the text. This section is designed to provide a number of open-ended activities. Use these items to develop positive attitudes toward science, as extra credit projects, or as a means of individualizing the course for students having the ability to comprehend material at a higher level than that presented in the text. Note that these items provide for a wide range of activities from simple library research to designing a technical research problem. Thus, they can be assigned to students at all levels of ability.

The *Readings* provide interested students with references to expand their knowledge of some aspects of the chapter. Encourage students to read articles concerning science in the local newspaper and popular news magazines. At this point in their education you want to establish the idea that a study of science is not relegated to the classroom or laboratory. The success of new science magazines for the nonscientist exemplifies this idea.

Appendices

Appendix A contains twelve useful tables to provide students with all the necessary data to work the problems in the text. This comprehensive set of tables provides you with all of the necessary reference data in one volume.

Appendix B contains a section to review the use of logarithms in chemical calculations.

Appendix C contains information on using calculators to solve problems.

Appendix D contains a partial listing and description of some chemistry related careers.

Glossary

The Glossary provides students with a quick reference to the key terms presented in the text.

TEACHING CHEMISTRY TO STUDENTS WITH SPECIAL NEEDS

Over the past few years there have been increasing numbers of students with special needs taking chemistry. These students include the gifted, the low achieving, the non- or limited-English proficient, and those with physical disabilities. The needs of all of these young people are the same as those of other chemistry students. However, in order to address the needs of these students, the sensitive teacher will find that he or she must use care in planning and preparing lessons. Some areas that may require special attention are lecturing and leading discussions, providing the time necessary to complete tasks, and determining the necessity for special arrangements particularly in laboratory work.

This text provides challenge for the gifted student, particularly in the *One More Step* exercises. There are also additional laboratory and enrichment activities in the **Teacher Resource Book.** These activities can be used to challenge your advanced students.

For the low achieving student, who may also be a slow learner, there are review exercises provided in each chapter of the text. The review masters in the **Teacher Resource Book** are an excellent learning aid for these students. You might also consider assigning additional practice problems from **Solving Problems in Chemistry.** It might be well to assign these materials to groups of students as the need arises. Generally these students will need constant reinforcement on particular concepts. Greater time may be needed for these students to finish their assignments. Also, they may need additional assistance in the laboratory. It would be well not to pair two such students for the lab.

The limited-English proficient student may well be capable of understanding the chemistry concepts but not capable of expressing the concepts in laboratory activities or on essay tests. Often a translator, such as a fellow student, exists in the classroom. This translator may be proficient in English and the native language of the student and be available to assist both in class and out of class. If a translator is not available, you may need to speak slowly and use many diagrams. It is important that you always face the students when you speak and not talk into the chalkboard.

Finally, the student with a physical disability will need particular attention. If possible, the teacher should have a presemester conference to determine the handicapping conditions and to make plans to overcome those conditions. The students are usually the best sources for knowing what is best for their learning. You may need to rearrange lab stations to provide for alternate means for taking tests, and to provide any additional safety precautions.

All students in your classes can be successful. Special-needs students need from their teachers understanding, interest, and a willingness to deal with the problems they pose. The rewards for your efforts can be great for both you and your students with special needs.

PLANNING GUIDE FOR
CHEMISTRY: A MODERN COURSE

You are in the best position to design a chemistry course that meets the needs of your students. You will find the arrangement of *Chemistry: A Modern Course* allows for a certain amount of flexibility in planning. You may prefer to use the chapters in a different sequence to reflect your own philosophy of teaching chemistry. For example, if you prefer a historical approach, use Chapters 1, 8-18, 2-6, and 19-30 in that order. We have arranged the text so as to provide a background early in the course that permits a strong laboratory approach. This planning guide is provided to assist you with both long-range and daily planning. We hope it helps in designing the best possible chemistry program.

The guide is organized to present a suggested number of class sessions for each chapter. The entire course is based on 180 class sessions in the school year, which is equivalent to 160 hours of combined class and laboratory time.

The sections of each chapter are classified as being of primary or secondary importance. We believe that a basic chemistry curriculum must include those sections designated as primary in importance. The sections listed in this category provide a minimum program. After presenting the essential sections in each chapter, you may have the time to select from additional text topics and laboratory experiments. The planning guide shows the correlation between the experiments in *Laboratory Chemistry* and the content of the text.

The first sixteen chapters are considered to be the equivalent of a semester of study. You will want to complete them in 90 class sessions. We consider the first 27 chapters to be essential in an introductory high school program which is designed to survey chemistry and prepare students for further study in science.

Once you have determined your goals for the year, use this guide to aid you in scheduling. The number of class sessions suggested includes time for laboratory experiments and testing. You may find that some classes will take longer to cover a chapter than what is projected in the planning guide. Use the planning guide as a framework not as a rigid schedule that must be adhered to.

The following is a general guide to covering the chapters if you are on six or nine week reporting periods.

Six Week Periods		Nine Week Periods	
	Chapters		Chapters
First	1–6	First	1–8
Second	7–11	Second	9–16
Third	12–16	Third	17–23
Fourth	17–20	Fourth	24–30
Fifth	21–25		
Sixth	26–30		

Correlation for supplemental problems in
Solving Problems in Chemistry © 1983

Chemistry: *A Modern Course*	*Solving Problems* *in Chemistry*
Chapter 2	Chapter 1
4	2
5	3, 4, 5, 6, 16
6	7
7	8
17	14
18	9
19	10, 11, 12, 13
20	15
21	16, 18
22	19
23	17
24	20
25	21, 22, 23
26	24
27	25
28	26
29	27

PLANNING GUIDE FOR CHEMISTRY: A MODERN COURSE

Chapter	Class Sessions	Emphasis Level — Of Primary Importance	Of Secondary Importance	Suggested Experiments from LABORATORY CHEMISTRY
1	3	1:3-1:6	1:1, 1:2 1:7	P PRELAB: OBSERVING, QUESTIONING 1 THE SCIENTIFIC METHOD: OBSERVING, INVESTIGATING, ANALYZING, INTERPRETING 2 THE LAW OF CONSERVATION OF MASS-ENERGY
2	5	2:1-2:13	2:14	3 DENSITY: A QUANTITATIVE MEASUREMENT
3	5	3:1-3:9	3:10	4 CHEMICAL AND PHYSICAL CHANGES IN MATTER 5 SPECIFIC HEAT OF A METAL
4	5	4:1-4:4	4:5-4:7	6 FORMULAS AND OXIDATION NUMBERS
5	6	5:1-5:8	5:9	7 QUANTITATIVE DETERMINATION OF AN EMPIRICAL FORMULA 8 HYDRATED CRYSTALS
6	8	6:1-6:5	6:6	9 CHEMICAL CHANGES AND EQUATIONS 10 QUANTITATIVE STUDY OF A REACTION 11 MOLE RELATIONSHIP IN A CHEMICAL REACTION
7	6	7:3-7:11	7:1-7:2 7:12	12 FLAME TESTS 13 INTRODUCTION TO THE SPECTROPHOTOMETER 14 ENERGIES OF ELECTRONS
8	8	8:5-8:14	8:1-8:4 8:15	15 ELECTRON ARRANGEMENTS
9	7	9:2-9:9	9:1, 9:10	16 THE PERIODIC LAW
10	7	10:1-10:6	10:7	17 INTRODUCTION TO QUALITATIVE ANALYSIS 18 ENERGY RELATIONSHIPS OF METALLIC IONS
11	3		all sections	19 THE ACTIVITY OF GROUPS IA(1), IIA(2), AND VIIA(17)
12	6	12:1-12:10	12:11	20 CONDUCTIVITY AND CHEMICAL BONDING
13	8	13:1-13:9	13:10-13:13	21 SHAPES AND POLARITIES OF COVALENT MOLECULES
14	4	14:1-14:2	14:3-14:11	22 INTRODUCTION TO CHROMATOGRAPHY
15	5	15:1-15:6	15:7	

Chapter	Experiments		
16	23 ION OR ATOM ARRANGEMENT IN CRYSTALS 24 ALLOTROPIC FORMS OF SULFUR	16:3 16:7-16:9 16:11, 16:13	16:1-16:2 16:4-16:6 16:10, 16:12	6
17	25 DETERMINATION OF ENTHALPY OF FUSION	17:12-17:13	17:1-17:11	7
18	26 CHARLES' LAW: THE EFFECT OF TEMPERATURE ON VOLUME 27 DIFFUSION OF GASES	18:8-18:9 18:11	18:1-18:7 18:10	7
19	28 THE MOLAR RELATIONSHIP INVOLVING MASS AND VOLUME 29 STOICHIOMETRY: MASS-VOLUME	19:8-19:11	19:1-19:7	6
20	30 ENTROPY AND ENTHALPY 31 ENTHALPY OF A CHEMICAL REACTION	20:7 20:10-20:11	20:1-20:6 20:8-20:9	6
21	32 THE EFFECT OF TEMPERATURE ON SOLUBILITY 33 DETERMINING SOLUTION CONCENTRATION USING A SPECTROPHOTOMETER	21:5-21:7 21:11	21:1-21:4 21:8-21:10	4
22	34 MOLECULAR MASS DETERMINATION USING BOILING POINT AND FREEZING POINT	22:2, 22:6 22:8-22:11	22:1 22:3-22:5 22:7	5
23	35 REACTION RATES 36 A STUDY OF CHEMICAL EQUILIBRIUM	23:10-23:12	23:1-23:9	7
24	37 QUALITATIVE ANALYSIS OF NET IONIC REACTIONS 38 REACTIONS BETWEEN IONS IN SOLUTION	24:6, 24:9 24:12, 24:14 24:15	24:1-24:5 24:7-24:8 24:10-24:11 24:13	7
25	39 SOLUBILITY PRODUCT CONSTANT OF A SALT 40 HYDRONIUM ION CONCENTRATION INDICATORS 41 HYDROLYSIS: WATER REACTIONS WITH NORMAL SALTS 42 ACID-BASE TITRATION AND VOLUMETRIC ANALYSIS	25:5 25:8	25:1-25:4 25:6-25:7	9
26	43 OXIDATION-REDUCTION REACTIONS 44 QUANTITATIVE TITRATION INVOLVING REDOX REACTIONS	26:9-26:13	26:1-26:8	7
27	45 THE POTENTIAL OF ELECTROCHEMICAL CELLS 46 CORROSION: AN ELECTROCHEMICAL PROBLEM	27:10-27:13 27:15, 27:16	27:1-27:9 27:14	6
28	47 NATURAL RADIOACTIVITY	28:1-28:3 28:10-28:14	28:4-28:9	6
29	48 PREPARATION OF SOME ORGANIC COMPOUNDS	29:5-29:6 29:18	29:1-29:4 29:7-29:17	6
30	49 PREPARATION OF SOAP, SYNTHETIC RUBBER, AND NYLON 50 BIOCHEMISTRY: CARBOHYDRATES, FATS, PROTEINS	30:1-30:5	30:6-30:14	5

TEACHER REFERENCES

General references for demonstrations and laboratory practice.

Prudent Practices for Disposal of Chemicals from Laboratories, Washington DC: National Academy Press, 1983.

Prudent Practices for Handling Hazardous Chemicals in Laboratories, Washington DC: National Academy Press, 1981.

Shakhashiri, Bassam Z., *Chemical Demonstrations, A Handbook for Teachers of Chemistry,* Volumes I and II, Madison: The University of Wisconson Press, 1983.

Pease, Burton F., *Basic Instrumental Analysis,* Van Nostrand, 1980.

General references useful in several chapters, referred to hereafter by code numbers.

(1) deKock, Roger L., et al., *Chemical Structure and Bonding,* Benjamin, 1980.

(2) Shriner, Ralph L., et al., *The Systematic Identification of Organic Compounds,* Wiley, 1980.

(3) Tuma, Jan J., *Handbook of Physical Calculations,* McGraw-Hill, 1983, 2nd. ed.

(4) Trefil, James S., *From Atoms to Quarks,* Scribner's, 1980.

(5) Atkins, P. W., *Physical Chemistry,* Freeman, 1978.

(6) Harrison, Walter A., *Electronic Structure and the Properties of Solids,* Freeman, 1980.

(7) Solomons, T. W. G., *Organic Chemistry,* Wiley, 1978.

(8) Stumm, Werner, and James J. Morgan, *Aquatic Chemistry,* Wiley, 1981.

The following three references are excellent general references that may be used with many of the text chapters.

Greenwood, N. N., and A. Earnshaw, *Chemistry of the Elements,* Oxford: Pergamon, 1984.

Kauffman, George B., and H. Henry Szmant, *The Central Science,* Fort Worth: TCU Press, 1984.

Moeller, Therald, et al., *Chemistry, with Qualitative Analysis,* New York: Academic Press, 1984.

It will be helpful to you if you can develop a personal reference library or have your school provide one for the chemistry department. At a minimum, we recommend that your library contain the following items.

1. A good chemical dictionary, such as Hawley, Gessner G., *The Condensed Chemical Dictionary,* New York: Van Nostrand Reinhold Company, 1981.
2. A chemical handbook such as any of the following:
   Dean, John A., *Lange's Handbook of Chemistry,* New York: McGraw-Hill Book Company, 1985.
   Windholz, Martha, *The Merck Index,* Rathway, NJ: Merck & Co., Inc., 1983.
   Weast, Robert C., *Handbook of Chemistry and Physics,* Cleveland: CRC Press (published annually).
3. A selection of data tables, such as Latimer's *Oxidation Potentials* (Prentice-Hall), and National Bureau of Standards' thermodynamics tables.
4. A reference on nomenclature, such as the IUPAC volumes on chemical nomenclature.
5. A major work on the chemical industry, such as Barnes & Noble's eight volume series, *Chemical Technology.*

Chapter 1

Abelson, Philip H., "Effects of SO_2 and NO_x Emissions," *Science,* Vol. 226, No. 4680(December 14, 1984), p. 1263.

Baum, Rudy M., "Genetic Engineering Engulfed in New Environmental Debate," *Chemical and Engineering News,* Vol. 62, No. 33(August 13, 1984), pp. 15-22.

Ember, Lois R., "Stringfellow Cleanup Mishaps Show need to Alter Superfund Law," *Chemical and Engineering News,* Vol. 63, No. 21(May 27, 1985), pp. 11-21.

Ferris, James P., "The Chemistry of Life's Origins," *Chemical and Engineering News,* Vol. 62, No. 35(August 27, 1984), pp. 25-35.

Fetter, Steven A., and Kosta Tsipis, "Catastrophic Releases of Radioactivity," *Scientific American,* Vol. 244, No. 4(April 1981), pp. 41-47.

Gray, Charles L. Jr., and Frank von Hippel, "Fuel Economy of Light Vehicles," *Scientific American,* Vol. 244, No. 5(May 1981), pp. 48-59.

Holden, Constance, "Global Cooperation in Big Science," *Science,* Vol. 229, No. 4708(July 5, 1985), pp. 32-33.

Kerr, Richard A., "Nuclear Winter Won't Blow Away." *Science*, Vol. 228, No. 4696(April 12, 1985), p. 163.

Taylor, Harriet V., "Conservation Energy," *Journal of Chemical Education*, Vol. 58, No. 2(February 1981), pp. 185-188.

Chapter 2
General Reference (8)

Garrett, James M., "Teaching Factor-Label Method without Sleight of Hand," *Journal of Chemical Education*, Vol. 60 No. 11(November 1983), p. 962.

Schwartz, Lowell M., "Propagation of Significant Figures," *Journal of Chemical Education*, Vol. 62, No. 8(August 1985), pp. 693-697.

Chapter 7
General Reference (1)

Kleppner, Daniel, et al., "Highly Excited Atoms." *Scientific American*, Vol. 244, No. 5(April 1981), pp. 130-149.

Mason, Franklin P., and Robert W. Richardson, "Why Doesn't the Electron Fall in the Nucleus?" *Journal of Chemical Education*, Vol. 50, No. 1(January 1983), pp. 40-42.

Chapter 8
General References (1), (2), (3), (4), and (10)

Bartell, Lawrence S., "Perspectives on the Uncertainty Principle and Quantum Reality," *Journal of Chemical Education*, Vol. 62, No. 3(March 1985), pp. 192-196.

Kikuchi, Osamu, and Keizo Suzuki, "Orbital Shape Representations," *Journal of Chemical Education*, Vol. 62, No. 3(March 1985), pp. 206-209.

McQuarrie, Donald A., *Quantum Chemistry*, Mill Valley, CA: University Science Books, 1983.

Chapter 9

Loening, K. L., "Recommended Format for the Periodic Table of the Elements," *Journal of Chemical Education*, Vol. 61, No. 2(February 1984), p. 136.

Chapter 10

Feinstein, H. I., "Diagonal Relationships—Descriptive or Theoretical?" *Journal of Chemical Education*, Vol. 61, No. 1(February 1984), p. 128.

Hay, R. W., *Bio-Inorganic Chemistry*, NY: John Wiley and Sons, 1984.

Kutney, Gerald W., and Kenneth Turnbull, "The Sulfur Chemist," *Journal of Chemical Education*, Vol. 61, No. 4(April 1984), pp. 372-276.

Langley, Richard H., and Larry Welch, "Fluorine," *Journal of Chemical Education*, Vol. 60, No. 9(September 1983), p. 759-761.

Singman, Charles N., "Atomic Volume and Allotropy of the Elements," *Journal of Chemical Education*, Vol. 61, No. 2(February 1984), pp. 137-142.

Chapter 11
General References (1) and (6)

Kremers, Howard E., "Technology of the Rare Earths," *Journal of Chemical Education*, Vol. 62, No. 8(August 1985), pp. 665-667.

Robinson, Edward A., and Ronald J. Gillespie, "Bent bonds and Multiple Bonds," *Journal of Chemical Education*, Vol. 57, No. 5(May 1980), pp. 329-333.

Chapter 12
General References (1) and (6)

Robinson, Edward A., and Ronald J. Gillespie, "Bent bonds and Multiple Bonds," *Journal of Chemical Education*, Vol. 57, No. 5(May 1980), pp. 329-333.

Chapter 13
General References (1), (5), (6), and (8)

Crosby, G. A., "Structure, Bonding, and Excited States of Coordination Complexes," *Journal of Chemical Education*, Vol. 60, No. 10(October 1983), pp. 791-796.

Reutter, D. J., et al., "Ion Chromatography in Bombing Investigations", *Analytical Chemistry*, Vol. 55, No. 14(December 1983), pp. 1468A-1472A.

Robinson, Edward A., and Ronald J. Gillespie, "Bent bonds and Multiple Bonds," *Journal of Chemical Education*, Vol. 57, No. 5(May 1980), pp. 329-333.

Small, Hamish, "Modern Inorganic Chromatography," *Analytical Chemistry*, Vol. 55, No. 2(February 1983), pp. 235A-242A.

Chapter 14
General References (1), (5) and (8)

Chapter 15
General References (1), (5), and (6))
Adler, David, "Chemistry and Physics of Amorphous Semiconductors," *Journal of Chemical Education*, Vol. 58, No. 8(August 1980), pp. 560-564.
Bickford, Franklin R., "Diamond: Some Interesting Physical Properties," *Journal of Chemical Education*, Vol. 61, No. 5(May 1984), p. 401.
Brown, Glenn H., "Liquid Crystals—The Chameleon Chemicals," *Journal of Chemical Education*, Vol. 60, No. 10(October 1983), pp. 900-905.
Guĺ, Hasan, "A General Approach to Radius Ratios of Simple Ionic Crystals", *Journal of Chemical Education*, Vol. 62, No. 5(May 1985), p. 384.
Nathan, Lawrence C., "Predictions of Crystal Structure Based on Radius Ratio," *Journal of Chemical Education*, Vol. 62, No. 3(March 1985), pp. 215-218.
Philipps, James C., "The Physics of Glass," *Physics Today*, Vol. 35, No. 2(February 1982), pp. 27-33.
Schomaker, Verner, and E. C. Lingafelter, "Crystal Systems," *Journal of Chemical Education*, Vol. 62, No. 3(March 1985), pp. 219-220.

Chapter 16
General References (1) and (6)
Adler, David, "Chemistry and Physics of Amorphous Semiconductors," *Journal of Chemical Education*, Vol. 57, No. 8(August 1980), pp. 560-564.

Chapter 17
General Reference (5)

Chapter 18
General Reference (5)

Chapter 20
General References (5) and (8)
Hornack, Frederick M., "Further Reflections on Heat," *Journal of Chemical Education*, Vol. 61, No. 10(October 1984), pp. 869-874.
Rock, Peter A., *Chemical Thermodynamics,* Mill Valley, CA: University Science Books, 1983.
Spencer, J. N., and E. S. Holmboe, "Entropy and Unavailable Energy," *Journal of Chemical Education*, Vol. 60, No. 12(December 1983), pp. 1018-1021.

Chapter 21
General Reference (8)
Traptow, Richard S., "LeChatelier's Principle Applied to the Temperature Dependence of Solubility," *Journal of Chemical Education*, Vol. 61, No. 6(June 1984), pp. 499-502.

Chapter 22
Tanaka, Toyoichi, "Gels," *Scientific American,* Vol. 244, No. 1(January 1980), pp. 124-138.

Chapter 23
General References (5) and (8)
Bardsley, W. D., et al., "Catalysis of Radical Chain Reactions," *Journal of Chemical Education*, Vol. 61, No. 8(August 1984), pp. 657-658.
Barrow, Gordon M., "Free Energy and Equilibrium: The Basis of $\Delta G° = -RT(\ln K)$ for Reactions in Solution," *Journal of Chemical Education*, Vol. 60, No. 8(August 1983), pp. 648-650.
Campbell, J. Arthur, "LeChatelier's Principle, Temperature Effects, and Entropy," *Journal of Chemical Education*, Vol. 62, No. 3(March 1985), pp. 231-232.
Epstein, Irving R., et al., "Oscillating Chemical Reactions," *Scientific American,* Vol. 248, No. 3(March 1983), pp. 112-123.
Falbe, Jürgen, and Helmut Bahrmann, "Homogeneous Catalysis—Industrial Applications," *Journal of Chemical Education*, Vol. 61, No. 11(November 1984), pp. 961-967.
Gupta, K. S., and Y. K. Gupta, "Hydrogen-Ion Dependence of Reaction Rates and Mechanisms," *Journal of Chemical Education*, Vol. 61, No. 11(November 1984), pp. 972-978.
Labuza, T. P., "Application of Chemical Kinetics to Deterioration of Foods," *Journal of Chemical Education*, Vol. 61, No. 4(April 1984), pp. 348-358.
Mickey, Charles D., "Chemical Equilibrium," *Journal of Chemical Education*, Vol. 57, No. 11(November 1980), pp. 801-804.
Mickey, Charles D., "Chemical Kinetics: Reaction Rates," *Journal of Chemical Education*, Vol. 57, No. 9(September 1980), pp. 659-663.
Rock, Peter A., *Chemical Thermodynamics,* Mill Valley, CA: University Science Books, 1983.
Treptow, Richard S., "LeChatelier's Principle," *Journal of Chemical Education*, Vol. 57, No. 6(June 1980), pp. 417-420.
Tsonis, Christos P., "Catalysis on Polymeric Matrices," *Journal of Chemical Education*, Vol. 61, No. 6(June 1984), pp. 479-483.

Chapter 24
General Reference (8)

Brewer, Leo, "The Generalized Lewis Acid-Base Theory," *Journal of Chemical Education,* Vol. 61, No. 2(February 1984), pp. 101-104.

Monroe, Manus, and Karl Abrams, "The Relative Strength of Oxyacids and Its Application," *Journal of Chemical Education,* Vol. 62, No. 1(January 1985), pp. 41-43.

Rich, Ronald L., "Periodicity in the Acid-Base Behavior of Oxides and Hydroxides," *Journal of Chemical Education,* Vol. 62, No. 1(January 1985), pp. 44-46.

Chapter 25
Hugus, Z. Z., Jr., and F. C. Hentz, Jr., "A different Look at the Solubility-Product Principle," *Journal of Chemical Education,* Vol. 62, No. 8(August 1985), pp. 645-647.

Chapter 26
General References (5) and (8)

Chapter 27
General Reference (5)

Faulkner, Larry R., "Understanding Electrochemistry: Some Distinctive Concepts," *Journal of Chemical Education,* Vol. 60, No. 4(April 1983), pp. 262-264.

Sammells, Arthur F., "Fuel Cells and Electrochemical Energy Storage," *Journal of Chemical Education,* Vol. 60, No. 4(April 1983), pp. 320-324.

Chapter 28
Bodner, George M., and Tony A. Rhea, "Natural Sources of Ionizing Radiation," *Journal of Chemical Education,* Vol. 61, No. 8(August 1984), pp. 687-689.

Foster, N., "Diagnostic Radiopharmaceuticals," *Journal of Chemical Education,* Vol. 61, No. 8(August 1984), pp. 689-693.

Georgi, Howard, "A Unified Theory of Elementary Particles and Forces," *Scientific American,* Vol. 224, No. 4(April 1981), pp. 48-63.

Rowe, M. W., "Radioactive Dating," *Journal of Chemical Education,* Vol. 62, No. 7(July 1985), pp. 580-584.

Seaborg, Glenn T., "Nuclear Synthesis and Identification of New Elements," *Journal of Chemical Education,* Vol. 62, No. 5(May 1985), pp. 392-395.

Seaborg, Glenn T., "The Transuranium Elements," *Journal of Chemical Education,* Vol. 62, No. 6(June 1985), pp. 463-467.

Chapter 29
General References (2) and (7)

Chapter 30
General References (2) and (7)

Batra, Suzanne W. T., "Polyester-Making Bees and Other Innovative Insect Chemists," *Journal of Chemical Education,* Vol. 62, No. 2(February 1985), pp. 121-124.

Prestwich, Glenn D., "Termite Soldiers," *The Science Teacher,* Vol. 49, No. 3(March 1982), pp. 50-53.

Stranges, Anthony N., "Synthetic Petroleum from Coal Hydrogenation," *Journal of Chemical Education,* Vol. 60, No. 8(August 1983), pp. 617-625.

Taylor, R. J., *Food Additives,* New York: John Wiley & Sons 1980.

Tocci, Salvatore, "Over-the-Counter Chemistry," *The Science Teacher,* Vol. 49, No. 8(November 1982), pp. 45-48.

STUDENT GENERAL REFERENCES

The following references should be accessible to students in the classroom or school library.

Himes, Gary K., et al., *Solving Problems in Chemistry*, Columbus, OH: Charles E. Merrill Publishing Co., 1987.

Shugar, Gershon J., et al., *Chemical Technician's Ready Reference Handbook*, New York: McGraw-Hill Book Company, 1981.

Magazines

DISCOVER
Time-Life Building
541 N. Fairbanks Court
Chicago, IL 60672

CHEMECOLOGY
Chemical Manufacturer's Association
2501 M St., NW
Washington, DC 20037

CHEM MATTERS
American Chemical Society
1155 16th Street, N.W.
Washington, DC 20036

FDA CONSUMER
Superintendent of Documents
Government Printing Office
Washington, DC 20402

JOURNAL OF CHEMICAL EDUCATION
20th & Northampton Sts.
Easton, PA 18042

NATIONAL GEOGRAPHIC SOCIETY
1155 Sixteenth St., NW
Washington, DC 20036

OMNI
Omni Publications International Ltd.
909 Third Ave.
New York, NY 10022

PHYSICS TODAY
American Institute of Physics
S/F Division
335 East 45th St.
New York, NY 10017

POPULAR SCIENCE
Boulder, CO 80302

SCIENCE
American Association for the Advancement of Science
1515 Massachusetts Ave., NW
Washington, DC 20005

SCIENCE DIGEST
P.O. Box 10076
Des Moines, IA 50350

SCIENCE NEWS
Science Service, Inc.
231 W.. Center St.
Marion, OH 43302

SCIENCE 8
Subscription Department
Xerox Publications
Columbus, OH 43216

SCIENTIFIC AMERICAN
Scientific American Inc.
415 Madison Ave.
New York, NY 10017

AUDIOVISUAL AIDS

Chapter 1

Ins and Outs of Energy, Learning Arts, Chemistry #112, filmstrips/8 cassettes

Pollution: Problems and Prospects, National Geographic Society, #03244, 2 filmstrips

The Forms of energy, Nova, #530-1724, filmstrips/2 cassettes

Chapter 2

Basic Math for Science Students and Technicians, Prentice-Hall, #WLC800FS, filmstrips/slides/10 cassettes

Density, Science Software Systems, #VCT-2, videocassette

Mathematical Techniques for Science Students, Prentice-Hall, #WLC905FS, filmstrips/slides/3 cassettes

Metric System Tutor, Nova, #519-0500, computer software, Apple

Modern Measure: The SI Metric System, Prentice-Hall, #WLC660, filmstrips/4 cassettes

Physics: Measurement of Scalars, Bergwall, #150, filmstrips/4 cassettes

Stoichiometric Calculations, Prentice-Hall, #WLC720FS, filmstrips/slides/4 cassettes

Temperature Conversions, °C, °F, K, TEMP, Programs for Learning, computer software, Apple/TRS-80/Pet-C64

Significant Figures Drill, SIGHELP, Programs for Learning, computer software, Apple/TRS-80/Pet-C64

Scientific Notation Drill, EXPO, Programs for Learning, computer software, Apple/TRS-80/Pet-C64

Metric Conversions Drill, SYSTEM, Programs for Learning, computer software, Apple/TRS-80/Pet-C64

Density Calculations Drill, DENSITY, Programs for Learning, computer software, Apple/TRS-80/Pet-C64

Chapter 3

All about Matter, Nova. #530-1710, filmstrips/4 cassettes

Chapter 4

Chemistry I Series, Science Software Systems, #CI-2200, computer software, Apple

Introduction to Chemical Nomenclature, Prentice-Hall, #WLC840FS, filmstrips/slides/3 cassettes

Naming Chemical Substances, Prentice-Hall, #WLC730FS, filmstrips/slides/2 cassettes

Symbols, Formulas, and Equations, Learning Arts, Chemistry #101, filmstrips/4 cassettes

Names and Symbols Drill, SYMBOL, Programs for Learning, computer software, Apple/TRS-80/Pet-C64

Ion Symbols and Changes, IONS, Programs for Learning, computer software, Apple/TRS-80/Pet-C64

Compounds' Names and Formulas, NOMEN, Programs for Learning, computer software, Apple/TRS-80/Pet-C64

Chapter 5

Chemistry I Series, Science Software Systems, #CI-2200, computer software, Apple

Stoichiometric Calculations, Prentice-Hall, #WLC720FS, filmstrips/slides/4 cassettes

Stoichiometry, Prentice-Hall, #WLC830FS, filmstrips/slides/4 cassettes

The Mole Concept, Inquiry Audio-Visuals, #67130, filmstrip

Moles and Formulas, Carolina, #41-3532, computer software, Apple

Formula Mass Calculations, MOLWT, Programs for Learning, computer software, Apple/TRS-80/Pet-C64

Mole and Percentage Composition Drill, MOLES, Programs for Learning, computer software, Apple/TRS-80/Pet-C64

Chapter 6

Balancing Chemical Equations, Prentice-Hall, #WLC710FS, filmstrips/slides/4 cassettes

Chemical Equations, Carolina, #41-3542, computer software, Apple

Symbols, Formulas, and Equations, Learning Arts, Chemistry #101, filmstrips/4 cassettes

Balancing Equations Drill, BALEQ, Programs for Learning, computer software, Apple/TRS-80/Pet-C64

Chemical Equations, Carolina, #41-3542, computer software, Apple

Chemical Reaction Principles, Science Software Systems, #480-0085, slides

Ins and Outs of Energy, Learning Arts, Chemistry #112, filmstrips/8 cassettes

Moles and Formulas, Carolina, #41-3532, computer software, Apple

Stoichiometry, Prentice-Hall, #WLC830FS, filmstrips/slides/4 cassettes

Chapter 7

Atomic Structure, Prentice-Hall, #WLC850FS, filmstrips/slides/4 cassettes

Chemistry I Series, Science Software Systems, #CI-2200 computer software, Apple

Definite Proportions: Electrolysis of Water, BFA Educational Media, #4B0672C, filmloop

Models of the Atom, Audio Visual Narrative Arts, Inc., #005C, filmstrips/5 cassettes

Spectroscopy, Modern Learning Aids, #140-4207, 16 mm film

The Atom: From Atomic Hypothesis to Atomic Fact, Audio Visual Narrative Arts, Inc., #441C, filmstrips/3 cassettes

Millikan Oil Drop Experiment, MILKAN, Programs for Learning, computer software, Apple/TRS-80/Pet-C64

Name and Symbols of Elements, ELEMENT, Programs for Learning, computer software, Apple/TRS-80/Pet-C64

Chemistry Demos, Cambridge Development Laboratory, Inc., #CDL-SPECTRA-A, computer software, Apple

Chapter 8

Atomic Structure, Prentice-Hall, #WLC850FS, filmstrips/slides/4 cassettes

Chemistry I Series, Science Software Systems, #CI-2200, computer software, Apple

Electron Configurations, Science Software Systems, #VCT-4, videocassette

Electron Configurations and Orbital Diagrams, Science Software Systems, #475-0255, filmstrip/slides/cassette

Electron Structure, Carolina, #41-3812, computer software, Apple

Light: The Wave That Wasn't—Quantum Theory, Audio Visual Narrative Arts, #425C, filmstrips/4 cassettes

Models of the Atom, Audio Visual Narrative Arts, #005C, filmstrips/5 cassettes

Particles and Waves—Quantum Theory, Audio Visual Narrative Arts, #429C, filmstrips/4 cassettes

Quantum Numbers, Science Software Systems, #VCT-5, videocassette

Structure of Atoms Drill, ATOMIC, Programs for Learning, computer software, Apple/TRS-80/Pet-C64

Chapter 9

Atomic Structure, Prentice-Hall, #WLC850FS, filmstrips/slides/4 cassettes

Quantum Numbers, Science Software Systems, #VCT-5, videocassette

Electron Structure, Carolina #41-3812, computer software, Apple

The Periodic Table, Science Software Systems, #480-0080, slides

The Periodic Table of the Elements, Prentice-Hall, #WLC740FS, filmstrips/slides/2 cassettes

Electron Configuration, SPDF, Programs for Learning, computer software, Apple/TRS-80/Pet-C64

The Octet Rule, LEWIS, Programs for Learning, computer software, Apple/TRS-80/Pet-C64

Chapter 10

Properties of Elements, TRENDS, Programs for Learning, computer software, Apple/TRS-80/Pet-C64

Ionization Energies, IE, Programs for Learning, computer software, Apple/TRS-80/Pet-C64

Chapter 11

Chemical Elements, Science Software Systems, #480-0465F, #480-0475F, 7 filmstrips

Properties of the Elements, Kalmia, #7010, filmloop or 16 mm film

The Periodic Table, Science Software Systems, #480-0080, slides

The Periodic Table of the Elements, Prentice-Hall, #WLC740FS, filmstrips/slides/2 cassettes

Observe the Properties—Simulation, STATE, Programs for Learning, computer software, Apple/TRS-80/Pet-C64

Chapter 12

Bonding of Atoms, Learning Arts, Chemistry #104 series, 13 filmstrips

Chemical Bonding, Prentice-Hall, #WLC860FS, film-strips/slides/5 cassettes

Forces in Solids, Liquids, and Gases, Learning Arts, Chemistry #109, filmstrips/5 cassettes

The Periodic Table, Science Software Systems, #480-0080, slides

Molecular Geometry, VSEPR, Programs for Learning, computer software, Apple/TRS-80/Pet-C64

Chemistry Demos, Cambridge Development Laboratory, Inc., #CDL-SPECTRA-A, computer software, Apple

Chapter 13

Bonding between Atoms of the Same Element: Nonmetals and the Covalent Bond, Science Software Systems, #475-0305, filmstrip/slides/cassette

Bonding of Atoms, Learning Arts, Chemistry #104 series, filmstrips/13 cassettes

Electron Configurations, Science Software Systems, #VCT-4, videocassette

Chapter 14

Bonding of Atoms, Learning Arts, Chemistry #104 series, filmstrips/13 cassettes

Chemical Bonding, Prentice-Hall, #WLC860FS, film-strips/slides/5 cassettes

Coordination Compounds and Other Special Topics, Science Software Systems, #475-0245, filmstrip/slides/cassette

The Periodic Table, Science Software Systems, #480-0080, slides

Chapter 15

Properties of Gases, Learning Arts, Chemistry #106, filmstrips/6 cassettes

The States of Matter, CRM McGraw-Hill Films, #106656-X, 16 mm film

Chapter 16

Crystal Systems of Minerals, Science Software Systems, #480-0645, slides

Forces in Solids, Liquids, and Gases, Learning Arts, Chemistry #109, filmstrips/5 cassettes

Chapter 17

Forces in Solids, Liquids, and Gases, Learning Arts, Chemistry #109, filmstrips/5 cassettes

Vapor Pressure and Partial Pressure, Learning Arts, Chemistry #107, filmstrips/3 cassettes

Chapter 18

Gas Laws, Prentice-Hall, #WLC890FS, filmstrips/slides/4 cassettes

Properties of Gases, Learning Arts, Chemistry #106, filmstrips/6 cassettes

Vapor Pressure and Partial Pressure, Learning Arts, Chemistry #107, filmstrips/3 cassettes

Gas Laws, GASES, Programs for Learning, computer software, Apple/TRS-80/Pet-C64

Chapter 19

Chemistry I Series, Science Software Systems, #CI-2200, computer software (Apple)

Gaseous Volume and the Mole, Learning Arts, Chemistry #108, filmstrips/3 cassettes

Gas Laws, Prentice-Hall, #WLC890FS, filmstrips/slides/4 cassettes

Moles and Formulas, Carolina, #41-3532, computer software (Apple)

Properties of Gases, Learning Arts, Chemistry #106, filmstrips/6 cassettes

Stoichiometric Calculations, Prentice-Hall, #WLC720FS, filmstrips/slides/4 cassettes

Stoichiometry, Prentice-Hall, #WLC830FS, filmstrips/slides/4 cassettes

Chapter 20

Energy and Entropy in Chemical Reactions, Prentice-Hall, #WLC821, filmstrips/2 cassettes

Chapter 21

Looking at the Solution, Learning Arts, Chemistry #110, filmstrips/5 cassettes

Molarity of Solutions, Learning Arts, Chemistry #111, filmstrips/3 cassettes

Solution Problems, Prentice-Hall, #WLC895FS, filmstrips/slides/3 cassettes

Solubility Curves, SOLUBLE, Programs for Learning, computer software, Apple/TRS-80/Pet-C64

Molarity Problems, MOLAR, Programs for Learning, computer software, Apple/TRS-80/Pet-C64

Chapter 22

Looking at the Solution, Learning Arts, Chemistry #110, filmstrips/5 cassettes

Solution Problems, Prentice-Hall, #WLC895FS, filmstrips/slides/3 cassettes

Solution Process and Theory, Science Software Systems, #480-0485F, 3 filmstrips

Chapter 23

Chemical Equilibrium, Prentice-Hall, #WLC880FS, filmstrips/slides/8 cassettes

Chemical Reaction Principles, Science Software Systems, #480-0085, slides

Equilibrium: Le Chatelier's Principle, BFA Educational Media, #4B0678C, filmloop

Reaction Kinetics, Carolina, #41-4522, computer software, Apple

Reaction Rates, BFA Educational Media, #4B0679C, filmloop

Reaction Rates: Molecules in Motion, Learning Arts, Chemistry #116, filmstrips/9 cassettes

Mathematical Model of Equilibrium, HIEQ, Programs for Learning, computer software, Apple/TRS-80/Pet-C64

Equilibrium Concentrations and K_{eq}, EQUIL, Programs for Learning, computer software, Apple/TRS-80/Pet-C64

Equilibrium Problems, EQPROB, Programs for Learning, computer software, Apple/TRS-80/Pet-C64

LeChatelier's Principle, LECHAT, Programs for Learning, computer software, Apple/TRS-80/Pet-C64

Haber Process—Simulation, HABER, Programs for Learning, computer software, Apple/TRS-80/Pet-C64

Chapter 24

All About Acids and Bases, Nova, #530-1717, filmstrips/4 cassettes

Chemical Equilibrium, Prentice-Hall, #WLC880FS, filmstrips/slides/8 cassettes

Acid Strength and K_a, DRILL 1, Programs for Learning,

computer software, Apple/TRS-80/Pet-C64

Brønsted Acids and Bases, BRNSTD, Programs for Learning, computer software, Apple/TRS-80/Pet-C64

Chapter 25

Acid Base Problems, Carolina, #41-3582, computer software, Apple

All about Acids and Bases, Nova, #530-1717, filmstrips/4 cassettes

Chemical Equilibrium, Prentice-Hall, #WLC880FS, filmstrips/slides/8 cassettes

pH, pOH, and Buffers, Science Software Systems, #475-0340, filmstrip/slides/cassette

Solution Problems, Prentice-Hall, #WLC895FS, filmstrips/slides/3 cassettes

Solubility Product Constant, K_{sp}, KSP2, and KSP, Programs for Learning, computer software, Apple/TRS-80/Pet-C64

pH Problems, PH, Programs for Learning, computer software, Apple/TRS-80/Pet-C64

Acid-Base Titration Curves and pH, TCPLOT, Programs for Learning, computer software, Apple/TRS-80/Pet-C64

Acid-Base Titration Simulation, ENDPT, Programs for Learning, computer software, Apple/TRS-80/Pet-C64

pH Plot, Cambridge Development Laboratory, Inc. #CDL-PH-PLOT, computer software, Apple

Chapter 26

Balancing Chemical Equations, Prentice-Hall, #WLC710FS, filmstrips/slides/4 cassettes

Oxidation Reduction, Carolina, #41-3552, computer software, Apple

Oxidation-Reduction Reaction, Science Software Systems, #480-0460F, 4 filmstrips

Chapter 27

Chemical Reaction Principles, Science Software Systems, #480-0085, slides

Electrochemistry, Prentice-Hall, #WLC870FS, filmstrips/slides/4 cassettes

Galvanic Cells: Electrolytes and Electrodes, BFA Educational Media, #4B0675C, filmloop

Galvanic Cells: Half-Cell Reactions, BFA Educational Media, #4B0676C, filmloop

Oxidation-Reduction: Electrolytic Cells, BFA Educational Media, #4B0671C, filmloop

Voltaic Cells, REDOX, Programs for Learning, computer software, Apple/TRS-80/Pet-C64

Chapter 28

Atomic Energy, Nova, #525-1615, 6 transparencies

Fermilab, Educational Audio Visuals Inc., #E1KF 1628, filmstrip/cassette

Nuclear Energy: Peril or Promise, Science and Mankind, #1-1051-2850, slides/cassette

Radioactivity, Prentice-Hall, #WLC855FS, filmstrips/slides/2 cassettes

Nuclear Equations, NUCLER, Programs for Learning, computer software, Apple/TRS-80/Pet-C64

Chapter 29

Nomenclature in Organic Chemistry, Prentice-Hall, #WLC9101, filmstrips/slides/3 cassettes

Organic Chemistry, Learnings Arts, Chemistry #120, filmstrips/7 cassettes

Organic Chemistry, Nova, #519-0560, computer software, Apple

Alkane Nomenclature, ALKANE, Programs for Learning, computer software, Apple/TRS-80/Pet-C64

Organic Nomenclature, ALKYL, Programs for Learning, computer software, Apple/TRS-80/Pet-C64

Chapter 30

Organic Chemistry, Learning Arts, Chemistry #120, filmstrips/7 cassettes

Organic Chemistry, Nova, #519-0560, computer software, Apple

Biochemistry, Nova, #519-0552, computer software, Apple

R. Bruce Merrifield: The Chemical Synthesis of Proteins, Films for the Humanities and Sciences, 22 min. color videotape

AUDIOVISUAL SUPPLIERS

Audio Visual Narrative Arts, Inc.
Box 9
Pleasantville, NY 10570

Bergwall Productions Inc.
839 Stewart Ave.
Garden City, NY 11530

BFA Educational Media
2211 Michigan Ave.
Santa Monica, CA 90404

Cambridge Development Laboratory, Inc.
1696 Massachusetts Ave.
Cambridge, MA 02138

Carolina Biological Supply Company
2700 York Road
Burlington, NC 27215

CRM McGraw-Hill Films
110 Fifteenth St.
Del Mar, CA 92014

Educational Audio Visuals, Inc.
Pleasantville, NY 10570

Films for the Humanities and Sciences
Box 2053
Princeton, NJ 08540

Inquiry Audio-Visuals
1754 West Farragut Ave.
Chicago, IL 60640

Kalmia Company
Department C6
Concord, MA 01742

Learning Arts
P.0 Box 179
Wichita, KS 67201

Modern Learning Aids
Ward's Natural Science Establishment Inc.
P.O. Box 1712
Rochester, NY 14603

National Geographic Society
Educational Services
Washington, DC 20036

Nova Scientific Corporation
111 Tucker St.
P.O. Box 500
Burlington, NC 27215

Prentice-Hall Media
150 White Plains Rd.
Tarrytown, NY 10591

Programs for Learning, Inc.
P.O. Box 954
New Milford, CT 06776

Science and Mankind Inc.
Communications Park
Box 2000
Mount Kisco, NY 10549

Science Software Systems Inc.
11899 West Pico Blvd.
West Los Angeles, CA 90064

University of Iowa
Conduit Oakdale Campus
Iowa City, IA 52242

PERFORMANCE OBJECTIVES

WHAT IS A GOOD PERFORMANCE OBJECTIVE?

Statements of performance objectives can usually be divided into three distinct parts. First is a description of the conditions under which the desired behavior will be observed. Here are some examples that describe the condition:

"When presented with models of crystal structures . . . ."

"When asked to draw electron dot diagrams for . . . ."

"When presented with the materials suggested on page. . . ."

"After having read and discussed. . . ."

"In groups of three students, given conductivity apparatus and several solutions. . . ."

A good performance objective includes a condition that tells what causes, stimulates, or motivates the student to perform the behaviors or under what circumstances those behaviors will be performed.

The second part of a well-stated performance objective is a clear description of exactly what behavior you're looking for. A good performance objective would avoid using such terms as "know about," "appreciate," or "sense the relationship between." Rather, a good performance objective will include terms that describe what you could observe students doing if they do "know about" or "appreciate." It's almost impossible to observe students "appreciating," but you can gather some evidence that they are appreciating science if they are

reading science books instead of comic books;

staying late or coming to class early to work in the laboratory;

requesting that you repeat a demonstration or wanting to do it themselves.

In other words, a good performance objective uses verbs that express some type of observable action. Here are some examples of action verbs that describe observable behaviors:

states orally	manipulates
matches	measures
distinguishes between	expresses
constructs	observes
identifies	states hypotheses

The third part of a well-stated performance objective is a description of some level of performance or criteria that may help you to know if the student or class has performed to the degree that you hoped for.

For example, if you were teaching students to use a balance, would you want all of your class to be able to accurately measure the mass of a solid or liquid? Would you feel satisfied if 90% of your class could perform this

skill? 80%? 50%? Would you be happy if just one student did it? Obviously, this level of performance would vary for each class, each student, each teacher, and each task.

What do we mean by accurately? Would you be satisfied if students could measure a mass to the nearest centigram? Half-centigram? Milligram? Just how accurately would be acceptable to you? Here then, is another aspect of a level of performance: A well-stated performance objective might also include some description of how precise, how accurate, how well the behavior should be performed in order for you to know that the student has really achieved the objective.

Another kind of a criterion measure or performance level that might be included in a performance objective is a statement of how often or how many times students must perform the behavior in order to demonstrate that they have learned something. For example, if a student measured a mass with a balance accurately just one time, would you conclude that the student has learned how to measure? What if you asked the student to measure the mass of five objects with a balance, and you were looking for the ability to measure them correctly to the nearest centigram? Would you be satisfied if the student measured four of them correctly? Three out of five? Or would you only be satisfied if the student measured all five of them correctly?

Again, this decision will have to be made on the basis of what you know about the student's ability, and the task at hand.

Now let's put all these parts together and see what a well-stated performance objective looks like.

Conditions—*tells you how to plan and organize your class and what materials you'll need*
Working individually, when presented with a laboratory balance, beaker, liquid, solid, and graduated cylinder, ...

Performance—*tells you what student behaviors to look for*
Students will measure the masses of the liquid and solid to the nearest 0.01 g, measure the volume of liquid to the nearest 0.01 cm^3, measure the volume of the solid by liquid displacement. Students will be able to calculate the density of the solid and liquid to the correct number of significant digits.

Criterion Measure—*tells you to what degree the objective should be achieved*
Of all the students, 95% will achieve 100% of the above objectives.

HOW DO YOU USE THE PERFORMANCE OBJECTIVES IN THIS TEACHER'S GUIDE?

Performance objectives are listed for each chapter of *CHEMISTRY: A MODERN COURSE.* They are related to four broad goals of science education.

A **Attitudes:** to develop students' attitudes of curiosity and involvement with phenomena in their natural environment, to develop an appreciation for the contributions of science to daily living, and to develop the value and inclinations toward solving problems in a scientific manner

P **Processes:** to develop those intellectual processes of inquiry by which scientific problems and phenomena are explained, predicted, and/or controlled

K **Knowledge:** to develop knowledge of facts, terminology, concepts, generalizations, and principles that help students confront and interpret their environment

S **Skills:** to develop students' ability to handle, construct, and manipulate materials and equipment in a productive and safe manner, and to develop their ability to measure, organize, and communicate scientific information.

Next to each performance objective you will find one or more of the following letters: A, P, K, S. They indicate the goal on which the objective is based—Attitudes, Processes, Knowledge, Skills. Keep in mind a balance among these four goals since they are all of equal priority.

Attitudes

The statements of performance objectives that are identified as "A"—developing Attitude goals—are behaviors that you might observe as students increase their enjoyment of science activities, and as they demonstrate an interest in the scientific objects and events in their environment. You will find such statements as:

Students will request that the demonstration be repeated.

Students will volunteer to conduct outside research.

Students will request the use of the chemistry laboratory during free periods.

Students will volunteer to do research and report their findings in class.

As you can see, few of these behaviors are prompted by the teacher. They are voluntary behaviors that indicate an affinity for, an inclination toward, and a preference for science. You will find suggested attitudinal behaviors at the end of each area or chapter when students may have an opportunity to go beyond the information presented in the text.

Processes

The statements of performance objectives that are identified as "P"—developing Process goals—are behaviors that you might observe as students use the thinking processes of analyzing, experimenting, applying, hypothesizing, theorizing, comparing and contrasting, classifying, observing, etc. You will find such statements as:

When presented with various objects, students will compare and contrast their similarities and differences and classify them as metallic or nonmetallic.

Given data from Appendix A, students will calculate the amount of energy needed to raise the temperature of 1000 kg of iron from 20°C to 1000°C.

Given a skeleton equation, students will balance a redox equation by the half-reduction method.

Knowledge

The statements of performance objectives that are identified as "K"—developing Knowledge goals—are behaviors that you might observe as students demonstrate they have gained an understanding and use of certain terms, concepts, and generalizations of science. You will find such statements as:

> When asked, students will define the term "ionization" correctly.

> Students will correctly identify the triple point on a phase diagram.

> Students will describe the effects of a catalyst on reaction rate.

Generally, a knowledge objective is one that calls upon the student to recall or explain information, concepts, or principles that have been learned in the past or that have been presented in the text and other materials.

Skills

The statements of performance objectives that are identified as "S"—developing Skills goals—are behaviors that you might observe as students gain skill in using scientific equipment correctly, and organizing, recording, or reporting information accurately. Some examples of such statements are:

> Students will use a pipette to transfer a solution from one container to another.

> While observing the demonstration, students will record their observations in their notebooks.

> Using plastic spheres and toothpicks, students will construct models of crystal lattice types.

In the Teacher Guide that follows, specific statements of the goals for each chapter are given. Goal statements are also given at the beginning of each chapter in the student's text. Following the goal statements in the Teacher Guide, the specific performance objectives for each section of the chapter are listed. There may be several objectives in each section. After each objective is a number that corresponds to that section of the chapter. From these objectives you should be able to determine and plan for the achievement of the objectives for each section of a chapter.

Remember, these performance objectives are not meant to be all inclusive. You should supplement them with objectives from other sources and with those you create yourself.

You will also find that the criterion or level of performance for each objective is not included. The intent was to create guidelines and not to state levels of expectancies for you. Only you can decide if 100% or only 50% of your students should be able to accomplish each task. You will need to develop and insert these criterion levels for your own students based upon your materials, and your own situation.

HOW DO YOU KNOW YOU'VE ACHIEVED YOUR OBJECTIVES?

When you try to find out if students have learned anything, you probably give some form of written test—true-false, completion, matching, multiple choice, or essay type of examination. All of these forms of evaluation are important in determining whether or not students have achieved their objectives. Evaluation materials are available to accompany *CHEMISTRY: A MODERN COURSE*. Each chapter test is based on the performance objectives in this Teacher Guide.

BIBLIOGRAPHY

Bloom, Benjamin, Hastings, J. Thomas, and Madaus, George, *Handbook on Formative and Summative Evaluation of Student Learning.* McGraw-Hill Book Co., New York, 1971.

Bloom, Benjamin and others, *Taxonomy of Educational Objectives, Handbook I: Cognitive Domain.* David McKay, New York, 1956.

Gronlund, Norman, *Stating Objectives for Classroom Instruction,* MacMillan, New York, 1985.

Krathwohl, D. R., Bloom, Benjamin, and Masia, Bertram R., *Taxonomy of Educational Objectives, Handbook II: Affective Domain.* David McKay, New York, 1956.

Lindvall, C. M., ed., *Defining Educational Objectives.* University of Pittsburgh Press, Pittsburgh, 1964.

Mager, Robert, *Preparing Instructional Objectives.* Fearon Publishers, Inc., Palo Alto, Calif., 1962.

Popham, W. James, *The Teacher-Empiricist.* Aegeus Publishing Co., Los Angeles, 1965.

Popham, W. James, and Baker, Eva L., *Establishing Instructional Goals.* Prentice Hall, Inc., Englewood Cliffs, N.J., 1970.

NATURE, CHEMISTRY, AND YOU

1

AN OVERVIEW

Chapter 1 demonstrates the relevance of chemistry to daily life. The chapter should leave the student with the realization that when voting on future scientific issues, the ballot must be cast after a detailed analysis of the facts. Chemistry will provide the student with the background needed to better understand the laws and relationships of the natural world. The first of these relationships is presented in chapter one, that of matter and energy ($E = mc^2$).

DEMONSTRATION INFORMATION

Before class prepare three solutions as follows: Dissolve 5 or 6 very small crystals of $KMnO_4$ in 500 cm^3 of water to make a pale wine-colored solution. Dissolve 1 g of $NaHSO_3$ in as little water as possible. Dissolve 1 g $BaCl_2 \cdot 2H_2O$ in a small amount of water. In class, pour the 500 cm^3 of "wine" ($KMnO_4$ soln) into a large beaker or flask.

Before class, place the $NaHSO_3$ solution in the bottom of an empty flask. Place the $BaCl_2$ solution in the bottom of a second empty flask. Pour the "wine" into the first flask containing $NaHSO_3$ to change it into "water." Next, pour the "water" into the second flask containing the $BaCl_2$. The "water" will turn into "milk". Emphasize to the students that the chemist is trained to take what is abundant and change it into another substance that can be used as a substitute for what is in short supply. Knowing the chemistry of this demonstration would be of little value to your students at this time. Your purpose should be to emphasize that the chemist has the experience to know how to change one substance into another substance with different properties.

Disposal: *Decant the liquid. Pour it down the drain with a large quantity of water. Dispose of the precipitate in the normal manner by placing it in your solid waste container. It can then be put in a local landfill.*

PERFORMANCE OBJECTIVES

Goals: Students will gain an understanding of the nature of chemistry. Students will examine the relationship between science and human progress. Students will define matter and energy.

Objectives: Upon completion of the reading and problems, and when asked to demonstrate their understanding either orally or on a written test, students will

1:1	P	list ways early civilizations have modified the environment for useful or destructive purposes. **Intro**
1:2	P	list some major problems facing today's world. **1:1**
1:3	P	differentiate between facts and value judgments. **1:2**
1:4	K	define science and hypothesis. **1:2**
1:5	K	define chemistry and state the role of chemists. **1:3**
1:6	K	define inertia, and matter in terms of inertia. **1:4**
1:7	K	differentiate among the three general forms of energy: potential, kinetic, and radiant. **1:5**
1:8	K	define energy. **1:5**
1:9	K	distinguish the energy transfer in nuclear change from that in other types of change. **1:5, 6**
1:10	K/P	state and briefly explain the law of conservation of matter, the law of conservation of energy, and the law of conservation of mass-energy and recognize examples of each. **1:6**
1:11	K	state Einstein's equation, the meaning of each symbol, and describe the significance of the equation. **1:6**
1:12	K	state the relationship between mass and matter. **1:6**
1:13	A	exhibit an interest in science by completing voluntarily one or more of the One More Step activities at the end of the chapter.
1:14	A	read unassigned literature related to the ideas presented in the chapter.

TEACHING TECHNIQUES

Section 1:1

As you discuss the world's needs versus available space and resources, point out the role of chemists and research. Chemists are able to convert materials into substances that will be suitable substitutes for scarce resources.

Section 1:5

Discuss the necessity of including cost considerations in the decision making processes concerning energy alternatives. Have students bring in articles from the newspaper and magazines concerning alternative sources of power and the advantages and disadvantages of each. This approach reinforces the idea developed in Section 1:2 that applications of scientific knowledge involve considerations other than straight scientific facts. When considering alternate energy forms, the resource supply, economics, and values all play an important part.

A battery is an excellent example of chemical potential energy. If you connect one to a small electric motor, you can demonstrate the conversion to kinetic energy.

Be sure students understand the differences among kinetic, potential, and radiant energy. These terms will be used throughout the text in describing chemical behavior.

Careers and Chemistry

Use this feature as the start of a year long project whereby students investigate the various branches and careers in chemistry. For example, you can assign reports on a weekly basis having a student report on biochemistry as a science while another student may focus on the duties of a biochemist. Appendix D—Careers can aid you in making these assignments. There are a number of popular science magazines available that highlight the branches of science and give personal insights into some of today's important scientists. Make arrangements to have these magazines made available to your students. A career bulletin board is another way of generating interest. Allow students to have an active part in putting the display together.

ONE MORE STEP

Page 15

1. Nearly every student can list some of the more common industries. The list will vary with the community, but would include the chemical producing and consuming industries, institutions of higher education, government agencies, medical and pharmaceutical institutions.

2. Cockcroft and Walton bombarded ^7Li nuclei with protons and obtained two alpha particles as products. From the balancing of the mass-energy of the system before and after the change, the Einstein equivalence hypothesis was established.

3. Advantages—source of food and oil, source of employment.

Disadvantages—loss of several species of interest and beauty, upset ecological balance. See *Oceans*, Vol. 10, No. 4(July-August 1977).

4. Advantages—source of power not dependent on dwindling oil supplies, does not pollute air
   Disadvantages—thermal pollution of cooling water source, radioactive waste disposal

5. Refer to the following article for detailed information. Paint, Roland D., "NOAA and the Nantucket Oilspill." *NOAA*, Vol. 7, No. 2(April 1977), pp. 9-20.

6. The fertilizer is biodegradable and reduces surface water contamination. This reduces algae growth in ponds and streams. The disadvantage is that it is expensive for the farmer. Currently, farmers spend about $90.00 per acre of corn for agri-chemicals.

CHAPTER END PROBLEMS

Pages 14-15

1. potential, kinetic, electrical, mechanical, thermal, radiant

2. agronomist—field crops and soil
   astronomer—stars, planets, other bodies of the universe
   biologist—living things
   botanist—plant life
   ecologist—living things and their environment
   entomologist—insects
   geochemist—chemical properties and changes in the earth's crust
   geologist—history of the earth's crust
   geophysicist—physical properties of the earth's crust
   horticulturist—fruits, vegetables, decorative plants
   limnologist—properties and conditions of fresh water areas
   metallurgist—metals
   meteorologist—weather
   physicist—energy-matter relationships
   zoologist—animal life

3. There are many that most students can name: pharmacist, doctor, farmer, foundry chemist, biologist. Accept what you wish.

4. Types of facts that may be mentioned: Should the lake be developed? How will it be developed? Will it harm the ecology of the area? What kind of development should it be: single homes, apartments, condominiums? This should produce much discussion regarding facts and value judgments.

5. Student answers will vary. They should include economic, social, health, and environmental concerns.

6. potential—energy due to position
   kinetic—energy due to motion
   radiant—energy of electromagnetic wave

7. The average household spends 15% of its income for chemicals each year. The citizen will be a better consumer of these household and garden chemicals. The chemicals will be handled properly and disposed of safely. The citizen will be an informed voter.

8. Matter can be changed to energy. Energy can be changed to matter. Mass and energy are always conserved.

MEASURING AND CALCULATING

2

AN OVERVIEW

Chapter 2 reviews basic mathematical techniques and measuring principles which are important in problem solving and laboratory work. In addition, the factor-label method of problem solving is introduced and will be used throughout the book.

SI measurement units are used throughout the text with few exceptions. As in the United States, SI is being used to facilitate communication among scientists all over the world.

We encourage the use of calculators in high school chemistry. Stress to students that in chemistry they will begin to use, perhaps for the first time, the math skills they have learned over the years to solve practical, relevant problems. It is important that you approach measurement and calculations in a positive manner.

DEMONSTRATION INFORMATION

Place 100 cm^3 of pure glycerine in a 250 cm^3 beaker. Next, place a small rubber stopper, size 00, and a small cork from a litmus paper tube into the glycerine. Both float. Carefully add 100 cm^3 of H_2O to the beaker containing the glycerine. You may want to add food coloring to the water before adding it to the glycerine. The cork floats in the water. Discuss the density difference. To make the demonstration more interesting, have the students predict the outcome before you add the H_2O layer. Ask the students why ice floats in H_2O liquid.

Disposal: *Decant the H_2O. Pour it down the drain. Dispose of the glycerine in the normal manner by placing it in a container. It can then be put in a local landfill.*

PERFORMANCE OBJECTIVES

Goals: Students will demonstrate a proficiency in using SI units. Students will use factor-label method to make chemical calculations. Students will differentiate between accuracy and precision.

Objectives: Upon completion of the reading and problems, and when asked to demonstrate their understanding either orally or on a written test, students will

2:1	K	list the three requirements for making a measurement. **Intro**
2:2	K	distinguish quantitative and qualitative characteristics. **Intro**
2:3	K	list and define the seven basic SI units with their categories of measurement. **2:1, 3-5**
2:4	K	define the commonly used SI prefixes: kilo-, deci-, centi-, milli-, micro-, and nano-. **2:1**
2:5	K	define mass, weight, and balance and state the differences between mass and weight. **2:2**
2:6	K	define temperature and give the basis for the Celsius temperature scale. **2:5**
2:7	K	distinguish precision and accuracy. **2:6**
2:8	P	determine the relative error of a measurement given its accuracy. **2:6**
2:9	K/P	define significant digits and determine the number of significant digits in a given measurement. **2:7**
2:10	P	express the results of addition, subtraction, multiplication, and division of measurements in the correct number of significant digits. **2:8**
2:11	K/P	convert numbers from decimal notation to scientific notation and vice versa, and perform calculations using scientific notation. **2:8**
2:12	K/P	combine SI units to form derived units, such as speed, area, and volume. **2:9**
2:13	P/S	demonstrate a logical approach to solving a problem. **2:10**
2:14	P	use the factor-label method for solving problems and making SI conversions. **2:11-12**
2:15	K/P	define density and perform calcuations using the mathematical relationship among density, mass, and volume. **2:13**
2:16	A	exhibit an interest in science by completing voluntarily one or more of the One More Step activities at the end of the chapter.
2:17	A	read unassigned literature to the ideas presented in the chapter.

TEACHING TECHNIQUES

Section 2:1

In using SI you will note many changes in the units and abbreviations in this book in comparison to older chemistry texts. All quantitative energy measurements (including heat) are expressed in joules (1 cal = 4.18 J). The degree symbol is not used in expressing kelvin temperatures. Pressure is measured in pascals and kilopascals. Commas are no longer used to group digits in long numbers. Rather a space is used to group digits in threes to the right and left of the decimal point. Teaching SI may require that you first familiarize yourself with the system. Supplemental materials can be obtained from the National Bureau of Standards and the American National Metric Council.

The seven base units are presented in this section to reinforce the simplicity of the system. Units that are combinations of these base units are covered later in the chapter. Emphasize that the changes do actually make learning chemistry less confusing by eliminating units having duplicate meaning.

Section 2:2

It is important to emphasize now and throughout the text that weight and mass are not the same. These terms will not be used interchangeably. Weight is rarely used in a chemistry laboratory. Students will probably notice many out of date materials that do not make this distinction. It is important that you as an educator set a good example.

Section 2:7

It is important to develop the use of significant digits. Using a calculator or computer requires that students apply some rules in making calculations in order to obtain answers with reasonable numbers of digits. Calculated accuracy should at least resemble measured accuracy. There can be some disadvantages to being too strict in marking students' answers. They will encounter a number of new mathematical relationships throughout the course. It is important that they understand these relationships and can perform operations based on them. Being too critical of the number of digits in the answer can be frustrating for students. As a result of these limitations, we occasionally will express measurments as 20°C instead of 20.0°C, or 1000 cm^3 rather than 1000.0 cm^3. We maintain that it is more important to use realistic values rather than try to fill the text with numbers.

Section 2:9

We are emphasizing the use of dm^3 and cm^3 for expressing volumes rather than L and mL. Liter and milliliter are not SI units. However, since they are in common use and part of the metric system they may appear in the text. Be sure students know the quantitative relationships among these units.

Section 2:11

Using unfamiliar units in a problem will help you evaluate students' mastery of the concept of conversion factors and their use. For example, 1 wag = 12 zoom, 1000 warp = 1 bam, 3 zoom = 1 bam. Convert 8 wags to warps.

$$\frac{8 \text{ wag}}{} \left| \frac{12 \text{ zoom}}{1 \text{ wag}} \right| \frac{1 \text{ bam}}{3 \text{ zoom}} \left| \frac{1000 \text{ warp}}{1 \text{ bam}} \right. = \frac{32\ 000}{\text{warp}}$$

Note the fraction bar used above is used in problem set-ups throughout the text. It is a convenient way to organize information and allows students to manipulate units without having to memorize a number of mathematical equations. Though it may be difficult to use at first, in the long run it encourages a real understanding of how an answer is obtained. You should also note that students will show their work more neatly on tests, lab reports, and homework.

Section 2:12

Students commonly have trouble setting up chemical problems. They must decide which math operations to perform. They must analyze the units. The best way to handle these questions is to use a systematic approach; the factor-label method. The biggest advantage to be gained from this method is that the math operations needed to convert a measurement from one set of units to another are clearly indicated by the units of the answer sought. In chemistry, units are carried along with nearly every number used. Stress to students that units are handled in division and multiplication as though they are numbers.

Careers and Chemistry

Emphasize the distinction between a career in engineering versus science. Engineering is related to technology and the use of scientific knowledge for practical purposes. Other fields of engineering (biomedical, mechanical, nuclear, and so on) also involve a knowledge of chemistry. You can assign reports concerning these careers.

PROBLEM SOLUTIONS

Page 23

1. $\dfrac{0.1}{12.7} = 0.008$

2. $\dfrac{1}{50} = 0.02$

3. $\dfrac{0.0001}{236.0490} = 4 \times 10^{-7}$

Page 24

4. a. 4	d. 2	g. 2	j. 1
b. 3	e. 3	h. 2	
c. 4	f. 2	i. 1	

Pages 27-28

5. 0.211

6. 2.2×10^6

7. 3400
8. 0.2287
9. 5.53×10^5
10. 8.65×10^3
11. 5.23×10^{18}
12. 2800
13. 0.0944
14. 303
15. 4.56
16. 1240
17. 10.5
18. 26.0
19. 2.42×10^{-4}
20. 169
21. 166
22. 1.07×10^4
23. 2×10^8

Page 31

24. $\dfrac{0.598 \, \cancel{h}}{} \left| \dfrac{60 \, \cancel{min}}{1 \, \cancel{h}} \right| \dfrac{60 \, s}{1 \, \cancel{min}} = 2.153 \times 10^3 \, s$

25. $\dfrac{0.193 \, \cancel{m}}{} \left| \dfrac{100 \, cm}{1 \, \cancel{m}} \right. = 19.3 \, cm$

26. $\dfrac{3.41 \, \cancel{cm^3}}{} \left| \dfrac{1 \, dm^3}{1000 \, \cancel{cm^3}} \right. = 0.003 \, 41 \, dm^3$

27. $\dfrac{57.5 \, \cancel{cg}}{} \left| \dfrac{1 \, \cancel{g}}{100 \, \cancel{cg}} \right| \dfrac{1000 \, mg}{1 \, \cancel{g}} = 575 \, mg$

28. $\dfrac{0.618 \, \cancel{km}}{} \left| \dfrac{1000 \, \cancel{m}}{1 \, \cancel{km}} \right| \dfrac{100 \, cm}{1 \, \cancel{m}} = 61 \, 800 \, cm$

29. $\dfrac{923 \, \cancel{ps}}{} \left| \dfrac{1 \, s}{10^{12} \, \cancel{ps}} \right. = 9.23 \times 10^{-11} \, s$

30. $\dfrac{0.397 \, \cancel{m^2}}{} \left| \dfrac{10 \, 000 \, cm^2}{1 \, \cancel{m^2}} \right. = 3970 \, cm^2$

31. $\dfrac{139 \, \cancel{cm^3}}{} \left| \dfrac{1 \, dm^3}{1000 \, \cancel{cm^3}} \right. = 0.139 \, dm^3$

32. $\dfrac{0.0446 \, \cancel{km}}{} \left| \dfrac{1000 \, m}{1 \, \cancel{km}} \right. = 44.6 \, m$

33. $\dfrac{52.5 \, \cancel{mg}}{} \left| \dfrac{1 \, g}{1000 \, \cancel{mg}} \right. = 0.0525 \, g$

34. $\dfrac{0.805 \, \cancel{dm^3}}{} \left| \dfrac{1000 \, cm^3}{1 \, \cancel{dm^3}} \right. = 805 \, cm^3$

35. $\dfrac{239 \, \cancel{dm^3}}{} \left| \dfrac{1000 \, cm^3}{1 \, \cancel{dm^3}} \right. = 239 \, 000 \, cm^3$

36. $\dfrac{661 \, \cancel{cm^3}}{} \left| \dfrac{1 \, dm^3}{1000 \, \cancel{cm^3}} \right. = 0.661 \, dm^3$

37. $\dfrac{656 \, \cancel{mg}}{} \left| \dfrac{1 \, g}{1000 \, \cancel{mg}} \right. = 0.656 \, g$

38. $\dfrac{218 \, \cancel{nm}}{} \left| \dfrac{1 \, \cancel{m}}{10^9 \, \cancel{nm}} \right| \dfrac{100 \, cm}{1 \, \cancel{m}} = 2.18 \times 10^{-5} \, cm$

Page 32

39. $\dfrac{0.905 \, \cancel{kg}}{} \left| \dfrac{1000 \, \cancel{g}}{1 \, \cancel{kg}} \right| \dfrac{1000 \, mg}{1 \, \cancel{g}} = 9.05 \times 10^5 \, mg$

40. $\dfrac{0.307 \, \cancel{mg}}{} \left| \dfrac{1 \, g}{1000 \, \cancel{mg}} \right. = 0.000 \, 307 \, g$

41. $\dfrac{822 \, \cancel{dm^3}}{} \left| \dfrac{1 \, L}{1 \, \cancel{dm^3}} \right. = 822 \, L$

42. $\dfrac{0.0775 \, \cancel{g}}{} \left| \dfrac{1000 \, mg}{1 \, \cancel{g}} \right. = 77.5 \, mg$

43. $\dfrac{0.667 \, \cancel{m^3}}{} \left| \dfrac{100 \, cm}{1 \, \cancel{m}} \right| \dfrac{100 \, cm}{1 \, \cancel{m}} \left| \dfrac{100 \, cm}{1 \, \cancel{m}} \right. = 6.67 \times 10^5 \, cm^3$

44. $\dfrac{0.848 \, \cancel{dm^3}}{} \left| \dfrac{1000 \, cm^3}{1 \, \cancel{dm^3}} \right. = 848 \, cm^3$

45. $\dfrac{0.384 \, \cancel{m^3}}{} \left| \dfrac{10^3 \, dm^3}{1 \, \cancel{m^3}} \right. = 384 \, dm^3$

46. $\dfrac{7.56 \, \cancel{mm}}{} \left| \dfrac{1 \, cm}{10 \, \cancel{mm}} \right. = 0.756 \, cm$

47. $\dfrac{0.888 \, \cancel{kg}}{} \left| \dfrac{1000 \, g}{1 \, \cancel{kg}} \right. = 888 \, g$

48. $\dfrac{920 \, \cancel{dm^3}}{} \left| \dfrac{1 \, m^3}{10^3 \, \cancel{dm^3}} \right. = 0.920 \, m^3$

49. $\dfrac{81.4 \, \cancel{nm}}{} \left| \dfrac{1 \, \cancel{m}}{1 \times 10^9 \, \cancel{nm}} \right| \dfrac{100 \, cm}{1 \, \cancel{m}} = 8.14 \times 10^{-6} \, cm$

50. $\dfrac{0.0300 \, \cancel{h}}{} \left| \dfrac{60 \, \cancel{min}}{1 \, \cancel{h}} \right| \dfrac{60 \, s}{1 \, \cancel{min}} = 108 \, s$

Page 35

51. $D = \dfrac{m}{V} = \dfrac{8.76 \, g}{3.07 \, cm^3} = 2.85 \, g/cm^3$

52. $D = \dfrac{m}{V} = \dfrac{0.650 \, g}{2.71 \, cm^3} = 0.240 \, g/cm^3$

53. $m = DV = \dfrac{2.72 \, g}{cm^3} \left| 98.2 \, \cancel{cm^3} \right. = 267 \, g$

54. $\dfrac{1.84 \, g}{1 \, \cancel{cm^3}} \left| 4.33 \, \cancel{cm^3} \right. = 7.97 \, g$

55. $\dfrac{2.74 \, g}{1 \, \cancel{cm^3}} \left| 99.7 \, \cancel{cm^3} \right. = 273 \, g$

56. $\dfrac{6.32 \, g}{1 \, \cancel{cm^3}} \left| 51.7 \, \cancel{cm^3} \right. = 327 \, g$

57. $\dfrac{7.48 \, \cancel{g}}{} \left| \dfrac{1 \, cm^3}{2.50 \, \cancel{g}} \right. = 2.99 \, cm^3$

58. $\dfrac{132 \, \cancel{g}}{} \left| \dfrac{1 \, cm^3}{3.17 \, \cancel{g}} \right. = 41.6 \, cm^3$

59. $\dfrac{81.4 \, \cancel{g}}{} \left| \dfrac{1 \, cm^3}{5.50 \, \cancel{g}} \right. = 14.8 \, cm^3$

CHAPTER END PROBLEMS

Pages 38-39

1. meter, kilogram, second, ampere, kelvin, mole, candela
2. Values for weight are subject to gravitational force. The mass of a substance is constant regardless of gravitational force.
3. Celsius temperature is defined by the freezing point of water as 0°C and the boiling point of water as 100°C.

4. the kilogram

5. A calculated answer cannot be any more accurate than the accuracy of the measurements used in the calculation.

6. a. 1
b. 2
c. 6
d. 8

7. The volume of water changes with temperature because the density of H_2O changes with temperature.

8. $\dfrac{0.1}{41.3} \times 100 = 0.2\%$

9. $\dfrac{0.1}{67.9} \times 100 = 0.1\%$

10. $\dfrac{0.0001}{0.0961} \times 100 = 0.1\%$

11. a. 3.68×10^1
b. 3.87×10^{-2}
c. 2.165×10^{-4}
d. 5.1683×10^{11}

12. a. 0.009 14
b. 0.000 035 0
c. 952 000
d. 46.6

13. 1.031×10^6

14. 2.17×10^{-5}

15. 3.8×10^{-1}

16. 1.7×10^{-2}

17. a. 2
b. 1
c. 2
d. 1

18. a. 52 (nearest whole number)
b. 0.9 (nearest tenth)
c. 156 (nearest whole number)
d. 10 (nearest whole number)
e. 2 (nearest whole number)

19. $V = lwh$
= $2.00 \times 2.00 \times 9.00 = 36.0 \text{ cm}^3$
$\dfrac{108 \text{ g}}{36.0 \text{ cm}^3} = 3.00 \text{ g/cm}^3$

20. $V = lwh$
= $5.00 \times 10.0 \times 23.0 = 1150 \text{ cm}^3$
$\dfrac{3.22 \text{ kg}}{1150 \text{ cm}^3} \left| \dfrac{1000 \text{ g}}{1 \text{ kg}} \right. = 2.80 \text{ g/cm}^3$

21. $\dfrac{6120 \text{ g}}{9.00 \text{ dm}^3} \left| \dfrac{1 \text{ dm}^3}{1000 \text{ cm}^3} \right. = 0.680 \text{ g/cm}^3$

22. $\dfrac{2.06 \text{ kg}}{2.00 \text{ dm}^3} \left| \dfrac{1000 \text{ g}}{1 \text{ kg}} \right| \dfrac{1 \text{ dm}^3}{1000 \text{ cm}^3} = 1.03 \text{ g/cm}^3$

23. $V = lwh$
= $23.0 \times 15.0 \times 15.5 = 5350 \text{ cm}^3$
$\dfrac{10.22 \text{ kg}}{5350 \text{ cm}^3} \left| \dfrac{1000 \text{ g}}{1 \text{ kg}} \right. = 1.91 \text{ g/cm}^3$

24. $\dfrac{411 \text{ g}}{384 \text{ cm}^3} = 1.07 \text{ g/cm}^3$

25. $\dfrac{233 \text{ g}}{97.0 \text{ cm}^3} = 2.40 \text{ g/cm}^3$

26. $\dfrac{535 \text{ g}}{62.3 \text{ cm}^3} = 8.59 \text{ g/cm}^3$

27. $\dfrac{49.2 \text{ g}}{27.3 \text{ cm}^3} = 1.80 \text{ g/cm}^3$

28. $\dfrac{171 \text{ g}}{1320 \text{ cm}^3} = 0.130 \text{ g/cm}^3$

29. $\dfrac{3.19 \text{ g}}{4.56 \text{ cm}^3} = 0.700 \text{ g/cm}^3$

30. $\dfrac{6.36 \text{ g}}{2.65 \text{ cm}^3} = 2.40 \text{ g/cm}^3$

31. $\dfrac{272 \text{ g}}{312 \text{ cm}^3} = 0.872 \text{ g/cm}^3$

32. $\dfrac{1590 \text{ kg}}{1 \text{ m}^3} \left| \dfrac{1000 \text{ g}}{1 \text{ kg}} \right| \dfrac{1 \text{ m}^3}{(100)^3 \text{ cm}^3} = 1.59 \text{ g/cm}^3$

33. $\dfrac{30.0 \text{ km}}{1 \text{ h}} \left| \dfrac{1000 \text{ m}}{1 \text{ km}} \right| \dfrac{100 \text{ cm}}{\text{m}} \left| \dfrac{1 \text{ h}}{60 \text{ min}} \right| \dfrac{1 \text{ min}}{60 \text{ s}} = 833 \text{ cm/s}$

34. $\dfrac{1.25 \text{ g}}{\text{dm}^3} \left| \dfrac{1000 \text{ dm}^3}{1 \text{ m}^3} \right| \dfrac{1.00 \text{ m}^3}{} = 1250 \text{ g}$

35. $\dfrac{9.80 \text{ g}}{1 \text{ cm}^3} \left| \dfrac{4.32 \text{ cm}^3}{} \right. = 42.3 \text{ g}$

36. $\dfrac{1 \text{ cm}^3}{7.87 \text{ g}} \left| \dfrac{24.6 \text{ g}}{} \right. = 3.13 \text{ cm}^3$

37. $\dfrac{1.2 \times 10^9 \text{ kg}}{1.00 \text{ km}^3} \left| \dfrac{1000 \text{ g}}{1 \text{ kg}} \right| \dfrac{1 \text{ km}^3}{(1000 \text{ m})^3} \left| \dfrac{1 \text{ m}^3}{(10^2 \text{ cm})^3} \right. = 1.2 \times 10^{-3} \text{ g/cm}^3$

38. $\dfrac{6.70 \text{ g}}{1 \text{ cm}^3} \left| \dfrac{7.10 \text{ cm}^3}{} \right. = 47.6 \text{ g}$

39. $\dfrac{19.3 \text{ g}}{1 \text{ cm}^3} \left| \dfrac{0.393 \text{ cm}^3}{} \right. = 7.58 \text{ g}$

40. $\dfrac{58.6 \text{ g}}{} \left| \dfrac{1 \text{ cm}^3}{1.74 \text{ g}} \right. = 33.7 \text{ cm}^3$

41. $\dfrac{4.44 \text{ kg}}{} \left| \dfrac{1000 \text{ g}}{1 \text{ kg}} \right| \dfrac{1 \text{ cm}^3}{7.28 \text{ g}} = 6.10 \times 10^2 \text{ cm}^3$

REVIEW

Page 39

1. To provide the facts as a basis for the application of value judgments.

2. kinetic and potential

3. To understand the structure and properties of matter sufficiently well to make predictions about unexamined substances.

4. Mass and energy are always conserved and their sum cannot be increased or decreased.

ONE MORE STEP

Page 39

1. Thermocouple: Measures the potential difference across the junction of two dissimilar metals in contact

Optical pyrometer: Measures temperature by determining the wavelength of the radiation given off by a glowing object

Thermistor: An electric device whose resistance varies with temperature

Advantages—All three of the above devices can measure temperatures higher and lower than mercury thermometers. The thermistor and thermocouple are small and compact. Disadvantages—All three of the above devices must be carefully calibrated. The optical pyrometer can measure extremely high temperatures but it is not as accurate. In order to use the thermistor and thermocouple, one must understand the mathematical and physical relationships involved.

2. A computer is basically a series of "off-on" switches. Most high speed computers operate on the *binary system* which contains only two symbols, 0 and 1. It is possible to construct all of the integers (1, 2, 3, . . .) using only these two symbols and the off and on positions of a series of switches or lights as follows:

decimal number	computer panel	binary number
0		
1	X	1
2	X	10
3	XX	11
4	X	100
5	X X	101
6	XX	110
7	XXX	111
8	X	1000
9	X X	1001
etc.		

Such a computer performs all mathematical operations by either adding or subtracting over and over in rapid succession in a manner determined by its program. For instance, 4 would be divided by 2 by adding two's until the sum was four and recording the number of times the number was added.

$$\frac{4}{2} = 2 + 2 = 2 \text{ additions}$$

$$\frac{8}{2} = 2 + 2 + 2 + 2 = 4 \text{ additions}$$

For more information, see *Algebra One* and *Two* by Foster, Rath, and Winters, Columbus, Ohio, Charles E. Merrill Publishing Co., 1983. *Algebra One* pp. 237, 243. *Algebra Two* pp. 550-551.

3. Double precision mode allows the computer to operate with many more significant digits.

4. Surveyors use lasers to measure distance.

MATTER **3**

AN OVERVIEW

Chapter 3 outlines one basic classification system for matter. Keep in mind that this classification is intended to organize matter into categories for students. Several concepts mentioned in Chapter 3 are developed fully later in the text. For example, Chapter 17 covers change of state in more depth. Try not to anticipate the material in later chapters by going into too much detail in Chapter 3. Many new terms are introduced that students will use throughout the course. You may want to remind students that an understanding of chemical concepts involves the ability to use the vocabulary.

DEMONSTRATION INFORMATION

The chapter opening demonstration makes the student aware that a special vocabulary is used by scientists to describe a system and its surroundings. Use the demonstration to introduce the vocabulary found in the chapter.

Mix 1 g of sugar with 1 g of $CaCO_3$ in a large test tube. Have a student examine the dry mixture. Can the student see a difference between the two chemicals? Add 10 cm^3 of H_2O and stopper the test tube. Shake the contents to dissolve the sugar. Allow the tube to stand for a minute, then decant the liquid into a filter apparatus. Collect the filtrate in a small beaker. To the solid remaining in the test tube, add a few drops of dilute H_2SO_4 (3 M). Note the reaction. Next add a few drops of dilute H_2SO_4 to the filtrate in the beaker. Discuss with the students the separation technique used.

At the beginning of the demonstration encourage the students to observe several different properties of the sugar and $CaCO_3$. Have them distinguish between extensive and intensive physical properties. It is not necessary that the students know the chemical reaction which occurs. This will be presented in Chapter 6.

Disposal: *These chemicals are properly disposed of at a local landfill. They represent little or no hazard to the environment.*

PERFORMANCE OBJECTIVES

Goals: Students will classify matter by its properties. Students will learn how matter is changed by physical and chemical processes. Students will perform calculations to determine heat transfer.

Objectives: Upon completion of the reading and problems, and when asked to demonstrate their understanding either orally or on a written test, students will

3:1 K/P define, recognize, and give examples of materials. **Intro**

3:2	K/P	define phase and interface, and relate to the three phases of water. **3:1**
3:3	K/P	define homogeneous and heterogeneous materials, distinguish between them, and recognize or give examples of them. **3:1-2**
3:4	K/P	define give, and recognize examples of solution, solute, and solvent. **3:2**
3:5	P	list several methods of expressing solution concentration, and state how solutions of different molarities relate to one another. **3:2**
3:6	K/P	define and distinguish between the terms in the following pairs: substance and mixture, element and compound, and give or recognize an example of each term. **3:2-3**
3:7	K	define atom. **3:3**
3:8	K/P	distinguish physical and chemical properties, and give examples of each. **3:4, 6**
3:9	K/P	distinguish extensive and intensive properties, and give examples of each. **3:4**
3:10	K/P	distinguish physical and chemical change and give examples of each. **3:5, 7**
3:11	K	define and explain the methods of distillation and fractional crystallization. **3:5**
3:12	P	read a graph of solubility versus temperature. 3:5
3:13	P	explain the two ways energy can be transferred between a system and its surroundings. **3:8**
3:14	K	define these energy-related terms: heat, joule, specific heat, and calorimeter. **3:8-9**
3:15	P	perform calculations involving specific heat and calorimetric measurements. **3:9**
3:16	A	voluntarily complete one or more of the One More Step activities.
3:17	A	read unassigned literature related to the chapter.

TEACHING TECHNIQUES

Section 3:3

The terms atom, element, and compound are introduced but not defined precisely. Emphasize the particle nature of each of these substances. This section is the basis for proposing the presence of atoms in all matter. The proof of atomic theory will be presented in Chapter

7. Show some elements that are available in your stockroom such as C, Zn, Pb, Cu, Na, and Br_2. Use these substances to begin the discussions of physical properties (3:4) and physical changes (3:5).

Show the class some compounds such as baking soda, epsom salts, water, sugar, and alcohol. Avoid mixtures, minerals, and polymers as these are not good examples. Name the compounds, but do not give the formulas yet unless the class asks for them. Use these substances to begin the discussion of chemical properties (3:6) and chemical changes (3:7).

Section 3:4

Show students a piece of colored paper. Ask them about its length, mass, color, hardness, density, and conductivity. Is it malleable or ductile? These questions require a thorough understanding of some new terms. Begin Section 3:5 by tearing the paper into small pieces.

Section 3:5

Using the torn paper, ask students which properties have changed and which have remained the same. Now group these properties into extensive and intensive properties. Emphasize that changing the size of the pieces is a physical change. Relate this concept to dissolving as a physical change.

Section 3:6-9

Demonstration: *Burn a small piece of paper over the sink. Discuss the changes in properties (mass, volume, color, hardness) which occurred. Use the demonstration to introduce energy transfer in 3:8 and the need for heat calculations in 3:9.*

Careers and Chemistry

You can use this feature to begin a project concerning food values and food labels. Food labels can be used to begin discussions of formulas in Chapter 4, and energy values in Chapter 7. Students should be more aware of the importance of chemistry to the food industry. The subject of food additives has received much bad publicity. However, ask students to consider the lack of nutritional value of many foods if they were not supplemented. Ask them to consider how without preservatives a decreased shelf life would affect the cost and availability of many foods.

PROBLEM SOLUTIONS

Pages 46-47

1. **a.** solution (Gases in gases are homogeneous solutions rather than heterogeneous mixtures.)
   b. heterogeneous mixture

  c. heterogeneous mixture
  d. compound
  e. compound
  f. heterogeneous mixture
  g. heterogeneous mixture (When homogenized, milk is an emulsion—a colloid.)
  h. element
  i. compound

2. a. inspection of "grain"
  b. see bubbles, evaporate liquid
  c. see vessels, extract with solvent
  d. evaporate liquid
  For all of these there is the possibility that the process of examination causes some chemical change, particularly in d. However, admission of this does not destroy the usefulness of the concept.

3. examine under a microscope

Page 50

4. a. 38 g/100 g H_2O
  b. 230 g/100 g H_2O
  c. 46 g/100 g H_2O
  d. 95 g/100 g H_2O

5. a. extensive
  b. intensive
  c. intensive
  d. extensive
  e. intensive

Page 52

6. a. physical
  b. chemical
  c. chemical
  d. chemical
  e. physical
  f. chemical
  g. physical
  h. physical
  i. physical
  j. physical
  k. chemical
  l. chemical

7. chemical

8. chemical

9. chemical

10. physical

11. chemical

12. physical

13. chemical

14. physical

15. physical

16. Most cooking procedures (particularly baking), photography, explosives exploding, gasoline engine burning gasoline, any action of the body, and a dry cell or a battery discharging.

Pages 55-56

17. $H = m(\Delta T)C_p = \dfrac{54.5\ \cancel{g}\ |\ 60.5\ \cancel{C°}\ |\ 0.874\ J}{|\ \cancel{g}\cancel{C°}} = 2880\ J$

18. $H = m(\Delta T)C_p = \dfrac{8.77\ \cancel{g}\ |\ 19.3\ \cancel{C°}\ |\ 0.856\ J}{|\ \cancel{g}\cancel{C°}} = 145\ J$

19. $H = m(\Delta T)C_p = \dfrac{7.90 \times 10^2\ \cancel{g}\ |\ 47.0\ \cancel{C°}\ |\ 4.18\ J}{|\ \cancel{g}\cancel{C°}} = 1.55 \times 10^5\ J$

20. $H(\text{lost}) = H(\text{gained})$
$m(\Delta T)C_p = m(\Delta T)C_p$

$\dfrac{2.39\ g\ |\ (100.0 - x)\ C°\ |\ 0.900\ J}{|\ g{\cdot}C°} = \dfrac{10.0\ g\ |\ (x - 14.1)\ C°\ |\ 4.18\ J}{|\ g{\cdot}C°}$

$x = 18.3\ C°$

21. $H(\text{lost}) = H(\text{gained})$
$m(\Delta T)C_p = m(\Delta T)C_p$

$\dfrac{75.2\ g\ |\ (100.0 - x)\ C°\ |\ 0.232\ J}{|\ g{\cdot}C°} = \dfrac{25.0\ g\ |\ (x - 23.0)\ C°\ |\ 4.18\ J}{|\ g{\cdot}C°}$

$x = 34.0\ C°$

22. $H(\text{lost}) = H(\text{gained})$
$m(\Delta T)C_p = m(\Delta T)C_p$

$\dfrac{5.19\ g\ |\ 76.17\ C°\ |\ x}{|} = \dfrac{10.0\ \cancel{g}\ |\ 1.83\ \cancel{C°}\ |\ 4.18\ J}{|\ \cancel{g}\cancel{C°}}$

$x = 0.193\ J/g{\cdot}C°$

23. $H(\text{lost}) = H(\text{gained})$
$m(\Delta T)C_p = m(\Delta T)C_p$

$\dfrac{23.8\ g\ |\ 67.50\ C°\ |\ x}{|} = \dfrac{50.0\ \cancel{g}\ |\ 8.5\ \cancel{C°}\ |\ 4.18\ J}{|\ \cancel{g}\cancel{C°}}$

$x = 1.1\ J/g{\cdot}C°$

CHAPTER END PROBLEMS

Pages 58-59

1. **a.** heterogeneous mixture
   b. compound
   c. heterogenous mixture
   d. heterogeneous mixture
   e. solution
   f. element

2. **a.** chemical
   b. physical
   c. physical
   d. physical
   e. chemical
   f. chemical

3. Suggested list of phases—soda, ice cream, cherry, straw, spoon, glass, CO_2, air, cream.
   Suggested list of interfaces—soda-glass, soda-ice cream, soda-straw, soda-spoon, soda-gas (two: in cream and "fizz"), ice cream-cream, ice cream-glass, ice cream-straw, ice cream-spoon, ice cream-gas (2), cream-gas, cream-cherry, cherry gas.

4. **a.** physical
   b. physical
   c. physical
   d. chemical

5. 1 joule = 1 kg·m²/s²

6. $\Delta H° = m(\Delta T)C_p$
$$= \frac{706\ \cancel{g} \quad (300 - 25)\cancel{C°} \quad 0.443\ J}{\cancel{g}\cancel{C°}} = 8.60 \times 10^4\ J$$

7. $\Delta H° = m(\Delta T)C_p$
$$= \frac{55.8\ \cancel{g} \quad (47.7 - 36.4)\ \cancel{C°} \quad 0.220\ J}{\cancel{g}\cancel{C°}} = 139\ J$$

8. See the appropriate handbook.

REVIEW

Page 59

1. **a.** $\dfrac{2.84\ \cancel{kg} \quad 1000\ g}{1\ \cancel{kg}} = 2840\ g$

   b. $\dfrac{544\ \cancel{ms} \quad 1\ s}{1000\ \cancel{ms}} = 0.544\ s$

c. $\dfrac{0.0656\ \cancel{g} \quad 1000\ mg}{1\ \cancel{g}} = 65.6\ mg$

d. $\dfrac{1102\ \cancel{cm} \quad 1\ m}{100\ \cancel{cm}} = 11.02\ m$

e. $\dfrac{0.220\ \cancel{g} \quad 1000\ mg}{1\ \cancel{g}} = 2.20 \times 10^2\ mg$

f. $\dfrac{3.6\ \cancel{nm} \quad 1\ \cancel{m} \quad 100\ cm}{1 \times 10^9\ \cancel{nm} \quad 1\ \cancel{m}} = 3.6 \times 10^{-7}\ cm$

2. **a.** $\dfrac{42.0\ g}{19.1\ cm^3} = 2.20\ g/cm^3$

   b. $\dfrac{8.17\ g}{34.0\ cm^3} = 0.240\ g/cm^3$

   c. $\dfrac{6120\ g}{5100\ cm^3} = 1.2\ g/cm^3$

   d. $\dfrac{201\ g}{165\ cm^3} = 1.22\ g/cm^3$

3. mass—amount of matter, kilogram, balance
   length—distance between two points, meter, meter stick
   time—interval between two occurrences, second, clock
   temperature—intensity of heat energy, kelvin, thermometer

4. inertia

5. 6

6. $\dfrac{0.002}{101.476} = 2 \times 10^{-5}$

ONE MORE STEP

Page 59

1. Action of salt water on bacteria is physical. Too high a concentration of salt causes the cells to lose water from their cytoplasm and to dry up. Too low a concentration of salt causes the cells to absorb water and to "explode."

2. Dissolve salt in water, filter, wash, dry copper in filter paper, evaporate filtrate.

3. There are several ways to convert oil shale to crude oil. One way involves preparation and retorting. Preparation involves breaking the shale into correct size pieces by crushing and screening. Primary crushing is with jaw crushers and gyratory crushers; secondary crushing is by roll crusher. One kind of retort procedure subjects shale to high pressure steam which vaporizes the oil. The steam also extracts ammonia and nitrogen gases as well as naphtha. The vapors are scrubbed to separate the crude oil vapor from the ammonia, naphtha, and other gases. Then the crude oil is refined.

4. Processes in use include solar distillation, conventional evaporators, flash evaporation, electrodialysis, vapor compression, reverse osmosis, and freezing.

5. solid, homogeneous mixture

6. The amount of heat per mole of a fuel is a determinant in the selection of a fuel. Other factors of selection are cost per mole of processing and use. Certainly given equal cost for obtaining and delivering two fuels, the one with greater heat content would provide more heat per dollar.

CHEMICAL FORMULAS   4

AN OVERVIEW

Chemical symbols and oxidation numbers are presented in this chapter. These tools allow students to successfully write chemical formulas. We will not consider bonding or atomic structure at this time. Our purpose is to give students a working vocabulary as soon as possible in the course. This approach enables students to function in lab at an earlier stage. It also keeps the abstract topics of structure and bonding for a later period in the course when students are better able to handle them.

The chapter is short in that formula writing is a necessary skill that may require time to master. We recommend some memorization to give students greater confidence and success.

The quantitative aspects of formulas will be covered in Chapter 5. Chemical equations will be covered in Chapter 6. Do not rush students into equations if they have not mastered formula writing.

DEMONSTRATION INFORMATION

Synthesis and decomposition can be demonstrated by reacting 3 g of zinc dust with 2 g of iodine crystals. After shaking to mix, add 1 cm^3 of H_2O slowly with a medicine dropper. Have a student check the temperature by feeling the outside of the test tube before and after the H_2O is added. Have students observe the ZnI_2 product. Then, add an additional 20 cm^3 of H_2O to the test tube and shake to dissolve the ZnI_2. Filter the solution and collect the filtrate in a petri dish. Place the petri dish on an overhead projector and electrolyze using copper wire for the electrodes. The anode reaction is $3 I^- \rightarrow I_3^-$ (brown). The cathode reaction is $Zn^{2+} \rightarrow Zn$. Zinc metal will be seen as a silvery plating on the copper wire electrode. A current of six to nine volts D.C. works well for the electrolysis. There is an excess of zinc, so you should not have to worry about the production of I_2 vapor.

You will want to make the following points:

1. We have synthesized a compound from two elements.

$$Zn + I_2 \rightarrow ZnI_2$$

2. A reaction that releases energy is exergonic. Water was added to dissolve the ZnI_2. This solution was filtered to separate it from the unreacted Zn. The zinc iodide was then electrolyzed according to the following reaction:

$$2Zn^{2+}(aq) + 6I^-(aq) \rightarrow 2Zn(cr) + 2I_3^-(aq).$$

This reaction is endergonic; it required energy in the form of electricity. This reaction was a decomposition reaction.

Disposal: *Decant the liquid. Pour it down the drain with a large quantity of water. Dispose of the precipitate in the normal manner by placing it in your solid waste container. It can then be put in a local landfill.*

PERFORMANCE OBJECTIVES

Goals: Students will demonstrate a proficiency in writing chemical formulas and naming compounds. Students will define oxidation number and state the oxidation numbers for common monatomic and polyatomic ions. Students will differentiate between molecular and empirical formulas.

Objectives: Upon completion of the reading and problems, and when asked to demonstrate their understanding either orally or on a written test, students will

4:1	K	list the names and symbols for the common elements highlighted in Table 4-1. **4:1**
4:2	K	differentiate between chemical symbols and chemical formulas. **4:1-2**
4:3	K	define a compound and its relationship to a formula. **4:2**
4:4	K	differentiate between subscripts and coefficients. **4:2, 4:6**
4:5	P	given a formula, state the number of atoms of each element present. **4:2, 4:6**
4:6	K	recognize that the element carbon is the distinguishing mark of organic compounds. **4:2**
4:7	K	define ion, monatomic and polyatomic ion, and oxidation number. **4:3**
4:8	K	list the names, symbols, and oxidation numbers or charges of the ions highlighted in Tables 4-3 and 4-4. **4:3**
4:9	K	define and distinguish molecular and ionic compounds. **4:3**
4:10	K	list the common elements that normally occur as diatomic molecules. **4:3**

4:11	K/P	write formulas for chemical compounds using oxidation numbers. **4:3**
4:12	K	distinguish atoms, ions, and molecules. **4:3**
4:13	K/P	define, recognize, and give examples of binary compound. **4:4**
4:14	P	name compounds from given chemical formulas. **4:4**
4:15	K/P	recognize or give examples of compounds containing polyatomic ions. **4:4**
4:16	K	differentiate between molecular and empirical formulas. **4:5**
4:17	K/P	define, recognize, and give examples of a formula unit. **4:6**
4:18	A	voluntarily complete one or more of the One More Step activities.
4:19	A	read unassigned literature related to the chapter.

TEACHING TECHNIQUES

Section 4:1

Point out that no rules have been followed in naming the elements. Some elements have names based on Latin or Greek roots. Silicon is named for the Latin word *silex* meaning flint. Some are named for geographic locations. Holmium (Stockholm), ytterium (Ytterby, Sweden), rhenium (Rhine river, Germany), and strontium (Strontian, Scotland) are examples. Some are named in honor of scientists such as einsteinium (Albert Einstein) and fermium (Enrico Fermi).

Section 4:3

Students come into chemistry with a basic knowledge about atoms gained in previous science courses. At this point, all they need to know is a nucleus is surrounded by electrons. It is not important that they know how oxidation numbers are assigned. This topic will be covered later in the text. Students should treat the oxidation state tables as given information used in solving an algebraic problem. Using this approach, we believe that formula writing can be taught before a detailed description of atomic structure is presented. It is recommended that charges for some ions be memorized. Daily quizzes will probably be helpful.

Section 4:4

Note that we do not present grid systems for formula writing or naming compounds. This method teaches by inference that all combinations are possible which is not actually the case. It is standard policy that compounds shown throughout this text do actually exist. We do not advocate using the technique that has students cross oxidation numbers to get subscripts. Again, this shortcut results in too many errors.

Careers and Chemistry

Consider the number of new publications concerning science and technology that are presently on the market. As a result, the demand for skilled reporters, photographers, and illustrators in the science field is up. As a project, students could assemble science or science-related articles for the school newspaper.

PROBLEM SOLUTIONS

Page 70

1. **a.** $CaCl_2$
   b. $CaCO_3$
   c. NaCN
   d. MgO
   e. NaF
   f. $AlCl_3$
   g. SiO_2
   h. ZnI_2
   i. $CoCO_3$
   j. KH

2. **a.** barium chloride
   b. zinc nitrate
   c. cesium acetate
   d. hydrogen sulfide
   e. potassium carbonate
   f. iron(II) chloride
   g. aluminum nitrate
   h. ammonium acetate
   i. barium hydroxide
   j. copper(II) acetate

3. **a.** $CuCO_3$
   b. KOH
   c. CaI_2
   d. RbCN
   e. KF
   f. $Ca(OH)_2$
   g. $Bi_2(SO_4)_3$
   h. $Mg_3(PO_4)_2$
   i. $Hg(CN)_2$
   j. $Ni_3(AsO_4)_2$

4. **a.** potassium chloride
   b. potassium bromide
   c. potassium iodide
   d. calcium nitrate
   e. mercury(II) iodide
   f. copper(II) nitrate
   g. phosphorus(V) oxide
   h. phosphorus(V) chloride
   i. sulfur(VI) fluoride
   j. phosphorus(III) chloride

5. **a.** KNO_3
   b. NaOH
   c. $Pb(NO_3)_2$
   d. CH_3COOH

e. HCl
f. $ZnSO_4$
g. Na_2S
h. $FeCl_3$
i. $HClO_4$
j. H_2SO_4

6. a. ammonium nitrate
   b. sodium sulfate
   c. sodium oxide
   d. acetic acid
   e. perchloric acid
   f. sodium phosphate
   g. ammonium chloride
   h. sodium chloride
   i. phosphoric acid
   j. nitric acid

Page 72

7. a. CH_2O
   b. NO_2
   c. CH_3
   d. CH_4
   e. HgI
   f. C_4H_9

8. a. 1 formula unit of silver carbonate
   b. 3 formula units of thallium(I) bromide
   c. 2 formula units of iron(II) nitrate
   d. 4 formula units of bismuth(III) bromide
   e. 6 formula units of barium arsenate
   f. 5 formula units of tin(IV) bromide
   g. 3 formula units of phosphoric acid
   h. 3 formula units of acetic acid

CHAPTER END PROBLEMS

Pages 75-77

1. A definite amount of a compound as represented by its formula.
2. H_2, O_2, N_2, F_2, Cl_2, Br_2, I_2
3. b
4. Roman numerals are used to denote the oxidation state of elements having variable oxidation states. e.g., copper(I) chloride, copper(II) chloride.
5. the PO_4^{3-} ion occurs more than once in the formula
6. iron forms more than one compound with OH^- ion, $Fe(OH)_2$, $Fe(OH)_3$
7. a. $FeSO_4$
   b. $Mn(NO_3)_2$
   c. $Cr(NO_3)_3$
   d. CuCl
   e. $Na_2C_2O_4$
   f. $AgClO_4$
8. a. sodium nitrate
   b. ammonium sulfate
   c. iron(III) nitrate
   d. sodium acetate
   e. barium selenide
   f. copper(II) sulfate

9. a. $RbCH_3COO$
   b. $CePO_4$
   c. $Ca_3(AsO_4)_2$
   d. $CuC_4H_4O_6$
   e. CrN
   f. $AgNO_3$
10. a. silver bromide
    b. cadmium phosphide
    c. cobalt(II) phosphate
    d. lithium hydride
    e. gallium(III) telluride
    f. mercury(II) chloride
11. a. $Mg(OH)_2$
    b. $Cd(OH)_2$
    c. $AgCH_3COO$
    d. $Mg(NO_3)_2$
    e. $Al_2(SO_4)_3$
    f. KCN
12. a. $SnCl_4$
    b. ThF_4
    c. $Mg(IO_3)_2$
    d. $(NH_4)_2S$
    e. $Co(NO_3)_2$
    f. $Ba(NO_3)_2$
13. a. copper(II) selenide
    b. lead(II) cyanide
    c. magnesium hydride
    d. manganese(II) oxide
    e. aluminum carbide
    f. hydrogen chloride or hydrochloric acid
14. a. $Cd(NO_3)_2$
    b. $Co(NO_3)_2$
    c. H_2CO_3
    d. $Ni(NO_3)_2$
    e. $Mg(ClO_4)_2$
    f. HNO_3
15. a. strontium nitrate
    b. calcium oxalate
    c. oxalic acid
    d. mercury(II) fluoride
    e. lithium selenide
    f. hydrogen chloride or hydrochloric acid
16. a. $Co(OH)_2$
    b. Cs_2CO_3
    c. $MgCO_3$
    d. CaO
    e. $LiCH_3COO$
    f. ZnTe
17. a. strontium iodide
    b. ammonium fluoride
    c. barium selenate
    d. silver sulfide
    e. thallium(I) acetate
    f. ammonium selenide
18. a. Al_2Se_3
    b. $Ni_3(PO_4)_2$
    c. CaO
    d. $Co(ClO_4)_2$
    e. $MgSiF_6$
    f. $Ba(ClO_4)_2$

19. **a.** aluminum arsenate
    b. chromium(III) sulfate
    c. mercury(II) iodate
    d. cadmium bromide
    e. cerium(III) chloride
    f. cesium oxide

REVIEW

Page 77

1. **a.** compound
   b. heterogeneous mixture
   c. solution
   d. element
   e. solution
   f. heterogeneous mixture

2. **a.** 3
   b. 2
   c. 2
   d. 2
   e. 6
   f. 3

3. Accuracy = ±0.0001 g

   Relative error = $\dfrac{0.0001}{0.8320}$ = 1 × 10^{-4}

4. **a.** 9.55 × 10^{-1}
   b. 6.80 × 10^{-1}
   c. 5.35 × 10^{1}
   d. 3.14 × 10^{2}
   e. 6.25 × 10^{-2}
   f. 2.23 × 10^{3}

5. **a.** 73 300 000
   b. 904
   c. 77 300
   d. 0.000 21
   e. 0.000 074
   f. 0.000 009 18

6. Density = $\dfrac{mass}{Volume}$;

   $\dfrac{7.13 \text{ g}}{7.77 \text{ cm}^3}$ = 0.918 g/cm^3

ONE MORE STEP

Page 77

1. Daltonides are compounds of definite composition. Bertholides are compounds of variable composition. Bertholides are possible because of the occurrence of interstitial atoms in crystal lattices. Transitional metal hydrides and copper(I) sulfide are well known Bertholides.

2. Answers may vary from the following example:
   aspirin $C_9H_8O_4$
   ascorbic acid $C_6H_8O_6$
   vitamin A $C_{20}H_{29}OH$

3.

THE MOLE   5

AN OVERVIEW

Chapter 5 begins with a strong emphasis on the mole as the chemist's basic measuring unit. The mole concept is developed through a logical progression. Formula mass is presented first. The mole and Avogadro's number are presented next. The remainder of the chapter provides students with applications of the mole concept. The problem solving sections of the chapter provide practice in using the mole concept with the factor-label method. Emphasis on these problems will give your students a better understanding of the quantitative aspects of chemistry.

DEMONSTRATION INFORMATION

Copper(II) sulfate pentahydrate loses water in an observable manner. You can determine the mass before and after heating. This procedure enables you to answer the question "how much water is lost?" Do not overheat the hydrate since it could decompose. Demonstrate proper safety procedure by wearing goggles or safety glasses. Stress the need for quantitative data (numbers of grams, moles, and molecules) to accurately describe what is happening.

Disposal: *These chemicals are properly disposed of at a local landfill. They represent little or no hazard to the environment.*

PERFORMANCE OBJECTIVES

Goals: Students will calculate molecular and formula mass. Students will define the mole. Students will use your knowledge of the mole in calculations of chemical formulas, solution concentration, and hydrates.

Objectives: Upon completion of the reading and problems, and when asked to demonstrate their understanding either orally or on a written test, students will

5:1	K	define atomic, molecular, and formula mass. **5:1**
5:2	P	calculate the molecular or formula mass of any substance. **5:1**
5:3	P	explain how chemists count atoms and molecules. **5:2**
5:4	K	state Avogadro's number. **5:2**
5:5	K/P	relate gram, atomic mass unit, and Avogadro's number. **5:2**
5:6	K	define the mole. **5:3**
5:7	P	convert moles to atoms and molecules, and vice versa. **5:3**
5:8	P	do simple conversions to find the number of moles or molecules in a given mass or vice versa. **5:3**
5:9	K/P	define molarity and determine molarities for given solutions. **5:4**
5:10	K/P	define percentage composition and calculate the percentage composition for any given compound. **5:5**
5:11	K/P	define and give or recognize examples of an empirical formula. **5:6**
5:12	P	determine the empirical formula of a substance from percentage composition data, or from a given number of grams. **5:6**
5:13	K/P	define and give or recognize examples of a molecular formula. **5:7**
5:14	P	given the molecular mass and the empirical formula, calculate the molecular formula. **5:7**
5:15	K	define and recognize hydrates. **5:8**
5:16	P	determine the percentage of water in a hydrate. **5:8**
5:17	A	voluntarily complete one or more of the One More Step activities.
5:18	A	read unassigned literature related to the chapter.

TEACHING TECHNIQUES

Section 5:1

The choice of the first atomic mass standard was arbitrary. For a long time chemists used an atomic mass scale based on oxygen. In 1961, it was agreed to use carbon-12 as the standard. This isotope is easy to measure in the mass spectrometer.

The terms molecular weight and atomic weight are incorrect even though these terms have been used for many years. Weight is measured in newtons.

Section 5:2

Perrin, a French physicist, made measurements of Brownian motion in natural gum. He found the number of molecules per mole to be 6.8×10^{23}. Perrin was the first to use the term Avogadro's number. Rutherford later did an experiment using He gas produced by the alpha decay of certain radioactive nuclides. He calculated N_A as 6.16×10^{23} atoms per mole. Millikan's oil drop experiment (covered in Chapter 8) gave the accepted value of 6.023×10^{23} electrons per mole.

Section 5:3

Since the mole as a counting unit is unfamiliar to students, it may help to relate the following:

1 dozen = 12 pieces of anything
1 mole = 6.02×10^{23} pieces of anything

Section 5:4

The mole concept is extended in calculating solution concentrations. Molarity is defined as the ratio of the moles of solute to the volume of solution in dm^3. The change in volume unit (dm^3) will not be noticed by your students since they are learning it for the first time. They will think of molarity as mol/dm^3. It is important to teach units in use throughout the world (SI) and those that will appear in the literature in the future in spite of the fact that we may be more familiar with outdated units.

Section 5:5

Some students have difficulty recalling how to calculate percentages. They may find it easier to remember the following:

part over the whole times 100 equals percent

We recommend that students read atomic masses to three significant digits

Technology and Chemistry

Throughout the text, up-to-date analytical equipment is shown to emphasize the use of computers in chemistry. Many high schools are now using computers for independent learning and review. The laboratory program that is designed to go with this textbook has computer programs on disks. They will assist you and your students with laboratory calculations.

PROBLEM SOLUTIONS

Page 80

1.	**a.**	30.1 u	**h.**	110 u
	b.	136 u	**i.**	380 u
	c.	193 u	**j.**	58.1 u
	d.	424 u	**k.**	899 u
	e.	310 u	**l.**	32.0 u
	f.	484 u	**m.**	342 u
	g.	266 u	**n.**	60.1 u

Pages 83

2. $\dfrac{7.74 \times 10^{26} \text{ formula units TlI}}{} \; \Big| \; \dfrac{1 \text{ mol}}{6.02 \times 10^{23} \text{ formula units}} = 1.29 \times 10^3 \text{ mol TlI}$

3. $\dfrac{0.943 \text{ mol } H_2O}{} \; \Big| \; \dfrac{6.02 \times 10^{23} \text{ molecules}}{1 \text{ mol}} = 5.68 \times 10^{23} \text{ molecules } H_2O$

4. $\dfrac{50.4 \text{ g } CaBr_2}{} \; \Big| \; \dfrac{1 \text{ mol } CaBr_2}{200 \text{ g } CaBr_2} = 0.252 \text{ mol } CaBr_2$

5. $\dfrac{91.9 \text{ g } Ag_2Te}{} \; \Big| \; \dfrac{1 \text{ mol } Ag_2Te}{343 \text{ g } Ag_2Te} \; \Big| \; \dfrac{6.02 \times 10^{23} \text{ formula units}}{1 \text{ mol}} = 1.61 \times 10^{23} \text{ formula units } Ag_2Te$

6. $\dfrac{6.63 \times 10^{23} \text{ formula units } Mg(CH_3COO)_2}{} \; \Big| \; \dfrac{1 \text{ mol}}{6.02 \times 10^{23} \text{ formula units}} \; \Big| \; \dfrac{142 \text{ g } Mg(CH_3COO)_2}{1 \text{ mol } Mg(CH_3COO)_2} = 156 \text{ g } Mg(CH_3COO)_2$

7. $\dfrac{0.638 \text{ mol } Ce_2(CO_3)_3}{} \; \Big| \; \dfrac{460 \text{ g } Ce_2(CO_3)_3}{1 \text{ mol } Ce_2(CO_3)_3} = 293 \text{ g } Ce_2(CO_3)_3$

8. $\dfrac{6.77 \times 10^{24} \text{ formula units } Ca(ClO_4)_2}{} \; \Big| \; \dfrac{1 \text{ mol}}{6.02 \times 10^{23} \text{ formula units}} = 11.2 \text{ mol } Ca(ClO_4)_2$

9. $\dfrac{53.1 \text{ g } HBr}{} \; \Big| \; \dfrac{1 \text{ mol } HBr}{80.9 \text{ g } HBr} = 0.656 \text{ mol } HBr$

10. $\dfrac{4.06 \text{ mol } SiH_4}{} \; \Big| \; \dfrac{6.02 \times 10^{23} \text{ molecules}}{1 \text{ mol}} = 2.44 \times 10^{24} \text{ molecules } SiH_4$

Page 85

11. $\dfrac{89.7 \text{ g } (NH_4)_2C_4H_4O_6}{5.00 \times 10^2 \text{ cm}^3 \text{ soln}} \; \Big| \; \dfrac{1 \text{ mol } (NH_4)_2C_4H_4O_6}{184 \text{ g } (NH_4)_2C_4H_4O_6} \; \Big| \; \dfrac{1000 \text{ cm}^3}{1 \text{ dm}^3} = 0.975M \; (NH_4)_2C_4H_4O_6$

12. $\dfrac{9.94 \text{ g } CoSO_4}{2.50 \times 10^2 \text{ cm}^3 \text{ soln}} \; \Big| \; \dfrac{1 \text{ mol } CoSO_4}{155 \text{ g } CoSO_4} \; \Big| \; \dfrac{1000 \text{ cm}^3}{1 \text{ dm}^3} = 0.257M \; CoSO_4$

13. $\dfrac{5.23 \text{ g } Fe(NO_3)_2}{100.0 \text{ cm}^3 \text{ soln}} \; \Big| \; \dfrac{1 \text{ mol } Fe(NO_3)_2}{180 \text{ g } Fe(NO_3)_2} \; \Big| \; \dfrac{1000 \text{ cm}^3}{1 \text{ dm}^3} = 0.291M \; Fe(NO_3)_2$

14. $\dfrac{44.3 \text{ g } Pb(ClO_4)_2}{200.0 \text{ cm}^3 \text{ soln}} \; \Big| \; \dfrac{1 \text{ mol } Pb(ClO_4)_2}{406 \text{ g } Pb(ClO_4)_2} \; \Big| \; \dfrac{1000 \text{ cm}^3}{1 \text{ dm}^3} = 0.546M \; Pb(ClO_4)_2$

15. $\dfrac{8.55 \text{ g } MnSiF_6}{50.0 \text{ cm}^3 \text{ soln}} \; \Big| \; \dfrac{1 \text{ mol } MnSiF_6}{197 \text{ g } MnSiF_6} \; \Big| \; \dfrac{1000 \text{ cm}^3}{1 \text{ dm}^3} = 0.868M \; MnSiF_6$

16. $\dfrac{1.000 \times 10^3 \text{ cm}^3 \text{ soln}}{} \; \Big| \; \dfrac{3.00 \text{ mol } NiCl_2}{1000 \text{ cm}^3 \text{ soln}} \; \Big| \; \dfrac{130.0 \text{ g } NiCl_2}{1 \text{ mol } NiCl_2} = 390 \text{ g } NiCl_2$

17. $\dfrac{2.50 \times 10^2 \text{ cm}^3 \text{ soln}}{} \; \Big| \; \dfrac{4.00 \text{ mol } RbOH}{1000 \text{ cm}^3 \text{ soln}} \; \Big| \; \dfrac{103 \text{ g } RbOH}{1 \text{ mol } RbOH} = 103 \text{ g } RbOH$

18. $\dfrac{5.00 \times 10^2 \text{ cm}^3 \text{ soln}}{} \; \Big| \; \dfrac{1.50 \text{ mol } AgF}{1000 \text{ cm}^3 \text{ soln}} \; \Big| \; \dfrac{127 \text{ g } AgF}{1 \text{ mol } AgF} = 95.3 \text{ g } AgF$

19. $\dfrac{2.50 \times 10^2 \text{ cm}^3 \text{ soln}}{} \; \Big| \; \dfrac{0.500 \text{ mol } SrSiF_6}{1000 \text{ cm}^3 \text{ soln}} \; \Big| \; \dfrac{230 \text{ g } SrSiF_6}{1 \text{ mol } SrSiF_6} = 28.8 \text{ g } SrSiF_6$

20. $\dfrac{2.50 \times 10^2 \text{ cm}^3 \text{ soln}}{} \; \Big| \; \dfrac{0.002\ 00 \text{ mol } Tl_2CO_3}{1000 \text{ cm}^3 \text{ soln}} \; \Big| \; \dfrac{469 \text{ g } Tl_2CO_3}{1 \text{ mol } Tl_2CO_3} = 0.234 \text{ g } Tl_2CO_3$

Page 86

21.
$$
\begin{array}{ll}
1 \text{ Cs @ } 133 & = 133 \\
1 \text{ F @ } 19.0 & = \underline{19.0} \\
& 152
\end{array}
$$

$Cs = \dfrac{133}{152} \; \Big| \; \dfrac{100}{} = 87.5\%$

$F = \dfrac{19.0}{152} \; \Big| \; \dfrac{100}{} = 12.5\%$

22.
$$
\begin{array}{ll}
1 \text{ Ni @ } 58.7 & = 58.7 \\
2 \text{ I @ } 127 & = \underline{254} \\
& 313
\end{array}
$$

$Ni = \dfrac{58.7}{313} \; \Big| \; \dfrac{100}{} = 18.8\%$

$I = \dfrac{254}{313} \; \Big| \; \dfrac{100}{} = 81.2\%$

23. $\begin{aligned} 2\text{ Bi @ } 209 &= 418 \\ 3\text{ O @ } 16.0 &= \underline{48.0} \\ &\ 466 \end{aligned}$

$\text{Bi} = \dfrac{418}{466} \left| \dfrac{100}{} \right. = 89.7\%$

$\text{O} = \dfrac{48.0}{466} \left| \dfrac{100}{} \right. = 10.3\%$

24. $\begin{aligned} 1\text{ Cu @ } 63.5 &= 63.5 \\ 2\text{ C @ } 12.0 &= 24.0 \\ 4\text{ O @ } 16.0 &= \underline{64.0} \\ &\ 152 \end{aligned}$

$\text{Cu} = \dfrac{63.5}{152} \left| \dfrac{100}{} \right. = 41.8\%$

$\text{C} = \dfrac{24.0}{152} \left| \dfrac{100}{} \right. = 15.8\%$

$\text{O} = \dfrac{64.0}{152} \left| \dfrac{100}{} \right. = 42.1\%$

25. $\begin{aligned} 1\text{ Tl @ } 204 &= 204 \\ 1\text{ I @ } 127 &= 127 \\ 3\text{ O @ } 16.0 &= \underline{48.0} \\ &\ 379 \end{aligned}$

$\text{Tl} = \dfrac{204}{379} \left| \dfrac{100}{} \right. = 53.8\%$

$\text{I} = \dfrac{127}{379} \left| \dfrac{100}{} \right. = 33.5\%$

$\text{O} = \dfrac{48.0}{379} \left| \dfrac{100}{} \right. = 12.7\%$

26. $\begin{aligned} 1\text{ Th @ } 232 &= 232 \\ 2\text{ O @ } 16.0 &= \underline{32.0} \\ &\ 264 \end{aligned}$

$\text{Th} = \dfrac{232}{264} \left| \dfrac{100}{} \right. = 87.9\%$

$2\text{ O} = \dfrac{32.0}{264} \left| \dfrac{100}{} \right. = 12.1\%$

27. $\begin{aligned} 3\text{ Co @ } 58.9 &= 177 \\ 2\text{ As @ } 74.9 &= 150 \\ 8\text{ O @ } 16.0 &= \underline{128} \\ &\ 455 \end{aligned}$

$3\text{ Co} = \dfrac{177}{455} \left| \dfrac{100}{} \right. = 38.9\%$

$2\text{ As} = \dfrac{150}{455} \left| \dfrac{100}{} \right. = 33.0\%$

$8\text{ O} = \dfrac{128}{455} \left| \dfrac{100}{} \right. = 28.1\%$

28. $\begin{aligned} 1\text{ Ba @ } 137 \\ 1\text{ Te @ } 128 \\ \hline 265 \end{aligned}$

$\text{Ba} = \dfrac{137}{265} \left| \dfrac{100}{} \right. = 51.7\%$

$\text{Te} = \dfrac{128}{265} \left| \dfrac{100}{} \right. = 48.3\%$

29. $\begin{aligned} 1\text{ Zn @ } 65.4 &= 65.4 \\ 1\text{ Si @ } 28.1 &= 28.1 \\ 3\text{ O @ } 16.0 &= \underline{48.0} \\ &\ 142 \end{aligned}$

$\text{Zn} = \dfrac{65.4}{142} \left| \dfrac{100}{} \right. = 46.1\%$

$\text{Si} = \dfrac{28.1}{142} \left| \dfrac{100}{} \right. = 19.8\%$

$3\text{ O} = \dfrac{48.0}{142} \left| \dfrac{100}{} \right. = 33.8\%$

30. $\begin{aligned} 1\text{ Cd @ } 112 &= 112 \\ 2\text{ F @ } 19.0 &= \underline{38.0} \\ &\ 150 \end{aligned}$

$\text{Cd} = \dfrac{112}{150} \left| \dfrac{100}{} \right. = 74.7\%$

$2\text{ F} = \dfrac{38}{150} \left| \dfrac{100}{} \right. = 25.3\%$

31. $\begin{aligned} 1\text{ La @ } 139 &= 139 \\ 3\text{ F @ } 19.0 &= \underline{57.0} \\ &\ 196 \end{aligned}$

$\text{La} = \dfrac{139}{196} \left| \dfrac{100}{} \right. = 70.9\%$

$3\text{ F} = \dfrac{57.0}{196} \left| \dfrac{100}{} \right. = 29.1\%$

32. $\begin{aligned} 1\text{ Sc @ } 45.0 &= 45.0 \\ 3\text{ N @ } 14.0 &= 42.0 \\ 9\text{ O @ } 16.0 &= \underline{144} \\ &\ 231 \end{aligned}$

$\text{Sc} = \dfrac{45.0}{231} \left| \dfrac{100}{} \right. = 19.5\%$

$3\text{ N} = \dfrac{42.0}{231} \left| \dfrac{100}{} \right. = 18.2\%$

$9\text{ O} = \dfrac{144}{231} \left| \dfrac{100}{} \right. = 62.3\%$

Pages 88-89

33. $\text{Ce} = \dfrac{1.67}{140} = 0.0119$, $\text{I} = \dfrac{4.54}{127} = 0.0357$

$0.0357/0.0119 \approx 3$, 1:3 ratio

therefore, CeI_3

34. $\text{Al} = \dfrac{77.9}{27.0} = 2.89$, $\text{S} = \dfrac{139}{32.1} = 4.33$

$4.33/2.89 \approx 1.5$, 2:3 ratio

therefore, Al_2S_3

35. $\text{Cs} = \dfrac{4.04}{133} = 0.0304$, $\text{Cl} = \dfrac{1.08}{35.5} = 0.0304$

$0.0304/0.0304 = 1:1$

therefore, $CsCl$

36. $\text{Ni} = \dfrac{9.11}{58.7} = 0.155$, $\text{F} = \dfrac{5.89}{19.0} = 0.310$

$0.310/0.155 = 2$, 1:2 ratio

therefore, NiF_2

37. $Sc = \dfrac{4.73}{45.0} = 0.105$, $O = \dfrac{2.52}{16.0} = 0.158$

$0.158/0.105 = 1.5$, $2:3$ ratio

therefore, Sc_2O_3

Page 89

38. $CH = 12.0 + 1.01 = 13.0$

$\dfrac{78}{13.0} = 6.0$

$6(CH) = C_6H_6$

39. $CHOCl = 12.0 + 1.01 + 16.0 + 35.5 = 64.5$

$\dfrac{129}{64.5} = 2.00$

$2(CHOCl) = C_2H_2O_2Cl_2$ or $HCCl_2COOH$.

40. $CClN = 12.0 + 35.5 + 14.0 = 61.5$

$\dfrac{184}{61.5} = 3.00$

$3(CClN) = C_3Cl_3N_3$

41. $(0.856)(42.1g) = 36.0$ g C

$\dfrac{36.0}{12.0} = 3.00$ mol C

$(0.144)(42.1$ g$) = 6.06$ g H

$\dfrac{6.06}{1.01} = 6.00$ mol H

therefore, C_3H_6

42. Assume 100 g sample

$\dfrac{60.0 \text{ g}}{} \, \Big| \, \dfrac{1 \text{ mol}}{12.0 \text{ g}} = 5.00$ mol C

$\dfrac{4.48}{} \, \Big| \, \dfrac{1 \text{ mol}}{1.01 \text{ g}} = 4.44$ mol H

$\dfrac{35.5}{} \, \Big| \, \dfrac{1 \text{ mol}}{16.0 \text{ g}} = 2.22$ mol O

$\dfrac{5.00}{2.22} = 2.25$, $\dfrac{4.44}{2.22} = 2.00$, $\dfrac{2.22}{2.22} = 1.00$

multiply by 4 $= C_9H_8O_4$, formula mass $= 180$, therefore $C_9H_8O_4$ is also the molecular formula.

Page 90

43. molecular mass =

$2(6.94) + 28.1 + 6(19.0) = 156$

$\dfrac{0.391 \text{ g Li}_2\text{SiF}_6}{} \, \Big| \, \dfrac{1 \text{ mol}}{156 \text{ g Li}_2\text{SiF}_6} = 0.002\ 51$ mol

molecular mass =

$2(1.01) + 16.0 = 18.0$

$\dfrac{0.0903 \text{ g H}_2\text{O}}{} \, \Big| \, \dfrac{1 \text{ mol}}{18.0 \text{ g H}_2\text{O}} = 0.005\ 02$ mol

$0.005\ 02/0.002\ 51 \div 2.00$, $1:2$ ratio

$\therefore Li_2SiF_6 \cdot 2H_2O$

44. $\dfrac{0.737 \text{ g MgSO}_3}{} \, \Big| \, \dfrac{1 \text{ mol}}{104 \text{ g MgSO}_3} = 0.007\ 09$ mol

$\dfrac{0.763 \text{ g H}_2\text{O}}{} \, \Big| \, \dfrac{1 \text{ mol H}_2\text{O}}{18.0 \text{ g H}_2\text{O}} = 0.0424$ mol H_2O

$0.424/0.007\ 09 = 6.00$, $1:6$ ratio

Therefore, $MgSO_3 \cdot 6H_2O$

45. $\dfrac{95.3 \text{ g LiNO}_3}{} \, \Big| \, \dfrac{1 \text{ mol LiNO}_3}{68.9 \text{ g LiNO}_3} = 1.38$ mol $LiNO_3$

$\dfrac{74.7 \text{ g H}_2\text{O}}{} \, \Big| \, \dfrac{1 \text{ mol}}{18.0 \text{ g H}_2\text{O}} = 4.15$ mol H_2O

$4.15/1.38 = 3.01$, $1:3$ ratio

$\therefore LiNO_3 \cdot 3H_2O$

46. Assume 100 g of material

$\therefore 76.9$ g $CaSO_3$, 23.1 g H_2O

$\dfrac{76.9 \text{ g CaSO}_3}{} \, \Big| \, \dfrac{1 \text{ mol}}{120 \text{ g CaSO}_3} = 0.641$ mol

$\dfrac{23.1 \text{ g H}_2\text{O}}{} \, \Big| \, \dfrac{1 \text{ mol}}{18.0 \text{ g H}_2\text{O}} = 1.28$ mol

$1.28/0.641 = 2.00$, $1:2$ ratio

$\therefore CaSO_3 \cdot 2H_2O$

47. Assume 100 g of material

$\therefore 89.2$ g $BaBr_2$, 10.8 g H_2O

$\dfrac{89.2 \text{ g BaBr}_2}{} \, \Big| \, \dfrac{1 \text{ mol}}{297 \text{ g BaBr}_2} = 0.300$ mol

$\dfrac{10.8 \text{ g H}_2\text{O}}{} \, \Big| \, \dfrac{1 \text{ mol}}{18.0 \text{ g H}_2\text{O}} = 0.600$ mol

$0.600/0.300 = 2.00$, $1:2$ ratio

$\therefore BaBr_2 \cdot 2H_2O$

CHAPTER END PROBLEMS

Pages 93-94

1. The term formula mass should be used in speaking of the mass of ionic substances.

2. Avogadro's number of atoms has a mass in grams which is equal to the mass of a single atom in atomic mass units.

3. A mole is a counting unit equivalent to 6.02×10^{23} particles.

Molarity is the ratio of moles of solute per cubic decimeter of solution.

4. Empirical formula: Simplest whole number ratio of atoms in a compound.

Molecular formula: The number of atoms in a molecule based on its molecular mass.

5. Rounding would not permit the chemist to readily convert ratios of compounds or elements from macroscopic to microscopic levels without error.

6. $Rb = \dfrac{63.0}{85.5} = 0.737$ mol

$O = \dfrac{5.90}{16.0} = 0.369$ mol

$0.737/0.369 \approx 2:1$

Therefore, Rb_2O

7. $U = \dfrac{0.159}{238} = 0.000\ 668$ mol

$Cl = \dfrac{0.119}{35.5} = 0.003\ 35$ mol

$0.003\ 35/0.000\ 668 = 5.02$, $1:5$ ratio
therefore, UCl_5

8. $Ni = \dfrac{5.13}{58.7} = 0.0874$ mol

$N = \dfrac{2.45}{14.0} = 0.175$ mol

$O = \dfrac{8.39}{16.0} = 0.524$ mol

$\dfrac{0.0874}{0.0874} = 1.00 \quad \dfrac{0.175}{0.0874} = 2.00 \quad \dfrac{0.524}{0.0874} = 6.00$
$1:2:6$ ratio   therefore, $Ni(NO_3)_2$

9. $Na = \dfrac{2.13}{23.0} = 0.0926$ mol

$As = \dfrac{2.32}{74.9} = 0.0310$ mol

$O = \dfrac{1.98}{16.0} = 0.124$ mol

$0.124/0.0310 = 4.00$
$0.0310/0.0310 = 1.00$
$0.0926/.0310 = 2.99$
$\approx 3:1:4$ ratio
Therefore, Na_3AsO_4

10. $N = \dfrac{30.0}{14.0} = 2.14$ mol

$H = \dfrac{8.65}{1.01} = 8.56$ mol

$Se = \dfrac{84.7}{79.0} = 1.07$ mol

$O = \dfrac{68.6}{16.0} = 4.29$ mol

$2.14/8.56/1.07/4.29 = 2:8:1:4$
Therefore, $(NH_4)_2SeO_4$

11. $Cr = \dfrac{32.8}{52.0} = 0.631$ mol

$Cl = \dfrac{67.2}{35.5} = 1.89$ mol

$1.89/0.631 = 3.00$, $1:3$ ratio
Therefore, $CrCl_3$

12. $Co = \dfrac{42.7}{58.9} = 0.725$ mol

$Se = \dfrac{57.3}{79.0} = 0.725$ mol

$0.725/0.725 = 1:1$ Therefore, $CoSe$

13. $La = \dfrac{56.6}{139} = 0.407$ mol

$Cl = \dfrac{43.4}{35.5} = 1.22$ mol

$1.22/0.407 = 3.00$, $1:3$ ratio
Therefore, $LaCl_3$

14. $Tl = \dfrac{96.2}{204} = 0.472$ mol

$O = \dfrac{3.77}{16.0} = 0.236$ mol

$0.472/0.236 = 2:1$
Therefore, Tl_2O

15. $Rb = \dfrac{58.0}{85.5} = 0.679$ mol

$N = \dfrac{9.50}{14.0} = 0.679$ mol

$O = \dfrac{32.5}{16.0} = 2.03$ mol

$0.679/0.679/2.03 = 1:1:3$
Therefore, $RbNO_3$

16. $Rh = \dfrac{46.1}{103} = 0.448$ mol

$S = \dfrac{21.6}{32.1} = 0.673$ mol

$O = \dfrac{32.3}{16.0} = 2.02$ mol

$\dfrac{0.448}{0.448} = 1.00, \dfrac{0.673}{0.448} = 1.50, \dfrac{2.02}{0.448} = 4.51$
multiply by 2, ratio becomes $2:3:9$ ratio
therefore, $Rh_2(SO_3)_3$

17. $Cd = \dfrac{48.8}{112} = 0.436$ mol

$C = \dfrac{20.8}{12.0} = 1.73$ mol

$H = \dfrac{2.62}{1.01} = 2.59$ mol

$O = \dfrac{27.8}{16.0} = 1.74$

$0.436/1.73/2.59/1.74 \approx 1:4:6:4$
Therefore, $CdC_4H_6O_4$

18. $Fe = \dfrac{49.5}{55.8} = 0.887$ mol

$F = \dfrac{50.5}{19.0} = 2.66$ mol

$0.887/2.66 = 1:3$
Therefore, FeF_3

19. $Ni = \dfrac{42.6}{58.7} = 0.726$ mol

$Se = \dfrac{57.4}{79.0} = 0.727$ mol

$0.726/0.727 \approx 1:1$
Therefore, $NiSe$

20. $Al = \dfrac{8.29}{27.0} = 0.307$

$Cl = \dfrac{32.7}{35.5} = 0.921$

$O = \dfrac{59.0}{16.0} = 3.69$

$0.307/0.921/3.69 \approx 1:3:12$
Therefore, $Al(ClO_4)_3$

21. a. 174 u
b. 79.5 u
c. 233 u
d. 550 u
e. 351 u
f. 325 u

22. a. 135 u
b. 319 u
c. 96.7 u
d. 198 u
e. 350 u
f. 158 u

23. a. $\dfrac{64.3 \text{ g Rb}_2\text{SeO}_4}{} \left| \dfrac{1 \text{ mol Rb}_2\text{SeO}_4}{314 \text{ g Rb}_2\text{SeO}_4} \right. = 0.205 \text{ mol Rb}_2\text{SeO}_4$

b. $\dfrac{3.33 \times 10^{25} \text{ molecules I}_2}{} \left| \dfrac{1 \text{ mol}}{6.02 \times 10^{23} \text{ molecules}} \right| \dfrac{254 \text{ g I}_2}{1 \text{ mol I}_2} = 1.41 \times 10^4 \text{ g I}_2$

c. $\dfrac{0.846 \text{ mol HF}}{} \left| \dfrac{6.02 \times 10^{23} \text{ molecules}}{1 \text{ mol}} \right. = 5.09 \times 10^{23} \text{ molecules HF}$

d. $\dfrac{39.8 \text{ mol CO}_2}{} \left| \dfrac{6.02 \times 10^{23} \text{ molecules}}{1 \text{ mol}} \right. = 2.40 \times 10^{25} \text{ molecules CO}_2$

e. $\dfrac{308 \text{ formula units MnC}_2\text{O}_4}{} \left| \dfrac{1 \text{ mol}}{6.02 \times 10^{23} \text{ formula units}} \right. = 5.12 \times 10^{-22} \text{ mol MnC}_2\text{O}_4$

24. $\dfrac{5.70 \text{ g ZrF}_4}{5.00 \times 10^2 \text{ cm}^3 \text{ soln}} \left| \dfrac{1 \text{ mol ZrF}_4}{167 \text{ g ZrF}_4} \right| \dfrac{1000 \text{ cm}^3}{1 \text{ dm}^3} = 0.683M \text{ ZrF}_4$

25. $\dfrac{7.90 \text{ g NH}_4\text{Br}}{2.50 \times 10^2 \text{ cm}^3 \text{ soln}} \left| \dfrac{1 \text{ mol NH}_4\text{Br}}{97.9 \text{ g NH}_4\text{Br}} \right| \dfrac{1000 \text{ cm}^3}{1 \text{ dm}^3} = 0.323M \text{ NH}_4\text{Br}$

26. $\dfrac{6.44 \text{ g CuF}_2}{1.00 \times 10^3 \text{ cm}^3 \text{ soln}} \left| \dfrac{1 \text{ mol CuF}_2}{102 \text{ g CuF}_2} \right| \dfrac{1000 \text{ cm}^3}{1 \text{ dm}^3} = 0.0631M \text{ CuF}_2$

27. $\dfrac{13.1 \text{ g CdCl}_2}{1.00 \times 10^3 \text{ cm}^3 \text{ soln}} \left| \dfrac{1 \text{ mol CdCl}_2}{183 \text{ g CdCl}_2} \right| \dfrac{1000 \text{ cm}^3}{1 \text{ dm}^3} = 0.0716M \text{ CdCl}_2$

28. $\dfrac{38.3 \text{ g Ce(CH}_3\text{COO)}_3}{2.50 \times 10^2 \text{ cm}^3 \text{ soln}} \left| \dfrac{1 \text{ mol Ce(CH}_3\text{COO)}_3}{317 \text{ g Ce(CH}_3\text{COO)}_3} \right| \dfrac{1000 \text{ cm}^3}{1 \text{ dm}^3} = 0.483M \text{ Ce(CH}_3\text{COO)}_3$

29. $\dfrac{1.00 \times 10^3 \text{ cm}^3 \text{ soln}}{} \left| \dfrac{4.00 \text{ mol CsCl}}{1000 \text{ cm}^3 \text{ soln}} \right| \dfrac{169 \text{ g CsCl}}{1 \text{ mol CsCl}} = 676 \text{ g CsCl}$

30. $\dfrac{1.00 \times 10^3 \text{ cm}^3 \text{ soln}}{} \left| \dfrac{6.00 \text{ mol LiBr}}{1000 \text{ cm}^3 \text{ soln}} \right| \dfrac{86.8 \text{ g LiBr}}{1 \text{ mol LiBr}} = 521 \text{ g LiBr}$

31. $\dfrac{5.00 \times 10^2 \text{ cm}^3 \text{ soln}}{} \left| \dfrac{2.00 \text{ mol MgBr}_2}{1000 \text{ cm}^3 \text{ soln}} \right| \dfrac{184 \text{ g MgBr}_2}{1 \text{ mol MgBr}_2} = 184 \text{ g MgBr}_2$

32. $\dfrac{1.00 \times 10^3 \text{ cm}^3 \text{ soln}}{} \left| \dfrac{1.50 \text{ mol MnSO}_4}{1000 \text{ cm}^3 \text{ soln}} \right| \dfrac{151 \text{ g MnSO}_4}{1 \text{ mol MnSO}_4} = 227 \text{ g MnSO}_4$

33. $\dfrac{1.00 \times 10^3 \text{ cm}^3 \text{ soln}}{} \left| \dfrac{0.750 \text{ mol NiSO}_4}{1000 \text{ cm}^3 \text{ soln}} \right| \dfrac{155 \text{ g NiSO}_4}{1 \text{ mol NiSO}_4} = 116 \text{ g NiSO}_4$

34. 1 Na @ 23.0 = 23.0
1 Br @ $\underline{79.9 = 79.9}$
$\qquad\qquad\quad$ 103

$Na = \dfrac{23.0}{103} \left| \dfrac{100}{} \right. = 22.3\%$

$Br = \dfrac{79.9}{103} \left| \dfrac{100}{} \right. = 77.6\%$

35. 2 C @ 12.0 = 24.0
4 H @ 1.01 = 4.04
2 O @ 16.0 = $\underline{32.0}$
$\qquad\qquad\quad$ 60.0

$C = \dfrac{24.0}{60.0} \left| \dfrac{100}{} \right. = 40.0\%$

$H = \dfrac{4.04}{60.0} \left| \dfrac{100}{} \right. = 6.73\%$

$O = \dfrac{32.0}{60.0} \left| \dfrac{100}{} \right. = 53.3\%$

36. 1 U @ 238 = 238
2 S @ 32.1 = 64.2
8 O @ $\underline{16.0 = 128}$
$\qquad\qquad\quad$ 430

$U = \dfrac{238}{430} \left| \dfrac{100}{} \right. = 55.3\%$

$S = \dfrac{64.2}{430} \left| \dfrac{100}{} \right. = 14.9\%$

$O = \dfrac{128}{430} \left| \dfrac{100}{} \right. = 29.8\%$

37. 1 Zn @ 65.4 = 65.4
1 S @ $\underline{32.1 = 32.1}$
$\qquad\qquad\quad$ 97.5

$Zn = \dfrac{65.4}{97.5} \left| \dfrac{100}{} \right. = 67.1\%$

$S = \dfrac{32.1}{97.5} \left| \dfrac{100}{} \right. = 32.9\%$

38. 1 Sn @ 119 = 119
2 Cr @ 52.0 = 104
8 O @ $\underline{16.0 = 128}$
$\qquad\qquad\quad$ 351

$Sn = \dfrac{119}{351} \left| \dfrac{100}{} \right. = 33.9\%$

$Cr = \dfrac{104}{351} \left| \dfrac{100}{} \right. = 29.6\%$

$O = \dfrac{128}{351} \left|\dfrac{100}{}\right. = 36.5\%$

39. 2 C @ 12.0 = 24.0
6 H @ 1.01 = 6.06
1 O @ 16.0 = 16.0
46.1

$C = \dfrac{24.0}{46.1}\left|\dfrac{100}{}\right. = 52.1\%$

$H = \dfrac{6.06}{46.1}\left|\dfrac{100}{}\right. = 13.1\%$

$O = \dfrac{16.0}{46.1}\left|\dfrac{100}{}\right. = 34.7\%$

40. $Ca = \dfrac{33.3}{40.1} = 0.831$

$O = \dfrac{40.0}{16.0} = 2.50$

$S = \dfrac{26.7}{32.1} = 0.832$

0.831/2.50/0.832 ≈ 1:3:1
Therefore, $CaSO_3$

41. $C = \dfrac{92.3}{12.0} = 7.69$

$H = \dfrac{7.70}{1.01} = 7.62$

7.69/7.62 = 1:1
$(CH)_n = 78$ g, $(13)_n = 78$ g
$n = 6$, therefore, C_6H_6

42. $P = \dfrac{26.7}{31.0} = 0.861$

$N = \dfrac{12.1}{14.0} = 0.864$

$Cl = \dfrac{61.2}{35.5} = 1.72$

0.861/0.864/1.72 ≈ 1:1:2
$(PNCl_2)_n = 695$ g, $(116)_n = 695$g
$n = 6$, therefore, $P_6N_6Cl_{12}$

43. Assume 100 g of the material
∴90.7 g SrC_2O_4, ∴9.30 g H_2O

$\dfrac{90.7 \text{ g } SrC_2O_4}{}\left|\dfrac{1 \text{ mol}}{176 \text{ g } SrC_2O_4}\right. = 0.515$ mol SrC_2O_4

$\dfrac{9.30 \text{ g } H_2O}{}\left|\dfrac{1 \text{ mol}}{18.0 \text{ g } H_2O}\right. = 0.517$ mol H_2O

0.515/0.517 ≈ 1:1 ∴$SrC_2O_4 \cdot H_2O$

44. Assume 100 g of the material.
∴76.9 g $La_2(CO_3)_3$, ∴23.9 g H_2O

$\dfrac{76.9 \text{ g } La_2(CO_3)_3}{}\left|\dfrac{1 \text{ mol } La_2(CO_3)_3}{458 \text{ g } La_2(CO_3)_3}\right. = 0.168$ mol $La_2(CO_3)_3$

$\dfrac{23.9 \text{ g } H_2O}{}\left|\dfrac{1 \text{ mol } H_2O}{18.0 \text{ g } H_2O}\right. = 1.33$ mol H_2O

1.33/0.168 = 7.92, 1:8 ratio
∴$La_2(CO_3)_3 \cdot 8H_2O$

45. Assume 100 g of the material.
∴86.7 g Mo_2S_5, ∴13.3 g H_2O

$\dfrac{86.7 \text{ g } Mo_2S_5}{}\left|\dfrac{1 \text{ mol } Mo_2S_5}{352 \text{ g } Mo_2S_5}\right. = 0.246$ mol Mo_2S_5

$\dfrac{13.3 \text{ g } H_2O}{}\left|\dfrac{1 \text{ mol } H_2O}{18.0 \text{ g } H_2O}\right. = 0.739$ mol H_2O

0.739/0.246 = 3.00, 1:3 ratio
∴$Mo_2S_5 \cdot 3H_2O$

REVIEW

Page 95

1. $\dfrac{81.2 \text{ g}}{}\left|\dfrac{1000 \text{ mg}}{1 \text{ g}}\right. = 81\ 200$ mg

2. 4

3. $\dfrac{0.5}{12.0} = 0.04$

4. **a.** chemical
b. physical
c. chemical
d. chemical

5. **a.** physical
b. chemical
c. physical
d. physical

ONE MORE STEP

Page 95

1. Experimental percentages are usually within 1-2% of the calculated values.

2. See Section 5:2 of the Teaching Techniques.

CHEMICAL REACTIONS   6

AN OVERVIEW

In Chapter 4, students learned how to name and write chemical formulas. In Chapter 5, they were made aware of the quantitative relationships involving chemical formulas. Chapter 6 builds on the techniques learned in the previous chapters. The ability to write and balance chemical equations is a basic goal of any introductory chemistry course. The chapter develops the following concepts:

1. The chemical equation represents chemical change. The system will be characterized by a whole new set of properties after the reaction has occurred.

2. In a balanced equation, equal numbers of each kind of atom are present on both sides of the equation.

3. Reactions can be classified into four general types: single displacement, double displacement, decomposition, and synthesis. Products may be predicted once students learn the characteristics of the four general types.

This prepares students for quantitative relationships associated with a chemical equation in 6:4.

DEMONSTRATION INFORMATION

You may want to add a few drops of H_2O to the glycerol-liquid soap mixture. Once the soap bubble is free of the funnel, it rises quickly. It is best to have an assistant hold the meter stick with the attached candle above the funnel before you shake it free. The bubbles burn with a yellow-blue flame in mid air. **CAUTION:** *Do not do this demonstration near any flammable materials (drapes, ceiling, and so on). As with any open flame, have a fire extinguisher close by.* Note, the combustion will not leave any soot marks on the ceiling. Place newspaper on the floor to collect wax droppings.

DISPOSAL: *These chemicals are properly disposed of at a local landfill. They represent little or no hazard to the environment.*

PERFORMANCE OBJECTIVES

Goals: Students will demonstrate a proficiency in writing and balancing chemical equations. Students will differentiate between four general types of chemical reactions. Students will demonstrate their understanding of mass relationships in chemical reactions by performing mass-mass calculations.

Objectives: Upon completion of the reading and problems, and when asked to demonstrate their understanding either orally or on a written test, students will

6:1	K	define chemical reaction, and list the reactants and products in a given reaction. **6:1**
6:2	K	use the correct symbols for the physical state of each substance involved in chemical equations. **6:1**
6:3	K	distinguish a chemical reaction from a chemical equation, and state what it means for an equation to be balanced. **6:2**
6:4	K	distinguish subscripts and coefficients in chemical equations. **6:2**
6:5	K/P	write balanced equations given names and/or formulas for reactants and products. **6:2**

6:6	P	classify a given reaction as one of these four types: single displacement, double displacement, decomposition, or synthesis. **6:3**
6:7	K	define each of the four types of reaction. **6:3**
6:8	K/P	predict the products and balance the equation when given the reactants for one of these four types of reactions. **6:3**
6:9	K	define stoichiometry. **6:4**
6:10	P	given the mass of a reactant or product, calculate the mass of another reactant or product using the mole ratio(s) in a chemical equation. **6:4**
6:11	K	differentiate the characteristics of exothermic and endothermic reactions. **6:5**
6:12	K	define energy of activation. **6:5**
6:13	A	voluntarily complete one or more of the One More Step activities.
6:14	A	read unassigned literature related to the chapter.

TEACHING TECHNIQUES

Section 6:1

Representing balanced chemical equations can best be done using models. If you do not have a commercial kit, obtain 18 plastic foam balls. Paint 4 black, 4 blue, and leave 10 white. Use pipe cleaners or toothpicks to build the molecules listed in the chapter introduction ($2C_2H_2$ and $5O_2$ molecules).

Explain the color coding to students. Ask them to rearrange the atoms, using all of them, to form CO_2 and H_2O molecules. They should end up with $4CO_2$ and $2H_2O$ models. Without any discussion, students have balanced the equation and should see why it is necessary to have the same number of each kind of atom on both sides of the equation.

Section 6:3

Students should receive sufficient drill in predicting the products of a reaction. This skill will be used throughout the course especially in the lab where students will be writing equations to represent their observations.

We wish to make the point once again that our approach in teaching formula writing, balancing equations, and the quantitative aspects of the mole concept before structure and bonding allows you more freedom in scheduling laboratory experiments.

Section 6:4

It is important to stress the coefficients of a balanced equation as being the ratio of moles for the mass-mass problem. Doing mass-mass problems in one step may be somewhat difficult for students to master at first. It is important that you emphasize using the factor-label method here to cut down on mistakes in problem solving. The proportion method of solving mass-mass problems is actually a form of factor-label in logic but the units are not expressed. As a result, students memorize rather than understand the solving process.

Section 6:5

This section concludes the chapter on chemical reactions. Use it to impress on your students the fact that energy changes always accompany chemical changes. Chapter 20 provides a detailed discussion of energy changes and activation energy.

Careers and Chemistry

This feature is designed to show the diverse types of careers that involve a knowledge of chemistry. You may want to have students bring in articles showing instances where regulatory groups (FDA or OSHA) have brought action to protect the public. *FDA Consumer* magazine has feature articles every month concerning product safety as well as a listing of seizures and actions brought against companies for unsanitary practices.

PROBLEM SOLUTIONS

Page 100

1. Balanced. $Te + H_2O \rightarrow TeO + H_2$

2. $La(NO_3)_3 + 3NaOH \rightarrow La(OH)_3 + 3NaNO_3$
3. Balanced. $RhO_3 \rightarrow RhO + O_2$
4. $3Hf + 2N_2 \rightarrow Hf_3N_4$
5. $2Ga + 3H_2SO_4 \rightarrow Ga_2(SO_4)_3 + 3H_2$
6. $PdCl_2 + 2HNO_3 \rightarrow Pd(NO_3)_2 + 2HCl$
7. Balanced. $RbBr + AgCl \rightarrow AgBr + RbCl$
8. $2PaI_5 \rightarrow 2Pa + 5I_2$
9. $5O_2 + Sb_2S_3 \rightarrow Sb_2O_4 + 3SO_2$
10. Balanced $Cu + Cl_2 \rightarrow CuCl_2$

Page 102

11. Balanced. $CuO + H_2 \rightarrow Cu + H_2O$ single displacement
12. $2Sb + 3H_2O \rightarrow Sb_2O_3 + 3H_2$ single displacement
13. $2Re + 3Br_2 \rightarrow 2ReBr_3$ synthesis
14. $2Ac(OH)_3 \rightarrow Ac_2O_3 + 3H_2O$ decomposition
15. $Ra + 2C \rightarrow RaC_2$ synthesis
16. $3HfCl_3 + Al \rightarrow 3HfCl_2 + AlCl_3$
17. $Zn + 2CrCl_3 \rightarrow 2CrCl_2 + ZnCl_2$
18. $Ca(AlO_2)_2 + 8HCl \rightarrow 2AlCl_3 + CaCl_2 + 4H_2O$
19. $BaCO_3 + C + H_2O \rightarrow 2CO + Ba(OH)_2$
20. $2CeO_2 + 2KI + 8HCl \rightarrow 2KCl + 2CeCl_3 + 4H_2O + I_2$
21. $CuCO_3(cr) \rightarrow CuO(cr) + CO_2(g)$
22. $2Na(cr) + 2H_2O(l) \rightarrow 2NaOH(aq) + H_2(g)$
23. $NH_4NO_2(cr) \rightarrow 2H_2O(l) + N_2(g)$
24. $2Cu(cr) + S(cr) \rightarrow Cu_2S(cr)$
25. $2AgNO_3(aq) + H_2SO_4(aq) \rightarrow Ag_2SO_4(cr) + 2HNO_3(aq)$
26. $H_2SO_4(l) \rightarrow H_2O(l) + SO_3(g)$
27. $CaCO_3(cr) + 2HCl(aq) \rightarrow CaCl_2(aq) + H_2O(l) + CO_2(g)$
28. $NH_4NO_3(cr) \rightarrow 2H_2O(l) + N_2O(g)$

Pages 106-107

29. $2Na(cr) + 2H_2O(l) \rightarrow 2NaOH(aq) + H_2(g)$

$$\frac{72.0 \text{ g Na}}{} \left| \frac{1 \text{ mol Na}}{23.0 \text{ g Na}} \right| \frac{1 \text{ mol } H_2}{2 \text{ mol Na}} \left| \frac{2.02 \text{ g } H_2}{1 \text{ mol } H_2} \right| = 3.16 \text{ g } H_2$$

30. $N_2(g) + 3H_2(g) \rightarrow 2NH_3(g)$

$$\frac{6.57 \text{ g } H_2}{} \left| \frac{1 \text{ mol } H_2}{2.02 \text{ g } H_2} \right| \frac{2 \text{ mol } NH_3}{3 \text{ mol } H_2} \left| \frac{17.0 \text{ g } NH_3}{1 \text{ mol } NH_3} \right| = 36.9 \text{ g } NH_3$$

31. $C(cr) + O_2(g) \rightarrow CO_2(g)$

$$\frac{84.9 \text{ g C}}{} \left| \frac{1 \text{ mol C}}{12.0 \text{ g C}} \right| \frac{1 \text{ mol } O_2}{1 \text{ mol C}} \left| \frac{32.0 \text{ g } O_2}{1 \text{ mol } O_2} \right| = 226 \text{ g } O_2$$

32.
$$\frac{84.9 \text{ g C}}{} \left| \frac{1 \text{ mol C}}{12.0 \text{ g C}} \right| \frac{1 \text{ mol } CO_2}{1 \text{ mol C}} \left| \frac{44.0 \text{ g } CO_2}{1 \text{ mol } CO_2} \right| = 311 \text{ g } CO_2$$

33. $2KClO_3(cr) \rightarrow 2KCl(cr) + 3O_2(g)$

$$\frac{82.6 \text{ g } O_2}{} \left| \frac{1 \text{ mol } O_2}{32.0 \text{ g } O_2} \right| \frac{2 \text{ mol KCl}}{3 \text{ mol } O_2} \left| \frac{74.6 \text{ g KCl}}{1 \text{ mol KCl}} \right| = 128 \text{ g KCl}$$

34.
$$\frac{80.3 \text{ g Fe}}{} \left| \frac{1 \text{ mol Fe}}{55.8 \text{ g Fe}} \right| \frac{3 \text{ mol CO}}{2 \text{ mol Fe}} \left| \frac{28.0 \text{ g CO}}{1 \text{ mol CO}} \right| = 60.4 \text{ g CO}$$

35. $2HCl(aq) + Ca(OH)_2(cr) \rightarrow CaCl_2(aq) + 2H_2O(l)$

$$\frac{44.7 \text{ g } Ca(OH)_2}{} \left| \frac{1 \text{ mol } Ca(OH)_2}{74.1 \text{ g } Ca(OH)_2} \right| \frac{2 \text{ mol HCl}}{1 \text{ mol } Ca(OH)_2} \left| \frac{36.5 \text{ g HCl}}{1 \text{ mol HCl}} \right| = 44.1 \text{ g HCl}$$

36. $2Al(cr) + 6HCl(aq) \rightarrow 2AlCl_3(aq) + 3H_2(g)$

$$\frac{4.77 \text{ g Al}}{} \left| \frac{1 \text{ mol Al}}{27.0 \text{ g Al}} \right| \frac{3 \text{ mol } H_2}{2 \text{ mol Al}} \left| \frac{2.02 \text{ g } H_2}{1 \text{ mol } H_2} \right. = 0.535 \text{ g } H_2$$

CHAPTER END PROBLEMS

Pages 111-112

1. $Cr(cr) + 2HCl(aq) \rightarrow H_2(g) + CrCl_2(aq)$

2. $Ba(OH)_2(aq) + CO_2(g) \rightarrow BaCO_3(cr) + H_2O(l)$

3. Changing a subscript changes the substance being represented. Balancing an equation involves changing the ratio of substances involved in the reaction not the substances themselves.

4. To accurately represent the ratio of substances involved in a reaction, the equation for the reaction must be balanced.

5. $4Na(cr) + O_2(g) \rightarrow 2Na_2O(cr)$

6. $AsCl_3(cr) + 3H_2O(l) \rightarrow 3HCl(aq) + As(OH)_3(aq)$

7. $2Ho(cr) + 6H_2O(l) \rightarrow 2Ho(OH)_3(aq) + 3H_2(g)$

8. $2IrCl_3(aq) + 3NaOH(aq) \rightarrow Ir_2O_3(cr) + 3HCl(aq) + 3NaCl(aq)$

9. $2MoO_3(cr) + 3Zn(cr) + 3H_2SO_4(l) \rightarrow Mo_2O_3(cr) + 3ZnSO_4(aq) + 3H_2O(l)$

10. Balanced. $NbI_3(cr) + I_2(cr) \rightarrow NbI_5(cr)$

11. $Pb(CH_3COO)_2(aq) + K_2CrO_4(aq) \rightarrow PbCrO_4(cr) + 2KCH_3COO \ (aq)$

12. $RbCl(cr) + 2O_2(g) \rightarrow RbClO_4(cr)$

13. $3SiF_4(cr) + 3H_2O(l) \rightarrow 2H_2SiF_6(aq) + H_2SiO_3(cr)$

14. $Sn(cr) + 2KOH(aq) \rightarrow K_2SnO_2(cr) + H_2(g)$

15. $2Ag_2O(cr) \rightarrow 4Ag(cr) + O_2(g)$

16. $Cu(cr) + 2AgNO_3(aq) \rightarrow Cu(NO_3)_2(aq) + 2Ag(cr)$

17. $2Mg(cr) + O_2(g) \rightarrow 2MgO(cr)$

18. $HCl(aq) + AgNO_3(aq) \rightarrow HNO_3(aq) + AgCl(cr)$

19. $Mg(cr) + 2HCl(aq) \rightarrow MgCl_2(aq) + H_2(g)$

20. $4Fe(cr) + 3O_2(g) \rightarrow 2Fe_2O_3(cr)$

21. $Fe(cr) + S(cr) \rightarrow FeS(cr)$

22. $Ca(OH)_2(aq) + H_2SO_4(aq) \rightarrow CaSO_4(cr) + 2H_2O(l)$

23. $3Mg(cr) + N_2(g) \rightarrow Mg_3N_2(cr)$

24. $Zn(cr) + H_2SO_4(aq) \rightarrow ZnSO_4(aq) + H_2(g)$

25. To obtain the ratio of moles of required substance to given substance, a balanced equation must be used.

26. $\dfrac{7.71 \text{ g } AlCl_3}{} \left| \dfrac{1 \text{ mol } AlCl_3}{134 \text{ g } AlCl_3} \right| \dfrac{1 \text{ mol } NaAlO_2}{1 \text{ mol } AlCl_3} \left| \dfrac{82.0 \text{ g } NaAlO_2}{1 \text{ mol } NaAlO_2} \right. = 4.72 \text{ g } NaAlO_2$

27. $\dfrac{2.96 \text{ g } Ce_2(C_2O_4)_3}{} \left| \dfrac{1 \text{ mol } Ce_2(C_2O_4)_3}{544 \text{ g } Ce_2(C_2O_4)_3} \right| \dfrac{42 \text{ mol } CO_2}{1 \text{ mol } Ce_2(C_2O_4)_3} \left| \dfrac{44.0 \text{ g } CO_2}{1 \text{ mol } CO_2} \right. = 10.1 \text{ g } CO_2$

28. Endothermic reactions take in heat while exothermic reactions give off heat.

29. a. exothermic   b. released   c. lower

30. $\dfrac{0.611 \text{ g } CO_2}{} \left| \dfrac{1 \text{ mol } CO_2}{44.0 \text{ g } CO_2} \right| \dfrac{1 \text{ mol } O_2}{2 \text{ mol } CO_2} \left| \dfrac{32.0 \text{ g } O_2}{1 \text{ mol } O_2} \right. = 0.222 \text{ g } O_2$

REVIEW

Page 112

1. a. $\dfrac{2.52 \times 10^{21} \text{ formula units } ZrS_2}{} \left| \dfrac{1 \text{ mol } ZrS_2}{6.02 \times 10^{23} \text{ formula units}} \right. = 0.004\ 19 \text{ mol } ZrS_2$

b. $\dfrac{1.26 \times 10^{25} \text{ formula units } Al(CH_3COO)_3}{} \left| \dfrac{1 \text{ mol}}{6.02 \times 10^{23} \text{ formula units}} \right| \dfrac{204 \text{ g } Al(CH_3COO)_3}{1 \text{ mol } Al(CH_3COO)_3} = .4270 \text{ g } Al(CH_3COO)_3$

c. $\dfrac{6.06 \text{ g } Fe_2(SO_4)_3}{} \left| \dfrac{1 \text{ mol } Fe_2(SO_4)_3}{400 \text{ g } Fe_2(SO_4)_3} \right. = 0.0152 \text{ mol } Fe_2(SO_4)_3$

d. $\dfrac{88.4 \text{ g } MnI_2}{} \left| \dfrac{1 \text{ mol } MnI_2}{309 \text{ g } MnI_2} \right. = 0.286 \text{ mol } MnI_2$

e. $\dfrac{0.002\ 02 \text{ mol } Ni(OH)_2}{} \left| \dfrac{92.7 \text{ g } Ni(OH)_2}{1 \text{ mol } Ni(OH)_2} \right. = 0.187 \text{ g } Ni(OH)_2$

2. $\dfrac{0.550 \text{ g } Ni(IO_3)_2}{1000 \text{ cm}^3 \text{ soln}} \left| \dfrac{1 \text{ mol } Ni(IO_3)_2}{409 \text{ g } Ni(IO_3)_2} \right| \dfrac{1000 \text{ cm}^3}{1 \text{ dm}^3} = 0.001\ 34M \text{ Ni(IO}_3)_2$

3. $\dfrac{2.00 \times 10^2 \text{ cm}^3 \text{ soln}}{} \left| \dfrac{0.003\ 64 \text{ mol } Ag_2C_4H_4O_6}{1000 \text{ cm}^3 \text{ soln}} \right| \dfrac{364 \text{ g } Ag_2C_4H_4O_6}{1 \text{ mol } Ag_2C_4H_4O_6} = 0.265 \text{ g } Ag_2C_4H_4O_6$

4. $Sr = 87.6 \ \dfrac{87.6}{342} \times 100 = 25.6\%$ $2I = 254 \ \dfrac{254}{342} \times 100 = 74.3\%$

5. $Zn = \dfrac{45.3}{65.4} = 0.693$, $Se = \dfrac{54.7}{79.0} = 0.69$

$0.693/0.693 = 1:1$

Therefore, ZnSe

6. $\dfrac{79.0 \, \cancel{g \, Zr(NO_3)_4}}{} \left| \dfrac{1 \, mol \, Zr(NO_3)_4}{339 \, \cancel{g \, Zr(NO_3)_4}} = 0.233 \, mol \, Zr(NO_3)_4 \right.$

$\dfrac{21.0 \, \cancel{g \, H_2O}}{} \left| \dfrac{1 \, mol \, H_2O}{18.0 \, \cancel{g \, H_2O}} = 1.17 \, mol \, H_2O \right.$

$1.17/0.223 = 5.02$, $1:5$ ratio

Therefore, $Zr(NO_3)_4 \cdot 5H_2O$

ONE MORE STEP

Pages 112-113

1. a. $Cu(cr) + 2H_2SO_4(aq) \rightarrow CuSO_4(aq) + SO_2(g) + 2H_2O(l)$

b. $Cu_2S(cr) + 12HNO_3(aq) \rightarrow Cu(NO_3)_2(aq) + CuSO_4(aq) + 10NO_2(g) + 6H_2O(l)$

c. $CH_4(g) + 2O_2(g) \rightarrow CO_2(g) + 2H_2O(l)$

d. $2Ce(IO_3)_4(aq) + 24H_2C_2O_4(aq) \rightarrow Ce_2(C_2O_4)_3(aq) + 4I_2(aq) + 42CO_2(g) + 24H_2O(l)$

e. $2KBr(cr) + 3H_2SO_4(aq) + MnO_2(cr) \rightarrow 2KHSO_4(aq) + MnSO_4(aq) + Br_2(l) + 2H_2O(l)$

2. Double displacement

3. A metal carbonate may decompose when heated to form a metal oxide and CO_2 gas.
A metal hydroxide may decompose when heated to form a metal oxide and H_2O.
A metal oxide may decompose when heated to form the metal and O_2 gas.
An acid containing oxygen may decompose when heated to form a nonmetal oxide and H_2O.

4. Brown bottles delay the spoiling of foods in which the decomposition reaction is activated by light.

5. Exposing the film involves the light-sensitive reaction

$AgBr \xrightarrow{\text{light}} AgBr$ (exposed)

Developing the exposed film replaces the exposed AgBr with Ag.

$2AgBr + C_6H_4(OH)_2 \rightarrow 2Ag + C_6H_4O_2 + 2HBr$
(exposed)   (image)

6. Any changes of mass to energy (or vice versa) which are associated with ordinary chemical reactions are too small to be detectable with present instruments. In molecular rearrangements (for example, chemical reactions) it is the change in potential energy of the particles involved (for example, the relative positions of the particles) which manifests itself as ΔH.

ATOMIC STRUCTURE   7

AN OVERVIEW

The study of atomic structure begins with Chapter 7. The atomic theory, subatomic particles, and basic ideas about the structure of atoms are discussed using an historical approach. Students can follow logically the historical development of scientific knowledge about atoms. When teaching atomic theory, you should make students aware of the parts of the theory that are firmly grounded in experiment and the parts that are tentative. For example, the existence of a small, dense, positive nucleus is firmly based upon experiment. Any description of an electron's location is not based on experiment. The chapter builds toward the structure of the hydrogen atom; however, do not stress the Bohr planetary model of the atom.

DEMONSTRATION INFORMATION

The demonstration offers students visual evidence that matter exists in small units called atoms.

PERFORMANCE OBJECTIVES

Goals: Students will gain an understanding of the historical development for our present day model of the atom. Students will learn how spectroscopy is used to identify substances. Students will calculate the average atomic mass of a mixture of isotopes of an element.

Objectives: Upon completion of the reading and problems, and when aksed to demonstrate their understanding either orally or on a written test, students will

7:1	K	state a brief history of the development of the theory of atomic structure. **7:1-7:2**
7:2	K	state the laws of conservation of mass, definite proportions, and multiple proportions, and explain the basis for each. **7:1-7:2**
7:3	K	identify the important persons associated with the development of atomic theory, the discovery of subatomic particles and their properties, the quantum theory, and the photoelectric effect. **7:1-7:11**
7:4	K	list the points of Dalton's hypothesis. **7:2**
7:5	K/P	state Avogadro's law, and how it relates to the work of Dalton and Gay-Lussac. **7:2**
7:6	K	state how modern atomic theory differs from Dalton's theory and the Rutherford-Bohr model. **7:3-7:4**

7:7	K	define and differentiate anode and cathode, and state their relationship to cathode rays. **7:3**
7:8	K/P	explain the significance of the work of Thomson and Millikan with respect to the electron. **7:3**
7:9	K	differentiate among the electron, proton, and neutron, and indicate the electrical charge and relative mass associated with each particle. **7:3**
7:10	K	define atomic number and mass number and their relationship to isotopes. **7:4**
7:11	P	given the atomic number and mass number, list the number of protons, neutrons, and electrons in an atom, or given the number of particles determine the atomic number and mass number. **7:4**
7:12	K	define isotope, nucleon, and nuclide. **7:4**
7:13	K	explain how Rutherford's gold foil experiment contributed to our knowledge of atomic structure. **7:5**
7:14	K	describe the Rutherford-Bohr planetary model of the atom. **7:5**
7:15	K	express the approximate size of an atom and the relative distances between subatomic particles. **7:5**
7:16	K	define spectrum and spectroscopy and explain the use of spectroscopy to determine the structure of a substance. **7:6**
7:17	K	define electromagnetic energy, frequency, hertz, wavelength, and amplitude. **7:6-7:7**
7:18	K	state Planck's hypothesis as it relates to atomic theory; define quantum theory, quanta, and photon. **7:7-7:8**
7:19	K	state the relationship between quantum theory and the location of an electron. **7:8**
7:20	K	define photoelectric effect. **7:9**
7:21	K	define the standard for atomic mass units. **7:10**
7:22	K	explain how a mass spectrometer can be used to determine average atomic mass. **7:11**
7:23	P	calculate average atomic mass, given percentages of isotopes and their masses. **7:11**
7:24	A	voluntarily complete one or more of the One More Step activities.
7:25	A	read unassigned literature related to the chapter.

TEACHING TECHNIQUES

Section 7:1-2

Students often ask why they have to study history in chemistry class. We have included a presentation of the origin of the atomic theory for two reasons, (1) to show that our present theory is the work of many scientists over many years, and (2) to make students aware of the logic used in obtaining evidence to support an atomic theory. The chemical evidence includes:

1. elements cannot be decomposed into simpler substances,
2. compounds have a definite composition by mass (Proust),
3. Dalton's law of multiple proportions, and
4. gases react in simple whole number ratios by volume (Gay Lussac).

Point out to your students that our understanding of atomic theory will need to be modified in light of yet undiscovered information.

Section 7:5

The nuclear theory of the atom was first proposed by Rutherford on the basis of the scattering experiment described in Section 7:5. His theory was the basis of modern atomic structure. This work raised several questions.

1. How are electrons arranged about the nucleus? This question will be considered in the next several chapters.
2. How do atoms of different elements differ in structure? F. Soddy first used the term isotopes in 1913. The separation of isotopes in a lab occurred in 1913 by J. J. Thomson (neon-20 and 22)
3. What is the internal structure of the nucleus? This question is still unanswered.

Bohr provided the model to explain why the hydrogen atom does not collapse. The Bohr model did successfully predict the energy levels of hydrogen; however, do not spend a great deal of time on the Bohr model. Experiments show that the electron does not move in circular or elliptical orbits. Spatial distribution described by quantum mechanics is covered in Chapter 8. Bohr calculations did not explain the energy levels of the multielectron atom. The Bohr model also does not explain chemical bonding in terms of energy. Finally, his basic assumption concerning the angular momentum $n(h/2\pi)$ is incorrect. It is actually

$$\sqrt{l(l + 1)}\ (h/2\pi)$$

For these reasons, this model is treated lightly in the text.

It is surprising that the Bohr model is still retained and emphasized almost sixty years after the proposal of the wave equation.

Section 7:7
Planck first described light as a particle. He used this description to explain the frequency distribution of black body radiation. Planck proposed this model based on experimental facts. Section 7:9 describes the photoelectric effect which demonstrates the particle nature of light. Interpretation of spectroscopic data concerns the behavior of light as a particle.

Section 7:8
We have avoided illustrations of atoms using Bohr models. Beginning chemistry students have open minds and should not be given the impression that the atom is planetary. Refer to the electrons as a cloud and to their positions as probable positions. This concept will be expanded in Chapter 9.

Section 7:9
When light falls on a metal surface, there is a frequency of the light which will cause the ejection of electrons from the surface of the metal. Changing the intensity at this frequency causes more electrons to be emitted. Increasing the light intensity increases the number of photons but does not change the energy per photon. Light which strikes the metal surface which is below the minimum frequency has no effect on the metal. Emphasize the difference between increasing light intensity and increasing the frequency.

Careers and Chemistry
The job description for a laboratory technician can vary widely. The educational requirements for this type of work can vary also. Have students investigate various programs at technical schools, junior colleges, and colleges. There may also be some on the job training programs sponsored by industries in your area.

PROBLEM SOLUTIONS

Page 121
1. C = 6 electrons, 7 neutrons, 6 protons
Am = 95 electrons, 148 neutrons, 95 protons

Page 131
2. $\dfrac{(92.21 \times 27.977) + (4.70 \times 28.976) + (3.09 \times 29.974)}{100} = 28.1$ u

3. $\dfrac{(5 \times 176) + (19 \times 177) + (27 \times 178) + (14 \times 179) + (35 \times 180)}{100}$
= 179 u

CHAPTER END PROBLEMS

Page 135
1. a. Dalton reintroduced the atomic theory and gathered experimental evidence to support his theory.
b. Thomson, who made the Cavendish Laboratory famous, made several important advances. He discovered the electron and showed that canal rays actually consist of positively charged particles. Thomson also calculated the mass of the proton.
c. Rutherford demonstrated that the nucleus is a small heavy core in an atom which consists mostly of space.
d. Chadwick showed that rays discovered by Walter Bothe in 1930 were really a beam of uncharged particles. Chadwick is credited with the discovery of the neutron.
e. Moseley did research which resulted in a modification of the atomic theory to include atomic number.
f. Bohr originated the idea that electrons travel in a definite energy level around the nucleus. He applied Planck's idea of small packets or quanta of energy to his electron model.
g. Planck introduced the idea that (electromagnetic) energy is radiated in small packets called quanta.
h. Avogadro formed an hypothesis regarding gases at the same temperature and pressure: Equal volumes of gases, at the same temperature and pressure, have the same number of molecules.

2. Dalton's Theory:
(1) All matter is composed of atoms which are indivisible.
(2) Atoms of the same element are identical, atoms of different elements are dissimilar.
(3) Atoms can unite with other atoms in simple numerical ratios.

3. Carbon-12

4. Demonstrate conservation of mass by burning a candle in a closed container. Measure the mass of the candle and container before and after burning. There should be no change in mass if mass is conserved.

5. Analyze a compound to determine of what elements it is composed and the percentage of each element present.

Synthesize the same compound (such as water) being careful to measure the reactants and products accurately. If the same ratio of elements is always involved, you have demonstrated the law of definite proportions.

6. Equal volumes of gases at the same temperature and pressure contain the same number of particles.

7. The atomic number is equal to the number of protons in the nucleus of an atom. The atomic number is 19. The mass number would be $(19 + 20) = 39$ u.

8. $\dfrac{(51.82 \times 106.905) + (48.18 \times 108.905)}{100} = 107.9$ u

9. $[(0.350 \times 77.920) + (2.27 \times 79.916) + (11.56 \times 81.913) + (11.55 \times 82.914) + (56.90 \times 83.912) + (17.37 \times 85.911)] \div 100 = 83.8$ u

10. $\dfrac{4.23 \text{ cm}}{} \left| \dfrac{1 \text{ m}}{100 \text{ cm}} \right| \dfrac{10^9 \text{ nm}}{1 \text{ m}} = 4.23 \times 10^7$ nm

11. Modified Theory: (See answer 2)
    (1) Atoms are composed of electrons, protons, and neutrons.
    (2) All atoms of the same element have the same number

of protons in the nucleus but the number of neutrons may vary.
    (3) Remains unchanged.

12.

	charge	relative mass	location
proton	+1	1	nucleus
neutron	0	1	nucleus
electron	−1	0	orbitals

13. Cl = 17 electrons, 18 neutrons, 17 protons
    Th = 90 electrons, 142 neutrons, 90 protons

14. Rutherford interpreted the results of the experiment.

15. Lines in the spectrum corresponded to the energy differences between Bohr's orbits.

16. Only the ionized form of an element will be affected by electric and magnetic fields.

17. The energy of electrons depends on the wavelength of light (energy in a quantum), while the number of electrons depends on the intensity of light (number of quanta).

REVIEW

Page 136

1. a. strontium acetate
   b. manganese(II) hydroxide
   c. cadmium oxalate
   d. lithium arsenate
   e. thorium(IV) nitride
   f. cerium(III) carbonate

2. assume a 100 g sample

   $\dfrac{84.2 \text{ g } (NH_4)_2CO_3}{} \left| \dfrac{1 \text{ mol } (NH_4)_2CO_3}{96.1 \text{ g } (NH_4)_2CO_3} \right. = 0.876 \text{ mol } (NH_4)_2CO_3$

   $\dfrac{15.8 \text{ g } H_2O}{} \left| \dfrac{1 \text{ mol } H_2O}{18.0 \text{ g } H_2O} \right. = 0.877 \text{ mol } H_2O$

   $0.876/0.877 \approx 1:1 \quad \therefore (NH_4)_2CO_3 \cdot H_2O$

3. a. $2Na + 2H_2O \rightarrow 2NaOH + H_2$ c. $2Sb + 3Cl_2 \rightarrow 2SbCl_3$
   b. $Mg + 2HCl \rightarrow MgCl_2 + H_2$ d. $Cl_2 + 2KBr \rightarrow 2KCl + Br_2$

4. a. Na_3N
   b. Ce_2S_3
   c. $BaSiF_6$
   d. H_2Te
   e. Ag_2SO_4
   f. Cs_2SiF_6

5. a. $2K + 2H_2O \rightarrow 2KOH + H_2$
   b. $Ca + 2HCl \rightarrow CaCl_2 + H_2$
   c. $Cl_2 + 2KI \rightarrow 2KCl + I_2$
   d. $2Na_2O_2 + 2H_2O \rightarrow 4NaOH + O_2$

6. $\dfrac{0.633 \text{ mol } Th(SeO_4)_2}{} \left| \dfrac{6.02 \times 10^{23} \text{ formula units}}{1 \text{ mol}} \right.$

   $= 3.81 \times 10^{23}$ formula units

7. $\dfrac{0.0731 \text{ mol } Sr(CN)_2}{} \left| \dfrac{140 \text{ g } Sr(CN)_2}{1 \text{ mol } Sr(CN)_2} \right. = 10.2 \text{ g } Sr(CN)_2$

8. Ba = 137 $\dfrac{137}{233} \times 100 = 58.8\%$

   S = 32.1 $\dfrac{32.1}{233} \times 100 = 13.8\%$

   4 O = 4 × 16.0 $\dfrac{64.0}{233} \times 100 = 27.5\%$

9. assume a 100 g sample

   $\dfrac{44.2 \text{ g } Cd}{} \left| \dfrac{1 \text{ mol } Cd}{112 \text{ g } Cd} \right. = 0.395 \text{ mol } Cd$

   $\dfrac{44.8 \text{ g } F}{} \left| \dfrac{1 \text{ mol } F}{19.0 \text{ g } F} \right. = 2.36 \text{ mol } F$

   $\dfrac{11.0 \text{ g } Si}{} \left| \dfrac{1 \text{ mol } Si}{28.1 \text{ g } Si} \right. = 0.391 \text{ mol } Si$

   $0.393/2.36/0.392 = 1:6:1$
   $CdSiF_6$

10. assume a 100 g sample

    $\dfrac{76.0 \text{ g } SrI_2}{} \left| \dfrac{1 \text{ mol } SrI_2}{342 \text{ g } SrI_2} \right. = 0.222 \text{ mol } SrI_2$

$$\frac{24.0 \text{ g } \cancel{H_2O}}{} \Big| \frac{1 \text{ mol } H_2O}{18.0 \cancel{\text{ g } H_2O}} = 1.33 \text{ mol } H_2O$$

$0.222/1.33 \approx 1:6$

Therefore, $SrI_2 \cdot 6H_2O$

11. $\dfrac{84.1 \cancel{\text{ g } MgO}}{} \Big| \dfrac{1 \cancel{\text{ mol } MgO}}{40.3 \cancel{\text{ g } MgO}} \Big| \dfrac{1 \cancel{\text{ mol } Mg(OH)_2}}{1 \cancel{\text{ mol } MgO}} \Big| \dfrac{58.3 \text{ g } Mg(OH)_2}{1 \cancel{\text{ mol } Mg(OH)_2}} = 122 \text{ g } Mg(OH)_2$

12. $H = m(\Delta T)C_p$

$= \dfrac{91.0 \cancel{g}}{} \Big| \dfrac{26.8 \cancel{C^\circ}}{} \Big| \dfrac{0.469 \text{ J}}{\cancel{g \cdot C^\circ}} = 1140 \text{ J}$

ONE MORE STEP

Pages 136-137

1. See: Glasstone, Samuel, *Sourcebook for Atomic Energy*, New York, D. Van Nostrand Co., Inc., 1958, pp. 227-230.

2. See: Richards, James A., Jr., et al., *Modern University Physics*, Reading, Addison-Wesley Pub. Co., Inc., 1960, pp. 747-749.

3. Note: Because research in this area is so current, only a partial list is given.

Particle	Mass	Charge	Lifetime
electron	1	±	∞
electron's neutrino	0	0	∞
muon	207	±	$2.20 \quad 10^{-6}$
muon's neutrino	0	0	∞
pion	273	±	2.60×10^{-8}s
pion	265	0	0.8×10^{-16}s

Particle	Mass	Charge	Lifetime
kaon	966	±	1.24×10^{-8}s
			5.17×10^{-8}s
kaon	975	0	0.86×10^{-10}s
eta	1074	0	2.53×10^{-19}s
rho	1507	±, 0	4×10^{-23}s
proton	1836	+	∞
neutron	1839	0	0.93×10^3s
lambda	2183	0	2.5×10^{-10}s
sigma	2328	±, 0	8.0×10^{-11}s
delta	2410	α+, ±, 0	4×10^{-23}s
xi	2583	0	3.0×10^{-10}s
sigma (1385)	2710	0, −	1×10^{-10}s
omega	3287	−	1.3×10^{-10}s
tau meson	3522	±	?
D meson	3523	±, 0	?
psi/J	6062	0	6×10^{-20}s
upsilon	18590	0	?
upsilon	19570	0	?

4.

Atomic Number	Mass Number	Atomic Number	Mass Number
1	1	6	(9)
	2		(10)
	(3)*		(11)
2	3		12
	4		13

Atomic Number	Mass Number	Atomic Number	Mass Number
3	(6)		(14)
	(8)		(15)
	6	7	(16)
	7	7	(12)
	(8)		(13)
	(9)		14
4	(6)		15
	(7)		(16)
	9		(17)
	(10)		(18)
	(11)	8	(13)
5	(8)		(14)
	10		(15)
	11		16
	(12)		17
	(13)		18
			(19)
			(20)

*Radioactive isotopes are circled

Atomic Number	Mass Numbers
9	17*, 18*, 19, 20*, 21*, 22*
10	17*, 18*, 19*, 20, 21, 22, 23*, 24*
11	20*, 21*, 22*, 23, 24*, 25*, 26*
12	20*, 21*, 23*, 24, 25, 26, 27*, 28*
13	24*, 25*, 26*, 27, 28*, 29*, 30*
14	25*, 26*, 27*, 28, 29, 30, 31*, 32*
15	28*, 29*, 30*, 31, 32*, 33*, 34*
16	29*, 30*, 31*, 32, 33, 34, 35*, 36, 37*, 38*
17	32*, 33*, 34*, 35, 36*, 37, 38*, 39*, 40*
18	33*, 34*, 35*, 36, 37*, 38, 39*, 40, 41*, 42*, 43*, 44*
19	36*, 37*, 38*, 39, 40*, 41, 42*, 43*, 44*, 45*, 46*, 47*
20	37*, 38*, 39*, 40, 41*, 42, 43, 44, 45*, 46, 47*, 48, 49*, 50*

5. The Japanese physicist Hantaro Nagaoka suggested the planetary model for the atom in 1904.

6. *Encyclopaedia Britannica,* "Proton: Characteristics;" also, Hofstadter's Nobel address, 1962. (The method is essentially electron diffraction.)

7. $E = h\nu = \dfrac{6.63 \times 10^{-34} \text{ J}}{\text{Hz}} \bigg| 4.31 \times 10^{14} \text{ Hz}$

$= 2.86 \times 10^{-19} \text{ J}$

8. $\nu = \dfrac{c}{\lambda} = \dfrac{3.00 \times 10^8 \text{ m}}{\text{s}} \bigg| \dfrac{1}{662 \text{ nm}} \bigg| \dfrac{1 \times 10^9 \text{ nm}}{1 \text{ m}}$

$= 4.53 \times 10^{14} \text{ Hz}$

$E = h\nu = \dfrac{6.63 \times 10^{-34} \text{ J}}{\text{Hz}} \bigg| 4.53 \times 10^{14} \text{ Hz}$

$= 3.00 \times 10^{-19} \text{ J}$

9. Energy of light = energy of photon + release energy:
$(1.20 \times 10^{-19}) + (3.60 \times 10^{-19}) = 4.80 \times 10^{-19} \text{ J}$
then determine the frequency:
$E = h\nu$

Therefore, $\nu = \dfrac{E}{h} = \dfrac{4.80 \times 10^{-19} \text{ J}}{6.63 \times 10^{-34} \text{ J·s}}$

$= 7.24 \times 10^{14} \text{ Hz}$

We conclude:

$\lambda = \dfrac{c}{\nu} = \dfrac{3.00 \times 10^8 \text{ m}}{\text{s}} \bigg| \dfrac{\text{s}}{7.24 \times 10^{14}} \bigg| \dfrac{1 \times 10^9 \text{ nm}}{1 \text{ m}}$

$= 414 \text{ nm}$

10. Frequency has no effect on the number of electrons that leave the metal surface. Frequency affects the energy of the electrons leaving the surface—the higher the frequency, the greater the energy of the ejected electrons.

11. $\nu = \dfrac{c}{\lambda}$

$= \dfrac{3.00 \times 10^8 \text{ m}}{\text{s}} \bigg| \dfrac{1}{413 \text{ nm}} \bigg| \dfrac{1 \times 10^9 \text{ nm}}{1 \text{ m}}$

$= 7.26 \times 10^{14} \text{ Hz}$

12. $\lambda = \dfrac{c}{\nu}$

$= \dfrac{3 \times 10^8 \text{ m}}{\text{s}} \bigg| \dfrac{\text{s}}{6.26 \times 10^{14}} \bigg| \dfrac{1 \times 10^9 \text{ nm}}{1 \text{ m}}$

$= 479 \text{ nm}$

13. $\dfrac{6.63 \times 10^{-34} \text{ J}}{\text{Hz}} \bigg| 7.26 \times 10^{14} \text{ Hz}$

$= 4.81 \times 10^{-19} \text{ J}$

14. $\dfrac{6.63 \times 10^{-34} \text{ J}}{\text{Hz}} \bigg| 6.26 \times 10^{14} \text{ Hz}$

$= 4.15 \times 10^{-19} \text{ J}$

15. Colorimetry is the analysis of colored solutions. A solution of unknown concentration can be compared to a solution of known concentration. When the colors are of equal intensity the concentration of the unknown solution can be determined.
Fluorimetry is the analysis of fluorescent substances, i.e., those substances which absorb light at one wavelength, usually UV, and then emit light at another longer wavelength. It is used for the analysis of steroids, amino acids, and vitamins.
Nephelometry is the analysis of colloids or suspensions by their light-scattering ability. It is used in the analysis of bacteria concentration, particle size in turbid water, and the concentration of ion producing colloidal precipitates with analytical reagents.

16. EPR (or ESR, Electron Spin Resonance) is completely analogous to NMR (Nuclear Magnetic Resonance). A spinning electron has a magnetic field. If an external field is imposed, the electron will tend to align itself with the field. The energy required to "flip" the electron spin can be measured. The energy required is related to the environment of the electron and helps deduce electronic structures.

ELECTRON CLOUDS AND PROBABILITY

8

AN OVERVIEW

The study of structure continues in Chapter 8 with a more detailed look at the behavior of electrons in atoms. In the text, students follow along as scientists develop the wave-mechanical view of the atom. This historical approach allows students to understand the limitations of the Bohr atom. Students see how the work of de Broglie, Heisenberg, and Schrödinger led to the new atomic model. The order of filling of the electron energy levels, sublevels, and orbitals is presented as a result of the study of quantum numbers derived from spectra. The chapter concludes with electron dot diagrams. Chapter 8 provides the foundation needed for Chapters 9, 10, and 11.

DEMONSTRATION INFORMATION

If a hydrogen gas tube and spectroscope are not available, the colored flames of Sr, Li, Ba, Cu, and Na salts can be used to introduce students to Chapter 8. Radiant energy is found to have many of the particle properties. Use the demonstration to review a discussion of energy levels and line spectra. Discuss how spectral observations are the basis of contemporary atomic theory. **CAUTION:** *As with any open alcohol flame, use caution to avoid spilling the alcohol from the evaporating dish.* For best results, dissolve 0.1g of the salt in 3 cm^3 of water before adding 3 cm^3 of methanol. The color will be most noticeable in a darkened room just as the alcohol is almost consumed. This solution can also be used for flame tests using nichrome wire loops. Use a separate wire for each solution. This saves time in that the loops do not have to be cleaned after each flame test.

Review Section 7:6 with the students. Recall for them that an emission spectrum results when electrons in an excited atom drop back down to lower energy levels. Each colored line represents a different transition. Each element gives its own distinctive spectrum like a fingerprint. This is how scientists have determined the composition of stars.

Have the students recall the color of street lights, the bluish-white of mercury-vapor and the yellow of sodium-vapor lamps. Students have also seen neon lights and fireworks displays. Each of these should remind the student about the atomic emission spectra. This will help them better understand Section 8:7.

DISPOSAL: *Evaporate the alcohol in an operating fume hood. Place the water with the dissolved salts into a large container. Add Na_2CO_3, stir, and allow to stand for 24 hours. Decant the liquid down the drain with a large quantity of water. The solid residue can be dried and placed in a local landfill.*

PERFORMANCE OBJECTIVES

Goals: Students will gain an understanding of the electron structure of the quantum mechanical model of the atom. Students will define the four quantum numbers. Students will use the diagonal rule to write electron configurations. Students will write electron dot diagrams for the elements.

Objectives: Upon completion of the reading and problems, and when asked to demonstrate their understanding either orally or on a written test, students will

8:1	K/P	explain de Broglie's work with Planck's theory and Einstein's relationship. **8:1**
8:2	P	use the de Broglie equation to calculate the wavelength of an electron, or any particle, given the particle's mass and velocity. **8:1**
8:3	K/P	explain the wave-particle duality of the electron and other particles. **8:1-8:3**
8:4	K	define index of refraction. **8:2**
8:5	K	differentiate Newtonian and quantum mechanics. **8:3**
8:6	K/P	state and briefly explain Heisenberg's uncertainty principle. **8:4**
8:7	K/P	state the significance of the Schrödinger wave equation as interpreted by Max Born. **8:5**
8:8	K/P	explain the location of the electron

		in terms of probability and electron clouds. **8:5-8:6**
8:9	K/P	use Schrödinger's work to develop a mental model of the atom involving charge clouds. **8:5-8:7**
8:10	K	define the four quantum numbers. **8:5-8:12**
8:11	P	calculate the greatest number of electrons in any given energy level. **8:8**
8:12	K	list the number of sublevels in each energy level, and give the letter designation for each sublevel. **8:9**
8:13	K	define the relationships among electrons, orbitals, energy levels, and sublevels. **8:9-8:10**
8:14	K	state the maximum number of electrons in any given energy level or sublevel. **8:9-8:10**
8:15	K	define the Pauli exclusion principle as it relates to quantum numbers. **8:11**
8:16	K/P	explain how quantum numbers are related to charge clouds and energy. **8:11-8:12**
8:17	K/P	write an electron configuration for any atom using the diagonal rule. **8:12**
8:18	K/P	draw a Lewis electron dot diagram for any atom. **8:13**
8:19	A	voluntarily complete one or more of the One More Step activities.
8:20	A	read unassigned literature related to the chapter.

TEACHING TECHNIQUES

Section 8:1

In 1927, Davisson and Germer demonstrated that electrons show wave properties. The wave properties of fundamental particles are now recognized. Diffraction patterns have been demonstrated for fundamental particles just like those for light. The mathematics of quantum mechanics is based upon a modification of the mathematics of classical mechanics. The equations describe waves. They have a statistical nature in which variables are in terms of probabilities and averages. Quantum mechanics depends upon an acceptance of the wave description of fundamental particles.

Section 8:3

Substituting momentum for *mv* in de Broglie's wave equation alters the mathematical nature of the equation. It becomes the Schrödinger equation by substituting a second derivative where momentum appears. This equation is the basis of quantum mechanics. The electron must be accelerated as it moves in a curved path around a proton. The electron should radiate energy, slow down, and spiral into the nucleus. Classical mechanics predicts that the atom would collapse in a fraction of a second. Obviously, atoms do not follow the same physics equations as the planets. The equations that describe electron behavior are called quantum or wave mechanics equations.

Section 8:4

Use Heisenberg's uncertainty principle to stress that quantum theory tells us in probability terms how the electron occupies the space outside the nucleus. For example, an electron can be as far away as 0.224 nm from the hydrogen nucleus and as close as 0.01 nm. However, 90% of the time the electron will be between 0.142 nm and 0.029 nm from the nucleus. Probability distribution is an important concept in quantum mechanics because we do not know the exact position and momentum of an electron simultaneously.

Section 8:5

The following is a more detailed explanation of the Schrödinger wave equation found in the text.

$$\frac{\partial^2 \psi}{\partial x^2} + \frac{\partial^2 \psi}{\partial y^2} + \frac{\partial^2 \psi}{\partial z^2} + \frac{8\pi^2 m}{h^2}(E - V)\psi = 0$$

∂ = the Greek letter delta. It is the mathematical symbol indicating a partial derivative.

ψ = the Greek letter *psi*. It is the symbol used to indicate the amplitude of a wave. ψ is also called the wave function. ψ^2 determines the probability of finding an electron in a specified region which can be represented on a three dimensional graph by the coordinates:

$$x \text{ and } x + dx,$$
$$y \text{ and } y + dy,$$
$$z \text{ and } z + dz.$$

x,y,z = the coordinates of probable wave location.
m = the mass of an electron = 9.11×10^{-28} g.
h = Planck's constant = 6.63×10^{-34} J·s.
E = total energy.
V = potential energy.

Section 8:6

The probability distribution of an electron in space is described by the wave function, ψ. If a time exposed photograph were taken of an atom, we would see where an electron spends more time and less time. The information contained in this picture is also contained in ψ. It gives us a time-averaged view of the electron's motion. The square of the wave function, $|\psi|^2$, gives us the probability distribution in space, an orbital. Each permitted set of quantum numbers defines an orbital. The electron motion around the nucleus in the Bohr model sug-

gested an orbital. The true meaning of ψ conflicts with the term orbital.

Section 8:8

The value of the principle quantum number n can actually go to infinity, but in a practical sense, there are seven energy levels. The value of, n, describes an average distance from the nucleus of the electron cloud.

Section 8:9

The letters s, p, d, and f stand for sharp, principal, diffuse, and fundamental. These terms were originally spectroscopy labels for different series of spectral lines emitted by the elements. Other permitted values are g, h, i, . . . and were added later in alphabetical order.

Section 8:10

Students often ask how a complex electron probability cloud shape, such as a d orbital, can be described by integers. You can stretch a rope between a doorknob and your hand to help answer the question. Begin to move the rope so as to induce a standing wave. At a low vibrating frequency there is one crest. At a higher frequency, there are two crests with a node in the center. An easy way to describe these waves is to represent the number of nodes with an integer. The quantum number is analogous to the integer. A nodal surface is a surface at which the probability of finding an electron is zero. When $n = 1$, the first energy level having a spherical shaped electron cloud, there is one nodal surface at infinity. When $n = 2$, there are two nodal surfaces, etc. The vibrating rope can be a helpful model to relate the abstract nature of Schrödinger's equation, the wave function, and the probability distribution.

Section 8:11

The values of n, l, and m are fixed values designating the energy level, sublevel, and orbital. The fourth quantum number has only two numerically permitted values. The fourth quantum number (s) is independent of the other three quantum numbers. It has a value of either $+\frac{1}{2}$ or $-\frac{1}{2}$. It describes the direction of rotation of an electron on its axis.

Only two electrons can occupy the same orbital according to the Pauli exclusion principle. If two electrons had the same set of four quantum numbers in an atom, they would have the same probability of being in the same place at the same time. That possibility is excluded considering the like charges.

You can summarize the quantum numbers as being analogous to an address. 123 Main St., Columbus, Ohio, consists of four parts: state = n, city = l, street = m, and lot number = s. The four quantum numbers give us an electron's address in an atom. Refer to the Teacher Resource Book, Review—Concepts for this chapter for a detailed presentation for your students.

Careers and Chemistry

Use the perfumer career as the beginning of a project to explore the various science-related careers in the cosmetics industry.

PROBLEM SOLUTIONS

Page 140

1. $\lambda = \dfrac{h}{mv}$

$$\dfrac{6.63 \times 10^{-34} \ \cancel{kg \cdot m^2}}{\cancel{s}} \left| \dfrac{}{9.11 \times 10^{-28} \ \cancel{g}} \right| \dfrac{1000 \ \cancel{g}}{1 \ \cancel{kg}} \left| \dfrac{\cancel{s}}{2.19 \times 10^{6} \ \cancel{m}} \right| \dfrac{1 \times 10^{9} \ nm}{1 \ \cancel{m}}$$

$= 0.332$ nm

Page 147

2. The greatest number of electrons in a given energy level can be determined by finding the value of $2n^2$ where n is the energy level involved; for

$n = 2$, $2n^2 = 2(2)^2 = 8$
$n = 3$, $2n^2 = 2(3)^2 = 18$
$n = 5$, $2n^2 = 2(5)^2 = 50$
$n = 7$, $2n^2 = 2(7)^2 = 98$

Page 150

3. **a.** An s sublevel contains 1 orbital.
   b. A p sublevel contains 3 orbitals.
   c. A d sublevel contains 5 orbitals.
   d. An f sublevel contains 7 orbitals.

Page 154

4. $z = 1 \quad 1s^1$
   2 \quad $1s^2$
   3 \quad $1s^2 2s^1$
   4 \quad $1s^2 2s^2$
   5 \quad $1s^2 2s^2 2p^1$
   6 \quad $1s^2 2s^2 2p^2$
   7 \quad $1s^2 2s^2 2p^3$
   8 \quad $1s^2 2s^2 2p^4$
   9 \quad $1s^2 2s^2 2p^5$
   10 \quad $1s^2 2s^2 2p^6$
   11 \quad $1s^2 2s^2 2p^6 3s^1$
   12 \quad $1s^2 2s^2 2p^6 3s^2$
   13 \quad $1s^2 2s^2 2p^6 3s^2 3p^1$
   14 \quad $1s^2 2s^2 2p^6 3s^2 3p^2$
   15 \quad $1s^2 2s^2 2p^6 3s^2 3p^3$
   16 \quad $1s^2 2s^2 2p^6 3s^2 3p^4$
   17 \quad $1s^2 2s^2 2p^6 3s^2 3p^5$
   18 \quad $1s^2 2s^2 2p^6 3s^2 3p^6$
   19 \quad $1s^2 2s^2 2p^6 3s^2 3p^6 4s^1$
   20 \quad $1s^2 2s^2 2p^6 3s^2 3p^6 4s^2$

Page 155

5. **a.** $1s^2 2s^2 2p^6 3s^2 3p^6 4s^2 3d^8$ ·· Ni:
   b. $1s^2 2s^2 2p^6 3s^2 3p^6$:Ar:
   c. $1s^2 2s^2 2p^6 3s^2 3p^4$ ·S:
   d. $1s^2 2s^2 2p^6 3s^2 3p^6 4s^2 3d^{10} 4p^6 5s^2 4d^9$ Ag:
   (actually $4d^{10} 5s^1$ Ag·)
   e. $1s^2 2s^2 2p^6 3s^2 3p^6 4s^1$ K·
   f. $1s^2 2s^2 2p^6 3s^2 3p^6 4s^2 3d^{10} 4p^2$ ·Ge:

CHAPTER END PROBLEMS

Page 158

1. He equated Einstein's expression for energy with Planck's expression for energy, $\lambda = h/mv$

2. An inverse relationship $\lambda = \dfrac{h}{p}$

3. $2n^2 = 2(4)^2 = 32$

4. $+1/2$, $-1/2$

5. Electron configuration for uranium:

Experimental (p. 170)
$1s^2 2s^2 2p^6 3s^2 3p^6 3d^{10} 4s^2 4p^6 4d^{10}$
$4f^{14} 5s^2 5p^6 5d^{10} 5f^3 6s^2 6p^6 6d^1 7s^2$

Diagonal rule (p. 153)
$1s^2 2s^2 2p^6 3s^2 3p^6 4s^2 3d^{10} 4p^6 5s^2$
$4d^{10} 5p^6 6s^2 4f^{14} 5d^{10} 6p^6 7s^2 5f^4$

	Experimental Levels			
n	s \quad p \quad d \quad f			total
1.	2			2
2.	2 + 6			8
3.	2 + 6 + 10			18
4.	2 + 6 + 10 + 14			32
5.	2 + 6 + 10 + 3			21
6.	2 + 6 + 1			9
7.	2			2
				92

	Predicted (diagonal rule) Levels		
1.	2		2
2.	2 + 6		8
3.	2 + 6 + 10		18
4.	2 + 6 + 10 + 14		32
5.	2 + 6 + 10 + 4		22
6.	2 + 6		8
7.	2		2
			92

Levels 5, 6, and 7 are not full.

6. **a.** Mn manganese
   b. Mo molybdenum

7. Zr Z = 40 $1s^2 2s^2 2p^6 3s^2 3p^6 4s^2 3d^{10} 4p^6 5s^2 4d^2$
   Ga Z = 31 $1s^2 2s^2 2p^6 3s^2 3p^6 4s^2 3d^{10} 4p^1$

8. Bi Z = 83 $1s^2 2s^2 2p^6 3s^2 3p^6 4s^2 3d^{10} 4p^6 5s^2 4d^{10} 5p^6 6s^2 4f^{14} 5d^{10} 6p^3$
   Ru Z = 44 $1s^2 2s^2 2p^6 3s^2 3p^6 4s^2 3d^{10} 4p^6 5s^2 4d^6$

9. $Z = 7$,   •N:

$Z = 15$,   •P:

$Z = 33$,   •As: Note that this is
column VA (15) of the

$Z = 51$,   •Sb: periodic table.

$Z = 83$,   •Bi:

10. There are 2 pairs of electrons in a boron atom.
Boron configuration = $1s^2 2s^2 2p^1$.
There are 7 pairs of electrons in a sulfur atom.
$1s^2 2s^2 2p^6 3s^2 3p^4$
There are 4 pairs of electrons in a fluorine atom.
Fluorine configuration = $1s^2 2s^2 2p^5$.

11. Two electrons are not shown in each electron dot diagram.

$Z = 3$	$1s^2 2s^1$	Li•	2
$Z = 4$	$1s^2 2s^2$	Be:	2
$Z = 5$	$1s^2 2s^2 2p^1$	B:	2
$Z = 6$	$1s^2 2s^2 2p^2$	•C:	2
$Z = 7$	$1s^2 2s^2 2p^3$	•N:	2
$Z = 8$	$1s^2 2s^2 2p^4$	•O:	2
$Z = 9$	$1s^2 2s^2 2p^5$	:F:	2
$Z = 10$	$1s^2 2s^2 2p^6$	:Ne:	2

REVIEW

Page 159

1. law of conservation of mass and law of definite proportions

2. nuclide—an atom with a specific number of protons and a specific number of neutrons
isotopes—two different nuclides of the same element

3. atomic number = number of protons in the nucleus of an atom
atomic mass = average mass of the atoms of an element

4. $\dfrac{10.0\ \cancel{g}\ \mid\ 200.0\ \cancel{C°}\ \mid\ 0.220\ J}{\mid\ \mid\ \cancel{g}\cdot\cancel{C°}} = 4.40 \times 10^2\ J$

5. the regularity of the spacing in the lines of the hydrogen atom

6. Planck proposed the quantum theory.

7. $\dfrac{(91.906808)(15.84) + (93.905090)(9.04) + (94.905837)(15.72) + (95.904674)(16.53) + (96.906023)(9.46) + (97.905409)(23.78) + (99.907478)(9.63)}{100} = 95.9\ u$

8. 101 electrons, 155 neutrons, 101 protons

9. The emission of electrons from a surface when it is exposed to radiant energy.

ONE MORE STEP

Page 159

1. First, change nm to meters:

$\dfrac{0.01\ \cancel{nm}\ \mid\ 1\ m}{\mid\ 1 \times 10^9\ \cancel{nm}} = 1 \times 10^{-11}\ m$

then solve:

$\Delta p = \dfrac{h}{\Delta x} = \dfrac{6.63 \times 10^{34}\ kg\cdot m^2}{s}\ \Bigg|\ \dfrac{}{1 \times 10^{-11}\ \cancel{m}}$

$= 6.63 \times 10^{-23}\ kg\cdot m/s$

2. In relativistic mechanics there is a fourth dimension—time. The experimental evidence indicating the fourth dimension is the splitting of spectral lines (Zeeman effect).

3. Wave properties: An electron beam which is passed through a crystal is diffracted and produces a pattern similar to that produced by light and water waves when they are passed through slits of the appropriate size.
Particle properties: The cloud chamber, bubble chamber, cyclotron, synchrotron, linear accelerator, mass spectrometer, electron gun, and Milikan's apparatus all treat the electron successfully as a particle.

THE PERIODIC TABLE   9

AN OVERVIEW

Classification of atoms into the periodic system on the basis of their structure is introduced in Chapter 9. The chapter begins with the historical development of the periodic table. This approach provides students with a rationale for the development of a classification system. The periodic table organizes a tremendous number of chemical facts and trends. The text shows students that the electron structure of atoms is the basis for the regularities observed in elements. In this chapter students are presented with many concepts and chemical facts. Center their attention on the chemistry which best illustrates the family relationships and their periodicity. We will continue to use the periodic table in several later chapters.

DEMONSTRATION INFORMATION

$2Na(cr) + 2H_2O(l) \rightarrow 2NaOH(aq) + H_2(g)$. The introductory paragraph in the text refers to the demonstration. Use the demonstration to introduce the activity trend found in group IA. Stress the ability of the chemist to make predictions based on a knowledge of such trends. **CAUTION:** *Wear goggles or safety glasses and quickly cover the petri dish with a wire screen to prevent the Na or Li metal from flying out of the beaker.*

DISPOSAL: *The solutions may be washed down the drain with plenty of water. Be careful not to splash any of the basic solution on your clothes. Wear goggles even when cleaning up after the demonstration.*

PERFORMANCE OBJECTIVES

Goals: Students will gain an understanding of how the periodic table is organized. Students will learn to predict the stability of atoms using the octet rule. Students will examine the relationship between an element's electron configuration and its placement on the periodic table.

Objectives: Upon completion of the reading and problems, and when asked to demonstrate their understanding either orally or on a written test, students will

9:1	K	list early attempts at classification of the elements and the limitations of these attempts, including a definition of triad and law of octaves: **9:1-9:2**
9:2	K	match scientists and their contributions to the development of the periodic table. **9:1-9:2**
9:3	K	state the modern periodic law. **9:3**
9:4	K	define the modern periodic table and its basis. **9:4**
9:5	K/P	assign a position in the periodic table to each of the elements based on application of the diagonal rule. **9:4-9:6**
9:6	K/P	write and explain the electron configurations of the transition elements. **9:5**
9:7	K	differentiate the lanthanides and the actinides. **9:6**
9:8	K	distinguish groups and periods on the periodic table. **9:6**
9:9	K	list properties of metals and nonmetals. **9:9**
9:10	K	distinguish metals from nonmetals in terms of electron configuration. **9:9**
9:11	K	distinguish among metals, nonmetals, and metalloids. **9:9**
9:12	K/P	use the periodic table to locate each of these groups of elements: alkali metals, alkaline earth metals, chalcogens, halogens, noble gases, transition elements, lanthanides, and actinides. **9:5-9:9**
9:13	K/P	determine whether an atom is unstable or stable using the octet rule, or filled versus half-filled sublevels, and recognize the stability of the noble gases. **9:8-9:9**
9:14	K/P	explain the exceptions to the diagonal rule. **9:9**
9:15	A	voluntarily complete one or more of the One More Step activities.
9:16	A	read unassigned literature related to the chapter.

TEACHING TECHNIQUES

Section 9:1

The history of some thought processes that went into the development of the periodic table is presented briefly. The emphasis of this section should be on gaining knowledge about the structure and properties of the elements and their compounds.

Section 9:2

The original paper presented by Mendeleev appears in English in the following text.

Newman, J. R., ed., *World of Mathematics,* Vol. II, Simon and Schuster, 1956, pp. 913-918.

Section 9:4

To impress students with the idea of classification, you can display in random order a number of elements and compounds from the stockroom. Students should be made aware of the difficulty of listing all the properties for each substance. A classification of the elements into metals and nonmetals allows us to generalize concerning some properties. Point out that electron configurations can be used to organize the elements into columns and rows. Review the Aufbau principle, the pattern in which the lowest electron levels fill first.

Section 9:8

Using Figure 9-4, students can write the electron configurations for most elements. Be sure students are aware that exceptions exist. You may want them to memorize Cr and Cu as examples of exceptions.

Careers and Chemistry

Emphasize the importance of analysis and analytical techniques to the study of chemistry. There are a number of analytical techniques covered briefly in the text (chromatography, mass spec, NMR, IR, electrophoresis, and so on). You can have students research these topics in more detail and present their findings in class. You may also want to consider having students research the analytical procedures used by a particular industry in your area (steel, pharmaceuticals, food processing, and so on).

PROBLEM SOLUTIONS

Page 172

1. **a.** nonmetal   **e.** metal
   b. metal   **f.** metal
   c. metalloid   **g.** metal
   d. metal

2. There are more metals than nonmetals in the periodic table.

CHAPTER END PROBLEMS

Page 177

1. **a.** metal   **e.** metal   **i.** nonmetal
   b. nonmetal   **f.** metal   **j.** metal
   c. metal   **g.** nonmetal   **k.** nonmetal
   d. nonmetal   **h.** metal   **l.** nonmetal

2. Z = 34, selenium

3. 4th period, Group VIA (16)

4. nonmetal

5. tends to gain electrons, hard, brittle

6. ·S̈e:

Barium

7. 6th period, Group IIA, (2)

8. metal

9. malleable, conducts electricity, loses electrons

10. $1s^2 2s^2 2p^6 3s^2 3p^6 4s^2 3d^{10} 4p^6 5s^2 5p^6 4d^{10} 6s^2$

11. Ba:

Vanadium

7. 4th period, Group VB (5)

8. metal

9. malleable, ductile, conducts heat and electricity, loses electrons

10. $1s^2 2s^2 2p^6 3s^2 3p^6 4s^2 3d^3$

11. V:

Indium

7. 5th period, Group IIIA (13)

8. metal

9. malleable, ductile, conducts heat and electricity, loses electrons

10. $1s^2 2s^2 2p^6 3s^2 3p^6 4s^2 3d^{10} 4p^6 5s^2 4d^{10} 5p^1$

11. In:

Tin

7. 5th period, Group IVA (14)

8. metal

9. malleable, ductile, conducts heat and electricity

10. $1s^2 2s^2 2p^6 3s^2 3p^6 4s^2 3d^{10} 4p^6 5s^2 4d^{10} 5p^2$

11. ·S̈n:

Krypton

7. 4th period, Group VIIIA (18)

8. nonmetal

9. does not conduct

10. $1s^2 2s^2 2p^6 3s^2 3p^6 4s^2 3d^{10} 4p^6$

11. :K̈r:

Astatine

7. 6th period, Group VIIA (17)

8. metalloid

9. loses or gains electrons, semiconductor

10. $1s^2 2s^2 2p^6 3s^2 3p^6 4s^2 3d^{10} 4p^6 5s^2 4d^{10} 5p^6 6s^2 4f^{14} 5d^{10} 6p^5$

11. :Ȧt:

REVIEW

Pages 178-179

1. frequency, wavelength, velocity, amplitude

2. Schrödinger considered the electron as a wave; Bohr considered it a particle.

3. n, l, m, s
   n represents energy level, l sublevel, m and s have no effect on energy
   n = cloud size, l = cloud shape, m = cloud spatial orientation, s = electron spin

4. **a.** $1s^2 2s^2 2p^6 3s^2 3p^1$ Al:
   b. $1s^2 2s^2 2p^6 3s^2 3p^4$ ·S̈:
   c. $1s^2 2s^2 2p^6 3s^2 3p^6 4s^2$ Ca:
   d. $1s^2 2s^2 2p^6 3s^2 3p^6 4s^2 3d^2$ Ti:
   e. $1s^2 2s^2 2p^6 3s^2 3p^6 4s^2 3d^3$ V:
   f. $1s^2 2s^2 2p^6 3s^2 3p^6 4s^2 3d^5$ Mn:
   g. $1s^2 2s^2 2p^6 3s^2 3p^6 4s^2 3d^7$ Co:
   h. $1s^2 2s^2 2p^6 3s^2 3p^6 4s^2 3d^{10} 4p^2$ ·G̈e:
   i. $1s^2 2s^2 2p^6 3s^2 3p^6 4s^2 3d^{10} 4p^5$:B̈r:

5. λ = wavelength
   h = Planck's constant
   m = mass
   v = velocity

6. $$\frac{(1.140)(179.9467) + (26.41)(181.948\ 25) + (14.40)(182.950\ 27) + (30.64)(183.950\ 97) + (28.41)(185.954\ 40)}{100} = 185.6\ u$$

7. 2

8. $\dfrac{0.01}{10.14} \times 100 = \pm 0.09\%$

9. $\dfrac{42.5\ \cancel{g}}{} \left| \dfrac{cm^3}{3.15\ \cancel{g}} \right. = 13.5\ cm^3$

10. a. Zn_3P_2 **c.** AlF_3
    b. $Zr(SeO_4)_2$ **d.** $BiCl_3$

11. a. zinc tartrate
    b. lead(II) selenide
    c. chromium(III) acetate
    d. manganese(II) phosphide

12. 291 μ

13. $\dfrac{3.00\ \cancel{mol\ Zn_3(PO_4)_2}}{} \left| \dfrac{386\ g\ Zn_3(PO_4)_2}{1\ \cancel{mol\ Zn_3(PO_4)_2}} \right. = 1160\ g\ Zn_3(PO_4)_2$

14. $\dfrac{10.0\ \cancel{cm^3\ soln}}{} \left| \dfrac{0.100\ \cancel{mol\ ZrCl_4}}{1000\ \cancel{cm^3\ soln}} \right| \dfrac{233\ g\ ZrCl_4}{1\ \cancel{mol\ ZrCl_4}} = 0.233\ g\ ZrCl_4$

    add water to make 10 cm³ of solution

15.   Co = 58.9
    4 C = 48.0
    6 H = 6.05
    4 O = $\underline{64.0}$
          177

$\dfrac{58.9}{177} \times 100 = 33.3\%\ Co$

$\dfrac{48.0}{177} \times 100 = 27.1\%\ C$

$\dfrac{6.05}{177} \times 100 = 3.42\%\ H$

$\dfrac{64.0}{177} \times 100 = 36.2\%\ O$

16. $\dfrac{40.1\ \cancel{g\ Co}}{} \left| \dfrac{1\ mol\ Co}{58.9\ \cancel{g\ Co}} \right. = 0.680\ mol\ Co$ (Assume 100 g sample)

$\dfrac{16.3\ \cancel{g\ C}}{} \left| \dfrac{1\ mol\ C}{12.0\ \cancel{g\ C}} \right. = 1.36\ mol\ C$

$\dfrac{43.5\ \cancel{g\ O}}{} \left| \dfrac{1\ mol\ O}{16.0\ \cancel{g\ O}} \right. = 2.72\ mol\ O$

    $0.680/1.36/2.72 \approx 1:2:4$ CoC_2O_4

17. $\dfrac{682}{341} = 2$ Thus, $Bi_2C_6O_{12}$
    or $Bi_2(C_2O_4)_3$

18. $\dfrac{66.3\ \cancel{g\ Ga_2(SeO_4)_3}}{} \left| \dfrac{1\ mol\ Ga_2(SeO_4)_3}{568\ \cancel{g\ Ga_2(SeO_4)_3}} \right. = 0.117\ mol\ Ga_2(SeO_4)_3$

$\dfrac{33.7\ \cancel{g\ H_2O}}{} \left| \dfrac{1\ mol\ H_2O}{18.0\ \cancel{g\ H_2O}} \right. = 1.87\ mol\ H_2O$

    $0.117/1.87 \approx 1:16$ $\therefore Ga_2(SeO_4)_3 \cdot 16H_2O$

19. $Cr(NO_3)_3 + 3NaOH \rightarrow Cr(OH)_3 + 3NaNO_3$

20. $\dfrac{2.37\ \cancel{g\ NaOH}}{} \left| \dfrac{1\ \cancel{mol\ NaOH}}{40.0\ \cancel{g\ NaOH}} \right| \dfrac{2\ \cancel{mol\ AgNO_3}}{2\ \cancel{mol\ NaOH}} \left| \dfrac{170\ g\ AgNO_3}{1\ \cancel{mol\ AgNO_3}} \right. = 10.1\ g\ AgNO_3$

21. $\Delta H = m(\Delta T)C_p$

$\dfrac{5.24\ \cancel{g}}{} \left| \dfrac{1995\ \cancel{C°}}{} \right| \dfrac{0.238\ J}{\cancel{g} \cdot \cancel{C°}} = 2490\ J$

22. 8 electrons, 8 protons, 8 neutrons

ONE MORE STEP

Page 179

1. Sections 9:1 and 9:2 give a start. See: Ihde, *The Development of Modern Chemistry*

2. Mendeleev's predictions about gallium and scandium were about as good as his predictions about germanium. However, his predictions about technetium, rhenium, and neptunium were not as accurate.

3. Mo predicted $5s^24d^4$
        actual $5s^14d^5$ (half-filled d sublevel)
     Pd predicted $5s^24d^8$
        actual $4d^{10}$ (full d sublevel)
     Gd predicted $4f^8$
        actual $4f^75d^1$ (half-filled f sublevel)

4. Au predicted $6s^24f^{14}5d^9$
        actual $6s^14f^{14}5d^{10}$ (full d sublevel)
     Cm predicted $5f^8$
        actual $5f^76d^1$ (half-filled f sublevel)
     Th predicted $5f^2$
        actual $6d^2$ (exception to the rules given in the text)

5. Element name origins:

Named for Discoverer's Geographic Origin
germanium
lutetium
polonium

Named for Properties

Chemical	Physical
hydrogen	phosphorus
oxygen	iron(?)
sulfur	bromine
argon	tungsten
zinc	osmium
arsenic	lead(?)
antimony	astatine
	radium
	actinium
	protactinium

Named to Honor

A Person	A Place
gadolinium	europium
curium	hafnium
einsteinium	francium
fermium	americium
mendelevium	berkelium

lawrencium   californium
nobelium

Named for Mythological Character

Due to Property	Due to Other Reason
titanium	vanadium
cobalt	niobium
nickel	tantalum

Named for Color

Of Element	Of Compound	Of Spectra
chlorine	chromium	rubidium
silver	iridium	rhodium
iodine		indium
platinum		cesium
gold		thallium
bismuth		

Named for Discovery

Location	Material	Process
helium	lithium	neon
scandium	carbon	krypton
copper	nitrogen	technetium
gallium	sodium	xenon
ruthenium	potassium	lanthanum
tin	calcium	promethium
holmium	radon	dysprosium
rhenium	samarium	thulium

Named for Mineral

Color	Property	Location
beryllium	fluorine	strontium
boron	aluminum	yttrium
magnesium	silicon	cadmium
zirconium	manganese	terbium
praseodymium	neodymium	erbium
	molybdenum	ytterbium
	barium	thorium

Named for Heavenly Body

Earth	Moon	Planet	Asteroid
tellurium	selenium	mercury	palladium
		uranium	cerium
		neptunium	
		plutonium	

6. Metalloids are semiconductors. Although Si and Ge have the same crystalline structure as diamond, they will conduct electrons. Heat energy at ordinary temperatures frees electrons from the valence band to the conducting band. The conductivity of semiconductors increases with temperature, and donor and acceptor impurities are easily introduced.

PERIODIC PROPERTIES   10

AN OVERVIEW

Chemistry: A Modern Course is organized around a central theme: *the properties of matter are a consequence of its structure.* The properties of elements as a consequence of their atomic structure comprise the subject matter of Chapter 10. In Chapter 9 the periodicity of electronic structure was presented. The periodic nature of properties, as related to the electronic structure, is discussed in Chapter 10. An awareness of the periodic nature of atomic and ionic radii will enable the student to better understand the trends, ionization energy, and electron affinity presented later in the chapter. The student is now ready to use the background presented in Chapter 9 to predict oxidation numbers. Chapter 10 provides the student with the prerequisite skills needed to understand the information presented in Chapters 11 and 12.

DEMONSTRATION INFORMATION

Review the demonstration in Chapter 9 which involved the reaction of lithium and then sodium in H_2O. Discuss the relative sizes of lithium and sodium atoms. Relate this to their reactivity and the trend noticed in Chapter 9. The students will begin to relate properties based on the structures and sizes of atoms.

Bring to class a battery operated smoke detector. Carefully burn a piece of paper near the detector. Point out to the students that the paper burns with a smokeless flame, and yet the detector senses the gases produced. Have a student research how a smoke detector works, and report to the class. The gases produced by the flame are struck by radioactive particles from a source within the detector. The gases are ionized, and conduct an electric current. The alarm sounds. This process is similar to how ionization energies are measured. This demonstration can serve to introduce Sections 10:4 and 10:5.

PERFORMANCE OBJECTIVES

Goals: Students will explain the periodic nature of the properties of the elements. Students will learn how atomic and ionic size changes in groups and periods. Students will define ionization energy and electron affinity and describe the factors affecting these properties.

Objectives: Upon completion of the reading and problems, and when asked to demonstrate their understanding either orally or on a written test, students will
10:1 K state the relationship between the properties of elements and their electron configurations. **Intro**
10:2 K define periodic, and list reasons why a group is called a family. **Intro**
10:3 K/P relate the size of the principal quantum number to the size of the electron cloud and both of these to atomic radius. **10:1**
10:4 K/P explain the size relationship between the atoms of sodium and chlorine. **10:1**
10:5 K/P explain the size relationship between sodium ions and chloride ions. **10:2**
10:6 K state a general relationship between size of atoms and ions and their positions in the periodic table. **10:2**
10:7 K/P given a pair of atoms, ions, or an atom and an ion, select the particle with the larger or smaller radius. **10:1-10:2**
10:8 K/P relate noble gas configuration and octet to the stability of an atom or ion. **10:2-10:3**
10:9 K/P predict and explain the oxidation number of an element given the element's location in the periodic table. **10:3**
10:10 K define first ionization energy. **10:4**
10:11 K/P predict the relative first ionization energies of two elements given their positions in the periodic table. **10:4**
10:12 K distinguish metals from nonmetals in terms of ionization energy. **10:4**
10:13 K define shielding effect, and list the four factors which affect ionization energy. **10:4**
10:14 K explain the variations in ionization energies of elements as their atomic numbers increase in a period or family of the periodic table. **10:4**
10:15 K/P explain the decrease in subsequent ionization energies for an element, from first to second, to third, and so on. **10:5**
10:16 K define electron affinity. **10:6**
10:17 K state the general relationship between ionization energy and electron affinity. **10:6**
10:18 K/P predict trends in electron affinities for elements, based on their location in the periodic table. **10:6**
10:19 A voluntarily complete one or more of the One More Step activities.
10:20 A read unassigned literature related to the chapter.

TEACHING TECHNIQUES

Section 10:2
To help students understand why the chloride ion is larger than the chlorine atom, use the following model: Imagine a circle of seven students (an energy level) in a large room. There is distance between each of them. As the nuclear charge increases, atomic number increases, the students move closer to the center of the circle. Eventually their shoulders touch. They can go no closer without distorting the circle. In order to admit an eighth

student to the circle, the students must back up, increasing the size.

You may wish to demonstrate the reaction of Na with Cl_2, Br_2, or I_2. **CAUTION:** *Use very small amounts of Na and perform in a fume hood. Do not use potassium. It explodes with Br_2 and I_2.*

Bromine gas fumes can be "poured" from a bottle of liquid bromine. **CAUTION:** *Use Br_2 in a fume hood and wear rubber gloves.*

Chlorine gas can be prepared by adding 20 cm^3 of concentrated HCl to 6 g of MnO_2 and heating gently. **CAUTION:** *Prepare Cl_2 in a fume hood.*

Section 10:4

The experiments to determine ionization energy involve shooting electrons through a vapor. A substance is vaporized in a space between two electrodes. No current flows through the vapor between the electrodes because the vapor particles have no charge. When this vapor is bombarded with a stream of electrons, some of the bombarding electrons will collide with atoms. The collision will result in "knocking off" electrons from atoms. The process produces positively charged ions. The positive ions will move toward the negative electrode, and a current will be detected.

In order to determine the necessary energy for ionization, the energy of the electron stream is increased slowly. When a current is detected, the energy of the electrons which first caused the ionization is noted. That value is the energy necessary to remove completely the most loosely held electron from an atom of the element being bombarded. This energy is the **first ionization energy** of that element. It is measured in kilojoules per mole (kJ/mol).

Careers and Chemistry

All of us are aware of the importance of chemotherapy in the treatment of cancer. The pharmacologist and hemotologist are important members of the health-profession team. Emphasize to students that these specialists must pay close attention to detail. Laboratory work must be conducted with great accuracy and care. Labels must be read carefully and procedures followed accurately.

Be sure that students understand the difference between organic chemistry and biochemistry. Students can research and report on the state laws that govern the licensing of pharmacists and pharmacologists. How are the laws different for the two? What are the educational requirements for these various career tracks? How do their salaries differ?

PROBLEM SOLUTIONS

Page 185

1. a. Ar   b. B   c. O^{2-} d. Mg e. P
   f. Cl   g. Ca   h. Te^{2-} i. Ti

2. a,e,f Atoms get larger as we go down the table.
   b,g Atoms get smaller as we go from left to right across the table.
   c,h Negative ions are larger than their parent atoms.
   d,i Positive ions are smaller than their parent atoms.

Page 187

3. Tb 2+ predicted, 3+ actual
   Ba 2+
   Mo 2+,3+,4+,5+,6+

4. 3+ should be more stable since the *d* sublevel is half-filled.

CHAPTER END PROBLEMS

Page 194

1. Ar 0   outer level already has 8 electrons
   Eu 2+ loss of the two 6s electrons
   Al 3+ loss of the two 3s and one 3p electron
   Sb 3+ loss of the three 5p electrons
     5+ loss of the two 5s and three 5p electrons
   Br 1− gain of one electron to complete outer level
   Ar as predicted
   Eu also a 3+ (no obvious explanation)
   Al as predicted
   Sb as predicted (sometimes considered to have a 3− in which the outer level is completed by gaining three electrons)
   Br as predicted

2. U 2+ loss of two 7s electrons
   Na 1+ loss of one 3s electron
   Si 4+ loss of two 3p and two 3s electrons
     4− gain of four electrons to fill outer level
   Ce 2+ loss of two 6s electrons
   Co 2+ loss of two 4s electrons
   U missing 2+ (no obvious explanation)
   Na as predicted
   Si as predicted
   Ce no 2+; 3+ and 4+ instead (no obvious explanation)
   Co also 3+ (no obvious explanation)

3. decrease

4. increase

5. smaller

6. larger

7. **a.** 3+
   b. 2+, 3+
   c. 3+, 5+, 3−
   d. 2−, 4+, 6+
   e. 1+, 2+
   f. 2+, 3+, 4+
   g. 2+
   h. 1+
   i. 2+ predicted, 1+ actual.

8. **a.** Al
   b. Tl
   c. N

d. Na
e. K
f. Br

9. Those electrons come from a lower energy level and are held more tightly.

10. The first four carbon electrons are the hybrids of $2s^2 2p^2$ and are in the outer energy level. Although each requires more

energy to remove than the previous due to the factors which affect ionization energies, they are reasonably close in energy. The next two are in the first energy level and are most tightly held. The increased effective nuclear positive charge and no shielding electrons makes them the most difficult to be removed.

11. Mg has a full s sublevel; Zn has a full d sublevel

REVIEW

Pages 194-195

1. Nb (41) $1s^2 2s^2 2p^6 3s^2 3p^6 4s^2 3d^{10} 4p^6 5s^2 4d^3$ predicted, [Kr] $4d^4 5s^1$ actual.
Rn (86) $1s^2 2s^2 2p^6 3s^2 3p^6 4s^2 3d^{10} 4p^6 5s^2 4d^{10} 5p^6 6s^2 4f^{14} 5d^{10} 6p^6$
Sn (50) $1s^2 2s^2 2p^6 3s^2 3p^6 4s^2 3d^{10} 4p^6 5s^2 4d^{10} 5p^2$

2. $\dfrac{(78.70 \times 23.985\,044) + (10.13 \times 24.985\,839) + (11.17 \times 25.982\,593)}{100} = 24.31$ u

3. $\dfrac{1.27\ \text{g NaBiO}_3}{} \left| \dfrac{1\ \text{mol NaBiO}_3}{280.0\ \text{g NaBiO}_3} \right| \dfrac{2\ \text{mol NaMnO}_4}{5\ \text{mol NaBiO}_3} \left| \dfrac{142\ \text{g NaMnO}_4}{1\ \text{mol NaMnO}_4} \right. = 0.258$ g NaMnO$_4$

4. $2HCl + SnCl_2 \rightarrow SnCl_4 + 2e^-$
$\underline{2e^- + I_2 \quad \rightarrow 2HI}$
$2HCl + SnCl_2 + I_2 \rightarrow 2HI + SnCl_4$

5. Assume a 100 g sample.

$\dfrac{63.9\ \text{g Cd}}{} \left| \dfrac{1\ \text{mol}}{112\ \text{g}} \right. = 0.571$ mol Cd

$\dfrac{11.8\ \text{g P}}{} \left| \dfrac{1\ \text{mol}}{31.0\ \text{g}} \right. = 0.381$ mol P

$\dfrac{24.3\ \text{g O}}{} \left| \dfrac{1\ \text{mol}}{16.0\ \text{g}} \right. = 1.52$ mol O

0.571/0.381 = 1.50 × 2 = 3
0.381/0.381 = 1.00 × 2 = 2
1.52/0.381 = 3.99 × 2 = 8
therefore $Cd_3P_2O_8$ or $Cd_3(PO_4)_2$

6. a. beryllium nitride
b. cerium(III) chloride
c. mercury(II) arsenate
d. calcium phosphide
e. copper(II) selenate

7. a. SiF_4
b. $TlClO_4$

c. $Ni(CN)_2$
d. $Ca_2P_4O_7$
e. BeH_2

ONE MORE STEP

Page 195

1. 96.4869 kJ/mol = 1 electron volt/mol

First Ionization Energies (in electron volts per mole)							
H 13.60							**He** 24.59
Li 5.39	**Be** 9.32	**B** 8.30	**C** 11.26	**N** 14.53	**O** 13.62	**F** 17.42	**Ne** 21.57
Na 5.14	**Mg** 7.65	**Al** 5.99	**Si** 8.15	**P** 10.49	**S** 10.36	**Cl** 12.97	**Ar** 15.76
K 4.34	**Ca** 6.11						

2. The anions are formed in an electric discharge and then photodissociated.

TYPICAL ELEMENTS   11

AN OVERVIEW

Chapter 11 extends the concepts of Chapter 10 in a descriptive study of example elements and their chemistry. After concluding this chapter, your students will have the background necessary to make some fairly good predictions concerning the properties and chemistry of other elements and compounds.

DEMONSTRATION INFORMATION

Into three test tubes place 1 g of $MgSO_4$, $CaSO_4$, and $BaSO_4$ respectively. Add 50 cm^3 of water to each

tube, stopper, shake to dissolve, and allow the solution to settle. The Mg salt dissolves completely, the Ca salt slightly dissolves, and the Ba salt is insoluble. The trend within the alkaline earth family is clearly shown when we compare their solubilities: Mg − 1 g in 0.8 cm^3, Ca in 375 cm^3, and Ba in 400 000 cm^3 of water.
DISPOSAL: *Evaporate water and place crystals in solid waste container.*

The relative solubilities of the three salts are obtained by comparing their K_{sp} values.

$MgSO_4$ soluble, no K_{sp}

$$CaSO_4 \qquad K_{sp} = 2.5 \times 10^{-5}$$
$$BaSO_4 \qquad K_{sp} = 1.7 \times 10^{-10}$$

The amount of solid in each test tube should be carefully noted by the students before the water is added. After the demonstration, students should be able to predict the solubility of $BeSO_4$, and $SrSO_4$. $BeSO_4$ has no K_{sp} value, and the K_{sp} of $SrSO_4$ is 3.5×10^{-7}.

Even though barium compounds are poisonous, they are used in medicine to make X rays of the digestive track clearer. Ask the students why? Barium compounds are insoluble in water and acid so the $BaSO_4$ doesn't poison the patient.

PERFORMANCE OBJECTIVES

Goals: Students will associate families of elements with columns of the periodic table. Students will differentiate among the properties of the families of elements. Students will be able to explain the reasons for similarities and differences of properties within the same family.

Objectives: Upon completion of the reading and problems, and when asked to demonstrate their understanding either orally or on a written test, students will

11:1	K	define family, or group, and explain what members of a chemical family have in common. **Intro**
11:2	K/P	list four ways in which hydrogen can bond, and give examples of each type of bonding. **11:1**
11:3	K/P	distinguish between the hydride ion and the hydrogen ion. **11:1**
11:4	K	define the shielding effect, and describe its characteristics. **11:2**
11:5	K	list and give uses for representative sodium compounds. **11:2**
11:6	K	define catalyst. **11:2**
11:7	K	list two 1+ ions that are not alkali metals but which behave similarly.**11:2**
11:8	K	list the characteristics common to the alkali metals. **11:2-11:3**
11:9	K/P	distinguish between the behavior of lithium and the other members of the alkali metal family. **11:3**
11:10	K	list some important properties of lithium. **11:3**
11:11	K	define and list some uses for the alkaline earth metals. **11:4**
11:12	K/P	explain why aluminum is less metallic than the elements of groups I(1) and II(2), and give some of its uses. **11:5**
11:13	K	define the carbide ion, and list

		some inorganic compounds of carbon. **11:6**
11:14	K	define silicates, and list three important developments in silicon chemistry. **11:6**
11:15	K/P	state how most organic compounds of carbon differ from inorganic compounds of carbon. **11:6**
11:16	K/P	define catenation, and compare catenation in carbon and silicon compounds. **11:6**
11:17	K	define allotropes, list examples in groups IVA(14), VA(15), and VIA(16), and state the importance of ozone. **11:6-11:8**
11:18	K/P	list some properties and uses of nitrogen and phosphorus, state their importance to living things, and give some differences and similarities between them. **11:7**
11:19	K/P	explain two ways in which oxygen can bond. **11:8**
11:20	K	define amphoteric oxide. **11:8**
11:21	K	distinguish between the oxides of sulfur. **11:8**
11:22	K/P	state the relationship between the activities of metallic and nonmetallic elements in relation to their locations in the periodic table. **11:9-11:10**
11:23	P	given two elements, determine which is more chemically active. **11:9-11:10**
11:24	K/P	define halogens, and list and distinguish among their properties. **11:9-11:10**
11:25	K/P	list the noble gases, some of their uses and compounds, and explain why they are no longer called inert gases. **11:11**
11:26	K	define transition metals, and list some of their properties. **11:12-11:14**
11:27	K	define galvanizing. **11:14**
11:28	K	list some properties of lanthanides and actinides. **11:15-11:16**
11:29	A	voluntarily complete one or more of the One More Step activities.
11:30	A	read unassigned literature related to the chapter.

TEACHING TECHNIQUES

Section 11:1
    Stress the fact that hydrogen is a unique element and can be included in either the alkali or halogen family.

Experimental observations show that hydrogen does not fit exclusively into either of these families.

Section 11:2

Emphasize to the students that they are studying group behavior to accumulate knowledge. The characteristics and properties presented will become the foundation on which chemical bonding will be built in Chapter 12.

Section 11:11

If your physics department has a neon gas discharge tube, you may want to light it for your students. Two papers, published in 1962, by Bartlett and Chernick, altered a well established theory that the noble gases were not inert.

Careers and Chemistry

You can use this feature as a starting point to have students research the chemistry involved in water treatment and sewage disposal. Use this topic to integrate their knowledge of biology from the previous year in discussing the chemical functions of bacteria in the breakdown of organic matter in sewage.

CHAPTER END PROBLEMS

Pages 216-217

1. Hydrogen reacts by
   (1) gaining electrons
   (2) losing electrons
   (3) sharing electrons
   (4) acting as a bridge between other atoms
2. The shielding effect reduces the effect of the positive field of the nucleus on the outer electrons due to electrons in between the nucleus and the outer electrons.
   Barium is more reactive since, with a greater shielding effect, it loses the outer electrons more readily.
3. Thallium has a similar (charge/radius) ratio.
4. Lithium has a greater (charge/radius) ratio than other members of the group.

REVIEW

Page 217

1. **a.** $Cr + H_2SO_4 \rightarrow CrSO_4 + H_2$ or
       $2Cr + 3H_2SO_4 \rightarrow Cr_2(SO_4)_3 + 3H_2$
   b. $Mn + 2H_2O \rightarrow Mn(OH)_2 + H_2$ or
       $Mn + H_2O \rightarrow MnO + H_2$
   c. $CuSO_4 + 2NaOH \rightarrow Cu(OH)_2 + Na_2SO_4$
   d. $BaCrO_4 + 2HCl \rightarrow BaCl_2 + H_2CrO_4$

2. $\dfrac{38.7 \text{ g AgCNS}}{} \left| \dfrac{1 \text{ mol AgCNS}}{166 \text{ g AgCNS}} \right| \dfrac{1 \text{ mol AgNO}_3}{1 \text{ mol AgCNS}} \left| \dfrac{170 \text{ g AgNO}_3}{1 \text{ mol AgNO}_3} \right. = 39.6 \text{ g AgNO}_3$

3. $\dfrac{(50.54 \times 78.918\ 332) + (49.46 \times 80.916\ 292)}{100} = 79.91 \text{ u}$

4. $\cdot\dot{Y}\colon, \ \dot{Dy}\colon, \ \ddot{In}\colon$

5. $S = 2-, \ Ge = 4\pm$

5. Aluminum loses its electrons less readily than sodium and magnesium.
6. Catenation is the bonding of atoms to form long chains. Carbon catenates easily. This property is the basis of organic chemistry.
7. Tin and lead are corrosion resistant.
8. Allotropes are different forms of the same element. Carbon, oxygen, and phosphorus have allotropic forms.
9. Phosphorus is a component of nucleic acids and energy transfer compounds in the body.
10. nitrogen and phorphorus
11. Metal oxides are basic and ionic in nature. Nonmetal oxides are acidic and involve the sharing of electrons.
12. Amphoteric oxides can react as acids or bases, while nonmetal oxides are acidic.
13. SO_3 is a nonmetallic oxide therefore the bonds involve electron sharing.
14. Halogen means salt former. These elements are noted for forming salt compounds.
15. francium
16. The noble gases have a full outer level of electrons. Thus, they would not be expected to gain or lose electrons.
17. The transition metals have the highest energy electrons located in d sublevels.
18. These metals are generally strong, some are corrosion resistant. They are generally malleable, ductile, lustrous, conductors of heat and electricity.
19. Zinc is used to protect iron from corrosion.
20. 3+
21. Plutonium is used as a raw material in the production of curium.
22. **a.** cobalt   **f.** zirconium
    b. copper   **g.** potassium
    c. mendelevium   **h.** arsenic
    d. fluorine   **i.** lithium
    e. radium   **j.** oxygen
23. **a.** actinium   **f.** lithium
    b. americium   **g.** bromine
    c. fermium   **h.** boron
    d. gallium   **i.** rubidium
    e. berkelium   **j.** iodine

ONE MORE STEP

Page 217

1. See *Science,* Vol. 138, October 12, 1962, for example of initial reports. XeF_4 is the compound most commonly reported.

2. Although its ionization energy is higher, the Li^+ ion is so highly hydrated that the entire process
$$Li(cr) \rightarrow Li(g) \rightarrow Li^+(g) \rightarrow Li^+(aq)$$

is more exothermic than the process
$$Na(cr) \rightarrow Na(g) \rightarrow Na^+(g) \rightarrow Na^+(aq)$$

3. The addition of 14 protons to the nucleus without starting a new energy level causes a considerable contraction of the elements following the lanthanides in the periodic table. Consequently, elements in the 6th row are smaller than we would otherwise expect. As a result, their chemical behavior is altered somewhat. As an example, gold is less reactive than silver.

CHEMICAL BONDING   12

AN OVERVIEW

The student has examined the structure of the atom in Chapters 8 and 9. The properties of atoms have been presented in detail in Chapters 10 and 11. These chapters have prepared the student to study how atoms bond to each other to form compounds.

Chapter 12 begins a series of chapters concerning the combination of atoms into molecules, (Chapters 12, 13, and 14). In Chapter 12 we discuss the underlying principles of bond formation. This chapter presents chemical bonding and how it affects molecular structure and properties. The first section should develop naturally from the discussions of periodic properties in Chapter 10. Ionic and covalent bonding are presented in detail. Time is spent discussing the different radii between bonded atoms. The chapter concludes with a look at metallic properties as explained by the metallic bond model.

DEMONSTRATION INFORMATION

The demonstration illustrates the formation of an ionic bond in MgO and a covalent bond in SO_2. **CAUTION:** *Wear goggles when burning Mg ribbon.* Place a large can in the sink. Carefully ignite the Mg ribbon in a burner flame. Hold the Mg ribbon with tongs while it burns inside the can. This will prevent students from looking at the burning Mg. If the room lights are turned off the students will safely see the reflected light. Mg is used in photographic flash cubes. The stability of the MgO is evidenced by the large amount of heat and light given off.

$$2Mg(cr) + O_2(g) \rightarrow 2MgO(cr) \quad H_f = -602 \text{ kJ/mol}$$

If oxygen gas is not available from the welding shop, it can be generated in the lab using a side arm vacuum flask as the generator. Place 5 g of MnO_2 in the flask. Insert a dropping funnel or buret into a stopper. Place the stopper loosely on the flask. Attach a hose to the side arm and place the other end into a bottle to collect O_2 gas. Pour 100 cm^3 of 6% H_2O_2 (20 cm^3 30% H_2O_2 + 80 cm^3 H_2O) into the dropping funnel or buret.

Allow the H_2O_2 to drip slowly onto the MnO_2. The bottle of O_2 can be stoppered when full.

Place a small piece of roll sulfur in a deflagrating spoon and briefly place it in a burner flame. It will burn with a low blue flame. Do not breathe the SO_2 gas produced. Use a fume hood. Lower the spoon into a bottle of O_2 gas.

$$S(cr) + O_2(g) = SO_2(g) \quad H_f = -297 \text{ kJ/mol}$$

Point out to the students that increasing the concentration of the O_2 increased the rate of the reaction. It is believed that the burning of high sulfur coal is a major contributor to acid rain. You can demonstrate this by adding 5-10 drops of universal indicator to the bottle of SO_2. Then add 25 cm^3 of water, stopper and shake.

CAUTION: *SO_2 is both toxic and irritating. Perform the demonstration in a fume hood.*

DISPOSAL: *Place solids in container for solid waste disposal. Flush liquids down the drain with water.*

PERFORMANCE OBJECTIVES

Goals: Students will explain the relationship between electronegativity and type of bond character. Students will differentiate among the four types of radii. Students will understand the special nature of metals and metallic bonding.

Objectives: Upon completion of the reading and problems, and when asked to demonstrate their understanding either orally or on a written test, students will

12:1	K	list two factors on which the formation of bonds between atoms depends. **Intro**
12:2	K	define electronegativity. **12:1**
12:3	K	list the factors influencing electronegativity. **12:1**
12:4	K/P	relate the location of elements on the periodic table to their electronegativity values. **12:1**

12:5	P	use electronegativities to predict the type of bond that will form between given atoms. **12:1-12:2**
12:6	K	define ionic bond, covalent bond, and molecule. **12:2-12:3, 12:5**
12:7	K/P	differentiate between the properties of ionic and covalent bonds. **12:3-12:6**
12:8	K/P	define internuclear distance and ionic radius, and use ionic radii to calculate the internuclear distances of crystals. **12:4**
12:9	K	define bond axis, bond angle, and bond length for covalent bonds. **12:5**
12:10	K/P	explain the use of infrared spectroscopy to determine the structure of molecules. **12:5**
12:11	K/P	define covalent radius, and use covalent radii to calculate bond length. **12:6**
12:12	K	define polyatomic ions, and describe their bonding characteristics. **12:7**
12:13	K	define van der Waals radius. **12:8**
12:14	K/P	list and differentiate among the four radii: atomic, ionic, covalent, and van der Waals. **12:9**
12:15	K	define forbidden zones, conduction band, and delocalized electrons, and use these concepts to describe metallic bonding. **12:10**
12:16	K/P	define insulators and semiconductors, and describe the effect of the forbidden zone on both. **12:10**
12:17	K/P	explain metallic properties using the metallic bond concept. **12:10**
12:18	A	voluntarily complete one or more of the One More Step activities.
12:19	A	read unassigned literature related to the chapter.

TEACHING TECHNIQUES

Section 12:1

Linus Pauling interpreted the bond energy of un-symmetrical molecules. Pauling's electronegativity scale is derived from fluorine as 4.0. Using this scale, one can decide if electrons favor one atom over another. For unequal attraction, the center of negative charge is displaced, resulting in a dipole. The bond will then have some ionic character (Section 12:2). Using the electronegativity table, students can predict bond stability (large electronegativity difference) and dipole formation in the molecule (Section 14:2).

Section 12:3

Discuss with students that high melting points are not exclusive to ionic substances. Metals have high melting points, as do macromolecular solids. The high melting points in both cases result from three-dimensional attractions of each atom to its neighbors. This same factor occurs for ionic solids as well.

Section 12:10

Felix Bloch is credited with the bond theory of the energy levels of solids. His theory provided an explanation of semiconductor behavior (Section 16:9). Inform students that Table 12-7 is a great review and study aid.

Technology and Chemistry

Use this feature as a starting point to have students research careers related to the ceramics industry such as ceramic engineers and technicians. Many of the uses of ceramics listed in the feature can be assigned as topics for reports (optical fibers, laser materials, heat resistant materials, and radioactive waste disposal using glass pellets).

PROBLEM SOLUTIONS

Page 220.
1. He, In, Sb, Se, F
2. Fr, Zn, Ga, Ge, P

Pages 221-222.
3. Ionic—b,g,i
   Covalent—a,c,d,e,f,h
4. Ionic—c,e,f
   Covalent—a,b,d

CHAPTER END PROBLEMS

Page 234.
1. When a force is applied to the crystal the attempted deformation forces ions of like charge next to each other. The resultant repulsive forces cause the crystal to split.
2. Since xenon tends neither to gain nor to lose electrons, it must bond covalently.
3. **a.** 0.128 nm
   b. 0.221 nm
   c. 0.244 nm
   d. 0.315 nm
   e. 0.154 nm
   f. 0.136 nm

4.	21	Sc	3
	22	Ti	4
	23	V	5
	24	Cr	6

25	Mn	6
26	Fe	6
27	Co	6
28	Ni	6
29	Cu	5.5
30	Zn	4.5

5. nuclear charge, shielding effect, radius, sublevel
6. Van der Waals radius concerns the distance between non-bonded adjacent atoms, while covalent radius concerns the distance between bonded adjacent atoms.
7. The atoms vibrate constantly. Thus only an average value for bond length can be determined.
8. high conductivity, lustrous, malleable, ductile, lose electrons
9. As the degree of delocalization of electrons increases the metal is harder, more dense, and exhibits a higher melting point.

REVIEW

Pages 234-235.

1.

N	Se	I
P	Br	Ta
S	Nb	W
Cl	Mo	Re
Ti	Tc	Os
V	Ru	Ir
Cr	Rh	Pt
Mn	Te	

2. Dobereiner's triads → Newland's law of octaves → Mendeleev's and Meyer's tables based on properties and atomic mass → modern table based on electron configurations and atomic number.

3. **a.**
astatine	7+, 1−
germanium	4±
mercury	2+
polonium	6+, 2−
tin	2+, 4+

b.
francium	1+
hafnium	2+, 3+, 4+
neodymium	2+

rubidium	1+
tellurium	6+, 2−

4. Elements with the same outer electron configuration are in the same column (except H and He). Elements with the same principle quantum number for the outer level are in the same period.

5. **a.** 1+
   b. 2+, 3+, 4+
   c. 2+, 3+, 4+, 5+
   d. 2−, 4+, 6+
   e. 1−
   f. 3+

6. **a.** metal
   b. metal
   c. metal
   d. metalloid
   e. nonmetal
   f. metalloid

7. **a.** alkali metals
   b. alkaline earth metals
   c. transition metals
   d. halogens
   e. noble gases

8. **a.** $1s^22s^22p^63s^23p^64s^23d^{10}4p^65s^24d^4$ (actually $5s^14d^5$)
   b. $1s^22s^22p^63s^23p^64s^23d^{10}4p^65s^24d^{10}5p^3$
   c. $1s^22s^22p^63s^23p^64s^23d^{10}4p^65s^24d^{10}5p^66s^24f^1$ (actually $6s^25d^1$)
   d. $1s^22s^22p^63s^23p^64s^23d^{10}4p^65s^24d^5$
   e. $1s^22s^22p^63s^23p^64s^23d^{10}4p^65s^24d^{10}5p^2$
   f. $1s^22s^22p^63s^23p^64s^2$

ONE MORE STEP

Page 235.

1. Pauling's equation:
$$Q = 23.06\Sigma(X_A - X_B)^2 - 55.1N_N - 24.2N_O$$
where $Q = \Delta H_f$ in kcal/mol
   X_A = electronegativity of element A
   X_B = electronegativity of element B
   N_N = number of nitrogen atoms in compound
   N_O = number of oxygen atoms in compound

Mulliken's equation:
$$\frac{1}{2}(I_A - E_A) - \frac{1}{2}(I_B - E_B) = 2.78(X_A - X_B)$$
where I_A and I_B = ionization potentials of A and B
   E_A and E_B = electron affinities of A and B

Allred and Rochow's equation:
$$X = 0.359\frac{Zeff}{r^2} + 0.744$$
where X = electronegativity
   $Zeff$ = effective nuclear charge
   r = covalent radius

Liu's equation:
$$X = 0.313\left(\frac{n + 2.6}{r^{2/3}}\right)$$
where X = electronegativity
   n = number of valence electrons
   r = covalent radius

Gordy's equation:
$$X = 0.31\left(\frac{n + 1}{r}\right) + 0.50$$
where X = electronegativity
   n = number of valence electrons
   r = covalent radius

2. X-ray diffraction of crystals; electron diffraction of gases; neutron diffraction of crystals; microwave spectroscopy—

From the energy absorbed, the moment of inertia of the molecule can be calculated. Then, using known atomic masses, distances can be calculated.

3. Covalent—one-half length of X—X bond for elements forming diatomic molecules. Others from subtraction of known radius from bond length.
   Assumptions: Additivity of radii in bond length
   No pi bonding in simple compounds not involving known double or triple bonds
   No ionic character
   No effect of one atom on electron cloud of another
   Ionic—subtract known radius from X-ray diffraction determined internuclear distance.
   Assumptions: One set of values (usually lithium halides) has

anions in contact
   Additivity of radii in bond lengths
   No covalent character
   No effect of one ion on electron cloud of another
   A precisely defined electron cloud
   van der Waals—one half nonbonded distance in pure elements
   Assumptions: No effect of one atom on electron cloud of another
   A precisely defined electron cloud

4. In complexes—number of ligands bonded to central ion
   In crystals—number of ions of opposite sign surrounding a given ion
   In metals—number of nearest neighbor atoms

MOLECULAR STRUCTURE 13

AN OVERVIEW

Chapter 13 presents a study of chemical bonds and their geometric arrangement. Different approaches to explain bonding in molecules are presented in a sequence that proceeds from the simple to the sophisticated: electron pair repulsion theory, hybrid orbitals, resonance, and molecular orbital theory.

There are numerous ways to represent atoms and their combinations in molecules. Thus, students should realize that the pictures in the text are simply models. Different approaches to bonding may dictate different representations. Do not attach too much importance to pictorial aspects of the orbital representations. Emphasize that these models are useful because they provide a basis for the prediction of structure and properties. The ability to predict avoids the necessity of memorizing hundreds of individual molecular shapes. Chapter 13 ends with an elementary treatment of the molecular orbital theory. Students are certain to encounter this theory in more advanced chemistry courses.

DEMONSTRATION INFORMATION

Large and small balloons can be used to represent shared and unshared electron pairs. Inflate 10 small (S = shared pr.) and 6 large (U = unshared pr.) Attach a rubber band to each balloon. Form the following molecules by connecting the balloons. Discuss the shapes found due to the interaction of S and U electron pairs (See 13:1).
HF (3U, 1S) H_2O (2U, 2S) NH_3 (1U, 3S) CH_4 (4S)

These models are more effective than chalkboard drawings in demonstrating special arrangements of the bonds. You may want to take slide pictures of the more complex models for use in future classes. Students may want to make the balloon models for extra credit. Hang them from the ceiling when they are completed.

PERFORMANCE OBJECTIVES

Goals: Students will study several hypotheses regarding the structure of molecules. Students will predict the structures of isomers from molecular formulas. Students will use one or more hypotheses to explain structure of given organic and inorganic molecules.

Objectives: Upon completion of the reading and problems, and when asked to demonstrate their understanding either orally or on a written test, students will

13:1	K/P	use electron-dot diagrams to show molecular structure. **Intro**
13:2	K	distinguish shared and unshared pairs of electrons. **Intro**
13:3	K/P	explain how the shared and unshared pairs of electrons determine molecular shape. **13:1**
13:4	K/P	predict the shapes and bond angles of simple molecules based on electron-pair repulsion. **13:1**
13:5	K	define double bond and distinguish it from a triple bond. **13:2**
13:6	K/P	differentiate among bond angles resulting from multiple bond repulsion. **13:2**
13:7	K	describe hybrid orbitals. **13:3**
13:8	K/P	explain the bonding of carbon compounds by overlapping of orbitals. **13:4-13:5**
13:9	K	differentiate sigma and pi bonding. **13:4**
13:10	K/P	use hybridization theory to explain the bond angles in compounds with multiple bonds. **13:3-13:6**

13:11	K	define and identify unsaturated compound and conjugated system. **13:7**
13:12	K/P	use bonding theory to explain unsaturated compounds and conjugated systems. **13:7**
13:13	K	define delocalization. **13:7**
13:14	K	define isomer and isomerism. **13:8**
13:15	K	define and differentiate among the four types of isomers. **13:8**
13:16	P	draw structural isomers for simple compounds of carbon. **13:8**
13:17	K/P	apply hybridization theory to inorganic compounds. **13:9**
13:18	K	define resonance. **13:10**
13:19	P	construct electron-dot resonance formulas to explain alternate structures for molecules and "average" bond length. **13:10**
13:20	K/P	define molecular orbital, and use molecular orbital theory to explain the behavior of some simple molecules. **13:11**
13:21	P	write molecular orbital configurations for diatomic molecules of first and second period elements. **13:11**
13:22	P	using molecular orbital theory, calculate the bond order in simple diatomic molecules. **13:11**
13:23	A	voluntarily complete one or more of the One More Step activities.
13:24	A	read unassigned literature related to the chapter.

TEACHING TECHNIQUES

Section 13:1

As you discuss electron repulsion, a balloon model of water is helpful. On the chalkboard, write the electron dot structure of water. Have two large pear-shaped balloons of one color (unshared pairs on oxygen) and two smaller ones of another color (shared pairs between O and H). Blow them up and attach them to the chalkboard with masking tape. Students can visualize the concept of unshared-unshared repulsion > unshared-shared > shared-shared using this model. If you wish, CH_4, NH_3 and HF can be demonstrated in the same way. Color slides of these models can serve well in future years. Students may also be willing to make them for extra credit.

Section 13:2

Using plastic foam balls and toothpicks, you can show the free rotation of a single bond. Ethane, C_2H_6, is

a simple model to use. Point out to students that the double bond prevents this rotation. Demonstrate it by changing the C_2H_6 to C_2H_4, ethene. Emphasize the trigonal planar shape of the double bond.

Section 13:8

Emphasize that mixtures of isomers can be separated and each isomer has its own physical and chemical properties. Models help students visualize the concept better than the single dimension pictures in the text. Build the molecules shown in the text.

Section 13:10

Attach a thin rope to a point across the room. Show how the rope vibrates (resonates) between two extremes as you move your hand up and down to produce a standing wave. Relate this idea to the different electron dot structures that can be drawn for resonance structures. We average the extremes to get a structure of the molecule.

Technology and Chemistry

A study of the boranes is included in this chapter to reinforce the concepts of bonding and molecular structure previously studied. The 1976 Nobel Prize was awarded for research concerning the boranes. An excellent follow-up article for additional reading is the following.

Lipscomb, William N., "The Boranes and Their Relatives," *Science*, Vol. 196, No. 4294 (June 3, 1977), pp. 1047-1054.

CHAPTER END PROBLEMS

Pages 259-260.

1.
	predicted	actual
a.	$<109.5°$	$90°$
b.	$<109.5°$	$93°$
c.	$\approx109.5°$	—
d.	$<109.5°$	$98°$
e.	$109.5°$	$109.5°$
f.	$109.5°$	$109.5°$

2. Sigma (σ) bonds are end-to-end overlaps of two orbitals. Pi (π) bonds result from the sideways overlap of two p orbitals.

3. Hybridization is the formation of equivalent orbitals by 2 or more orbitals from different energy sublevels. For example, one s and two p orbitals form three equivalent sp^2 hybrid orbitals.

4. The double bond (C=C) is formed by the σ overlap of two sp^2 orbitals and the π overlap of two p orbitals. The H—C bonds are formed by the σ overlap of sp^2 hybrid orbitals of the carbon with s orbitals of the hydrogens.

5. Benzene has a conjugated ring which in effect results in delocalization of the pi electrons, a very stable form.

6. a. trigonal planar, 120° bond angles

b. angular

$$O=Se \overset{\cdot\cdot}{} \longleftrightarrow O-Se \overset{\cdot\cdot}{}$$
$$\quad\ O \qquad\qquad\quad O$$

c. trigonal planar

d. octahedral

e.

f. trigonal bipyramidal with one equatorial position occupied by the unshared pair

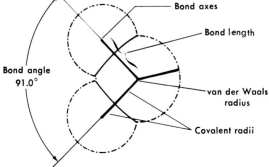

7. Linear; *sp;* H—C bond is sigma, C≡N is one sigma and two pi bonds.

8.

Bond axes
Bond length
Bond angle 91.0°
van der Waals radius
Covalent radii

9. Hexane has five isomers:

(1) C—C—C—C—C—C

(2) C—C—C—C—C
  with C below second carbon

(3) C—C—C—C—C
  with C below second and third carbons

(4) C—C—C—C
  with C below second and third carbons

(5) C—C—C—C
  with C above and below second carbon

10. Geometric isomerism results from groups being able to take two different positions with respect to double bonds. Positional isomers are formed when a particle may bond at different points on a chain of carbons.

Functional isomerism results when a particle may be bonded in two or more ways.

11. a.

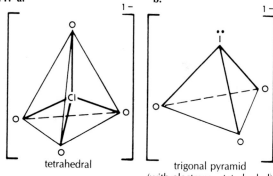

tetrahedral

b.

trigonal pyramid (with electrons—tetrahedral)

c.

octahedral

d.

tetrahedral

e.

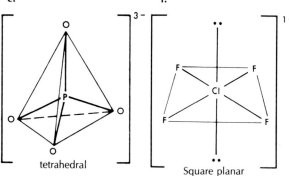

tetrahedral

f.

Square planar

the fluorines are planar, however, including the unshared pairs, the ion can be labeled as octahedral

12. PCl_5—trigonal bipyramid

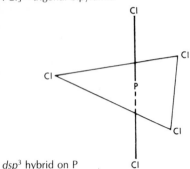

dsp^3 hybrid on P

PCl_4^+—tetrahedral, sp^3 hybrid on P
PCl_6^-—octahedral, d^2sp^3 hybrid on P

13. Both benzene and metals exhibit delocalization of electrons. For benzene, the delocalization occurs for each individual molecule. For metals, the delocalization exists throughout the entire piece of matter.

14. A 90° arrangement indicates all atoms are in the same plane. Electron pair repulsions result in 3-dimensional arrangements. Thus, the maximum distance of repulsion for four electron pairs results in a tetrahedral shape with bond angles of 109.5°.

15. NH_3 has a tetrahedral shape (see Figure 13-3) having three shared pairs and one unshared pair. The unshared pair causes the distortion which makes the bond angle less than 109.5°. BF_3 is a planar arrangement with three shared pairs. The maximum distance of repulsion for atoms in a single plane is 120°.

16.

:O:
   ``C:O: ⟷   C::O: ⟷   C:O:
:O: :O: :O:

17.

Benzene

Naphthalene

18. a. $(\sigma_{2s})^2\ (2-0)/2 = 1$ bond, stable
b. $(\sigma_{2s})^2\ (\sigma_{2s}^*)^2\ (\pi_{sp})^2\ (4-2)/2 = 1$ bond, stable
c. $(\sigma_{2s})^2\ (\sigma_{2s}^*)^2\ (\pi_{2p})^4\ (6-2)/2 = 3$ bonds, stable
d. $(\sigma_{2s})^2\ (\sigma_{2s}^*)^2\ (\pi_{2p})^4\ (\sigma_{2p})^2\ (8-2)/2 = 3$ bonds, stable
e. $(\sigma_{2s})^2\ (\sigma_{2s}^*)^2\ (\pi_{2p})^4\ (\sigma_{2s})^2\ (\pi_{2p}^*)^4\ (8-6)/2 = 1$ bond, stable

19. $(\sigma_{2s})^2\ (\sigma_{2s}^*)^2\ (\pi_{2p})^4\ (\sigma_{2p})^2\ \left(\dfrac{8-2}{2}\right) = 3$ bonds, stable

REVIEW

Page 261.
1. francium, manganese, zinc, boron

2. a. ionic   **d.** covalent
   b. ionic   **e.** covalent
   c. ionic   **f.** covalent

3. Electrons are in the outer level band which is separated from the conduction band by only a narrow forbidden zone.

ONE MORE STEP

Page 261.
1. a. 125°   **d.** 134°
   b. 108°   **e.** 115°
   c. 113°

2. octahedral; SF_6, $CdCl_6^{4-}$, ICl_4^-, BrF_4^-, BrF_5, IF_5, $Co(NH_3)_6^{3+}$, $PdCl_6^{2-}$, $Fe(CN)_6^{3-}$

3. puckered ring; two shapes of C_6H_{12}:

Chair form

Boat form

The chair form is more stable because of the H—H interference found in boat form:

H – – H

4. a. $H_2C{=}C{=}CH_2$ linear, planar on both ends, but one —CH_2 is in a plane perpendicular to the other —CH_2 group.
   b. $H_2C{=}C{=}C{=}CH_2$ linear; entire molecule planar.

5. Alfred Werner → Langmuir → G. N. Lewis →
   Sidgwick → Born → Pauling → Ingold
   No one theory agrees with all experimental data. No one theory enables one to make sure predictions.

6. Because electrons, in the two bound atoms, with the same quantum numbers are no longer at the same energy. Therefore, the way in which they combine to form molecular orbitals is extremely difficult to predict.

7. There are three molecular orbitals for the six pi electrons. The lowest energy orbital encompasses all six carbon atoms. The other two MO's are equivalent in energy, and each exists in two parts. One orbital has half bonding carbons 1 and 6 while the other half bonds carbons 3 and 4. The other orbital has half bonding atoms 1, 2, and 3, while the other half bonds 4, 5, and 6. The net result of all MO's is two flat rings of electron cloud, half below the plane of the carbon and half above.

POLAR MOLECULES 14

AN OVERVIEW

Properties of molecules which are a consequence of their structure are discussed in Chapter 14. The chapter begins with a study of polar molecules. Students investigate how some properties of similar compounds differ because of varying molecular shapes and structures.

Polarity shows the relationship between properties and electric dipoles in molecules. Before beginning the study of complex ions, students may find a brief review of solid geometrical figures helpful. In Section 14:6, students find that the presence of *d* orbitals gives no new bonding types, only some new shapes. A study of the weak van der Waals forces between molecules is important if students are to have a complete understanding of the relationship between structure and properties. Finally, the knowledge of polarity is applied in learning how to separate the components of a mixture by chromatography. Several types of chromatography are discussed.

DEMONSTRATION INFORMATION

CAUTION: *Cyclohexane vapors are to be considered poisonous. Perform the demonstration in a fume hood. Do not use cyclohexane near open flames.*

Place two burets in a buret clamp and fill one with water and one with cyclohexane. Place a small beaker under each buret. The liquids can be recycled for other classes. A silk cloth and a lucite rod are used to obtain a static charge. This equipment can often be borrowed from the physics teacher. Rub the lucite rod with the cloth to place a static charge on the rod. Open the cyclohexane buret and allow the stream to run into the beaker. Bring the charged rod near the stream. No effect is observed. Repeat these steps with the water buret. A definite deflection is noticed due to the polarity of the water molecules.

To explain these observed differences you may want to draw the structures of both molecules for the students. Every C—H bond is polar in cyclohexane, but because of its symmetry, the molecule is nonpolar. This demonstration confirms the angular shape of the water molecule. Both H—O bonds are polar; the oxygen end has a partial negative charge, and the hydrogen end has a partial positive charge. Because these bonds are polar and not symmetrically arranged, the molecule itself is polar.

DISPOSAL: *Label a bottle for the cyclohexane and save the sample to use again next year.*

PERFORMANCE OBJECTIVES

Goals: Students will gain an understanding of the relationship between molecular structure and the properties of molecular compounds. Students will explain the formation of coordination compounds and complex ions. Students will gain an understanding of chromatographic identification of compounds.

Objectives: Upon completion of the reading and problems, and when asked to demonstrate their understanding either orally or on a written test, students will

14:1	K	distinguish between polar and nonpolar covalent bonds. **14:1**
14:2	P	use electronegativities to predict the comparative polarities of bonds. **14:1**
14:3	K/P	define dipole and compare the strengths of intermolecular forces based on dipole moments. **14:1**
14:4	K	define van der Waals forces and list the three factors contributing to them. **14:2**
14:5	K	define and distinguish intramolecular and intermolecular forces. **14:2**
14:6	K/P	define dipole-dipole forces, induced dipole forces, dipole-induced dipole forces, temporary dipole, and dispersion forces, and give examples of substances exhibiting these forces. **14:2**
14:7	K	define complex ion, ligand, bidentate ligand, and coordination number. **14:3**
14:8	K/P	list the most common coordination numbers and give examples of central ions having these numbers. **14:3**
14:9	K/P	relate coordination number to the structure of complex ions and their isomers. **14:3-14:4**
14:10	K	distinguish *cis* and *trans* isomers of complex ions. **14:4**
14:11	K/P	name complex ions given their formulas, and write formulas for complex ions given their names. **14:5**
14:12	K	describe the coordinate covalent bond. **14:6**
14:13	K	list reasons why transition metals form complex ions. **14:6**

14:14	K	define mobile phase, stationary phase, and fractionation. **14:8**
14:15	K/P	explain fractionation as a separation method. **14:8**
14:16	K	define chromatography. **14:8**
14:17	K	define and describe column chromatography, paper chromatography, and thin layer chromatography. **14:8-14:11**
14:18	A	voluntarily complete one or more of the One More Step activities.
14:19	A	read unassigned literature related to the chapter.

TEACHING TECHNIQUES

Section 14:3

Ball and stick models are helpful to students as they attempt to visualize the coordination number of the central positive ion in a complex. The structures of complexes are usually either linear (sp bonding), tetrahedral (sp^3), square planar (dsp^2), or octahedral (d^2sp^3).

Section 14:9

Your students have probably seen paper chromatography before, but column chromatography may be new to them. You can purchase commercial resins, many of which are shipped slightly moist. Do not breathe any of the dust if you use a dry resin. Columns can be kept from year to year if kept moist and sealed. Old columns can be reconditioned by percolating $2M$ HCl through them. If you do not have a commercial resin, a list of acceptable substitutes is found in 14:9. A flow rate that works well is 2-3 cm^3 per minute. If the rate is too slow, use either air pressure on top (rubber squeeze bulb) or an aspirator on the bottom of the tube. A good solution to separate can be prepared by dissolving 2.8 g $FeCl_3 \cdot 6H_2O$, 2.5 g $NiCl_2 \cdot 6H_2O$, and 2.5 g $CoCl_2 \cdot 6H_2O$ in 100 cm^3 of $9M$ HCl. Use 2 cm^3 of this solution for a column 10 mm × 20 cm long. A usual manner of separation is to begin with three aliquots of 5 cm^3 each of $9M$ HCl, then 4 portions of 5 cm^3 of $5M$ HCl then 5 portions of 5 cm^3 of $1M$ HCl.

Technology and Chemistry

This feature provides an introduction to many concepts introduced later in the text freezing point depression (Chapter 22), saponification (Chapter 30), ion ratios in the body (Chapters 11 and 30). You may have students do further research on any of these topics as well as water softening and desalination processes.

PROBLEM SOLUTIONS

Page 265.

1. f, e, a, d, c, b

Page 272.

2. a. hexiodoplatinate(IV) ion

b. diamminecadmium ion
c. hexafluorogermanate(IV) ion
d. tetraaquochromium(II) ion
e. hexacyanoferrate(III) ion
f. hexacyanoferrate(II) ion
g. hexaamminecobalt(II) ion
h. hexachloroplatinate(IV) ion
i. hexaamminenickel(II) ion
j. hexachloroiridate(IV) ion

3.
a. AuI_4^-	**f.** $W(CN)_8^{3-}$
b. $Pt(NH_3)_4^{2+}$	**g.** $Co(NH_3)_6^{3+}$
c. $Au(CN)_4^-$	**h.** AlF_6^{3-}
d. $PdCl_6^{2-}$	**i.** $Pd(NH_3)_2Cl_2$
e. $Ir(H_2O)_6^{3+}$	**j.** $Cd(NH_3)_4^{2+}$

4. a. chloropentaammineiridium(III) ion
b. tetraamminepalladium(II) ion
c. hexahydroxoantimonate(V) ion
d. tetrachloropalladate(II) ion
e. trioxalatoferrate(III) ion
f. hexaamminecopper(II) ion

5.
a. $FeCO(CN)_5^{3-}$	**d.** $Cu(CN)_2^-$
b. $Ru(CO)_5$	**e.** $Co(NH_3)_4(H_2O)Cl^{2+}$
c. $Pt(NH_3)_2Br_4$	**f.** $Cr(NH_3)_6^{3+}$

6.
a. $GaBr_4^-$	**d.** $OsCl_6^{2-}$
b. GaF_6^{3-}	**e.** $IrBr_6^{3-}$
c. $Hg(S_2O_3)_3^{4-}$	**f.** $Fe(NO)(H_2O)_5^{2+}$

CHAPTER END PROBLEMS

Page 282.

1. b,a,e,f,c,d

2. van der Waals forces caused by dipole-dipole, dipole-induced dipole, and dispersion forces

3. octahedral

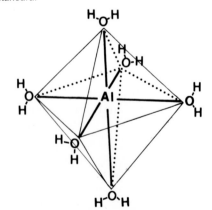

4. Central ion: Ion about which ligands cluster
Coordination number: Number of ligands
Ligand: Negative ion or polar molecule bonded to central ion

5. size and charge

6. The transition metals have partially filled d orbitals to accept e^- and are relatively small, thus, they have large charge-to-radius ratio.

7. a. pentafluorogallate(III) ion
  b. tetrathioantimonate(V) ion
  c. dicyanoaurate(I) ion
  d. tetracyanoaurate(III) ion
  e. dichlorotetraaquochromium(III) ion

8. Both depend upon selective adsorption. In the column, the solvent is run through the adsorbent, while on paper, the solvent moves by capillary action.

9. X_2A, X_2A

10. Due to filled orbitals, noble gas particles are held together only by dispersion forces. Since these forces are the weakest of those holding molecules together, we would expect Group VIIIA elements to be gases.

11. O=C=O

The linear shape of CO_2 accounts for a dipole moment of zero. The unshared pair and angular shape of SO_2 account for the dipole moment value and its resulting polarity.

REVIEW

Pages 282-283.

1. NI_3 trigonal pyramid, CCl_4 tetrahedral

2. An s orbital is spherical and a p orbital is dumbbell shaped.

3. The s and three p orbitals hybridize to four orbitals of equivalent energy each containing one electron.

4. The p orbital overlap is conjugated so that the electron cloud for the pi bond completely encircles the ring of carbon atoms. Such a delocalized system of electrons represents a more stable arrangement than isolated sigma and pi bonds.

5. Angular. The two unshared pairs of electrons push the shared pairs toward each other.

6. The He_2^+ ion would have a total of 3 electrons in the outer level. Their orbital arrangement would be $(\sigma_{1s})^2 (\sigma_{2s}^*)^1$. The bonding would be $(2 -)/2 = 1/2$. In other words it should be a stable species.

7. C=C—C—C—C
  C—C=C—C—C (cis and trans)
  C=C—C—C
    |
    C
  C—C=C—C
    |
    C
  C=C—C—C
    |
    C

CH_3

(cis and trans)

CH

8. 120°

9.

10.

ONE MORE STEP

Page 283.

1. R_f values must be found for a particular system with standards of known concentration. Once that piece of apparatus has been standardized for a substance, an unknown containing that substance can be analyzed. The volume of the chromatographic chamber, for instance, has a large effect on R_f values. Values from one chamber cannot be applied to another chamber of different geometry. Other factors affecting R_f values are the state of subdivision of the adsorbent, temperature, purity of the solvent, separation of a multi-component solvent, and evaporation. Solvents and/or adsorbents from the same manufacturer but from different batches will give different R_f values. However, the *relative* values are quite useful in analysis.

2. Mg, 4, phaeophorbide, planar
  Fe, 4, porphyrin, planar

3. The formation of a heterocyclic ring with a metal atom in the ring is the process of chelation.

disodium ethylenediaminetetraacetate
copper chelate

4. Ni = dimethylglyoxime
  Al = ammonium aurin tricarboxylate
  Zr = sodium alizarin sulfonate

5. Extract the pigments from a few grams of spinach leaves by grinding them in a mortar with a little sand and acetone as the solvent. Filter the solution and spot the paper in the usual manner being certain to dry between each application. Develop the chromatogram using a solvent of 0.5% propanol in petroleum ether.

KINETIC THEORY 15

AN OVERVIEW

Chapter 15 presents the physical states as a consequence of their thermal behavior. A model that treats gases as hard, round, perfectly elastic spheres in constant motion is discussed first. The concept of pressure is introduced quantitatively early in the chapter. From Sections 15:4-5 students should get the idea that the temperature of a gas is a measure of the average kinetic energies of its molecules. It then follows that molecules of all gases at the same temperature must have the same kinetic energies. Section 15:4 presents a discussion of temperature. Students should be able to convert Celsius to kelvin and the reverse. At the end of the chapter students use the kinetic theory to explain the properties of gases, liquids, solids, and plasmas.

DEMONSTRATION INFORMATION

On an overhead projector, place 5-10 glass beads in a covered petri dish for the first part of the demonstration. When the dish is moved back and forth the activity of molecules in a closed container can be simulated. This qualitative demonstration of the kinetic molecular theory can also be used to show temperature variations by varying your hand motion.

During the demonstration introduce the concept of mean free path. Your students will observe collisions between molecules and between molecules and the container wall. The effect of increasing temperature can also be simulated.

In the second part of the demonstration, the formation of $NH_4Cl(cr)$ could not occur if the particles of matter were not in constant, rapid, random motion. The reaction:

$$NH_3(g) + HCl(g) \rightarrow NH_4Cl(cr)$$

will be repeated as a quantitative laboratory experiment in Chapter 18. **CAUTION:** *The vapors are harmful; perform the reaction in a fume hood. Rinse cotton under running water before discarding.*

PERFORMANCE OBJECTIVES

Goals: Students will gain an understanding of the kinetic theory. Students will use the kinetic theory to describe the effects of heat and pressure on matter. Students will differentiate among the four states of matter.

Objectives: Upon completion of the reading and problems, and when asked to demonstrate their understanding either orally or on a written test, students will

15:1	K	define the kinetic theory. **Intro**
15:2	K/P	list and explain the basic assumptions of the kinetic theory. **Intro**
15:3	K	define and describe mean free path of a molecule in motion. **15:1**
15:4	K	define pressure, standard pressure, and the pascal. **15:2**
15:5	K	relate pressure to molecular motion. **15:2**
15:6	K	define manometer and barometer, and describe the use of a manometer to measure gas pressure. **15:3**
15:7	P	calculate pressures of gases in both open and closed manometers; convert pressure units. **15:3**
15:8	K	define kinetic energy in terms of the motion and mass of particles. **15:4**
15:9	K	relate temperature and energy transfer to molecular motion. **15:4**
15:10	K	define absolute zero and the kelvin temperature scale. **15:4**
15:11	K/P	convert temperatures from Celsius to kelvin and from kelvin to Celsius. **15:4**
15:12	K/P	determine the relative velocities of gas molecules at the same temperature. **15:4**
15:13	K	describe the three common states of matter in terms of the kinetic theory. **15:5**
15:14	K	define plasma and magnetohydrodynamics. **15:6**
15:15	K	describe the characteristics of the plasma state. **15:6**
15:16	A	voluntarily complete one or more of the One More Step activities.
15:17	A	read unassigned literature on a topic related to the chapter.

TEACHING TECHNIQUES

Section 15:1

Oxygen gas molecules have an average speed of 1900 km/h (about 1000 miles/h). You can relate mean free path to driving a car. An oxygen "car" would have a collision every 314 car lengths, or 4.5×10^9 collisions per second.

Section 15:2

If you have empty duplicating fluid cans, attach one to an aspirator or vacuum pump and let students observe its collapse.

Pressure in the laboratory is measured in mm of Hg and converted to pascals or kilopascals. The auto and tire industries have been using kilopascals for tire pressure measurements.

One atmosphere (760 mm Hg) of pressure is equal to 100 (101.325) kilopascals. Students will generally accept new units. Pascal is the unit of pressure used throughout the world. You may experience the most difficulty with this conversion.

Section 15:4

The degree symbol associated with the K was dropped officially in 1968. The kelvin is the SI unit of temperature.

At absolute zero, theory predicts that all particle motion has stopped. Absolute zero has not yet been reached (see the Technology feature on cryogenics).

Section 15:5

This section serves only to introduce solids, liquids, and gases. Each of these will be covered in the next three chapters. Do not go into much detail here.

Technology and Chemistry

Since many of the materials used for replacement parts are organic, you may want to introduce some organic chemistry at this point. We have made it a point to use organic as well as inorganic examples throughout the text, so as not to relegate their study to the last two chapters.

PROBLEM SOLUTIONS

Pages 288–289.

1. The gas pressure is 62 mm less than the pressure of the air on the tube.

$$\frac{62 \text{ mm}}{} \left| \frac{1 \text{ kPa}}{7.50 \text{ mm}} \right. = 8.3 \text{ kPa}$$

Total pressure = $97.7 - 8.3 = 89.4$ kPa

2. $$\frac{691 \text{ mm}}{} \left| \frac{1 \text{ kPa}}{7.50 \text{ mm}} \right. = 92.1 \text{ kPa}$$

3. The gas pressure is 6 mm less than the pressure of the air on the tube.

$$\frac{6 \text{ mm}}{} \left| \frac{1 \text{ kPa}}{7.50 \text{ mm}} \right. = 0.8 \text{ kPa}$$

Total pressure = $100.0 - 0.8 = 99.2$ kPa

4. The gas pressure is 38 mm greater than the pressure of the air in the tube.

$$\frac{38 \text{ mm}}{} \left| \frac{1 \text{ kPa}}{7.50 \text{ mm}} \right. = 5.1 \text{ kPa}$$

Total pressure = $96.3 + 5.1 = 101.4$ kPa

5. $$\frac{86.0 \text{ mm}}{} \left| \frac{1 \text{ kPa}}{7.50 \text{ mm}} \right. = 11.5 \text{ kPa}$$

PAGE 291.

6. **a.** 338 K   **d.** 237 K
   b. 289 K   **e.** 346 K
   c. 321 K

7. **a.** $-187°C$ **d.** 48°C
   b. $-82°C$ **e.** 621°C
   c. 260°C

8. **a.** 296 K   **d.** 291 K
   b. 331 K   **e.** 298 K
   c. 183 K

9. **a.** 599°C   **d.** $-253°C$
   b. 417°C   **e.** $-213°C$
   c. 111°C

10. N_2

CHAPTER END PROBLEMS

Page 296.

1. The gas pressure is 12 mm less than air.

$$\frac{12 \text{ mm}}{} \left| \frac{1 \text{ kPa}}{7.50 \text{ mm}} \right. = 1.6 \text{ kPa}$$

Total pressure $98.7 - 1.6 = 97.1$ kPa

2. $$\frac{522 \text{ mm}}{} \left| \frac{1 \text{ kPa}}{7.50 \text{ mm}} \right. = 69.6 \text{ kPa}$$

3. **a.** $605 \text{ K} - 273 = 333°C$
   b. $751°C + 273 = 1024 \text{ K}$
   c. $18°C + 273 = 291 \text{ K}$
   d. $3 \text{ K} - 273 = -270°C$
   e. $62°C + 273 = 335 \text{ K}$
   f. $-14°C + 273 = 259 \text{ K}$

4. The molecular mass of ammonia is: $14 + 3 = 17$. The molecular mass of chlorine gas is: $2(35.5) = 71.0$. Since the velocity of gas molecules varies inversely as the square root of their mass, the *ammonia* which is composed of lighter molecules will be expected to cross the room first.

5. The mean free path of an atom or molecule is the average distance it travels between collisions.

6. Each molecule moves independently of other molecules in a gas. A molecule appears to vibrate about a moving point in a liquid. Molecules appear to vibrate about fixed points in a solid.

7. The gas pressure is 24 mm greater than air.

$$\frac{24 \text{ mm}}{} \left| \frac{1 \text{ kPa}}{7.50 \text{ mm}} \right. = 3.2 \text{ kPa}$$

Total pressure $100.3 + 3.2 = 103.5$ kPa

8. Temperature is a measure of the average kinetic energy of particles.

9. Theoretically, at absolute zero all molecular motion would cease.

10. Kinetic energy is conserved in an elastic collision. In an inelastic collision, some kinetic energy is converted to another energy form (potential or radiant).

REVIEW

Page 297.

1. **a.** RuH

2. Advantage—surface chromatography is a more rapid separation method.
   Disadvantage—surface chromatography is not as quantitative as column chromatography.

3. H_2O

4. trigonal bipyramidal (unshared pairs are equatorial)

5. A sigma bond involves the end-to-end overlap of orbitals. Pi bonds involve a sideways overlap of p orbitals.

6. linear

7. Molecules with multiple bonds are rigid with respect to rotation of the bonded atoms. These molecules are more reactive than those with single bonds. Multiple bonding always involves the p orbitals.

8. :Ö: :S: :Ö: $\longleftrightarrow$:Ö: :S: :Ö:

9. At

10. Sc, Ti, Ni, C, F

11. a, c, d covalent
    b, e ionic

12. linear

13. $(\sigma_{2s})^2 (\sigma_{2s}^*) (\pi_{2p})^4 (\sigma_{2p})^2$

14. **a.** hexaamminecobalt(II) ion
    b. diamminecopper(II) ion
    c. diaquotetraamminenickel(II)
    d. diammineplatinum(IV) chloride
    e. diamminesilver ion

15. **a.** $RhCl_6{}^{3-}$ **c.** $Fe(CO)_6$
    b. $BeF_4{}^{2-}$ **d.** $Ni(CO)_4$

ONE MORE STEP

Page 297.

1. Oxygen: $KE = (1/2)mv^2$ $v = 4.43 \times 10^2$ m/s (see 15:1)

$$KE = \frac{1}{2} \left| \frac{32.0 \, \text{g}}{6.02 \times 10^{23} \, \text{molecules}} \right| \frac{1 \, \text{kg}}{1000 \, \text{g}} \left| \frac{(4.43 \times 10^2)^2 \text{m}^2}{\text{s}^2} \right|$$

$$= 5.22 \times 10^{-21} \text{ J/molecule}$$

Remember that 1 joule = 1 kg·m²/s²

Automobile:

$$KE = \frac{1}{2} \left| 1500 \, \text{kg} \right| \frac{(50.0)^2 \text{km}^2}{1 \, \text{hr}^2} \left| \frac{(1000)^2 \text{m}^2}{1 \, \text{km}^2} \right| \frac{1 \, \text{hr}^2}{(60)^2 \text{min}^2} \left| \frac{1 \, \text{min}^2}{(60)^2 \text{s}^2} \right|$$

$$= 1.45 \times 10^5 \text{ J}$$

2. $\dfrac{v_{hydrogen}}{v_{oxygen}} = \sqrt{\dfrac{m_{oxygen}}{m_{hydrogen}}}$, $\dfrac{v_{hydrogen}}{4.43 \times 10^2 \text{ m/s}} = \sqrt{\dfrac{32.0 \text{ g}}{2.02 \text{ g}}}$, $v_{hydrogen} = (4.43 \times 10^2 \text{ m/s}) \sqrt{15.8}$
   $= (4.43 \times 10^2 \text{ m/s})3.97$
   $= 1.76 \times 10^3 \text{ m/s}$

3. Other instruments used to measure pressure: steam gauge, depth gauge, altimeter.

Multiplying Levers or Gears
Spring
Vacuum Chamber

4. Plasma is the term applied to highly ionized gases in strong magnetic fields. This "state of matter" is used primarily to control thermonuclear reactions. The student may be interested in the "pinch effect." Further information can be found in an encyclopedia.

5. Blaise Pascal (1623-1662). French mathematician and physicist. Early investigator of the mass of air and of the properties of a vacuum. 1 millibar = 100 pascal

SOLIDS 16

AN OVERVIEW

In Chapter 16, students study particles bonded or attracted to one another in the solid state. The properties of solids are a direct consequence of their structures. Students are introduced to crystals by studying unit cells. If attention is given to charge and size, the packing arrangements can be used to explain the observed crystal structures. Students can apply this knowledge when studying the chemistry of semiconductors. The chapter concludes by showing a contrast between crystals, liquid crystals, and amorphous solids.

DEMONSTRATION INFORMATION

The demonstration offers a simple introduction to unit cells. The soap bubbles simulate the way in which atoms efficiently arrange themselves in a solid. The orientation of the bubbles conforms to an energy minimum.

Place the petri dish on the overhead. Add 10 cm³ of water and 10 drops of liquid soap to the dish. Mix well, then use a straw to gently blow bubbles. The arrangement of the bubbles demonstrates the economy and efficiency of nature.

The arrangement of the bubbles can be reinforced by using 7 pennies and seven quarters. Washers can be used instead of coins. Manipulate the seven coins of identical size on the screen of the overhead until they occupy a minimum amount of space. They will be in a hexagonal close pack arrangement. This arrangement is universal as is demonstrated by using the different sized coins. The HCC arrangement is the most efficient of solid packings. The bubbles achieved this efficiency without external manipulation.

PERFORMANCE OBJECTIVES

Goals: Students will gain an understanding of crystal structure. Students will use the concepts of bonding to explain melting point of crystals. Students will study crystal aberrations such as defects, transistors, liquid crystals, hydrated crystals, and amorphous solids.

Objectives: Upon completion of the reading and problems, and when asked to demonstrate their understanding either orally or on a written test, students will

16:1	K/P	define crystal and explain how the seven crystal systems are distinguished. **16:1**
16:2	K/P	define unit cell and space lattice, and distinguish among cubic, face-centered cubic, and body-centered cubic cells. **16:2**
16:3	K/P	identify examples of unit cells. **16:2-16:4**
16:4	K/P	describe the relationship between particle size and unit cell arrangement. **16:3-16:4**
16:5	K/P	define hexagonal and cubic closest packing and differentiate between the packing arrangements and properties for metallic and nonmetallic crystals. **16:4-16:5**
16:6	K/P	use allotropes of carbon to distinguish two different packing arrangements. **16:5**
16:7	K	define and list characteristics of macromolecules, or network crystals. **16:6**
16:8	K/P	explain the relationship of melting point to bonding type and to crystal type. **16:6**
16:9	K/P	distinguish isomorphous and polymorphous crystals and give examples. **16:7**
16:10	K	identify the types of crystal defects; define dislocations. **16:8**
16:11	K	describe the chemistry of semiconductors, and define doping. **16:9**
16:12	K	distinguish between transistors and "chips." **16:9**
16:13	K/P	define and give examples of hydrated ions, anhydrous, hygroscopic, deliquescent, and efflorescent substances. **16:10**
16:14	K/P	explain the characteristics of and give uses for liquid crystals. **16:11**
16:15	K/P	define and give examples of amorphous materials, and explain the meaning of metastable. **16:12**
16:16	K	define viscosity. **16:12**
16:17	A	voluntarily complete one or more of the One More Step activities.
16:18	A	read unassigned literature related to the chapter.

TEACHING TECHNIQUES

Section 16:1

You may wish to add to the definition of a crystal as given in the text. Crystals have well defined melting points. They also have flat faces that meet at definite angles.

Section 16:2

Three-dimensional models of unit cells are of value in helping students to visualize the diagrams in the text. Students can construct permanent models for you. Glue them together and paint them using latex paint. Emphasize that the unit cells presented in the text are not all inclusive. There are many others.

Section 16:4

The hexagonal closest packed structure can be shown on an overhead projector using seven circles having the same diameter (coins). Show students that the next layer has only three particles, then seven, then three, repeating. This demonstration will help them understand that HCP has a coordination number of 12.

Section 16:5

The hair pins can be heat treated as indicated in the red annotation. Count the number of bends each will take before breaking. This count will show quantitatively that a change occurs in the metal. You may wish to have a student give a report on heat treated metals (tempering) and the career of metallurgy.

Section 16:6

Commercially prepared models of a diamond and graphite are good investments. They help students visualize important concepts, including the relationship between structure and melting point. Point out that graphite is a good dry lubricant under heat and pressure due to its structure. The layers don't break down, but slide over each other easily.

Section 16:12

Point out that glasses fracture and produce curved surfaces. Crystals cleave and produce flat faces and definite angles. A glass is a liquid with very high viscosity (a supercooled liquid). The particles have no orderly arrangement. If there is a glass factory in your area try to obtain a large piece of cullet (broken glass) that will show the curved surfaces.

Technology and Chemistry

You can use this feature as a starting point for a more in-depth study of crystals. If your students have sufficient math backgrounds, have them research the calculations used to determine the distances between particles in a crystal from X-ray diffraction data. See the Chapter 16 Enrichment in the Teacher Resource Book.

CHAPTER END PROBLEMS

Pages 319-320.

1.

A one-to-one correspondence exists between the chlorine and sodium ions.

2. Na^+ 0.095 nm
Cl^- 0.181 nm
      $\overline{0.276}$ nm

3. The radius ratio of the positive ions and negative ions in one pair of compounds is the same as the positive to negative and negative to positive in the other pair.

4.   1 Cu @ 63.5 =   63.5
    1 S @ 32.1 =   32.1
    4 O @ 16.0 =   64.0
  5 H_2O @ 18.0 =   90.0
               $\overline{249.6}$ = 250

% $H_2O = \dfrac{90.0}{250} \times 100 = 36.1\%\ H_2O$

5. **a.** nickel sulfate heptahydrate
   b.   1 Ni @ 58.7 =   58.7
        1 S @ 32.1 =   32.1
        4 O @ 16.0 =   64.0
    7 H_2O @ 18.0 = 126.0
                 $\overline{280.8}$ = 281

% $H_2O = \dfrac{126}{281} \times 100 = 44.8\%\ H_2O$

   c. 11 O in $NiSO_4 \cdot 7\ H_2O$ @ 16.0 = 176
     % $O = \dfrac{176}{281} \times 100 = 62.6\%\ O$

6. **a.** barium hydroxide octahydrate
   b.   1 Ba @ 137   = 137.
        2 O @   16.0   =   32.0
        2 H @   1.01 =   2.02
    8 H_2O @   18.0 = 144.0
                  $\overline{315.02}$ = 315

% $H_2O = \dfrac{144}{315} \times 100 = 45.7\%\ H_2O$

   c. 10 O in $Ba(OH)_2 \cdot 8\ H_2O$ @ 16.0 = 160
     % $O = \dfrac{160}{315} \times 100 = 50.8\%\ O$

7. **a.** sodium carbonate decahydrate
   b.   2 Na @   23.0 =   46.0
         1 C @   12.0 =   12.0
         3 O @   16.0 =   48.0
   10 H_2O @   18.0 = 180.
                   $\overline{286.0}$

% $H_2O = \dfrac{180}{286} \times 100 = 62.9\%\ H_2O$

   c. 13 O in $Na_2CO_3 \cdot 10\ H_2O$ @ 16.0 = 208
     % $O = \dfrac{208}{286} \times 100 = 72.7\%\ O$

8.   hydrate   9.88 g
   anhydrous -6.68 g
      water   3.20 g

Ni 1 × 58.7 = 58.7
Cl 2 × 35.5 = 71.0
O 6 × 16.0 = 96.0
            $\overline{225.7}$ = 226

moles anhydrous $Ni(ClO_3)_2$

$\dfrac{6.68\ \cancel{g}}{}\ \Big|\ \dfrac{1\ mol}{226\ \cancel{g}} = 0.0296\ mol\ Ni(ClO_3)_2$

moles of water

$\dfrac{3.20\ \cancel{g}}{}\ \Big|\ \dfrac{1\ mol}{18.0\ \cancel{g}} = 0.178\ mol\ H_2O$

0.178 mol/0.0296 mol = 6.01
Therefore 1:6 ratio, $Ni(ClO_3)_2 \cdot 6H_2O$

9. Diamond has 3-dimensional network bonds. Thus, it is a very hard substance. Graphite has a 2-dimensional layered structure of covalent bonds. The bonds between layers are strictly van der Waals forces. Thus, its layers slide easily over one another.

10. The number and arrangement of particles differs for each.

11. the charge and radius ratio of the ions involved

12. Sodium and cesium have different radius ratios.

13. The particles of most nonmetallic elements are held together by weak van der Waals forces.

14. generally hard, strong, high melting solids; diamond and silicate compounds exhibit these characteristics

15. Some defects cause color in substances. Doping causes some substances to be better conductors.

16. The electric conductivity of silicon and germanium increases.

17. **a.** $Mg(NO_3)_2 \cdot 6H_2O$
    b. $FeSO_4 \cdot 7H_2O$
    c. $Cu(NO_3)_2 \cdot 3H_2O$
    d. $SnCl_2 \cdot 2H_2O$

18. Isomorphs have the same shape. Isomers have the same number and types of atoms but different arrangements.

19. Amorphous substances do not have a regular internal arrangement like that in crystalline solids.

Review

Page 320.
1. The gas pressure is less in the gas than in the air.

$$\frac{64 \text{ mm}}{} \left| \frac{1 \text{ kPa}}{7.50 \text{ mm}} \right. = 8.5 \text{ kPa}$$

Total pressure of the gas $= 92.7 - 8.5 = 84.2$ kPa

2. $$\frac{421 \text{ mm}}{} \left| \frac{1 \text{ kPa}}{7.50 \text{ mm}} \right. = 56.1 \text{ kPa}$$

3. In plasma, the atoms are not intact, but rather, they are broken up into individual electrons and nuclei.

4. Because it depends upon selective adsorption as do all the other chromatographic methods.

One More Step

Page 321.
1. See the *Encyclopaedia Britannica* article on crystallography. This gives an excellent treatment of the history of X-ray probing.

2. One source is the Bell Telephone Laboratories book, *Conductors and Semiconductors*, by Alan Holden. Almost any elementary electronics text deals with the subject.

3. Cholesteric compounds have two dimensional order as do smectic compounds. However, in smectic compounds the molecules are arranged in layers in which the parallel molecules are oriented with their long axes perpendicular to the plane. In cholesteric compounds, on the other hand, although the molecules are still arranged in planes, the long axes of the molecules are in the plane. Although cholesterol itself is not mesomorphic, as an alcohol, it forms many esters which are mesomorphic. Since these esters have their molecules aligned in the plane of order, the class name is cholesteric.

LIQUIDS   17

AN OVERVIEW
Chapter 17 introduces the study of liquids by developing the idea of vapor pressure in relationship to phase diagrams. We present a brief systematic view of the interactions that hold matter in the liquid state. Chapter 17 is a logical extension of Chapters 15 and 16, with the kinetic theory applied to the interactions in liquids. Keep in mind that several topics mentioned in Chapter 17 are intended to be brief and will be developed in more detail later, i.e. Le Chatelier's principle and equilibrium. At this point in the course, emphasize the apparent unchanging aspect of observed properties at equilibrium. Vapor pressure leads students to an understanding of the definition of normal boiling point. The phase diagram is an important tool in that it graphically summarizes the first part of the chapter. The ability to interpret graphs is an important skill for this chapter. The quantitative aspects of change of state are then covered. The chapter closes with the application of structure to understand the properties of liquids.

DEMONSTRATION INFORMATION

CAUTION: *Safety glasses are a must for the demonstrator and assistant (such a system could implode). Use an explosion shield.*

Obtain a 500 cm^3 round bottom flask (check carefully for hairline cracks) and a 2-hole rubber stopper. Place a thermometer in one hole and a short piece of glass tubing in the other. On the glass tube, connect a short piece of rubber tubing as shown. Fill the flask 1/4 full of water and boil unclamped at room pressure for 3-5 minutes. Have a student read the thermometer. Remove the burner and clamp the rubber tubing closed. Quickly wrap a towel around the neck of the flask, invert the flask and have a student hold 2-3 ice cubes on the bottom of the flask. Water will continue to boil in the neck of the flask. Have a student read the thermometer after a few minutes while the water is boiling in the neck of the flask under reduced pressure. Place a phase diagram on the board or overhead projector and ask students to explain their observations of the flask. Do not tell them about the reduced pressure. Let them discover the concept.

PERFORMANCE OBJECTIVES

Goals: Students will use the kinetic energy theory to explain the properties of liquids. Students will gain an understanding of Le Chatelier's principle. Students will determine the relationship between energy and change of state.

Objectives: Upon completion of the reading and problems, and when asked to demonstrate their understanding either orally or on a written test, students will

17:1	K/P	describe the process of melting. **Intro**
17:2	K/P	define vapor, and explain how a liquid or solid vaporizes in terms of the kinetic energy of their molecules. **17:1**
17:3	K	define reversible change and saturated system as these relate to dynamic equilibrium in a closed container. **17:1**
17:4	K	define equilibrium. **17:1**
17:5	K	state and apply Le Chatelier's principle. **17:2**
17:6	K/P	relate vapor pressure to intermolecular forces. **17:3**
17:7	K	define melting point and boiling point in terms of vapor pressure; define normal boiling point. **17:4-17:6**
17:8	K/P	define and give examples of sublimation. **17:5**
17:9	K/P	distinguish between volatile and nonvolatile liquids, and give examples of each. **17:6**
17:10	P	read graphs of vapor pressure versus temperature. **17:7**
17:11	K	define liquefaction, and list conditions for the liquefaction of gases. **17:7**
17:12	K/P	define and give examples of critical temperature and critical pressure. **17:7**
17:13	P	using a phase diagram, determine melting point, boiling point, critical temperature, critical pressure, and triple point for a substance. **17:8**
17:14	K	define triple point. **17:8**
17:15	K	state the relationship between energy and change of state. **17:9**
17:16	K	define heats of fusion and vaporization. **17:9**
17:17	K/P	use heats of fusion and vaporization to calculate the energy needed for various temperature changes and state conversions. **17:9**
17:18	K/P	use polarity to explain hydrogen bonding. **17:10**
17:19	K	define and describe the properties of substances having hydrogen bonds. **17:10-17:11**
17:20	K/P	explain surface tension and capillary rise on the basis of unbalanced surface forces. **17:12**
17:21	A	voluntarily complete one or more of the One More Step activities.
17:22	A	read unassigned literature related to the chapter.

TEACHING TECHNIQUES

Section 17:1

You can demonstrate vapor pressure and equilibrium using a 500 cm³ Florence flask fitted with a 3-hole stopper. Connect one side to a manometer. The other side is fitted with rubber tubing and a clamp. In the center hole, insert a dropping funnel equipped with a stopcock. Partially evacuate the flask. A difference of 150 mm Hg in the manometer levels is satisfactory. Add a few cm³ of acetone to the dropping funnel. Open the stopcock and allow a few drops of acetone to enter the Florence flask. Have a student read the mercury level every minute for 8-10 minutes then add a few more drops of acetone to establish vapor equilibrium. The flask will be cooler than room temperature because of the evaporation. The vapor pressure of acetone at 15° is approximately 20 kPa.

Section 17:2

Discuss the ice skating example presented in the text in detail. Students can understand and remember it. Stress that the expansion of water in forming the ice crystal is unique to water.

Section 17:6

The demonstration described in Section 17:9 (boiling water in a paper container) can also be used effectively here. The constant temperature during a change of state is visually reinforced because the water prevents a temperature increase to the kindling temperature of paper. Emphasize that the energy is being used to overcome attractive forces between the molecules and is not available to increase the temperature. This conceptual model can be used to introduce molar heat of vaporization (Section 17:9). A definite amount of heat will be required to overcome a definite number of attractive forces.

Section 17:9

An interesting calculation for your students is to determine the number of joules given off to the air when a rain barrel full of water freezes. The rain barrel was placed in root cellars to keep the vegetables stored there from freezing. A rain barrel holds approximately 8.7×10^7 grams of H_2O. This amount of water releases 2.9×10^{10} J. The January thaw remelts the ice and it is ready to give off more energy. Ask your students if this concept could be used as an alternative energy source.

The demonstration works best if the burner is adjusted to give a bushy blue flame. Place the paper box on a wire gauze, add the water, and heat it. The edges of the box may brown a little, but the box will remain unburned. Because of its high specific heat, the water removes the energy and prevents the paper from reaching its kindling temperature. After you pour out the steaming hot water, place the paper back on the wire gauze. The paper will dry and then burn in a short period of time.

The high specific heat of water is an important property. Large bodies of water act as storehouses for solar energy which is later released to the surrounding air and land masses.

Section 17:10

To demonstrate hydrogen bonding while reinforcing the concepts of equilibrium and Le Chatelier's principle, dissolve 1.4 g of $CoCl_2 \cdot 2H_2O$ in 30 cm^3 of H_2O. Place this solution in a 100 cm^3 graduated cylinder and slowly pour 60 cm^3 of acetone down the inside of the graduate. Observe the blue layer on top.

$$Co(H_2O)_6^{2+} + 4Cl^- \rightleftarrows CoCl_4^{2-} + 6H_2O$$
pink   blue

The acetone forms hydrogen bonds with water and in effect decreases the concentration of water on the top of the solution. The equilibrium shifts to the right to form the blue chloro complex.

Section 17:11

The hydrogen bonding that causes ice to occupy more volume and therefore be less dense is important both to ice skaters and to aquatic plants and animals. If ice were more dense, the ponds and streams would freeze from the bottom up. The plants and animals would die.

Technology and Chemistry

You can use this feature as an extension of the theme presented in Chapter 1 concerning the use of scientific knowledge. There has been much controversy concerning the use of chemical herbicides and their possible harmful effects. However, students should also consider the implications if no herbicides were used. How would this ban affect food supply, prices, and the availability of some foods?

PROBLEM SOLUTIONS

Page 329.

1. **a.** 50°C   **c.** 70°C
   b. 99°C   **d.** 48°C

Page 332.

2. **a.** $T_c = 33$ K   **d.** $P_t = 5$ kPa
   b. $P_c = 1290$ kPa   **e.** $T_m = 14$ K
   c. $T_t = 13.8$ K   **f.** $T_b = 18$ K

3. **a.** gas   **c.** liquid
   b. solid   **d.** liquid

Page 334.

4. **a.** $H = m(\Delta T)C_p =$

$$\frac{46.0\ g \mid 58.0\ °C \mid 2.06\ J}{\mid \mid g\ °C} = 5.50 \times 10^3\ J$$

b. $$\frac{46.0\ g \mid 334\ J}{\mid g} = 15\ 400\ J$$

c. $$\frac{46.0\ g \mid 100\ °C \mid 4.18\ J}{\mid \mid g\ °C} = 19\ 200\ J$$

d. $$\frac{46.0\ g \mid 2260\ J}{\mid g} = 104\ 000\ J$$

e. $$\frac{46.0\ g \mid 14\ °C \mid 2.02\ J}{\mid \mid g\ °C} = 1300\ J$$

5. $$\frac{25.4\ g \mid 61.7\ J}{\mid g} = 1570\ J$$

6. $$\frac{4.24\ g \mid 162\ J}{\mid g} = 687\ J$$

7. Cs melts at 28.4°C and boils at 678°C (Table A-3 of the Appendix)

$$\frac{45.0 \text{ g} \mid 4.4 \text{ C}^\circ \mid 0.246 \text{ J}}{\mid \mid \text{g C}^\circ} = 49 \text{ J}$$

$$\frac{45.0 \text{ g} \mid 15.7 \text{ J}}{\mid \text{g}} = 707 \text{ J}$$

$$\frac{45.0 \text{ g} \mid 650 \text{ C}^\circ \mid 0.252 \text{ J}}{\mid \mid \text{g C}^\circ} = 7370 \text{ J}$$

$$\frac{45.0 \text{ g} \mid 514 \text{ J}}{\mid \text{g}} = 23 \text{ } 100 \text{ J}$$

$$\frac{45.0 \text{ g} \mid 202 \text{ C}^\circ \mid 0.156 \text{ J}}{\mid \mid \text{g C}^\circ} = 1420 \text{ J}$$

Summing all five steps and rounding off to the proper number of decimal places = 32 600 J

8. $$\frac{5.58 \text{ kg} \mid 980 \text{ C}^\circ \mid 0.448 \text{ J} \mid 1000 \text{ g} \mid 1 \text{ kJ}}{\mid \mid \text{g C}^\circ \mid 1 \text{ kg} \mid 1000 \text{ J}}$$
= 2450 kJ

9. $$\frac{70.0 \text{ g} \mid 64 \text{ C}^\circ \mid 2.06 \text{ J}}{\mid \mid \text{g C}^\circ} = 9200 \text{ J}$$

$$\frac{70.0 \text{ g} \mid 334 \text{ J}}{\mid \text{g}} = 23 \text{ } 400 \text{ J}$$

$$\frac{70.0 \text{ g} \mid 100 \text{ C}^\circ \mid 4.18 \text{ J}}{\mid \mid \text{g C}^\circ} = 29 \text{ } 300 \text{ J}$$

$$\frac{70.0 \text{ g} \mid 2260 \text{ J}}{\mid \text{g}} = 158 \text{ } 000 \text{ J}$$

$$\frac{70.0 \text{ g} \mid 422 \text{ C}^\circ \mid 2.02 \text{ J}}{\mid \mid \text{g C}^\circ} = 59 \text{ } 700 \text{ J}$$

Sum of all five steps = 2.80×10^5 J

10. $$\frac{28.9 \text{ g} \mid 1058 \text{ C}^\circ \mid 0.386 \text{ J}}{\mid \mid \text{g C}^\circ} = 1.18 \times 10^4 \text{ J}$$

CHAPTER END PROBLEMS

Pages 342-343.

1. Above the critical temperature, T_c, no amount of pressure will cause the gas to liquefy.
The critical pressure, P_c, is the pressure that will cause the gas to liquefy at the critical temperature.

2. The triple point is the temperature and pressure at which the vapor pressures of the three phases of a substance, gas, liquid, and solid, are in equilibrium. The triple point for water = 0.61 kPa at +0.01°C. NOTE: Students will probably overestimate the temperature of the triple point for water because the slant of the solid-liquid line in Figure 17-8 has been exaggerated to emphasize that the triple point is not at 0°C and that increased pressure lowers the freezing point of water.

3. Le Chatelier's principle: If stress is applied to a system at equilibrium, the system readjusts so that the stress is reduced.
As pressure is applied to one portion of a balloon surface, another portion bulges and the increased pressure is distributed evenly over the entire balloon surface.

4. Molecules appear to vibrate about points in a solid. By chance, a molecule near the surface may undergo a collision or series of collisions which result in a velocity (direction and speed) or kinetic energy sufficiently large enough to counterbalance the attractive forces of surrounding molecules. If these forces are weak enough, the molecule "escapes" from the surface. The loss of molecules from the surface of a liquid in this manner is called evaporation. The loss of molecules from the surface of a solid is called sublimation. Camphor is an excellent example.

5. Sublimation is the change of state in which a substance passes directly from the solid to the gaseous state. Three examples: dry ice changes to CO_2 gas, naphthalene balls (mothballs) gradually disappear, and in cold weather, snow or ice sublimes. Frozen clothes hanging on a clothesline gradually become soft and flexible without becoming wet.

6. The boiling point is the temperature at which the vapor pressure of the liquid equals the atmospheric pressure. The melting point is the temperature at which the vapor pressure of the solid and liquid are equal.

7. The HBr molecule is not highly polar and does not form hydrogen bonds. HF does form hydrogen bonds and the greater attraction results in a higher boiling point.

8. In the ice crystal lattice, each oxygen atom touches four hydrogen atoms and each hydrogen atom touches two oxygen atoms (note that this follows from the formula, H_2O). In the solid, the repulsion of similar atoms results in the formation of an open lattice but as the molecular motion increases and becomes more random, the open crystal collapses, causing the molecules to move closer together and the ordered structure of the ice crystal is destroyed. This results in a decrease in volume as the ice melts and as the temperature rises from 0°C to 3.98°C.

9. Volatile substances evaporate rapidly at room temperature. Nonvolatile substances evaporate slowly at room temperature. Volatile substances have a higher vapor pressure at a given temperature than nonvolatile substances. Ether is a volatile liquid, iodine a volatile solid. Oil is a nonvolatile liquid, iron a nonvolatile solid.

10. The temperature remains at 0°C because the energy added with the warm water is absorbed by the ice and simply

causes the equilibrium to shift. Some of the ice melts and becomes liquid. The temperature does not change until all of the ice has melted. The equilibrium is then destroyed.

When the ice below 0°C is added some of the water freezes giving up energy to the ice. The ice is then warmed to 0°C. Again, the equilibrium is simply shifted, unless so much ice (low temperature) is added that all the water freezes. In that case, the equilibrium is destroyed.

11.

	x	y
B.P.	249 K	699 K
M.P.	133 K	300 K
T.P.	124 K	300 K
T_c	255 K	710 K
P_c	120 kPa	120 kPa

12. $\dfrac{86.4 \, \text{g}}{} \left| \dfrac{5.59 \text{ kJ}}{\text{mol}} \right| \dfrac{1 \, \text{mol}}{69.7 \, \text{g}} = 6.93 \text{ kJ}$

13. $\dfrac{59.5 \, \text{g}}{} \left| \dfrac{95.4 \, \text{C}°}{} \right| \dfrac{2.06 \text{ J}}{\text{g} \cdot \text{C}°} = 11\ 700 \text{ J}$

$\dfrac{59.5 \, \text{g}}{} \left| \dfrac{334 \text{ J}}{\text{g}} \right| = 19\ 900 \text{ J}$

$\dfrac{59.5 \, \text{g}}{} \left| \dfrac{100 \, \text{C}°}{} \right| \dfrac{4.18 \text{ J}}{\text{g} \cdot \text{C}°} = 24\ 900 \text{ J}$

$\dfrac{59.5 \, \text{g}}{} \left| \dfrac{2260 \text{ J}}{\text{g}} \right| = 134\ 000 \text{ J}$

$\dfrac{59.5 \, \text{g}}{} \left| \dfrac{924 \, \text{C}°}{} \right| \dfrac{2.02 \text{ J}}{\text{g} \cdot \text{C}°} = 111\ 000 \text{ J}$

Total of all five steps = 302 000 J

REVIEW

Page 343.
1. A crystal is a rigid body in which the constituent particles are arranged in a repeating pattern.
2. 1
3. FCC, BCC, HCP
4. A macromolecule is a network crystal in which each atom is bonded to its nearest neighbors throughout the entire crystal. diamond, graphite

5. A doped crystal is a better conductor of electricity than the same crystal in pure form.
6. 14
7. FCC
8. because of its collisions with the walls of its container
9. Distance = several hundred times the molecular diameter.
10. The pressure of the gas is less than that of the air.

$\dfrac{97.1 \, \text{mm}}{} \left| \dfrac{1 \text{ kPa}}{7.50 \, \text{mm}} \right| = 12.9 \text{ kPa}$

Total pressure for the gas = 98.5 − 12.9 = 85.6 kPa

11. $\dfrac{409 \, \text{mm}}{} \left| \dfrac{1 \text{ kPa}}{7.50 \, \text{mm}} \right| = 54.5 \text{ kPa}$

ONE MORE STEP

Page 343.
1. The pressure exerted on the ice by the wire causes an equilibrium shift directly under the wire, the ice melts and the wire moves downward. The water remaining above the wire is at 0°C and is no longer under pressure so it refreezes. As the wire passes through the block of ice, the equilibrium shifts first from solid to liquid, then from liquid to solid. See Section 17:2.
2. Faraday sealed crystals of a chlorine compound in a closed bent glass tube and cooled one leg of the bent tube. He heated the crystals which released chlorine gas. As the gas was evolved, pressure in the tube increased and the chlorine gas condensed to a liquid in the cooled portion of the tube. Under these conditions of pressure and temperature, chlorine is a liquid.
3. The CO_2 is under pressure in the extinguisher. When the pressure is released, the gas expands and as a result is cooled due to the Joule-Thomson effect. Each molecule which escapes causes the average K.E. to decrease, thus cooling the gas. The CO_2 is at atmospheric pressure and reduced temperature (−78°C). Under these conditions, CO_2 is a solid.

GASES   18

AN OVERVIEW
In Chapter 18, the ideal gas laws are developed with the aid of the kinetic theory model. The chapter begins with the introduction of the characteristics of an ideal gas. The behavior of an ideal gas is easy to predict. Do not allow students to finish the chapter thinking that real gases are ideal. Each ideal gas law is presented and then students are given the opportunity to develop their problem solving abilities. Students are encouraged to think through the problems rather than plugging numbers into formulas. Emphasize that STP (101.325 kPa and 0°C) has no special scientific basis, but was chosen for convenience. The chapter closes with application of the kinetic theory model to understand the properties of gases. Once again properties are seen as a consequence of a particular structure.

DEMONSTRATION INFORMATION
This simple demonstration is a good introduction to relationships between pressure, volume, temperature, and the number of moles of gas in the container. Encourage the students to think about how these variables

change as the cola can is removed from the heat, sealed by inverting in the water, and cooled. The can will be crushed quickly and with some noise. As the number of moles of water vapor decrease, and as the temperature inside the can decreases, the pressure inside the can will decrease. The pressure of the atmosphere is constant and sufficient to crush the can, thus decreasing the volume inside the can.

Students usually have no trouble explaining what happened. However, point out to them the compressibility of gases (water vapor) compared to liquids and solids which are considered to be noncompressible. This property can be related to the brake fluid in a car. You step on the brake pedal and the fluid transfers the force to the brake disc or shoe because it is noncompressible. Emphasize that gases are therefore unique in the way temperature, volume, and pressure are related. Ask students how they think pressure and volume are related based on the demonstration.

PERFORMANCE OBJECTIVES

Goals: Students will use the kinetic theory to gain an understanding of the behavior of ideal gases. Students will demonstrate a proficiency in the use of Boyle's and Charles' laws to solve temperature/pressure/volume problems. Students will differentiate between ideal and real gas behavior.

Objectives: Upon completion of the reading and problems, and when asked to demonstrate their understanding either orally or on a written test, students will

18:1	K/P	explain the distinction between ideal gases and real gases. **Intro**
18:2	K	define point masses. **Intro**
18:3	K	list standard temperature and pressure and recognize the symbol STP. **Intro**
18:4	K/P	state Boyle's law, and use it to solve problems of pressure-volume variation. **18:1-18:2**
18:5	K/P	state Dalton's law of partial pressures, and use it to find the dry volume of a gas collected over water. **18:3**
18:6	K/P	state Charles' law, and use it to solve volume-temperature variation problems. **18:4-18:5**
18:7	P	determine the volume of a given dry gas under changing conditions of temperature and pressure. **18:6**
18:8	K	define diffusion. **18:7**
18:9	K/P	explain Graham's law, and use it to determine the relative rates of diffusion of various gases. **18:7**

18:10	P	determine the density of a dry gas given the original volume, mass, and the changing conditions. **18:8**
18:11	K	list properties of real gases which lead to deviations from ideal gas behavior. **18:9**
18:12	K	define adiabatic system. **18:9**
18:13	A	voluntarily complete one or more One More Step activities.
18:14	A	read unassigned literature related to the chapter.

TEACHING TECHNIQUES

Section 18:3
Some of your students may find the ratio method of solving problems useful for calculations involving gases. The following explanation may help in presenting the ratio method.

Consider the equation for finding the area of a rectangle: $A = lw$. If we have a rectangle with width 3 and length 4, the area is 12. What will happen to the area if we double the length? The new area is 24. It was easy enough in this case to calculate the new area from the original equation. However, let us look at the problem a different way. We will use the basic equation to represent values of the original problem. That is, $A = 12$, $l = 4$, and $w = 3$. Now let the equation $A' = l'w$, where A' represents the new area and l' the new length. w remains the same because the width did not change. If we divide the first equation by the second we get

$$\left(\frac{A = lw}{A' = l'w}\right) = \left(\frac{A}{A'} = \frac{lw}{l'w}\right)\left(\frac{A}{A'} = \frac{l}{l'}\right)$$

We then solve the final equality for the new area, A'. Upon doing so we get

$$A' = A\frac{l'}{l}$$

In other words, we find the new area by multiplying the old area by the ratio of the two lengths. Should we then multiply the old area (12) by $\frac{1}{8}$ or $\frac{8}{4}$? Since the new length is greater than the old we can expect to get a new area that is greater than the old. Multiplying the old area by a fraction less than one ($\frac{1}{8}$) would give a new area less than the old. Multiplying by a fraction greater than one ($\frac{8}{4}$) will give us an area larger than the original area, so we choose the fraction greater than one.

In applying the relationships between volume, pressure, and temperature, the same kind of reasoning leads to easy solution for gas-related problems.

Section 18:5
Have students take a small balloon, blow it up and measure the circumference with a tape measure. Then,

place it in the freezer and remeasure it in one hour. This procedure will help them remember Charles' law.

Section 18:8

For uniformity, have students use the first gas named in the problem as V_1 and the second one as V_2.

Section 18:9

The cubic decimeter and the liter differ by 28 parts in a million. In 1964 international metric organizations (CIPM and CGPM) recommended that the liter should not be used in volume measurements. The cubic decimeter was adopted as the volume unit to replace it, based on the m^3 which is the SI unit of volume. For this reason, we use cm^3, dm^3, and m^3 as volume units rather than mL and L.

Section 18:10

An equation exists that takes into account the two major differences in real and ideal gases. Research conducted by van der Waals led to the equation $(P + a/V^2)(V - b) = RT$. The pressure of a real gas is less than ideal because the attractive forces delay the molecules. There are fewer collisions per second. The factor (a/V^2) is added to the pressure to correct for this change. The kinetic theory assumes that the molecules are point masses. However, they do have volume. The volume we calculate isn't totally available because some of it is occupied by the molecules. The variable (b) is the correction that is subtracted from the volume. These corrections allow us to calculate more accurate values for gases at high pressures.

Technology and Chemistry

Use this feature as a starting point in having students research current pollution standards and methods of eliminating pollutants. You may want to have your students obtain air quality data from the last ten years from the state EPA.

PROBLEM SOLUTIONS

Page 349.

1. a. $\dfrac{844\ cm^3}{} \Bigg| \dfrac{98.5\ kPa}{101.3\ kPa} = 821\ cm^3$

b. $\dfrac{273\ cm^3}{} \Bigg| \dfrac{59.4\ kPa}{101.3\ kPa} = 1.60 \times 10^2\ cm^3$

c. $\dfrac{116\ m^3}{} \Bigg| \dfrac{90.0\ kPa}{101.3\ kPa} = 103\ m^3$

d. $\dfrac{598\ cm^3}{} \Bigg| \dfrac{94.4\ kPa}{101.3\ kPa} = 557\ cm^3$

e. $\dfrac{77.0\ m^3}{} \Bigg| \dfrac{105.9\ kPa}{101.3\ kPa} = 80.5\ m^3$

2. a. $\dfrac{817\ cm^3}{} \Bigg| \dfrac{80.8\ kPa}{101.3\ kPa} = 652\ cm^3$

b. $\dfrac{50.0\ m^3}{} \Bigg| \dfrac{55.1\ kPa}{101.3\ kPa} = 27.2\ m^3$

c. $\dfrac{13.7\ m^3}{} \Bigg| \dfrac{87.1\ kPa}{101.3\ kPa} = 11.8\ m^3$

d. $\dfrac{641\ cm^3}{} \Bigg| \dfrac{93.1\ kPa}{101.3\ kPa} = 589\ cm^3$

e. $\dfrac{231\ cm^3}{} \Bigg| \dfrac{80.7\ kPa}{101.3\ kPa} = 184\ cm^3$

3. a. $\dfrac{0.600\ m^3}{} \Bigg| \dfrac{110.0\ kPa}{62.4\ kPa} = 1.06\ m^3$

b. $\dfrac{380.0\ cm^3}{} \Bigg| \dfrac{66.0\ kPa}{42.1\ kPa} = 596\ cm^3$

c. $\dfrac{0.338\ m^3}{} \Bigg| \dfrac{102.4\ kPa}{47.3\ kPa} = 0.732\ m^3$

d. $\dfrac{248\ cm^3}{} \Bigg| \dfrac{94.1\ kPa}{46.3\ kPa} = 504\ cm^3$

e. $\dfrac{0.123\ m^3}{} \Bigg| \dfrac{104.1\ kPa}{117.7\ kPa} = 0.109\ m^3$

4. a. $\dfrac{388\ cm^3}{} \Bigg| \dfrac{86.1\ kPa}{104.0\ kPa} = 321\ cm^3$

b. $\dfrac{0.873\ m^3}{} \Bigg| \dfrac{94.3\ kPa}{102.3\ kPa} = 0.805\ m^3$

c. $\dfrac{31.5\ cm^3}{} \Bigg| \dfrac{97.8\ kPa}{82.3\ kPa} = 37.4\ cm^3$

d. $\dfrac{524\ cm^3}{} \Bigg| \dfrac{110.0\ kPa}{104.5\ kPa} = 552\ cm^3$

e. $\dfrac{171\ cm^3}{} \Bigg| \dfrac{122.5\ kPa}{104.3\ kPa} = 201\ cm^3$

Page 351.

5. a. $93.3 - 1.6 = 91.7$,

$\dfrac{888\ cm^3}{} \Bigg| \dfrac{91.7\ kPa}{101.3\ kPa} = 804\ cm^3$

b. $77.5 - 1.8 = 75.7$,

$\dfrac{30.0\ cm^3}{} \Bigg| \dfrac{75.7\ kPa}{101.3\ kPa} = 22.4\ cm^3$

c. $82.4 - 2.1 = 80.3$,

$\dfrac{34.0\ m^3}{} \Bigg| \dfrac{80.3\ kPa}{101.3\ kPa} = 27.0\ m^3$

d. $78.3 - 1.4 = 76.9$,

$\dfrac{384\ cm^3}{} \Bigg| \dfrac{76.9\ kPa}{101.3\ kPa} = 292\ cm^3$

e. $87.3 - 3.6 = 83.7$,

$\dfrac{8.23\ m^3}{} \Bigg| \dfrac{83.7\ kPa}{101.3\ kPa} = 6.80\ m^3$

Pages 353-354.

6. a. $\dfrac{617\ cm^3}{} \Bigg| \dfrac{273\ K}{282\ K} = 597\ cm^3$

b. $\dfrac{609 \text{ cm}^3}{} \left| \dfrac{273 \text{ K}}{356 \text{ K}} \right. = 467 \text{ cm}^3$

c. $\dfrac{942 \text{ cm}^3}{} \left| \dfrac{273 \text{ K}}{295 \text{ K}} \right. = 872 \text{ cm}^3$

d. $\dfrac{7.12 \text{ m}^3}{} \left| \dfrac{273 \text{ K}}{988 \text{ K}} \right. = 1.97 \text{ m}^3$

e. $\dfrac{213 \text{ m}^3}{} \left| \dfrac{273 \text{ K}}{372 \text{ K}} \right. = 156 \text{ m}^3$

f. $\dfrac{5.93 \text{ m}^3}{} \left| \dfrac{273 \text{ K}}{492 \text{ K}} \right. = 3.29 \text{ m}^3$

g. $\dfrac{2.27 \text{ m}^3}{} \left| \dfrac{273 \text{ K}}{282 \text{ K}} \right. = 2.20 \text{ m}^3$

h. $\dfrac{819 \text{ cm}^3}{} \left| \dfrac{273 \text{ K}}{294 \text{ K}} \right. = 761 \text{ cm}^3$

i. $\dfrac{4.67 \text{ m}^3}{} \left| \dfrac{273 \text{ K}}{287 \text{ K}} \right. = 4.44 \text{ m}^3$

j. $\dfrac{5.94 \text{ m}^3}{} \left| \dfrac{273 \text{ K}}{352 \text{ K}} \right. = 4.61 \text{ m}^3$

7. a. $\dfrac{2.90 \text{ m}^3}{} \left| \dfrac{296 \text{ K}}{226 \text{ K}} \right. = 3.80 \text{ m}^3$

b. $\dfrac{376 \text{ cm}^3}{} \left| \dfrac{324 \text{ K}}{379 \text{ K}} \right. = 321 \text{ cm}^3$

c. $\dfrac{7.91 \text{ m}^3}{} \left| \dfrac{538 \text{ K}}{325 \text{ K}} \right. = 13.1 \text{ m}^3$

d. $\dfrac{667 \text{ cm}^3}{} \left| \dfrac{314 \text{ K}}{431 \text{ K}} \right. = 486 \text{ cm}^3$

e. $\dfrac{4.82 \text{ m}^3}{} \left| \dfrac{304 \text{ K}}{295 \text{ K}} \right. = 4.97 \text{ m}^3$

f. $\dfrac{2.97 \text{ m}^3}{} \left| \dfrac{502 \text{ K}}{345 \text{ K}} \right. = 4.32 \text{ m}^3$

g. $\dfrac{19.0 \text{ cm}^3}{} \left| \dfrac{326 \text{ K}}{56.0 \text{ K}} \right. = 111 \text{ cm}^3$

h. $\dfrac{5.18 \text{ m}^3}{} \left| \dfrac{279 \text{ K}}{349 \text{ K}} \right. = 4.14 \text{ m}^3$

i. $\dfrac{882 \text{ cm}^3}{} \left| \dfrac{455 \text{ K}}{315 \text{ K}} \right. = 1270 \text{ cm}^3$

j. $\dfrac{833 \text{ cm}^3}{} \left| \dfrac{357 \text{ K}}{300 \text{ K}} \right. = 991 \text{ cm}^3$

Page 355.

8. a. $\dfrac{7.51 \text{ m}^3}{} \left| \dfrac{273 \text{ K}}{278 \text{ K}} \right| \dfrac{59.9 \text{ kPa}}{101.3 \text{ kPa}} = 4.36 \text{ m}^3$

b. $\dfrac{351 \text{ cm}^3}{} \left| \dfrac{309 \text{ K}}{292 \text{ K}} \right| \dfrac{82.5 \text{ kPa}}{94.5 \text{ kPa}} = 324 \text{ cm}^3$

c. $\dfrac{7.03 \text{ m}^3}{} \left| \dfrac{273 \text{ K}}{304 \text{ K}} \right| \dfrac{111 \text{ kPa}}{101.3 \text{ kPa}} = 6.92 \text{ m}^3$

d. $\dfrac{955 \text{ cm}^3}{} \left| \dfrac{349 \text{ K}}{331 \text{ K}} \right| \dfrac{108.0 \text{ kPa}}{123.0 \text{ kPa}} = 884 \text{ cm}^3$

e. $\dfrac{960.0 \text{ cm}^3}{} \left| \dfrac{286 \text{ K}}{344 \text{ K}} \right| \dfrac{107.2 \text{ kPa}}{59.3 \text{ kPa}} = 1440 \text{ cm}^3$

9. a. $\dfrac{654 \text{ cm}^3}{} \left| \dfrac{277 \text{ K}}{279 \text{ K}} \right| \dfrac{65.3 \text{ kPa}}{108.7 \text{ kPa}} = 3.90 \times 10^2 \text{ cm}^3$

b. $\dfrac{2.13 \text{ m}^3}{} \left| \dfrac{273 \text{ K}}{368 \text{ K}} \right| \dfrac{103 \text{ kPa}}{101.3 \text{ kPa}} = 1.61 \text{ m}^3$

c. $\dfrac{4.76 \text{ m}^3}{} \left| \dfrac{273 \text{ K}}{279 \text{ K}} \right| \dfrac{124.5 \text{ kPa}}{101.3 \text{ kPa}} = 5.72 \text{ m}^3$

d. $\dfrac{61.4 \text{ cm}^3}{} \left| \dfrac{273 \text{ K}}{340 \text{ K}} \right| \dfrac{96.8 \text{ kPa}}{101.3 \text{ kPa}} = 47.1 \text{ cm}^3$

e. $\dfrac{164 \text{ cm}^3}{} \left| \dfrac{294 \text{ K}}{273 \text{ K}} \right| \dfrac{101.3 \text{ kPa}}{98.0 \text{ kPa}} = 183 \text{ cm}^3$

Pages 356-357.

10. $\dfrac{v_{hydrogen}}{v_{oxygen}} = \dfrac{\sqrt{m_{oxygen}}}{\sqrt{m_{hydrogen}}} = \dfrac{\sqrt{32.0 \text{ g}}}{\sqrt{2.02 \text{ g}}} = \sqrt{\dfrac{32.0}{2.02}}$

$= 3.98$

11. $\dfrac{v_{helium}}{v_{radon}} = \dfrac{\sqrt{m_{radon}}}{\sqrt{m_{helium}}} = \dfrac{\sqrt{222 \text{ g}}}{\sqrt{4.00 \text{ g}}} = \sqrt{55.5} = 7.45$

12. $\dfrac{v_{helium}}{v_{oxygen}} = \sqrt{\dfrac{m_{oxygen}}{m_{helium}}}$

$\dfrac{v_{helium}}{0.0760 \text{ m/s}} = \sqrt{\dfrac{32.0 \text{ g}}{4.00 \text{ g}}} = \sqrt{8} = 2.83$

$v_{helium} = (2.83)(0.0760 \text{ m/s})$

$\qquad = 0.215 \text{ m/s}$

13. $\dfrac{v_{He}}{v_{Ar}} = \sqrt{\dfrac{m_{Ar}}{m_{He}}} = \sqrt{\dfrac{39.9}{4.00}} = 3.16$

14. $\dfrac{v_{Ar}}{v_{Rn}} = \sqrt{\dfrac{m_{Rn}}{m_{Ar}}} = \sqrt{\dfrac{222}{39.9}} = 2.36$

Page 358.

15. a. $\dfrac{1.64 \text{ g}}{969 \text{ cm}^3} \left| \dfrac{1000 \text{ cm}^3}{1 \text{ dm}^3} \right| \dfrac{337 \text{ K}}{273 \text{ K}} \left| \dfrac{101.3 \text{ kPa}}{96.4 \text{ kPa}} \right.$

$\qquad = 2.20 \text{ g/dm}^3$

b. $\dfrac{0.530 \text{ g}}{498 \text{ cm}^3} \left| \dfrac{1000 \text{ cm}^3}{1 \text{ dm}^3} \right| \dfrac{304 \text{ K}}{273 \text{ K}} \left| \dfrac{101.3 \text{ kPa}}{103.5 \text{ kPa}} \right.$

$\qquad = 1.16 \text{ g/dm}^3$

c. $\dfrac{8.30 \text{ g}}{833 \text{ cm}^3} \left| \dfrac{1000 \text{ cm}^3}{1 \text{ dm}^3} \right| \dfrac{372 \text{ K}}{273 \text{ K}} \left| \dfrac{101.3 \text{ kPa}}{103 \text{ kPa}} \right.$

$\qquad = 13.4 \text{ g/dm}^3$

d. $\dfrac{3.69 \text{ g}}{883 \text{ cm}^3} \left| \dfrac{1000 \text{ cm}^3}{1 \text{ dm}^3} \right| \dfrac{310 \text{ K}}{273 \text{ K}} \left| \dfrac{101.3 \text{ kPa}}{115.0 \text{ kPa}} \right.$

$\qquad = 4.18 \text{ g/dm}^3$

e. $\dfrac{4.91 \text{ g}}{2540 \text{ cm}^3} \left| \dfrac{1000 \text{ cm}^3}{1 \text{ dm}^3} \right| \dfrac{298 \text{ K}}{273 \text{ K}} \left| \dfrac{101.3 \text{ kPa}}{80.4 \text{ kPa}} \right.$

$\qquad = 2.66 \text{ g/dm}^3$

16. $\dfrac{3.08 \text{ g}}{\text{dm}^3} \left| \dfrac{273 \text{ K}}{301 \text{ K}} \right| \dfrac{101.0 \text{ kPa}}{101.3 \text{ kPa}} = 2.79 \text{ g/dm}^3$

17. $\dfrac{5.01 \text{ g}}{\text{dm}^3} \left| \dfrac{325 \text{ K}}{273 \text{ K}} \right| \dfrac{101.3 \text{ kPa}}{107.0 \text{ kPa}} = 5.65 \text{ g/dm}^3$

CHAPTER END PROBLEMS

Pages 362-363.

1. An ideal gas is composed of particles which are considered point masses. These particles have no attraction for each other.

2. low pressure, high temperature

3. The gas would disappear. In reality, the gas would condense to form a liquid, then freeze into a solid.

4. The masses of the gases would be different. Thus, they would be traveling at different velocities. $KE = mv^2/2$

5. A gas exhibits the Joule-Thomson effect by cooling when released through a small opening under high pressure.

6. $\dfrac{806 \text{ cm}^3}{} \left| \dfrac{273 \text{ K}}{299 \text{ K}} \right| \dfrac{103.0 \text{ kPa}}{101.3 \text{ kPa}} = 748 \text{ cm}^3$

7. $122.0 - 3.6 = 118.4$

   $\dfrac{96.0 \text{ cm}^3}{} \left| \dfrac{343 \text{ K}}{300 \text{ K}} \right| \dfrac{118.4 \text{ kPa}}{127.0 \text{ kPa}} = 102 \text{ cm}^3$

8. $111.0 - 70.1 = 40.9$

   $\dfrac{372 \text{ cm}^3}{} \left| \dfrac{275 \text{ K}}{363 \text{ K}} \right| \dfrac{40.9 \text{ kPa}}{98.0 \text{ kPa}} = 118 \text{ cm}^3$

9. $100.8 - 0.9 = 99.9$

   $\dfrac{7.29 \text{ cm}^3}{} \left| \dfrac{295 \text{ K}}{279 \text{ K}} \right| \dfrac{99.9 \text{ kPa}}{114.3 \text{ kPa}} = 6.74 \text{ cm}^3$

10. $93.0 - 2.3 = 90.7$

    $\dfrac{30.0 \text{ cm}^3}{} \left| \dfrac{273 \text{ K}}{293 \text{ K}} \right| \dfrac{90.7 \text{ kPa}}{101.3 \text{ kPa}} = 25.0 \text{ cm}^3$

11. a. $84.1 - 1.4 = 82.7$

    $\dfrac{871 \text{ cm}^3}{} \left| \dfrac{82.7 \text{ kPa}}{101.3 \text{ kPa}} = 711 \text{ cm}^3$

    b. $115.7 - 3.4 = 112.3$

    $\dfrac{317 \text{ cm}^3}{} \left| \dfrac{112.3 \text{ kPa}}{101.3 \text{ kPa}} = 351 \text{ cm}^3$

    c. $107 - 2.3 = 104.7$

    $\dfrac{7.83 \text{ m}^3}{} \left| \dfrac{104.7 \text{ kPa}}{101.3 \text{ kPa}} = 8.09 \text{ m}^3$

    d. $111.5 - 4.0 = 107.5$

    $\dfrac{964 \text{ cm}^3}{} \left| \dfrac{107.5 \text{ kPa}}{101.3 \text{ kPa}} = 1020 \text{ cm}^3$

12. $\dfrac{325 \text{ cm}^3}{} \left| \dfrac{293 \text{ K}}{273 \text{ K}} \right| \dfrac{101.3 \text{ kPa}}{93.3 \text{ kPa}} = 379 \text{ cm}^3$

13. $101.3 - 0.6 = 100.7$

    $\dfrac{8.00 \text{ cm}^3}{} \left| \dfrac{100.7 \text{ kPa}}{101.3 \text{ kPa}} = 7.95 \text{ cm}^3$

REVIEW

Page 363.

1. It must be on the surface, heading away from the body of the liquid and have sufficient kinetic energy to overcome the attractive forces of its neighboring particles in the liquid.

2. A system at equilibrium will shift so as to relieve an outside stress.

3. change directly from solid to gas phase.

4. The molecules must be brought close enough together for van der Waals forces to take effect, and they must be slowed sufficiently for the van der Waals forces to keep them together. (cool and compress the gas.)

5.

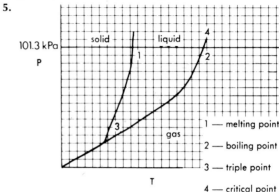

1 — melting point
2 — boiling point
3 — triple point
4 — critical point

6. Changes are occurring, but they are the reverse of each other and are occurring at the same rate.

7. the temperature at which the vapor pressures of the solid and liquid phases are equal

8. $\dfrac{1.70 \text{ g}}{} \left| \dfrac{12 \text{ C}°}{} \right| \dfrac{2.06 \text{ J}}{\text{g C}°} = 42 \text{ J}$

   $\dfrac{1.70 \text{ g}}{} \left| \dfrac{334 \text{ J}}{\text{g}} = 568 \text{ J}$

   $\dfrac{1.70 \text{ g}}{} \left| \dfrac{100.\text{C}°}{} \right| \dfrac{418 \text{ J}}{\text{g C}°} = 711 \text{ J}$

   $\dfrac{1.70 \text{ g}}{} \left| \dfrac{2260 \text{ J}}{\text{g}} = 3840 \text{ J}$

   $\dfrac{1.70 \text{ g}}{} \left| \dfrac{40.\text{C}°}{} \right| \dfrac{2.02 \text{ J}}{\text{g C}°} = 140 \text{ J}$

   Sum of all 5 steps = 5300 J

9. $\dfrac{146 \text{ g CaCl}_2}{} \left| \dfrac{1 \text{ mol CaCl}_2}{111 \text{ g CaCl}_2} = 1.32 \text{ mol CaCl}_2$

ONE MORE STEP

Page 363.

1. Student results will vary but should approximate $PV = k$, Boyle's Law.

2. The most common equation is that of van der Waals.

$$\left(P + \frac{an^2}{V^2}\right)(V - nb) = nRT$$

For N_2:
$a = 141 \text{ dm}^6 \cdot \text{kPa/mol}^2$, $b = 0.0394 \text{ dm}^3/\text{mol}$
Solving for V (assuming 1 mole) gives 0.0736 dm^3.
Solving the ideal gas equation gives 0.0560. The % is then,

$\dfrac{(0.0736 - 0.0560)}{0.0560} \left| \dfrac{100}{1} = 31.4\%$

Other equations are

Keyes $\left(P - \dfrac{a}{V - L_2}\right)(V - d) = RT$ for 1 mole

Berthelot $\left(P - \dfrac{n^2A}{TV^2}\right)(V - nB) = nRT$

GASES AND THE MOLE   19

AN OVERVIEW

Chapter 19 continues the study of gases by comparing the gas laws with experimental results obtained from real gases. The mole is reintroduced in connection with Avogadro's principle in order to develop the ideal gas equation, $pV = nRT$. Point out to students that R as a constant provides evidence for the validity of our kinetic theory model. Remind students that there is nothing special about the value 22.4 dm^3, the molar volume. It is a result of the values that were selected for standard temperature and pressure. You may want to review stoichiometry problems (mass-mass) from Chapter 6 before introducing mass-volume and volume-volume problems. Emphasize the factor-label method. Attempt to get your students to ask themselves, "Is this answer reasonable?" It helps students understand what they are trying to accomplish in the answer. The student will need this ability to master the non 1 to 1 mole ratio problems. The chapter closes by introducing the concept that gases can do work or have work done on them.

DEMONSTRATION INFORMATION

$Mg(cr) + 2HCl(aq) \rightarrow MgCl_2(aq) + H_2(g)$

This demonstration is often done as a laboratory experiment. Volume, temperature, and pressure measurements can be made and then used to introduce related calculations. A 50 cm^3 gas measuring tube works better than a graduated cylinder.

PERFORMANCE OBJECTIVES

Goals: Students will gain an understanding of the relationship between the mole and gas volumes. Students will use the concept of molar gas volumes to solve gas reaction problems. Students will learn the relationship between gases and work.

Objectives: Upon completion of the reading and problems, and when asked to demonstrate their understanding either orally or on a written test, students will

19:1	K	state Avogadro's principle. **19:1**
19:2	K	define molar volume. **19:2**
19:3	K/P	determine the molar volume of a gas using Avogadro's principle. **19:1-19:2**
19:4	K	give the molar volume of a gas at STP. **19:2**
19:5	K	state the ideal gas equation, and give the meaning of each symbol. **19:3**
19:6	P	determine the value of the ideal gas constant, R, for one mole of a gas at STP. **19:3**
19:7	P	given any three variables in the ideal gas equation—pressure, temperature, volume, or number of moles—determine the fourth. **19:3**
19:8	P	determine the molecular mass of a gas from the ideal gas equation. **19:4**
19:9	P	determine the volume of a gas in a reaction at STP given the mass of another substance in the reaction. **19:5**
19:10	P	determine the mass of a substance in a reaction given the volume of a gas in the reaction at STP. **19:6**
19:11	P	determine the volume of one reactant or product given the volume of a second substance in the reaction. **19:7**
19:12	K/P	define limiting and excess reactant, and use the concept of limiting reactant to solve stoichiometric problems. **19:8**
19:13	P	given the mass of one substance in a reaction, calculate the volume of a second substance in the reaction under nonstandard conditions. **19:9**
19:14	P	given the volume of a substance in a reaction under nonstandard conditions, calculate the mass or volume of another substance in the reaction. **19:9**
19:15	K	define isothermal. **19:10**
19:16	K	distinguish +w from −w. **19:10**
19:17	K/P	explain the relationships among gases, reversible and irreversible changes, and work. **19:10**
19:18	P	calculate the work done by a gas in isothermal and adiabatic changes. **19:10**
19:19	A	voluntarily complete one or more of the One More Step activities.

19:20   A   read unassigned literature related to the chapter.

TEACHING TECHNIQUES

Section 19:1

Small magnets representing molecules placed on a magnetic board can be used to represent a chemical reaction. They can be moved together to simulate a reaction such as $H_2 + I_2 \rightarrow 2HI$. Stress the equal temperature and equal pressure part of Avogadro's principle.

Section 19:3

The value for R is not constant when working with real gases. When it is experimentally determined, it varies in the third or fourth decimal place from the accepted value of R. You can determine R experimentally using a small disposable butane (C_4H_{10}) lighter. Submerge the lighter in water, shake it off, dry it and mass it. Fill a 100 cm^3 graduated cylinder with water and invert it in a large beaker of water. Release the gas and collect 100 cm^3 by water displacement. Shake and dry the lighter before massing it again. The difference is the mass of 100 cm^3 of butane. Correct the volume for water vapor and pressure levels. Substitute the pressure and corrected volume for P and V. Calculate the moles of butane using the mass of the gas and the molecular mass. Substitute for n in the equation. Convert the temperature of the gas to kelvin. $(PV/nT = R)$ Using the units $kPa \cdot dm^3/mol \cdot K$, you will have a close experimental value for R. One butane lighter will last 5 or 6 demonstrations. Make students aware that R has many values depending on the units used to derive it. See Teacher Resource Book for this chapter.

Section 19:8

Limiting Reactant Demonstration: Place ten empty test tubes on a cafeteria tray. Place 5 rubber stoppers that fit the test tubes in each of four small beakers (20 stoppers). Show the class that reactant A (test tube) plus reactant B (stopper) will react to form product C (a stoppered test tube). This procedure is a model of a synthesis reaction (Chapter 6). Ask the class how much product will form when the first beaker full (5) of stoppers is added to the cafeteria tray containing the 10 test tubes (answer = 5). Add another beaker full of stoppers and repeat the same question (answer = 10). Add the third and later the fourth beaker, each time asking how much product will be produced (answer = 10 both times). Ask the class which reactant was in excess (stoppers) and which one was the limiting reactant (test tubes). The students are now ready to handle the math problems with a better understanding of the concept of limiting reactants.

Section 19:10

Ask your students how we use compressed gases to do work for us. They may name the air impact wrench used to change tires. Compressed air mixed with a liquid is used for quick response on airplane flight control surfaces. This brief discussion will help students relate to the text material.

Gases At Work Demonstration: Fire rescue trucks often use large air bags, inflated by the truck's exhaust pipe, to lift large, heavy objects quickly. Place four plastic bags around a table. Place a cafeteria tray on top of the bags. Have four students blow up the bags and levitate the tray. Deflate the bags and place a large mass on the tray. Have the students inflate the bags again.

Technology and Chemistry

With supplies dwindling for some resources ocean mining is becoming more economically feasible. You can have students do further research into the costs and benefits of deep sea mining.

PROBLEM SOLUTIONS

Page 368.

1. $P = \dfrac{nRT}{V} = \dfrac{0.622\ \text{mol}}{9.22\ \text{dm}^3} \left| \dfrac{8.31\ \text{dm}^3 \cdot \text{kPa}}{\text{mol} \cdot \text{K}} \right| 289\ \text{K}$

$= 162\ \text{kPa}$

2. $n = \dfrac{PV}{RT} = \dfrac{66.7\ \text{kPa}}{} \left| \dfrac{0.486\ \text{dm}^3}{283\ \text{K}} \right| \dfrac{\text{mol} \cdot \text{K}}{8.31\ \text{dm}^3 \cdot \text{kPa}}$

$= 0.0138\ \text{mol}$

3. $V = \dfrac{nRT}{P} = \dfrac{0.684\ \text{mol}}{99.1\ \text{kPa}} \left| \dfrac{8.31\ \text{dm}^3 \cdot \text{kPa}}{\text{mol} \cdot \text{K}} \right| 282\ \text{K}$

$= 16.2\ \text{dm}^3$

4. $T = \dfrac{PV}{nR} = \dfrac{100.4\ \text{kPa}}{0.0851\ \text{mol}} \left| 604\ \text{cm}^3 \right| \dfrac{\text{mol} \cdot \text{K}}{8.31\ \text{dm}^3 \cdot \text{kPa}} \left| \dfrac{1\ \text{dm}^3}{1000\ \text{cm}^3} = 85.8\ \text{K} = -187°\text{C}\right.$

5. $P = \dfrac{nRT}{V} = \dfrac{0.00306\ \text{mol}}{25.9\ \text{cm}^3} \left| \dfrac{8.31\ \text{dm}^3 \cdot \text{kPa}}{\text{mol} \cdot \text{K}} \right| 282\ \text{K} \left| \dfrac{1000\ \text{cm}^3}{1\ \text{dm}^3} = 277\ \text{kPa}\right.$

Page 369.

6. $M = \dfrac{mRT}{PV} = \dfrac{0.922\ \text{g}}{107.0\ \text{kPa}} \Bigg| \dfrac{8.31\ \text{dm}^3\cdot\text{kPa}}{\text{mol}\cdot\text{K}} \Bigg| \dfrac{372\ \text{K}}{0.1500\ \text{dm}^3} = 178\ \text{g/mol}$

7. $\dfrac{m}{V} = \dfrac{MP}{RT} = \dfrac{32.0\ \text{g}}{\text{mol}} \Bigg| \dfrac{100.5\ \text{kPa}}{296\ \text{K}} \Bigg| \dfrac{\text{mol}\cdot\text{K}}{8.31\ \text{dm}^3\cdot\text{kPa}} = 1.31\ \text{g/dm}^3$

8. $M = \dfrac{mRT}{PV} = \dfrac{3.59\ \text{g}}{99.2\ \text{kPa}} \Bigg| \dfrac{8.31\ \text{dm}^3\cdot\text{kPa}}{\text{mol}\cdot\text{K}} \Bigg| \dfrac{304\ \text{K}}{4.34\ \text{dm}^3} = 21.1\ \text{g/mol}$

9. $M = \dfrac{mRT}{PV} = \dfrac{0.858\ \text{g}}{106.3\ \text{kPa}} \Bigg| \dfrac{8.31\ \text{dm}^3\cdot\text{kPa}}{\text{mol}\cdot\text{K}} \Bigg| \dfrac{275\ \text{K}}{0.1500\ \text{dm}^3} = 123\ \text{g/mol}$

10. $M = \dfrac{mRT}{PV} = \dfrac{8.11\ \text{g}}{109.1\ \text{kPa}} \Bigg| \dfrac{8.31\ \text{dm}^3\cdot\text{kPa}}{\text{mol}\cdot\text{K}} \Bigg| \dfrac{283\ \text{K}}{2.38\ \text{dm}^3} = 73.5\ \text{g/mol}$

Page 371.

11. $3H_2(g) + N_2(g) \rightarrow 2NH_3(g)$

$\dfrac{14.0\ \text{g}\ N_2}{} \Bigg| \dfrac{1\ \text{mol}\ N_2}{28.0\ \text{g}\ N_2} \Bigg| \dfrac{2\ \text{mol}\ NH_3}{1\ \text{mol}\ N_2} \Bigg| \dfrac{22\,400\ \text{cm}^3}{1\ \text{mol}} = 22\,400\ \text{cm}^3\ NH_3$

12. $Zn(cr) + H_2SO_4(aq) \rightarrow ZnSO_4(aq) + H_2(g)$

$\dfrac{28.0\ \text{g}\ Zn}{} \Bigg| \dfrac{1\ \text{mol}\ Zn}{65.4\ \text{g}\ Zn} \Bigg| \dfrac{1\ \text{mol}\ H_2}{1\ \text{mol}\ Zn} \Bigg| \dfrac{22\,400\ \text{cm}^3}{1\ \text{mol}} = 9590\ \text{cm}^3\ H_2$

13. $H_2(g) + Br_2(g) \rightarrow 2HBr(g)$

$\dfrac{5600\ \text{cm}^3\ H_2}{} \Bigg| \dfrac{1\ \text{mol}}{22\,400\ \text{cm}^3} \Bigg| \dfrac{2\ \text{mol}\ HBr}{1\ \text{mol}\ H_2} \Bigg| \dfrac{80.9\ \text{g}\ HBr}{1\ \text{mol}\ HBr} = 40.5\ \text{g}\ HBr$

14. $2Sb(cr) + 3Cl_2(g) \rightarrow 2SbCl_3(cr)$

$\dfrac{3570\ \text{cm}^3\ Cl_2}{} \Bigg| \dfrac{1\ \text{mol}}{22\,400\ \text{cm}^3} \Bigg| \dfrac{2\ \text{mol}\ SbCl_3}{3\ \text{mol}\ Cl_2} \Bigg| \dfrac{229\ \text{g}\ SbCl_3}{1\ \text{mol}\ SbCl_3} = 24.3\ \text{g}\ SbCl_3$

Pages 373-374.

15. $2C_4H_{10}(g) + 13O_2(g) \rightarrow 8CO_2(g) + 10H_2O(g)$

$\dfrac{401\ \text{cm}^3\ C_4H_{10}}{} \Bigg| \dfrac{13\ \text{cm}^3\ O_2}{2\ \text{cm}^3\ C_4H_{10}} = 2610\ \text{cm}^3\ O_2$

16. $\dfrac{75.2\ \text{dm}^3\ Cl_2}{} \Bigg| \dfrac{1\ \text{dm}^3\ Br_2}{1\ \text{dm}^3\ Cl_2} = 75.2\ \text{dm}^3\ Br_2$

17. $O_2(g) + 2NO(g) \rightarrow 2NO_2(g)$

$\dfrac{499\ \text{cm}^3\ NO}{} \Bigg| \dfrac{1\ \text{cm}^3\ O_2}{2\ \text{cm}^3\ NO} = 2.50 \times 10^2\ \text{cm}^3\ O_2$

18. $\dfrac{941\ \text{m}^3\ C_6H_6}{} \Bigg| \dfrac{4\ \text{m}^3\ H_2}{1\ \text{m}^3\ C_6H_6} = 3760\ \text{m}^3\ H_2$

Page 376.

19. $\dfrac{2.10\ \text{g}\ NaBr}{} \Bigg| \dfrac{1\ \text{mol}\ NaBr}{103\ \text{g}\ NaBr} \Bigg| \dfrac{1\ \text{mol}\ Br_2}{2\ \text{mol}\ NaBr} = 0.0102\ \text{mol}\ Br_2\ \text{(limiting reactant)}$

$\dfrac{9.42\ \text{g}\ H_2SO_4}{} \Bigg| \dfrac{1\ \text{mol}\ H_2SO_4}{98.1\ \text{g}\ H_2SO_4} \Bigg| \dfrac{1\ \text{mol}\ Br_2}{2\ \text{mol}\ H_2SO_4} = 0.0480\ \text{mol}\ Br_2$

$\dfrac{0.0102\ \text{mol}\ NaBr}{} \Bigg| \dfrac{160\ \text{g}\ Br_2}{1\ \text{mol}\ Br_2} = 1.63\ \text{g}\ Br_2$

20. $\dfrac{4.14\ \text{g}\ Ca_3(PO_4)_2}{} \Bigg| \dfrac{1\ \text{mol}\ Ca_3(PO_4)_2}{310\ \text{g}\ Ca_3(PO_4)_2} \Bigg| \dfrac{10\ \text{mol}\ CO}{2\ \text{mol}\ Ca_3(PO_4)_2} = 0.0668\ \text{mol}\ CO$

$\dfrac{1.20\ \text{g}\ SiO_2}{} \Bigg| \dfrac{1\ \text{mol}\ SiO_2}{60.1\ \text{g}\ SiO_2} \Bigg| \dfrac{10\ \text{mol}\ CO}{6\ \text{mol}\ SiO_2} = 0.0333\ \text{mol}\ CO\ \text{(limiting reactant)}$

$\dfrac{0.0333\ \text{mol}\ CO}{} \Bigg| \dfrac{22.4\ \text{dm}^3\ CO}{1\ \text{mol}\ CO} = 0.746\ \text{dm}^3\ CO$

21. $\dfrac{4.11\ \text{g}\ I_2}{} \Bigg| \dfrac{1\ \text{mol}\ I_2}{254\ \text{g}\ I_2} \Bigg| \dfrac{1\ \text{mol}\ S}{1\ \text{mol}\ I_2} = 0.0162\ \text{mol}\ S$

$\dfrac{317\ \text{cm}^3\ H_2S}{} \Bigg| \dfrac{1\ \text{mol}\ H_2S}{22\,400\ \text{cm}^3\ H_2S} \Bigg| \dfrac{1\ \text{mol}\ S}{1\ \text{mol}\ H_2S} = 0.0142\ \text{mol}\ S\ \text{(limiting reactant)}$

$\dfrac{0.0142\ \text{mol}\ S}{} \Bigg| \dfrac{32.1\ \text{g}\ S}{1\ \text{mol}\ S} = 0.456\ \text{g}\ S$

22. $\dfrac{116 \text{ cm}^3 \text{ Cl}_2}{} \left| \dfrac{1 \text{ mol Cl}_2}{22\,400 \text{ cm}^3 \text{ Cl}_2} \right| \dfrac{1 \text{ mol Cl}_2\text{O}}{2 \text{ mol Cl}_2} = 0.00259 \text{ mol Cl}_2\text{O (limiting reactant)}$

$\dfrac{7.62 \text{ g HgO}}{} \left| \dfrac{1 \text{ mol HgO}}{217 \text{ g HgO}} \right| \dfrac{1 \text{ mol Cl}_2\text{O}}{1 \text{ mol HgO}} = 0.0351 \text{ mol Cl}_2\text{O}$

$\dfrac{0.00259 \text{ mol Cl}_2\text{O}}{} \left| \dfrac{22\,400 \text{ cm}^3 \text{ Cl}_2\text{O}}{1 \text{ mol Cl}_2\text{O}} = 58.0 \text{ cm}^3 \text{ Cl}_2\text{O}$

Page 379.

23. a. $w = -2.303nRT \log \dfrac{V_2}{V_1}$

$= -(2.303)(1)(8.31)(298) \log \dfrac{44.5}{9.92}$

$= -3720 \text{ J}$

b. $w = -P_{ex}\Delta V$

$= -(10.0)(44.5 - 9.92) = -346 \text{ J}$

24. $w = C_v\Delta T$

$= (12.5)(8.48) = 106 \text{ J/mol}$

25. $w = -2.303nRT \log \dfrac{V_2}{V_1}$

$= -(2.303)(1.80)(8.31)(371) \log \dfrac{0.151}{0.492}$

$= 6560 \text{ J}$

26. $w = C_v\Delta T$

$= (34.2)(80.0)$

$= 2740 \text{ J/mol}$

CHAPTER END PROBLEMS

Pages 382-383.

1. $P = \dfrac{nRT}{V} = \dfrac{0.400 \text{ mol}}{10.0 \text{ dm}^3} \left| \dfrac{8.31 \text{ dm}^3 \cdot \text{kPa}}{\text{mol} \cdot \text{K}} \right| \dfrac{300 \text{ K}}{} = 99.7 \text{ kPa}$

2. $M = \dfrac{mRT}{PV} = \dfrac{1.00 \text{ g}}{105.0 \text{ kPa}} \left| \dfrac{8.31 \text{ dm}^3 \cdot \text{kPa}}{\text{mol} \cdot \text{K}} \right| \dfrac{250 \text{ K}}{0.500 \text{ dm}^3} = 39.6 \text{ g/mol}$

3. $2\text{C}_2\text{H}_6(g) + 7\text{O}_2 \rightarrow 4\text{CO}_2(g) + 6\text{H}_2\text{O}(g)$

$\dfrac{7.07 \text{ dm}^3 \text{ C}_2\text{H}_6}{} \left| \dfrac{4 \text{ dm}^3 \text{ CO}_2}{2 \text{ dm}^3 \text{ C}_2\text{H}_6} = 14.1 \text{ dm}^3 \text{ CO}_2$

4. $\dfrac{7.07 \text{ dm}^3 \text{ C}_2\text{H}_6}{} \left| \dfrac{7 \text{ dm}^3 \text{ O}_2}{2 \text{ dm}^3 \text{ C}_2\text{H}_6} = 24.7 \text{ dm}^3 \text{ O}_2$

5. $\text{CS}_2(g) + 3\text{O}_2(g) \rightarrow \text{CO}_2(g) + 2\text{SO}_2(g)$

$\dfrac{2.22 \text{ dm}^3 \text{ CS}_2}{} \left| \dfrac{2 \text{ dm}^3 \text{ SO}_2}{1 \text{ dm}^3 \text{ CS}_2} = 4.44 \text{ dm}^3 \text{ SO}_2$

6. $\dfrac{2.22 \text{ dm}^3 \text{ CS}_2}{} \left| \dfrac{1 \text{ dm}^3 \text{ CO}_2}{1 \text{ dm}^3 \text{ CS}_2} \right| \dfrac{1 \text{ mol CO}_2}{22.4 \text{ dm}^3 \text{ CO}_2} = 0.0991 \text{ mol CO}_2$

7. $\text{Ni(cr)} + \text{S(cr)} \rightarrow \text{NiS(cr)}$

$\text{Ni} = \dfrac{5.75 \text{ g Ni}}{} \left| \dfrac{1 \text{ mol Ni}}{58.7 \text{ g Ni}} = 0.0980 \text{ mol (limiting reactant)}$

$\text{S} = \dfrac{5.22 \text{ g S}}{} \left| \dfrac{1 \text{ mol S}}{32.1 \text{ g S}} = 0.163 \text{ mol}$

$\dfrac{0.0980 \text{ mol Ni}}{} \left| \dfrac{1 \text{ mol NiS}}{1 \text{ mol Ni}} \right| \dfrac{90.8 \text{ g NiS}}{1 \text{ mol NiS}} = 8.90 \text{ g NiS}$

8. $\text{CaO(cr)} + \text{H}_2\text{O(l)} \rightarrow \text{Ca(OH)}_2(aq)$

$\dfrac{4.44 \text{ g CaO}}{} \left| \dfrac{1 \text{ mol CaO}}{56.1 \text{ g CaO}} = 0.0791 \text{ mol CaO (limiting reactant)}$

$\dfrac{7.77 \text{ g H}_2\text{O}}{} \left| \dfrac{1 \text{ mol H}_2\text{O}}{18.0 \text{ g H}_2\text{O}} = 0.432 \text{ mol H}_2\text{O}$

$\dfrac{0.0791 \text{ mol CaO}}{} \left| \dfrac{1 \text{ mol Ca(OH)}_2}{1 \text{ mol CaO}} \right| \dfrac{74.1 \text{ g Ca(OH)}_2}{1 \text{ mol Ca(OH)}_2} = 5.86 \text{ g Ca(OH)}_2$

9. $2 \text{ Na(cr)} + \text{Cl}_2(g) \rightarrow 2\text{NaCl(cr)}$

$\dfrac{23.0 \text{ g Na}}{} \left| \dfrac{1 \text{ mol Na}}{23.0 \text{ g Na}} \right| \dfrac{2 \text{ mol NaCl}}{2 \text{ mol Na}} = 1.00 \text{ mol NaCl (limiting reactant)}$

$$\frac{22.4 \text{ dm}^3 \text{ Cl}_2}{} \left| \frac{1 \text{ mol Cl}_2}{22.4 \text{ dm}^3 \text{ Cl}_2} \right| \frac{2 \text{ mol NaCl}}{1 \text{ mol Cl}_2} = 2.00 \text{ mol NaCl}$$

$$\frac{1.00 \text{ mol NaCl}}{} \left| \frac{58.5 \text{ g NaCl}}{1 \text{ mol NaCl}} \right. = 58.5 \text{ g NaCl}$$

10.
$$\frac{15.7 \text{ g Fe}_2\text{O}_3}{} \left| \frac{1 \text{ mol Fe}_2\text{O}_3}{160 \text{ g Fe}_2\text{O}_3} \right| \frac{3 \text{ mol CO}_2}{1 \text{ mol Fe}_2\text{O}_3} = 0.294 \text{ mol CO}_2 \text{ (limiting reactant)}$$

$$\frac{11.2 \text{ dm}^3 \text{ CO}}{} \left| \frac{1 \text{ mol CO}}{22.4 \text{ dm}^3 \text{ CO}} \right| \frac{3 \text{ mol CO}_2}{3 \text{ mol CO}} = 0.500 \text{ mol CO}_2$$

$$\frac{0.294 \text{ mol CO}_2}{} \left| \frac{22.4 \text{ dm}^3 \text{ CO}_2}{1 \text{ mol CO}_2} \right. = 6.59 \text{ dm}^3 \text{ CO}_2$$

11.
$$\frac{6.59 \text{ dm}^3}{} \left| \frac{300 \text{ K}}{273 \text{ K}} \right| \frac{101.3 \text{ kPa}}{104.5 \text{ kPa}} = 7.02 \text{ dm}^3$$

12.
$$\frac{44.0 \text{ g}}{22.4 \text{ dm}^3} \left| \frac{273 \text{ K}}{300 \text{ K}} \right| \frac{104.5 \text{ kPa}}{101.3 \text{ kPa}} = 1.84 \text{ g/dm}^3$$

13. $w = -2.303nRT \log \dfrac{V_2}{V_1}$

$$= -(2.303)(0.316)(8.31)(290) \log \frac{22.1}{11.3}$$

$$= -511 \text{ J}$$

14. $w = C_v \Delta T$
$$= (20.8)(91.1) = 1890 \text{ J/mol}$$

REVIEW

Page 283.

1.
$$\frac{642 \text{ cm}^3}{} \left| \frac{93.9 \text{ kPa}}{109.0 \text{ kPa}} \right. = 553 \text{ cm}^3$$

2. $114.9 - 12.3 = 102.6 \text{ kPa}$
$$\frac{62.5 \text{ cm}^3}{} \left| \frac{102.6 \text{ kPa}}{97.8 \text{ kPa}} \right. = 65.6 \text{ cm}^3$$

3.
$$\frac{286 \text{ cm}^3}{} \left| \frac{333 \text{ K}}{315 \text{ K}} \right| \frac{98.1 \text{ kPa}}{42.2 \text{ kPa}} = 703 \text{ cm}^3$$

4. $\dfrac{v_{\text{O}_2}}{v_{\text{Ar}}} = \sqrt{\dfrac{m_{\text{Ar}}}{m_{\text{O}_2}}} = \sqrt{\dfrac{39.9}{32.0}} = 1.12 \text{ O}_2/\text{Ar}$

5.
$$\frac{1.34 \text{ g}}{343 \text{ cm}^3} \left| \frac{1000 \text{ cm}^3}{1 \text{ dm}^3} \right| \frac{297 \text{ K}}{273 \text{ K}} \left| \frac{101.3 \text{ kPa}}{99.9 \text{ kPa}} \right.$$
$$= 4.31 \text{ g/dm}^3$$

6. The particles of an ideal gas occupy zero volume and have no attractive forces.

7.
$$\frac{60.0 \text{ dm}^3}{} \left| \frac{585 \text{ K}}{280 \text{ K}} \right. = 125 \text{ dm}^3$$

ONE MORE STEP

Page 383.

1. In 1858 Cannizzaro wrote a paper in an Italian scientific journal in which he explained how Avogadro's hypothesis could be used in teaching chemistry. At the Karlsruhe Congress in 1860, Cannizzaro argued persuasively for the adoption of Avogadro's hypothesis and won over a number of prominent chemists. Distribution of reprints of the earlier paper helped when some of the delegates had a chance to read it at length after the congress.

2. In a time-of-flight spectrometer, a burst or pulse of ionized particles is fired through a series of electrodes or grids. Ions of different masses require varying times to transit the path; by proper interpretation of the electrode currents, the sample may be analyzed for e/m values.

3. The amount of materials to be used in the iron foundry could be calculated. Analysis could be used to determine whether the iron had the correct amount of carbon, manganese, and other additives. Knowledge of reactions to produce a given amount of a product could be used. Mostly these would involve mass-mass rather than mass-volume problems, however. Students may wish to check into the chemistry of iron more closely.

4. too low

5. none

ENERGY AND DISORDER   20

AN OVERVIEW

Chapter 20 brings together various concepts of energy and disorder which have been introduced at appropriate points earlier in the text. The purpose of Chapter 20 is to introduce students to thermodynamics through a study of state functions. Students have just completed a study of solids, liquids, and gases. Point out that mass- mass and mass-volume calculations allow laboratory results to be mathematically predicted. However, enthalpy and entropy factors must be considered in order to completely describe a system. The problem solving part of the chapter gives students the mathematical relationships among ΔH, ΔS, and ΔG and allows them to interpret the results in a practical way.

DEMONSTRATION INFORMATION

Commercially prepared thermite mixture and thermite starter are available from chemical supply houses. Use 9 or 11 cm filter paper to form a paper cone. Fill a large bucket with sand and place it in the sink of a demonstration table. Place the cone in the sand near the center of the bucket. Place the thermite mixture in the cone. Make a slight depression in the center of the thermite mixture and fill with thermite starter. Insert a Mg ribbon fuse into the starter. Mound up additional starter around the fuse. Place a safety shield between the class and the sink. *Safety goggles are a must.* Darken the room. Bend the end of the fuse over and light it with a burner. **CAUTION:** *Move away quickly since the heat generated will produce molten iron. Allow the sand and metal to cool slowly. Do not place it in a container of water.* After it has cooled for about 15 minutes, use tongs to hold the metal in a small stream of water. When it is completely cooled, use a hammer to break off the crude ceramic material that was formed when the sand melted around the iron core. Use this demonstration to emphasize that a chemist can not completely describe a chemical reaction using stoichiometry alone. Other calculations involving enthalpy, entropy, and free energy are also necessary for a more complete description.

DISPOSAL: *These chemicals are properly disposed of at a local landfill. They represent little or no hazard to the environment.*

Aluminum reacts with iron(III) oxide to produce iron metal for welding. The mixture, called thermite, is also used in anti-tank weapons. Al can be used to produce other metals. Chromium is produced in the Goldschmidt process when Al reacts with Cr_2O_3. In this reaction $\Delta H = -536$ kJ.

PERFORMANCE OBJECTIVES

Goals: Students will gain an understanding of the relationship among entropy, enthalpy, and free energy. Students will use the concepts and interrelationships of entropy, enthalpy, and free energy to solve problems dealing with any of the three. Students will gain an understanding of energy as it is related to chemical systems.

Objectives: Upon completion of the reading and problems, and when asked to demonstrate their understanding either orally or on a written test, students will

20:1	K	define isothermal and isobaric processes. **Intro**
20:2	K/P	differentiate state functions and non-state functions, and give examples of both. **20:1**
20:3	K	define internal energy and its relationship to heat and work, and give the symbols for all three quantities. **20:2**
20:4	K	list the ways energy may be transferred between a system and its surroundings and calculate the change in internal energy. **20:2**
20:5	K/P	derive the enthalpy definition from that for internal energy. **20:3**
20:6:	K/P	explain the change in enthalpy in a reaction in terms of bond breaking

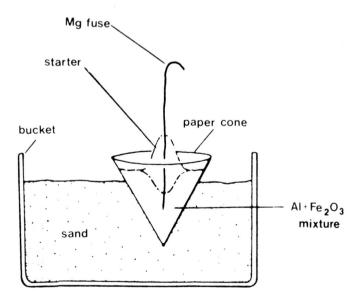

		and bond formation through use of an example. **20:3**
20:7	K	define the enthalpy of free elements. **20:4**
20:8	K	define standard enthalpy of formation. **20:5**
20:9	K/P	relate positive and negative enthalpy values to exothermic and endothermic reactions. **20:5**
20:10	K	define thermodynamics and thermodynamic stability. **20:5**
20:11	P	calculate the change in enthalpy for a given reaction. **20:6-20:7**
20:12	K/P	state and explain Hess's law. **20:7**
20:13	K	define entropy. **20:8**
20:14	K/P	predict whether a given physical or chemical change involves an increase or decrease in entropy. **20:8**
20:15	K	define free energy in terms of entropy and enthalpy. **20:9**
20:16	K	distinguish exergonic and endergonic reactions. **20:9**
20:17	K	list standard states for measuring entropy, enthalpy, and free energy. **20:9**
20:18	K	define thermodynamic equilibrium. **20:9**
20:19	P	calculate the standard entropy change for a given reaction. **20:10**
20:20	P	solve problems to find the standard entropies of compounds. **20:10**
20:21	P	calculate the standard free energy change for a given reaction. **20:10**
20:22	K/P	use standard values for the change in free energy ($\Delta G°$) to predict whether a reaction will be spontaneous or nonspontaneous. **20:9-20:10**
20:23	A	voluntarily complete one or more of the One More Step activities.
20:24	A	read unassigned literature related to the chapter.

TEACHING TECHNIQUES

Section 20:3

Remind students that the sign convention of ΔH is arbitrary. However, it is well established and accepted worldwide; $\Delta H = \Sigma(enthalpy\ of\ products) - \Sigma(enthalpy\ of\ reactants)$. You may think that thermodynamics is too sophisticated for high school students. However, it is presented in a logical manner at a low level of intensity. Most students are successful with Chapter 20 including the problem solving. We do not recommend a more detailed presentation for an introductory high school course. We will use these concepts in later chapters for reinforcement (Sections 23:11, 27:13).

Section 20:4

Emphasize the difference in the standard temperature for gases, 0°C, and for thermodynamic properties, 25°C.

Section 20:9

The earlier sections of the chapter have prepared students to understand free energy.

$$\begin{pmatrix} reaction \\ trend \end{pmatrix} = \begin{pmatrix} trend\ toward \\ min.\ enthalpy \end{pmatrix} - \begin{pmatrix} trend\ toward \\ max.\ entropy \end{pmatrix}$$
$$\Delta G \quad = \quad \Delta H \quad - \quad T\Delta S$$

Point out that the ability to predict the occurrence of a chemical reaction makes free energy an important concept and tool. Both the concentration and the nature of the reactants control the tendency for a reaction to occur.

You can demonstrate and then discuss the competition, or balance, between the two trends by burning a piece of paper. The combustion reaction releases energy. Thus, the products have minimum enthalpy (ΔH). Some of the paper was changed into a gas during combustion. The tendency toward maximum entropy is also seen ($T\Delta S$). Both of these natural tendencies worked together. To show a contrast, you can discuss when water freezes. Ice is in a state of minimum enthalpy (ΔH), but water also has a tendency to be in the vapor phase so as to have maximum entropy ($T\Delta S$). The trends are balanced and water is a liquid at room temperature. In this oversimplified example the trends compete with each other. See the *Teacher Resource Book* for an investigation that demonstrates how reaction tendencies are related to ΔG.

Section 20:10

Recommend to students that they use the table method to organize the data they obtain from Appendix A-6. Have them especially note the units (kJ versus J). Also remind them to multiply by the number of moles from the balanced chemical equation.

Technology And Chemistry

Emphasize the importance of liquid air as a raw material for the production of other gases (Group VIIIA elements) as well as oxygen and nitrogen.

PROBLEM SOLUTIONS

Page 387

1. $\Delta U = q + w = 419 + (-389) = 3.0 \times 10^1$ kJ
2. $\Delta U = q + w = -196 + (+4.20 \times 10^2) = 224$ kJ

Page 391

3. $2NO(g) + O_2(g) \rightarrow 2NO_2(g)$
$\Delta H°_{rxn} = [2(33.8)] - [2(90.4) + 0]$
$\Delta H°_{rxn} = -113kJ$

4. $4FeO(cr) + O_2(g) \rightarrow 2Fe_2O_3(cr)$
$\Delta H°_{rxn} = [2(-822)] - [4(-267) + 0]$
$\Delta H°_{rxn} = -576 \text{ kJ}$

Page 392-393

5. Hess's Law solution:

$$\begin{array}{c} \\ \Delta H_{rxn} \\ 2[C_2H_4 + 3O_2 \rightarrow 2CO_2 + 2H_2O] \qquad 2[-1323 \text{ kJ}] \end{array}$$

equation reversed:

$$2[C_2H_6 \rightarrow C_2H_4 + H_2]$$
$$\underline{2[H_2 + \tfrac{1}{2}O_2 \rightarrow H_2O]}$$
$$2C_2H_6 + 7O_2 \rightarrow 4\ CO_2 + 6H_2O$$

sign changed:

$$2[+137 \text{ kJ}]$$
$$\underline{2[-242 \text{ kJ}]}$$
$$-2860 \text{ kJ}$$

6. a. positive
b. negative
c. negative
d. positive

7. a. positive
b. negative

Page 398

8. $\Delta G°_{rxn} = \Sigma \Delta G°_{f \text{ (products)}} - \Sigma \Delta G°_{f \text{ (reactants)}}$

$$= \left[\frac{1\text{ mol BaSO}_4}{1\text{ mol BaSO}_4} \Big| \frac{(-1350)\text{ kJ}}{1\text{ mol BaSO}_4} + \frac{2\text{ mol HCl(aq)}}{} \Big| \frac{(-131)\text{ kJ}}{1\text{ mol HCl(aq)}} \right]$$

$$- \left[\frac{1\text{ mol BaCl}_2\text{(aq)}}{} \Big| \frac{(-823)\text{ kJ}}{1\text{ mol BaCl}_2\text{(aq)}} + \frac{1\text{ mol H}_2\text{SO}_4\text{(aq)}}{} \Big| \frac{(-742)\text{ kJ}}{1\text{ mol H}_2\text{SO}_4\text{(aq)}} \right]$$

$= -47 \text{ kJ}$ Yes, the reaction is spontaneous.

9. $\Delta G°_{rxn} = \Sigma \Delta G°_{f \text{ (products)}} - \Sigma \Delta G°_{f \text{ (reactants)}}$

$$= \left[\frac{1\text{ mol H}_2}{} \Big| \frac{0\text{ kJ}}{1\text{ mol H}_2} + \frac{1\text{ mol F}_2}{} \Big| \frac{0\text{ kJ}}{1\text{ mol F}_2} \right] - \left[\frac{2\text{ mol HF}}{} \Big| \frac{(-271)\text{ kJ}}{1\text{ mol HF}} \right]$$

$= +542 \text{ kJ}$, not spontaneous

10. $\Delta H°_{rxn} = \Sigma \Delta H°_{f \text{ (products)}} - \Sigma \Delta H°_{f \text{ (reactants)}}$

$$= \left[\frac{1\text{ mol Ca(OH)}_2}{} \Big| \frac{(-987)\text{ kJ}}{1\text{ mol Ca(OH)}_2} + \frac{1\text{ mol H}_2}{} \Big| \frac{0\text{ kJ}}{1\text{ mol H}_2} \right] - \left[\frac{1\text{ mol Ca}}{} \Big| \frac{0\text{ kJ}}{1\text{ mol Ca}} + \frac{2\text{ mol H}_2O}{} \Big| \frac{(-286)\text{ kJ}}{1\text{ mol H}_2O} \right]$$

$= -415 \text{ kJ}$

$\Delta G°_{rxn} = \Sigma \Delta G°_{f \text{ (products)}} - \Sigma \Delta G°_{f \text{ (reactants)}}$

$$= \left[\frac{1\text{ mol Ca(OH)}_2}{} \Big| \frac{(-897)\text{ kJ}}{1\text{ mol Ca(OH)}_2} + \frac{1\text{ mol H}_2}{} \Big| \frac{0\text{ kJ}}{1\text{ mol H}_2} \right] - \left[\frac{1\text{ mol Ca}}{} \Big| \frac{0\text{ kJ}}{1\text{ mol Ca}} + \frac{2\text{ mol H}_2O}{} \Big| \frac{(-237)\text{ kJ}}{1\text{ mol H}_2O} \right]$$

$= -423 \text{ kJ}$

$\Delta G°_{rxn} = \Delta H°_{rxn} - T\Delta S°_{rxn}$

$\Delta S°_{rxn} = \dfrac{\Delta H°_{rxn} - \Delta G°_{rxn}}{T}$

$\Delta S°_{rxn} = \dfrac{-415 \text{ J} - (-423) \text{ J}}{298 \text{ K}}$

$= 26.8 \text{ J/K}$

$\Delta S°_{rxn} = \Sigma \Delta S°_{\text{(products)}} - \Sigma \Delta S°_{\text{(reactants)}}$

$26.8 \text{ J/K} = [(x) + (131 \text{ J/K})] - [(41.6 \text{ J/K}) + (2 \text{ mol})(70.0 \text{ J/mol·K})]$
$= 77.4 \text{ J/mol·K for Ca(OH)}_2$

11. $\Delta H°_{rxn} = \Sigma \Delta H°_{f \text{ (products)}} - \Sigma \Delta H°_{f \text{ (reactants)}}$

$$= \left[\frac{2\text{ mol H}}{} \Big| \frac{218 \text{ kJ}}{1\text{ mol H}} \right] - \left[\frac{1\text{ mol H}_2}{} \Big| \frac{0 \text{ kJ}}{1\text{ mol H}_2} \right]$$

$= 436 \text{ kJ}$

$\Delta S°_{rxn} = \Sigma \Delta S°_{\text{(products)}} - \Sigma \Delta S°_{\text{(reactants)}}$

$$= \left[\frac{2\text{ mol H}}{} \Big| \frac{115 \text{ J/K}}{1\text{ mol H}} \right] - \left[\frac{1\text{ mol H}_2}{} \Big| \frac{131 \text{ J/K}}{1\text{ mol H}_2} \right]$$

$= 99 \text{ J/K}$

$\Delta G°_{rxn} = \Delta H°_{rxn} - T\Delta S°_{rxn}$

$$= 436 \text{ kJ} - \frac{298 \text{ K}}{} \Big| \frac{99 \text{ J}}{K} \Big| \frac{1 \text{ kJ}}{1000 \text{ J}}$$

$= 406 \text{ kJ}$

$$\Delta G^\circ_{rxn} = \Sigma \Delta G^\circ_{f\ (products)} - \Sigma \Delta G^\circ_{f\ (reactants)}$$

$$406 = \left[\frac{2\ \cancel{mol\ H}}{} \middle| \frac{x\ kJ}{1\ \cancel{mol\ H}} \right] - \left[\frac{1\ \cancel{mol\ H_2}}{} \middle| \frac{0\ kJ}{1\ \cancel{mol\ H_2}} \right]$$

$$x = 203\ kJ$$

CHAPTER END PROBLEMS

Page 401

$\Delta G^\circ_{rxn} = \Sigma \Delta G^\circ_{f\ (products)} - \Sigma \Delta G^\circ_{f\ (reactants)}$,
if ΔG is negative the reaction is spontaneous.

1. $\Delta G^\circ_{rxn} = [(1)(-314)] - [(1)(-260)]$
$= -54\ kJ$, spontaneous

2. $\Delta G^\circ_{rxn} = [(1)(-229)] - [(1)(-237)]$
$= 8\ kJ$, nonspontaneous

3. $\Delta G^\circ_{rxn} = [(8)(-394)] + [(10)(-237)]$
$- [(2)(-15.7)] = -5490\ kJ$, spontaneous

4. $\Delta G^\circ_{rxn} = [(2)(-53.7)] - [(1)(-86.2)]$
$= -21.2\ kJ$, spontaneous

5. $\Delta G^\circ_{rxn} = [(1)(-662)] - [(1)(-53.7)]$
$= -608\ kJ$, spontaneous

6. $\Delta G^\circ_{rxn} = \Delta H^\circ_f - T\Delta S^\circ_f$, $\Delta G^\circ_{rxn} = \Sigma \Delta G^\circ_{f\ (products)}$
$- \Sigma \Delta G^\circ_{f\ (reactants)}$
$\Delta H^\circ_{rxn} = \Sigma \Delta H^\circ_{f\ (products)} - \Sigma \Delta H^\circ_{f\ (reactants)}$
$\Delta S^\circ = \Sigma S^\circ_{(products)} - \Sigma S^\circ_{(reactants)}$
$\Delta G^\circ_{rxn} = [(2)(-177)] - [(1)(-211)] = -143\ kJ$
$\Delta H^\circ_{rxn} = [(2)(-230)] - [(1)(-265)] = -195\ kJ$
$\Delta S^\circ = \dfrac{-195 - (-143)}{298} = -0.174\ kJ = -174\ J$
$\Delta S^\circ = -174 = [(2)(x)] - [(1)(196) + (1)(223)]$
$2x = 245\ J/mol \cdot K$, $x = 123\ J/mol \cdot K$

7. $\Delta G^\circ_f = -512\ kJ$
$\Delta H^\circ_f = -568\ kJ$
$\Delta S^\circ_f = \dfrac{-568 - (-512)}{298} = -0.188\ kJ = -188\ J$
$-188 = [x] - [(3)(9.54) + (1)(192)]$
$x = 32.6\ J/mol \cdot K$

8. $\Delta G^\circ_{rxn} = [(2)(-237)] - [(2)(-118)] = -238\ kJ$
$\Delta S^\circ_{rxn} = [(2)(70.0)] + [(1)(205)] - [(2)(110)] =$
$125\ J = 0.125\ kJ$
$\Delta H^\circ_{rxn} = \Delta G^\circ_{rxn} + T\Delta S^\circ_{rxn}$
$\Delta H^\circ_{rxn} = -238 + (298)(0.125) = -201\ kJ$
$-201 = [(2)(-286)] - [2x]$
$x = -186\ kJ/mol$

9. $\Delta H^\circ_{rxn} = [2(33.8)] - [2(90.4)] = -113\ kJ$
$\Delta S^\circ_{rxn} = [2(240)] - [205 + 2(211)] = -147\ J = -0.147\ kJ$
$\Delta G^\circ_{rxn} = -113.2 - 298(-0.147) = -69.2\ kJ$
$-69.2 = 2(51.8) - 2x$
$x = 86.4\ kJ/mol$

10. $\Delta U = 622 + (-813) = -191\ kJ$

11. $\Delta U = -262 + (160.0) = -102\ kJ$

REVIEW

Pages 401–402

1. $\dfrac{163\ cm^3}{} \middle| \dfrac{52.4\ \cancel{kPa}}{68.7\ \cancel{kPa}} = 124\ cm^3$

2. $\dfrac{258\ cm^3}{} \middle| \dfrac{350\ \cancel{K}}{370\ \cancel{K}} = 244\ cm^3$

3. $\dfrac{94.5\ dm^3}{} \middle| \dfrac{316\ \cancel{K}}{319\ \cancel{K}} = 93.6\ dm^3$

4. CO_2

5. Real gas molecules occupy a finite volume and exert an attractive force on each other.

6. Equal volumes of gases at the same temperature and pressure contain the same number of molecules.

7. $V = \dfrac{nRT}{P} = \dfrac{0.161\ \cancel{mol}}{43.3\ \cancel{kPa}} \middle| \dfrac{8.31\ dm^3 \cdot \cancel{kPa}}{\cancel{mol} \cdot \cancel{K}} \middle| \dfrac{325\ \cancel{K}}{}$
$= 10.0\ dm^3$

8. $\dfrac{4.90\ \cancel{dm^3\ Cl_2}}{} \middle| \dfrac{1\ \cancel{mol\ Cl_2}}{22.4\ \cancel{dm^3 Cl_2}} \middle| \dfrac{2\ \cancel{mol\ Al}}{3\ \cancel{mol\ Cl_2}} \middle| \dfrac{27.0\ g\ Al}{1\ \cancel{mol\ Al}}$
$= 3.94\ g\ Al$

9. $\dfrac{49.5\ \cancel{g\ HCl}}{} \middle| \dfrac{1\ mol\ HCl}{36.5\ \cancel{g\ HCl}} = 1.36\ mol\ HCl$

$\dfrac{91.8\ \cancel{g\ NaOH}}{} \middle| \dfrac{1\ mol\ NaOH}{40.0\ \cancel{g\ NaOH}} = 2.30\ mol\ NaOH$

$\dfrac{1.36\ \cancel{mol\ HCl}}{} \middle| \dfrac{1\ \cancel{mol\ NaCl}}{1\ \cancel{mol\ HCl}} \middle| \dfrac{58.5\ g\ NaCl}{1\ mol\ NaCl}$
$= 79.6\ g\ NaCl$

10. $\dfrac{134\ \cancel{g\ Al(OH)_3}}{} \middle| \dfrac{1\ \cancel{mol\ Al(OH)_3}}{78.0\ \cancel{g\ Al(OH)_3}} \middle| \dfrac{1\ mol\ Na_3AlO_3}{1\ \cancel{mol\ Al(OH)_3}}$
$= 1.72\ mol\ Na_3AlO_3$

$\dfrac{635\ \cancel{g\ NaOH}}{} \middle| \dfrac{1\ mol\ NaOH}{40.0\ \cancel{g\ NaOH}} \middle| \dfrac{1\ mol\ Na_3AlO_3}{3\ mol\ NaOH}$
$= 5.29\ mol\ Na_3AlO_3$

$\dfrac{1.72\ \cancel{mol}\ Na_3AlO_3}{} \middle| \dfrac{144\ g\ Na_3AlO_3}{1\ \cancel{mol\ Na_3AlO_3}}$
$= 248\ g\ Na_3AlO_3$

11. a. 54.4 K   **d.** 54.8 K
b. 0.152 kPa   **e.** 155 K
c. 90.2 K   **f.** 5040 kPa

12. $\dfrac{8.16\ \cancel{g}}{} \middle| \dfrac{16\ \cancel{C}}{} \middle| \dfrac{2.06\ J}{\cancel{g} \cdot \cancel{C}} = 270\ J$

$$\frac{8.16\,g \mid 334\,J}{\mid g} = 2730\,J$$

$$\frac{8.16\,g \mid 100\,C° \mid 4.18\,J}{\mid \mid g\cdot C°} = 3410\,J$$

$$\frac{8.16\,g \mid 2260\,J}{\mid g} = 18\,400\,J$$

$$\frac{8.16\,g \mid 2\,C° \mid 2.02\,J}{\mid \mid g\cdot C°} = 30\,J$$

Sum of all 5 steps = 24 800 J

13. $103 - 2.5 = 100.5$ kPa dry pressure

$$\frac{37.0\,dm^3 \mid 100.5\,kPa}{\mid 103\,kPa} = 36.1\,dm^3$$

14. $\dfrac{629\,cm^3 \mid 273\,K \mid 101.0\,kPa}{\mid 297\,K \mid 101.3\,kPa} = 576\,cm^3$

15. $\dfrac{8.02\,g \mid 101.3\,kPa \mid 281\,K}{1.20\,dm^3 \mid 103.1\,kPa \mid 273\,K} = 6.76\,g/dm^3$

16. $M = \dfrac{mRT}{PV} = \dfrac{2.20\,g \mid 8.31\,dm^3\cdot kPa \mid 293\,K}{107.1\,kPa \mid mol\cdot K \mid 2.13\,dm^3} = 23.5\,g/mol$

17. $\dfrac{21.0\,g\,Zn \mid 1\,mol\,Zn \mid 1\,mol\,H_2 \mid 22.4\,dm^3}{\mid 65.4\,g\,Zn \mid 1\,mol\,Zn \mid 1\,mol\,H_2} = 7.19\,dm^3\,H_2$

18. $\dfrac{93.0\,dm^3\,Cl_2 \mid 2\,dm^3\,HCl}{\mid 1\,dm^3\,Cl_2} = 186\,dm^3\,HCl$

19. $\dfrac{10.1\,g\,Mn \mid 1\,mol\,Mn \mid 1\,mol\,H_2 \mid 22.4\,dm^3 \mid 279\,K \mid 101.3\,kPa}{\mid 54.9\,g\,Mn \mid 1\,mol\,Mn \mid 1\,mol\,H_2 \mid 273\,K \mid 123.0\,kPa} = 3.47\,dm^3\,H_2$

ONE MORE STEP

Page 403

1. Heat capacity is the heat required to raise the temperature of a certain amount of a substance a specified number of degrees, usually one.

Heat content is used in two ways by chemists: (a) The total thermal (kinetic) energy of molecules determined by their mass and velocity. (b) The enthalpy, which is the heat lost (or gained) during an isothermal reaction.

2. Work function is usually known as the Helmholtz free energy. It is represented by the letter A and is defined by the equation $A = E - TS$. It is of use principally in constant-volume systems and is not as useful as G for chemists who are usually working at constant pressure. ΔA represents the maximum work obtainable from a constant-volume, isothermal process. If $\Delta A > 0$, then work must be done on the system. In a similar manner, ΔG is the maximum work at constant pressure and temperature.

3. constant volume

4. reversible

SOLUTIONS   21

AN OVERVIEW

A study of nonreacting homogeneous mixtures is presented in Chapter 21. The mixtures of homogeneous aggregates are classified into nine groups of solutions. The properties of each group are discussed. We examine only one solvent in detail, water. Emphasize that many solvents are used in everyday practice. Solution equilibria and solution rate are studied in preparation for Chapter 23. Enthalpy of solution is presented as an application of the thermodynamic topics in Chapter 20. Molarity is reviewed from Chapter 5. The concentration units of molality and mole fraction are introduced and applied.

DEMONSTRATION INFORMATION

The demonstration is used to introduce the student to some of the unique properties of solutions when compared to suspensions. The student quickly realizes that chemical pollution of water supplies cannot just simply be filtered out as can mud and algae. The "need to know" about solutions is established.

DISPOSAL: *These chemicals are properly disposed of at a local landfill. They represent little or no hazard to the environment.*

PERFORMANCE OBJECTIVES

Goals: Students will gain an understanding of the nine homogeneous mixtures called solutions. Students will determine the factors that aid or hinder the rate of solution. Students will solve problems dealing with various means of expressing concentration of solutions.

Objectives: Upon completion of the reading and problems, and when asked to demonstrate their understanding either orally or on a written test, students will

21:1	K	state the meaning of the terms solution, solute, and solvent. **Intro**
21:2	K	recognize water as the most common solvent. **21:1**
21:3	K	define and explain the processes of dissociation and solvation. **21:1**
21:4	K	describe the mechanisms by which ionic, polar, and nonpolar solutes interact with other nonpolar and polar solutes. **21:2**
21:5	K/P	predict the solubility of a given substance in a given solvent on the basis of comparative polarities. **21:2**
21:6	K	define hydration. **21:2**
21:7	K	state the factors on which the solubility of a nonpolar solid in a nonpolar liquid depends. **21:2**
21:8	K	list and give examples of the nine possible combinations of solute-solvent pairs, based on the states of matter. **21:3**
21:9	K	distinguish miscible and immiscible. **21:3**
21:10	K	define solution equilibrium and use the concept to define saturated, unsaturated, and supersaturated solutions. **21:4**
21:11	K	describe factors which affect the rate of solution. **21:5**
21:12	K/P	state the relationship of solubility to ΔH and ΔS. **21:6**
21:13	K	describe factors which affect the extent of solution. **21:6-21:7**
21:14	K/P	distinguish dilute and concentrated solutions. **21:8**
21:15	K	define molality. **21:9**
21:16	K	define mole fraction. **21:10**
21:17	K/P	solve problems involving molarity, molality, and mole fraction of solutions. **21:9-21:10**
21:18	A	voluntarily complete one or more of the One More Step activities.
21:19	A	read unassigned literature related to the chapter.

TEACHING TECHNIQUES

Section 21:4
Demonstration: Partially fill a petri dish with water and place it onto an overhead projector. Place a crystal of $KMnO_4$ into the dish. Have the students note the purple streamers as the water is very gently stirred. You can demonstrate the effect of temperature on rate of solution by using two petri dishes side by side on the overhead. Place ice water in one, and warm water in the second dish. Put a crystal of $KMnO_4$ in each dish. Introduce the students to the equilibrium nature of dissolving by having them note how the color density changes as the distance from the crystal increases. Ask the student if the dissolving process ever stops. It only macroscopically appears to stop. This is another example of dynamic equilibrium.

Demonstration: A supersaturated solution can be prepared by adding sodium thiosulfate to hot water and letting it cool slowly. Prepare several large clean test tubes before class. Add a small seed crystal to cause crystallization to occur.

DISPOSAL: *These chemicals are properly disposed of at a local landfill. They represent little or no hazard to the environment.*

Section 21:5
Demonstration: How the rate of solution varies with surface area can be demonstrated by giving to each of three students an erlenmeyer flask containing the same mass of sugar in three different forms. In one flask place two sugar cubes. In each of the other two flasks place the same mass of granulated and powdered sugar respectively. Hand each student a graduated cylinder containing 25 cm^3 of water. Add the water to the flasks simultaneously and swirl them gently. Compare the rates by having three other students note the dissolution times using the second hand on their watches.

Demonstration: To demonstrate the temperature effect on the rate of solution place two petri dishes on an overhead projector. Into one place hot water and into the second dish place ice water. At the same time, drop a sugar cube into the water in each dish. If you do not have a sugar cube, an aspirin tablet works also.

Section 21:6

Demonstration: The effect of temperature on solubility can be demonstrated using salts with positive and negative enthalpies of solution. Mass 20g each of $Ca(CH_3COO)_2$ and KNO_3. Add each solid to 125 cm³ flasks that contain 50 cm³ of water. The calcium acetate dissolves but the KNO_3 is only partially soluble. Place both flasks on a hotplate. Heat with occasional stirring. The calcium acetate comes out of solution while the KNO_3 dissolves.

solid	solubility per 100 cm³ H_2O	
	0°C	100°C
$Ca(CH_3COO)_2$	37.4 g	29.7 g
KNO_3	13.3 g	247 g

The solubility of calcium acetate decreases with increasing temperature. It begins to crystallize out of solution at higher temperatures. The solubility of KNO_3 increases dramatically at higher temperatures. Use this demonstration to introduce your students to positive and negative enthalpies of solution, and the shape of the solubility graphs (see section 3:5).

DISPOSAL: *These chemicals are properly disposed of at a local landfill. They represent little or no hazard to the environment.*

Section 21:7

To help students visualize Henry's Law, draw some circles on the chalkboard to represent solvent molecules. In the space between the molecules, draw small three dimensional boxes (cubes) to represent volumes of a gas. Ask students about the expansion or contraction ability of a liquid. (It is much less than 3% in most solvents.) If the pressure is halved, the volume doubles. Students will see quickly that the volumes of gas will no longer fit in the space between the solvent molecules. Thus, some of the gas leaves the solution according to the law.

Technology And Chemistry

Use this feature as a practical example of solution chemistry. Students could report on current processes being researched concerning desalination of ocean water.

PROBLEM SOLUTIONS

Page 412

1. $\dfrac{193 \text{ g MgBr}_2}{5.00 \times 10^2 \text{ cm}^3 \text{ soln}} \left| \dfrac{1 \text{ mol MgBr}_2}{184 \text{ g MgBr}_2} \right| \dfrac{1000 \text{ cm}^3}{1 \text{ dm}^3} \left| \dfrac{2 \text{ mol Br}^-}{1 \text{ mol MgBr}_2} \right. = 4.20M \text{ Br}^-$

2. $\dfrac{8.28 \text{ g Ca}(C_5H_9O_2)_2}{2.50 \times 10^2 \text{ cm}^3 \text{ soln}} \left| \dfrac{1 \text{ mol Ca}(C_5H_9O_2)_2}{242 \text{ g Ca}(C_5H_9O_2)_2} \right| \dfrac{1000 \text{ cm}^3}{1 \text{ dm}^3} \left| \dfrac{1 \text{ mol Ca}^{2+}}{1 \text{ mol Ca}(C_5H_9O_2)_2} \right.$
   $= 0.137M \text{ Ca}^{2+}$

3. $\dfrac{0.523 \text{ mol CaCl}_2}{1 \text{ dm}^3} \left| \dfrac{2.00 \text{ dm}^3}{} \right| \dfrac{1 \text{ mol Ca}^{2+}}{1 \text{ mol CaCl}_2} = 1.05 \text{ mol Ca}^{2+}$

Page 413

4. $\dfrac{199 \text{ g NiBr}_2}{5.00 \times 10^2 \text{ g H}_2O} \left| \dfrac{1 \text{ mol NiBr}_2}{219 \text{ g NiBr}_2} \right| \dfrac{1000 \text{ g H}_2O}{1 \text{ kg H}_2O} = 1.82m \text{ NiBr}_2 \text{ (mol/kg} = m)$

5. $\dfrac{92.3 \text{ g KF}}{1.00 \times 10^3 \text{ g H}_2O} \left| \dfrac{1 \text{ mol KF}}{58.1 \text{ g KF}} \right| \dfrac{1000 \text{ g H}_2O}{1 \text{ kg H}_2O} = 1.59m \text{ KF}$

Page 413

6. $\dfrac{12.3 \text{ g C}_4H_4O}{} \left| \dfrac{1 \text{ mol C}_4H_4O}{68.0 \text{ g C}_4H_4O} \right. = 0.181 \text{ mol C}_4H_4O$

   $\dfrac{1.00 \times 10^2 \text{ g C}_2H_6O}{} \left| \dfrac{1 \text{ mol C}_2H_6O}{46.1 \text{ g C}_2H_6O} \right. = \dfrac{2.17 \text{ mol C}_2H_6O}{2.35 \text{ mol soln}}$

   $\dfrac{0.181}{2.35} = 0.0770 \text{ mole fraction C}_4H_4O$

   $\dfrac{2.17}{2.35} = 0.923 \text{ mole fraction C}_2H_6O$

7. $\dfrac{156 \text{ g C}_{12}H_{22}O_{11}}{} \left| \dfrac{1 \text{ mol C}_{12}H_{22}O_{11}}{342 \text{ g C}_{12}H_{22}O_{11}} \right. = 0.456 \text{ mol C}_{12}H_{22}O_{11}$

   $\dfrac{3.00 \times 10^2 \text{ g H}_2O}{} \left| \dfrac{1 \text{ mol H}_2O}{18.0 \text{ g H}_2O} \right. = \dfrac{16.7 \text{ mol H}_2O}{17.2 \text{ mol soln}}$

$$\frac{0.456}{17.2} = 0.0265 \text{ mole fraction } C_{12}H_{22}O_{11}$$

$$\frac{16.7}{17.2} = 0.971 \text{ mole fraction } H_2O$$

CHAPTER END PROBLEMS

Pages 416-417

1. a. not soluble   **d.** not soluble
   b. not soluble   **e.** not soluble
   c. miscible   **f.** miscible
Students may predict solubility in some cases because of the difference in electronegativities. Such answers are satisfactory.

2. a. slightly soluble   **d.** not soluble
   b. soluble   **e.** soluble
   c. soluble

3. $\dfrac{31.1 \text{ g } Al_2(SO_4)_3}{1.00 \times 10^3 \text{ cm}^3 \text{ soln}} \left| \dfrac{1 \text{ mol } Al_2(SO_4)_3}{342 \text{ g } Al_2(SO_4)_3} \right| \dfrac{1000 \text{ cm}^3 \text{ soln}}{1 \text{ dm}^3} = 0.0909M \text{ Al}_2(SO_4)_3$

4. $\dfrac{48.4 \text{ g } CaCl_2}{1.00 \times 10^2 \text{ cm}^3 \text{ soln}} \left| \dfrac{1 \text{ mol } CaCl_2}{111 \text{ g } CaCl_2} \right| \dfrac{1000 \text{ cm}^3 \text{ soln}}{1 \text{ dm}^3} = 4.36M \text{ CaCl}_2$

5. $\dfrac{313.5 \text{ g } LiClO_3}{2.50 \times 10^2 \text{ cm}^3 \text{ soln}} \left| \dfrac{1 \text{ mol } LiClO_3}{90.4 \text{ g } LiClO_3} \right| \dfrac{1000 \text{ cm}^3 \text{ soln}}{1 \text{ dm}^3} = 13.9M \text{ LiClO}_3$

6. $\dfrac{98.0 \text{ g } RbBr}{824 \text{ g } H_2O} \left| \dfrac{1 \text{ mol } RbBr}{165 \text{ g } RbBr} \right| \dfrac{1000 \text{ g } H_2O}{1 \text{ kg } H_2O} = 0.721m \text{ RbBr}$

7. $\dfrac{85.2 \text{ g } SnBr_2}{1.40 \times 10^2 \text{ g } H_2O} \left| \dfrac{1 \text{ mol } SnBr_2}{279 \text{ g } SnBr_2} \right| \dfrac{1000 \text{ g } H_2O}{1 \text{ kg } H_2O} = 2.18m \text{ SnBr}_2$

8. $\dfrac{10.0 \text{ g } AgClO_3}{201 \text{ g } H_2O} \left| \dfrac{1 \text{ mol } AgClO_3}{192 \text{ g } AgClO_3} \right| \dfrac{1000 \text{ g } H_2O}{1 \text{ kg } H_2O} = 0.259m \text{ AgClO}_3$

9. $\dfrac{75.6 \text{ g } C_{10}H_8}{} \left| \dfrac{1 \text{ mol } C_{10}H_8}{128 \text{ g } C_{10}H_8} \right. = 0.591 \text{ mol } C_{10}H_8$

$\dfrac{6.00 \times 10^2 \text{ g } C_4H_{10}O}{} \left| \dfrac{1 \text{ mol } C_4H_{10}O}{74.1 \text{ g } C_4H_{10}O} \right. = 8.10 \text{ mol } C_4H_{10}O$

$\dfrac{0.591}{8.69} = 0.0680 \text{ mole fraction } C_{10}H_8$

$\dfrac{8.10}{8.69} = 0.932 \text{ mole fraction } C_4H_{10}O$

10. $\dfrac{67.4 \text{ g } C_9H_7N}{} \left| \dfrac{1 \text{ mol } C_9H_7N}{129 \text{ g } C_9H_7N} \right. = 0.522 \text{ mol } C_9H_7N$

$\dfrac{2.00 \times 10^2 \text{ g } C_2H_6O}{} \left| \dfrac{1 \text{ mol } C_2H_6O}{46.1 \text{ g } C_2H_6O} \right. = 4.34 \text{ mol } C_2H_6O$

$\dfrac{0.522}{4.86} = 0.107 \text{ mole fraction } C_9H_7N$

$\dfrac{4.34}{4.86} = 0.893 \text{ mole fraction } C_2H_6O$

11. $\dfrac{5.48 \text{ g } C_5H_{10}O_5}{} \left| \dfrac{1 \text{ mol } C_5H_{10}O_5}{150 \text{ g } C_5H_{10}O_5} \right. = 0.0365 \text{ mol } C_5H_{10}O_5$

$\dfrac{3.15 \text{ g } CH_6ON_4}{} \left| \dfrac{1 \text{ mol } CH_6ON_4}{90.1 \text{ g } CH_6ON_4} \right. = 0.0350 \text{ mol } CH_6ON_4$

$\dfrac{21.2 \text{ g } H_2O}{} \left| \dfrac{1 \text{ mol } H_2O}{18.0 \text{ g } H_2O} \right. = 1.18 \text{ mol } H_2O$

$\dfrac{0.0365}{1.25} = 0.0292$ mole fraction $C_5H_{10}O_5$

$\dfrac{0.0350}{1.25} = 0.0280$ mole fraction CH_6ON_4

$\dfrac{1.18}{1.25} = 0.944$ mole fraction H_2O

12. $\dfrac{1.000 \text{ dm}^3 \text{ soln}}{} \left| \dfrac{0.780 \text{ mol Sc(NO}_3)_3}{1.000 \text{ dm}^3 \text{ soln}} \right| \dfrac{231 \text{ g Sc(NO}_3)_3}{1 \text{ mol Sc(NO}_3)_3}$

$= 1.80 \times 10^2 \text{ g Sc(NO}_3)_3$

13. $\dfrac{2.00 \times 10^2 \text{ cm}^3 \text{ soln}}{} \left| \dfrac{0.179 \text{ mol Er}_2(SO_4)_3}{1000 \text{ cm}^3 \text{ soln}} \right| \dfrac{622 \text{ g Er}_2(SO_4)_3}{1 \text{ mol Er}_2(SO_4)_3}$

$= 22.3 \text{ g Er}_2(SO_4)_3$

14. $\dfrac{1.00 \times 10^2 \text{ cm}^3 \text{ soln}}{} \left| \dfrac{0.626 \text{ mol VBr}_3}{1000 \text{ cm}^3 \text{ soln}} \right| \dfrac{291 \text{ g VBr}_3}{1 \text{ mol VBr}_3} = 18.2 \text{ g VBr}_3$

15. $\dfrac{2.50 \times 10^2 \text{ cm}^3 \text{ soln}}{} \left| \dfrac{0.0965 \text{ mol DyCl}_3}{1000 \text{ cm}^3 \text{ soln}} \right| \dfrac{270.0 \text{ g DyCl}_3}{1 \text{ mol DyCl}_3} = 6.51 \text{ g DyCl}_3$

16. $\dfrac{5.00 \times 10^2 \text{ cm}^3 \text{ soln}}{} \left| \dfrac{0.0978 \text{ mol IrCl}_4}{1000 \text{ cm}^3 \text{ soln}} \right| \dfrac{334 \text{ g IrCl}_4}{1 \text{ mol IrCl}_4}$

$= 16.3 \text{ g IrCl}_4$

17. $\dfrac{1.00 \text{ dm}^3 \text{ soln}}{} \left| \dfrac{0.0130 \text{ mol YBr}_3}{1.00 \text{ dm}^3 \text{ soln}} \right| \dfrac{329 \text{ g YBr}_3}{1 \text{ mol YBr}_3} = 4.28 \text{ g YBr}_3$

18. $\dfrac{1.00 \times 10^2 \text{ cm}^3 \text{ soln}}{} \left| \dfrac{0.528 \text{ mol Li}_2SO_4}{1000 \text{ cm}^3 \text{ soln}} \right| \dfrac{110 \text{ g Li}_2SO_4}{1 \text{ mol Li}_2SO_4}$

$= 5.81 \text{ g Li}_2SO_4$

19. $\dfrac{2.00 \times 10^2 \text{ cm}^3 \text{ soln}}{} \left| \dfrac{0.0469 \text{ mol KHC}_2O_4}{1000 \text{ cm}^3 \text{ soln}} \right| \dfrac{128 \text{ g KHC}_2O_4}{1 \text{ mol KHC}_2O_4}$

$= 1.20 \text{ g KHC}_2O_4$

20. $\dfrac{2.50 \times 10^2 \text{ cm}^3 \text{ soln}}{} \left| \dfrac{0.274 \text{ mol UO}_2(NO_3)_2 \cdot 6H_2O}{1000 \text{ cm}^3 \text{ soln}} \right| \dfrac{502 \text{ g UO}_2(NO_3)_2 \cdot 6H_2O}{1 \text{ mol UO}_2(NO_3)_2 \cdot 6H_2O}$

$= 34.4 \text{ g UO}_2(NO_3)_2 \cdot 6H_2O$

21. $\dfrac{5.00 \times 10^2 \text{ cm}^3 \text{ soln}}{} \left| \dfrac{0.512 \text{ mol HSO}_3F}{1000 \text{ cm}^3 \text{ soln}} \right| \dfrac{100 \text{ g HSO}_3F}{1 \text{ mol HSO}_3F} = 25.6 \text{ g HSO}_3F$

22. $\dfrac{1.00 \times 10^3 \text{ g H}_2O}{} \left| \dfrac{0.851 \text{ mol Fe}_2(C_2O_4)_3}{1000 \text{ g H}_2O} \right| \dfrac{376 \text{ g Fe}_2(C_2O_4)_3}{1 \text{ mol Fe}_2(C_2O_4)_3}$

$= 3.20 \times 10^2 \text{ g Fe}_2(Cl_2O_4)_3$

23. $\dfrac{1.00 \times 10^3 \text{ g H}_2O}{} \left| \dfrac{0.534 \text{ mol VOBr}_3}{1000 \text{ g H}_2O} \right| \dfrac{307 \text{ g VOBr}_3}{1 \text{ mol VOBr}_3} = 164 \text{ g VOBr}_3$

24. $\dfrac{2.00 \times 10^2 \text{ g C}_2H_6O}{} \left| \dfrac{1 \text{ mol C}_2H_6O}{46.1 \text{ g C}_2H_6O} \right| = 4.34 \text{ moles C}_2H_6O \text{ (solvent)}$

$\dfrac{4.34}{x + 4.34} = 0.510$

$x = 4.17 \text{ mol solute}$

$\dfrac{4.17 \text{ mol C}_7H_4O_2Br_2}{} \left| \dfrac{280 \text{ g C}_7H_4O_2Br_2}{1 \text{ mol C}_7H_4O_2Br_2} \right| = 1170 \text{ g C}_7H_4O_2Br_2$

25. $\dfrac{1.00 \times 10^3 \text{ g C}_4H_{10}O}{} \left| \dfrac{1 \text{ mol C}_4H_{10}O}{74.1 \text{ g C}_4H_{10}O} \right| = 13.5 \text{ mol C}_4H_{10}O \text{ (solvent)}$

$\dfrac{x}{x + 13.5} = 0.363$

$x = 7.7 \text{ mol solute}$

$\dfrac{7.7 \text{ mol C}_{14}H_{16}N_2}{} \left| \dfrac{212 \text{ g C}_{14}H_{16}N_2}{1 \text{ mol C}_{14}H_{16}N_2} \right| = 1630 \text{ g C}_{14}H_{16}N_2$

26. $\dfrac{5.00 \times 10^2 \text{ g H}_2\text{O}}{} \quad \left| \dfrac{0.614 \text{ mol LiMnO}_4}{1000 \text{ g H}_2\text{O}} \right| \dfrac{126 \text{ g LiMnO}_4}{1 \text{ mol LiMnO}_4} = 38.7 \text{ g LiMnO}_4$

27. Iodine and carbon tetrachloride are both nonpolar, while water is highly polar.

28. a. Cl^- will precipitate Ag^+ but not Na^+
 b. OH^- will precipitate Fe^{3+} but not Na^+
 c. SO_4^{2-} will precipitate Ba^{2+} but not K^+
 d. OH^- will precipitate Cu^{2+} but not K^+

29. $\dfrac{3.50 \text{ g AgCl}}{} \quad \left| \dfrac{170.0 \text{ g AgNO}_3}{144 \text{ g AgCl}} \right. = 4.13 \text{ g AgNO}_3 \text{ in mixture}$

30. Most solids having positive enthalpies of solution are more soluble in hot water than in cold. Gases with negative enthalpies of solution are more soluble in cold water.

31. Molarity is the ratio of solute to solution by volume. Molality is the ratio of solute to solvent mass.
 molarity = mol/dm³ soln
 molality = mol/kg solvent

REVIEW

Page 417

1. $\Delta H = \Sigma \Delta H^\circ_{f(products)} - \Sigma \Delta H^\circ_{f(reactants)}$
 $\Delta H = [(1)(-770) + (1)(-297) + (2)(-286)] - [(2)(-908)] = 177 \text{ kJ}$

2. $\Delta G = \Delta H - T\Delta S = -454\,300 - 298(+3.76) = -455\,000 \text{ J} = -455\text{kJ}$

3. The standard state for thermodynamic measurements is 101.325 kPa, 1M concentration, and 25°C. The standard state of a substance is its physical state under those conditions.

4. q = heat absorbed by the system
 w = work done on the system

ONE MORE STEP

Page 417

1. See page 49, Figure 3-10, for solubility curves. Any of the compounds listed on the curve can be used. The student may use 50 g of water and the corresponding amount of solute. The temperature should be measured and then increased slowly as more solute is added. By plotting a solubility curve, the student should be able to determine the substance by comparison with Figure 3-10.

2. In a 400 cm³ beaker, place about 80-90 cm³ of distilled water. Heat to near boiling. Add about 200 g of $Na_2S_2O_3 \cdot 5H_2O$ (hypo) of reagent grade. Filter while hot into a very clean 250 cm³ boiling flask. Allow the system to cool without disturbance.

3. The enthalpy of solution increases with concentration. The curve is asymptotic to 54.3 kJ/mol for the anhydrous salt. The dodecahydrate is formed. If the $Na_3PO_4 \cdot 12H_2O$ is dissolved, the curve becomes asymptotic to -67.2 kJ/mol.

COLLIGATIVE AND COLLOIDAL PROPERTIES   22

AN OVERVIEW

The chapter begins with a practical discussion of Raoult's law. The problem solving techniques presented enable students to calculate the freezing point depressions and boiling point elevations as well as determine experimentally the molecular mass of an unknown solute. Osmotic pressure as a colligative property is also introduced. An introduction to colloids concludes the chapter. This study focuses on the properties of colloids as a consequence of their structure.

DEMONSTRATION INFORMATION

Attach a U-tube to each of three side arm vacuum flasks. Half fill the U-tube with colored water. Place 50.0

cm^3 of H_2O in each flask. Stopper the flask and observe the water level in the U-tube. The first flask has pure water in it. Into the second flask place 10.00 g of sucrose. Stopper the flask and gently swirl it to dissolve the sugar. Note the levels in the U-tube. To the third flask, add 3.25 g NaCl, stopper and swirl to dissolve. Also note the levels in the U-tube. Discuss the relative vapor pressure lowering effects. Use the demonstration to introduce Raoult's law.

Colligative properties depend on the number of particles rather than their nature. The 10.00 g of sugar is stoichiometrically equivalent to 3.25 g of NaCl (i.e. both amounts represent 0.0556 mole of compound); however the salt dissociates into 0.0556 mole of Na^+ and 0.0556 mole of Cl^-. The salt solution contains twice as many particles than the sugar solution. The results support Raoult's law.

According to Raoult's law, the vapor pressure of a solvent depends on the mole fraction of the solvent. The lowering of the vapor pressure causes the boiling point of the solution to be higher than that of the pure solvent. The freezing point is lowered.

The mole fraction of water in the sugar solution is

$$\frac{\text{moles } H_2O}{\text{moles } H_2O + \text{moles sugar}}$$

$$= \frac{50.00 \text{ g} / 18.0 \text{ g/mol}}{(50.00 \text{ g}/18.0 \text{ g/mol}) + (10.00 \text{ g}/180 \text{ g/mol})}$$

$$= \frac{2.78 \text{ mol}}{2.78 \text{ mol} + 0.0556 \text{ mol}} = 0.979.$$

The mole fraction of water in the NaCl solution is

$$\frac{\text{moles } H_2O}{\text{moles } H_2O + \text{moles NaCl}}$$

$$= \frac{2.78 \text{ mol}}{2.78 \text{ mol} + 2(3.30 \text{ g}/58.5 \text{ g/mol})}$$

$$= \frac{2.78 \text{ mol}}{2.78 \text{ mol} + 0.113 \text{ mol}} = 0.962.$$

The mole fraction of pure water is 1.00. Since the mole fraction of water in the salt solution is less than that in the sugar solution, the salt solution will boil at a higher temperature and freeze at a lower temperature than the sugar solution. Ask students if there is any difference between summer coolant and winter antifreeze used in car radiators. Ethylene glycol serves as a coolant and an antifreeze because of Raoult's law.

PERFORMANCE OBJECTIVES

Goals: Students will gain an understanding of the properties of solutions that depend upon the number of particles in solution. Students will calculate boiling and freezing points for solutions of known concentrations and vice versa. Students will differentiate between solutions and colloids.

Objectives: Upon completion of the reading and problems, and when asked to demonstrate their understanding either orally or on a written test, students will

22:1	K	give a definition of colligative properties and list four colligative properties of solutions. **22:1**
22:2	K	give both a verbal and a mathematical statement of Raoult's law. **22:1**
22:3	K	define ideal and nonideal solutions. **22:1-22:7**
22:4	K	define fractional distillation. **22:2**
22:5	K/P	use Raoult's law to explain and solve problems related to vapor pressure lowering in solutions and fractional distillation. **22:1-22:2**
22:6	K	define boiling point and freezing point. **22:3**
22:7	K/P	solve problems related to boiling point elevation, freezing point depression, osmotic pressure, and the use of colligative properties in molecular mass determination. **22:3-22:6**
22:8	K	compare the freezing and boiling points of solutions and pure liquids. **22:3-22:4**
22:9	K	define molal boiling point constant and molal freezing point constant. **22:4**
22:10	K	define osmosis, semipermeable membrane, and osmotic pressure. **22:6**
22:11	K	define ion activity, and relate the concept of ion activity to deviations from ideal behavior. **22:7**
22:12	K	define colloids and crystalloids. **22:8**
22:13	K	distinguish the dispersed and continuous phases in a colloid. **22:8-22:9**
22:14	K	describe the characteristics of colloids and their types, e.g., emulsions, gels. **22:8-22:10**
22:15	K	define colloid chemistry. **22:9**
22:16	K	differentiate among the characteristics of solutions,

suspensions, and colloids.
22:9-22:10

22:17   K   list and define the properties associated with colloids, i.e., Brownian motion, the Tyndall effect, adsorption, and electrophoresis. **22:10**

22:18   A   voluntarily complete one or more of the One More Step activities.

22:19   A   read unassigned literature related to the chapter.

TEACHING TECHNIQUES

Section 22:5

In actual practice in organic chemistry, camphor is often used as the solvent in molecular mass determination because it has a freezing point constant of 39.7 C°/mol (for water, this value is 1.86 C°). The temperature change is therefore easier to observe accurately.

Section 22:10

Demonstration: The demonstration shows the presence of colloidal sulfur and the tendency of light of longer wavelengths (red) to bend. This will occur when the 1 cm^3 of conc. HCl is added to the 1 g of $Na_2S_2O_3$ dissolved in the water in the 150 cm^3 beaker. Students will notice that the liquid becomes white as the colloidal sulfur forms. They will also see that the projected, transmitted light gets dimmer as it shifts to the red color. This resembles the color of the setting sun. The hole in the cardboard which covers the overhead projector must be slightly smaller than the beaker that sits over it. The chemical reactions are

$$Na_2S_2O_3(aq) + 2HCl(aq) \rightarrow H_2S_2O_3(aq) + 2NaCl(aq)$$
$$H_2S_2O_3(aq) \rightarrow H_2O(l) + SO_2(g) + S(cr).$$

The property of a colloid to scatter light can be observed at night. Students have seen the sweeping search lights used to attract people to grand openings. They have observed the Tyndall effect. The light beam is visible because the colloidal sized particles of moisture and pollutants scatter the light. Ask your students if the beam would be visible in clean dry air, or in outer space? No.

DISPOSAL: *These chemicals are properly disposed of at a local landfill. They represent little or no hazard to the environment.*

Demonstration: Into each of two tall cylinders, pour a solution of $NaHCO_3$. Add 2-3 g of licorice extract to one cylinder. Then add $Al_2(SO_4)_3$ solution to each and observe the stabilizing action of colloids as the CO_2 bubbles subside rapidly in one of the cylinders. This principle is used in fire extinguishers.

Technology And Chemistry

This feature provides some exposure to organic compounds as well as uses of nitrogen compounds.

PROBLEM SOLUTIONS

Page 421

1. v.p. H_2O @ 25°C = 3.2 kPa
   v.p. soln = (3.2 kPa)(1 − 0.163) = 2.7 kPa

2. v.p. ethanal = (86.3 kPa)(0.300) = 25.9 kPa
   v.p. methanol = (11.6 kPa)(0.700) = 8.12 kPa
   v.p. soln = 25.9 + 8.12 = 34.0 kPa

Page 426

$\Delta T_{FP} = mK_{FP}, \Delta T_{BP} = mK_{BP}$

3. $\dfrac{25.5 \text{ g } C_7H_{11}NO_7S}{1.00 \times 10^2 \text{ g } H_2O} \left| \dfrac{1 \text{ mol } C_7H_{11}NO_7S}{253 \text{ g } C_7H_{11}NO_7S} \right| \dfrac{1000 \text{ g}}{1 \text{ kg}} = 1.01m$

   $\Delta T_{FP} = (1.01)(1.86) = 1.88$ C°
   $\Delta T_{BP} = (1.01)(0.512) = 0.517$ C°
   $FP = 0 - 1.88 = -1.88°C$
   $BP = 100 + 0.517 = 100.517°C$

4. $\dfrac{1.00 \times 10^2 \text{ g } C_{10}H_8O_6S_2}{1.00 \times 10^2 \text{ g } H_2O} \left| \dfrac{1 \text{ mol } C_{10}H_8O_6S_2}{288 \text{ g } C_{10}H_8O_6S_2} \right| \dfrac{1000 \text{ g}}{1 \text{ kg}} = 3.47m$

   $\Delta T_{FP} = (3.47)(1.86) = 6.45$ C°
   $\Delta T_{BP} = (3.47)(0.512) = 1.78$ C°
   $FP = 0 - 6.45 = -6.45°C$
   $BP = 100 + 1.78 = 101.78°C$

5. $\dfrac{21.6 \text{ g } NiSO_4}{1.00 \times 10^2 \text{ g } H_2O} \left| \dfrac{1 \text{ mol } NiSO_4}{155 \text{ g } NiSO_4} \right| \dfrac{2 \text{ mol ions}}{1 \text{ mol } NiSO_4} \left| \dfrac{1000 \text{ g}}{1 \text{ kg}} \right. = 2.79m$

   $\Delta T_{FP} = (2.79)(1.86) = 5.19$ C°
   $\Delta T_{BP} = (2.79)(0.512) = 1.43$ C°
   $FP = 0 - 5.19 = -5.19°C$
   $BP = 100 + 1.43 = 101.43°C$

6. $\dfrac{77.0\ \text{g Mg(ClO}_4)_2}{2.00 \times 10^2\ \text{g H}_2\text{O}} \left|\ \dfrac{1\ \text{mol Mg(ClO}_4)_2}{223\ \text{g Mg(ClO}_4)_2}\ \right|\ \dfrac{3\ \text{mol ions}}{1\ \text{mol Mg(ClO}_4)_2}\ \left|\ \dfrac{1000\ \text{g}}{1\ \text{kg}}\right. = 5.18\ m$

$\Delta T_{\text{FP}} = (5.18)(1.86) = 9.63\ \text{C}°$
$\Delta T_{\text{BP}} = (5.18)(0.512) = 2.65\ \text{C}°$
$FP = 0 - 9.63 = -9.63°\text{C}$
$BP = 100 + 2.65 = 102.65°\text{C}$

7. $\dfrac{41.3\ \text{g C}_{15}\text{H}_9\text{NO}_4}{1.00 \times 10^2\ \text{g C}_6\text{H}_5\text{NO}_2}\ \left|\ \dfrac{1\ \text{mol C}_{15}\text{H}_9\text{NO}_4}{267\ \text{g C}_{15}\text{H}_9\text{NO}_4}\ \right|\ \dfrac{1000\ \text{g}}{1\ \text{kg}} = 1.55m$

$\Delta T_{\text{FP}} = (1.55)(7.00) = 10.9\ \text{C}°$
$\Delta T_{\text{BP}} = (1.55)(5.24) = 8.12\ \text{C}°$
$FP = 5.7 - 10.9 = -5.2\ \text{C}°$
$BP = 210.8 + 8.12 = 219\ \text{C}°$

Pages 426-427

8. $\dfrac{0.430\ \text{C}°}{1.86\ \text{C}°}\ \left|\ \dfrac{1\ \text{mol solute}}{1\ \text{kg H}_2\text{O}}\right. = 0.231\ \text{mol solute/kg H}_2\text{O}$

$\dfrac{8.02\ \text{g solute}}{861\ \text{g H}_2\text{O}}\ \left|\ \dfrac{1000\ \text{g H}_2\text{O}}{1\ \text{kg H}_2\text{O}}\right.\ 9.31\ \text{g solute/kg H}_2\text{O},$

$\dfrac{9.31\ \text{g}}{0.231\ \text{mol}} = 40.3\ \text{g/mol}$

9. $\dfrac{0.680\ \text{C}°}{0.512\ \text{C}°}\ \left|\ \dfrac{1\ \text{mol solute}}{1\ \text{kg H}_2\text{O}}\right. = 1.33\ \text{mol solute/kg H}_2\text{O}$

$\dfrac{64.3\ \text{g solute}}{3.90 \times 10^2\ \text{g H}_2\text{O}}\ \left|\ \dfrac{1000\ \text{g H}_2\text{O}}{1\ \text{kg H}_2\text{O}}\ \right|\ \dfrac{1\ \text{kg H}_2\text{O}}{1.33\ \text{mol solute}} = 1.24\ \text{g/mol}$

10. $\dfrac{3.1\ \text{C}°}{3.90\ \text{C}°}\ \left|\ \dfrac{1\ \text{mol solute}}{1\ \text{kg CH}_3\text{COOH}}\right. = 0.79\ \text{mol solute/kg CH}_3\text{COOH}$

$\dfrac{20.8\ \text{g}}{128\ \text{g CH}_3\text{COOH}}\ \left|\ \dfrac{1000\ \text{g CH}_3\text{COOH}}{1\ \text{kg CH}_3\text{COOH}}\right. = 163\ \text{g/kg CH}_3\text{COOH}$

$\dfrac{163\ \text{g}}{0.79\ \text{mol}} = 210\ \text{g/mol}$

11. $\dfrac{6.7\ \text{C}°}{7.40\ \text{C}°}\ \left|\ \dfrac{1\ \text{mol solute}}{1\ \text{kg phenol}}\right. = 0.91\ \text{mol solute/kg phenol}$

$\dfrac{10.4\ \text{g solute}}{164\ \text{g phenol}}\ \left|\ \dfrac{1000\ \text{g phenol}}{1\ \text{kg phenol}}\right. = 63.4\ \text{g solute/kg phenol}$

$\dfrac{63.4\ \text{g}}{0.91\ \text{mol}} = 7.0 \times 10^1\ \text{g/mol}$

12. $\dfrac{2.3\ \text{C}°}{7.00\ \text{C}°}\ \left|\ \dfrac{1\ \text{mol solute}}{1\ \text{kg nitrobenzene}}\right. = 0.33\ \text{mol solute/kg nitrobenzene}$

$\dfrac{2.53\ \text{g}}{63.5\ \text{g nitrobenzene}}\ \left|\ \dfrac{1000\ \text{g nitrobenzene}}{1\ \text{kg nitrobenzene}}\right. = 39.8\ \text{g/kg nitrobenzene}$

$\dfrac{39.8\ \text{g}}{0.33\ \text{mol}} = 120\ \text{g/mol}$

Page 428

13. $\Pi = MRT$ or $\dfrac{mRT}{MV}$

$\Pi = \dfrac{18.6\ \text{g X}}{1.00\ \text{dm}^3}\ \left|\ \dfrac{1\ \text{mol X}}{8940\ \text{g X}}\ \right|\ \dfrac{8.31\ \text{dm}^3\cdot\text{kPa}}{\text{mol}\cdot\text{K}}\ \left|\ \dfrac{298\ \text{K}}{}\right.$

$\Pi = 5.15\ \text{kPa}$

14. $x\ \text{g/mol Y} = \dfrac{}{15.8\ \text{kPa}}\ \left|\ \dfrac{96.0\ \text{g}}{1.00\ \text{dm}^3}\ \right|\ \dfrac{8.31\ \text{dm}^3\cdot\text{kPa}}{\text{mol}\cdot\text{K}}\ \left|\ \dfrac{298\ \text{K}}{}\right.$

$x = 1.50 \times 10^4\ \text{g/mol}$

15. $\Pi = MRT$

$$\Pi = \frac{69.7\ \cancel{g}}{1.00\ \cancel{dm^3}}\ \bigg|\ \frac{1\ \cancel{mol}}{2790\ \cancel{g}}\ \bigg|\ \frac{8.31\ \cancel{dm^3}\cdot kPa}{\cancel{mol}\ \cancel{K}}\ \bigg|\ \frac{293\ \cancel{K}}{}\ = 60.8\ kPa$$

16. $\Pi = \dfrac{nRT}{V} = \dfrac{mRT}{MV'}\quad M = \dfrac{mRT}{\Pi V}$

$$= \frac{2.00 \times 10^2\ g}{1.00\ \cancel{dm^3}}\ \bigg|\ \frac{8.31\ \cancel{dm^3}\cdot\cancel{kPa}}{mol\cdot\cancel{K}}\ \bigg|\ \frac{294\ \cancel{K}}{1.00 \times 10^2\ \cancel{kPa}}\ = 4890\ g/mol$$

CHAPTER END PROBLEMS

Pages 434-435

1. Colligative properties are those which depend only on the number of particles and not their nature (vapor pressure, freezing point, boiling point, osmotic pressure).

2. Ideal solutions obey Raoult's law.

3. A nonvolatile solute is one which does not evaporate.

4. These solute particles decrease the opportunity for the solvent particles to evaporate. Thus the vapor pressure of a solution with a nonvolatile solute is always less than the vapor pressure of the pure solvent.

7. $\dfrac{8.27\ \cancel{g\ C_6H_6}}{}\ \bigg|\ \dfrac{1\ mol\ C_6H_6}{78.1\ \cancel{g\ C_6H_6}}\ = 0.106\ mol\ C_6H_6$

$\dfrac{3.87\ \cancel{g\ CHCl_3}}{}\ \bigg|\ \dfrac{1\ mol\ CHCl_3}{119\ \cancel{g\ CHCl_3}}\ = 0.0325\ mol\ CHCl_3$

$x\ C_6H_6 = \dfrac{0.106}{0.139} = 0.763$, v.p. $C_6H_6 = (12.1)(0.763) = 9.23\ kPa$

$x\ CHCl_3 = \dfrac{0.0325}{0.139} = 0.234$, v.p. $CHCl_3 = (25.2)(0.234) = 5.90\ kPa$

v.p. soln $= 9.23 + 5.90 = 15.1\ kPa$

8. $\dfrac{97.5\ \cancel{g\ C_{12}H_{22}O_{11}}}{185\ \cancel{g\ H_2O}}\ \bigg|\ \dfrac{1\ mol\ C_{12}H_{22}O_{11}}{342\ \cancel{g\ C_{12}H_{22}O_{11}}}\ \bigg|\ \dfrac{1000\ \cancel{g\ H_2O}}{1\ kg\ H_2O}\ = 1.54m$

$BP = 100°C + (1.54m \times 0.512C°/m) = 100.788°C$
$FP = 0°C - (1.54m \times 1.86C°/m) = -2.86°C$

9. $\dfrac{14.0\ \cancel{g\ C_{10}H_8}}{25.0\ \cancel{g\ C_6H_6}}\ \bigg|\ \dfrac{1\ mol\ C_{10}H_8}{128\ \cancel{g\ C_{10}H_8}}\ \bigg|\ \dfrac{1000\ \cancel{g\ C_6H_6}}{1\ kg\ C_6H_6}\ = 4.38m$

$BP = 80.1°C + (4.38m \times 2.53C°/m) = 91.2°C$
$FP = 5.5°C - (4.38m \times 4.90C°/m) = -16.0°C$

10. $\dfrac{5.00 \times 10^2\ \cancel{g\ X}}{5.00 \times 10^2\ \cancel{g\ H_2O}}\ \bigg|\ \dfrac{1\ mol\ X}{511\ \cancel{g\ X}}\ \bigg|\ \dfrac{1000\ \cancel{g\ H_2O}}{1\ kg\ H_2O}\ = 1.96m$

$BP = 100°C + (1.96m \times 0.512C°/m) = 101.00°C$
$FP = 0°C - (1.96m \times 1.86C°/m) = -3.65°C$

11. $\dfrac{2.50 \times 10^2\ \cancel{g\ Y}}{5.00 \times 10_2\ \cancel{g\ C_6H_6}}\ \bigg|\ \dfrac{1\ mol\ Y}{246\ \cancel{g\ Y}}\ \bigg|\ \dfrac{1000\ \cancel{g\ C_6H_6}}{1\ kg}\ = 2.03m$

$BP = 80.1°C + (2.03m \times 2.53C°/m) = 85.2°C$
$FP = 5.5°C - (2.03m \times 4.90C°/m) = -4.5°C$

12. $\dfrac{60.0\ \cancel{g\ C_9H_{18}}}{1.00 \times 10^2\ \cancel{g\ HAc}}\ \bigg|\ \dfrac{1\ mol\ C_9H_{18}}{126\ \cancel{g\ C_9H_{18}}}\ \bigg|\ \dfrac{1000\ \cancel{g\ HAc}}{1\ kg\ HAc}\ = 4.76m$

$BP = 117.9°C + (4.76m \times 3.07C°/m) = 133°C$
$FP = 16.604°C - (4.76m \times 3.90C°/m) = -1.96°C$

13. $\dfrac{-0.603\ C°}{-1.86\ C°} = 0.324m$

$\dfrac{5.60\ g\ X}{104\ \cancel{g\ H_2O}}\ \bigg|\ \dfrac{1000\ \cancel{g}}{1\ \cancel{kg}}\ \bigg|\ \dfrac{\cancel{kg\ H_2O}}{0.324\ mol}\ = 166\ g\ X/mol$

5. The size of colloidal particles is smaller than suspension particles. Colloidal particles will not settle out and can pass through filter paper.

6. v.p. H_2O @ $60.0°C = 19.9\ kPa$

$\dfrac{133\ \cancel{g\ C_6H_8O_7}}{}\ \bigg|\ \dfrac{1\ mol\ C_6H_8O_7}{192\ \cancel{g\ C_6H_8O_7}}\ = 0.693\ mol\ C_6H_8O_7$

$\dfrac{1.00 \times 10^2\ \cancel{g\ H_2O}}{}\ \bigg|\ \dfrac{1\ mol\ H_2O}{18.0\ \cancel{g\ H_2O}}\ = 5.56\ mol\ H_2O$

$x\ H_2O = \dfrac{5.56\ mol\ H_2O}{5.56\ mol\ H_2O + 0.693\ mol\ C_6H_8O_7} = 0.890$

v.p. soln $= (19.9)(0.890) = 17.7\ kPa$

14. $\Pi = MRT$

$$= \frac{8.10 \text{ g}}{1.00 \text{ dm}^3} \left| \frac{\text{mol}}{1310 \text{ g}} \right| \frac{8.31 \text{ dm}^3 \cdot \text{kPa}}{\text{mol} \cdot \text{K}} \right| \frac{295 \text{ K}}{} = 15.2 \text{ kPa}$$

REVIEW

Page 435

1. $\dfrac{20.0 \text{ g Fe}_2(C_2O_4)_3}{1.00 \times 10^2 \text{ g H}_2O} \left| \dfrac{1 \text{ mol Fe}_2(C_2O_4)_3}{376 \text{ g Fe}_2(C_2O_4)_3} \right| \dfrac{1000 \text{ g}}{1 \text{ kg}} = 0.532m \text{ Fe}_2(C_2O_4)_3$

2. $\dfrac{2.50 \times 10^2 \text{ cm}^3 \text{ H}_2O}{} \left| \dfrac{1 \text{ g H}_2O}{1 \text{ cm}^3 \text{ H}_2O} \right| \dfrac{0.560 \text{ mol Li}_2S}{1000 \text{ g H}_2O} \right| \dfrac{46.0 \text{ g Li}_2S}{1 \text{ mol Li}_2S}$

$= 6.44 \text{ g Li}_2S$

3. $\dfrac{50.0 \text{ g CH}_3COCH_3}{} \left| \dfrac{1 \text{ mol CH}_3COCH_3}{58.1 \text{ g CH}_3COCH_3} \right. = 0.861 \text{ mol CH}_3COCH_3$

$\dfrac{50.0 \text{ g H}_2O}{} \left| \dfrac{1 \text{ mol H}_2O}{18.0 \text{ g H}_2O} \right. = \dfrac{2.78 \text{ mol H}_2O}{3.64 \text{ mol soln}}$

$\dfrac{0.861}{3.64} = 0.237 \text{ mole fraction CH}_3COCH_3$

ONE MORE STEP

Page 435

1. See any elementary organic chemistry laboratory manual. Possible mixtures are 1-butanol and 1-octanol, methanol and water. **CAUTION:** *The mixtures are flammable.* Collect five fractions and analyze by refractive index or density.

2. The ultracentrifuge was developed by the Swedish scientist, Svedberg. It can, through centrifugal force, produce an effective gravitational field about 500 000 times the earth's. Dissolved particles of large molecular mass settle out quickly and mass values can be determined by this rate. For further information consult *Encyclopaedia Britannica*.

3. Cyclone separators—stack gas forced into a spiral path. Centrifugal force throws dust against sides when it settles out.
Cottrell precipitators—electrostatic precipitation of charged, colloidal dust particles.
Scrubbing towers—gas is bubbled through water, or other wash liquid, which strips out dust as well as noxious gases.

4. Gelatin forms most useful protective colloids. It is used with silver bromide emulsions in photography, to prevent ice crystals in ice cream, and as an emulsifying agent in many solutions. Egg is an emulsifier in foods such as salad dressings or mayonnaise. Detergents are special protective colloids.

5. A living cell is filled principally with water (75-85%). The inorganic salts and some of the smaller organic molecules (if hydrophilic) are in solution. However, the larger molecules in the colloidal range of size and hydrophobic materials are dispersed. The larger molecules would include proteins and nucleic acids; while the hydrophobic materials would include lipids. Many of the long molecules, particularly proteins, tend to align themselves in a degree of order which appears the same as in liquid crystals.

REACTION RATE AND CHEMICAL EQUILIBRIUM   23

AN OVERVIEW

Chapter 23 is used to introduce both the qualitative and quantitative aspects of the factors affecting rates of chemical reactions. Emphasize the role of energy in affecting the rate of a chemical reaction. The concept of activation energy should be graphically contrasted to the enthalpy of reaction. Reaction rates can be measured by observing the rate at which some property of the reaction changes. Some properties which change are index of refraction, rotation of polarized light, pH, volume, color, and pressure. Stress that the accurate prediction of reaction rates is one of the most important unsolved problems in chemistry. The quantitative study of equilibrium is based on the study of reaction rates. At equilibrium, the rates of the forward and reverse reactions are equal. Using Le Chatelier's principle, students may predict how changes in concentration, pressure, and temperature affect equilibrium concentrations. Stress that in many reactions some of the product molecules will have enough energy to cause the reverse reaction to occur. The chapter ends by relating small K_{eq} values to negative free energy changes.

DEMONSTRATION INFORMATION

The clock reaction: To 40 cm^3 of distilled H_2O in a small beaker, add 20 drops of saturated KIO_3 solution. Place 100 cm^3 of distilled H_2O into another small beaker, add 40 drops of a soluble starch solution (4 g/100 cm^3 boiling water), 12 drops of $Na_2S_2O_5$ solution (2.5 g/100 cm^3), and 4 drops of concentrated H_2SO_4. Pour the solutions in the two beakers together and time the reaction. If the reaction time is longer than 20 seconds, increase the amount of KIO_3 solution. Dilute the KIO_3 solution if the reaction time is too fast. Run the demonstration before class and adjust the concentrations accordingly. Vary the concentration of KIO_3 in the first beaker and run several trials. (Example: 10, 15, 20 and 30 drops) Record the time for each trial. Place the two solutions in large test tubes in an ice water bath and run a trial at the colder temperature. Record the time. Repeat in a hot water bath (35°C) and record the time for the reaction to take place. You may prefer to do this as a laboratory experiment for your students. Discuss how the rate of a reaction can vary without changing the temperature. Use the demonstration to introduce reaction mechanisms, rate determining step, and activation energy.

After the solutions are mixed, the following reactions occur:

step 1. slow
$2IO_3^-(aq) + 9H_2O(l) + 3S_2O_5^{2-}(aq) \rightarrow 2I^-(aq) + 6SO_4^{2-}(aq) + 6H_3O^+(aq)$

step 2. slow
$5I^-(aq) + 6H_3O^+(aq) + IO_3^-(aq) \rightarrow 3I_2(aq) + 9H_2O(l)$

step 3. very fast
$2I_2(aq) + S_2O_5^{2-}(aq) + 9H_2O(l) \rightarrow 4I^-(aq) + 2SO_4^{2-}(aq) + 6H_3O^+(aq)$

step 4. slow
$I_2(aq) + starch \rightarrow$ blue-black complex

As long as any $S_2O_5^{2-}$ remains in solution, the I_2 formed in step 2 is immediately reduced in step 3. As soon as the $S_2O_5^{2-}$ is consumed, the I_2 will react with the starch and the solution will turn dark suddenly. The iodine-clock reaction remains one of the most dramatic chemical reactions and is especially useful in showing temperature and concentration effects on reaction rate.

DISPOSAL: *These chemicals are properly disposed of at a local landfill. They represent little or no hazard to the environment.*

PERFORMANCE OBJECTIVES

Goals: Students will determine the factors that affect the rate of reaction. Students will determine the reaction mechanism for simple reactions. Students will determine equilibrium constants for specific reactions and explain the effect of Le Chatelier's principle.

Objectives: Upon completion of the reading and problems, and when asked to demonstrate their understanding either orally or on a written test, students will

23:1	K	define the phrase thermodynamically stable. **Intro**
23:2	K	define and give an example of a reversible reaction. **23:1**
23:3	K	define reaction rate. **23:2**
23:4	K/P	use reaction rates to determine whether products or reactants will predominate in a reversible reaction. **23:2**
23:5	K	define activation energy and activated complex. **23:3**
23:6	K	list and describe the factors which influence the rate of a reaction. **23:3-23:6**
23:7	K	define reaction mechanism and rate determining step. **23:3**
23:8	K/P	interpret a reaction rate expression for a given reaction. **23:4**
23:9	K	define concentration and the specific rate constant, k. **23:4**
23:10	K	define heterogeneous reaction. **23:4**
23:11	K/P	relate temperature, molecular collisions, and reaction rate. **23:5**
23:12	K	define catalysis. **23:6**
23:13	K	define inhibitor and adsorption. **23:6**
23:14	K/P	differentiate heterogeneous and homogeneous catalysts. **23:6**
23:15	P	given experimental concentration and rate data, determine the rate law and rate constant for a given reaction. **23:7**
23:16	K/P	given a reaction and rate data, propose a possible reaction mechanism for the reaction. **23:7**
23:17	K/P	given the rate law for a reaction, predict the effect of changes in concentration, pressure/volume, and temperature. **23:7**
23:18	K/P	given an equation for a reaction, write the expression for the equilibrium constant, K_{eq}. **23:8**
23:19	K/P	state the relationship of K_{eq} to the relative amounts of products and reactants in a given reaction. **23:8**

23:20	P	calculate the equilibrium constant for a reaction given final concentrations of reactants and products. **23:8**
23:21	P	calculate the final concentration of a reactant or product given K_{eq} and the concentrations of other reactants and/or products. **23:8**
23:22	K	state Le Chatelier's principle. **23:9**
23:23	K/P	use Le Chatelier's principle to explain the effect of changes in concentration, pressure/volume, and temperature on an equilibrium system. **23:9**
23:24	K/P	state the effect on K_{eq} of changes in concentration, pressure/volume, and temperature. **23:9**
23:25	K	define optimum conditions. **23:9**
23:26	K	write equilibrium constant expressions for gas phase reactions. **23:10**
23:27	K/P	solve problems involving the free energy and equilibrium constant for a reaction. **23:11**
23:28	A	voluntarily complete one or more of the One More Step activities.
23:29	A	read unassigned literature related to the chapter.

TEACHING TECHNIQUES

Section 23:1

Demonstration: A reversible reaction can be demonstrated by dissolving 14 g NaOH in 700 cm^3 distilled H$_2$O, in a 1000 cm^3 Erlenmeyer flask. Add 14 g of dextrose or glucose and 1 cm^3 of methylene blue indicator solution to the NaOH solution and stopper tightly. Shake vigorously and the solution is blue in color. Allow it to sit and the color clears.

DISPOSAL: *Neutralize with 6M HCl. Verify with pH test paper. Wash the neutralized solution down the drain with a large amount of water.*

Section 23:4

Demonstration: Lycopodium powder can be purchased from chemical supply houses. Place a scoop full on a ceramic square. Try to light the powder using a burner. It does not burn. Then, lift the square containing the powder about 50 cm above the burner flame and turn the square over. The falling dust will produce a roaring flame which is best viewed in a darkened room. The surface area is directly proportional to concentration. Thus an increase in surface area increases the reaction rate. Relate this demonstration to a dust explosion in a grain elevator or cement plant. **CAUTION:** *Safety goggles must be worn.*

Section 23:5

Figure 23-6 is a simplified diagram. The graph of a multistep reaction would have several valleys and peaks. The "controlling" step in such a reaction is the one with the highest peak.

Section 23:6

The demonstration in the margin shows a homogeneous catalyst. The cobalt(II) tartrate complex is oxidized to a green Co(III) tartrate compound. The green form is then reduced by tartaric acid and H$_2$O$_2$ to Co(II) tartrate with the evolution of CO$_2$ and O$_2$ gas. This demonstration shows a multistep mechanism (Section 23:7). The pink to green (oxidation) is faster than the green to pink (reduction). The short life of a collision product (activated complex) can also be discussed.

DISPOSAL: *Pour the solution down the drain with a large amount of water.*

Section 23:8

Demonstration: As students begin their quantitative study of equilibria, it is important to dispel the idea that equilibrium means 50:50, the same amount of reactant and product. To do this, obtain two aquaria from the biology lab or get two plastic sweater storage boxes. Fill one completely with water. Add a drop of food coloring to make the demonstration more visible. At the same time, using two of the same size plastic beakers, dip the beakers into their respective aquarium and then transfer the contents of the beakers into the opposite aquarium. The beaker that is dipped into the empty aquarium represents the reverse reaction. Initially there is no reverse reaction. The beaker that is dipped into the full aquarium represents the initial forward reaction. As water is gradually transferred to the empty aquarium, we see that the rate of the reverse reaction is increasing. That is to say, the beaker is collecting and transferring more and more water. It is important that the two beakers be dipped into their respective aquaria at the same time. Eventually the class will notice that both beakers are full and are transferring the same amount of water. Equilibrium has been reached. The amount of water going in one direction is equal to the amount of water going in the opposite direction. If you use 100 cm^3 beakers, it will be obvious to the class that the amounts of water in the two aquaria at equilibrium are not 50:50. Equilibrium is often established when the amount of reactant remaining does not equal the amount of product produced.

The students are now better able to understand the concepts behind the mathematical manipulation of equilibria problems.

Section 23:9

Demonstration: A demonstration that helps students visualize Le Chatelier's principle is based on the equilibrium:

$$Co(H_2O)_6{}^{2+} + 4\ Cl^- \rightarrow CoCl_4{}^{2-} + 6H_2O$$

      pink   blue

Dissolve 2.0 g of $CoCl_2$ in 40 cm^3 of H_2O. Put the 40 cm^3 of solution in a 100 cm^3 graduated cylinder. Have the equilibrium equation on the chalkboard. Ask students to predict if a change will occur before adding 60 cm^3 of $12M$ HCl to the graduated cylinder. Observe the color change from pink to blue. Pour half of the blue solution into another graduated cylinder. Ask students to predict the color again before adding 35 cm^3 of water. Observe the color change back to pink. Point out to students that this is a reversible reaction (Section 23:1). To the graduated cylinder with blue solution, add 35 cm^3 of $0.1M$ $AgNO_3$ and observe the formation of the AgCl precipitate and a color change to pink. This reaction shows students that chlorides are removed by precipitation with $AgNO_3$. This precipitation causes the equilibrium to shift to the left (decreases concentration of Cl^-).

DISPOSAL: *Place the materials in a large container. Add a large amount of water and sodium carbonate. Stir and allow to stand for 24 hours. Decant the liquid into another container. Neutralize with $Ca(OH)_2$. Verify with pH test paper. Wash the neutralized solution down the drain with a large amount of water. The solid residue can be dried and placed in a local landfill.*

Technology and Chemistry

This feature is an extension of the discussion concerning kelvin temperature. Emphasize to students that some of the research in this area concerns trying to reach absolute zero. For students to do additional literature research concerning absolute zero and the devices used to maintain low temperatures, some knowledge of physics may be required.

PROBLEM SOLUTIONS

Pages 447-448

1. **a.** doubled $[2H_2] = 2[H_2]$
   b. eight times faster
   $[2NO]^2[2H_2] = 8[NO]^2[H_2]$
   c. slows down
2. **a.** Rate $= k[H_2][I_2]$
   $0.2 = k(1)(1)$
   $k = 0.2$ $dm^6/mol\cdot s$
   $0.4 = k(1)(2)$
   $k = 0.2$ $dm^6/mol\cdot s$
   $0.8 = k(2)(2)$
   $k = 0.2$ $dm^6/mol\cdot s$
   b. Rate $= 0.2(0.5)(0.5)$
   Rate $= 0.05$ mol/s

3. rate $= k[CH_3COCH_3]$ (Iodine has no effect)

4. $H^+ + CH_3-\overset{\overset{\displaystyle O}{\|}}{C}-CH_3 \rightarrow CH_3-\overset{\overset{\displaystyle OH}{|}}{\underset{\oplus}{C}}-CH_3$ slow

$CH_3-\overset{\overset{\displaystyle OH}{|}}{\underset{\oplus}{C}}-CH_3 \rightarrow CH_3-\overset{\overset{\displaystyle OH}{|}}{C}=CH_2 + H^+$ fast

$CH_3-\overset{\overset{\displaystyle OH}{|}}{C}=CH_2 + I_2 \rightarrow CH_3-\overset{\overset{\displaystyle OH}{|}}{\underset{\oplus}{C}}-CH_2I + I$ fast

$CH_3-\overset{\overset{\displaystyle OH}{|}}{\underset{\oplus}{C}}-CH_2I + I^- \rightarrow CH_3-\overset{\overset{\displaystyle O}{\|}}{C}-CH_2I + HI$ fast

Pages 450-451

5. **a.** $K_{eq} = \dfrac{[CO_2][NH_3]^2}{[NH_2COONH_4]}$

   b. $K_{eq} = \dfrac{[Cl_2]^2[H_2O]^2}{[HCl]^4[O_2]}$

   c. $K_{eq} = \dfrac{[NH_3][H_2S]}{[NH_4HS]}$

   d. $K_{eq} = \dfrac{[CuSO_4][H_2O]^5}{[CuSO_4\cdot5H_2O]}$

6. $[HI]^2 = \dfrac{[H_2][I_2]}{K_{eq}}$

   $[HI]^2 = \dfrac{(2.00 \times 10^{-4})(2.00 \times 10^{-4})}{1.40 \times 10^{-2}} = 2.86 \times 10^{-6}$

   $[HI] = 1.69 \times 10^{-3}M$

7. $K_{eq} = \dfrac{[H_2][CO_2]}{[CO][H_2O]} = \dfrac{(0.32)(0.42)}{(0.200)(0.500)} = 1.3$

8. $[CO] = \dfrac{[H_2][CO_2]}{K_{eq}[H_2O]}$

   $[CO] = \dfrac{(0.32)(0.42)}{(2.40)(0.500)} = 0.11\ M$

9. $K_{eq} = \dfrac{[H_2]^2[S_2]}{[H_2S]^2}$

   $= \dfrac{(2.22 \times 10^{-3})^2(1.11 \times 10^{-3})}{(7.06 \times 10^{-3})^2} = 1.10 \times 10^{-4}$

10. $K_{eq} = \dfrac{[NO_2]^2}{[N_2O_4]}$

    $[NO_2]^2 = K_{eq}[N_2O_4]$
    $= (8.75 \times 10^{-2})(1.72 \times 10^{-2})$
    $= 1.51 \times 10^{-3}$
    $[NO_2] = 3.88 \times 10^{-2}M$

Page 455

11. $\log K_{eq} = -\dfrac{\Delta G}{2.30RT} = -\dfrac{28.95}{(2.30)(8.31 \times 10^{-3})(298)}$

    $= -5.0828$

    antilog $-5.0828 = 8.26 \times 10^{-6}$

12. $\Delta G = -2.30RT\ (\log K_{eq})$

    $= (-2.30)(0.00831)(900)(\log 3.16 \times 10^{-4})$

    $= 60.2$ kJ/mol

13. $\Delta G_f^\circ = -2.30\ RT(\log K_{eq})$
$= (-2.30)(0.008\ 31)(473)(\log 0.457)$
$= 3.07$ kJ/mol

CHAPTER END PROBLEMS

Page 458

1. a. $K_{eq} = \dfrac{[(NH_4)_2SO_4]}{[NH_3]^2[H_2SO_4]}$

b. $K_{eq} = \dfrac{4.00}{(2.00)^2(3.00)} = 0.333$

c. increases **d.** shifts right **e.** changes

2. $H_2(g) + Cl_2(g) \rightarrow 2HCl(g)$
Cl_2 is more active than Br_2

3. The reaction rate would increase.

4. The surface area of the log is less than the surface area of the paper. The match cannot raise the temperature of the log to its kindling point but can heat the paper.

5. See Figure 23-6, page 443 for an example of how to set up the uncatalyzed reaction. The catalyzed reaction should show a lower activation energy hill.

6. If [NO] is constant, rate $\propto$ [H]; thus the reaction rate doubles.

7. The reaction rate would increase.

8. $\Delta G = -RT\ln K_{eq}$

$= \dfrac{-8.31\ J}{mol\cdot K}\ \bigg|\ 2.000 \times 10^3\ K\ \bigg|\ ln(6.45 \times 10^{-8})$

$= 2.75 \times 10^5\ J = 275$ kJ/mol

9. $338\ 000\ J = \dfrac{-8.31\ J}{mol\cdot K}\ \bigg|\ 1273\ K\ \bigg|\ ln\ x$

$x = $ anti $ln\ -31.95$
$K_{eq} = 1.33 \times 10^{-14}$

10. $\Delta G = -RT(\ln K_{eq})$
$-300\ 000 = -(8.31)(298)(\ln K_{eq})$
$K_{eq} = 4.10 \times 10^{52}$

11. $\Delta G\ -RT(\ln K_{eq})$
$= -(8.31)(298)\ ln(6.00 \times 10^5)$
$= -32\ 900\ J = -32.9$ kJ/mol

12. $\Delta G = -RT(\ln K_{eq})$
$-503\ 000 = -(8.31)(298)\ ln\ K_{eq}$
$K_{eq} = 1.63 \times 10^{88}$

13. $\Delta G = -RT(\ln K_{eq})$
$= (8.31)(298)\ ln(13.69)$
$= -6480\ J = -6.48$ kJ/mol

14. $K_p = \dfrac{(pp\ HCHO)(pp\ H_2)}{(pp\ CH_3OH)}$
$= \dfrac{(176)^2}{26.3}$
$= 1180$

REVIEW

Page 459

1. Due to ion-dipole or van der Waals forces, solvent particles adhere to solute particles during the solvation process.

2. No. Water is highly polar. Butter is nonpolar.

3. crush solute, heat, stir

4. The volume of gas that will dissolve in a given quantity of liquid will increase as the pressure increases.

5. $\dfrac{16.0\ g\ HIO_3}{1.00 \times 10^2\ cm^3}\ \bigg|\ \dfrac{1\ mol\ HIO_3}{176\ g\ HIO_3}\ \bigg|\ \dfrac{1000\ cm^3}{1\ dm^3}$
$= 0.909M\ HIO_3$

6. It increases the boiling point.

7. The activity of the ions is slightly less than their concentration.

8. $\dfrac{98.1\ g\ C_{12}H_{22}O_{11}}{}\ \bigg|\ \dfrac{1\ mol\ C_{12}H_{22}O_{11}}{342\ g\ C_{12}H_{22}O_{11}} = 0.287\ mol\ C_{12}H_{22}O_{11}$

$\dfrac{1.00 \times 10^2\ g\ H_2O}{}\ \bigg|\ \dfrac{1\ mole\ H_2O}{18.0\ g\ H_2O} = 5.56\ mol\ H_2O$

$\dfrac{5.56}{5.85} = 0.950$ mole fraction water

vapor pressure of the solution $= x(v.p.\ solvent) =$
$(0.950)(3.2\ kPa) = 3.0$ kPa

9. $\dfrac{1.58}{1.86} = 0.849m$

$\dfrac{4.23\ g}{45.0\ g\ H_2O}\ \bigg|\ \dfrac{1000\ g}{1\ kg}\ \bigg|\ \dfrac{kg}{0.849\ mol} = 111$ g/mol

10. $\Pi = MRT$

$\dfrac{4.70\ g}{500\ cm^3}\ \bigg|\ \dfrac{1\ mol}{6870\ g}\ \bigg|\ \dfrac{1000\ cm^3}{1\ dm^3}\ \bigg|\ \dfrac{8.31\ dm^3\cdot kPa}{mol\cdot K}\ \bigg|\ 288\ K$
$= 3.27$ kPa

ONE MORE STEP

Page 459

1. $K_{eq} = \dfrac{[C]^2}{[A]^2[B]} = 8$

initial concentration of A $= \dfrac{0.5}{10} = 0.05M$

initial concentration of B $= \dfrac{0.5}{10} = 0.05M$

If x moles of B react per dm^3, then $2x$ moles of A must react per dm^3 and $2x$ moles of C will be produced per dm^3. Therefore,
final concentration of A $= 0.05 - 2x$
final concentration of B $= 0.05 - x$
final concentration of C $= 2x$
Note: The final solution to this problem involves a "sticky" third-degree equation:

$\dfrac{(2x)^2}{(0.05 - 2x)^2(0.05 - x)} = 8$

$\dfrac{4x^2}{(0.000125 - 0.0125x + 0.4x^2 - 4x^3)} = 8$
$4x^2 = 0.001 - 0.1x + 3.2x^2 - 32x^3$
$32x^3 + 0.8x^2 + 0.1x - 0.001 = 0$
$x = 0.00910$
Since $[C] = 2x$, $[C] = 0.0182M$
Then $[A] = 0.0318M$ and $[B] = 0.0409M$

2. $E_a = \Delta H^{°*} + RT$ for solid and liquid systems
$E_a = \Delta H^{°*} - (\Delta n^* - 1)\, RT$ for gaseous systems
$\Delta G^{°*} = H^{°*} - T\Delta S^{°*}$
$\Delta G^{°*} = -RT(\ln K^*)$
where E_a = activation energy
$\Delta H^{°*}$ = enthalpy of activation
R = gas constant
T = kelvin temperature
Δn^* = moles of complex minus number of moles of reactants
$\Delta G^{°*}$ = free energy of activation
$\Delta S^{°*}$ = entropy of activation
$\ln$ = natural logarithm
K^* = equilibrium constant for reactants $\rightleftharpoons$ complex in units of concentration

3. There are many multistep reactions listed in texts on kinetics and physical chemistry. For example:
$$2O_3 \rightarrow 3O_2$$
$$2H_2O_2 \xrightarrow{I^-} 2H_2O + O_2$$
(The I^- is a catalyst for decomposing H_2O_2.)

$$H_2 + Cl_2 \rightarrow 2HCl$$
$$O_3 \leftrightarrows O_2 + O \quad \text{fast}$$
$$O + O_3 \rightarrow 2O_2 \quad \text{slow}$$
$$H_2O_2 + H_3O^+ \leftrightarrows H_3O^{2+} + H_2O \quad \text{fast}$$
$$H_3O^{2+} + I^- \rightarrow H_2O + HOI^+ \quad \text{slow}$$
$$HOI + H_2O_2 \rightarrow H_3O^+ I^- + O_2 \quad \text{fast}$$
$$Cl_2 + hv \rightarrow 2Cl \quad \text{slow}$$
chain $\begin{cases} Cl + H_2 \rightarrow HCl + H & \text{fast} \\ H + Cl_2 \rightarrow HCl + Cl & \text{fast} \end{cases}$
reaction

$\left.\begin{array}{l} H + HCl \rightarrow H_2 + Cl \\ Cl + HCl \rightarrow Cl_2 + H \end{array}\right\}$ inhibiting reactions

$\left.\begin{array}{l} Cl_2 \rightarrow 2Cl \\ H_2 \rightarrow 2H \end{array}\right\}$ chain-breaking reactions

4. $K_c = K_p \dfrac{1}{(RT)}\Delta n$ where Δn = the increase in moles in going from reactants to products.

5. See *Biology: Living Systems* © 1986, Oram, Charles E. Merrill Publishing Co., pp. 61-64.

6. Free energy (G) always decreases with temperature. The free energy change (ΔG) becomes more positive as temperature increases. $\Delta G = \Delta H - T\Delta S$

ACIDS, BASES, AND SALTS 24

AN OVERVIEW

The three classes of electrolytes—acids, bases, and salts are discussed in Chapter 24 with an emphasis on their behavior in water solution. The chapter begins with an introduction to three acid-base theories. Point out that the Arrhenius definitions are applicable only in water solution. Under the Brønsted-Lowry definitions we write H_3O^+ as a convenience. However, a more exact representation we use is $H(H_2O)_n{}^+$. The Lewis theory is applicable to reactions carried out in the absence of solvents. After the students know the definition of an acid, teach students how to name them. The properties and behavior of acids, bases, and salts are discussed qualitatively and then expressed and applied in a quantitative manner. Students apply the knowledge gained in Chapter 23 on equilibrium to solve problems involving the ionization constant, percent of ionization, and common ion effect.

DEMONSTRATION INFORMATION

A safe conductivity apparatus can be easily made using an AC adaptor (battery eliminator). Remove the special plug from the end of the DC wire. Attach alligator clips to the ends of the two wires. Wire in series a flashlight bulb socket into one side of the wire. Place a bulb in the socket. The alligator clips can be attached to straightened paper clips (electrodes) that have been pushed through cardboard. The conductivity apparatus can now be used with a small beaker.

Input 120 V
Output 9 V
500 mA

Conductivity is directly related to the concentration of ions in solution. The concentration of ions is not the same in strong and weak acid solutions. This demonstration will help students understand this concept. The HCl solutions will conduct electricity. However, students will observe that the bulb becomes dimmer as the lower concentrations are tested. With the type of conductivity apparatus described above, the 0.01M HCl does not light the bulb.

The K_a for acetic acid is 1.76×10^{-5}. The H_3O^+ concentrations and the percent of ionization can be calculated for the test solutions. Students can do these calculations after studying Sections 24:11 and 24:12.

[CH₃COOH]	[H₃O⁺] or [CH₃COO⁻]	% ionization
0.01M	0.0004M	4%
0.10M	0.001M	1%
1.0M	0.004M	0.4%
6.0M	0.010M*	0.2%

*The 0.01M HCl ionized to produce 0.01M H_3O^+ and Cl^- concentrations. This concentration was not strong enough to light the bulb. 6.0 M acetic acid has the same concentration of H_3O^+ as the 0.01M HCl. Students can now understand why the bulb would not light for any of the acetic acid concentrations. Emphasize to students that in weak acids, the percent ionization increases as the acid concentration decreases.

DISPOSAL: Place materials in a large container. Add a large amount of water and Na_2CO_3. Stir and allow to stand for 24 hours. Decant the liquid into another container. Neutralize with 6M NaOH. Verify with pH test paper. Wash the neutralized solution down the drain with a large quantity of water. The solid residue can be dried and placed in a local landfill.

PERFORMANCE OBJECTIVES

Goals: Students will differentiate among three acid-base theories. Students will compare and contrast properties of acids, bases, and salts. Students will name acids, bases, and salts given the formulas and write the formula given the name. Students will calculate ionization constant, $[H_3O^+]$ and/or percent of ionization.

Objectives: Upon completion of the reading and problems, and when asked to demonstrate their understanding either orally or on a written test, students will

24:1	K	define electrolytes. **Intro**
24:2	K	define acids and bases according to the Arrhenius theory. **24:1**
24:3	K	define acids and bases according to the Brønsted-Lowry theory. **24:2**
24:4	K	define hydronium ion. **24:2**
24:5	K	define conjugate acid and conjugate base and distinguish between them. **24:2**
24:6	K/P	given an acid-base reaction, identify the acid, base, conjugate acid, and conjugate base. **24:2**
24:7	K	define acids and bases according to the Lewis theory. **24:3**
24:8	K/P	classify substances as Lewis acids or Lewis bases. **24:3**
24:9	K/P	use Lewis acid-base theory to complete equations for the formation of complex ions. **24:3**
24:10	K	define binary acids. **24:4**

24:11	K/P	given the formula for a binary acid, name it, and given the name, write the formula. **24:4**
24:12	K	define ternary acid. **24:5**
24:13	K/P	given the formula for a ternary acid, name it, and given its name, write the formula. **24:5**
24:14	K/P	given the formula of an Arrhenius base, name it, and vice versa. **24:5**
24:15	K	define anhydrous, and distinguish acidic and basic anhydrides. **24:6**
24:16	K/P	given the formula for an acid or base, write its corresponding acidic or basic anhydride, and vice versa. **24:6**
24:17	K	define amphoteric. **24:7**
24:18	K/P	state whether a given element will tend to form an acidic, basic, or amphoteric substance. **24:7**
24:19	K	define neutral, neutralization, and salt and complete equations for neutralization reactions. **24:8**
24:20	K/P	name and write formulas for acidic salts. **24:8**
24:21	K	define and distinguish between strong and weak acids, and strong and weak bases. **24:9**
24:22	K	define spectator ion. **24:10**
24:23	K/P	given a reaction taking place in water, write a net ionic equation for the reaction. **24:10**
24:24	K	define ionization constant. **24:11**
24:25	K/P	write ionization constant expressions for weak acids and weak bases. **24:11**
24:26	P	calculate the ionization constant for a weak acid or a weak base. **24:11**
24:27	P	calculate the hydronium ion concentration given K_a. **24:11**
24:28	K	define percent of ionization. **24:12**
24:29	P	calculate the percent ionization given either the hydronium ion concentration or the K_a. **24:12**
24:30	K/P	explain the common ion effect. **24:13**
24:31	P	calculate the hydronium ion concentration in a solution containing an acid and a salt with a common ion. **24:13**
24:32	K/P	define and give examples of polyprotic acids and their stepwise ionization. **24:14**
24:33	A	voluntarily complete one or more of the One More Step activities.
24:34	A	read unassigned literature related to the chapter.

TEACHING TECHNIQUES

Section 24:1

The first three sections of the chapter discuss the three popular theories regarding the definition of acids and bases. Point out to students that each definition has two parts—descriptive and theoretical. All three theories describe acid properties as is shown in the chapter opening demonstration (sour taste, electrolyte, affect indicators, and react with metals to produce H_2). What makes each theory unique is the theoretical description of behavior (ionizable hydrogen, proton donor, or electron pair acceptor). Your students will ask, "which one is the right definition?" They all are. As in Chapter 13, different observations can be explained by different theories. Arrhenius' theory applies only to water solutions. The Brønsted-Lowry theory can be used with all solvents that will gain or lose a proton, including water. As a result, this theory is more widely applicable.

Section 24:9

Acids and bases can be grouped as either strong or weak with no intermediate groups. Orthophosphoric acid is an exception. This acid is intermediate between strong and weak acids. It is much weaker than strong acids like HCl and H_2SO_4 but much stronger than acetic acid.

Technology and Chemistry

This topic is included as it is somewhat controversial. In addition to focusing on the chemistry of acid rain, you may want to have students consider who is to accept the responsibility for reducing anhydride levels in the atmosphere and the costs associated with repairing the damage caused by acid rain.

PROBLEM SOLUTIONS

Page 463

1. **a.** acid – HNO_3
   base – NaOH
   conjugate acid – H_2O
   conjugate base – $NaNO_3$
   b. acid – HCl
   base – $NaHCO_3$
   conjugate acid – H_2CO_3
   conjugate base – NaCl

Page 465

2. **a.** Lewis base   **c.** Lewis acid
   b. Lewis base   **d.** Lewis base

3. $Ag^+ + 2NH_3 \rightarrow Ag(NH_3)_2^+$

4. $Cu^{2+} + 4NH_3 \rightarrow Cu(NH_3)_4^{2+}$

5. $Co^{3+} + 6NH_3 \rightarrow Co(NH_3)_6^{3+}$

6. $Fe^{3+} + 6CN^- \rightarrow Fe(CN)_6^{3-}$

7. $Zn^{2+} + 4OH^- \rightarrow Zn(OH)_4^{2-}$

Page 466

8. **a.** hydrobromic acid
   b. hydrofluoric acid

Page 467

9. **a.** boric acid
   b. nitrous acid
   c. phosphoric acid
   d. arsenous acid
   e. iodic acid

10. **a.** H_2CO_3
    b. HNO_3
    c. H_3AsO_4
    d. H_2SeO_4
    e. HIO

Page 469

11. **a.** basic
    b. basic
    c. acidic
    d. basic
    e. acidic

12. **a.** BaO
    b. I_2O_7
    c. TeO_3
    d. Al_2O_3
    e. ZnO

Page 471

13. **a.** sodium hydrogen sulfate
    b. potassium hydrogen tartrate
    c. sodium dihydrogen phosphate
    d. sodium hydrogen sulfide
    e. aluminum hydroxide silicate

14. **a.** $NaHCO_3$
    b. Na_2HPO_4
    c. NH_4HS
    d. $KHSO_4$
    e. $Sn(OH)NO_3$

Page 474

15. $2Cl^-(aq) + 2Cr^{2+}(aq) + 2Hg^{2+}(aq) \rightarrow 2Cr^{3+}(aq) + Hg_2Cl_2(cr)$

16. $2Mn^{2+}(aq) + 5NaBiO_3(cr) + 14H^+(aq) \rightarrow 2MnO_4^-(aq) + 5Bi^{3+}(aq) + 7H_2O(l) + 5Na^+(aq)$

17. $2Ag^+(aq) + HSO_4^-(aq) \rightarrow Ag_2SO_4(cr) + H^+(aq)$

18. $H_4SiO_4(aq) + 4OH^-(aq) \rightarrow SiO_4^{4-}(aq) + 4H_2O(l)$

19. $2Cu^{2+}(aq) + SO_4^{2-}(aq) + 2CNS^-(aq) + H_2SO_3(aq) + H_2O(l) \rightarrow 2CuCNS(cr) + 2HSO_4^-(aq) + 2H^+(aq)$

Page 476

20. $HClO + H_2O \rightleftharpoons H_3O^+ + ClO^-$
    $K_a = \dfrac{[H_3O^+][ClO^-]}{[HClO]} = 3.16 \times 10^{-8} = \dfrac{x^2}{0.0200 - \text{\textcircled{x}}} \leftarrow$ neglect
    $x = 2.51 \times 10^{-5} M$

21. $N_2H_4 + H_2O \rightleftharpoons N_2H_5^+ + OH^-$
    $K_b = \dfrac{[N_2H_5^+][OH^-]}{[N_2H_4]} = \dfrac{(1.23 \times 10^{-3})^2}{0.499}$
    $K_b = 3.03 \times 10^{-6}$

Page 477

22. $K_a = \dfrac{[CH_3COO^-][H_3O^+]}{[CH_3COOH]}$
    $1.76 \times 10^{-5} = \dfrac{x^2}{0.200 - \text{\textcircled{x}}} \leftarrow$ neglect
    $x^2 = 3.52 \times 10^{-6}$
    $x = 1.88 \times 10^{-3}$
    $\% = \dfrac{1.88 \times 10^{-3}}{0.200} \left| \dfrac{100}{1} \right. = 0.940\%$

23. $K_a = \dfrac{[A^-][H_3O^+]}{[HA]} = \dfrac{(0.0200)^2}{0.980} = 4.08 \times 10^{-4}$

Page 479

24. $HNO_2 + H_2O \rightleftarrows H_3O^+ + NO_2^-$

$$K_a = \frac{[H_3O^+][NO_2^-]}{[HNO_2]}$$

$$4.60 \times 10^{-4} = \frac{x(\cancel{x} + 0.03)}{(0.150 - \cancel{x})} \leftarrow \text{neglect}$$

$x = 2.30 \times 10^{-3}M$

25. $HBrO + H_2O \rightleftarrows H_3O^+ + BrO^-$

$$K_a = \frac{[H_3O^+][BrO^-]}{[HBrO]}$$

$$2.40 \times 10^{-9} = \frac{x(\cancel{x} + 0.000195)}{0.403 - \cancel{x}} \leftarrow \text{neglect}$$

$x = 4.96 \times 10^{-6}M$

26. Add either HCO_3^- or CO_3^{2-} in the form of soluble salts; add H_3O^+

Page 480

27. oxalic acid $\dfrac{5.90 \times 10^{-2}}{6.40 \times 10^{-5}} = 9.22 \times 10^2$

carbonic acid $\dfrac{4.30 \times 10^{-7}}{5.61 \times 10^{-11}} = 7.66 \times 10^3$

phosphoric acid $\dfrac{7.52 \times 10^{-3}}{6.23 \times 10^{-8}} = 1.21 \times 10^5$

sulfurous acid $\dfrac{1.54 \times 10^{-2}}{1.02 \times 10^{-7}} = 1.51 \times 10^5$

boric acid $\dfrac{7.30 \times 10^{-10}}{1.80 \times 10^{-13}} = 4.06 \times 10^3$

selenous acid $\dfrac{3.50 \times 10^{-2}}{4.80 \times 10^{-9}} = 7.29 \times 10^6$

phosphorous acid $\dfrac{1.00 \times 10^{-2}}{2.60 \times 10^{-7}} = 3.85 \times 10^4$

Pattern: There is a very large difference between the 1st and 2nd ionizations.

CHAPTER END PROBLEMS

Pages 482-483

1.

	Acid	Base	Conjugate acid	Conjugate base
a.	H_3O^+	NH_3	NH_4^+	H_2O
b.	CH_3OH	NH_2^-	NH_3	CH_3O^-
c.	H_3O^+	OH^-	H_2O	H_2O
d.	H_2O	NH_2^-	NH_3	OH^-
e.	$HClO_4$	H_2O	H_3O^+	ClO_4^-

2. a.

:Cl:
Al:Cl: acid (electron-pair acceptor)
:Cl:

b. :Ö:S:Ö:⟷:Ö::S:Ö:⟷:Ö:S:Ö: acid
       :Ö: :Ö: :Ö:

c. H
     :P:H   base (electron-pair donor)
        H

d. :Xe: base

e. Zn^{2+} acid

3. a. hydrobromic acid
b. hydroselenic acid
c. iodic acid
d. selenious acid
e. hyponitrous acid

4. a. H_3PO_3
b. H_3PO_2
c. H_2Te
d. HIO_4
e. HIO_3
f. HCl

5. a. NaOH
b. $Ca(OH)_2$
c. HNO_3
d. RbOH
e. H_2TeO_3
f. CsOH

6. a. Sc_2O_3
b. Cs_2O
c. I_2O_5
d. Ga_2O_3
e. CdO
f. K_2O

7. a. $6Cr^{2+} + 3Cu^{2+} \rightarrow 3Cu + 6Cr^{3+}$
b. $3H^+ + HSO_4^- + MnO_2 + 2Br^- \rightarrow Mn^{2+} + SO_4^{2-} + Br_2 + 2H_2O$
c. $H^+ + HSO_4^- \rightarrow H_2O + SO_3$
d. $P_4O_{10} + 6H_2O \rightarrow 4H_3PO_4$
e. $4CuCNS + 7IO_3^- + 14H^+ + 7Cl^- \rightarrow 4HCN + 4Cu^{2+} + 4SO_4^{2-} + 7ICl + 5H_2O$

8. a. sodium phosphate, Na_3PO_4
b. potassium borate, K_3BO_3
c. chromium(III) perchlorate, $Cr(ClO_4)_3$
d. cadmium bromide, $CdBr_2$
e. lithium orthosilicate, Li_4SiO_4

9. A Lewis acid does not necessarily produce H^+ in water solution.

10. $CH_3CH_2Cl + AlCl_3 \rightarrow AlCl_4^- + CH_3CH_2^+$
$CH_3CH_2^+ + C_6H_6 \rightarrow C_6H_6CH_2CH_3^+$
$C_6H_6CH_2CH_3^+ + AlCl_4^- \rightarrow C_6H_5CH_2CH_3 + HCl + AlCl_3$

11. Metals have low electronegativities. Oxygen pulls shared electrons away from the metal keeping the hydrogen joined to the oxygen.

12. H_2SO_4 is completely ionized in solution, while H_2CO_3 is only partially ionized in solution.

13. Insoluble salts do not dissociate.

14. Two or more substances producing the same ion in an equilibrium system exhibit the common ion effect.

15. With each succeeding ionization, it becomes more difficult to remove a positive charge from an increasingly negative ion.

16. $KHSO_4 \rightarrow K^+ + HSO_4^-$ 100%

$H_2O + HSO_4^- \rightleftharpoons H_3O^+ + SO_4^{2-}$

$[SO_4^{2-}] = [H_3O^+] = x$

$K_a = \dfrac{[H_3O^+][SO_4^{2-}]}{[HSO_4^-]} = 1.20 \times 10^{-2}$

$= \dfrac{[H_3O^+]^2}{0.100 - [H_3O^+]} = \dfrac{x^2}{0.100 - x}$

The x in $0.100 - x$ is *not* negligible since the concentration (0.1) is so close to the K_a (1.2×10^{-2}).

Solving for x by the quadratic formula:

$1.2 \times 10^{-3} - 1.2 \times 10^{-2} x = x^2$

$x^2 + 1.2 \times 10^{-2} x - 1.2 \times 10^{-3} = 0$

$x = \dfrac{-1.2 \times 10^{-2}}{2}$

$\dfrac{\pm \sqrt{1.44 \times 10^{-4} + 4.8 \times 10^{-3}}}{2}$

$x = \dfrac{-1.2 \times 10^{-2} \pm \sqrt{4.94 \times 10^{-3}}}{2}$

$x = \dfrac{5.83 \times 10^{-2}}{2}$

$x = 2.92 \times 10^{-2} M = [H^+] = [H_3O^+]$

17. % ionization $= \dfrac{[H_3O^+]}{[HSO_4^-]} \ \bigg| \ \dfrac{100}{}$

$= \dfrac{2.92 \times 10^{-2}}{0.100} \ \bigg| \ \dfrac{100}{1} = 29.2\%$

18. $K_a = \dfrac{[H_3O^+][C_6H_5COO^-]}{[C_6H_5COOH]}$

$[H_3O^+] = [C_6H_5COO^-] = x$

$K_a = 6.46 \times 10^{-5} = \dfrac{x^2}{0.0178 - \textcircled{x}} \leftarrow$ neglect

$x^2 = 1.15 \times 10^{-6}$

$x = 1.07 \times 10^{-3} M = [C_6H_5COO^-]$

19. $HOOC-COOH + H_2 \rightleftharpoons HOOC-COO^- + H_3O^+$

neglect second ionization (3 orders of magnitude less)

$K_a = \dfrac{[HOOC-COO^-][H_3O^+]}{[HOOC-COOH]}$

$[HOOC-COO^-] = [H_3O^+] = x$

$K_a = 5.90 \times 10^{-2} = \dfrac{x^2}{0.884 - x}$

$5.22 \times 10^{-2} - 5.90 \times 10^{-2} x = x^2$

$x^2 + 5.90 \times 10^{-2} x - 5.22 \times 10^{-2} = 0$

$= \dfrac{-5.90 \times 10^{-2} \pm \sqrt{3.48 \times 10^{-3} + 2.09 \times 10^{-1}}}{2}$

$= \dfrac{-5.90 \times 10^{-2} \pm \sqrt{2.12 \times 10^{-1}}}{2}$

$= \dfrac{-5.90 \times 10^{-2} \pm 4.60 \times 10^{-1}}{2}$

$= 2.01 \times 10^{-1} M = [H_3O^+]$

neglect the negative answer as meaningless

REVIEW

Page 483

1. A reaction whose products will react to produce the original reactants.

2. molarity

3. increased number of collisions per unit time; more collisions have the requisite activation energy

4. homogeneous reactions—all reactants in the same phase
   heterogeneous reactions—reactants in two or more phases

5. $\dfrac{k_f}{k_r} = K_{eq}$

6. shift left

7. No. Methane is nonpolar and water is polar.

8. unsaturated—more solute will dissolve
   saturated—dissolved solute in equilibrium with undissolved solute
   supersaturated—more solute per unit of solvent than in saturated solution

9. concentrated—high ratio of solute to solution
   dilute—low ratio of solute to solution

10. positive

11. rate $= k[IO_3^-][Br^-]^2$

12. $K_a = \dfrac{[H_3O^+][C_6H_5O^-]}{[C_6H_5OH]}$

$1.02 \times 10^{-10} = \dfrac{x^2}{0.250 - \textcircled{x}} \leftarrow$ neglect

$x = 5.05 \times 10^{-6} M$

13. $\log K_{eq} = \dfrac{\Delta G}{-2.30 \, RT}$

$= \dfrac{-55.6}{(-2.30)(0.00831)(298)}$

$= 9.7618$

$K_{eq} = $ antilog $9.7618 = 5.78 \times 10^9$

ONE MORE STEP

Page 483

1. All strong acids ionize completely in water because water is a strong enough base to remove all protons from an acid. However, in less basic solvents, these acids (for example, $HClO_4$, HCl, HNO_3) would not be completely ionized, and an order of relative strength can be set up. Because water is basic, it "levels" the effect of these acids to equality.

2. H_2SO_5 peroxysulfuric acid (contains —O—O— peroxy group)

   $H_2S_2O_7$ disulfuric acid (contains 2 sulfuric acid molecules condensed)

   $H_2S_2O_8$ peroxydisulfuric acid (both of above reasons)

   HNCO   isocyanic acid (HOCN is normal cyanic acid)

   HSCN   thiocyanic acid (S substituted for O in normal cyanic acid)

3. acid = carboxylic acids (R—COOH)
   base = amines (R—NH_2)

SOLUTIONS OF ELECTROLYTES *25*

AN OVERVIEW

Chapter 25 presents the practical side of acid, base, and salt behavior to students. Solubility product constant is described both qualitatively and quantitatively. Common ion effect is demonstrated mathematically. The sequence is for students to progress from the ionization of water, to pH, and then to the hydrolysis of salts. The concepts of hydrolysis and the common ion effect are linked in a practical study of buffers. Students are prepared for laboratory work with a study of indicators followed by titration calculations.

DEMONSTRATION INFORMATION

Prepare 50 cm^3 of 0.5M Pb(NO$_3$)$_2$ by dissolving 8.25 g in enough water to make 50 cm^3 of solution. Prepare 100 cm^3 of 0.5M Na$_2$SO$_4$ by dissolving 7.1 g anhydrous Na$_2$SO$_4$ in enough H$_2$O to prepare 100 cm^3 of solution. 0.5M Na$_2$S can be prepared by dissolving 12 g in 100 cm^3 of solution. The white to black color change is dramatic.

$$PbSO_4 \rightleftarrows Pb^{2+} + SO_4^{2-}$$
$$Pb^{2+} + S^{2-} \rightarrow PbS$$

Lead(II) sulfate is very slightly soluble with a K_{sp} of 1.9 × 10^{-8}. As the Pb^{2+} ion reacts with S^{2-} ion, the equilibrium shifts to produce more Pb^{2+}. Most Pb^{2+} cations will be converted from PbSO$_4$ to PbS.

DISPOSAL: *Decant the liquid. Pour it down the drain with a large quantity of water. Dispose of the precipitate in the normal manner by placing it in your solid waste container. It can then be put in a local landfill.*

PERFORMANCE OBJECTIVES

Goals: Students will gain an understanding of the interaction of salts with water and with acid-base solutions. Students will solve problems dealing with solubility, common ion, and solubility product. Students will gain an understanding of pH and learn a number of methods with which to determine its value.

Objectives: Upon completion of the reading and problems, and when asked to demonstrate their understanding either orally or on a written test, students will

25:1	K	define solubility product constant, K_{sp}. **25:1**
25:2	K/P	use the equilibrium constant to develop the solubility product constant. **25:1**
25:3	K/P	use the solubility product constant of a given salt to determine the effect of a common ion. **25:1**
25:4	K/P	use the solubility product constant to determine whether a precipitate will form from the combining of two salt solutions. **25:1**
25:5	K/P	use the solubility product constant to find the concentration of an ion in a saturated salt solution and vice versa. **25:1**
25:6	K	define ion product constant of water, K_w. **25:2**
25:7	K/P	use the equilibrium constant for water to find the ion product constant of water. **25:2**
25:8	K/P	calculate the concentrations of hydronium ion and hydroxide ion in an aqueous solution of a salt. **25:2**
25:9	K	define the pH scale. **25:3**
25:10	K/P	calculate the pH of a solution given the hydronium ion concentration. **25:3**
25:11	K/P	calculate the hydronium ion concentration of a solution given its pH. **25:3**
25:12	K	define hydrolysis. **25:4**
25:13	K/P	write equations for hydrolysis reactions, and predict the acidity or basicity of hydrolysis products. **25:4**
25:14	K	define buffer system. **25:5**
25:15	K/P	describe and give examples of buffered systems. **25:5**
25:16	K	define pH meter. **25:6**
25:17	K	define and describe the use of indicators. **25:6**
25:18	K/P	list the limitations of indicators. **25:6**
25:19	K	define titration. **25:7**
25:20	K/P	explain titration as a laboratory tool and interpret graphs of titration data. **25:7**
25:21	K/P	using titration data, solve for the concentration of an unknown acid or base. **25:7**
25:22	K	define standard solution and endpoint. **25:7**
25:23	K/P	determine the amount of a specified acid or base that will neutralize a specific amount of a second base or acid, respectively. **25:7**

25:24   A   voluntarily complete one or more of the One More Step activities.

25:25   A   read unassigned literature related to the chapter.

TEACHING TECHNIQUES

Section 25:7
Normal Solutions

An older quantitative method of expressing the concentration of solutions is normality. A 1-normal ($1N$) solution contains one equivalent mass of solute per liter of solution.

For the moment, we may define the equivalent mass of a substance as the mass of a mole of the substance divided by the total positive charge in the compound. For instance, 1 mole of $NaCl$ is 58.5 g; its total positive charge is 1. Therefore, its equivalent mass is 58.5 g. One mole of $Bi(NO_3)_3$ is 395 g; its total positive charge is 3. Therefore, its equivalent mass is 132. One mole of $Al_2(SO_4)_3$ is 342; its total positive charge is 6. Therefore, its equivalent mass is 57 g.

Equivalents

If 1 mole of $NaOH$ is added to 1 mole of HCl, 1 mole of water and 1 mole of salt are formed: $HCl + NaOH \rightarrow NaCl + H_2O$. What will happen if 1 mole of $NaOH$ is added to 1 mole of H_3PO_4? $NaOH(aq) + H_3PO_4(aq) \rightarrow NaH_2PO_4(aq) + H_2O(l)$ or, eliminating the spectator ion:
$$OH^-(aq) + H_3PO_4(aq) \rightarrow H_2PO_4^-(aq) + H_2O(l)$$
However, we can see that each $H_2PO_4^-$ ion has two more protons which can be liberated, so in order to neutralize all available protons, 3 moles of $NaOH$ are needed.
$$3\ NaOH(aq) + H_3PO_4(aq) \rightarrow Na_3PO_4(aq) + 3H_2O(l)$$
One mole of H_3PO_4 is equivalent to 3 moles of $NaOH$.

The important reactants in the neutralization reaction are H_3O^+ and OH^-. But one mole of $NaOH$ contains one mole of OH^- while one mole of H_3PO_4 contains three moles of H^+. We could solve the problem by expressing concentrations in terms of moles of H^+ and OH^-, or in terms of equivalents. One equivalent of acid is the amount of acid that can donate 1 mole of H^+ ions to a strong base. One equivalent of base can donate 1 mole of OH^- ions. One equivalent of acid will exactly neutralize one equivalent of base.

Normality and Equivalents

An equivalent of an acid must yield one mole of H^+ (H_3O^+) ions. One dm^3 of a $1N$ solution of any acid will contain one mole of H^+ ions.

For example, the equivalent mass of HCl is

$$\frac{molecular\ mass}{total\ positive\ charge} = \frac{36.5\ g}{1} = 36.5\ g$$

A $1N$ HCl solution contains one mole of HCl and will yield one mole of H^+ ions. The equivalent mass of H_3PO_4, on the other hand, is the molecular mass divided by 3. Since one mole of H_3PO_4 would release 3 moles of H^+ ions, one equivalent mass would release 1 mole of H^+ ions. Equivalents of acid (or base) can be expressed in terms of normality. A $0.5N$ H_2SO_4 solution means that one dm^3 of solution contains one-half mole of H^+ ions.

One advantage of this concentration unit is that we can then pour the amount of H^+ or OH^- ions that we want. If we need two equivalents of H_2SO_4, we can use 500 cm^3 of $4N$ H_2SO_4, 1000 cm^3 of $2N$ H_2SO_4, 2 dm^3 of $1N$ H_2SO_4 or 8 dm^3 of $0.25N$ H_2SO_4. Notice that in every case, the product of the volume in dm^3 and the normality is 2, the number of equivalents needed.

$$0.5\ dm^3 \times 4N = 2\ equivalents$$
$$1\ dm^3 \times 2N = 2\ equivalents$$
$$2\ dm^3 \times 1N = 2\ equivalents$$
$$8\ dm^3 \times 0.25N = 2\ equivalents$$

Titration

The equivalents of acid can be calculated by multiplying the volume of acid solution by the normality of the acid solution.
$$(dm^3) \times (eq/dm^3) = eq$$
$$V_a \times N_a = equivalents\ of\ acid$$
The equivalents of base in the titrated solution are equivalent to the volume of the basic solution times the unknown normality of the solution.
$$V_b \times N_b = equivalents\ of\ base$$
Since we stop titrating exactly at the point of complete neutralization, the equivalents of acid are equal to the equivalents of base or:
$$V_a \times N_a = V_b \times N_b$$
We now know V_a, N_a, and V_b and we can solve the equation for N_b, the normality of the basic solution we may have just titrated.

Suppose that we use 15.0 cm^3 of $NaOH$ and 25.0 cm^3 of vinegar solution. What is the normality of the vinegar solution?

$V_a \times N_a = V_b \times N_b$

$N_a = \dfrac{V_b \times N_b}{V_a}$ Notice that it is not necessary to convert cm^3 to dm^3

$N_a = \dfrac{15.0\ cm^3 \times 0.5N}{25.0\ cm^3}$ as long as both volumes are in the same units.

$N_a = 0.3N$

Example: Titration
How many cm^3 of $0.02N$ KOH will exactly neutralize 15 cm^3 of $0.4N$ H_2SO_4?

$V_b \times N_b = V_a \times N_a$

$V_b = \dfrac{V_a \times N_a}{N_b}$

$V_b = \dfrac{15 \text{ cm}^3 \times 0.4N}{0.02N}$

$V_b = 300 \text{ cm}^3$

Notice that the volume will have the same units as the known solution.

Technology And Chemistry

This feature is included to provide added insight into an important topic in the chapter—ion activity. You can have students research the mathematics associated with ion activity problems as this is a topic they will encounter if they proceed to college chemistry.

PROBLEM SOLUTIONS

Page 488

1. **a.** $K_{sp} = [Pb^{2+}][I^-]^2$
   b. $K_{sp} = [Cu^{2+}]^3[PO_4^{3-}]^2$

2. $AgI \rightleftharpoons Ag^+ + I^-$
   $K_{sp} = [Ag^+][I^-]$
   $[Ag^+] = [I^-] = x$
   $x^2 = 1.50 \times 10^{-16}$
   $x = 1.22 \times 10^{-8}M = [Ag^+]$

3. $D_2A \rightleftharpoons 2D^+ + A^{2-}$
   $K_{sp} = [D^+]^2[A^{2-}]$
   $2[A^{2-}] = [D^+] = 2.00 \times 10^{-5}$
   $[A^{2-}] = 1.00 \times 10^{-5}$
   $K_{sp} = (2.00 \times 10^{-5})^2(1.00 \times 10^{-5})$
   $K_{sp} = 4.00 \times 10^{-15}$

4. $Be(OH)_2 \rightleftharpoons Be^{2+} + 2OH^-$
   $K_{sp} = [Be^{2+}][OH^-]^2$
   $1.60 \times 10^{-22} = x(2x)^2$
   $x = 3.42 \times 10^{-8}M$

5. $PbI_2 \rightleftharpoons Pb^{2+} + 2I^-$
   $K_{sp} = [Pb^{2+}][I^-]^2$
   $K_{sp} = (1.21 \times 10^{-3})(2.42 \times 10^{-3})^2$
   $K_{sp} = 7.09 \times 10^{-9}$

Page 490

6. $H_2O + H_2O \rightleftharpoons H_3O^+ + OH^-$
   $K_w = [H_3O^+][OH^-]$
   $1.00 \times 10^{-14} = x(6.80 \times 10^{-10})$
   $x = 1.47 \times 10^{-5}M$

7. $H_2O + H_2O \rightleftharpoons H_3O^+ + OH^-$
   $K_w = [H_3O^+][OH^-]$
   $1.00 \times 10^{-14} = x(5.67 \times 10^{-3})$
   $x = 1.76 \times 10^{-12}M$

Page 493

8. **a.** $-\log(1.00 \times 10^{-3}) = 3.00$
   b. $-\log(1.00 \times 10^{-6}) = 6.00$
   c. $-\log(6.59 \times 10^{-10}) = 9.18$
   d. $-\log(7.01 \times 10^{-6}) = 5.15$
   e. $-\log(9.47 \times 10^{-8}) = 7.02$
   f. $-\log(6.89 \times 10^{-14}) = 13.2$

9. **a.** antilog$(-3.000) = 1.00 \times 10^{-3}M$
   b. antilog$(-10.000) = 1.00 \times 10^{-10}M$
   c. antilog$(-6.607) = 2.47 \times 10^{-7}M$
   d. antilog$(-2.523) = 3.00 \times 10^{-3}M$
   e. antilog$(-6.149) = 7.10 \times 10^{-7}M$
   f. antilog$(-7.662) = 2.18 \times 10^{-8}M$

Page 494

10. **a.** acidic
    b. acidic
    c. acidic
    d. acidic
    e. basic
    f. basic

Page 500

11. $\dfrac{21.4 \text{ cm}^3 \text{ HCl}}{} \left| \dfrac{0.106 \text{ mol HCl}}{1000 \text{ cm}^3 \text{ HCl}} \right| \dfrac{1 \text{ mol NaOH}}{1 \text{ mol HCl}} \left| \dfrac{1000 \text{ cm}^3 \text{ NaOH}}{0.0947 \text{ mol NaOH}} \right. = 24.0 \text{ cm}^3 \text{ NaOH}$

12. $\dfrac{21.7 \text{ cm}^3 \text{ HBr}}{} \left| \dfrac{0.500 \text{ mol HBr}}{1000 \text{ cm}^3 \text{ HBr}} \right| \dfrac{1 \text{ mol LiOH}}{1 \text{ mol HBr}} \left| \dfrac{}{26.4 \text{ cm}^3} \right| \dfrac{1000 \text{ cm}^3}{1 \text{ dm}^3} = 0.411M \text{ LiOH}$

CHAPTER END PROBLEMS

Pages 503-504

1. $\dfrac{27.3 \text{ cm}^3}{} \left| \dfrac{0.413 \text{ mol HBr}}{1000 \text{ cm}^3} \right| \dfrac{1 \text{ mol LiOH}}{1 \text{ mol HBr}} \left| \dfrac{1000 \text{ cm}^3}{0.196 \text{ mol LiOH}} \right. = 57.5 \text{ cm}^3$

2. $\dfrac{75.0 \text{ cm}^3}{95.5 \text{ cm}^3} \left| \dfrac{0.823 \text{ mol HClO}_4}{1000 \text{ cm}^3} \right| \dfrac{1 \text{ mol Ba(OH)}_2}{2 \text{ mol HClO}_4} \left| \dfrac{1000 \text{ cm}^3}{1 \text{ dm}^3} \right. = 0.323M \text{ Ba(OH)}_2$

3. Increase the Cl^- concentration by adding a soluble salt or acid producing Cl^- in solution.

4. 1×10^{-14}

5. $pOH = 14 - pH$.

6. Hydrolysis is the reaction of a salt with water to produce an acidic, basic, or neutral solution.

7. The anion of the salt reacts with the H^+ of the water leaving OH^- in the solution. Thus, it is basic.

8. The type of solution formed depends on the degree of weakness of the acid and base. Thus, the solution could be acidic, basic, or neutral.

9. A buffer contains an ion in common between the acid or base, and its salt.

10. Rebreathing exhaled air increases the CO_2 concentration in the blood. Thus, the proper pH is restored.

11. $MnS \rightleftharpoons Mn^{2+} + S^{2-}$

$$K_{sp} = [Mn^{2+}][S^{2-}]$$
$$1.40 \times 10^{-15} = 0.100[S^{2-}]$$
$$[S^{2-}] = 1.40 \times 10^{-14}$$

12. $[H_3O^+] = \dfrac{1.00 \times 10^{-14}}{[OH^-]} = \dfrac{1.00 \times 10^{-14}}{2.77 \times 10^{-10}} = 3.61 \times 10^{-5}M$

13. $pOH = -\log[OH^-] = 6.13$
$$[OH^-] = 7.41 \times 10^{-7}M$$

14. $Mg(OH)_2 \rightleftharpoons Mg^{2+} + 2OH^-$

$$K_{sp} = [Mg^{2+}][OH^-]^2$$
$$2[Mg^{2+}] = [OH^-]$$
$$[Mg^{2+}] = x$$
$$1.20 \times 10^{-11} = x(2x)^2$$
$$1.20 \times 10^{-11} = 4x^3$$
$$x^3 = 3.00 \times 10^{-12}$$
$$x = 1.44 \times 10^{-4}$$
$$[OH^-] = 2.88 \times 10^{-4}$$
$$[H^+] = \dfrac{1.00 \times 10^{-14}}{2.88 \times 10^{-4}} = 3.47 \times 10^{-11}$$
$$pH = 10.5$$

19. $NaOH + HCl \rightarrow NaCl + H_2O$

21.2 cm³ HCl	0.0800 mol HCl	1 mol NaOH	1000 cm³
25.0 cm³ NaOH	1000 cm³ HCl	1 mol HCl	1 dm³

$$= 0.0678M \text{ NaOH}$$

20.
86.2 cm³ NaOH	0.765 mol NaOH	1 mol HCl	1000 cm³
30.0 cm³ HCl	1000 cm³ NaOH	1 mol NaOH	1 dm³

$$= 2.20M \text{ HCl}$$

21. $2KOH + H_2SO_4 \rightarrow K_2SO_4 + 2H_2O$

40.8 cm³ H₂SO₄	0.106 mol H₂SO₄	2 mol KOH	1000 cm³	
61.8 cm³ KOH	1000 cm³ H₂SO₄	1 mol H₂SO₄	1 dm³	= 0.140M KOH

15. $[OH^-] = 1 \times 10^{-4}$ $[H^+] = 1 \times 10^{-10}$
$$pH = 10$$

16.
$$K_a = \dfrac{[H_3O^+][CN^-]}{[HCN]}$$
$$K_a = 4.93 \times 10^{-10}$$
$$= \dfrac{[x](0.00100 + (x))}{0.300 - x} \quad \leftarrow \text{neglect}$$
$$x = [H_3O^+] = \dfrac{1.48 \times 10^{-10}}{0.00100} = 1.48 \times 10^{-7}M$$
$$pH = 6.83$$

17. a. neutral
b. basic, $CO_3^{2-} + H_2O \rightarrow HCO_3^- + OH^-$
c. acidic, $Al(H_2O)_6^{3+} + H_2O \rightarrow Al(H_2O)_5(OH)^{2+} + H_3O^+$
d. acidic, $Hg^{2+} + H_2O \rightarrow HgOH^+ + H^+$
e. neutral

18. $HCN + H_2O \rightleftharpoons H_3O^+ + CN^-$
$$K_a = \dfrac{[H_3O^+][CN^-]}{[HCN]}$$
$$4.93 \times 10^{-10} = \dfrac{x(0.00150 + (x))}{0.0100 - (x)} \quad \leftarrow \text{neglect}$$
$$x = 3.29 \times 10^{-9}$$
$$pH = 8.48$$

REVIEW

Pages 504-505

1. $\dfrac{46.6 \text{ g Hg(CN)}_2}{1.00 \text{ dm}^3 \text{ soln}} \quad \dfrac{1 \text{ mol Hg(CN)}_2}{253 \text{ g Hg(CN)}_2} = 0.184M \text{ Hg(CN)}_2$

2. $\dfrac{0.944 \text{ g K}_3AsO_4}{10.0 \text{ g H}_2O} \quad \dfrac{1 \text{ mol K}_3AsO_4}{256 \text{ g K}_3AsO_4} \quad \dfrac{1000 \text{ g}}{1 \text{ kg}} = 0.369m \text{ K}_3AsO_4$

3. $\dfrac{1.00 \times 10^2 \text{ g Rb}_2C_4H_4O_6}{} \quad \dfrac{1 \text{ mol Rb}_2C_4H_4O_6}{319 \text{ g Rb}_2C_4H_4O_6} = 0.313 \text{ mol Rb}_2C_4H_4O_6$

$\dfrac{50.0 \text{ g H}_2O}{} \quad \dfrac{1 \text{ mol H}_2O}{18.0 \text{ g H}_2O} = 2.78 \text{ mol H}_2$

$\dfrac{0.313}{3.09} = 0.101 \text{ mole fraction Rb}_2C_4H_4O_6$

4. $\dfrac{39.5 \text{ g C}_6H_{12}O_6}{} \quad \dfrac{1 \text{ mol C}_6H_{12}O_6}{180 \text{ g C}_6H_{12}O_6} = 0.219 \text{ mol C}_6H_{12}O_6$

$\dfrac{1.00 \times 10^2 \text{ g H}_2O}{} \quad \dfrac{1 \text{ mol H}_2O}{18.0 \text{ g H}_2O} = 5.56 \text{ mol H}_2O$

$\dfrac{5.56}{5.78} = 0.962 \text{ mole fraction H}_2O$

v.p. soln = (v.p. solvent) (x)
v.p. soln = (4.2 kPa)(0.962) = 4.04 kPa

5. $\dfrac{42.2 \text{ g } C_6H_{12}O_6}{2.00 \times 10^2 \text{ g } H_2O} \left| \dfrac{1 \text{ mol } C_6H_{12}O_6}{180 \text{ g } C_6H_{12}O_6} \right| \dfrac{1000 \text{ g}}{1 \text{ kg}}$

$= 1.17m\ C_6H_{12}O_6$

$\Delta T_{FP} = m \cdot K_{FP} = (1.17m)(1.86C°/m) = 2.18\ C°$

$\Delta T_{BP} = m \cdot K_{BP} = (1.17m)(0.512C°/m) = 0.599\ C°$

$FP = 0° - 2.18° = -2.18°C$

$BP = 100° + 0.599° = 100.60°C$

6. $m = \dfrac{\Delta T_{FP}}{K_{FP}} = \dfrac{1.83}{1.86} = 0.984m$

mols solute $= (0.984)\left(\dfrac{250}{1000}\right) = 0.246 \quad \dfrac{22.2}{0.246} = 90.2 \text{ g/mol}$

7. $\Pi = MRT$

$\Pi = \dfrac{7.10 \text{ g}}{0.500 \text{ dm}^3} \left| \dfrac{1 \text{ mol}}{1.00 \times 10^3 \text{ g}} \right| \dfrac{8.31 \text{ dm}^3 \cdot kPa}{mol \cdot K} \left| \right. 298\ K = 35.2\ kPa$

8. rate $= k[PCl_3][Cl_2]$

9. $K_{eq} = \dfrac{[CO_3{}^{2-}]}{[HCO_3{}^-][OH^-]}$

10. $\log K_{eq} = \dfrac{\Delta G}{-2.30\ RT}$

$= \dfrac{-8170\ J}{(-2.30)(8.31)(298)}$

$= 1.43$

$K_{eq} = $ antilog of $1.43 = 26.9$

11. base $-$ LiH

acid $-$ BH_3

conjugate base $-$ $BH_4{}^-$

conjugate acid $-$ Li^+

12. Tl^+ can be classified as either a Lewis acid or base. Since it has a positive charge, it can accept electrons, but it also retains two of its outer level electrons which it can donate.

ONE MORE STEP

Page 505

1. See Jensen, William B., "Lewis Acid-Base Theory: Part III Hard and Soft Acid-Base Theory," *Journal of Chemical Education*, Vol. 47 No. 5(May 1974)

2. $Ac^- + H_2O \rightarrow HAc + OH^-$

$K_{eq} = \dfrac{[H_3O^+][Ac^-]}{[HAc]} = \dfrac{\left(\dfrac{1.00 \times 10^{-14}}{[OH^-]}\right)[Ac^-]}{[HAc]}$

$1.76 \times 10^{-5} = \dfrac{\left(\dfrac{1.00 \times 10^{-14}}{x}\right)(0.100 - \cancel{x})}{x}$

neglect

$1.76 \times 10^{-5}x = \dfrac{1.00 \times 10^{-15}}{x}$

$1.76 \times 10^{-5}x^2 = 1.00 \times 10^{-15}$

$x^2 = \dfrac{1.00 \times 10^{-15}}{1.76 \times 10^{-5}} = 5.68 \times 10^{-11}$

$x = 7.54 \times 10^{-6}M$

$[H^+] = \dfrac{1.00 \times 10^{-14}}{7.54 \times 10^{-6}} = 1.33 \times 10^{-9}M$

$pH = 8.88$

3. $AgCl \rightleftarrows Ag^+ + Cl^-$

$K_{sp} = [Ag^+][Cl^-]$

$1.56 \times 10^{-10} = (1)[Cl^-]$

$[Cl^-] = 1.56 \times 10^{-10}M$

$PbCl_2 \rightleftarrows Pb^{2+} + 2Cl^-$

$K_{sp} = [Pb^{2+}][Cl^-]^2$

$1.62 \times 10^{-5} = (1)[Cl^-]^2$

$[Cl^-]^2 = 1.62 \times 10^{-5}$

$[Cl^-] = 4.02 \times 10^{-3}M$

$PbCl_2$ will require a higher concentration of Cl^-, so AgCl will precipitate first.

4. From Problem 3, we know that $4.02 \times 10^{-3}M = [Cl^-]$ when $PbCl_2$ precipitates.

Therefore, $1.56 \times 10^{-10} = [Ag^+](4.02 \times 10^{-3})$

$[Ag^+] = \dfrac{1.56 \times 10^{-10}}{4.02 \times 10^{-3}}$

$[Ag^+] = 3.88 \times 10^{-8}M$

5. Answers may vary depending on the indicator chosen.

methyl violet

acid

base

cresol red

acid

base

4-nitrophenol

acid

base

methyl orange

acid

base

bromothymol blue

acid

brilliant yellow

acid

base

alizarin yellow R

acid

base

base

methyl red

acid

base

orange IV

acid

base

OXIDATION REDUCTION

26

AN OVERVIEW

Chapter 26 presents electron transfer reactions. The chapter begins with the definitions of oxidation and reduction. This approach allows students to apply these definitions when assigning oxidation numbers. Balancing redox reactions is demonstrated using the half reaction method. The method demands that we conserve mass, electrons, and charge. We should emphasize that our use of this method does not imply that we really believe electronic charges are truly described by the concept. It is important to point out to students that the oxidation numbers used in balancing redox equations are arbitrary values obtained by using arbitrary rules. Students should be warned against thinking that the oxidation number represents the real ion charge in the molecule.

DEMONSTRATION INFORMATION

Students should respond that $CuCl_2(aq)$ cannot be shipped in an aluminum tank car. Later in Chapter 27, they will learn to predict whether a reaction will occur. At that time, you can refer to this demonstration and ask students if they would ship H_2O_2 in a nickel tank car (no); or $OH^-(aq)$ in a lead tank car (yes).

Consider the following reduction potentials:

Reaction	$E°$, V
$Cu^{2+} + 2e^- \rightarrow Cu$	0.34
$2H_2O + 2e^- \rightarrow H_2 + 2OH^-$	-0.414 (10^{-7} M OH^-)
$Al^{3+} + 3e^- \rightarrow Al$	-1.66

Although one might expect a simple oxidation-reduction reaction between Cu^{2+} and Al, bubbles in the reaction mixture indicate that $H_2(g)$ is being produced as well. Two reactions are occurring simultaneously:

$$3Cu^{2+} + 2Al \rightarrow 3Cu + 2Al^{3+}$$
$$2Al + 6H_2O \rightarrow 2Al(OH)_3 + 3H_2(g)$$

The reaction is highly exothermic and may bubble over.

The reaction mixture is messy, but finely divided copper and gelatinous $Al(OH)_3$ may be observed.

DISPOSAL: *Decant the liquid. Pour it down the drain with a large quantity of water. Dispose of the precipitate in the normal manner by placing it in your solid waste container. It can then be put in a local landfill.*

PERFORMANCE OBJECTIVES

Goals: Students will gain an understanding of oxidation-reduction reactions. Students will assign oxidation numbers to elements in compounds using a set of commonly agreed upon rules. Students will balance oxidation-reduction equations.

Objectives: Upon completion of the reading and problems, and when asked to demonstrate their understanding either orally or on a written test, students will

26:1	K	define oxidation-reduction reactions, and describe the major difference between them and other reactions. **Intro**
26:2	K	define oxidation in terms of electron loss. **26:1**
26:3	K	define reduction in terms of electron gain. **26:2**
26:4	K	define oxidizing and reducing agents. **26:3**
26:5	K/P	explain the relationships among oxidizing agent, reducing agent, oxidation, and reduction. **26:3**
26:6	K	define oxidation number. **26:4**
26:7	K	determine that an oxidation-reduction reaction has taken place by a change of oxidation numbers as shown by electronic structures. **26:4-26:5**

26:8	K/P	state and use the rules for assigning oxidation numbers to elements in common compounds. **26:6**
26:9	K/P	identify oxidation-reduction reactions through use of change in oxidation numbers. **26:7**
26:10	K/P	given an equation, determine the oxidizing and reducing agents and the elements that are reduced and oxidized. **26:7**
26:11	K	define half-reaction. **26:8**
26:12	K/P	using the half-reaction method, balance redox reactions. **26:8-26:12**
26:13	A	voluntarily complete one or more of the One More Step activities.
26:14	A	read unassigned literature related to the chapter.

TEACHING TECHNIQUES

Section 26:3

To help students with the concept that an oxidizing agent is itself reduced, you can discuss the action of a bleaching agent on clothing in a washing machine. A bleaching agent, which causes whitening to occur, does not itself become whiter. An oxidizing agent is not oxidized.

Section 26:6

Remind students that oxidation numbers do not necessarily represent the number of electrons gained or lost. They are arbitrary numbers assigned using arbitrary rules that enable us to make predictions.

Section 26:7

Demonstration: Corrosion—Obtain 2 petri dishes. Clean 4 iron nails with alcohol to remove any oil. Clean the nails with emery cloth. Cut a thin strip of zinc and obtain a piece of copper wire. Prepare 200 cm^3 of plain agar-agar solution (2.0 g/200 cm^3 boiling water). After the agar has dissolved add 10 drops of 0.1M $K_3Fe(CN)_6$ and 5 drops of phenolphthalein solution. While the agar cools, place a bent nail and a straight nail in one petri dish. In a second petri dish, place two nails, one wrapped with Cu, the other with Zn. Keep the nails separated and slowly pour the agar solution into the dishes to cover the metals. Observe the color changes, pink is reduction (OH^-) and blue is oxidation. Discuss ways to prevent the corrosion of metals.

To understand the different reactions, consider the following reduction potentials:

Reaction	$E°$, V
$O_2(g) + 2H_2O + 4e^- \rightarrow 4OH^-$	0.81 (10^{-7} M OH^-)
$Fe^{3+} + e^- \rightarrow Fe^{2+}$	0.77
$Cu^{2+} + 2e^- \rightarrow Cu$	0.34
$2H_2O + 2e^- \rightarrow H_2(g) + 2OH^-$	-0.414 (10^{-7} M OH^-)
$Fe^{2+} + 2e^- \rightarrow Fe$	-0.44
$Zn^{2+} + 2e^- \rightarrow Zn$	-0.76

In the presence of phenolphthalein, production of a pink color indicates that either reduction of O_2 (from the air) to produce OH^- or reduction of water to produce $H_2(g)$ and OH^- is occurring. In the presence of $K_3Fe(CN)_6$, production of a blue color indicates the oxidation of iron to Fe^{2+} producing the deep blue compound iron(II) ferricyanide, $Fe_3[Fe(CN)_6]_2$.

For a plain nail, straight or bent, the oxidation of iron is expected to take place at the stress points. Thus, blue is observed at the head and point of the nail, because of the stress induced in forming the head and cutting the point, or at a sharp bend in the nail, because of the stress induced in bending. Reduction must also occur, and the resultant pink color is observed where there is less stress in the nail. For a nail wrapped in copper wire, the blue oxidation product is observed all around the nail. The copper does not react at all, having a lower oxidation potential, but it does provide a low energy surface where the reduction can take place. The overvoltage required is lower for copper than for iron. Thus the pink color in the gel is observed in the vicinity of the copper wire, away from the iron nail. For a nail wrapped in zinc, the blue oxidation product is absent. Because of its higher oxidation potential, zinc serves as a sacrificial electrode, undergoing oxidation instead of the iron. The reduction still produces OH^-, and the pink color of phenolphthalein is observed.

Galvanized iron takes advantage of the process just described. Coating iron with a thin layer of zinc protects the iron from corrosion, because the zinc will be oxidized in preference to iron. This is known as cathodic protection, because the iron becomes the cathode.

Section 26:8

The oxidation number method of balancing redox equations is not presented in the text for simplicity. Students become confused in learning two methods to solve the same problem. We feel it is more valuable for students to be proficient using one technique at this level. The technique taught in this chapter approximates more closely what actually happens in solvated reactions. This presentation results in maximum learning for minimum investment of student time and effort.

Technology and Chemistry

Students can do additional research into the career options in the field of metallurgy. It is important to emphasize to students that most metals are not found in pure form. Students may not have considered this point since they generally encounter metals in the pure state after refining.

PROBLEM SOLUTIONS

Page 514

1. a. 4+ **e.** 4+ **h.** 2−
   b. 7+ **f.** 6+ **i.** 2+
   c. 5+ **g.** 6+ **j.** 0
   d. 4+

Page 515

2. no

3. yes
   H is oxidized and H_2 is the reducing agent.
   N is reduced and N_2 is the oxidizing agent.

4. yes
   C is oxidized and the reducing agent
   H is reduced
   H_2O is oxidizing agent

5. no

6. no

7. no

Page 521

17. $(8H^+ + 5e^- + MnO_4^- \rightarrow Mn^{2+} + 4H_2O) \times 2$
$(H_2O + H_2SO_3 \rightarrow HSO_4^- + 2e^- + 3H^+) \times 5$
$16H^+ + 10e^- + 2MnO_4^- \rightarrow 2Mn^{2+} + 8H_2O$
$\underline{5H_2O + 5H_2SO_3 \rightarrow 5HSO_4^- + 10e^- + 15H^+}$
$H^+ + 2MnO_4^- + 5H_2SO_3 \rightarrow 2Mn^{2+} + 5HSO_4^- + 3H_2O$

18. $(14H^+ + 6e^- + Cr_2O_7^{2-} \rightarrow 2Cr^{3+} + 7H_2O)$
$(2I^- \rightarrow I_2 + 2e^-) \times 3$
$14H^+ + 6e^- + Cr_2O_7^{2-} \rightarrow 2Cr^{3+} + 7H_2O$
$\underline{6I^- \rightarrow 3I_2 + 6e^-}$
$Cr_2O_7^{2-} + 14H^+ + 6I^- \rightarrow 2Cr^{3+} + 3I_2 + 7H_2O$

19. $(5OH^- + NH_3 \rightarrow NO + 5e^- + 4H_2O) \times 4$
$4H_2O + 4e^- + O_2 \rightarrow 2H_2O + 4OH^-$
Simplifying the 2nd equation gives:
$2H_2O + 4e^- + O_2 \rightarrow 4OH^-$
$(2H_2O + 4e^- + O_2 \rightarrow 4OH^-) \times 5$
$20OH^- + 4NH_3 \rightarrow 4NO + 20e^- + 16H_2O$
$\underline{10H_2O + 20e^- + 5O_2 \rightarrow 20OH^-}$
$4NH_3 + 5O_2 \rightarrow 4NO + 6H_2O \qquad \text{(basic)}$

20. $(5H_2O + As_2O_3 \rightarrow 2H_3AsO_4 + 4e^- + 4H^+) \times 3$
$(4H^+ + 3e^- + NO_3^- \rightarrow NO + 2H_2O) \times 4$
$15H_2O + 3As_2O_3 \rightarrow 6H_3AsO_4 + 12e^- + 12H^+$
$\underline{16H^+ + 12e^- + 4NO_3^- \rightarrow 4NO + 8H_2O}$
$3As_2O_3 + 4H^+ + 4NO_3^- + 7H_2O \rightarrow 6H_3AsO_4 + 4NO$

21. $(2e^- + I_2 \rightarrow 2I^-) \times 1$
$\underline{(H_2O + H_2SO_3 \rightarrow HSO_4^- + 2e^- + 3H^+) \times 1}$
$I_2 + H_2SO_3 + H_2O \rightarrow 2I^- + HSO_4^- + 3H^+$

22. $(8H^+ + 8e^- + H_3AsO_4 \rightarrow AsH_3 + 4H_2O) \times 1$
$(Zn \rightarrow Zn^{2+} + 2e^-) \times 4$
$8H^+ + 8e^- + H_3AsO_4 \rightarrow AsH_3 + 4H_2O$
$\underline{4Zn \rightarrow 4Zn^{2+} + 8e^-}$
$H_3AsO_4 + 8H^+ + 4Zn \rightarrow AsH_3 + 4H_2O + 4Zn^{2+}$

8. yes
   O is reduced
   S is oxidized
   H_2O_2 is oxidizing agent
   PbS is reducing agent

9. no

10. yes
   N is reduced
   P is oxidized
   HNO_3 is oxidizing agent
   H_3PO_3 is reducing agent

11. yes
   N is reduced
   I is oxidized
   HNO_3 is oxidizing agent
   I_2 is the reducing agent

12. no

13. yes
   N is reduced
   Fe^{2+} is oxidized and the reducing agent
   NO_3^- is oxidizing agent

14. yes
   Br_2 is reduced and the oxidizing agent
   Fe^{2+} is oxidized
   $FeBr_2$ is reducing agent

15. yes
   I^- is reduced
   S is oxidized
   $S_2O_3^{2-}$ is reducing agent
   I_2 is the oxidizing agent

16. yes
   Mn is reduced
   O is oxidized
   MnO_4^- is oxidizing agent
   H_2O_2 is reducing agent

23. $(MnO_4{}^{2-} \rightarrow MnO_4{}^- + e^-) \times 2$
$(4H^+ + 2e^- + MnO_4{}^{2-} \rightarrow MnO_2 + 2H_2O) \times 1$
$$\frac{}{}$$
$\quad\quad 2MnO_4{}^{2-} \rightarrow 2MnO_4{}^- + 2e^-$
$$\overline{\quad 3MnO_4{}^{2-} + 4H^+ \rightarrow 2MnO_4{}^- + MnO_2 + 2H_2O \quad}$$

24. $(8H^+ + 5e^- + MnO_4{}^- \rightarrow Mn^{2+} + 4H_2O) \times 2$
$(2H_2O + SO_2 \rightarrow SO_4{}^{2-} + 2e^- + 4H^+) \times 5$
$\quad\quad 16H^+ + 10e^- + 2MnO_4{}^- \rightarrow 2Mn^{2+} + 8H_2O$
$\quad\quad\quad 10H_2O + 5SO_2 \rightarrow 5SO_4{}^{2-} + 10e^- + 20H^+$
$$\overline{\quad 2MnO_4{}^- + 5SO_2 + 2H_2O \rightarrow 2Mn^{2+} + 5SO_4{}^{2-} + 4H^+ \quad}$$

25. $e^- + NO_2 \rightarrow NO_2{}^-$
$\quad\quad 2OH^- + NO_2 \rightarrow NO_3{}^- + e^- + H_2O$
$$\overline{\quad 2NO_2 + 2OH^- \rightarrow NO_2{}^- + NO_3{}^- + H_2O \quad} \quad \text{(basic)}$$

26. $(4Cl^- + HgS \rightarrow S + 2e^- + HgCl_4{}^{2-}) \times 3$
$(4H^+ + 3e^- + NO_3{}^- \rightarrow NO + 2H_2O) \times 2$
$\quad\quad 12Cl^- + 3HgS \rightarrow 3S + 6e^- + 3HgCl_4{}^{2-}$
$\quad\quad\quad 8H^+ + 6e^- + 2NO_3{}^- \rightarrow 2NO + 4H_2O$
$$\overline{\quad 8H^+ + 3HgS + 12Cl^- + 2NO_3{}^- \rightarrow 3HgCl_4{}^{2-} + 3S + 2NO + 4H_2O \quad}$$

CHAPTER END PROBLEMS

Page 524

1. Reactions in which electrons are transferred.

2. Oxidizing agents contain the element reduced.
   Reducing agents contain the element oxidized.

3. **a.** 5+
   b. 5+
   c. 4+
   d. 1+
   e. 4+
   f. 5+

4. $(Cu \rightarrow Cu^{2+} + 2e^-) \times 3$
   $(4H^+ + 3e^- + NO_3{}^- \rightarrow NO + 2H_2O) \times 2$
   $\quad\quad 3Cu \rightarrow 3Cu^{2+} + 6e^-$
   $\quad 8H^+ + 6e^- + 2NO_3{}^- \rightarrow 2NO + 4H_2O$
   $$\overline{\quad 3Cu + 8H^+ + 2NO_3{}^- \rightarrow 3Cu^{2+} + 2NO + 4H_2O \quad}$$

5. $3Fe^{2+} \rightarrow 3Fe^{3+} + 3e$
   $\quad\quad 4H^+ + 3e^- + NO_3{}^- \rightarrow NO + 2H_2O$
   $$\overline{\quad 3Fe^{2+} + 4H^+ + NO_3{}^- \rightarrow 3Fe^{3+} + NO + 2H_2O \quad}$$

6. $(Zn \rightarrow Zn^{2+} + 2e^-) \times 1$
   $(2H^+ + e^- + NO_3{}^- \rightarrow NO_2 + H_2O) \times 2$
   $\quad 4H^+ + 2e^- + 2NO_3{}^- \rightarrow 2NO_2 + 2H_2O$
   $\quad\quad Zn \rightarrow Zn^{2+} + 2e^-$
   $$\overline{\quad Zn + 4H^+ + 2NO_3{}^- \rightarrow Zn^{2+} + 2NO_2 + 2H_2O \quad}$$

12. $(4H^+ + 3e^- + NO_3{}^- \rightarrow NO + 2H_2O) \times 2$
    $(2Hg + HSO_4{}^- \rightarrow H^+ + Hg_2SO_4 + 2e^-) \times 3$
    $\quad\quad 8H^+ + 6e^- + 2NO_3{}^- \rightarrow 2NO + 4H_2O$
    $\quad\quad\quad 3HSO_4{}^- + 6Hg \rightarrow 3Hg_2SO_4 + 6e^- + 3H^+$
    $$\overline{\quad 3HSO_4{}^- + 5H^+ + 2NO_3{}^- + 6Hg \rightarrow 2NO + 4H_2O + 3Hg_2SO_4 \quad}$$

13. $(H_2O + CO \rightarrow CO_2 + 2e^- + 2H^+) \times 5$
    $\quad 10H^+ + 10e^- + I_2O_5 \rightarrow I_2 + 5H_2O$
    $\quad\quad 5H_2O + 5CO \rightarrow 5CO_2 + 10e^- + 10H^+$
    $$\overline{\quad I_2O_5 + 5CO \rightarrow I_2 + 5CO_2 \quad}$$

14. Oxidation is a loss of electrons;
    reduction is a gain of electrons.

15. $K_2SO_3 \rightarrow K_2SO_4$ lose $2e^-$ per atom S
    $KMnO_4 \rightarrow MnO_2$ gain $3e^-$ per atom Mn

7. $(Sb \rightarrow Sb^{3+} + 3e^-) \times 2$
   $(3H^+ + 2e^- + HSO_4{}^- \rightarrow SO_2 + 2H_2O) \times 3$
   $\quad\quad 2Sb \rightarrow 2Sb^{3+} + 6e^-$
   $\quad 9H^+ + 6e^- + 3HSO_4{}^- \rightarrow 3SO_2 + 6H_2O$
   $$\overline{\quad 2Sb + 9H^+ + 3HSO_4{}^- \rightarrow 2Sb^{3+} + 3SO_2 + 6H_2O \quad}$$

8. $(H_2S \rightarrow S + 2e^- + 2H^+) \times 2$
   $\quad 4H^+ + 4e^- + H_2SO_3 \rightarrow S + 3H_2O$
   $\quad\quad 2H_2S \rightarrow 2S + 4e^- + 4H^+$
   $$\overline{\quad H_2SO_3 + 2H_2S \rightarrow 3S + 3H_2O \quad}$$

9. $(H_2O + Cl^- \rightarrow HClO + 2e^- + H^+) \times 3$
   $(4H^+ + 3e^- + NO_3{}^- \rightarrow NO + 2H_2O) \times 2$
   $\quad\quad 3H_2O + 3Cl^- \rightarrow 3HClO + 6e^- + 3H^+$
   $\quad 8H^+ + 6e^- + 2NO_3{}^- \rightarrow 2NO + 4H_2O$
   $$\overline{\quad 3Cl^- + 5H^+ + 2NO_3{}^- \rightarrow 3HClO + 2NO + H_2O \quad}$$

10. $(Cl^- + Ag \rightarrow AgCl + e^-) \times 6$
    $\quad 6H^+ + 6e^- + ClO_3{}^- \rightarrow Cl^- + 3H_2O$
    $\quad\quad 6Cl^- + 6Ag \rightarrow 6AgCl + 6e^-$
    $$\overline{\quad 6H^+ + ClO_3{}^- + 5Cl^- + 6Ag \rightarrow 3H_2O + 6AgCl \quad}$$

11. $(3I^- \rightarrow I_3{}^- + 2e^-) \times 2$
    $\quad\quad 6I^- \rightarrow 2I_3{}^- + 4e^-$
    $\quad 4H^+ + 4e^- + O_2 \rightarrow 2H_2O$
    $$\overline{\quad 6I^- + 4H^+ + O_2 \rightarrow 2I_3{}^- + 2H_2O \quad}$$

therefore, need 3 moles K_2SO_3 for 2 moles $KMnO_4$

$$\frac{7.90 \text{ g } KMnO_4}{} \left| \frac{1 \text{ mol } KMnO_4}{158 \text{ g } KMnO_4} \right| \frac{3 \text{ mol } K_2SO_3}{2 \text{ mol } KMnO_4} \left| \frac{158 \text{ g } K_2SO_3}{1 \text{ mol } K_2SO_3} \right| = 11.9 \text{ g } K_2SO_3$$

16. $KClO_3 \rightarrow Cl^-$ gain $6e^-$ per atom Cl
$Cr_2O_3 \rightarrow K_2CrO_4$ lose $3e^-$ per atom Cr; Cr_2O_3 gives up $6e^-$
Therefore, need one mole Cr_2O_3 for each mole $KClO_3$

$$\frac{20.0 \text{ cm}^3 \ Cr_2O_3}{} \left| \frac{0.1 \text{ mol } Cr_2O_3}{1000 \text{ cm}^3 \ Cr_2O_3} \right| \frac{1 \text{ mol } KClO_3}{1 \text{ mol } Cr_2O_3} \left| \frac{1000 \text{ cm}^3 \ KClO_3}{0.2 \text{ mol } KClO_3} \right| = 10.0 \text{ cm}^3 \ KClO_3 \text{ soln.}$$

REVIEW

Page 525

1. $Cd_3(PO_4)_2 \rightleftarrows 3Cd^{2+} + 2PO_4^{3-}$
$K_{sp} = [Cd^{2+}]^3[PO_4^{3-}]^2$
Let $[PO_4^{3-}] = 2x$, then $[Cd^{2+}] = 3x$
$2.50 \times 10^{-33} = (3x)^3(2x)^2 = (27x^3)(4x^2) = 108x^5$
$x^5 = 2.31 \times 10^{-35}$
$x = 1.18 \times 10^{-7}$
$[Cd^{2+}] = 3x = 3.54 \times 10^{-7}M$

2. increases the rate

3. Slowest step is the rate determining step.

4. $Sr(OH)_2$, strontium hydroxide

5. $H_2PO_4^- + H^+ \rightarrow H_3PO_4$
$CH_3CH_2COOH + H_2O \rightleftarrows H_3O^+ + CH_3CH_2COO^-$

6. $K_a = \dfrac{[H_3O^+][CH_3CH_2COO^-]}{[CH_3CH_2COOH]}$

$K_a = \dfrac{(1.16 \times 10^{-3})(1.16 \times 10^{-3})}{(0.100 - 1.16 \times 10^{-3})} = 1.36 \times 10^{-5}M$

7. $\dfrac{1.16 \times 10^{-3}}{0.100} \times 100 = 1.16\%$

8. $HF + H_2O \rightleftarrows H_3O^+ + F^-$

$K_a = \dfrac{[H_3O^+][F^-]}{[HF]}$

$3.53 \times 10^{-4} = \dfrac{x(0.01 + x)}{0.100 - x}$

$x = 3.53 \times 10^{-3}M$

9. $K_{eq} = \dfrac{[H^+][CHCl_2COO^-]}{[CHCl_2COOH]}$

$K_{eq} = \dfrac{(0.200)(0.200)}{1.20}$

$= 0.0333$ or 3.33×10^{-2}

10. $\dfrac{0.200 \times 100}{1.20 + 0.200} = \dfrac{0.200}{1.40} \left| \dfrac{100}{1} \right| = 14.3\%$

11. $0.0333 = \dfrac{x(0.400)}{1.40 - x}$

$0.0466 - 0.0333x = 0.400x$

$0.433x = 0.0466$
$x = 0.108$
$1.40 - x = 1.29M$

ONE MORE STEP

Page 525

1. a. Ba_3N_2
  b. CrO_3
  c. Ca_3P_2
  d. SrH_2
  e. Fr_4C
  f. Li_2O
  g. Fe_2S_3
  h. ScF_3
  i. $TiCl_4$

2. all the O atoms are $2-$
the central S is $5+$
the peripheral S is $1-$
The ion contains 2 atoms of the same element (S) in different oxidation states.

3. $3-$ NH_3 ammonia
   $2-$ N_2H_4 hydrazine
   $1-$ NH_2OH hydroxylamine
   0 N_2 the free element
   $1+$ N_2O nitrogen (I) oxide
   $2+$ NO nitrogen (II) oxide
   $3+$ N_2O_3 nitrogen (III) oxide
   $4+$ NO_2 nitrogen (IV) oxide
   $5+$ N_2O_5 nitrogen (V) oxide

4. Black; (O) $= 2-$, one Fe $= 2+$, two Fe $= 3+$; magnetic

5. The ore is crushed, dried, and dissolved in sulfuric acid. Iron (the principal impurity) is reduced to Fe^{2+} and crystallized out as the sulfate. The solution is filtered, concentrated by vacuum evaporation, and boiled to precipitate the TiO_2. The TiO_2 mixed with coke (C) is exposed to Cl_2 to convert the titanium to $TiCl_4$. The $TiCl_4$ is reduced to the metal by Mg or Na in an inert atmosphere. The metallurgy of most common metals may be found in encyclopedias, chemical engineering texts, or industrial chemistry texts.

ELECTROCHEMISTRY   27

AN OVERVIEW

Chapter 27 introduces the interaction of electricity and chemical species. The chapter uses the concepts presented in Chapters 25 and 26 to develop an under- standing of electrochemistry and its applications. Discuss with your classes the differences between experimental fact, model, and convention. In a voltaic cell, electrons flow from the negative pole to the positive pole; this statement is fact. We describe the chemical process that produces the electrons using half-reactions for each electrode; this description is our model. We name the oxidation electrode the anode; this labeling is convention. Definitions and vocabulary are developed first for students. Then, the concepts are applied to practical situations such as electrolysis and voltaic cells. Students should learn to use the table of standard reduction potentials to predict the products of a chemical reaction. Section 27:11 shows students that predictions made from the table without considering other factors may be wrong. The quantitative aspects of electrochemistry are practical and relevant.

DEMONSTRATION INFORMATION

The electrolysis of KI(aq), is presented in Section 27:10 in the textbook, and the demonstration illustrates that the theoretical products are actually obtained.

The possible reductions at the cathode are:
$$K^+ + e^- \rightarrow K$$
$$2H_2O + 2e^- \rightarrow H_2 + 2OH^-$$
$$E° = -2.93 \text{ V}$$
$$E° = -0.414 \text{ V} (10^{-7}M \text{ OH}^-)$$

The reduction of water has the more positive value of $E°$; therefore, it is the reaction that occurs. The students will observe bubbling at the cathode as $H_2(g)$ is produced, and the solution around the cathode will turn pink as OH^- is generated in the presence of phenolphthalein.

The possible oxidations at the anode are:
$$2I^- \rightarrow I_2 + 2e^-$$
$$2H_2O \rightarrow O_2 + 4H^+ + 4e^-$$
$$E° = -0.53 \text{ V}$$
$$E° = -0.815 \text{ V} (10^{-7}M \text{ H}^+)$$

The oxidation of I^- requires a lower driving potential, so it is the reaction that occurs. The students will observe the solution around the anode turn brown as I_2 is generated and combines with I^- to form I_3^-.

The overall reaction for the electrolysis is:
$$2H_2O + 2I^- \rightarrow H_2 + I_2 + 2OH^-$$
Reflecting the formation of I_3^-, the reaction is written as:
$$2H_2O + 3I^- \rightarrow H_2 + I_3^- + 2OH^-$$

The demonstration can be used to introduce the vocabulary presented in the first three sections of the chapter.

DISPOSAL: *These chemicals are properly disposed of at a local landfill. They represent little or no hazard to the environment.*

PERFORMANCE OBJECTIVES

Goals: Students will gain an understanding of how electricity can produce chemical changes and how chemical changes can produce an electric current. Students will determine the cell potential given different electrodes. Students will use Faraday's laws to determine the amount of element deposited by a given current for a given length of time.

Objectives: Upon completion of the reading and problems, and when asked to demonstrate their understanding either orally or on a written test, students will

27:1	K	define galvanometer and salt bridge. **Intro**
27:2	K	define electric current, volts, and amperes. **27:1**
27:3	K	distinguish between anions and cations. **27:2**
27:4	K	define electrolytes. **27:2**
27:5	K	explain how an electric current causes a chemical change in a molten salt. **27:3**
27:6	K	define anode and cathode in terms of oxidation and reduction. **27:3**
27:7	K/P	write equations for half-reactions at each electrode in the electrolysis of a given molten salt. **27:3**
27:8	K	define electrolysis. **27:3**
27:9	K/P	write equations for half-reactions at each electrode in the electrolysis of a salt solution. **27:4**
27:10	K	define electronic or metallic conduction and electrolytic conduction. **27:4**
27:11	K	explain the similarities and differences in electronic and electrolytic conduction. **27:4**
27:12	K	define voltaic cell. **27:5**
27:13	K/P	explain the process for producing electricity from a voltaic cell. **27:5-27:6**
27:14	K	describe the zero potential hydrogen half-cell. **27:7**
27:15	K/P	given a table of standard reduction potentials, determine whether a reaction will take place. **27:8**
27:16	K/P	given a table of standard reduction potentials, predict the voltage from two different half-cells used as a single voltaic cell. **27:9**
27:17	K/P	using a table of standard reduction potentials, predict the products of an electrolysis. **27:10**
27:18	K	state the Nernst equation. **27:11**
27:19	K	describe the effects of nonstandard conditions on cell voltage. **27:11**
27:20	K/P	given nonstandard concentration, determine the voltage of a cell using the Nernst equation. **27:11**

27:21	K	explain the working of a pH meter. **27:12**
27:22	K/P	given the voltage of a reaction, calculate the free energy change. **27:13**
27:23	K/P	use Faraday's laws to determine the amount of metal electroplated by a given current in a given time. **27:14**
27:24	K	define coulomb. **27:14**
27:25	K/P	given data from an electroanalysis, determine the percentage of a given metal in a sample. **27:15**
27:26	A	voluntarily complete one or more of the One More Step activities.
27:27	A	read unassigned literature related to the chapter.

TEACHING TECHNIQUES

Section 27:4

carbon anode

two-hole rubber stopper

porous cup

copper wire cathode

distilled H_2O and phenolpthalein

NaCl solution

Demonstration: The electrolysis of NaCl is a simulation of the industrial process for the preparation of sodium hydroxide, chlorine, and hydrogen. Fill a porous cup three-quarters full of sodium chloride solution. Insert a carbon rod, supported by a two-hole rubber stopper, into the solution in the porous cup. This rod serves as the anode. Wrap a copper wire around the porous cup to serve as the cathode. Place the porous cup in a 250 cm^3 beaker half-full of water to which some phenolphthalein has been added. Connect the electrodes to a 4½ volt battery or power supply and note all changes that occur. **CAUTION:** *Chlorine gas is very poisonous. It can react and cause fire or explosion with hydrogen. Perform demonstration in a fume hood.*

Section 27:5

A diagram of a voltaic cell can be duplicated and distributed to students to assist them in taking notes as you cover the electrochemical cell. They can label the anode (oxidation) and cathode (reduction). The direction of electron flow can be charted. The voltage can be calculated and written by the meter. Ion migration can be diagrammed and half reactions at the electrodes written and balanced. The oxidizing agent can be identified. The diagram needs to be large enough for students to draw and write information in the proper location. See *Teacher Resource Book.*

Section 27:8

Table 27-1 conforms to IUPAC conventions in that it is a reduction table. The voltage becomes more positive as you go from top to bottom of the table. This convention may be unfamiliar to you, but it will not be difficult for your students since it is their first exposure to it.

Section 27:14

Plating Cu metal—The apparatus shown in the diagram can be used in the electrolysis of a variety of solutions. The electrodes are ordinary pencils with the wood covers peeled back about 1 cm at each end. The products of the reaction can be identified visually and by smell. The odor of chlorine is retained by the pencil for a short time. After copper has plated on one of the elec-

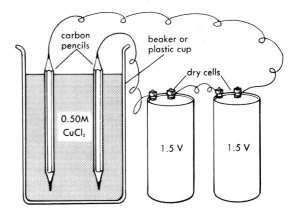

carbon pencils

beaker or plastic cup

dry cells

0.50M $CuCl_2$

1.5 V   1.5 V

trodes, disconnect the power supply and measure the voltage between the electrodes. Students will now be able to observe an electrochemical cell. Short out the electrodes and watch the cell reach equilibrium. Reverse the polarity of the cell to show that the copper leaves one electrode and plates on the other.

Technology and Chemistry

This features illustrates the practical application of a knowledge of electrochemistry. Have students do additional research concerning electroplating for protective and ornamental purposes (jewelry, silverplated objects).

PROBLEM SOLUTIONS

Page 539

1. $-1.66 + 0.25 = -1.41$ V no reaction
2. $0.80 + 0.28 = +1.08$ V reaction occurs
3. $-0.15 + (0.13) = -0.28$ V no reaction
4. $+1.50 + 0.44 = +1.94$ V reaction occurs

Page 540

5. **a.** $Zn \rightarrow Zn^{2+}$ 0.76 V, $Fe^{2+} \rightarrow Fe$ −0.44 V,
   sum = 0.32 V
   b. $Mn \rightarrow Mn^{2+}$ 1.18 V, $Br_2 \rightarrow Br^-$ 1.07 V,
   sum = 2.25 V
   c. $H_2C_2O_4 \rightarrow CO_2$ 0.49 V $MnO_4^- \rightarrow Mn^{2+}$ 1.51 V,
   sum = 2.00 V
   d. $Ni \rightarrow Ni^{2+}$ 0.25 V, $Hg_2^{2+} \rightarrow Hg$ 0.79 V,
   sum = 1.04 V
   e. $Cu \rightarrow Cu^{2+}$ −0.34 V, $Ag^+ \rightarrow Ag$ 0.80 V,
   sum = 0.46 V
   f. $Pb \rightarrow Pb^{2+}$ +0.13 V, $Cl_2 \rightarrow Cl^-$ 1.36 V,
   sum = 1.49 V

Page 541

6. **a.** H_2 and O_2—hydrogen reduction requires less energy than sodium, sulfate cannot be oxidized
   b. Cu and O_2—copper reduction requires less energy than hydrogen, oxygen oxidation requires less energy than chlorine
   c. Co and O_2—cobalt reduction requires less energy than hydrogen, oxygen oxidation requires less energy than fluorine

d. Pb and O_2—lead reduction requires less energy than hydrogen, nitrate cannot be oxidized
e. H_2 and O_2—hydrogen reduction requires less energy than lithium, oxygen oxidation requires less energy than bromine
f. H_2 and Cl_2—hydrogen reduction requires less energy than sodium, chloride oxidation requires less energy than oxygen.

Page 543

7. $Pb + Sn^{4+} \rightarrow Pb^{2+} + Sn^{2+}$

$$E = E° - \frac{0.0592}{n} \log K = E° - \frac{0.0592}{n} \log \frac{[Pb^{2+}][Sn^{2+}]}{[Sn^{4+}]}$$

$$E = 0.28 - \frac{0.0592}{2} \log \frac{(0.485)(0.346)}{(0.652)} = 0.30 \text{ V}$$

8. $Ni + Cu^{2+} \rightarrow Ni^{2+} + Cu$

$$E = E° - \frac{0.0592}{n} \log K = E° - \frac{0.0592}{n} \log \frac{[Ni^{2+}]}{[Cu^{2+}]}$$

$$E = 0.59 - \frac{0.0592}{2} \log \frac{(1.00)}{(0.100)} = 0.56 \text{ V}$$

9. $Fe + 2Ag^+ \rightarrow Fe^{2+} + 2Ag$

$$E = E° - \frac{0.0592}{n} \log K = E° - \frac{0.0592}{n} \log \frac{[Fe^{2+}]}{[Ag^+]^2}$$

$$E = 1.24 - \frac{0.0592}{2} \log \frac{(0.720)}{(0.785)^2} = 1.24 \text{ V}$$

Page 545

10. $E° = 1.46$ V = (0.61 + 0.85) V
    $\Delta G = -nFE° = (-2)(96\,500)(1.46) = -282$ kJ
11. $E° = 1.68$ V = (0.76 + 0.92) V
    $\Delta G = -nFE° = (-2)(96\,500)(1.68) = -324$ kJ

Page 547

12. $Ag^+(aq) + e^- \rightarrow Ag(cr)$

$$\frac{1.00 \text{ A}}{} \left| \frac{9650 \text{ s}}{} \right| \frac{1 \text{ mol } e^-}{96\,500 \text{ A·s}} \left| \frac{1 \text{ mol Ag}}{1 \text{ mol } e^-} \right| \frac{108 \text{ g Ag}}{1 \text{ mol Ag}} = 10.8 \text{ g Ag}$$

13. $Ag^+(aq) + e^- \rightarrow Ag(cr)$

$$\frac{5.00 \text{ A}}{} \left| \frac{10.0 \text{ min}}{} \right| \frac{60 \text{ s}}{1 \text{ min}} \left| \frac{1 \text{ mol } e^-}{96\,500 \text{ A·s}} \right| \frac{1 \text{ mol Ag}}{1 \text{ mol } e^-} \left| \frac{108 \text{ g Ag}}{1 \text{ mol Ag}} \right| = 3.36 \text{ g Ag}$$

14. $Cu^2(aq) + 2e^- \rightarrow Cu(cr)$

$$\frac{1.75 \text{ mol Cu}}{6.24 \text{ min}} \left| \frac{2 \text{ mol } e^-}{1 \text{ mol Cu}} \right| \frac{96\,500 \text{ A·s}}{1 \text{ mol } e^-} \left| \frac{1 \text{ min}}{60 \text{ s}} \right| = 902 \text{ A}$$

15. $2Cl^-(aq) \rightarrow Cl_2(g) + 2e^-$

$$\frac{1.00 \text{ mol } Cl_2}{5.00 \text{ A}} \left| \frac{2 \text{ mol } e^-}{1 \text{ mol } Cl_2} \right| \frac{96\,500 \text{ A·s}}{1 \text{ mol } e^-} = 3.86 \times 10^4 \text{ s} = 643 \text{ min} = 10.7 \text{ h}$$

16. $Ca^{2+}(aq) + 2e^- \rightarrow Ca(cr)$

$$\frac{0.375 \text{ g Ca}}{3.93 \text{ A}} \left| \frac{1 \text{ mol Ca}}{40.1 \text{ g Ca}} \right| \frac{2 \text{ mol } e^-}{1 \text{ mol Ca}} \left| \frac{96\,500 \text{ A·s}}{1 \text{ mol } e^-} \right| \frac{1 \text{ min}}{60 \text{ s}} = 7.65 \text{ min}$$

Page 548

17.   new mass 28.118 g
      original mass 26.041 g
      mass copper 2.077 g

$$\% \text{ copper} = \frac{2.077}{2.60} \times 100 = 79.9\%$$

CHAPTER END PROBLEMS

Pages 551–552

1. a, e, and f will proceed spontaneously
   b, c, and d do not proceed spontaneously
2. The anode is the site of oxidation and the cathode is the site of reduction.

3. If an insulator develops a high enough electric potential to break down its electronic structure, it can be made to conduct.

4. The structure of an ionic solid is such that the ions cannot migrate. Thus, they are "locked" in the crystal lattice.

5. Electrolysis involves a chemical change. Electrolytic conduction is a physical change.

6. The outer electrons of the active metal are held less tightly.

7. **a.** Fe **c.** Zn
   b. Ca **d.** Cu

8. **a.** Ca^{2+} **c.** Cl_2
   b. Hg_2^{2+} **d.** Cu^+

9. Electronic conduction consists of the movement of electrons through a conductor, electrolytic conduction consists of the migration of ions through a solution or an ionic melt.

10. $Al(cr) \rightarrow Al^{3+} + 3e^-$
    $3Ag^+ + 3e^- \rightarrow 3Ag(cr)$
    $Al + 3Ag^+ \rightarrow Al^{3+} + 3Ag$
    1.66 V (Al)
    0.80 V (Ag)
    2.46 V

11. cathode: $2H_2O + 2e^- \rightarrow 2OH^- + H_2$
    anode: $2Cl^- \rightarrow Cl_2 + 2e^-$

12. $(2e^- + 2H_2O \rightarrow H_2 + 2OH^-) \times 2$
    $2H_2O \rightarrow O_2 + 4H^+ + 4e^-$
    $4e^- + 4H_2O \rightarrow 2H_2 + 4OH^-$
    $6H_2O \rightarrow O_2 + 2H_2 + 4H_2O$

19. $2NaCl(aq) + 2H_2O(l) \rightarrow 2NaOH(aq) + H_2(g) + Cl_2(g)$

$$\frac{40.0\ \text{g NaOH}}{20.0\ A} \left| \frac{1\ \text{mol NaOH}}{40.0\ \text{g NaOH}} \right| \frac{1\ \text{mol } e^-}{1\ \text{mol NaOH}} \left| \frac{96\,500\ A\cdot s}{1\ \text{mol } e^-} \right. = 4825\ s = 1.34\ h \quad (80.4\ \text{min})$$

20. **a.** $Ag^+(aq) + e^- \rightarrow Ag(cr)$

b. $$\frac{5.00\ A}{} \left| \frac{2.00\ h}{} \right| \frac{60\ \text{min}}{1\ h} \left| \frac{60\ s}{1\ \text{min}} \right| \frac{1\ \text{mol } e^-}{96\,500\ A\cdot s} \left| \frac{1\ \text{mol Ag}}{1\ \text{mol } e^-} \right| \frac{108\ \text{g Ag}}{1\ \text{mol Ag}} = 40.3\ \text{g Ag}$$

$2H_2O \rightarrow O_2 + 2H_2$

$$\frac{10.0\ \text{g } H_2O}{} \left| \frac{1\ \text{mol } H_2O}{18.0\ \text{g } H_2O} \right| \frac{1\ \text{mol } O_2}{2\ \text{mol } H_2O} \left| \frac{22.4\ dm^3}{1\ \text{mol}} \right.$$
$= 6.22\ dm^3\ O_2 STP$

13. $Mg + Cl_2 \rightarrow Mg^{2+} + 2Cl^-$
    $E = E° - \dfrac{0.0592}{n} \log K = E° = \dfrac{0.0592}{n} \log [Cl^-]^2[Mg^{2+}]$
    $E = 3.72 - \dfrac{0.0592}{2} \log (0.100)^2(0.170) = 3.80\ V$

14. $Cd \rightarrow Cd^{2+}$ 0.40 V, $Fe^{3+} \rightarrow Fe^{2+}$ 0.77 V, $E = 1.17$ V
    $E = E° - \dfrac{0.0592}{n} \log \dfrac{[Cd^{2+}][Fe^{2+}]^2}{[Fe^{3+}]^2}$
    $E = 1.17 - \dfrac{0.0592}{2} \log \dfrac{(0.500)(0.200)^2}{(0.100)^2}$
    $E = 1.16\ V$

15. $Sn^{4+} \rightarrow Sn^{2+}$ 0.15 V, $Fe \rightarrow Fe^{2+}$ 0.44 V, sum = 0.59 V
    $\Delta G = -nFE° = -(2)(96\,500)(0.59)$
    $= -110\ kJ$

16. $\log K = \dfrac{nFE°}{2.30RT} = \dfrac{110\,000\ J}{(2.30)(8.31)(298)}$
    $K = 9.83 \times 10^{19}$

17. $-30\,000 = -n(96\,500)E°$
    $E° = 0.31\ V$ per electron transferred

18. $9.186 - 7.601 = 1.585\ g$ (mass of nickel)
    $\dfrac{1.585}{4.525} \times 100 = 35.0\%\ Ni$

REVIEW

Page 552

1. loss of electrons
2. gains electrons
3. **a.** 6+ **c.** 7+
   b. 4+ **d.** 5+
4. $(Fe^{2+} \rightarrow Fe^{3+} + e^-) \times 6$
   $14H^+ + 6e^- + Cr_2O_7^{2-} \rightarrow 2Cr^{3+} + 7H_2O$
   $6Fe^{2+} \rightarrow 6Fe^{3+} + 6e^-$
   $14H^+ + Cr_2O_7^{2-} + 6Fe^{2+} \rightarrow 2Cr^{3+} + 7H_2O + 6Fe^{3+}$
5. proton acceptor
6. hydrotelluric acid
7. hypochlorous acid
8. metallic
9. $H_2P_2O_7^{2-} + H_2O \rightarrow H_3O^+ + HP_2O_7^{3-}$
   $K_a = \dfrac{[H_3O^+][HP_2O_7^{3-}]}{[H_2P_2O_7^{2-}]}$

$= \dfrac{(1.58 \times 10^{-4})^2}{0.100 - (1.58 \times 10^{-4})}$
$= 2.50 \times 10^{-7}$

10. $\dfrac{1.58 \times 10^{-4}}{0.100} \times 100 = 0.158\%$

11. $H_4IO_6^-$

12. $[OH^-] = \dfrac{10^{-14}}{|H_3O^+|} = \dfrac{10^{-14}}{3.61 \times 10^{-6}}$
    $= 2.77 \times 10^{-9} M$

13. 5.44

One More Step

Page 553

1. *Encyclopaedia Brittanica* is a good source. Start with Thales → Franklin → nuclear reactors. Another good source is the Bell Telephone Laboratories book, *Conductors and Semiconductors.*

2. $E = 0 - \dfrac{0.0592}{0} \log \dfrac{[0.100]}{[1.00]}$

   $= -\dfrac{0.0592}{2} \log 0.100$

   $= \dfrac{0.0592}{2} = 0.0296$ volts

3. $E = E° - \dfrac{RT}{nF} \ln \dfrac{[C][D]}{[A][B]}$; $\dfrac{203 \text{ kPa}}{101.3 \text{ kPa}} = 2$

   $E = 0.76 - \dfrac{0.0592}{2} \log 2$

   $= 0.76 - (0.0296)(0.301)$
   $= 0.76 - 0.00891 = 0.75$ volts

4. The danger is the explosion of hydrogen gas generated by electrolysis of the moisture present during recharging.

5. Fuels are combined with oxygen to release energy directly in the form of electricity rather than heat. Information on the hydrogen-oxygen cells used in spacecraft is available from NASA.

NUCLEAR CHEMISTRY   28

AN OVERVIEW

   Chapter 28 presents the specialized area of nuclear chemistry. This material continues the theme of the book because the emphasis is on properties as a consequence of structure. Chapter 28 introduces elementary particles, accelerators, radioactivity, biological effects of radiation, half-life, and reactions involving nuclear change. Fusion and fission processes are presented in relation to their development, use, and control.

DEMONSTRATION INFORMATION

   Cloud chambers may be purchased from commercial sources. You can construct your own using a clear plastic sandwich box or other similar container. Paint the bottom of the box black. Wet two pieces of blotter paper with alcohol and place them on opposite sides of the box. Place the box on dry ice. Keep the box level for best results. Place a radioactive source in the middle of the box and cover it with the plastic lid. After a few minutes, shine a high-intensity light beam through the box. If the room is darkened, the vapor tracks will be more visible. **CAUTION:** *Alcohol is flammable, keep away from flames.*

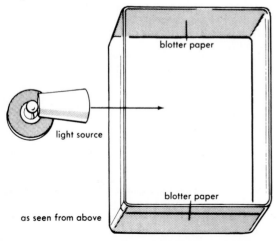

blotter paper

light source

blotter paper

as seen from above

PERFORMANCE OBJECTIVES

Goals: Students will gain an understanding of natural and artificial nuclear reactions and the promise and problems associated with nuclear power. Students will gain an understanding of instruments used to study, control, and utilize radioactive materials and nuclear processes. Students will complete and balance nuclear equations.

Objectives: Upon completion of the reading and problems, and when asked to demonstrate their understanding either orally or on a written test, students will

28:1	K	list the factors explaining nuclear structure. **28:1**
28:2	K	define nuclear force and nucleons. **28:1**
28:3	K/P	define, list and classify these elementary subatomic particles: leptons, hadrons, quarks, baryons, mesons, gluons, and neutrinos. **28:2**
28:4	K	define antiparticle. **28:2**
28:5	K	explain the principles utilized in accelerators. **28:3**
28:6	K	define drift tube and synchroton. **28:3**
28:7	K	differentiate among the three forms of radiation from natural radioactive nuclei. **28:4**
28:8	K	define and distinguish the radiation measures: rad, rem, RBE. **28:5**
28:9	K	compare the penetrating power and potential biological damage of the naturally occurring types of radiation. **28:5**
28:10	K/P	define half-life, and solve simple problems using the concept. **28:6**
28:11	K/P	list and explain the three factors which affect the stability of nuclides. **28:7**

28:12	K	define mass defect and binding energy. **28:7**
28:13	K/P	given a nuclide, predict its stability. **28:7**
28:14	K/P	describe natural and synthetic transmutations. **28:8-28:9**
28:15	K/P	write balanced equations to represent nuclear reactions. **28:8**
28:16	K	list some examples of synthetic transmutations. **28:9**
28:17	K	list some practical uses for radioactive nuclides. **28:10**
28:18	K	define and differentiate fission and fusion. **28:11-28:12**
28:19	K/P	describe a prototype nuclear reactor and define some problems in its use. **28:11**
28:20	K	define moderator and containment vessel. **28:11**
28:21	K	describe the problems inherent in a fusion reactor. **28:13**
28:22	A	voluntarily complete one or more of the One More Step activities.
28:23	A	read unassigned literature related to the chapter.

TEACHING TECHNIQUES

Section 28:4

Emphasize that natural radioactivity is a natural occurrence. Students are aware of the amount of heat produced by nuclear bombs and nuclear reactors. Radium undergoes natural radioactive decay producing heat, 552 J/h for each gram. Thus 1.0 gram of radium produces 1.00×10^{10} J of heat in its lifetime. This energy is equivalent to the heat produced by half a ton of coal when it burns. The heat, from natural radioactivity, can be detected deep within the earth. Nuclear energy and geothermal energy are related. Solar energy is from a great nuclear furnace also.

Section 28:5

You may want to have a student contact a doctor of radiation medicine and then make a report to the class on this tool in the fight against cancer.

Section 28:11

Demonstration: Staple or tape books of paper matches to a board with the heads over the edge. Hold the board upright and light the bottom match. The others will follow in turn demonstrating a chain reaction. Place the board in the sink and use a small rubber tubing connected to water to extinguish the flame.

Demonstration: By setting the dominos up so that one falls to hit two others in a branching set-up, one can illustrate the more rapid rate available for a branched chain reaction.

Technology and Chemistry

Use this feature to reinforce nuclear reactions and as an extension of Chapters 3 and 11 concerning the elements. Students can research other theories as to the origins of the elements.

PROBLEM SOLUTIONS

Page 562

1. $\frac{5.32 \times 10^9}{5.20 \times 10^6} = 1023 = 2^{10} = 10$ half-lives

   $10(32.1 \text{ h}) = 321 \text{ h} = 13.4$ days

2. $\frac{3.03 \times 10^6}{3.79 \times 10^5} = 7.99 = 8$ half-lives

   $2^8 = 256 \qquad \frac{5.80 \times 10^{28}}{256} = 2.27 \times 10^{26}$ atoms

3. Time required for one-half the atoms in a sample to decay.

Page 567

4. $^{27}_{12}\text{Mg} \rightarrow ^{\ \ 0}_{-1}\text{e} + ^{27}_{13}\text{Al}$
5. $^{49}_{24}\text{Cr} \rightarrow ^{\ 0}_{+1}\text{e} + ^{49}_{23}\text{V}$
6. $^{76}_{36}\text{Kr} + ^{\ \ 0}_{-1}\text{e} \rightarrow ^{76}_{35}\text{Br}$
7. $^{213}_{88}\text{Ra} \rightarrow ^{4}_{2}\text{He} + ^{209}_{86}\text{Rn}$
8. $^{231}_{90}\text{Th} \rightarrow ^{4}_{2}\text{He} + ^{227}_{88}\text{Ra}$

CHAPTER END PROBLEMS

Page 576

1. Alpha particles are helium nuclei; beta particles are electrons; gamma rays are electromagnetic radiation. α and β radiation consist of particles while γ radiation consists of electromagnetic waves. α particles are positively charged and several thousand times as heavy as the negatively charged β particles.

   increasing penetration
   $\longrightarrow$
   $\alpha\ \beta\ \gamma$
   $\longleftarrow$
   increasing ionizing power

2. Stability tests:
   (a) Binding energy. A greater binding energy per particle indicates greater stability.
   (b) Neutron-proton ratio. The more closely the ratio approximates 1, the more stable the atom, for light atoms.
   (c) In general, the atoms having an even number of neutrons and protons are more stable than those having an odd number of neutrons and protons.

3. Radioactive isotopes are used to:
   (a) gauge wear of pistons in automobile engines.
   (b) determine location of certain substances in the human body.
   (c) produce γ-rays.
   (d) trace the progress of radioactive chemicals in plants and animals.

4. Fusion is the joining of small nuclei to form one large nucleus.

Fission is the splitting of a large nucleus into smaller nuclei.

5. **a.** $^3_1H \rightarrow {}^3_2He + {}^0_{-1}e$
  b. $^{61}_{30}Zn \rightarrow {}^{61}_{29}Cu + {}^0_{+1}e$
  c. $^9_3Li \rightarrow {}^9_4Be + {}^0_{-1}e$
  d. $^{240}_{96}Cm \rightarrow {}^{236}_{94}Pu + {}^4_2He$
  e. $^{199}_{84}Po + {}^0_{-1}e \rightarrow {}^{199}_{83}Bi$

6. $\dfrac{6.00 \times 10^{20}}{1.88 \times 10^{19}} = 32 = 2^5 = 5$ half-lives
  $5(2.4 \text{ min}) = 12 \text{ min}$

7. **a.** $^{242}_{94}Pu \rightarrow {}^4_2He + {}^{238}_{92}U$
  b. $^{30}_{13}Al \rightarrow {}^0_{-1}e + {}^{30}_{14}Si$
  c. $^{55}_{26}Fe + {}^0_{-1}e \rightarrow {}^{55}_{25}Mn$
  d. $^{93}_{44}Ru \rightarrow {}^0_{+1}e + {}^{93}_{43}Tc$

8. **a.** $^{257}_{102}No \rightarrow {}^{253}_{100}Fm + {}^4_2He$
  b. $^{80}_{38}Sr + {}^0_{-1}e \rightarrow {}^{80}_{37}Rb$
  c. $^{140}_{62}Sm \rightarrow {}^{140}_{61}Pm + {}^0_{+1}e$
  d. $^{211}_{82}Pb \rightarrow {}^{211}_{83}Bi + {}^0_{-1}e$

REVIEW

Pages 576–577

1. It is reduced.

2. Otherwise the reactants would transfer electrons directly between particles instead of through the external wire.

3. No

4. $Co \rightarrow Co^{2+}$ 0.28 V, $Pb^{2+} \rightarrow Pb$ −0.13 V, sum = 0.15 V

5.

$$\frac{0.506 \text{ A}}{} \left| \frac{22.0 \text{ min}}{} \right| \frac{60 \text{ s}}{1 \text{ min}} \left| \frac{1 \text{ mol } e^-}{96\,500 \text{ A·s}} \right.$$

$$\frac{1 \text{ mol Sn}}{2 \text{ mol } e^-} \left| \frac{119 \text{ g Sn}}{1 \text{ mol Sn}} \right. = 0.412 \text{ g Sn}$$

6. Cu, O_2

7. $E = E° - \dfrac{0.0592}{n} \log [Pb^{2+}][F^-]^2$

  $E = 3.00 - \dfrac{0.0592}{2} \log (0.282)(0.0400)^2$

  $E = 3.10$ V

8. $\Delta G = -nFE°$

  $E° = \dfrac{\Delta G}{-nF} = (-26\,600 \text{ J})/(-1.96\,500)$

  $= 0.276$ V/e⁻ transferred

9. gain of electrons

10. 5+

11. 2+

12. At least one element changes oxidation number

13. $(8H^+ + 5e^- + MnO_4^- \rightarrow Mn^{2+} + 4H_2O) \times 2$
  $(2Cl^- \rightarrow Cl_2 + 2e^-) \times 5$
  $16H^+ + 10e^- + 2MnO_4^- \rightarrow 2Mn^{2+} + 8H_2O$
  $\underline{10Cl^- \rightarrow 5Cl_2 + 10e^-}$
  $16H^+ + 2MnO_4^- + 10Cl^- \rightarrow 2Mn^{2+} + 8H_2O + 5Cl_2$

14. $(2H_2O + 3e^- + MnO_4^- \rightarrow MnO_2 + 4OH^-) \times 2$
  $(2I^- \rightarrow I_2 + 2e^-) \times 3$
  $4H_2O + 6e^- + 2MnO_4^- \rightarrow 2MnO_2 + 8OH^-$
  $\underline{6I^- \rightarrow 3I_2 + 6e^-}$
  $4H_2O + 2MnO_4^- + 6I^- \rightarrow 2MnO_2 + 8OH^- + 3I_2$

ONE MORE STEP

Page 577

1. **a.** Intensity varies inversely as the square of the distance between source and detector.
  b. Relative effectiveness for equal thicknesses of: paper 1, masonry 16, iron 50, lead 100. (Figures will vary with type of paper and type of masonry.)

2. weak—slow processes (on a nuclear time-scale, $> 10^{-10}$s) such as beta decay of nuclei, and decay of muons, kaons, and λ particles.
strong—forces responsible for holding the nucleus together.

3. Cyclotron—makes use of magnetic fields and electrostatic charges to accelerate charged particles.
Betatron—accelerates electrons by means of magnetic fields alone.
Synchrotron—synchronizes an electric field and a magnetic field in order to accelerate the particles.
See: Wilson, Robert R., and Littauer, Raphael, *Accelerators: Machines of Nuclear Physics*. Garden City, Doubleday and Co., 1960.

4. For about 30 years physicists have been working toward the goal of harnessing the nuclear fusion process to obtain power. One of the systems studied is the magnetohydrodynamic (MHD) generator in which the fusion reaction is confined by magnetic means. Another system involves laser fusion which is based on ignition of a pellet of fuel by focused laser beams.

5. In the upper atmosphere, ^{14}C is formed as a result of bombardment of ^{14}N by cosmic rays. This radioactive carbon soon reacts with oxygen to form $^{14}CO_2$. Through mixing by winds, the distribution of $^{14}CO_2$ in the atmosphere remains virtually uniform. Carbon dioxide containing $^{14}CO_2$ is constantly being removed from the air by plants. All living plants have a constant concentration of ^{14}C in their composition because they use the radioactive ^{14}C in photosynthesis. However, when the plant dies, no more $^{14}CO_2$ is replaced by photosynthesis. Now, only disintegration is occurring. The ^{14}C concentration in the plant begins to decrease. By measuring the ^{14}C level in the dead plant and comparing it with the ^{14}C level in a living plant, it is possible to tell how long a plant has been dead. If an archeologist unearths logs in an excavation of an ancient city, *radio-carbon dating* of the timbers will indicate approximately when the trees were cut down.

6. By measuring the ratio of parent radioactive nuclide to daughter nuclide, the number of half-lives that have since the mineral was formed can be found. The assumption is made that all of the daughter nuclide came from the parent. Common parent-daughter pairs in use are $^{238}U - {}^{206}Pb$, $^{235}U - {}^{207}Pb$, $^{40}K - {}^{40}Ar$, $^{87}Rb - {}^{87}Sr$. Of course, the half-life of the parent must be known.

7. The first tests of the Shiva laser were completed in late 1977. The laser is used in inertial confinement fusion experiments at the Lawrence Livermore Laboratory. The laser produced 10 200 J in a pulse lasting 10^{-9} second. Its 11.3 trillion watt pulse is used in fusion power experiments with deuterium and tritium targets. Other experiments use 12 lasers aimed at the same target.

CLASSES OF ORGANIC COMPOUNDS

29

AN OVERVIEW

Organic chemistry is presented through a systematic study of hydrocarbons and their derivatives.

You should tell students that the chemical principles which govern the behavior of organic reactions are the same ones used in inorganic chemistry. The importance of structure is presented early in the chapter. Students should be made aware of the systematic way many compounds can be grouped according to similarities in their properties as a consequence of their structure. While teaching nomenclature, stress the pronunciation since compounds have similar names. It is important to make students aware of the 3-dimensional structure of organic compounds.

DEMONSTRATION INFORMATION

Esters can be prepared by placing 6 cm^3 of each reactant into a test tube with 5 drops of concentrated H_2SO_4. Heat the test tubes in a water bath.

butyric acid   + ethanol   pineapple
acetic acid   + amyl alcohol   banana
salicylic acid + methanol   wintergreen

Place a few drops of each ester on separate pieces of numbered filter paper and pass around the room. Ask students to identify the odor. Discuss the difference in price of natural oils (esters) and synthetic esters in perfumes and flavorings.

DISPOSAL: *Pour the liquid down the drain with a large quantity of water.*

PERFORMANCE OBJECTIVES

Goals: Students will classify hydrocarbons according to bonding families. Students will name and write structural formulas for simple hydrocarbons and substituted hydrocarbons. Students will differentiate among formulas and properties of substituted hydrocarbon families.

Objectives: Upon completion of the reading and problems, and when asked to demonstrate their understanding either orally or on a written test, students will

29:1	K	define organic chemistry. **Intro**
29:2	K	define hydrocarbons. **29:1**
29:3	K/P	distinguish aliphatic and cyclic hydrocarbons. **29:1**
29:4	K	define alkane and saturated hydrocarbon. **29:1**
29:5	K	define homologous series. **29:2**
29:6	K	give the general formulas for the alkane series of hydrocarbons, the alkenes, the alkynes, and the cycloalkanes. **29:2-29:10**
29:7	K/P	name the first ten members of the alkanes, and give their formulas. **29:2**
29:8	K	define hydrocarbon radical. **29:2**
29:9	K	define branch or substituent. **29:3**
29:10	K/P	given the structural formula of an alkane, name the compound. **29:3**
29:11	K/P	given the name of an alkane, draw its structural formula. **29:3**
29:12	K/P	draw structural formulas for the isomers of the alkanes. **29:4**
29:13	K	define optical isomers and these related terms: asymmetric carbon, optically active, and stereoisomers. **29:5**
29:14	K	define polarized light and polarimeter. **29:5**
29:15	K	define nuclear magnetic resonance (NMR) spectroscopy, and describe its use in the identification of organic compounds. **29:6**
29:16	K/P	list examples of cycloalkanes, giving names and structural formulas. **29:7**
29:17	K	define unsaturated hydrocarbon. **29:8**
29:18	K	define alkenes, and identify and name representative alkenes and their isomers. **29:8-29:9**
29:19	K	list some commercial uses of representative alkenes. **29:9**
29:20	K	define alkynes, and identify and name representative alkynes. **29:10**
29:21	K/P	given the number of carbons in an alkene or an alkyne, draw a representative structural formula. **29:8-29:10**
29:22	K	define, identify and give uses for representative aromatic hydrocarbons. **29:11**
29:23	K	define functional group. **29:12**
29:24	K	describe halogen substituted hydrocarbons, and list some of their uses. **29:12**
29:25	K/P	name and write formulas for halogen substituted hydrocarbons. **29:12**

29:26	K/P	differentiate the organic oxygen compounds: alcohols, ethers, aldehydes, ketones, acids, and esters. **29:13-29:16**
29:27	K/P	given the formula of an organic oxygen compound, name it, and vice versa. **29:13-29:16**
29:28	K	define phenol. **29:14**
29:29	K	define inductive effect. **29:16**
29:30	K/P	define and distinguish amines and amides. **29:17**
29:31	A	voluntarily complete one or more of the One More Step activities.
29:32	A	read unassigned literature related to the chapter.

TEACHING TECHNIQUES

Section 29:10

Demonstrate the reactivity of the triple bond by producing ethyne. Place some calcium carbide in water and cover with an inverted, water-filled test tube. Collect the gas by H_2O displacement. Collect three tubes: one 100% gas, one 50% gas (half filled with water, half air), and one 10% gas. Ignite each, keeping the mouth of the test tube down.

Section 29:11

Aromatic compounds are economically important to many chemical industries such as rubber, plastics, fibers, explosives, paint, and petroleum. Nomenclature rules for bonding positions on the benzene ring are:

ortho	meta	para
o-	m-	p-

Section 29:15

Demonstrate the oxidation of an aldehyde by slowly adding $1.0M$ $NH_3(aq)$ dropwise to 5 cm^3 of $1.0M$ $AgNO_3(aq)$ in a very clean test tube. A precipitate will form but will dissolve as more $NH_3(aq)$ is added. Add $NH_3(aq)$ until the precipitate is almost completely dissolved, then add 5 drops of 40% formaldehyde. Shake the test tube and warm (do not boil). A silver mirror will be deposited on the inside of the test tube. Silver ions are reduced to silver metal while the aldehyde is oxidized.

Aldehydes oxidize to form acids. Discard all unused material because it can form an explosive.

Technology and Chemistry

Use this feature as a starting point for a project concerning research on synthetic fuels. It is important to emphasize to students that there are many options for synthetic fuels, however the conversion costs associated with some of these options do not make them feasible. The economics of energy is an important topic in discussing the total energy picture.

PROBLEM SOLUTIONS

Page 284

1. **c.** 2,3-dimethylpentane
2. **a.** 2,2-dimethylbutane   **c.** 3-methylpentane
   b. hexane   **d.** 3-ethyl-2-methylhexane

3. **a.**
   b.
   c.
   d.

Pages 585-586

4. **a.** 2,3-dimethylpentane
   b. octane
   c. 2,2,3-trimethylheptane
   d. 2,3,4-trimethylhexane
   e. 2,2-dimethylbutane

5. **a.**
   b.
   c.
   d.

e. CH₃—CH₂—CH—CH₂—CH₂—CH₃
                    |
                    CH₂
                    |
                    CH₃

6. C—C—C—C—C—C

C—C—C—C—C
    |
    C

C—C—C—C—C
      |
      C

C—C—C—C
    |
    C
    |
    C

C—C—C—C
    | |
    C   C

7. hexane
2-methylpentane
3-methylpentane
2,2-dimethylbutane
2,3-dimethylbutane

CHAPTER END PROBLEMS

Pages 602-604

1. A homologous series is a group of compounds which differ by a specific structural unit.

2. C_nH_{2n}

3. a. C_6H_{12}
   b. C_8H_{18}
   c. $C_{10}H_{18}$

4. C_nH_{2n+1}

5. Longer molecules have more surface area over which weak forces can interact and heavier molecules travel more slowly than light molecules at the same temperature.

6. CH₃—CH₂—CH₂—CH₂—CH₂—CH₂—CH₂—CH₃
CH₃—CH₂—CH₂—CH₂—CH₂—CH₂—CH₂—CH₂—CH₃

7. C_7H_{15}

8. a. 2
   b. 2

9. a nonhydrocarbon or branch to the parent chain

10. Position numbers are assigned to give the lowest possible numbers to the substituents. Radicals appear in the name in alphabetical order.

11. C_8H_{16}, C_7H_{14}, $C_{10}H_{20}$

12. heptyne contains a triple bond

13. $C_7H_5N_3O_6$

14. C_8H_{10}

15. C_nH_{2n-2}

16. a. amide   **c.** nitrile
    b. amine   **d.** amino acid

17. a. alcohol   **c.** aldehyde
    b. alcohol   **d.** ketone

18. a. ether   **c.** carboxylic acid
    b. alcohol   **d.** ether

19.

C—C—C•—C—C—C—C

C—C—C—C—C—C
      |
      C

C—C—C—C—C—C
    |
    C

C—C—C—C
    |
    C
    |
    C   C
    | |
C—C—C—C—C

C
|
C
|
C—C—C—C—C
      |
      C
C—C—C—C—C
      |
      C
C—C—C—C
      |
      C   C
      | |
C—C—C—C—C

C
|
C
|
C—C—C—C
    | |
    C   C
    | |
C—C—C—C—C

20. a. 2,6-dimethyl-4-ethyloctane
    b. 2-pentene
    c. 1,2-diethylbenzene
    d. 1,1,4-trimethylcyclohexane
    e. 3,3-dimethyl-1-butyne

21. a.
                    CH₂—CH₃
                    |
    CH₃—CH₂—CH—CH₂—CH₂—CH₃

b.
    CH₃⬡CH₃ with CH₃, CH₃, CH₃, CH₃ substituents (hexamethylcyclohexane)

c. CH₂=C—CH₃
           |
           CH₃

d. CH≡C—CH₂—CH₂—CH₂—CH₃

e.
    (naphthalene with CH₃)

22. $C_{40}H_{82}$
40(12) + 82(1) = 562 u

23. a. 1-propanol
    b. 2-methyl-2-propanol
    c. 1-pentoxyhexane
    d. butanal
    e. 2-hexanone
    f. butanoic acid
    g. hexyl propanoate
    h. 1-propanamine (1-aminopropane)

24. a. CH₃—CH₂—CH₂—CH₂—OH
    b.   CH₃ OH
               | |
        CH₃—CH—CH₂
    c. CH₃—CH₂—CH₂—O—CH₂—CH₂—CH₂—CH₃
    d.   O
               ‖
        CH₃—CH

e. $CH_3-CH_2-\overset{\overset{O}{\|}}{C}-CH_2-CH_3$

f. $CH_3-CH_2-CH_2-O-\overset{\overset{O}{\|}}{C}-H$

g. $CH_3-\overset{\overset{CH_3}{|}}{N}-CH_3$

i. $CH_3-CH_2-\overset{\overset{O}{\|}}{C}-NH_2$

h. $CH_3-CH_2-\overset{\overset{O}{\|}}{C}-OH$ **j.** CH_3-NO_2

25. The inductive effect is the electron withdrawing (or donating) power of an atom away from the functional group.

26. If the functional group exhibits the inductive effect or is an atom of high electronegativity the acid strength increases.

27. The chlorine is closer to the functional group in 2-chlorobutanoic acid.

28. a. (cyclopentanone structure)

b. $CH_3-\overset{\overset{O}{\|}}{C}-CH=CH-CH_3$

c. $CH_3-CH_2-CH_2-CH_2-O-\overset{\overset{O}{\|}}{C}-CH_2-CH_2-CH_3$

d. $CH_3-CH_2-O-\overset{\overset{O}{\|}}{C}-CH_2-Cl$

e. CH_3-CN

f. $CH_2-CH-CHO$ (with benzene ring, NH_2)

g. $Br-CH-CH_2-Br$ (with benzene ring)

h. $CH_3(-CH_2{}^-)_{14}\,CH_3$

29. a. 2-methylpropanal
b. 2-methylbutanal
c. methanoic acid (formic acid)
d. ethandioic acid (oxalic acid)
e. methylamine
f. chloromethane

30. a. $CH=CH-CH_3$ (with benzene ring)
b. (benzene ring with CH_3, CH_3)
c. (benzene ring with I)
d. $CH_3-CH_2-CH_2-CH_2-CH_2-Br$
e. $CH_3-CH_2-\overset{\overset{OH}{|}}{\underset{\underset{CH_3}{|}}{C}}-CH_2-CH_3$
f. (benzene ring with OH, CH_3)

REVIEW

Pages 604-605

1. Nuclear force exists as a result of trading or sharing of pions between nucleons.

2. alpha—2+, mass of He atom (about 4 u)
beta—1−, negligible mass

3. It represents the amount of energy necessary to break up the nucleus.

4. The products of one fission include one or more neutrons which can initiate one or more additional fissions.

5. bombard Cf nuclei with Mg nuclei

6. $Co \rightarrow Co^{2+}$ 0.28 V, $Cu^{2+} \rightarrow Cu$ 0.34 V,
sum $(E°) = 0.62$ V
$$E = E° - \frac{0.0592}{n} \log \frac{[Co^{2+}]}{[Cu^{2+}]}$$
$$= 0.62 - \frac{0.0592}{2} \log \frac{(0.1)}{(2)} = 0.66 \text{ V}$$

7. $2.30RT(\log K) = nFE°$
$(2.30)(8.31)(298)\log K = (1)(96\,500)(1)$
$K = 8.76 \times 10^{16}$
$\Delta G = -nFE° = -(1)(96\,500)(1) = -96\,500$ J

8. $12.6731 - 12.3247 = 0.3484$ g Ni
$$\frac{0.3484}{0.8128} \times 100 = 42.86\%$$

9. $$\frac{6.30 \times 10^{11}}{2.46 \times 10^9} = 256 = 2^8$$
$8(74.2) = 594$ days $= 1.63$ years

10. $^{240}_{92}U \rightarrow {}^{0}_{-1}e + {}^{240}_{93}Np$

ONE MORE STEP

Page 605

1. ethylene—Some is a by-product of petroleum processing. The remainder is made principally from ethane. Ethane and steam are run through a cracking tower at 700-900°C. The output is cooled to condense high-boiling products and remove water. The product is then fractionally distilled to recover ethane, ethylene, propane, propylene, and methane.
Uses—Manufacture of polyethylene plastic, ethylene oxide, ethylene dichloride, ethanol, ethylbenzene, acetaldehyde, ethyl chloride
benzene—Recovered by liquid-liquid extraction from by-products of petroleum cracking and reforming operations
Uses—manufacture of styrene, phenol, decylbenzene, fibers, plastics
propylene—By-product of petroleum processing. See also under ethylene.
Uses—Manufacture of polypropylene plastic, isopropyl alcohol, detergents, cumene, glycerine, gasoline
toluene—same source as benzene

Uses—gasoline, manufacture of other chemicals

urea—The principle process for the production of urea is the combining of ammonia and carbon dioxide under high pressure. The ammonium carbamate (NH_2COONH_4) thus formed is decomposed to urea and water.

Uses—principally in fertilizer and plastics (e.g., ureaformaldehyde). Also in wood treatment, glues, and the production of other chemicals.

2. Silicon is prepared from silica (SiO_2) and coke in an electric furnace. Treatment of the silicon with HCl produces $HSiCl_3$. Reaction with Grignard reagents (see problem 1) produces R_2SiCl_2. Hydrolysis of these produces the polymer ($R_2SiO)_n$. There is an excellent outline of silicon chemistry in the first few pages of the Petrarch Systems catalog (P.O. Box 141, Levittown, Pa. 19059).

Depending upon the degree of polymerization and the R- groups, silicones can be oils, resins, or elastomers. They are used for surface coatings, electrical insulation, rubber, lubricating oil and grease, antifoam agents, water repellants, and glues.

They are heat-stable, pliable, and have a nearly constant viscosity with changing temperature.

3.
methane	undecane	heneicosane
ethane	dodecane	docosane
propane	tridecane	tricosane
butane	tetradecane	tetracosane
pentane	pentadecane	pentacosane
hexane	hexadecane	hexacosane
heptane	heptadecane	heptacosane
octane	octadecane	octacosane
nonane	nonadecane	nonacosane
decane	eicosane	triacontane

4. nonane = 35 isomers
   decane = 75 isomers

ORGANIC REACTIONS AND BIOCHEMISTRY 30

AN OVERVIEW

Chapter 30 presents the common types of organic chemical reactions. Reaction patterns lead students to an understanding of basic organic chemistry. Reaction patterns allow us to predict the products of similar processes. The chapter then describes some of the common products of organic reactions. Soap, petroleum products, synthetic rubber, plastics, and synthetic fibers are studied. The properties studied are a consequence of structure. The chapter concludes with a presentation of introductory biochemistry.

DEMONSTRATION INFORMATION

Preparation of nylon—**CAUTION:** *Vapors hazardous, use a fume hood for this demonstration. Goggles must be worn because the solution can easily splash into the eyes.* In a 100 cm^3 beaker place 50 cm^3 of (TTE) 1,1,2-trichloro-1,2,2-trifluoroethane. Add 1 cm^3 of sebacoyl chloride to the TTE and stir vigorously. It is important that the solution be thoroughly mixed. In a 100 cm^3 beaker, dissolve 1.1 g of 1,6-diaminohexane and 2.5 g of anhydrous sodium carbonate in 25 cm^3 H_2O. Add a drop of food coloring to the H_2O to help students see the two layers. Pour the water solution into the TTE solution without mixing the two. Using forceps, pick up the center of the "film" that forms at the interface of the two liquids. Slowly pull the nylon fiber from the beaker and roll it up on a graduated cylinder that has a paper towel taped around it. A crank can be made from a glass bend with two 90° angles. Insert the tubing in a stopper placed in the end of the graduated cylinder. See Section 30:9.

DISPOSAL: *These chemicals are properly disposed of at a local landfill. They represent little or no hazard to the environment.*

PERFORMANCE OBJECTIVES

Goals: Students will complete and balance equations dealing with five common types of organic reactions. Students will determine the practical and biological significance of some organic compounds.

Objectives: Upon completion of the reading and problems, and when asked to demonstrate their understanding either orally or on a written test, students will

30:1	K/P	given a hydrocarbon, determine the combustion products, and complete and balance the equation for the reaction. **30:1**
30:2	K/P	describe substitution reactions, and complete and balance representative reactions. **30:2**
30:3	K	define addition reaction. **30:3**
30:4	K/P	given an alkene, complete and balance an equation for an addition reaction involving the alkene **30:3**
30:5	K/P	complete and balance representative elimination reactions **30:4**
30:6	K	define esterification and saponification. **30:5**
30:7	K/P	compare neutralization and hydrolysis reactions with

30:8	K	esterification and saponification reactions. **30:5**
30:8	K	define octane rating. **30:6**
30:9	K/P	describe fractional distillation as it relates to the refining of petroleum. **30:6**
30:10	K	define polymers. **30:7**
30:11	K/P	discuss the formation of polymers and their uses. **30:7**
30:12	K/P	describe the manufacture of products derived from synthetic rubber, plastics, and synthetic fibers. **30:7-30:8**
30:13	K	distinguish proteins and amino acids. **30:10**
30:14	K	list some biochemical functions of proteins. **30:10**
30:15	K/P	explain the significance of amino acids. **30:10**
30:16	K	define amide or peptide link, di-, tri-, and polypeptides. **30:10**
30:17	K	define lipids, fats, and vitamins. **30:12**
30:18	K	define nucleic acids and nucleotides. **30:13**
30:19	K	list, differentiate among, and describe the biochemical functions of carbohydrates, lipids, and nucleic acids. **30:11-30:13**
30:20	A	voluntarily complete one or more of the One More Step activities.
30:21	A	read unassigned literature related to the chapter.

TEACHING TECHNIQUES

Section 30:5

Soap—Place 25 g of a solid vegetable oil in a 250 cm^3 beaker. Add 10 cm^3 of ethanol and 5 cm^3 of 6M NaOH solution. Heat the mixture using a hot plate and stir constantly for 15 minutes. **CAUTION:** ethanol is flammable. Cool the mixture in a water bath, then add 25 cm^3 of hot distilled water and 25 cm^3 of a saturated NaCl solution. The soap should now appear as curds. Collect the soap and press it into an evaporating dish to mold it.

Section 30:6

Gasolines are rated on a scale known as octane rating. The basis for this scale is the property of some fuels to cause "knocking" in engines. The knocking occurs when some of the fuel explodes suddenly instead of burning evenly. To rate a gasoline, a "standard" engine is required. Heptane is given an arbitrary octane rating of zero, and 2,2,4-trimethylpentane, an isomer of octane, is given a rating of 100. The standard engine is run on the test fuel as well as on various mixtures of heptane and 2,2,4-trimethylpentane. When one of the mixtures of the two standards causes the same degree of knocking as the test fuel, the test is complete. The octane rating for the test fuel is the percentage of 2,2,4-trimethylpentane in the mixture with heptane.

Section 30:10

Use clothespins to present a visual model of the monomer-polymer relationship. Clip one clothespin onto the leg of another one and continue this process to form a polymer chain. Each clothespin acts as a monomer.

Technology and Chemistry

There has been much controversy surrounding the topic of genetic engineering. Use this feature as a starting point. Have students investigate the advantages and disadvantages of continuing research in this area.

PROBLEM SOLUTIONS

Page 608

1. $2C_6H_{14} + 19O_2 \rightarrow 12CO_2 + 14H_2O$

Page 609

2. $HOH + (CH_3)_3CI \rightarrow (CH_3)_3COH + HI$

Page 610

3. $CH_3-CH_2-CH=CH_2 + Br_2 \rightarrow CH_3-CH_2-\underset{\underset{Br}{|}}{CH}-\underset{\underset{Br}{|}}{CH_2}$

4. $CH_3-CH_2-CH_2-CH_2-OH \xrightarrow{H_2SO_4}$
$CH_3-CH_2-CH=CH_2 + H_2O$

Page 611

5. $CH_3-CH_2-OH + CH_3-CH_2-CH_2-COOH \rightarrow$
$CH_3-CH_2-O-\overset{\overset{O}{||}}{C}-CH_2-CH_2-CH_3 + H_2O$

Page 612

6. petroleum ether, ligroin, gasoline, kerosene, gas oil, lubricating oil

Page 615

7. cellulose (wood)

Page 617

8. nylon

9. $-\overset{\overset{O}{||}}{C}\boxed{-OH \qquad H}-\overset{\overset{N}{|}}{N}- \rightarrow -\overset{\overset{O}{||}}{C}-\overset{\overset{N}{|}}{N}- + H_2O$

Page 618

10. energy source and reserve

Page 619

11. fats, vitamins, steroids, porphyrins (hemoglobin and chlorophyll)

12. Animal fats contain saturated fatty acid residues. Plant oils contain unsaturated fatty acid residues.

Page 620

13. DNA contains thymine; RNA contains uracil. DNA is used to make RNA and to pass genetic information between generations. RNA is used to make proteins and enzymes.

CHAPTER END PROBLEMS

Page 623

1. $CH_2{=}CH_2(g) + HI(g) \rightarrow CH_3{-}CH_2I(l)$

2. $CH_2{=}CH_2(g) + $ $-CH{=}CH_2(l) \rightarrow$

$-CH{-}CH_2{-}CH_2{-}CH_2{-}$(amor)

3. a. $Cl_2(g) + CH_2{=}CH{-}CH_3(g) \rightarrow Cl{-}CH_2{-}\underset{\underset{Cl}{|}}{CH}{-}CH_3(l)$

b. $CH_3{-}(CH_2)_4{-}OH(l) + CH_3{-}\underset{\underset{O}{\|}}{C}{-}OH(l) \rightarrow$

$CH_3{-}\underset{\underset{O}{\|}}{C}{-}O{-}(CH_2)_4{-}CH_3(l) + H_2O(l)$

c. $2C_6H_6(l) + 15O_2(g) \rightarrow 12CO_2(g) + 6H_2O(l)$

d. $HO{-}CH_2{-}CH_2{-}CH_2{-}CH_3(l) \xrightarrow{H_2SO_4}$

$CH_2{=}CH{-}CH_2CH_3(g) + H_2O(l)$

e.

4. Addition polymerization is a result of the "adding on" to each other of monomers containing double bonds. Condensation polymerization is the result of monomers reacting by eliminating a small molecule between them.

5.

6.

7. Proteins contain hundreds or thousands of amino acid residues. Thus, the number of possible combinations is enormous.

8. Proteins act as catalysts and are structural components.

9. adenosine triphosphate—ATP

10. assist enzymatic reactions, and act as coenzymes

REVIEW

Pages 623-624

1.
$$Bi \rightarrow Bi^{3+} + 3e^-$$
$$\underline{4H^+ + 3e^- + NO_3^- \rightarrow NO + 2H_2O}$$
$$Bi + 4H^+ + NO_3^- \rightarrow Bi^{3+} + NO + 2H_2O$$

2. $0.28 + 0.63 = 0.91$ V

3. H_2, SO_2

4. $E = E° - \dfrac{0.0592}{n} \log \dfrac{[Cu^+]^5[Mn^{2+}]}{[MnO_4^-][H^+]^8}$

$= 0.99 - \dfrac{0.0592}{5} \log \dfrac{(1)^5(0.01)}{(1)(1)^8} = 1.01$ V

5. $\Delta G = -nFE° = (-n)(96\ 500)(1.94)$
$= -187$ kJ/mol e⁻ transferred

6. $2Br^- \rightarrow Br_2 + 2e^-$

| $\dfrac{260\ \cancel{A}}{}$ | $\dfrac{2.17\ \cancel{h}}{}$ | $\dfrac{60\ \cancel{min}}{1\ \cancel{h}}$ | $\dfrac{60\ \cancel{s}}{1\ \cancel{min}}$ | $\dfrac{1\ \cancel{mol\ e^-}}{96\ 500\ \cancel{A \cdot s}}$ |

$$\dfrac{1\ \cancel{mol\ Br_2}}{2\ \cancel{mol\ e^-}} \mid \dfrac{160\ g\ Br_2}{1\ \cancel{mol\ Br_2}} = 16.8\ g\ Br_2$$

7. $\dfrac{16}{4} = 4$ half-lives; $2^4 = 16$

$\dfrac{270}{16} = 16.9$ g Pd

8. $^{129}_{55}Cs + ^{\ \ 0}_{-1}e \rightarrow ^{129}_{54}Xe$

9. a. 2-bromobutane
b. propene
c. 1,1,2,2-tetramethylcyclohexane

d. 1-bromo-3,4-dimethylbenzene (4-bromo-1,2-xylene)

10. a. $Br-\overset{\overset{\displaystyle Cl}{|}}{C}=CH-CH_3$

b. $CH_2=CH_2$

d. $Br-CH-\!\!\!\!-CH-CH_3$

c. Cl

ONE MORE STEP

Pages 624-625

1. Grignard Reagents. In 1901, the French chemist Victor Grignard made the important observation that alkyl halides dissolved in diethyl ether ($C_2H_5-O-C_2H_5$) will react with metallic magnesium to form ether-soluble alkylmagnesium halides. These halides are now called Grignard reagents. The reaction producing them will be illustrated here by the formation of methylmagnesium iodide from methyl iodide. The diethyl ether solvent must be very pure, and the apparatus and reagents must be moisture free.

$$CH_3I + Mg \rightarrow CH_3MgI$$
methylmagnesium iodide

Grignard reagents react with water to produce alkanes. Since the step leading to the formation of the Grignard reagent and the hydrolysis process both produce a good yield, this reaction sequence is an attractive one for the conversion of alkyl halides to the corresponding alkanes. The hydrolysis of methylmagnesium iodide produces methane in the following manner:

$$CH_3MgI + HOH \rightarrow CH_4 + MgI(OH)$$

This type of reaction sequence may be generalized as:

$R-X + Mg \rightarrow RMgX$ R | $MgX + H-O$ | H →

$R-H + MgX(OH)$

The Wurtz and Williamson reactions are described in the enrichment of chapter 6 in the Teacher Resource Book.

2. Saran®—copolymer of vinyl chloride and vinylidene chloride.
Kodel®—copolymer of ethylene glycol and terephthalic acid.
Acrilan®—acrylonitrile.

Dynel®—copolymer of acrylonitrile and vinyl chloride.
Mylar®—copolymer of ethylene glycol and terephthalic acid.
vinyl chloride $CH_2=CH-Cl$
vinylidene chloride $CH_2=CCl_2$
ethylene glycol $HO-CH_2-CH_2-OH$
terephthalic acid

acrylonitrile $CH_2=CH-C\equiv N$

3. A dipolar ion; e.g., an amino acid in a solution acidic enough to produce

$$H_3\overset{\oplus}{N}-\underset{\underset{\displaystyle G}{|}}{C}H-COO^{\ominus}$$

4. for an α-helix, imitate Fig. 3-7, p. 37, in Kilgour, *Fundamentals of Biochemistry*
for a β-pleat, imitate Fig. 3-5, p. 35, Kilgour, *Fundamentals of Biochemistry*

5. During the "burning" of glucose, NAD acts as the oxidizing agent (it is reduced) in converting glyceraldehyde-3-phosphate to glyceric acid-1,3-diphosphate.

6.

7. for the citric acid cycle, imitate the right-hand front end paper of Kilgour, *Fundamentals of Biochemistry*

8. As the liver attempts to regulate glucose levels in the blood, amino acid and fatty acid metabolism upset the citric acid cycle resulting in an accumulation of acetoacetic acid. The body cannot excrete the acid and neutralizes it with various cations. The remaining H^+ builds up and the pH of the blood dips into the acid range.

9.

TEACHER QUESTIONNAIRE

Perhaps one of the best ways to ensure that effective educational materials are produced is to let authors and publishers know how you feel concerning the texts you are using. Please help us plan revisions and new programs to meet your needs. Complete and return the form provided. Please attach any additional comments to the questionnaire form. After removing the questionnaire from the book, fold and staple it so that the address label shows. We would certainly appreciate hearing from you.

CHEMISTRY: A MODERN COURSE

Circle the number which corresponds to your opinion of each of the following items for the Merrill Chemistry Program. Please also star (*) those three factors which most influence your evaluation or choice of a text.

Student Text	Excel-lent	Very Good	Satis-factory	Fair	Poor	Comments
1. Readability	5	4	3	2	1	_____
2. Approach	5	4	3	2	1	_____
3. Organization	5	4	3	2	1	_____
4. Factual accuracy	5	4	3	2	1	_____
5. Coverage of chemical principles	5	4	3	2	1	_____
6. Concept development	5	4	3	2	1	_____
7. Visual impact	5	4	3	2	1	_____
8. Chapter end materials	5	4	3	2	1	_____
9. Tables	5	4	3	2	1	_____
10. Illustrations	5	4	3	2	1	_____
11. Technology career features	5	4	3	2	1	_____
12. Biographies	5	4	3	2	1	_____
13. Student notes	5	4	3	2	1	_____
14. Example problems	5	4	3	2	1	_____
15. Appendices	5	4	3	2	1	_____
16. Glossary	5	4	3	2	1	_____

Teacher Annotated Edition						
1. Teachability	5	4	3	2	1	_____
2. Effective program use	5	4	3	2	1	_____
3. Demonstrations	5	4	3	2	1	_____
4. Chapter suggestions	5	4	3	2	1	_____
5. Planning guide	5	4	3	2	1	_____
6. Chapter end answers	5	4	3	2	1	_____
7. Audiovisual aids	5	4	3	2	1	_____
8. Annotations	5	4	3	2	1	_____
9. Suggested readings	5	4	3	2	1	_____

Supplements						
1. *Laboratory Chemistry*	5	4	3	2	1	_____
2. *Laboratory Chemistry TAE*	5	4	3	2	1	_____
3. *Evaluation Program for Chemistry: A Modern Course*	5	4	3	2	1	_____
4. *Solving Problems in Chemistry*	5	4	3	2	1	_____
5. *Teacher Resource Book*	5	4	3	2	1	_____
6. *Computer-Assisted Data-Checking Programs*	5	4	3	2	1	_____

Circle the appropriate information:

1. Grade level of your students
2. Average number of students in your chemistry classes
3. Total number of students enrolled in chemistry
4. Total school enrollment
5. Locale of the school
6. Ability level of the students
7. Appropriateness of the text for your class
8. The number of years the text will be used
9. May we quote you?

9	10	11		12
5-10	11-20	21-30	31-40	40+
under 100	101-200	201-300	300+	
under 200	201-500	501-1000	1000+	
rural	small town	suburban	city	
below avg.	average	above avg.		
easy	about right	difficult		
1	2	3	4	5
yes	no			

Please feel free to attach an additional sheet to make further comments.

Name _____ Date _____

School _____ City _____ State _____ Zip _____

Fold

BUSINESS REPLY MAIL
FIRST CLASS   PERMIT NO. 284   COLUMBUS, OHIO
POSTAGE WILL BE PAID BY ADDRESSEE
Managing Editor, Elhi Science
MERRILL PUBLISHING CO.
A BELL & HOWELL COMPANY
1300 ALUM CREEK DRIVE
COLUMBUS, OHIO 43216

NO POSTAGE
NECESSARY
IF MAILED
IN THE
UNITED STATES

CHEMISTRY
A MODERN COURSE

ROBERT C. SMOOT
Rollins Fellow in Science
McDonogh School
McDonogh, Maryland

Robert C. Smoot is a chemistry teacher and Rollins Fellow in Science at McDonogh School. He has taught chemistry at the high school level for 27 years. He has also taught courses in physics, mathematics, engineering, oceanography, and electronics. He earned his B.S. degree in Chemical Engineering from Pennsylvania State University and his M.A. in Teaching from Johns Hopkins University. He is a member of many national professional organizations including the American Chemical Society and the National Science Teachers Association. In addition, Mr. Smoot is a coauthor of other Merrill senior high science textbooks.

JACK PRICE
Superintendent
Palos Verdes Peninsula Unified School District
Palos Verdes, California

Jack Price taught chemistry and mathematics for 13 years in Detroit before becoming Math/Science Coordinator for the San Diego County Department of Education. He earned his B.A. degree at Eastern Michigan University and M. Ed. and Ed. D. degrees at Wayne State University. While at Wayne State, Dr. Price did original research in organometallic compounds. He has participated in NSF summer institutes at New Mexico State University and the University of Colorado. Presently, he is Superintendent of Schools in Palos Verdes, California, where he periodically teaches semester courses at one of the three high schools. He is a member of the Mathematical Sciences Education Board of the National Research Council. He is also a coauthor of other Merrill science and mathematics textbooks at the junior and senior high levels.

RICHARD G. SMITH
Chairman, Science Department
Bexley High School
Bexley, Ohio

Richard G. Smith has been teaching chemistry at the high school level for 21 years. Presently, he is also the Science Department Chairman at Bexley High School. He received a regional outstanding teacher award from the American Chemical Society and has participated in NSF summer institutes in chemistry. Mr. Smith earned his B.S. degree in Education from Ohio University and his M.A.T. in Chemistry from Indiana University. He is a member of the American Chemical Society and the National Science Teachers Association as well as other national professional organizations.

MERRILL PUBLISHING CO.
A BELL & HOWELL COMPANY
COLUMBUS, OHIO
TORONTO • LONDON • SYDNEY

A MERRILL SCIENCE PROGRAM

CHEMISTRY: A MODERN COURSE
CHEMISTRY: A MODERN COURSE, TEACHER ANNOTATED EDITION
CHEMISTRY: A MODERN COURSE, TEACHER RESOURCE BOOK
CHEMISTRY: A MODERN COURSE, SPIRIT DUPLICATING EVALUATION MASTERS
LABORATORY CHEMISTRY
LABORATORY CHEMISTRY, TEACHER ANNOTATED EDITION
LABORATORY CHEMISTRY, COMPUTER-ASSISTED DATA-CHECKING PROGRAMS
SOLVING PROBLEMS IN CHEMISTRY

Reviewers

Betty S. Abernathy, Science Department Chairman, Fike High School, Wilson, North Carolina
Norman E. Allen, Chemistry and Physics Teacher, San Juan High School, Citrus Heights, California
Deborah L. Contois, Chemistry Teacher, McArthur High School, Hollywood, Florida
Bridget R. Dube, Chemistry Teacher, John Marshall High School, San Antonio, Texas
Robert P. Jacobson, Sr., Chemistry and Biology Teacher, Chippewa Valley High School, Mt. Clements, Michigan
Daniel W. McGary, Science Coordinator (K-12), School District of Lancaster, Lancaster, Pennsylvania
Daryl M. Miller, Science Department Chairman, Ben Davis High School, Indianapolis, Indiana
Jeanne M. O'Leary, Science Department Chairman, Moody High School, Corpus Christi, Texas
Richard J. Parsons, Science Department Chairman, Wilcox High School, Santa Clara, California
William S. Talbott, Educational Specialist, Baltimore City Public Schools, Baltimore, Maryland

Project Editor: Mary E. Gallant; *Editor:* Teresa Anne McCowen; *Project Designer and Artist:* Kip M. Frankenberry; *Illustrators:* Jim Shough, Ron McClean, Lloyd Ostendorf; *Photo Editors:* Barbara Buchholz, Aaron Haupt; *Production Editor:* Joy E. Dickerson

ISBN 0-675-06401-5
PUBLISHED BY
MERRILL PUBLISHING COMPANY
A BELL & HOWELL COMPANY
COLUMBUS, OHIO 43216

PREFACE

The 1987 Edition of **Chemistry: A Modern Course** is an introductory chemistry program which is comprehensive as well as relevant. The aim of the program is to enable students to develop a better understanding of their physical world. The central theme of the text is the basic principle that **the properties of matter are a consequence of the structure of matter.** A balanced approach is presented in combining chemical theories and concepts with quantitative problems. Students will find this material challenging and will be encouraged to think independently throughout the course.

Throughout the text the relationships among science, scientists, and society are stressed. In the biographies, the technology and careers essays, and the text itself, students are introduced to societal issues involving science and/or scientific personnel.

The content is presented in a logical manner which is flexible enough so later chapters may be studied in a variety of sequences. Initial chapters present some descriptive chemistry as well as the "mechanics" and basic vocabulary needed to move on to more complex concepts. Introduction of the mole concept early in the text enables students to perform quantitative as well as qualitative laboratory experiments within the first few weeks of the course. Several chapters are then devoted to the structure of matter and the periodicity of the elements. The principles developed in these chapters provide the foundation for the remainder of the text. The chapters that follow present matter in terms of acidity, oxidation-reduction, and electric potential. The text concludes with descriptive material in nuclear, organic, and biochemistry.

Each chapter is introduced with a photograph and a thought-provoking paragraph which sets the theme of the chapter. The *Goal* statements give an overall purpose for studying the chapter so that students will know from the first page of the chapter what they are expected to learn. Within each chapter, *margin notes* appear beside the text to highlight important ideas and to assist students in organizing information for study and review.

Sections are short and present only one or two main ideas in each. Thus, the pace at which new material is introduced is carefully controlled. The section titles provide an outline of the basic framework of each chapter. *New terms* are highlighted in boldface type. The *Glossary* at the back of the text assists students in learning the definitions of these terms.

The development of a systematic approach to problem solving should be a major aim of any beginning course in chemistry. The *factor-label method* exemplifies this philosophy and is used throughout the text. *Example* problems within each chapter include a step-by-step solving process to guide students in mastering problem solving. Many *practice problems* are also included within each chapter. Answers are provided for some of these in-chapter problems to enable students to check their understanding of the material just studied.

Many of the compounds used in example and practice problems contain elements that only recently have been used commercially. In this way, students are made aware of properties and uses of lesser known elements.

As awareness of health threats and disposal hazards becomes more widespread, many familiar compounds used in chemistry laboratories just a few years ago will disappear from widespread use. Some will be replaced by these less common substances. Thus, it will be increasingly important to have a broader awareness of the uses of the elements.

Each chapter includes a *Biography* of a scientist whose work is related to the material presented in the chapter. *Technology* and *Careers* related to chemistry are featured in the last section of each chapter.

Each chapter ends with an extensive *Summary* covering the major points of the chapter. The *Vocabulary* words are a list of terms boldfaced in the chapter. A comprehensive set of *questions* and *problems* is included to test understanding of the chapter material. *Review problems* are included to reinforce material from previous chapters. Another feature is the series of *problems* and *projects* under the heading *One More Step*. This section may be used to further students' knowledge of the chapter material by encouraging them to prepare projects, papers, or talks that can benefit the entire class. The *Readings* section provides references to books and magazine articles related to the material in the chapter.

The text takes into consideration a realistic appraisal of the capabilities and maturities of typical students. We wish to express our sincere thanks to the many chemistry students, teachers, and science educators who have made suggestions for changes based on their use of **Chemistry: A Modern Course.**

The Authors

CONTENTS

PHOTO CREDITS

Have you ever wondered how new medicines, cosmetics, or building materials are developed? Think of the vast number of products you use each day. These products have been developed by scientists using their knowledge of chemistry and related fields. Most of them were produced originally in a chemical laboratory using techniques similar to those used by the students shown here. What is chemistry? What other contributions do chemists make to society? What situations have arisen where chemical knowledge may have been used unwisely?

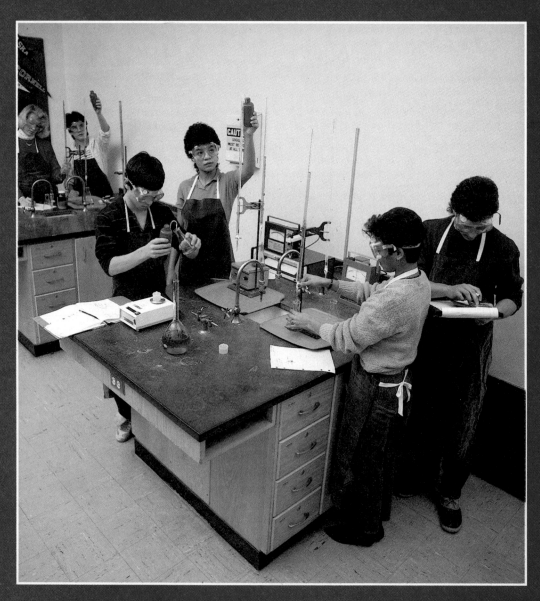

NATURE, CHEMISTRY, AND YOU

Chapter 1 covers the necessity of being informed in order to make intelligent decisions concerning the environment and quality of life. Chemistry is defined and the mass-energy relationship is introduced.

DEMONSTRATION: Use solutions of $KMnO_4$, $NaHSO_3$, and $BaCl_2$ to show wine to water to milk changes. See the Teacher Guide at the front of this book for details.

GOALS:
- You will gain an understanding of the nature of chemistry.
- You will examine the relationship between science and human progress.
- You will define matter and energy.

Throughout history, people have tried to alter their environment to improve their way of life. Such "tinkering" has often had unexpected results.

Some of the earliest examples we have of people changing their environment involve farming. More than 4000 years ago, the Sumerians of the lower Tigris-Euphrates valley built a system of canals and dikes. This system was used to control yearly floodwaters and to carry water to crops in dry areas. However, as the water flowed down from the mountains, it picked up salts in the hills. When it reached the fields, some of the water was used by the plants. The rest evaporated and left salts in the soil where they collected over centuries. In time the salt content of the soil became so high that crops could not grow. The Babylonians, who next occupied the land, paid the price for such "tinkering."

When the early Egyptian pharaohs built the pyramids about 4500 years ago, they had to quarry huge amounts of stone. The Great Pyramid alone needed over five million metric tons of stone! In the process of obtaining this stone, the landscape was badly scarred.

In India, about 400 A.D., a method for making rust-resistant iron was discovered. This method was later used by the Persians and then by the Arabs. This Indian discovery had an unexpected later application. The fine "Damascus" steel was made into swords used in many "holy wars."

Farming is an example of how people have altered their environment in an attempt to improve the quality of life.

SUGGESTION: Discuss other examples in which the environmental impact has not been thoroughly studied in advance.

3

FIGURE 1-1. Rust resistant iron (a) was used in the construction of this ancient pillar in Delhi, India. The ancient painting (b) depicts the flood control systems developed by the Egyptians along the Nile river.

About 600 A.D., the Chinese discovered how to make an explosive mixture containing potassium nitrate. They used it to make fireworks for amusement. Five centuries later, this same mixture was being used as gunpowder.

There is nothing good or bad about water, salt, stone, steel, or potassium nitrate. People determine whether these things are helpful or harmful. The people of Sumeria, Egypt, India, and China could not have foreseen the damage their discoveries would bring. They did not intend for their work to lead to undesirable results. Their aim was simply to improve the quality of their lives.

1:1 LIMITATIONS AND OPPORTUNITIES

Today we face many problems resulting from past attempts to "tinker" with nature. We have learned that we must plan for the future with care. However, planning for the future requires making choices.

We must plan for the future with care while using our existing resources wisely.

Livable space on our planet is limited. Space travel is enormously expensive. It seems unlikely that large numbers of people will colonize space stations in the near future. Therefore, we must use our existing resources wisely. An increasing world population leads to greater needs for housing, food, and clean air and water. Housing and farming both require suitable space. How is the available space to be divided? How is the available water supply to be divided?

Machines make our lives easier and more fun. However, machines need energy to run. The demand for energy is growing rapidly, yet our energy resources are limited. How should known energy resources be used? There is no single "best" answer to this question.

ENERGY PRODUCTION AND CONSUMPTION IN THE UNITED STATES, 1984

PRODUCTION AND CONSUMPTION IN 10^{18} J

FIGURE 1-2. By comparing the data in this graph, we see that the relative amounts for energy produced are lower than the amounts consumed.

1:2 FINDING OUT AND MAKING CHOICES

People and their leaders make daily decisions that affect the use of the environment and natural resources. To make an intelligent choice, one must know the facts on each side of a question. The decision a person makes involves a value judgment. That is, the person must apply his or her own values and beliefs to the facts at hand.

To make an intelligent choice, one must be aware of the available facts.

Values vary from country to country. Moral and ethical standards differ from person to person. You may judge a person as "good" or "bad" on the basis of how that person behaves. You are really comparing his or her behavior to your own set of standards. This kind of judgment is called a value judgment.

How we use facts involves value judgments.

The facts of nature, however, are neither good nor bad. Established facts are the same for everyone. For example, table salt dissolves in water. A diamond is hard. Neither of these statements can be labeled as good or bad. Nor is the process of determining these facts good or bad.

A collection of facts is neither good nor bad.

It is the way facts are used that may be good or bad. For example, scientists have learned the fact that sudden movements of the earth's crust can cause earthquakes. Can we hold scientists responsible for the destruction of life and property by an earthquake? Scientists have also learned the fact that huge amounts of energy are released by changes in certain atomic nuclei. It is the use of this fact to make a nuclear bomb, not the fact itself, that involves a value judgment.

SUGGESTION: Discuss with students that science is not "good" or "bad." What people do with science may be.

Even when the facts are known, making choices can be difficult. In making one choice, we decide against others. Usually, a risk is traded for

SUGGESTION: Ask students what "trade-offs" they consider when making decisions on a daily basis.

When making choices, we must consider the risks and benefits.

SUGGESTION: Be sure students are aware of the distinction between science and technology.

Science continually changes as our knowledge of the universe increases.

Scientists observe, hypothesize, and experiment to expand the collection of facts.

FIGURE 1-3. The use of nuclear reactions as an energy source is a controversial issue. Both pro-nuclear (a) and anti-nuclear groups (b) have strong arguments for their positions. You should be well informed in order to make wise decisions concerning this issue.

a benefit. For example, we may choose to develop more efficient car engines to save energy. However, this development will also mean more expensive cars. We choose to ship oil in huge tankers in order to lower shipping costs. However, if one of these tankers is involved in an oil spill, the resulting damage to the environment is beyond measurement in dollars. Science cannot provide the values a person uses to make such choices.

Science deals with learning facts about the universe. The scientist uses many methods to try to obtain facts free from human bias. However, methods of learning facts and applying them cannot be freed from human values.

Science is always changing. Science is not a set of procedures or a certain group of people. It is not a collection of facts that never changes and should not be viewed as a subject forever a mystery to you. Someday you may decide to pursue a career as a scientist and seek facts about our world. As a scientist, you will make observations. You will also hypothesize (make predictions based on your observations) and then experiment to test your hypotheses. In this way, you will add to the collection of facts that scientists have already recorded. This organized body of knowledge is a product of science. The information it provides may help us make wiser choices in planning for our future.

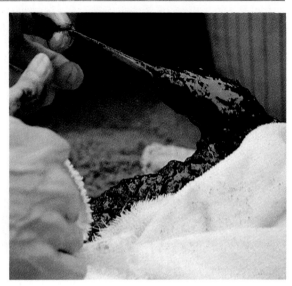

FIGURE 1-4. Oil spills such as that of the Argo Merchant in 1976 have caused extensive environmental damage. The damage done to the aquatic life in the area may be difficult to measure.

1:3 CHEMISTRY

Chemistry is the study and investigation of the structure and properties of matter. Millions of such studies have been made. As a result, certain properties are found to be related to the internal structure of matter. Knowledge of the relationship between structure and properties can be useful. An engineer may tell a chemist that a new material with certain properties is needed for a job. With this information, the chemist can predict what structure that material should have. For example, many new materials had to be developed for space exploration. These materials had to fit exacting specifications. An attempt was then made to produce the needed material. For example, a tragic fire in an Apollo space capsule killed three astronauts. NASA engineers asked chemists to develop a new, fire-resistant material for astronaut clothing. Besides its fire-resistance, it had to be flexible, abrasion-resistant, and comfortable next to the skin. Several companies produced materials that fit the requirements. One material, polybenzimidazole, was chosen after extensive testing by the manufacturer and NASA. The material has subsequently been used in some fire fighters' attire as well as astronauts' clothing.

A chemist may study many things. Such studies could be as different as the structure of the human brain or the bonding of rubber in a car tire. To make these studies, a chemist must be familiar with all of the sciences, including physics and mathematics. A chemist expresses the results of such investigations as a relationship between the properties and structure of the material being examined.

Relationships between properties and structure can be organized into a limited number of basic principles and facts. These basic facts and

Chemistry is the study and investigation of the structure and properties of matter.

CAREER: Point out that many disciplinary boundaries, such as biochemistry, physical chemistry, and biophysics, overlap. (Refer to Appendix D—Chemistry Related Careers)

Basic principles and facts relate the properties of materials to their structure.

FIGURE 1-5. This painting depicts an alchemist's laboratory during the Middle Ages. Alchemists were mainly concerned with changing abundant materials into precious or rare metals. They never reached their goal.

principles are the foundations of chemistry. Therefore, it is not necessary for a person to study the properties of all known materials in order to gain a knowledge of chemistry.

DEMONSTRATION: Pour a small quantity of perfume onto a watch glass. Ask students for their ideas as to the source of the odor.

Inertia is resistance of matter to change in direction or rate of motion.

1:4 MATTER

All material is called **matter** by scientists. Matter may be as difficult to observe as the particles that produce the odor of perfume. It may be as easy to observe as a block of lead. Matter is defined by scientists as anything that has the property of inertia. What is inertia? **Inertia** (in UHR shuh) is the resistance of matter to any change in motion. This change can be in either the direction or the rate of motion, or in both. For example, sup-

FIGURE 1-6. Today's chemistry laboratory is highly mechanized. Many analytical procedures are run completely by computerized machines. The chemist monitors the machines and analyzes the data produced.

pose you are riding in a moving car. When the car is stopped suddenly, your body tends to continue to move forward. If the car makes a sharp turn, your body tends to continue to move in its original direction. Thus, you are thrown against the side of the car opposite from the direction of the turn. In both cases, your body is showing the property of inertia. All matter has the property of inertia.

FIGURE 1-7. Energy may be transferred from one object to another as seen by the motion of these billiard balls.

1:5 ENERGY

In the study of science, an important concept to understand is **energy.** All objects possess energy. A hockey stick is an object. So is an automobile, an atom, and an electron. The word energy comes from a Greek word meaning "work-within." We may interpret energy as meaning the capacity to do work.

Energy is a property of all matter.

An object has two general forms of energy: potential and kinetic. **Potential energy** depends on the position of the object with respect to some reference point. A book on a table has a greater potential energy than the same book on the floor because on the table it is further from the earth. The gravitational attraction between the earth and the book produces the potential energy. An electron close to its nucleus has less potential energy than when it is farther away. Here, the electrostatic attraction between the electron and nucleus produces the potential energy.

Potential energy depends upon the position of an object with respect to another object.

Kinetic energy refers to the motion of an object with respect to a reference point. An airplane traveling 700 kilometers per hour has a greater kinetic energy than when it is traveling 500 kilometers per hour.

Kinetic energy depends upon the motion of an object with respect to another object.

Energy can be transferred between objects in two ways: through direct contact and through electromagnetic waves. An example of direct transfer is the collision of two billiard balls. Kinetic energy is transferred

FIGURE 1-8. Solar energy is a form of radiant energy. It has some applications as a replacement for fossil fuels in areas with high percentages of sunny days. This school obtains some of its energy through solar panels.

directly from one ball to the other. An example of electromagnetic waves is the transfer of energy from the sun to the earth. Energy being transferred by electromagnetic waves is often called **radiant energy.**

Many other terms we use to describe energy are special cases or combinations of potential, kinetic, and radiant energy. Energy can be transformed from one kind to another. For instance, think about the battery-alternator system of a car. As the starter switch is turned on, the chemical energy in the battery is converted to electric energy. The car starts and chemical energy in the gasoline is converted into the energy of the moving car. As the crankshaft gains speed, its mechanical energy is transferred by belt and pulley to the alternator. In the alternator, the mechanical energy is converted into electric energy. This electric energy is transferred to the battery where it is converted to chemical energy. The battery is thus recharged. During this time, other energy transformations result in the production of heat and sound. With the exception of nuclear change, all such transfers of energy occur without an observable loss or gain in the total amount of energy.

Radiant energy is transferred through empty space, and is not a property of an object.

DEMONSTRATION: Half fill a 150 cm^3 beaker with sugar. Carefully pour a few cm^3 of concentrated H_2SO_4 on top of the sugar. Ask students for signs that energy is involved in the change they observe. Have a student touch the outside of the beaker. **CAUTION:** *The beaker will be quite hot. H_2SO_4 is corrosive.*

FIGURE 1-9. Many energy transformations must take place in the engine, crankshaft, alternator, and battery in order for a car to function properly.

1:6 MATTER AND ENERGY

For years, scientists thought that the total amount of matter and the total amount of energy in the universe were each constant. They stated their observations in the form of two laws. These laws are the law of conservation of matter and the law of conservation of energy.

The **law of conservation of matter** *states that matter is always conserved.* This statement means that the total amount of matter in the universe remains constant. Matter is neither created nor destroyed. It is only changed in form.

The **law of conservation of energy** *states that energy is always conserved.* This statement means that the total amount of energy in the universe remains the same. Energy is neither created nor destroyed. It too, is only changed in form.

In the early 1900's, Albert Einstein showed that matter can be changed to energy. He also showed that energy can be changed to matter. Einstein expressed this relationship in his famous equation:

$$E = mc^2$$

In this equation, E is energy, m is mass, and c is the speed of light in a vacuum (a constant).

According to Einstein's equation, mass and energy are equivalent. Thus we see that the two conservation laws are really just one law. This law is known as the law of conservation of matter-energy. Because mass is a measure of the amount of matter, this law is usually called the law of conservation of mass-energy. The **law of conservation of mass-energy** *states that mass and energy are always conserved and that their sum cannot be increased or decreased.* Mass and energy can, however, be changed from one to the other. Changes of energy to mass and mass to energy are observable only in nuclear reactions. In our laboratory work and in our discussions, we will always assume the original laws of conservation of matter and energy to be correct.

Energy can be converted from one form to another.

Matter can be changed to energy; energy can be changed to matter.

Mass and energy are interconvertible.

Law of conservation of mass-energy: Mass and energy are always conserved.

Mass-energy conversions are observed in nuclear reactions.

FIGURE 1-10. Energy and matter are conserved in the nuclear and chemical reactions that took place when this star exploded.

BIOGRAPHY   Ellen H. Richards (1842-1911)

In 1871 Ellen Richards entered Massachusetts Institute of Technology as the first woman ever admitted to a technical school in the United States. Her major interest in research and teaching was in public health in the fields of nutrition and sanitation. For more than thirty years, Mrs. Richards worked to establish standards for pure food, clean air and water, and safe sewage. At one time in her career she tested over 40 000 samples of the water in Massachusetts making certain that the citizens had a safe water supply. She taught sanitary chemistry at MIT for 27 years and served as consultant in public health to many communities. During her research, she encountered a certain material which she believed to contain new elements. Her work, however, did not allow her the time to find samarium and gadolinium which were later discovered in the same material by two French chemists. The health and well-being of people were more important to her than the fame she would have received from the discovery.

CAREERS AND CHEMISTRY

1:7 Chemists

Imagine how you would feel if you were the chemist who discovered how to make a drug that could cure a form of cancer! Not all chemists have such a sensational discovery in their careers. Chemists do, however, make many contributions that improve the quality of our lives. What is a chemist?

We have defined chemistry as the science of matter. Chemists, then, must work with matter. That statement, however, is too broad for a definition. In the Preface of this text, the theme of the book is stated as: The properties of matter are a consequence of its structure. Using this theme, chemists can be described as those scientists concerned chiefly with the interrelationship of the structure and properties in matter.

Some chemists are primarily concerned with finding the internal atomic structure of matter. Once the structure for a number of related compounds is determined, the chemist looks for patterns of behavior. In other words, the chemist tries to determine if a particular structural feature always leads to the same property or properties.

Other chemists take advantage of what is already known about structure and properties. These chemists "design" new compounds and predict their properties. These research and development chemists try to produce these new compounds and check for the properties. This work involves research in the library as well as the laboratory. Some chemists spend their entire careers making new compounds. Often these compounds are designed for a specific application. In Chapter 13 you will see how chemists design new compounds called polyester carboranes. Other times the compounds are produced merely to check the predictions made about their behavior.

A third group of chemists spends little time in the laboratory. This group uses the information produced by chemists in the lab to combine chemical facts into broad, useful theories concerning the structure and behavior of matter. They are called theoretical chemists.

Chemists in a fourth group devote their efforts to finding out the composition of materials. That is, they determine the compounds and elements present in a material as well as the proportions in which these substances occur. These men and women are analytical chemists.

In addition to chemists, many other persons with various backgrounds and training work with matter. Some deal with the science of chemistry, for example, chemistry teachers and science journalists. Others, such as chemical engineers, are more concerned with the technological applications of chemical principles to the solution of practical problems. In the following chapters, we will examine in detail some of the careers and technological applications that involve chemistry.

FIGURE 1-11. Chemists are involved in synthesizing new compounds as well as follow-up testing to ensure product safety. The chemists shown are running analytical tests on pesticide compounds.

SUMMARY

Point out that the Summary is an excellent aid in reviewing the chapter.

1. For thousands of years, people have altered their physical environment. Their work has led to both helpful and harmful results. **Intro**
2. Today, people face many decisions that will affect their environment and the use of natural resources. **1:1**
3. In order to make intelligent decisions, people must obtain the facts related to the decision to be made. The function of science is to provide the facts needed to make informed, intelligent decisions. **1:2**
4. Chemistry is the science of materials. A chemist studies the dependence of properties on the structures of materials. **1:3**
5. Matter is anything with the property of inertia. Inertia is the resistance of an object to change in either its direction or rate of motion. **1:4**
6. The energy of an object is the total of its potential and kinetic energy. **1:5**
7. Energy can be transferred from one object to another or made to do work on an object. **1:5**
8. Energy being transferred by electromagnetic waves is radiant energy. **1:5**
9. Energy can be transformed from one form to another. **1:5**
10. The law of conservation of mass-energy states that the sum of mass and energy in the universe is always the same. **1:6**

VOCABULARY

The vocabulary words are a list of the bold-faced terms in the chapter. Part A of each chapter test in the *Evaluation Program* is a test on these vocabulary words.

science **1:2**
chemistry **1:3**
matter **1:4**
inertia **1:4**
energy **1:5**
potential energy **1:5**

kinetic energy **1:5**
radiant energy **1:5**
law of conservation of matter **1:6**
law of conservation of energy **1:6**
law of conservation of mass-energy **1:6**

PROBLEMS

Detailed discussions and answers to problems are given in the Teacher Guide at the front of this book.

1. Make a list of at least five different forms of energy. Use reference materials in your school library, particularly physics texts, to help you.
2. Using a dictionary, find out what aspects of nature are investigated by each of the following scientists: agronomist, astronomer, biologist, botanist, ecologist, entomologist, geochemist, geologist, geophysicist, horticulturist, limnologist, metallurgist, meteorologist, physicist, and zoologist.
3. Find out what kinds of careers require a knowledge of chemistry. Use the career appendix in the back of this book as a starting point. Obtain the career education materials that your guidance counselor may have, including college catalogs, the *Dictionary of Occupational Titles,* and the *Occupational Outlook Handbook.*
4. Assume that there is a remote mountain lake that can be developed as a vacation spot for city dwellers. What facts must be determined before development starts? What value judgments must be made?

5. If acid rain in the northeastern part of North America is caused by midwestern power plants, what would be the advantages and disadvantages of closing the power plants?

6. Define potential, kinetic, and radiant energy.

7. How can chemical knowledge be of use to the average citizen?

8. What are the conservation laws of matter, energy, and mass-energy?

ONE MORE STEP

1. Make a list of the industries and institutions in your community that make use of the services of a chemist.

2. Investigate the Cockcroft-Walton experiment, which confirmed Einstein's matter-energy hypothesis. Use reference materials from your library.

3. Research the advantages and disadvantages of continuing the whaling industry.

4. Investigate the advantages and disadvantages of expanding the nuclear power industry.

5. In December, 1976, the tanker *Argo Merchant* went aground off Massachusetts. A very large oil spill resulted. Try to find out what decisions led to the disaster, and why the decisions were made as they were.

6. What are the advantages and disadvantages of organotin fertilizers?

The One More Step section is intended to provide impetus to research topics related to the chapter.

READINGS

Baeder, D. L., "Love Canal—What Really Happened," *Chemtech*, Vol. 10, No. 12(December 1980), pp. 740-743.

Boraiko, Allen A., "Hazardous Waste," *National Geographic*, Vol. 167, No. 3(March 1985), pp. 318-351.

Caglioti, Luciano, *The Two Faces of Chemistry*, Cambridge, MA: MIT Press, 1983.

Ember, Lois R., "Yellow Rain," *Chemical and Engineering News*, Vol. 62, No. 2(January 9, 1984), pp. 8-34.

Heylin, Michael, et al., "Bhopal," *Chemical and Engineering News*, Vol. 63, No. 6(February 11, 1984), pp. 14-65.

Krieger, James, "Genetic Engineering Report," *Chemical and Engineering News*, Vol. 62, No. 33(August 13, 1984), pp. 10-12.

O'Sullivan, Dermot A., "European Concern about Acid Rain is Growing," *Chemical and Engineering News*, Vol. 63, No. 4(January 28, 1985), pp. 12-18.

Rawls, Rebecca L., "Progress in Gene Therapy Brings Human Trials Near," *Chemical and Engineering News*, Vol. 62, No. 33(August 13, 1984), pp. 39-44.

Weaver, Kenneth F., et al., *Energy*, Washington, D.C.: National Geographic Society, 1981.

White, Peter T., "Trash," *National Geographic*, Vol. 163, No. 4(April 1983), pp. 424-457.

Zurer, Pamela S., "Asbestos," *Chemical and Engineering News*, Vol. 63, No. 9(March 4, 1985), pp. 28-41.

Suggested Readings for teachers are found in the Teacher Guide at the front of this book.

Construction requires an in-depth knowledge of the structure and properties of materials. Measurement and design are key factors in using materials wisely. Design specifications for a building must conform to standards. In this chapter, you will learn how measurements and calculations using measurements will be important in gaining chemical knowledge. What standards are required in making a measurement? What measurement standards are used throughout the world?

MEASURING AND CALCULATING

Chapter 2 introduces scientific measurement and the mathematical concepts used in this text. These concepts include scientific notation, SI measurement, and the factor-label method of problem solving.

DEMONSTRATION: Prepare a two-layered system of water and glycerine. Float a rubber stopper on the glycerine and a cork on the water. See the Teacher Guide for details and teaching suggestions.

We have discussed two properties of matter: inertia and energy. When we describe a property without measurements we are characterizing the object **qualitatively.** When the property can be measured and described by a number of standard units, we have characterized the object **quantitatively.** Chemistry involves measuring and calculating. It is a quantitative science. When we refer to properties as we describe materials, it is helpful to measure the property and state the result quantitatively. In order to make a measurement, we must meet three requirements.

1. We must know exactly what we are trying to measure.
2. We must have some standard with which to compare whatever we are measuring.
3. We must have some method of making this comparison.

Qualitative—description with no measurements.

Quantitative—description based on measurements.

2:1 THE INTERNATIONAL SYSTEM (SI)

The standard units of measurement in science are part of a measuring system called the International System (SI). The letters are reversed in the symbol because they are taken from the French name Le Système International d'Unités. SI is used by all scientists throughout the world. SI is a modern version of the metric system.

BACKGROUND: SI will be used throughout the text as it is the accepted system of measurement in science.

SI is a modern version of the metric system.

SPECIFICATIONS (Hatchback Model)
Dimensions

Length 4210 mm	Wheelbase 2450 mm
Width 1650 mm	Ground clearance 165 mm
Height 1355 mm	

Capacity

Fuel tank 60 L	Power steering fluid 1.4 L
Radiator coolant 5.0 L	Manual transmission oil 2.5 L
Engine oil 4.0 L	Windshield washer fluid 2.5 L

Valve Clearance

Intake and Auxiliary 0.12 0.17 mm
Exhaust 0.25 0.30 mm

Engine

Type Water cooled 4-stroke OHC gas engine
Bore $\times$ Stroke 77.0 $\times$ 94.0 mm
Displacement 1751 cm^3

FIGURE 2-1. Information concerning breakthroughs and advances in chemistry is published in journals from all over the world. Thus, scientists must have a standardized system of presenting measurement data. Since many products are imported and exported, standardized measurements for specifications are a necessity.

The people in most countries use SI in everyday life or are in the process of converting to SI. This measurement system will be used in this text. One important feature of SI is its simplicity. Seven basic units are the foundation of the International System. These units are shown in Table 2-1.

The International System (SI) is based on seven units of measurement.

Table 2-1

SI Base Units		
Quantity	**Name**	**Symbol**
Length	meter	m
Mass	kilogram	kg
Time	second	s
Electric current	ampere	A
Thermodynamic temperature	kelvin	K
Amount of substance	mole	mol
Luminous intensity	candela	cd

Detailed definitions of these units are found in Table A-1 of the Appendix. We will discuss length, mass, time, and temperature in this chapter. Amount of substance will be discussed in Chapter 5 and electric current in Chapter 27. Luminous intensity will not be used in this book.

Order of magnitude is indicated by a prefix.

In SI, prefixes are used to obtain different units of a convenient size for measuring larger or smaller quantities. SI prefixes and their equivalents are listed in Table 2-2.

Table 2-2

SI Prefixes				
Prefix	Symbol	Meaning	Multiplier (Numerical)	Multiplier (Exponential)
Greater than 1				
tera	T	trillion	**1 000 000 000 000	10^{12}
giga	G	billion	1 000 000 000	10^{9}
mega	M	million	1 000 000	10^{6}
*kilo	k	thousand	1 000	10^{3}
hecto	h	hundred	100	10^{2}
deka	da	ten	10	10^{1}
Less than 1				
*deci	d	tenth	0.1	10^{-1}
*centi	c	hundredth	0.01	10^{-2}
*milli	m	thousandth	0.001	10^{-3}
*micro	μ	millionth	0.000 001	10^{-6}
*nano	n	billionth	0.000 000 001	10^{-9}
pico	p	trillionth	0.000 000 000 001	10^{-12}
femto	f	quadrillionth	0.000 000 000 000 001	10^{-15}
atto	a	quintillionth	0.000 000 000 000 000 001	10^{-18}

*These prefixes are commonly used in this book and should be memorized.
**Spaces are used to group digits in long numbers. In some countries, a comma indicates a decimal point. Therefore, commas will not be used.

2:2   MASS AND WEIGHT

In chemistry, finding the amount of matter is very important. For instance, we may wish to measure the amount of wood in a small block. One way of measuring is to weigh the block. Suppose we weigh such a block on a spring scale and find that its weight is one newton* (N). Now suppose we take the scale and the block to the top of a high mountain. There we weigh the block again. The weight now will be slightly less than one newton. The weight has changed because the weight of an object depends on its distance from the center of the earth. **Weight** is a measure of the force of gravity between two objects. These two objects are the block and the Earth. This force of gravity changes when the distance between the center of the Earth and the object changes.

The weight of an object can vary from place to place. In scientific work, we need a measurement that does not change from place to place. This measurement is called mass. **Mass** is a measure of the quantity of matter.

The standard for mass is a piece of metal kept at the International Bureau of Weights and Measures in Sèvres, France. This object is called the International Prototype Kilogram. Its mass is defined as one kilogram. The SI standard of mass is the **kilogram (kg).** However, the kilogram is too large a unit for everyday use in the chemical laboratory. For this reason,

*The newton is the measurement standard for weight or force.

FIGURE 2-2. The international standard for mass is the Prototype Kilogram.

the gram (g), one-thousandth of a kilogram, is commonly used. The mass of a paperclip is approximately one gram.

We have completed the first two requirements for making a measurement. We know what property we are going to measure and what our standard of comparison will be. Now we must compare the object with our standard. To compare, we use a balance. A **balance** is an instrument used to determine the mass of an object by comparing unknown mass to known mass. To compare these masses, we first place the object with unknown mass on the balance pan. Then we add standard masses to the beams until the masses are equal. In this comparison, the known masses and the unknown mass (the object) are the same distance from the center of Earth. They are, therefore, subject to the same attraction by the earth. At the top of the mountain, the unknown mass and known masses will still be equally distant from the center of the earth. Thus, Earth's attraction for each mass will still be equal. The mass of the object as compared to the standard will be the same. The balance will indicate no change in mass.

FIGURE 2-3. A triple-beam balance (a) measures mass by comparing the mass of an object placed on the pan to standard masses. An electronic balance (b) uses the same process to provide a digital readout of mass.

a

b

The process of measuring mass by comparing masses on a balance is called massing. Unfortunately, many terms that apply to the measurement of weight are often incorrectly applied to the measurement of mass. For example, standard masses used on the balance are often incorrectly called "weights." Also, the process of using a balance to compare masses is often incorrectly called "weighing."

2:3 LENGTH

A second important measurement is that of length. **Length** is the distance covered by a line segment connecting two points. The standard for measuring length is defined in terms of the distance traveled by light in a unit of time (Table A-1 of the Appendix). The standard unit of length is the **meter (m).** Length is usually measured with a ruler or similar device.

2:4 TIME

A third basic measurement is time. **Time** is the interval between two occurrences. Our present standard of time is defined in terms of an electron transition in an atom. The unit of time, the **second (s),** is 1/86 400 of an average day. The most common device for measuring time is a watch or clock. More precise time pieces include the chronometer, the atomic clock, and the solid state digital timer.

The SI standard for length is the meter (m).

BACKGROUND: The second is now defined as the duration of 9 192 631 770 periods of the radiation corresponding to the transition between two hyperfine levels of the fundamental state of a cesium-133 atom.

The SI standard for time is one second (s).

a

b

2:5 TEMPERATURE

Matter is composed of small particles called atoms, ions, and molecules. These particles are in constant motion and, therefore, possess kinetic energy. The average kinetic energy of a group of particles determines the group's temperature. The **temperature** of a sample of matter is a measure of the average kinetic energy of the particles that make up the sample. The greater the average kinetic energy of the particles, the higher the temperature of the material. If we add energy to heat an object, the kinetic energy of its particles increases.

FIGURE 2-4. Early time measurements made by a sundial (a) were not nearly as precise as those made by a modern cesium clock (b).

Temperature is a measure of the average kinetic energy of the sample's particles.

BACKGROUND: Fahrenheit will not be used in this text.

A thermometer is the most common instrument used to measure temperature. When the bulb is heated, the liquid expands and rises in the tube. When the bulb is cooled, the liquid contracts and the height of the liquid column decreases. The height of the liquid column can thus be used to measure temperature. The temperature can be read directly from the scale on the tube.

The SI unit of temperature is the kelvin (K).

The SI unit of temperature is the **kelvin (K).** We will not define this unit until Chapter 15. However, the kelvin has a direct connection with a more familiar unit, the Celsius degree (C°).

The Celsius degree is exactly equal to the kelvin.

The Celsius temperature scale is based on the fact that the freezing and boiling temperatures of pure water under normal atmospheric pressure are constant. The difference between the boiling and freezing points is divided into 100 equal intervals. Each interval is called a Celsius degree. The point at which water freezes is labeled zero degrees Celsius (0°C). The point at which water boils is labeled 100°C. The Celsius degree is exactly equal to the kelvin. We will use both units in our study of chemistry.

Some data tables indicate that the values were measured at 25°C (See Table A-10 of the Appendix). Average room temperature is approximately 25°C. Your average body temperature is 37°C.

2:6   ACCURACY AND PRECISION

Accuracy depends on how closely an instrument's measurement agrees with the standard for that measurement.

The terms accuracy and precision are often used in discussing measurements. **Accuracy** refers to how close a measurement is to the actual quantity. It is determined by the quality of the measuring instrument. A micrometer used to measure engine parts may approximate the standard very closely. The micrometer has a high degree of accuracy. A plastic ruler has a lesser degree of accuracy. For example, a measurement of 347 cm is less accurate than a measurement of 26.7 cm because the instrument used is more accurate, that is it measures in ±0.1 cm rather than ±1 cm.

Precision is uncertainty in measurement.

Precision refers to uncertainty in measurement. If we use a ruler marked off in divisions of 0.1 centimeter to measure a textbook, we might obtain the following data.

Dimension	Measurement	Accuracy
Length	24.3 cm	±0.1 cm
Width	18.7 cm	±0.1 cm
Depth	4.4 cm	±0.1 cm

Relative error is often expressed as the percent uncertainty in the measurement.

The absolute uncertainty in each case is ±0.1 centimeter. However, that uncertainty is a different proportion of each dimension. A better reflection of uncertainty is the relative error. **Relative error** is often expressed as the percentage uncertainty in the measurement.

Measurement	Accuracy	Precision (Relative Error)	(Percentage Uncertainty)
24.3 cm	±0.1 cm	$\dfrac{0.1 \text{ cm}}{24.3 \text{ cm}} = 0.004$	0.4%
18.7 cm	±0.1 cm	$\dfrac{0.1 \text{ cm}}{18.7 \text{ cm}} = 0.005$	0.5%
4.4 cm	±0.1 cm	$\dfrac{0.1 \text{ cm}}{4.4 \text{ cm}} = 0.02$	2%

In this case, we see that length and width are far more precise measurements than depth.

PROBLEMS

Compute the relative error of each of the following measurements.

1. 12.7 cm (accuracy of measurement = ±0.1 cm).
2. 50 cm³ (accuracy of measurement = ±1 cm³).
3. 236.0490 g (accuracy of balance = ±0.0001 g).

1. 0.008
2. 0.02
3. 4×10^{-7}

FIGURE 2-5. An analytical balance is a highly precise tool for measuring mass. The data obtained should have a high degree of accuracy.

2:7 SIGNIFICANT DIGITS

Suppose we want to measure the length of a strip of metal. We have two rulers. One ruler is graduated in centimeters. The other is graduated in millimeters. With which ruler can we obtain a better measurement of length? The length of the strip measured in millimeters is the more significant measurement because it is closer to the actual length of the strip. We say that the measurement in millimeters has more significant digits than the measurement in centimeters.

Look at Figure 2-6. The measurement on the centimeter scale lies approximately 6/10 of the way from the 13-cm mark to the 14-cm mark. This length is recorded as 13.6 cm. On the millimeter ruler, the length lies approximately 3/10 of the way from the 13.6-cm mark to the 13.7-cm mark. This length is recorded as 13.63 cm. The measurement 13.6 cm has

FIGURE 2-6. The number of significant digits in the length measurement of the metal strip depends on the accuracy of the ruler used.

three significant digits. The measurement 13.63 has four significant digits. The last digit of each measurement is an estimate. All digits that occupy places for which actual measurement was made are referred to as **significant digits.**

The exactness of measurements is an important part of experimentation. The exactness of a measurement is indicated by the number of significant digits in that measurement. The observer and anyone reading the results of an experiment want to know the number of significant digits in any observation. The following rules are used to determine the number of significant digits in a recorded measurement.

1. *Digits other than zero are always significant.*

96	2 significant digits
61.4	3 significant digits

2. *One or more final zeros used after the decimal point are significant.*

4.7200   5 significant digits

3. *Zeros between two other significant digits are always significant.*

5.029   4 significant digits

4. *Zeros used solely for spacing the decimal point are not significant. The zeros are placeholders only.*

7000	1 significant digit
0.007 83	3 significant digits

PROBLEM

4. How many significant digits are there in each of the following?

a. 903.2   **c.** 900.0   **e.** 0.090 0   **g.** 0.008 8   **i.** 0.02
b. 90.3   **d.** 0.009 0   **f.** 99   **h.** 0.049   **j.** 70

2:8   HANDLING NUMBERS IN SCIENCE

In this course we will sometimes use very large numbers. For example, in Chapter 5 you will learn about Avogadro's number, which is 602 217 000 000 000 000 000 000. We will also use very small numbers. The distance between the particles in a salt crystal is 0.000 000 002 814 cm. In working with such numbers it is easy to drop a zero or to lose a decimal place.

Scientific notation makes it easier to work with very large or small numbers. In **scientific notation,** all numbers are expressed as the product of a number between 1 and 10 and a whole-number power of 10.

$$M \times 10^n$$

In this expression, $1 \leq M < 10$, and n is an integer. This number is read as M times ten to the nth. For example, 5.2×10^5 is read five point two times ten to the fifth.

One advantage of scientific notation is that it removes any doubt about the number of significant digits in a measurement. Suppose the volume of a gas is expressed as 2000 cm³. We do not know whether the measurement was made to one (±1000) or to four significant digits. Suppose the measurement was actually made to the nearest cm³. Then the volume 2000 cm³ is expressed to four significant digits (±1). In scientific notation, we can indicate the additional significant digits by placing zeros to the right of the decimal point. Thus, 2×10^3 cm³ has only one significant digit, while 2.000×10^3 cm³ has four significant digits.

Once we have recorded measurements to the correct number of significant digits and expressed them in scientific notation, they can be used in calculations.

In scientific notation, only significant digits are shown.

Scientific notation allows the entry of very large and very small numbers into a calculator.

a   ~0.000 025 m in diameter

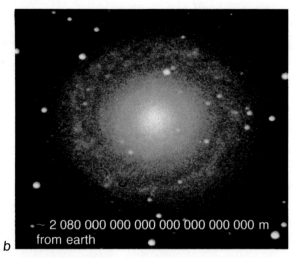

~ 2 080 000 000 000 000 000 000 000 m from earth

b

To determine the number of digits that should appear in the answer to a calculation, we will use two rules.

1. *In addition and subtraction, the answer may contain only as many decimal places as the least accurate value used in finding the answer.* For example, if 345 is added to 27.6 the answer must be given to the nearest whole number. In adding a column of figures such as

$$\begin{array}{r} 677 \\ 39.2 \\ \underline{6.23} \\ 722.43 \end{array}$$

the answer should be rounded off to the nearest whole number. The answer to the problem above is 722.

2. *In multiplication and division, the answer may contain only as many significant digits as the least accurate value used to arrive at the answer.* For example, in the following problem the answer has five significant digits.

FIGURE 2-7. Expressing numbers in scientific notation for extremely small and large measurements such as the diameter of a moth's eye (a) or the distance to another galaxy (b) is less confusing than showing all digits.

In addition and subtraction, the answer is rounded to the decimal place of the least accurate digit in the problem.

In multiplication and division, the answer should have the same number of significant digits as the term having the least number of significant digits in the problem.

$$\begin{matrix} (5) & (9) \\ (1.133\ 0)\ (5.126\ 000\ 00) \end{matrix} = 5.807\ 758\ 000\ 000$$

$$\begin{matrix} & (5) \\ & = 5.8078 \end{matrix}$$

The answer to this division problem has four significant digits.

$$\frac{\overset{(6)}{49.600\ 0}}{\underset{(4)}{47.40}} = 1.046\ 413\ 5 \overset{(4)}{=} 1.046$$

If you are using a calculator to obtain your numerical answer, you must be very careful. The calculator may give you an answer with eight or ten digits. For example, in the problem 49.600 0/47.40, the answer may appear as 1.046 413 502. The answer must be rounded to the proper number of significant digits. In this case, the number of significant digits is four. Thus, the answer is 1.046. Always double-check your answer against the data given. Report the answer only to the number of significant digits justified by the data. Remember, calculated accuracy cannot exceed measured accuracy.

BACKGROUND: Rounding rule used in this text: if the number to be rounded is followed by 5-9 the number is rounded up.

Problem entered into the calculator	Uncertain digits in each value
$\dfrac{49.600}{47.40}$	49.600 47.40
Calculator answer readout	Answer should be correctly stated as
1.046 413 5	1.046

FIGURE 2-8. When using a calculator, it is important to express your answers to the proper number of significant digits. Therefore, you will not always use all the values shown on the readout.

EXAMPLE: Multiplying in Scientific Notation

Find the product of $(4.0 \times 10^{-2})(3.0 \times 10^{-4})(2.0 \times 10^{1})$.

Solving Process:

To multiply numbers expressed in scientific notation ($M \times 10^{n}$), multiply the values of M and add the exponents. The exponents do not need to be alike.

Multiply the values of M. $4.0 \times 3.0 \times 2.0 = 24$

Add the exponents. $-2 + (-4) + 1 = -5$

$$(4.0 \times 10^{-2})(3.0 \times 10^{-4})(2.0 \times 10^{1}) = (4.0 \times 3.0 \times 2.0) \times 10^{-2+(-4)+1}$$
$$= 24 \times 10^{-5} = 2.4 \times 10^{-4}$$

Standard position for the decimal point is after the first significant digit.

SUGGESTION: Remind students when using a calculator capable of scientific notation not to enter ($\times 10$) but to use the exponent key.

EXAMPLE: Dividing in Scientific Notation

Divide. $\dfrac{(4 \times 10^{3})(6 \times 10^{-1})}{(8 \times 10^{2})}$

Solving Process:

In division the exponents are subtracted. To divide numbers in scientific notation ($M \times 10^{n}$), divide the values of M and subtract the sum of the exponents of the denominator from the sum of the exponents of the numerator.

$$\frac{(4 \times 10^{3})(6 \times 10^{-1})}{(8 \times 10^{2})} = \frac{(4 \times 6) \times 10^{3+(-1)}}{8 \times 10^{2}} = \frac{24}{8} \times \frac{10^{2}}{10^{2}} = 3 \times 10^{0} = 3$$

Remember to observe rules of significant digits when solving problems.

$10^{0} = 1$

PROBLEMS

Perform the following operations. Express your answers to the correct number of significant digits.

5. $(35.72)(0.005\ 90) =$

6. $(707\ 000)(3.1) =$

7. $(0.054\ 32)(62\ 000) =$

8. $(0.005\ 900\ 0)(38.76) =$

9. $(6.09 \times 10^{-1})(9.08 \times 10^{5})$

10. $(1.65 \times 10^{1})(5.24 \times 10^{2})$

11. $(1.10 \times 10^{9})(4.75 \times 10^{9})$

12. $\dfrac{6810.12}{2.4} =$

13. $\dfrac{0.4832}{5.12} =$

14. $201 + 3.57 + 98.493 =$

15. $5.32 - 0.759\ 38 =$

16. $\dfrac{(7.79 \times 10^{4})(6.45 \times 10^{4})}{(5.44 \times 10^{6})(7.45 \times 10^{-1})}$

17. $\dfrac{(7.69 \times 10^{2})(6.56 \times 10^{6})}{(2.92 \times 10^{4})(1.65 \times 10^{4})}$

18. $(1.18 \times 10^{-2})(2.20 \times 10^{3})$

5. 0.211
6. 2.2×10^{6}
7. 3400
8. 0.2287
9. 5.53×10^{5}
10. 8.65×10^{3}
11. 5.23×10^{18}
12. 2800
13. 0.0944
14. 303
15. 4.56
16. 1240
17. 10.5
18. 26.0

Perform the following operations.

19. 2.42 × 10⁻⁴
20. 169
21. 166
22. 1.07 × 10⁴
23. 2 × 10⁸

19. $\dfrac{(9.19 \times 10^7)(1.79 \times 10^1)}{(8.17 \times 10^4)(8.32 \times 10^7)}$

20. $\dfrac{(8.17 \times 10^1)(8.70 \times 10^5)}{4.20 \times 10^5}$

21. $\dfrac{(4.87 \times 10^6)(9.69 \times 10^1)}{2.84 \times 10^6}$

22. $\dfrac{(6.40 \times 10^2)(9.97 \times 10^4)}{(6.12 \times 10^{-2})(9.71 \times 10^4)}$

23. $\dfrac{(2.1 \times 10^3)(2.593 \times 10^{-2})}{(5.23 \times 10^{-3})(6 \times 10^{-5})}$

2:9 DERIVED UNITS

The SI unit of volume is the cubic meter (m^3).

By combining the fundamental SI units, we obtain measurement units used to express other quantities. Distance divided by time equals speed. If we multiply length by length, we get area. Area multiplied by length produces volume. The SI unit of volume is the cubic meter (m^3). However, this quantity is too large to be practical for the laboratory. Chemists often use cubic decimeters (dm^3) as the unit of volume. One cubic decimeter is given another name, the liter (L). The liter is a unit of volume. One liter equals 1000 milliliters (mL) and 1000 cubic centimeters (cm^3). From these facts, you can see that

1 liter (L) = 1 cubic decimeter (dm^3).

$$1000 \text{ cm}^3 = 1000 \text{ mL} = 1 \text{ L} = 1 \text{ dm}^3$$

Derived units combine fundamental units. For example speed = meters per second (m/s).

The units used to express measurements of speed, area, and volume are called derived units. You saw that area and volume measurements are expressed using length units. The units used to express speed, such as kilometers per hour or meters per second, combine fundamental units of length and time.

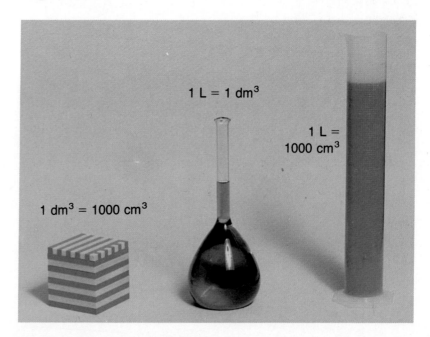

FIGURE 2-9. The volumes shown here are equivalent.

2:10 A GENERAL APPROACH TO PROBLEMS

One trait shared by most people who understand chemistry is the ability to solve problems. You will need to develop this ability during your study of chemistry. Skill in solving problems can be developed by practice and using the method described here.

A good way to practice solving problems is to break the problem into three parts. In Part One, decide what information you are given. Locate the starting material with which you will be working. Another way of expressing Part One is "Where am I?" In Part Two, decide what is required of you. Make certain you know what you are to find. Another way of expressing Part Two is "Where do I want to be?" In Part Three, find a "bridge" that connects what you are given to what is required of you. Part Three could also be expressed, "How do I get from where I am to where I want to be?"

Parts One and Two require a careful reading and rereading of the question or problem. The first time you read the problem, concentrate on finding the starting point. Concentrate the second time on what you are required to find.

The "bridge" mentioned in Part Three comes from two sources. Your background of general knowledge is the first source. The second source is the knowledge you will gain in your study of chemistry. Perhaps your chemical knowledge will not lead you to an immediate method of solving the problem. However, the knowledge you already have will be a guide to using the textbook, including the Table of Contents, the Appendices, and the Index. The text contains Example problems and descriptions that you can use in solving problems. Learn to look for patterns in solving different types of problems. Then apply the pattern to solving the problem at hand.

The solving of problems in chemistry is not an inherited talent. Everyone can learn the skill with practice. Be patient, concentrate, and you will develop the skill.

2:11 CONVERSION FACTORS

In Section 2:1, the relationships between various prefixes were described. For example, the relationship between the centimeter and the meter is 1 m = 100 cm. The kilogram and the gram are related by the equation 1 kg = 1000 g. Using these and similar relationships, we can convert a unit to any other related unit.

Conversion factors are ratios with a value equal to one.

EXAMPLE: Conversion

Convert 72 centimeters to meters.

Solving Process:
(a) The given quantity is 72 cm. We know that

$$100 \text{ cm} = 1 \text{ m}$$

SUGGESTION: Spend time on conversions as they will be used throughout the book.

(b) By dividing both sides of this equation by 100 cm, the equation becomes

$$1 = \frac{1 \text{ m}}{100 \text{ cm}}$$

Always make certain the unit you wish to eliminate is properly placed in the fraction that equals one.

(c) Multiplying both sides of the equation by 72 cm, we get

$$72 \text{ cm} \times 1 = 72 \text{ cm} \left(\frac{1 \text{ m}}{100 \text{ cm}}\right)$$

$$72 \text{ cm} = \frac{72 \text{ m}}{100} = 0.72 \text{ m}$$

EXAMPLE: Conversion

How many cubic centimeters are there in 5 cubic decimeters?

Solving Process:

The given quantity is 5 dm³. The required quantity is cm³. The bridge we must find is that which will take us from cm³ to dm³.

(a) We know that 1 dm is equal to 10 cm. The relationship between dm and cm is

$$1 \text{ dm} = 10 \text{ cm}$$

(b) If we cube both sides of the equation we get

$$1 \text{ dm}^3 = 1000 \text{ cm}^3$$

(c) Both sides of the equation can be divided by the quantity 1 dm³. Now the equation appears as

$$1 = \frac{1000 \text{ cm}^3}{1 \text{ dm}^3}$$

$1 \text{ dm}^3 = 1000 \text{ cm}^3$

(d) Using the known quantity of 5 dm³ that is given in the problem, we can write the equation

$$5 \text{ dm}^3 = 5 \text{ dm}^3$$

(e) We can now multiply the right side of the expression in (d) by the fraction

$$\frac{1000 \text{ cm}^3}{1 \text{ dm}^3}$$

The value of any quantity multiplied by 1 is unchanged.

Since this fraction equals one, the value of the right side of the equation is not changed. (Recall that the value of any quantity multiplied by 1 is unchanged.) The equation then becomes

$$5 \text{ dm}^3 = 5 \text{ dm}^3 \left(\frac{1000 \text{ cm}^3}{1 \text{ dm}^3}\right) = \frac{(5 \text{ dm}^3)(1000 \text{ cm}^3)}{(1 \text{ dm}^3)}$$

The equation then reduces to

$$5 \text{ dm}^3 = (5)(1000 \text{ cm}^3) = 5000 \text{ cm}^3$$

The procedure in the example above is far too involved for finding the number of cm^3 in dm^3. However, these principles can be used to solve many kinds of problems. In order to simplify the working of problems, we will use the following notation. In the sample problem just given, we had the equation

$$5 \text{ dm}^3 = 5 \text{ dm}^3 \left(\frac{1000 \text{ cm}^3}{1 \text{ dm}^3} \right)$$

That equation is equivalent to the equation

$$5 \text{ dm}^3 = \left(\frac{5 \text{ dm}^3}{1} \right) \left(\frac{1000 \text{ cm}^3}{1 \text{ dm}^3} \right)$$

Instead of enclosing every factor in parentheses, we will simply set off each factor by a vertical line. Our equation is now written as

$$5 \text{ dm}^3 = \frac{5 \text{ dm}^3}{} \left| \frac{1000 \text{ cm}^3}{1 \text{ dm}^3} \right. = 5000 \text{ cm}^3$$

The fraction bar eliminates the need for parentheses.

PROBLEMS

Convert.

24. 0.598 hours to seconds
25. 0.193 meter to centimeters
26. 3.41 cm^3 to dm^3
27. 57.5 centigrams to milligrams
28. 0.618 kilometers to centimeters
29. 923 picoseconds to seconds
30. 0.397 m^2 to cm^2
31. 139 cm^3 to dm^3

32. 0.0446 km to m
33. 52.5 milligrams to grams
34. 0.805 dm^3 to cm^3
35. 239 dm^3 to cm^3
36. 661 cm^3 to dm^3
37. 656 milligrams to grams
38. 218 nanometers to centimeters

24. 2.153×10^3 s
25. 19.3 cm
26. 0.003 41 dm^3
27. 575 mg
28. 61 800 cm
29. 9.23×10^{-11} s
30. 3970 cm^2
31. 0.139 dm^3
32. 44.6 m
33. 0.0525 g
34. 805 cm^3
35. 239 000 cm^3
36. 0.661 dm^3
37. 0.656 g
38. 2.18×10^{-5} cm

2:12 FACTOR-LABEL METHOD

The problem-solving method discussed in Sections 2:10 and 2:11 is called the **factor-label method.** In effect, unit labels are treated as factors. As common factors, these labels may be divided out. The solution to a problem depends upon having the correct unit label. Thus, this method aids in solving a problem and provides a check on mathematical operations. The individual conversion factors (ratios whose value is equivalent to one) may usually be written by inspection. Let us see how the method can be applied to more complex measurements.

Many measurements are simply combinations of the elementary measurements as discussed in Section 2:9. We are all familiar with the measurement of speed. Speed is the distance covered in a single unit of

Unit labels are treated as factors. Labels may be regarded as factors and "divided" out.

SUGGESTION: The factor label method is used throughout the text. Spend a considerable amount of time familiarizing students with it. This time is an important factor in their success throughout the course.

Most conversion factors have an unlimited number of significant digits because they are definitions.

time. It is length per unit time. The speed of an automobile is measured in kilometers (length) per hour (time). Most scientific measurements of speed are made in centimeters or meters per second.

EXAMPLE: Conversion of Units

Express 60.0 kilometers per hour in terms of centimeters per second.

SUGGESTION: Show students that each factor = 1.

Solving Process:

(a) Write 60.0 kilometers per hour as a ratio.

$$\frac{60.0 \text{ km}}{1 \text{ h}}$$

(b) We wish to convert kilometers to meters. Since 1000 m = 1 km, we can use the ratio

$$\frac{1000 \text{ m}}{1 \text{ km}}$$

(c) In the same manner, we will use

$$1 \text{ m} = 100 \text{ cm, or } \frac{1 \text{ m}}{100 \text{ cm}}$$

$$1 \text{ h} = 60 \text{ min, or } \frac{1 \text{ h}}{60 \text{ min}}$$

$$1 \text{ min} = 60 \text{ s, or } \frac{1 \text{ min}}{60 \text{ s}}$$

(d) All these ratios equal 1. Since any number may be multiplied by 1 or its equivalent without changing its value, we can now write

$$\frac{60.0 \text{ km}}{1 \text{ h}} = \frac{60.0 \text{ km}}{1 \text{ h}} \left| \frac{1000 \text{ m}}{1 \text{ km}} \right| \frac{100 \text{ cm}}{1 \text{ m}} \left| \frac{1 \text{ h}}{60 \text{ min}} \right| \frac{1 \text{ min}}{60 \text{ s}} = 1670 \text{ cm/s}$$

Unit division marks act as a check as to whether the problem has been set up correctly.

Notice that ratios are arranged so that units can be divided out as factors. This procedure leaves the correct units in the answer and provides a check on the method used.

Unit cancellation marks will be shown for all Example problems. Use these as a guide in working on your own problems. They act as a check as to whether the problem has been set up correctly.

39. 9.05×10^5 mg
40. 0.000 307 g
41. 822 L
42. 77.5 mg
43. 6.67×10^5 cm^3
44. 848 cm^3
45. 384 dm^3
46. 0.756 cm
47. 888 g
48. 0.920 m^3
49. 8.14×10^{-6} cm
50. 108 s

PROBLEMS

Make the following conversions.

39. 0.905 kilograms to milligrams

40. 0.307 milligrams to grams

41. 822 dm^3 to liters

42. 0.0775 g to mg

43. 0.667 cubic meters to cm^3

44. 0.848 dm^3 to cm^3

45. 0.384 m^3 to dm^3

46. 7.56 mm to cm

47. 0.888 kg to g

48. 920 dm^3 to m^3

49. 81.4 nm to cm

50. 0.0300 h to s

2:13 DENSITY

A less familiar, but common, scientific measurement is density. **Density** is mass per unit of volume. To measure density, we must be able to measure both mass (*m*) and volume (*V*). Mass can be measured on a balance. The volume of a solid can be measured in different ways. For instance, the volume of a cube is the length of one edge cubed (multiplied by itself three times). The volume of a rectangular solid is the length times the width times the height. Width and height are simply different names for length. The volume of a liquid can be measured in a clear container graduated to indicate units of volume. You will use graduated cylinders in lab to measure liquid volumes. In density measurements of liquids and solids, volume is usually measured in cubic centimeters (cm³). Density, then, is expressed in grams per cubic centimeter (g/cm³). The units to express density are derived units. In equation form, density can be expressed as

Density = mass/unit volume

Density of solids and liquids is generally measured in g/cm³.

$$D = \frac{m}{V}$$

Densities of common materials are listed in Table 2-3 on page 34. Such a table offers a convenient and accurate means of comparing the masses of equal volumes of different materials. Note that the values given for gases are quite small. It is more practical to express gas density in g/dm³.

People sometimes say that lead is heavier than feathers. However, a truckload of feathers is heavier than a single piece of lead buckshot. To be exact, we should say that the density of lead is greater than the density of feathers. The density of a substance changes with changes in temperature. Ice floats in a glass of ice water because the solid is less dense than the liquid. In Chapter 17 you will learn how the structure of ice causes this difference.

FIGURE 2-10. Though the volumes of the wood and sponge are equal, the balance shows the masses are not the same, (a). The solids and liquids shown occupy different levels due to the differences in their densities (b).

Air 0.001 g/cm³

Wood (oak) 0.710 g/cm³

Corn oil 0.925 g/cm³

Water 1.00 g/cm³

Plastic 1.17 g/cm³

Glycerol 1.26 g/cm³

Rubber 1.34 g/cm³

Corn syrup 1.38 g/cm³

Steel alloy 7.81 g/cm³

Table 2-3

Densities of Some Common Materials	
Material	**Density**
natural gas	0.000 555 g/cm^3
air	0.001 22 g/cm^3
blood	1.06 g/cm^3
sucrose (table sugar)	1.59 g/cm^3
sodium chloride (table salt)	2.16 g/cm^3
stainless steel	7.86 g/cm^3
copper	8.92 g/cm^3
mercury	13.59 g/cm^3

EXAMPLE: Conversion of Units

Express 0.053 cubic centimeters as cubic meters.

Solving Process:

$$0.053 \text{ cm}^3 = \frac{0.053 \cancel{\text{cm}^3}}{} \left| \frac{1 \text{ m}^3}{(10^2 \cancel{\text{cm}})^3} \right. = 5.3 \times 10^{-8} \text{ m}^3$$

Express 0.20 kg/m^3 as g/cm^3.

Solving Process:

$$0.20 \text{ kg/m}^3 = \frac{0.20 \cancel{\text{kg}}}{1 \cancel{\text{m}^3}} \left| \frac{10^3 \text{ g}}{1 \cancel{\text{kg}}} \right| \frac{1 \cancel{\text{m}^3}}{(10^2 \text{ cm})^3}$$

$$= \frac{0.20}{1} \left| \frac{10^3 \text{ g}}{1} \right| \frac{1}{10^6 \text{ cm}^3} = \frac{0.20 \text{ g}}{10^3 \text{ cm}^3}$$

$$= \frac{2.0 \times 10^{-1} \text{ g}}{10^3 \text{ cm}^3} = 2.0 \times 10^{-4} \text{ g/cm}^3$$

FIGURE 2-11. The density of a battery acid solution is measured using a hydrometer.

EXAMPLE: Density

Calcium has a density of 1.54 g/cm^3. What mass would 3.00 cm^3 of calcium have?

Solving Process:

Density is mass per unit volume, or

$$D = \frac{m}{V}$$

Solving this equation for mass by multiplying each side by V, we obtain

$$m = D \times V$$

Substituting the known information, we obtain

$$m = \frac{1.54 \text{ g}}{\cancel{\text{cm}^3}} \Bigg| \frac{3.00 \cancel{\text{cm}^3}}{} = 4.62 \text{ g}$$

The fact that the answer is expressed in grams is another check on the work.

EXAMPLE: Density

Cobalt has a density of 8.90 g/cm³. What volume would 17.8 g of cobalt have?

Solving Process
We know that density can be expressed as

$$D = \frac{m}{V}$$

Solving this equation for volume and substituting the known information in the resulting equation, we obtain

$$V = \frac{m}{D} = \frac{17.8 \text{ g}}{8.90 \text{ g/cm}^3} \quad \text{or} \quad \frac{17.8 \cancel{\text{g}}}{} \Bigg| \frac{1 \text{ cm}^3}{8.90 \cancel{\text{g}}} = 2.00 \text{ cm}^3$$

The answer is in cm³, a unit of volume, which is another check on the accuracy of the problem solving approach.

PROBLEMS

51. What is the density of a piece of cement that has a mass of 8.76 g and a volume of 3.07 cm³?

52. What is the density of a piece of cork that has a mass of 0.650 g and a volume of 2.71 cm³?

53. Limestone has a density of 2.72 g/cm³. What is the mass of 98.2 cm³ of limestone?

54. Ammonium magnesium chromate has a density of 1.84 g/cm³. What is the mass of 4.33 cm³ of this substance?

55. Barium perchlorate has a density of 2.74 g/cm³. What is the mass of 99.7 cm³ of this substance?

56. Bismuth phosphate has a density of 6.32 g/cm³. What is the mass of 51.7 cm³ of this substance?

57. Calcium chloride has a density of 2.50 g/cm³. What is the volume of 7.48 g of this substance?

58. Cerium sulfate has a density of 3.17 g/cm³. What is the volume of 132 g of this substance?

59. Chromium silicide has a density of 5.50 g/cm³. What is the volume of 81.4 g of this substance?

51. 2.85 g/cm³
52. 0.240 g/cm³
53. 267 g
54. 7.97 g
55. 273 g
56. 327 g
57. 2.99 cm³
58. 41.6 cm³
59. 14.8 cm³

BIOGRAPHY   Marie Curie (1867-1934)

A Nobel Prize usually caps the career of a scientist. Marie Curie won two! In 1903, she was awarded the prize in physics for her joint research with her husband Pierre on the radiation phenomenon discovered by Becquerel. In 1911, she won the chemistry prize for the discovery of the elements radium and polonium, and for the study of radium compounds. Madame Curie was devoted not only to scientific research but also to the applications of the research. The use of the radioactive rays of radium in the treatment of cancer is but one example of this concern. In spite of the honors and her fame in the scientific community and the world, she remained modest and unassuming until her death at age 67. In 1935, one year after her death, her daughter, Irene Joliot-Curie (1897-1956) was awarded a Nobel Prize with her husband for the discovery of artificial radioactivity.

CAREERS AND CHEMISTRY

2:14   Chemical Engineering

One of the reasons the United States usually has an agricultural surplus is the development of superior agricultural chemicals by chemists. These products are produced by chemical engineers in chemical plants.

Chemistry is a science. Engineering, on the other hand, is a particular approach to problem solving. The engineer uses the facts generated by scientists to solve everyday problems. Most engineers (and some chemists) deal with technology.

Though a chemical engineer performs many functions, a broad definition would be a person who designs, builds, and/or operates chemical plants or industrial plants using chemistry. The design function involves working with chemists who have investigated the process for which the plant is being built. The design engineer may call on other engineers to research certain aspects of the design. Typically, one problem that must be solved is the types of materials to be used in construction. Raw materials, intermediate substances, and the final product may be corrosive and require special handling. Stainless steel piping and titanium pumps may be needed because of their ability to resist corrosion.

Chemical engineers oversee the construction of the plant to ensure that all specifications are met. They also direct the operations of the plant

FIGURE 2-12. Chemical engineers must research all aspects of design when planning a new chemical plant.

after it begins production. In both of these functions, the engineer may have to use his or her knowledge of economics and business to make decisions about sources of raw materials, selling price of the product, and value of overtime work. Since the chemical engineers are involved in the production of chemicals, they must be aware of the environmental factors involved. The costs of scrubbers and other antipollution devices must be considered. Decisions must be made about how to preserve the environment while supplying a competitively priced product.

SUMMARY

1. Scientific work requires a quantitative approach. In other words, to investigate a phenomenon, certain characteristics must be measured. Intro.

2. Scientists use SI measurements. This system of measurement consists of seven fundamental units. SI units are particularly convenient because they are based on multiples of 10. 2:1

3. The most elementary measurements in science are those of mass, length, time, and temperature. 2:2-2:5

4. Mass is a measure of the quantity of matter. Weight is a measure of the force of gravity between two objects. 2:2

5. Accuracy of a measurement is determined by the quality of the measuring instruments. Precision of a measurement is the relative error. 2:6

6. The exactness of a measurement is indicated by the number of significant digits in that measurement. 2:7

7. Any number can be expressed in scientific notation as $M \times 10^n$, where M is some number ≥ 1 and < 10 and n is an integer. Scientific notation indicates clearly the number of significant digits. This notation is particularly helpful in multiplication and division. 2:8

8. The SI unit of volume is the cubic meter (m^3). Speed is length per unit time. Density is the mass of a substance in a unit volume of that substance. All three of these quantities are compound or derived. 2:9, 2:13

9. In the factor-label method of problem solving, unit labels are treated as factors. This method makes conversion of units easier. 2:12

VOCABULARY

qualitatively Intro	meter 2:3	precision 2:6
quantitatively Intro	time 2:4	relative error 2:6
weight 2:2	second 2:4	significant digits 2:7
mass 2:2	temperature 2:5	scientific notation 2:8
kilogram 2:2	kelvin 2:5	factor-label method 2:12
balance 2:2	accuracy 2:6	density 2:13
length 2:3		

1. meter, kilogram, second, ampere, kelvin, mole, candela
2. An object's weight varies from place to place, but its mass does not.
3. The Celsius temperature scale is defined as 100 equal intervals between the freezing point (0°) and boiling point (100°) of water under normal atmospheric pressure.
4. kilogram
5. The number of significant digits indicates the exactness of measurement. An important part of experimentation is data which shows the exactness of an observation.
7. Since the density of water varies with temperature, the volume occupied by a certain mass of water will vary with temperature.
11.   a. 3.68×10^1
       b. 3.87×10^{-2}
       c. 2.165×10^{-4}
       d. 5.1683×10^{11}
12.   a. 0.009 14
       b. 0.000 035 0
       c. 952 000
       d. 46.6
13. 1.031×10^6
14. 2.17×10^{-5}
15. 3.8×10^{-1}
16. 1.7×10^{-2}
17.   a. 2
       b. 1
       c. 2
       d. 1
18.   a. 52
       b. 0.9
       c. 156
       d. 1.0×10^1
       e. 2
19. 3.00 g/cm^3
20. 2.80 g/cm^3
21. 0.680 g/cm^3

PROBLEMS

1. What are the seven base units in SI?
2. Why is mass used instead of weight for scientific work?
3. How is the Celsius temperature scale defined?
4. What is the SI fundamental unit of mass?
5. Why is it important to maintain the correct number of significant digits in calculations?
6. List the number of significant digits for each of the following:
    a. 1×10^8
    b. 6.8×10^8
    c. $4.930\ 00 \times 10^9$
    d. $8.420\ 000\ 0 \times 10^8$

6.   a. 1
      b. 2
      c. 6
      d. 8

7. The definition of the outdated unit, the liter, was originally based on the volume of a certain mass of water. What is the difficulty such a definition?

Compute the percentage uncertainty of each of the following measurements:

8. 41.3 s (accuracy of stopwatch = ±0.1 s).
9. 67.9°C (accuracy of thermometer = ±0.1°).
10. 0.0961 km (accuracy of pedometer = ±0.0001 km).

8. 0.2%
9. 0.1%
10. 0.1%

11. Express in scientific notation.
    a. 36.8
    b. 0.0387
    c. 0.000 216 5
    d. 516 830 000 000

12. Express as a whole number or decimal.
    a. 9.14×10^{-3}
    b. 3.50×10^{-5}
    c. 9.52×10^5
    d. 4.66×10^1

Perform the following operations.

13. $9.43 \times 10^5 + 8.82 \times 10^4$
14. $2.78 \times 10^{-5} - 6.12 \times 10^{-6}$
15. $(1.6 \times 10^2)(2.4 \times 10^{-3})$
16. $(75.4 \times 10^2)(0.774 \times 10^{-2}) \div (3.4 \times 10^3)$
17. List the number of significant digits that should appear in the answers to the following problems.
    a. $(0.50)(0.005\ 5)$
    b. $(0.7)(9.48 \times 10^1)$
    c. 0.30 divided by 0.058
    d. 0.6 divided by 9.59×10^1
18. Solve the following problems. Round your answers to the proper number of decimal places.

    a.   0.089 90
        + 52.

    b.   0.9
        − 0.000 05

    c.   63
        + 93

    d.   4
        + 6

    e.   0.06
        + 2.

Find the density in g/cm³ of the following:

19. cement, if a rectangular piece 2.00 cm × 2.00 cm × 9.00 cm has a mass of 108 g
20. granite, if a rectangular piece 5.00 cm × 10.0 cm × 23.0 cm has a mass of 3.22 kg
21. gasoline, if 9.00 dm³ have a mass of 6120 g

22. milk, if 2.00 dm^3 have a mass of 2.06 kg
23. ivory, if a rectangular piece 23.0 cm × 15.0 cm × 15.5 cm has a mass of 10.22 kg
24. evaporated milk, if 411 g occupy 384 cm^3
25. asbestos, if 233 g occupy 97.0 cm^3
26. brass, if 535 g occupy 62.3 cm^3
27. brick, if 49.2 g occupy 27.3 cm^3
28. balsa wood, if 171 g occupy 1320 cm^3
29. cardboard, if 3.19 g occupy 4.56 cm^3
30. chalk, if 6.36 g occupy 2.65 cm^3
31. butter, if 272 g occupy 312 cm^3
32. What is the density of sugar in g/cm^3 if its density is 1590 kg/m^3?
33. An automobile is traveling at the rate of 30.0 kilometers per hour. What is its rate in centimeters per second (cm/s)?
34. The density of nitrogen gas is 1.25 g/dm^3. What is the mass of 1.00 m^3 of N$_2$?
35. Bismuth has a density of 9.80 g/cm^3. What is the mass of 4.32 cm^3 of B?
36. Iron has a density of 7.87 g/cm^3. What volume would 24.6 g of Fe occupy?
37. If 1.00 km^3 of air has mass 1.2 × 10^9 kg, what is the density of air in g/cm^3?
38. Antimony has a density of 6.70 g/cm^3. What is the mass of 7.10 cm^3 of Sb?
39. Gold has a density of 19.3 g/cm^3. What is the mass of 0.393 cm^3 of Au?
40. Magnesium has a density of 1.74 g/cm^3. What is the volume of 58.6 g of Mg?
41. Tin has a density of 7.28 g/cm^3. What is the volume of 4.44 kg of Sn?

22. 1.03 g/cm^3
23. 1.91 g/cm^3
24. 1.07 g/cm^3
25. 2.40 g/cm^3
26. 8.59 g/cm^3
27. 1.80 g/cm^3
28. 0.130 g/cm^3
29. 0.700 g/cm^3
30. 2.40 g/cm^3
31. 0.872 g/cm^3
32. 1.59 g/cm^3
33. 833 cm/s
34. 1250 g
35. 42.3 g
36. 3.13 cm^3
37. 1.2 × 10^{-3} g/cm^3
38. 47.6 g
39. 7.58 g
40. 33.7 cm^3
41. 6.10 × 10^2 cm^3

REVIEW

1. What is the role of science in making environmental decisions?
2. What are the two general forms of energy an object can possess?
3. What is the principal aim of chemists in their work?
4. State the law of conservation of mass-energy.

1. To provide the facts as the basis for making value judgments.
2. potential and kinetic

ONE MORE STEP

1. Thermometers are not the only instruments used to measure temperature. Other temperature measuring devices are the thermocouple, the optical pyrometer, and the thermister. Prepare a report for your class on operation and advantages and disadvantages of each of these instruments.
2. Determine how a computer makes computations with large numbers.
3. Some personal microcomputers can do calculations in "double precision mode." Find the meaning of that phrase.
4. Research how surveyors use lasers in making measurements.

3. The study of the structure and properties of matter and its applications to technology. (Answers may vary but should outline the concept above.)
4. Matter and energy are always conserved and their sum is a constant.

READINGS

Himes, Gary K., *Solving Problems in Chemistry*, Columbus, OH: Merrill Publishing Co., 1987.

Every object in the photograph can be labeled as matter. However, it would seem to be an impossible task to study the characteristics of all matter. Classifying matter into smaller groups with similar characteristics can make this study easier. Knowing the characteristics and properties of some members of a group allows us to generalize about others. Consider the properties of some materials in the photograph. Some metals can be used for building bridges and for electrical wiring. Cement is used for roads and bridge supports. What is matter? What are some classes of matter? In what other ways may these materials be used?

MATTER

Chapter 3 introduces atoms, molecules, elements, compounds, and mixtures. It also describes the general properties of matter and the changes it undergoes.

DEMONSTRATION: Separate a mixture of sugar and $CaCO_3$ by dissolving in H_2O and filtering. Test the filtrate and the residue with H_2SO_4. See Teacher Guide for details and teaching suggestions.

The world around us is filled with objects of many kinds. There are people, chairs, books, trees, lumps of sugar, ice cubes, drinking glasses, doorknobs, and an endless number of other familiar objects. Each of these objects may be characterized by its size, shape, use, color, and texture. Many unlike objects have certain things in common. For example, a tree and a chair are both made of wood. Millions of other objects with differ-ent shapes and purposes may also be made of wood. The word **material** is used in referring to a specific kind of matter (such as wood). Familiar materials include wood, steel, copper, sugar, salt, nickel, marble, con-crete, and milk.

Material refers to a specific kind of matter.

3:1 HETEROGENEOUS MATERIALS

Most of the things we see around us contain two or more different materials. Sometimes it is necessary to use a microscope to distinguish between these different materials. Wood, granite, concrete, and milk are examples. If we look closely at granite, we can see at least three minerals. If a piece of granite is crushed into sand-sized particles, it is possible to pick out the minerals quartz, biotite, and feldspar. Milk appears to be uniform. Under a microscope, however, we can see particles suspended in water. Milk is not uniform. Such nonuniform materials are called het-erogeneous (het uh roh JEE nee uhs) materials. One type of material can be separated from the other material in milk. Fat globules can be removed by a cream separator.

A heterogeneous material is not uniform throughout.

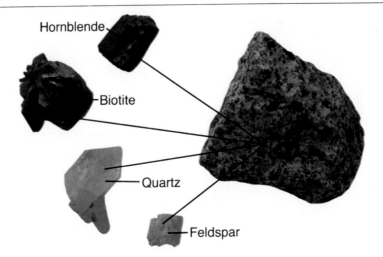

Hornblende

Biotite

Quartz

Feldspar

FIGURE 3-1. Granite is a heterogeneous material.

A phase is a physically separate
part of a material having a uniform set of properties.

Any physically separate part of a material is called a phase. A **phase** is any region with a uniform set of properties. We can distinguish between different phases of the same material. For example, ice and water are different phases of the same material. All the material in the water region has the same set of properties. Likewise, all the material in the ice region has the same set of properties. Ice and water are different states (solid and liquid) of the same material.

Heterogeneous materials contain more than one phase.

We may now define a **heterogeneous** material as one that is composed of more than one phase. The different phases in a heterogeneous material are separated from each other by definite boundaries called **interfaces.** In the two-phase system of ice and water, the surfaces of the ice and water are the interfaces. Figures 3-2 and 3-3 show different phases of systems.

FIGURE 3-2. Milk (a) is a heterogeneous material as can be
seen from this microscopic
view (b). A microscopic view of
cream is shown in (c).

a

b

c

FIGURE 3-3. The layered liquids on the left compose a four-phase system in the liquid state. The container on the right is a three-phase system at three different physical states.

3:2 HOMOGENEOUS MATERIALS

Materials that consist of only one phase are called **homogeneous** (hoh moh JEE nee uhs) materials. Since they are homogeneous, there must be a uniform distribution of the particles within the material. If you break a piece of homogeneous matter into smaller pieces, each piece will have the same properties as every other small piece. If you look at one of the pieces under a microscope, it is impossible to distinguish one part as being a different material from any other part. Examples of homogeneous materials are sugar, salt, seawater, quartz, and window glass.

Homogeneous materials consist of only one phase.

Some homogeneous matter can be classified as mixtures. A **mixture** contains more than one kind of material. Heterogeneous matter is always composed of more than one phase and is always a mixture. Homogeneous matter composed of more than one material is called a **solution.**

A mixture contains more than one kind of material.

A solution is a homogeneous mixture whose composition varies.

A solution consists of a **solute** (dissolved material) in a **solvent** (dissolving material). In the case of two liquids in solution, the solvent is the component which is the larger proportion of the whole solution. The solute is scattered in the solvent in very small particles (molecular or smaller). Because of this scattering, the solution appears uniform, even under the most powerful optical microscope. Since the scattering of particles appears to be completely uniform, solutions are classified as homogeneous materials.

A solution has a solute dispersed uniformly in a solvent.

Solutions such as antifreeze, seawater, window glass, and gold-silver alloys vary in composition from sample to sample. If we put a small amount of pure salt into pure water, stir it, and let it stand, we get a solution, or homogeneous mixture. Homogeneous mixtures, or solutions, have variable compositions. If we add a larger amount of pure salt to the same amount of pure water, we again get a solution. The composition of the second sample would differ from the first. The second sample contains more salt in an equal volume of water. In each case, the resulting material

SUGGESTION: Students should understand the distinction between mixing and combining. Natural gas and air can mix, but when they combine CO_2 and H_2O are produced.

CLASSIFICATION OF MATTER

FIGURE 3-4. Matter can be classified from general to specific types by characteristic properties.

Solutions may be solids, liquids, or gases.

Molarity, *M*, indicates the amount of solute in a specific amount of solution.

is homogeneous. A solution may also be defined as a single phase that can vary in composition.

Solutions are not necessarily liquid. To a chemist, air is a homogeneous material composed of nitrogen, oxygen, and smaller quantities of other gases. Its composition varies from place to place. However, from a practical standpoint, the air we breathe usually contains heterogeneous particles such as soot or spores. Different types of window glass have different compositions, yet each type is homogeneous. Both air and glass are solutions. So is automobile radiator antifreeze. The solvent is an organic liquid called 1,2-ethanediol (ethylene glycol). The solutes are various rust inhibitors and rubber hose conditioners.

In your laboratory work, you will be using solutions labeled with a number followed by the letter "*M.*" The symbol represents the term molarity. The exact meaning of molarity will be studied in Chapter 5. In

2.9 grams   291 grams   1746 grams

DEMONSTRATION: When discussing molarity, prepare KMnO$_4$ solutions of different concentrations to show students color-concentration relationships.

FIGURE 3-5. The flasks contain a cobalt compound in solution. The relative amounts of solid needed to prepare 0.01*M*, 1*M*, and 6*M* solutions are shown.

the meantime, you should keep in mind that molarity is used to indicate the amount of solute in a specific amount of solution. A 6*M* (six molar) solution contains 60 times as much solute as a 0.1*M* (tenth molar) solution of the same volume. Concentrated solutions have a higher ratio of solute to solvent than dilute solutions.

Percent by volume, percent by mass (Section 5:5), molality (Section 21:9), and normality are other methods used to express solution concentration. Normality is used by some analytical chemists and technicians, but is not widely accepted.

3:3 SUBSTANCES

Some homogeneous materials such as pure salt, pure sugar, or pure sulfur always have the same composition. Such materials are called **substances.** A large part of chemistry is the study of the processes by which substances may be changed into other substances.

According to the atomic theory, matter is made of very tiny particles called **atoms.** Substances are divided into two classes. Substances composed of only one kind of atom are called **elements.** Examples are sulfur, oxygen, hydrogen, nitrogen, copper, gold, and chlorine. Substances composed of more than one kind of atom are called **compounds.** The atoms in the particles of compounds are always in definite ratios. For example, water contains hydrogen atoms and oxygen atoms in a ratio of 2 to 1.

To summarize, all matter can be classified as heterogeneous mixture, solution, compound, or element. The development of this system of classification played a significant role in the early development of chemistry. Early chemists spent much time and energy sorting the pure substances from the mixtures.

Materials which always have the same composition are substances.

An element is composed of only one kind of atom.

A compound is made of more than one kind of atom.

Elements and compounds are substances.

Tc and Pm do not occur naturally. At and Fr are present in such negligible amounts that they can be ignored as contributing to the earth's mass.

Chemists know of 88 naturally-occurring elements. A complete list of the elements is found on page 62. Uranium is the natural element with the most complex atoms. Two elements, technetium and promethium, which have simpler atoms than uranium, are not found in nature. Astatine and francium have been detected in nature. However, they are present in such small amounts that they cannot be easily separated from their ores. These four elements are not normally counted among the natural elements. These synthetic elements can be produced by scientists through nuclear reactions. Synthetic elements and nuclear reactions will be discussed in Chapter 28.

Chemists today are interested in reactions of elements and compounds, the analysis of compounds into their component elements, and the synthesis of compounds from elements or other compounds. These properties and processes depend upon the structure of the elements and compounds. Thus, chemists are very much interested in these structures. The development of new pharmaceutical products is pursued largely on the basis of known reactions of the human body to molecules with particular structures.

FIGURE 3-6. Curium (a) is a synthetic element. Mercury (b) and iron (c) appear quite different from the compounds they form.

a

b

c

1. a. solution
   b. heterogeneous mixture
   c. heterogeneous mixture
   d. compound
   e. compound
   f. heterogeneous mixture
   g. heterogeneous mixture
   h. element
   i. compound
2. a) inspection
   b) evaporate liquid
   c) extract with solvent
   d) evaporate liquid

PROBLEMS

1. Classify the following materials as heterogeneous mixtures, solutions, compounds, or elements. Use a dictionary to identify any unfamiliar materials.

   a. air   **d.** table salt   **g.** milk
   b. India ink   **e.** wood alcohol   **h.** plutonium
   c. paper   **f.** apple   **i.** water

2. Indicate how you would demonstrate that each of the following is a heterogeneous mixture or a homogeneous mixture.

   a. a piece of lumber   **c.** a piece of calf's liver
   b. a glass of soda pop   **d.** shaving cream

3. How would you determine if a piece of cloth advertised as 50% wool and 50% synthetic fiber was a heterogeneous mixture or a homogeneous mixture?

3. Examine the material under a microscope.

3:4 PHYSICAL PROPERTIES

The properties of a substance can be divided into two classes. One class depends on the substance itself. The other depends for the most part on the action of the substance in the presence of other substances. The first class of properties is called **physical properties.** Length, color, and temperature are physical properties. Physical properties may be divided into groups: extensive properties and intensive properties. **Extensive properties** depend upon the amount of matter present. Some of these properties are mass, length, and volume.

Intensive properties do not depend upon the amount of matter present. For example, each sample of a substance, regardless of its size, has the same density throughout. Other intensive properties include malleability (mal ee uh BIHL uht ee), ductility, and conductivity. For example, copper can be hammered quite easily into thin sheets. It is more malleable than iron, which resists this pounding. Copper can also be drawn out into a fine wire; it is quite ductile. Both copper and silver have high heat and electrical conductivity. A high heat conductivity or electrical conductivity means that a substance offers little resistance to the flow of heat or electricity. A silver spoon will become hot if left in a hot pan of soup because silver has a high heat conductivity.

In addition to density, the intensive properties most important to the chemist are color, crystalline shape, melting point, boiling point, and refractive index (ability to bend light).

Extensive properties depend on the amount of material.

Intensive properties depend upon the nature of material.

DEMONSTRATION: A piece of colored paper can be used to show the difference between extensive and intensive physical properties: color, mass, volume, density, conductivity, hardness. Does tearing change the properties? Discuss the changes that occur when the paper is burned.

FIGURE 3-7. Copper is quite malleable and ductile. These properties make it useful for a variety of products including sheeting, tubing, and wire.

3:5 PHYSICAL CHANGES

Changes like pounding, pulling, or heating do not change the chemical character of a substance. Pounded copper is still copper. Only its physical appearance is changed. Thus, these changes are called **physical changes.** In a physical change, the same substance is present after the change as was present before the change. Cutting a piece of wood into smaller pieces, tearing paper, dissolving sugar in water, and pouring a liquid from one container to another, are other examples of physical changes.

Physical changes occur when a substance melts or boils. At the melting point, a solid changes to a liquid. At the boiling point, a liquid changes to a gas. Such physical changes are called changes of state, since the substance is not altered except for its physical state. A knowledge of physical properties and changes can be applied to separating mixtures. Separating substances by distillation is a change-of-state operation. It is used to separate substances with different boiling points. For instance, you can separate a solution of salt in water by heating the solution to a temperature equal to the boiling point of the solution. The water will then be turned to steam and escape from the container. The salt, whose boiling point has not yet been reached, will remain.

Another separation based on phase difference depends upon the solubility of one substance in another. Most substances have a specific solubility (amount of solute that dissolves) in water at a given temperature.

Physical changes affect only physical properties.

Distillation is a means of separating substances by boiling point differences.

FIGURE 3-8. A distillation apparatus is used to separate the components of a mixture by differences in boiling points.

a

b

Therefore, it is usually possible to separate two substances in the same solution by a process called fractional crystallization. The insoluble substance which forms from a solution is called a precipitate. This process may be called crystallization since most substances form crystals when they precipitate.

Notice in Figure 3-10 that, at 70°C, potassium bromide (KBr) is less soluble than potassium nitrate (KNO_3). If a water solution containing equal amounts of both substances is allowed to evaporate at 70°C, the potassium bromide will crystallize first. This process is used quite often by chemists to purify laboratory chemicals. It is also used in industry in the production of many crystalline items, such as sugar, salt, and drugs.

Both distillation and crystallization are useful in separating mixtures. As a rule, any mixture can be separated by physical changes. In some cases, however, such separations are not practical.

FIGURE 3-9. An electron microscope was used to photograph the crystallization of palladium (a). The yellow precipitate formed in this reaction is lead(II) chromate (b).

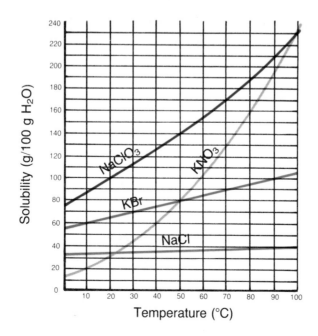

FIGURE 3-10. A solubility graph shows the amount of solid that will dissolve at a given temperature.

PROBLEMS

4. a. 38 g/100 g H$_2$O
   b. 230 g/100 g H$_2$O
   c. 46 g/100 g H$_2$O
   d. 95 g/100 g H$_2$O
5. a. extensive
   b. intensive
   c. intensive
   d. extensive
   e. intensive

4. Using Figure 3-10, determine the solubility of the following.

   a. NaCl at 70°C   **c.** KNO$_3$ at 30°C

   b. NaClO$_3$ at 100°C   **d.** KBr at 80°C

5. Classify the following properties as extensive or intensive.

   a. mass   **c.** ductility   **e.** melting point

   b. color   **d.** length

3:6 CHEMICAL PROPERTIES

Chemical properties are determined by observing the behavior of a substance in the presence of other substances.

Some properties of matter depend upon the action of substances in the presence of other substances. These properties are called **chemical properties.** In order to determine the chemical properties of a substance we must know the kinds of chemical changes that the substance can undergo. Does it burn? Does it help other substances to burn? Does it react with water? Does it react with acids and/or bases? With what other kinds of substances does it react? Is it toxic? Such questions help to determine the chemical properties of a substance.

FIGURE 3-11. Information concerning the chemical and physical properties of a substance can be found in a chemical handbook. The chemical and physical properties of uranium are highlighted.

The organic compound paraquat has two chemical properties that make it useful as a herbicide. It is toxic to plant tissue so it will kill the

☐ Physical property

▨ Chemical property

Uranium. U: atomic mass 238.029; atomic number 92; oxidation states 6+, 5+, 4+, 3+. Occurrence in the earth's crust 2×10^{-5}%; melting point 1132.3°C; boiling point 3818°C; density 19.05 g/cm^3. Silver-white radioactive metal, softer than glass. Uranium is malleable, ductile, and can be polished. Half-life of the U-238 isotope is 4.51×10^9 years. Specific heat is 0.117 J/g·C°; heat of fusion 12.1 kJ/mol; heat of vaporization 460 kJ/mol. Burns in air at 150–175°C to form U$_3$O$_8$. When finely powdered, it slowly decomposes in cold water, more quickly in hot water. Burns in fluorine to form a green, volatile tetrafluoride; also burns in chlorine, bromine, and iodine. Reacts with acids with the liberation of hydrogen and the formation of salts with the 4+ oxidation state. Not attacked by alkalies.

plants. On the other hand, it is decomposed by soil particles, particularly clays. Thus, it does not poison the soil permanently.

3:7 CHEMICAL CHANGES

Suppose you are given two test tubes containing colorless liquids. One test tube contains water. The other contains nitric acid. If you place a pinch of sugar in the water, it will disappear and the liquid remains colorless. The sugar has dissolved and you now have a sugar-water solution. A physical change has occurred. If you put a small piece of copper into the other test tube, it will also disappear. However, the liquid will turn blue and a brown gas will be given off. You now have a solution of copper nitrate and some nitrogen dioxide gas. A chemical change has occurred.

Let us take another example. Sodium is a silvery, soft metal that reacts violently with water. Chlorine is a greenish-yellow gas, which is highly corrosive and poisonous. However, if these two elements are allowed to combine, they produce a white crystalline solid. It is common table salt, sodium chloride, which neither reacts with water nor is poisonous. In this case, the properties of the reactants have disappeared. The product has different properties.

Whenever a substance undergoes a change so that one or more new substances with different properties are formed, a **chemical change** (reaction) has taken place. Burning, digesting, and fermenting are examples of chemical changes.

The separation of compounds into their component elements always requires a chemical change. Such a separation is one type of analysis. Mixtures can always be separated by physical means. However, it is sometimes more convenient to separate mixtures by a chemical change.

DEMONSTRATION: Add $AgNO_3$ solution to NaCl solution to give a white precipitate.

SUGGESTION: You may wish to do this as a demonstration. **CAUTION:** *Vent the fumes from the Cu + HNO_3 reaction.*

Chemical changes produce new substances with new properties.

FIGURE 3-12. The reaction of copper with nitric acid (a) produces a copper compound and reddish gas. The combustion of steel wool in pure oxygen (b) is also a chemical change.

a

b

PROBLEMS

6. Classify the following properties as chemical or physical. Use a dictionary to identify any unfamiliar properties.

a. color	**e.** porosity	**i.** expansion
b. reactivity	**f.** stability	**j.** melting point
c. flammability	**g.** ductility	**k.** rusting
d. odor	**h.** solubility	**l.** reacts with air

Classify the following changes as chemical or physical.

7. digestion of food

8. fading of dye in cloth

9. growth of a plant

10. melting of ice

11. explosion of gasoline in an automobile engine

12. formation of clouds in the air

13. healing of a wound

14. making of rock candy by evaporating water from a sugar solution

15. production of light by an electric lamp

3:8   ENERGY TRANSFER

Physical and chemical changes are always accompanied by energy changes. Energy can be transferred between a system and its surroundings in two ways. First, the surroundings may do work on the system, or the system may do work on the surroundings. For example, if a strip of copper is the system under consideration, by hammering the strip we would do work on it. On the other hand, if we consider the product gases in an automobile engine cylinder as a system, the system does work on the engine as it expands and pushes the cylinder down. The second way energy can be transferred is a result of a difference in temperature between the system and its surroundings. In that case, energy is transferred from the higher temperature matter to the lower. Energy transferred due to a temperature difference is called **heat** and is represented by "q." Quantitative measurements of energy changes are expressed in joules. The **joule** (J) is a derived SI unit rather than a base unit.

PROBLEM

16. List five chemical changes familiar to you in which the energy transfer that occurs is important.

3:9   MEASURING ENERGY CHANGES

Experimentally, energy changes of chemical reactions are measured in a **calorimeter,** Figure 3-13. The energy quantities involved in various physical changes can also be measured in a calorimeter. To change the temperature of a substance, heat must be added or removed. Some substances require little heat to cause a change in their temperature. Other substances require a great deal of heat to cause the same temperature change. For example, one gram of water requires 4.18 joules of heat to cause a temperature change of one Celsius degree. It takes only 0.900 joule to raise the temperature of one gram of aluminum one Celsius degree. The heat needed to raise the temperature of one gram of a substance by one Celsius degree is called the **specific heat** (C_p) of the substance. Every substance has its own specific heat. The heat required to raise the temperature of one gram of water one Celsius degree is 4.18 joules. The specific heat of water is 4.18 J/g·C°.

Specific heats are given in joules per gram-Celsius degree (J/g·C°). Tables A-3 and A-5 of the Appendix list the specific heat of some substances. The specific heat can be used in calculations involving the change in temperature of a specific amount of substance.

One kilojoule equals 1000 joules. 4.18 joules is the heat required to raise the temperature of one gram of water one Celsius degree. Therefore, 4.18 kilojoules is the heat required to raise the temperature of 1000 grams (one kilogram) of water one Celsius degree.

4.18 joules is the amount of heat needed to raise the temperature of one gram of water 1 C°.

FIGURE 3-13. A bomb calorimeter is used to measure the heat of a reaction. Energy produced in the reaction vessel is absorbed by the water (a). The energy values of different foods can be determined by burning them in a calorimeter such as the one shown here (b).

Ignition wires
Stirrer   Thermometer
Water

a

b   Reaction chamber   Insulation

There are several kinds of calorimeters. A calorimeter containing water is often used to measure the heat absorbed or released by a chemical reaction. Heat from a chemical reaction in the cup in the calorimeter causes a change in temperature of the water in the calorimeter. The temperature change of the water is used to measure the heat absorbed or released by the reaction.

The law of conservation of energy means that in an insulated system, any heat lost by one quantity of matter must be gained by another. The

It is assumed that no heat is lost or absorbed by the calorimeter.

Heat loss = Heat gained

$\Delta T = T_{final} - T_{initial}$

transfer of energy takes place between two quantities of matter that are at different temperatures. Energy flows from one to the other until the two reach the same temperature. Further, the amount of energy transferred can be calculated from the relationship:

$$\left(\begin{array}{c}heat\ gained\\ or\ lost\end{array}\right) = \left(\begin{array}{c}mass\\ in\ grams\end{array}\right)\left(\begin{array}{c}change\ in\\ temperature\end{array}\right)\left(\begin{array}{c}specific\\ heat\end{array}\right)$$

$$q = (m)(\Delta T^*)(C_p)$$

In the calorimeter the product of the specific heat of the water, the temperature change of the water, and the mass of the water gives the change in heat. The heat released or absorbed by water is calculated using the following equation.

$$\frac{g\ of\ H_2O}{} \left| \frac{\Delta T}{} \right| \frac{4.18\ J}{g \cdot C^\circ} = J$$

The same method can be used to calculate the change in heat when two dilute solutions react. The solutions are placed in a cup in the calorimeter. As the chemical reaction occurs, the temperature change is measured. Because the solutions are dilute, we can assume that the mixture has the same specific heat as water, 4.18 J/g·C°. By multiplying the specific heat by the temperature change, and the mass of the solutions, we can calculate the heat change of the reaction.

Notice that throughout our discussion of calorimetry, we have assumed that the calorimeter itself does not absorb any heat. We also have assumed that no heat escapes from the calorimeter. Neither of these assumptions is completely true. However, we will continue to make these assumptions in order to simplify our calculations. The error from actual losses of heat should be considered in any laboratory exercise using calorimeters.

EXAMPLE: Heat Calculation

How much heat is lost when a solid aluminum ingot with mass 4110 g cools from 660.0°C to 25°C?

Solving Process:
From Table A-5 of the Appendix, we find that the specific heat of aluminum is 0.900 J/g · C°. We also know that

$$q = (m)(\Delta T)(C_p) \qquad\qquad \Delta T = 660.0°C - 25°C = 635\ C°$$

so

$$q = \frac{4110\ g}{} \left| \frac{635\ C^\circ}{} \right| \frac{0.900\ J}{g \cdot C^\circ} = 2.35 \times 10^6\ J$$

$^*\Delta T$ may be represented as $T_f - T_i$ when heat is gained and $T_i - T_f$ when heat is lost.

EXAMPLE: Heat Calculation

Suppose a piece of iron with a mass of 21.5 grams at a temperature of 100.0°C is dropped into an insulated container of water. The mass of the water is 132 grams and its temperature before adding the iron is 20.0°C. What will be the final temperature of the system?

Solving Process:
We know the heat lost must equal the heat gained. Since the iron is at a higher temperature than the water, the iron will lose energy. The water will gain an equivalent amount of energy.

$q = m(\Delta T)C_p$

(a) The heat lost by the iron is

$$q = (m)(\Delta T)(C_p) = \frac{21.5\ \cancel{g}\ |\ (100.0\cancel{°C} - T_f)\ |\ 0.448\ J}{|\ |\ \cancel{g}\cdot\cancel{°C}}$$

(b) The heat gained by the water is

$$q = (m)(\Delta T)(C_p) = \frac{132\ \cancel{g}\ |\ (T_f - 20.0\cancel{°C})\ |\ 4.18\ J}{|\ |\ \cancel{g}\cdot\cancel{°C}}$$

(c) The heat gained must equal the heat lost

$$\frac{132\ \cancel{g}\ |\ (T_f - 20.0°C)\ |\ 4.18\cancel{J}}{|\ |\ \cancel{g}\cdot\cancel{°C}} = \frac{2.15\ \cancel{g}\ |\ (100.0°C - T_f)\ |\ 0.448\cancel{J}}{|\ |\ \cancel{g}\cdot\cancel{°C}}$$

$$T_f = 21.4°C$$

The same type of calculation may be used to measure the specific heat of an unknown metal. We must have the masses of the two substances and the initial and final temperatures of both. The only unknown factor is the specific heat of the metal.

The specific heats of metals are fairly constant over a wide range of temperatures. In fact, the specific heats of all solids and liquids are fairly constant.

C_p of solids and liquids are nearly constant over a temperature range.

In contrast, the specific heats of gases vary widely with temperature. They also depend on whether the gas is heated at constant volume or constant pressure. When performing heat calculations on gases, then, we must be careful to use correct data. We must use figures which give a good average of the specific heats of a substance over the temperature range involved. In advanced work, we must also check the conditions of volume and pressure stated for the change.

C_p of gases vary with temperature.

PROBLEMS

17. How much heat is required to raise the temperature of 54.5 g PCl_3 from 18.6°C to 79.1°C? (See Table A-5 of the Appendix.)

18. How much heat is required to raise the temperature of 8.77 g CCl_4 from 37.1°C to 56.4°C? (See Table A-5 of the Appendix.)

17. 2880 J
18. 145 J

19. 1.55×10^5 J
20. 18.3°C
21. 34.0°C
22. 0.193 J/g · C°
23. 1.1 J/g · C°

SUGGESTION: Advise students to avoid rounding off intermediate answers which introduce rounding errors into their final answers.

19. How much heat is required to raise the temperature of 7.90×10^2 g H_2O from 38.4°C to 85.4°C?

20. If a piece of aluminum with mass 2.39 g and a temperature of 100.0°C is dropped in 10.0 cm³ of water at 14.1°C, what will be the final temperature of the system? (Recall the density of water is 1.00 g/cm³.)

21. If a piece of cadmium with mass 75.2 g and a temperature of 100.0°C is dropped into 25.0 cm³ of water at 23.0°C, what will be the final temperature of the system?

22. A piece of unknown metal with mass 5.19 g is heated to 100.00°C and dropped in 10.0 cm³ of water at 22.00°C. The final temperature of the system is 23.83°C. What is the specific heat of the metal? Using the data in Table A-3 of the Appendix, what might this metal be?

23. A piece of an unknown metal with mass 23.8 g is heated to 100.00°C and dropped in 50.0 cm³ of water at 24.0°C. The final temperature of the system is 32.50°C. What is the specific heat of the metal?

BIOGRAPHY — St. Elmo Brady (1884-1966)

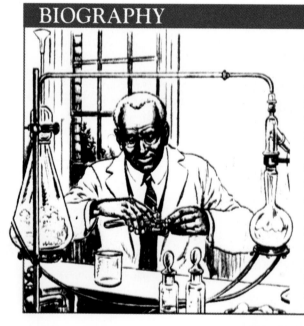

St. Elmo Brady was the first black student to receive a doctorate in chemistry. He spent the rest of his life making certain that other black students would have the same opportunity. After finishing his degree at the University of Illinois in 1916, he went to Tuskegee Institute to develop what became the first chemistry department there. He moved in 1920 to Howard University and accomplished the same task. In 1927 he moved to Fisk University and served 25 years building both undergraduate and graduate programs. After retirement, when he was nearly 70 years old, Brady was again asked to build a chemistry department, this time at Tougaloo, Mississippi. As a result of his efforts, thousands of students have had the opportunity for an education in chemistry. He studied and wrote until his death at 82.

Careers and Chemistry

3:10 Nutritionists

Have you ever wondered who decides on the menu in your school cafeteria? A nutritionist does. Nutritionists study the effects of foods on the human body.

The human body is an extremely complex chemical factory. Several sciences are involved in the study of the body, but nutrition is one of the most practical. Knowledge gained in nutrition science can be put to immediate use in a number of career positions.

Nutritionists are concerned with the raw materials fed into the human chemical factory. A thorough study of chemistry, biochemistry, and human physiology is required. Some nutritionists make a career of researching medical and health-related nutritional problems. Others choose to apply their knowledge on a daily basis in maintaining the health of individuals or communities.

The nutritionist is an essential part of the health care team, whether it be in a hospital, rural clinic, food industry, or government agency. In that role, he or she must be able to cooperate with other health care professionals (doctors, food chemists, food standards boards) as well as communicate with a patient. In addition, the nutritionist must be aware of the legal limitations to which he or she is subject, the cultural biases of a patient, and the economic realities of a particular situation. The nutritional problems of many cultures are not easily solved.

The food intake of humans varies as an individual grows. Not all individuals grow at the same rate and nutritionists adjust diets to account for individual differences in physiology and metabolism. They must have a thorough knowledge of the chemical needs of the body and how these needs can be met by the chemical substances present in foods. In addition, nutritionists provide specialized diets to administer to individuals with particular medical problems such as obesity, high blood pressure, or ulcers.

Nutritionists also supervise food preparation, plan menus, recognize and treat dietary-based diseases, purchase food, and develop new recipes. The principal employers of nutritionists are hospitals, schools, restaurant and hotel chains, food producers, and government agencies.

SUMMARY

1. A phase consists of uniform matter. One phase is separated from other phases by boundaries called interfaces. 3:1

2. Heterogeneous matter is made of more than one phase. The phases usually can be separated by physical means. 3:1

3. A mixture is a combination of two or more substances which retain their individual properties. 3:2

4. Homogeneous matter is made of only one phase. 3:2

5. A solution is a homogeneous mixture consisting of a solute dissolved in a solvent. The component parts need not be present in any specific ratios. 3:2

6. Elements are made of one kind of atom. 3:3

7. Compounds are substances made of more than one kind of atom. The component atoms are present in definite ratios. 3:3

8. Physical properties depend upon the substance itself. 3:4

9. Extensive physical properties, such as mass and length, depend upon the amount of matter present. Intensive properties, such as ductility and melting point, depend on the nature of matter itself. 3:4

10. A physical change in a substance does not alter its chemical character. A change of state is a physical change from one state—solid, liquid, or gas—to another. 3:5

11. The chemical properties of a substance depend upon the action of the substance in the presence of other substances. 3:6

12. A chemical change in a substance involves the formation of new substances with different properties. Chemical changes must be used to separate the elements composing a compound. 3:7

13. Physical and chemical changes always involve energy transfer, either in the form of work or heat. 3:8

14. The specific heat of a substance is the heat required to raise the temperature of 1 g of the substance 1C°. 3:9

15. The energy transferred when matter changes temperature is $q = (m)(\Delta T)(C_p)$. This value is expressed using an energy unit called joules. 3:9

16. The specific heat of water is 4.18 J/g·C°. 3:9

VOCABULARY

material Intro	solvent 3:2	physical change 3:5
phase 3:1	substances 3:3	chemical properties 3:6
heterogeneous 3:1	atoms 3:3	chemical change 3:7
interfaces 3:1	element 3:3	heat 3:8
homogeneous 3:2	compounds 3:3	joule 3:8
mixture 3:2	physical properties 3:4	calorimeter 3:9
solution 3:2	extensive properties 3:4	specific heat 3:9
solute 3:2	intensive properties 3:4	

PROBLEMS

1. a. heterogeneous mixture
   b. compound
   c. heterogeneous mixture
   d. heterogeneous mixture
   e. solution
   f. element

1. Use reference materials to classify the following materials as heterogeneous mixture, solution, compound, or element. Use a dictionary to identify any unfamiliar materials.

   a. paint   **c.** granite   **e.** corn syrup
   b. orthoclase   **d.** leather   **f.** gold

2. a. chemical
   b. physical
   c. physical
   d. physical
   e. chemical
   f. chemical

2. Classify the following changes as chemical or physical.

   a. burning of coal   **d.** excavating of earth
   b. tearing of a piece of paper   **e.** exploding of TNT
   c. kicking of a football   **f.** contracting a muscle

3. 9 phases, approximately 13 interfaces

3. Estimate the number of phases and interfaces present in an ice cream soda complete with whipped cream and candied cherry.

4. Classify the following properties as chemical or physical.

   a. density   **b.** melting point   **c.** length   **d.** flammability

4. a. physical   b. physical   c. physical   d. chemical

5. The joule is an SI derived unit. Express joules in terms of SI base units.

6. How many joules are required to heat 706 g of nickel from 25°C to 300°C?

7. How many joules are required to heat 55.8 g of tin from 36.4°C to 47.7°C?

8. Using a chemical dictionary, the *Handbook of Chemistry and Physics,* or *Lange's Handbook of Chemistry* prepare a report on the properties of an element assigned by your teacher.

5. $1 \text{ kg} \cdot \text{m}^2/\text{s}^2$
6. 8.60×10^4 J
7. 139 J

See the Teacher Guide for detailed answers.

REVIEW

1. Make the following conversions.
   a. 2.84 kilograms to grams
   b. 544 milliseconds to seconds
   c. 0.0656 grams to milligrams
   d. 1102 centimeters to meters
   e. 0.220 grams to milligrams
   f. 3.6 nanometers to centimeters

2. Compute the density of the following materials.
   a. clay, if 42.0 g occupy 19.1 cm^3
   b. cork, if 8.17 g occupy 34.0 cm^3
   c. linoleum, if 6120 g occupy 5100 cm^3
   d. ebony wood, if 201 g occupy 165 cm^3

3. State the four basic measurements you have studied so far. Define these quantities. State the standards for each and the instrument used to measure each.

4. What is the property possessed by all matter?

5. How many significant digits are in the measurement 101.476 g?

6. What is the relative error of the measurement in the previous problem if the measurement is precise to ±0.002 grams?

1. a. 2840 g
   b. 0.544 s
   c. 65.6 mg
   d. 11.02 m
   e. 2.20×10^2 mg
   f. 3.6×10^{-7} cm
2. a. 2.20 g/cm^3
   b. 0.240 g/cm^3
   c. 1.2 g/cm^3
   d. 1.22 g/cm^3
3. mass, length, time, temperature
4. inertia
5. 6
6. 2×10^{-5}

ONE MORE STEP

1. The doctor sometimes recommends gargling with salt water to relieve a sore throat. Determine whether the action of the salt water on bacteria is chemical or physical.

2. Devise an experiment which will allow you to separate a mixture of copper filings and salt.

3. Find out how crude oil may be obtained from shale through physical and chemical means.

4. The shortage of drinkable water has become critical in many parts of the world. Investigate various methods of separating drinkable water from seawater. Pay particular attention to phase changes and other physical processes involved in the methods.

5. Investigate the structure of gelatin. In what physical state would you classify it? Is it heterogeneous or homogeneous?

6. How would specific heat affect selection of fuels?

READINGS

Seaborg, Glenn T., "Charting the New Elements," *SciQuest,* Vol. 53, No. 8(October 1980), pp. 7-11.

Artistic expression is considered a form of communication. The clear glass globe has appeared in various art exhibits. It contains krypton gas. Electric impulses cause the lightning flashes you see throughout the globe. Chemists, like artists, have their own means of expression. The chemical changes you see here can be described by a lengthy paragraph or by using symbols and formulas. These shorthand forms provide the same information in much less space. You learned about the standardized system of expressing measurements in Chapter 2. What standardized system is used to describe matter using symbols and formulas?

CHEMICAL FORMULAS

Chapter 4 introduces symbols and their use as a means of writing chemical formulas.

DEMONSTRATION: Mix 3 g of zinc dust with 2 g of iodine in a large test tube. Add 1 cm^3 of H$_2$O to prepare ZnI$_2$. See Teacher Guide for additional information.
CAUTION: *Reaction is exothermic.*

Although there are only a few more than 100 elements, there are literally millions of compounds known to chemists. It is convenient to represent elements and compounds by the use of symbols. This shorthand system improves communications among all parts of the scientific and technological community. These representations of substances are another way to help us classify these substances quickly. This ability to classify simplifies the study of the vast number of substances with which chemists work.

GOALS:
• You will demonstrate a proficiency in writing chemical formulas and naming compounds.
• You will define oxidation number and state the oxidation numbers for common monatomic and polyatomic ions.
• You will differentiate between molecular and empirical formulas.

4:1 SYMBOLS

The **chemical symbols** of the elements are a form of shorthand. They take the place of the complete names of the elements. A symbol may represent one atom of an element. Scientists throughout the world have agreed to represent one atom of aluminum by the symbol Al.

Ancient symbols for some elements are shown in Figure 4-1. J. J. Berzelius, a Swedish chemist, is generally given credit for creating the modern symbols for elements. Berzelius proposed that all elements be given a symbol corresponding to the first letter of their names. In the case of two elements that began with the same letter, a second letter or a letter outstanding in the name was added. In some cases, the Latin name of the element was used. Thus, the symbol for sulfur is S; selenium, Se; strontium, Sr; and sodium, Na (Latin *natrium* = sodium).

The symbols that have been agreed upon for the elements are listed in Table 4-1. Notice that they contain capital and lowercase letters. Names for elements 104 through 109 and their three-letter symbols are the result of a system adopted by the International Union of Pure and Applied Chemistry (IUPAC). In this system, Latin and Greek stems representing the atomic numbers of the elements are used for both the name and the symbol.

A symbol may be used in place of the name of an element.

Symbols consist of one, two or three letters.

The first letter of a symbol is always capitalized.

Table 4-1

Elements and Their Symbols					
Actinium	Ac	Holmium	Ho	Radon	Rn
*Aluminum	Al	*Hydrogen	H	Rhenium	Re
Americium	Am	Indium	In	Rhodium	Rh
Antimony	Sb	*Iodine	I	*Rubidium	Rb
*Argon	Ar	Iridium	Ir	Ruthenium	Ru
Arsenic	As	*Iron	Fe	Samarium	Sm
Astatine	At	Krypton	Kr	Scandium	Sc
*Barium	Ba	Lanthanum	La	Selenium	Se
Berkelium	Bk	Lawrencium	Lr	*Silicon	Si
*Beryllium	Be	*Lead	Pb	*Silver	Ag
*Bismuth	Bi	*Lithium	Li	*Sodium	Na
*Boron	B	Lutetium	Lu	*Strontium	Sr
*Bromine	Br	*Magnesium	Mg	*Sulfur	S
*Cadmium	Cd	*Manganese	Mn	Tantalum	Ta
*Calcium	Ca	Mendelevium	Md	Technetium	Tc
Californium	Cf	*Mercury	Hg	Tellurium	Te
*Carbon	C	*Molybdenum	Mo	Terbium	Tb
Cerium	Ce	Neodymium	Nd	*Thallium	Tl
*Cesium	Cs	*Neon	Ne	Thorium	Th
*Chlorine	Cl	Neptunium	Np	Thulium	Tm
*Chromium	Cr	*Nickel	Ni	*Tin	Sn
*Cobalt	Co	Niobium	Nb	Titanium	Ti
*Copper	Cu	*Nitrogen	N	Tungsten	W
Curium	Cm	Nobelium	No	Unnilennium	Une
Dysprosium	Dy	Osmium	Os	Unnilhexium	Unh
Einsteinium	Es	*Oxygen	O	Unniloctium	Uno
Erbium	Er	Palladium	Pd	Unnilpentium	Unp
Europium	Eu	*Phosphorus	P	Unnilquadium	Unq
Fermium	Fm	*Platinum	Pt	Unnilseptium	Uns
*Fluorine	F	Plutonium	Pu	Uranium	U
Francium	Fr	Polonium	Po	Vanadium	V
Gadolinium	Gd	*Potassium	K	Xenon	Xe
Gallium	Ga	Praseodymium	Pr	Ytterbium	Yb
Germanium	Ge	Promethium	Pm	Yttrium	Y
Gold	Au	Protactinium	Pa	*Zinc	Zn
Hafnium	Hf	Radium	Ra	Zirconium	Zr
*Helium	He				

Students should memorize those symbols marked with an asterisk as they will be used often throughout the text.

4:2 CHEMICAL FORMULAS

Chemists also use combinations of symbols to represent compounds. Compounds are substances in which two or more elements are chemically combined. Compounds are represented by chemical formulas.

A **chemical formula** is a combination of symbols that represents the composition of a compound. Formulas often contain numerals to indicate the proportions in which the elements occur within a compound. For

Chemical formulas represent compounds.

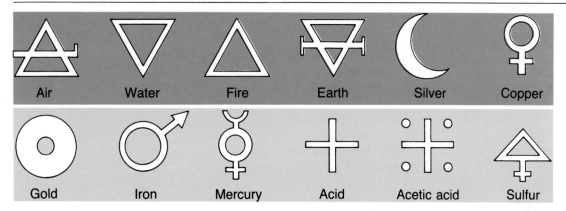

| Air | Water | Fire | Earth | Silver | Copper |
| Gold | Iron | Mercury | Acid | Acetic acid | Sulfur |

example, we have learned from experiments that water is composed of the elements hydrogen and oxygen. We also know that two atoms of hydrogen will react (combine chemically) with one atom of oxygen to form one molecule of water. Using this data, we write the formula for water as H_2O. The small subscript, $_2$, after the H indicates that there are two atoms of hydrogen in one molecule of water. Note that there is no subscript after the oxygen. If a symbol for an element has no subscript, it is understood that only one atom of that element is present. A formula shows two things. It indicates the elements present in the compound and the relative number of atoms of each element in the compound.

FIGURE 4-1. Picture symbols were once used for substances believed to be elements.

Chemical formulas indicate the relative number of atoms for each element present in a compound.

Table 4-2

Some Common Compounds and Their Formulas		
Compound	Formula	Elements
ammonia	NH_3	nitrogen, hydrogen
rust	Fe_2O_3	iron, oxygen
sucrose	$C_{12}H_{22}O_{11}$	carbon, hydrogen, oxygen
table salt	NaCl	sodium, chlorine
water	H_2O	hydrogen, oxygen

Most compounds containing the element carbon are classed as organic compounds. Formulas for organic compounds are written according to a different set of rules that you will study in Chapter 29. For example, a formula for acetic acid is written as CH_3COOH^*. The actual structure of the acetic acid molecule is represented by

Most compounds containing carbon are organic compounds.

$$
\begin{array}{cc}
\text{H} & \text{O} \\
| & \| \\
\text{H}-\text{C}-\text{C}-\text{O}-\text{H} \\
| \\
\text{H}
\end{array}
$$

From this structural formula you can see how the shorthand formula is derived. It shows how the atoms are joined, as well as the kind and number of atoms present.

*A formula for acetic acid is also written as $HC_2H_3O_2$.

4:3 OXIDATION NUMBER

Through experiments, chemists have determined the ratios in which most elements combine. They have also learned that these ratios depend upon the structure of their atoms. This relationship will be explored fully in Chapters 7-10. For now, you should know that the atoms can acquire an electric charge. Such charged atoms are called **ions.** They may also attach themselves to other atoms so that the whole group gains an electric charge. An ion made of more than one atom, for example OH^-, is called a **polyatomic ion.** When a single atom gains a charge, that charge is known as its **oxidation number.**

Table 4-3 lists the oxidation numbers of many elements. Table 4-4 lists the charges of several polyatomic ions. You should memorize the asterisked items. They will be important throughout your study of chemistry. We use this information to write correct chemical formulas. Atoms

An ion is a charged atom or group of charged atoms.

Oxidation numbers represent apparent charge on an atom.

Table 4-3

Oxidation Numbers of Monatomic Ions					
1+		**2+**		**3+**	
*cesium, Cs^+	*barium, Ba^{2+}	*manganese(II), Mn^{2+}	*aluminum, Al^{3+}	iridium(III), Ir^{3+}	
*copper(I), Cu^+	beryllium, Be^{2+}	*mercury(II), Hg^{2+}	antimony(III), Sb^{3+}	*iron(III), Fe^{3+}	
*hydrogen, H^+	cadmium, Cd^{2+}	nickel(II), Ni^{2+}	bismuth(III), Bi^{3+}	phosphorus(III), P^{3+}	
indium(I), In^+	*calcium, Ca^{2+}	platinum(II), Pt^{2+}	boron, B^{3+}	rhodium(III), Rh^{3+}	
*lithium, Li^+	chromium(II), Cr^{2+}	*strontium, Sr^{2+}	cerium(III), Ce^{3+}	thallium(III), Tl^{3+}	
*potassium, K^+	*cobalt(II), Co^{2+}	tin(II), Sn^{2+}	*cobalt(III), Co^{3+}	titanium(III), Ti^{3+}	
rubidium, Rb^+	*copper(II), Cu^{2+}	titanium(II), Ti^{2+}	*chromium(III), Cr^{3+}	uranium(III), U^{3+}	
*silver, Ag^+	iridium(II), Ir^{2+}	tungsten(II), W^{2+}	gallium(III), Ga^{3+}	vanadium(III), V^{3+}	
*sodium, Na^+	*iron(II), Fe^{2+}	vanadium(II), V^{2+}	indium(III), In^{3+}		
*thallium(I), Tl^+	*lead(II), Pb^{2+}	*zinc, Zn^{2+}			
	*magnesium, Mg^{2+}	zirconium(II), Zr^{2+}			

4+			**5+**	
cerium(IV), Ce^{4+}	platinum(IV), Pt^{4+}	tungsten(IV), W^{4+}	antimony(V), Sb^{5+}	tungsten(V), W^{5+}
germanium(IV), Ge^{4+}	thorium(IV), Th^{4+}	uranium(IV), U^{4+}	bismuth(V), Bi^{5+}	uranium(V), U^{5+}
iridium(IV), Ir^{4+}	titanium(IV), Ti^{4+}	vanadium(IV), V^{4+}	phosphorus(V), P^{5+}	vanadium(V), V^{5+}
*lead(IV), Pb^{4+}	tin(IV), Sn^{4+}	zirconium(IV), Zr^{4+}		

1−	**2−**	**3−**	**4−**
*bromide, Br^-	*oxide, O^{2-}	nitride, N^{3-}	carbide, C^{4-}
*chloride, Cl^-	selenide, Se^{2-}	phosphide, P^{3-}	
*fluoride, F^-	*sulfide, S^{2-}		
hydride, H^-			
*iodide, I^-			

*Table A-3 of the Appendix lists additional charges of monatomic ions.

Table 4-4

Charges of Common Polyatomic Ions*	
1+ *ammonium, NH_4^+	**2+** mercury(I), Hg_2^{2+}

1−	**2−**	**3−**
*acetate, CH_3COO^-	*carbonate, CO_3^{2-}	arsenate, AsO_4^{3-}
bromate, BrO_3^-	chromate, CrO_4^{2-}	phosphate, PO_4^{3-}
chlorate, ClO_3^-	hexafluorosilicate, SiF_6^{2-}	
cyanide, CN^-	molybdate, MoO_4^{2-}	
formate, $HCOO^-$	*oxalate, $C_2O_4^{2-}$	
*hydroxide, OH^-	peroxide, O_2^{2-}	
hypochlorite, ClO^-	selenate, SeO_4^{2-}	
*nitrate, NO_3^-	silicate, SiO_3^{2-}	
perchlorate, ClO_4^-	*sulfate, SO_4^{2-}	
periodate, IO_4^-	sulfite, SO_3^{2-}	
	tartrate, $C_4H_4O_6^{2-}$	

*Table A-4 of the Appendix lists additional polyatomic ions and their charges.

Ionic compounds are composed of charged particles; molecular compounds are composed of neutral particles.

Monatomic = 1 atom
Diatomic = 2 atoms
Polyatomic = 2 or more atoms

and ions combine chemically in definite ratios. Oxidation numbers of elements and the charges on polyatomic ions tell us these combining ratios. The way to determine the ratio of elements in a compound is to add the charges algebraically. If the charges add up to zero, the formula for the compound is correct.

Common table salt, NaCl, is made from sodium, Na, and chlorine, Cl. Table 4-3 shows a 1+ charge for sodium ions and a 1− charge for chloride ions.

$$Na^+Cl^-$$

Adding these charges, we see that $1 + (1-) = 0$. Therefore, the formula for salt is NaCl. This formula indicates that a one-to-one ratio exists between sodium ions and chloride ions in a crystal of salt. Sodium chloride is an **ionic compound,** that is, it is composed of charged particles called ions. Elements also combine in another way. Neutral atoms combine to form neutral particles called **molecules.** The compounds formed are called molecular compounds. In Chapter 12, we will study distinct differences in properties between ionic and molecular substances.

The element chlorine is a gas composed of molecules that are diatomic. A diatomic molecule is made of two atoms. One chlorine molecule contains two chlorine atoms. Chlorine gas is represented by the formula Cl_2. Six other common elements also occur as diatomic molecules. Hydrogen (H_2), nitrogen (N_2), oxygen (O_2), and fluorine (F_2) are diatomic gases under normal conditions. Bromine (Br_2) is a gas above 58.8°C. Iodine (I_2) is a gas above 184°C.

FIGURE 4-2. The crystal structure of the sodium chloride in this vast salt mine is the same as in the table salt you use. The ratio of sodium ions to chloride ions is 1:1 in both cases.

SUGGESTION: Students need much practice on these.

EXAMPLES: Writing Formulas

Write a formula for a compound of calcium and bromine.
Solving Process:
With the exception of ammonia, NH_3, the element with the positive oxidation number is always written first. Using Table 4-3, we see the oxidation states of calcium and bromide are as follows:

$$Ca^{2+} \qquad Br^-$$

Since the sum of the charges must equal zero, two Br^- are needed to balance Ca^{2+}. The correct formula is $CaBr_2$.

Write the formula for a compound made from aluminum and sulfur atoms.
Solving Process:
Using Table 4-3, we see the oxidation states of aluminum and sulfide are as follows:

$$Al^{3+} \qquad S^{2-}$$

To make the sum of the charge equal zero, we must find the least common multiple of 3 and 2. The least common multiple is 6. Thus, two Al^{3+} and three S^{2-} must combine for the charges to equal zero. The formula is written Al_2S_3.

Write the formula for a compound made from aluminum and the sulfate ion.
Solving Process:
Using Tables 4-3 and 4-4, we see the oxidation states of aluminum and the sulfate ion are as follows:

$$Al^{3+} \qquad SO_4^{2-}$$

It is necessary to have two Al^{3+} and three SO_4^{2-} in the compound to maintain neutrality. Writing aluminum ions in the formula is simple.

$$Al_2$$

For the sulfate, the entire polyatomic ion must be placed in parentheses to indicate that three sulfate ions are required.

$$(SO_4)_3$$

Thus, aluminum sulfate has the formula $Al_2(SO_4)_3$. Note that parentheses are used in a formula only when you are expressing multiples of a polyatomic ion. If only one sulfate ion were needed in writing a formula, parentheses would not be used. For example, the formula for the compound made from calcium, Ca^{2+}, and the sulfate ion, SO_4^{2-}, is $CaSO_4$.

The formula of a substance represents a specific amount of a compound. If a substance is composed of molecules, the formula represents one molecule. If a substance is composed of ions, the formula represents the lowest combining ratio of the ions.

a

b

4:4 NAMING COMPOUNDS

Unfortunately, some compounds have many names, both common and chemical. However, there is a systematic method of naming practically all the compounds that we will use. The names of only a few compounds, particularly acids, will not be included in this system.

Compounds containing only two elements are called **binary compounds.** To name a binary compound, first write the name of the element having a positive charge. Then add the name of the negative element. The name of the negative element must be modified to end in -*ide*. For example, the compound formed by aluminum (Al^{3+}) and nitrogen (N^{3-}), with the formula AlN, is named aluminum nitride.

FIGURE 4-3. It is important to know the names and formulas of chemical compounds in order to distinguish between different substances used in the lab (a), and the hazards associated with them (b).

Table 4-5

Formulas and Names of Some Binary Compounds	
Formula	**Name**
Al_2S_3	aluminum sulfide
$CaBr_2$	calcium bromide
H_2O	hydrogen oxide (water)
H_2Se	hydrogen selenide
NaCl	sodium chloride (table salt)

In looking at Table 4-3 we see that some elements have more than one possible charge. Therefore, they may form more than one compound with another element. For instance, nitrogen and oxygen form five different binary compounds with each other.

We must have a way of distinguishing the names of these compounds. We tell the difference by writing the oxidation number of the element having positive charge after the name of that element. Roman numerals in parentheses are used. Examples of some compounds named according to this system are listed in Table 4-6.

Roman numerals are used in naming compounds that contain elements with more than one oxidation number.

Table 4-6

Formulas and Names of Some Binary Molecular Compounds Having Variable Oxidation States			
Formula	**Name using Roman Numerals**	**Formula**	**Name using Roman Numerals**
N_2O	nitrogen(I) oxide	Cu_2S	copper(I) sulfide
NO	nitrogen(II) oxide	CuS	copper(II) sulfide
N_2O_3	nitrogen(III) oxide	FeF_2	iron(II) fluoride
NO_2	nitrogen(IV) oxide	FeF_3	iron(III) fluoride
N_2O_5	nitrogen(V) oxide	$PbCl_2$	lead(II) chloride
SO_2	sulfur(IV) oxide	$PbCl_4$	lead(IV) chloride
SO_3	sulfur(VI) oxide		

Prefix	Number of atoms
mono-	1
di-	2
tri-	3
tetra-	4
penta-	5
hexa-	6
hepta-	7
octa-	8

There are many compounds that have been named by an older system in which prefixes indicate the number of atoms present. These names have been used for so long that these more common names are usually used. Examples are listed in Table 4-7.

Table 4-7

Formulas and Common Names of Some Binary Molecular Compounds			
Formula	**Common Name**	**Formula**	**Common Name**
CS_2	carbon disulfide	SF_2	sulfur difluoride
CO	carbon monoxide	SF_4	sulfur tetrafluoride
CO_2	carbon dioxide	SF_6	sulfur hexafluoride
CCl_4	carbon tetrachloride	SO_2	sulfur dioxide
PBr_3	phosphorus tribromide	SO_3	sulfur trioxide
PBr_5	phosphorus pentabromide		

Some compounds have names ending in -ide and are not binary.

Not all compounds ending in -ide are binary. A few negative polyatomic ions also have names ending in -ide. Examples are OH^- (hydroxide), NH_2^- (amide), $N_2H_3^-$ (hydrazide), O_2^{2-} (peroxide), and CN^- (cyanide).

For naming compounds containing more than two elements, several rules apply. The simplest of these compounds are formed from one element and a polyatomic ion. These compounds are named in the same way as binary compounds. However, the ending of the polyatomic ion is not changed. An example is $AlPO_4$, which is named aluminum phosphate. Other examples are listed in Table 4-8.

In naming compounds containing polyatomic ions, the name of the polyatomic ion is not changed.

Polyatomic ions which contain oxygen (other than OH^-) have the ending *-ite* or *-ate*. Thus, H_2SO_4 is hydrogen sulf*ate* not hydrogen sulf*ide* which is H_2S, a binary compound.

BACKGROUND: The term *polyatomic ion* is used throughout this text in place of the term *radical*. We reserve the term radical for the free radical of organic chemistry.

Table 4-8

Formulas and Names for Some Compounds Containing Polyatomic Ions			
Formula	**Name**	**Formula**	**Name**
$AlAsO_4$	aluminum arsenate	$CuSO_4$	copper(II) sulfate
$(NH_4)_2SO_4$	ammonium sulfate	$Ni(OH)_2$	nickel(II) hydroxide
$Cr_2(C_2O_4)_3$	chromium(III) oxalate	$ZnCO_3$	zinc carbonate

Other rules for naming compounds and writing formulas will be discussed when the need arises. The names of the common acids, for example, do not normally follow these rules. Table 4-9 lists names and formulas for acids that you should memorize.

Table 4-9

Acids			
Formula	**Name**	**Formula**	**Name**
CH_3COOH	acetic	$H_2C_2O_4$	oxalic
H_2CO_3	carbonic	$HClO_4$	perchloric
HCl	hydrochloric	H_3PO_4	phosphoric
HNO_3	nitric	H_2SO_4	sulfuric

FIGURE 4-4. Sulfuric acid plants, such as the one shown here, produce large quantities of the acid. H_2SO_4 is used in the preparation of many other chemicals.

The names and formulas for acids commonly used in the lab should be memorized.

On a tonnage basis, sulfuric acid is the most important substance produced by the chemical industry. Almost twice as much H_2SO_4 is produced as the next largest chemical product. Two other acids produced in huge quantities are terephthalic acid, $C_6H_4(COOH)_2$, and adipic acid, $HOOC(CH_2)_4COOH$. Both are used in synthetic fiber production.

1. a. $CaCl_2$ f. $AlCl_3$
   b. $CaCO_3$ g. SiO_2
   c. NaCN   h. ZnI_2
   d. MgO   i. $CoCO_3$
   e. NaF   j. KH

2. a. barium chloride
   b. zinc nitrate
   c. cesium acetate
   d. hydrogen sulfide
   e. potassium carbonate
   f. iron(II) chloride
   g. aluminum nitrate
   h. ammonium acetate
   i. barium hydroxide
   j. copper(II) acetate

3. a. $CuCO_3$ f. $Ca(OH)_2$
   b. KOH   g. $Bi_2(SO_4)_3$
   c. CaI_2 h. $Mg_3(PO_4)_2$
   d. RbCN   i. $Hg(CN)_2$
   e. KF   j. $Ni_3(AsO_4)_2$

4. a. potassium chloride
   b. potassium bromide
   c. potassium iodide
   d. calcium nitrate
   e. mercury(II) iodide
   f. copper(II) nitrate
   g. phosphorus(V) oxide
   h. phosphorus(V) chloride
   i. sulfur(VI) fluoride
   j. phosphorus(III) chloride

5. a. KNO_3 f. $ZnSO_4$
   b. NaOH   g. Na_2S
   c. $Pb(NO_3)_2$ h. $FeCl_3$
   d. CH_3COOH i. $HClO_4$
   e. HCl   j. H_2SO_4

6. a. ammonium nitrate
   b. sodium sulfate
   c. sodium oxide
   d. acetic acid
   e. perchloric acid
   f. sodium phosphate
   g. ammonium chloride
   h. sodium chloride
   i. phosphoric acid
   j. nitric acid

PROBLEMS

1. Write the formula for each of the following compounds. Table A-3 of the Appendix contains additional oxidation states of some elements.
   a. calcium chloride
   b. calcium carbonate
   c. sodium cyanide
   d. magnesium oxide
   e. sodium fluoride
   f. aluminum chloride
   g. silicon(IV) oxide
   h. zinc iodide
   i. cobalt(II) carbonate
   j. potassium hydride

2. Write the name for each of the following compounds.
   a. $BaCl_2$
   b. $Zn(NO_3)_2$
   c. $CsCH_3COO$
   d. H_2S
   e. K_2CO_3
   f. $FeCl_2$
   g. $Al(NO_3)_3$
   h. NH_4CH_3COO
   i. $Ba(OH)_2$
   j. $Cu(CH_3COO)_2$

3. Write the formula for each of the following compounds.
   a. copper(II) carbonate
   b. potassium hydroxide
   c. calcium iodide
   d. rubidium cyanide
   e. potassium fluoride
   f. calcium hydroxide
   g. bismuth(III) sulfate
   h. magnesium phosphate
   i. mercury(II) cyanide
   j. nickel(II) arsenate

4. Write the name for each of the following compounds.
   a. KCl
   b. KBr
   c. KI
   d. $Ca(NO_3)_2$
   e. HgI_2
   f. $Cu(NO_3)_2$
   g. P_2O_5
   h. PCl_5
   i. SF_6
   j. PCl_3

5. Write the formula for each of the following compounds.
   a. potassium nitrate
   b. sodium hydroxide
   c. lead(II) nitrate
   d. acetic acid
   e. hydrochloric acid
   f. zinc sulfate
   g. sodium sulfide
   h. iron(III) chloride
   i. perchloric acid
   j. sulfuric acid

6. Write the name for each of the following compounds.
   a. NH_4NO_3
   b. Na_2SO_4
   c. Na_2O
   d. CH_3COOH
   e. $HClO_4$
   f. Na_3PO_4
   g. NH_4Cl
   h. NaCl
   i. H_3PO_4
   j. HNO_3

4:5 MOLECULAR AND EMPIRICAL FORMULAS

The formulas for compounds that exist as molecules are called **molecular formulas.** For instance, one compound of hydrogen and oxygen is hydrogen peroxide (H_2O_2). The formula H_2O_2 is a molecular formula because one molecule of hydrogen peroxide contains two atoms of hydrogen and two atoms of oxygen. However, there is another kind of formula chemists also use. The atomic ratio of hydrogen to oxygen in hydrogen peroxide is one to one. Therefore, the simplest formula that would indicate the ratio between hydrogen and oxygen is HO. This simplest formula is called an **empirical formula.** As another example, both benzene (C_6H_6) and ethyne (C_2H_2) have the same empirical formula, CH. Chemists can determine the empirical formula of an unknown substance through analysis. The empirical formula may then be used to help identify the molecular formula of the substance.

For many substances, the empirical formula is the only formula possible. We will discuss these substances later. Note that the molecular formula of the compound is always some whole-number multiple of the empirical formula. The actual calculation of empirical formulas will be presented in Chapter 5.

A molecular formula describes the composition of a molecule.

An empirical formula indicates the simplest whole-number ratio of atoms or ions in a compound.

A molecular formula is a whole number multiple of an empirical formula.

TYPE OF FORMULA	NAME	1-hexene	ethene
	Empirical formula	CH_2	CH_2
	Molecular formula	C_6H_{12}	C_2H_4
	Structural formula		
	Physical properties:	Colorless liquid	Colorless gas
		Molecular mass 84.16 amu	Molecular mass 28.05 amu
		Melting pt. 68–70°C	Melting pt. −169.2°C
		Boiling pt. 179°C	Boiling pt. −103.7 C

FIGURE 4-5. Hexene and ethene have the same empirical formula but different molecular formulas, structural formulas, and physical properties.

4:6 COEFFICIENTS

Coefficients are used to represent the number of formula units.

The formula of a compound represents a definite amount of that compound. This amount may be called a **formula unit.** It may be one molecule or the smallest number of particles giving the true proportions of the elements in the compound. One molecule of water is represented by H_2O. How do we represent two molecules of water? We use the same system as we would use in mathematics: coefficients. When we wish to represent two x, we write $2x$. When we wish to represent two molecules of water we write $2H_2O$. Three sodium ions combined with three chloride ions is represented as $3NaCl$. We will discuss the use of coefficients in Chapter 6.

7. a. CH_2O d. CH_4
   b. NO_2 e. HgI
   c. CH_3 f. C_4H_9
8. a. 1 formula unit of silver carbonate
   b. 3 formula units of thallium(I) bromide
   c. 2 formula units
   d. 4 formula units
   e. 6 formula units
   f. 5 formula units
   g. 3 formula units
   h. 3 formula units

PROBLEMS

7. Write the empirical formula for each of the following compounds.
   a. $C_6H_{12}O_6$ **d.** CH_4
   b. N_2O_4 **e.** Hg_2I_2
   c. C_2H_6 **f.** C_8H_{18}

8. Write the number of formula units represented by each of the following.
   a. Ag_2CO_3 **e.** $6Ba_3(AsO_4)_2$
   b. $3TlBr$ **f.** $5SnBr_4$
   c. $2Fe(NO_3)_2$ **g.** $3H_3PO_4$
   d. $4BiBr_3$ **h.** $3CH_3COOH$

BIOGRAPHY   Jons Jakob Berzelius (1779-1848)

Jons Jakob Berzelius was one of many medical doctors who became interested in chemistry and contributed greatly to its progress. His early studies rarely took him very far from his native Swedish village near Stockholm.

One of his endeavors included a 10-year analysis of some 2000 simple and compound materials to determine the proportions of their various elements.

He developed a system of nomenclature—our present system of symbols and formulas. He also discovered several new elements, including selenium, silicon, and thorium. Throughout his life, Berzelius served on national committees and commissions dealing with science, agriculture, and education in an effort to better the life of his fellow Swedes.

CAREERS AND CHEMISTRY

4:7 Scientific Writing and Illustrating

· The decisions that we must make as voters and consumers require us to have an understanding of science and technology. Only when a society understands the facts and issues can it make intelligent choices. Communicating the facts and issues is the function of the science journalist.

There are many people who have a strong interest in science and who also enjoy writing. Scientific journalism is a fascinating career for these people. There are a variety of career positions requiring a knowledge of science and the ability to use language in a clear and coherent manner.

Most major newspapers and magazines have one or more employees whose primary function is the reporting of scientific news. The chance to be an accredited press representative at a space shuttle launch or an international scientific exchange is an enviable position. However, a science reporter would probably spend most of his or her time investigating and reporting on local issues such as a source of pollution or a dramatic improvement in community health care facilities. Radio and television science journalists follow a similar pattern in their careers.

Another career for a science writer is in the field of technical writing. These people work for companies producing chemicals, instruments, or machinery, as well as large research foundations. New products and processes are usually accompanied by data sheets, instruction manuals, and maintenance and repair guides written by the company's technical writers. In these publications, it is important that ideas be conveyed clearly. Ambiguous directions could lead to legal problems for the company.

Government agencies such as the Department of Energy and the Food and Drug Administration employ a number of scientific writers.

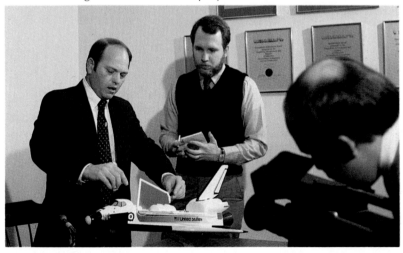

FIGURE 4-6. A career as a technical writer or photographer involves learning of new developments and breakthroughs as they are happening. The writer and photographer shown are interviewing a NASA representative.

These people may be involved in converting highly technical research data into a form that can be understood by the average person.

Professional organizations such as the American Chemical Society and trade associations such as the Chemical Manufacturers' Association produce journals and trade magazines. In addition, there are now a number of popular magazines concerned wholly or to a large extent with science. Most of these publications have a staff of science writers. Almost all of them will buy articles that are informative and well-written.

A free-lance writer earns a living by selling articles to publications. The advantage of free-lancing is being your own boss. The disadvantage is the difficulty in getting started. Writers may experience some lean economic times until well established.

The technical illustrator is another position tied to scientific publications. It combines the creative aspects of art with the technical aspects of science. The tasks performed by the technical illustrator are in some ways similar to those of a scientific writer. The technical illustrator must be able to present clear, accurate drawings to be used in instruction manuals, research reports, and as general information for the public in magazines and newspapers. As we saw in Chapter 1, many advances in research are based on the refinement of work published by another research team. The accurate communication of information through graphics is therefore vitally important.

The technical illustrator must have some knowledge or background in the subject being illustrated to do an accurate job. He or she must be aware of the reader's knowledge level to provide drawings that are understandable but, more importantly, scientifically accurate. An undergraduate degree in one of the sciences is generally a prerequisite.

FIGURE 4-7. The science illustrator combines a knowledge of science with creativity in producing highly technical drawings.

SUMMARY

1. A chemical symbol for an element represents one atom of that element when it appears in a formula. **4:1**
2. A chemical formula is a statement in chemical symbols of the composition of one formula unit of a compound. A subscript in a formula represents the relative number of atoms of an element in the compound. **4:2**
3. A polyatomic ion is a stable, charged group of atoms. **4:3**
4. The combining capacity of an atom or polyatomic ion is indicated by its oxidation number or charge. **4:3**
5. In chemical compounds, atoms combine in definite ratios. Their combined charges add to zero. **4:3**
6. A binary compound is composed of two elements. Its name is the name of the positive element followed by the name of the negative element modified to end in -ide. **4:4**
7. Some elements have more than one possible oxidation number. A compound containing such an element is named by showing the oxidation number as Roman numerals in parentheses after the element. **4:4**
8. A compound formed from one element and one polyatomic ion is named in the same way as a binary compound. However, the ending of the name of the polyatomic ion is not changed. **4:4**
9. A molecular formula shows the actual number of each kind of atom in one molecule of a compound. It is always a whole-number multiple of the empirical formula. **4:5**
10. An empirical formula represents the simplest whole-number ratio between atoms in a compound. **4:5**
11. A formula unit represents one molecule or the smallest number of particles giving the ratio of the elements in the compound. **4:6**
12. The coefficient of a formula indicates the number of molecules or the number of formula units of a nonmolecular substance. **4:6**

VOCABULARY

chemical symbols **4:1**	oxidation number **4:3**	molecular formulas **4:5**
chemical formula **4:2**	ionic compound **4:3**	empirical formula **4:5**
ions **4:3**	molecules **4:3**	formula unit **4:6**
polyatomic ion **4:3**	binary compounds **4:4**	

PROBLEMS

1. Define formula unit.
2. What elements exist as diatomic molecules?
3. Which of the following is not a binary compound?
   a. potassium chloride   c. calcium bromide
   b. magnesium hydroxide   d. carbon dioxide

1. the amount of a substance represented by the formula
2. H_2, N_2, O_2, F_2, Cl_2, Br_2, I_2
3. b. $Mg(OH)_2$

4. Roman numeral, copper(I) chloride, copper(II) chloride

5. the PO_4^{3-} ion occurs more than once in the formula

6. iron forms more than one compound with OH^- ion, $Fe(OH)_2$, $Fe(OH)_3$

8. a. sodium nitrate
   b. ammonium sulfate
   c. iron(III) nitrate
   d. sodium acetate
   e. barium selenide
   f. copper(II) sulfate

9. a. $RbCH_3COO$
   b. $CePO_4$
   c. $Ca_3(AsO_4)_2$
   d. $CuC_4H_4O_6$
   e. CrN
   f. $AgNO_3$

10. a. silver bromide
   b. cadmium phosphide
   c. cobalt(II) phosphate
   d. lithium hydride
   e. gallium(III) telluride
   f. mercury(II) chloride

11. a. $Mg(OH)_2$
   b. $Cd(OH)_2$
   c. $AgCH_3COO$
   d. $Mg(NO_3)_2$
   e. $Al_2(SO_4)_3$
   f. KCN

13. a. copper(II) selenide
   b. lead(II) cyanide
   c. magnesium hydride
   d. manganese(II) oxide
   e. aluminum carbide
   f. hydrogen chloride or hydrochloric acid

4. Copper forms two different compounds with the chloride ion, $CuCl$ and $CuCl_2$. In writing their names, how do we distinguish between them?

5. Why is it necessary to use parentheses in writing the formula for zinc phosphate?

6. Why is it necessary to use Roman numerals in writing the formula for iron(III) hydroxide?

7. Write the formula for each of the following compounds.

   a. iron(II) sulfate   a. $FeSO_4$ **d.** copper(I) chloride d. $CuCl$
   b. manganese(II) nitrate b. $Mn(NO_3)_2$ **e.** sodium oxalate   e. $Na_2C_2O_4$
   c. chromium(III) nitrate c. $Cr(NO_3)_3$ **f.** silver perchlorate   f. $AgClO_4$

8. Write the name for each of the following compounds.

   a. $NaNO_3$ **c.** $Fe(NO_3)_3$ **e.** BaSe
   b. $(NH_4)_2SO_4$ **d.** $NaCH_3COO$ **f.** $CuSO_4$

9. Write the formula for each of the following compounds.

   a. rubidium acetate   **d.** copper(II) tartrate
   b. cerium(III) phosphate   **e.** chromium(III) nitride
   c. calcium arsenate   **f.** silver nitrate

10. Write the name for each of the following compounds.

   a. AgBr   **c.** $Co_3(PO_4)_2$ **e.** Ga_2Te_3
   b. Cd_3P_2 **d.** LiH   **f.** $HgCl_2$

11. Write the formula for each of the following compounds.

   a. magnesium hydroxide   **d.** magnesium nitrate
   b. cadmium hydroxide   **e.** aluminum sulfate
   c. silver acetate   **f.** potassium cyanide

12. Write the formula for each of the following compounds.

   a. tin(IV) chloride   a. $SnCl_4$ **d.** ammonium sulfide d. $(NH_4)_2S$
   b. thorium(IV) fluoride b. ThF_4 **e.** cobalt(II) nitrate e. $Co(NO_3)_2$
   c. magnesium iodate   c. $Mg(IO_3)_2$ **f.** barium nitrate   f. $Ba(NO_3)_2$

13. Write the name for each of the following compounds.

   a. CuSe   **c.** MgH_2 **e.** Al_4C_3
   b. $Pb(CN)_2$ **d.** MnO   **f.** HCl

14. Write the formula for each of the following compounds.

   a. cadmium nitrate a. $Cd(NO_3)_2$ **d.** nickel(II) nitrate   d. $Ni(NO_3)_2$
   b. cobalt(II) nitrate b. $Co(NO_3)_2$ **e.** magnesium perchlorate   e. $Mg(ClO_4)_2$
   c. carbonic acid   c. H_2CO_3 **f.** nitric acid   f. HNO_3

15. Write the name for each of the following compounds.

   a. $Sr(NO_3)_2$ a. strontium nitrate **d.** HgF_2 d. mercury(II) fluoride
   b. CaC_2O_4 b. calcium oxalate   **e.** Li_2Se e. lithium selenide
   c. $H_2C_2O_4$ c. oxalic acid   **f.** HCl   f. hydrogen chloride or hydrochloric acid

16. Write the formula for each of the following compounds.

   a. cobalt(II) hydroxide a. $Co(OH)_2$ **d.** calcium oxide   d. CaO
   b. cesium carbonate   b. Cs_2CO_3 **e.** lithium acetate   e. $LiCH_3COO$
   c. magnesium carbonate   c. $MgCO_3$ **f.** zinc telluride   f. $ZnTe$

17. Write the name for each of the following compounds.

a. SrI_2

b. NH_4F

c. $BaSeO_4$

d. Ag_2S

e. $TlCH_3COO$

f. $(NH_4)_2Se$

18. Write the formula for each of the following compounds.

a. aluminum selenide

b. nickel(II) phosphate

c. calcium oxide

d. cobalt(II) perchlorate

e. magnesium hexafluorosilicate

f. barium perchlorate

19. Write the name for each of the following compounds.

a. $AlAsO_4$

b. $Cr_2(SO_4)_3$

c. $Hg(IO_3)_2$

d. $CdBr_2$

e. $CeCl_3$

f. Cs_2O

REVIEW

1. Classify each object or material as a heterogeneous mixture, solution, compound or element.

a. plastic garbage bag

b. automobile

c. seawater

d. hydrogen

e. maple syrup

f. newsprint

2. List the number of significant digits in each of the following measurements.

a. 0.558 g

b. 7.3 m

c. 410 cm

d. 0.0094 mg

e. 19.0000 g

f. 75.0 s

3. A student masses out 0.8320 grams of salt. Compute the relative error of this mass measurement if it is accurate to ±0.0001 g.

4. Express in scientific notation.

a. 0.955

b. 0.680

c. 53.5

d. 314

e. 0.0625

f. 2230

5. Express as whole numbers or decimals.

a. 7.33×10^7

b. 9.04×10^2

c. 7.73×10^4

d. 2.1×10^{-4}

e. 7.4×10^{-5}

f. 9.18×10^{-6}

6. Calculate the density of a material that has a mass of 7.13 grams and occupies a volume of 7.77 cm³.

ONE MORE STEP

1. Investigate the difference between compounds known as Daltonides and those known as Bertholides.

2. Look through the kitchen cabinet at home and find a product that lists ingredients. Using a chemical dictionary, handbook, or the Merck Index, find the formula for each ingredient.

3. The formula for benzoic acid is C_6H_5COOH. Try to draw a structure for it.

READINGS

Orna, Mary V., "On Naming the Elements with Atomic Numbers Greater than 100," *Journal of Chemical Education*, Vol. 59, No. 2(February 1982), p. 123.

17. a. strontium iodide
b. ammonium fluoride
c. barium selenate
d. silver sulfide
e. thallium(I) acetate
f. ammonium selenide
18. a. Al_2Se_3
b. $Ni_3(PO_4)_2$
c. CaO
d. $Co(ClO_4)_2$
e. $MgSiF_6$
f. $Ba(ClO_4)_2$
19. a. aluminum arsenate
b. chromium(III) sulfate
c. mercury(II) iodate
d. cadmium bromide
e. cerium(III) chloride
f. cesium oxide
1. a. compound
b. heterogeneous mixture
c. solution
d. element
e. solution
f. heterogeneous mixture
2. a. 3   **d.** 2
b. 2   **e.** 6
c. 2   **f.** 3
3. 1×10^{-4}
4. a. 9.55×10^{-1}
b. 6.80×10^{-1}
c. 5.35×10^1
d. 3.14×10^2
e. 6.25×10^{-2}
f. 2.23×10^3
5. a. 73 300 000
b. 904
c. 77 300
d. 0.000 21
e. 0.000 074
f. 0.000 009 18
6. 0.918 g/cm³

The Great Pyramid is a symbol of human ingenuity. The pyramid contains over 2 million stone blocks each having an average mass of 2300 kilograms. It stands 137 meters high with a base covering 50 000 square meters. In comparison, consider a diamond chip having a mass of 1 gram. This chip contains over 5×10^{23} carbon atoms. Think of the difficulty a chemist encounters in building molecules from single atoms. It is much more practical to work with a large amount as a single unit. The mole is a chemist's counting unit. What number of objects does a mole represent? Why was this particular number selected to represent a mole?

THE MOLE

GOALS:
- You will calculate molecular and formula mass.
- You will define the mole.
- You will use your knowledge of the mole in calculations of chemical formulas, solution concentration, and hydrates.

Chapter 5 introduces the mole and the use of this concept in manipulating formulas. Students are expected to set up and solve quantitative problems.

DEMONSTRATION: Place some $CuSO_4 \cdot 5H_2O$ in a large test tube. Heat it over a flame until the blue color disappears. Place the white anhydrous $CuSO_4$ on a watch glass and add H_2O from a dropper. **CAUTION:** *exothermic.* Discuss how quantitative information can be used to completely describe our observations.

SUGGESTION: Point out that elements can have formulas such as I_2, S_8, and P_4.

Chemical symbols and formulas (such as H and H_2O) are shorthand signs for chemical elements and compounds. The symbol of an element may represent one atom of the element. The formula of a compound may represent one molecule or one formula unit of the compound. Symbols and formulas may also represent a group of atoms or formula units. Since atoms are so very small, chemists deal with large groups of atoms. This chapter is about a group called a mole, containing a specific number of units.

5:1 MOLECULAR AND FORMULA MASS

The masses of the atoms are compared by using the atomic mass scale. This scale has the **"atomic mass unit" (u)** as a standard. The atomic mass unit is often called a dalton (dal) by biochemists. The source of this standard will be discussed in Chapter 7. A list of atomic masses for the elements is found on the inside back cover of this book.

The atomic mass of hydrogen in atomic mass units is 1, and the atomic mass of oxygen is 16. Therefore, the total mass of a water molecule, H_2O, is $1 + 1 + 16$, or 18 u. If the atomic masses of all the atoms in a molecule are added, the sum is the mass of that molecule. Such a mass is called a **molecular mass.** This name is incorrect when applied to an ionic substance. Sodium chloride, NaCl, is an ionic substance that does not exist in molecular form. A better name for the mass of ionic substances is formula mass. The sum of the atomic masses of all atoms in the formula unit of an ionic compound is called the **formula mass.** To calculate a formula mass add the masses of all the atoms in the formula.

The atomic mass unit is used to compare masses of atoms.

The data in the atomic mass table gives relative masses of the elements.

Molecular mass is the sum of the atomic masses of the atoms in the molecule.

Formula mass is the sum of the atomic masses of the atoms in a formula unit.

BACKGROUND: The IUPAC recommends the use of the unit symbol u for atomic mass unit.

EXAMPLE: Molecular Mass

Find the formula mass of 2,3-butanedione, $C_4H_6O_2$.

Solving Process:

Add the atomic masses of all the atoms in the $C_4H_6O_2$ formula unit.

4 C atoms	$4 \times 12.0 = 48.0$ u
6 H atoms	$6 \times 1.0 \ = \ 6.0$ u
2 O atoms	$2 \times 16.0 = \underline{32.0 \text{ u}}$
formula mass of $C_4H_6O_2$	86.0 u

EXAMPLE: Formula Mass

Find the formula mass of calcium nitrate, $Ca(NO_3)_2$.

Solving Process:

Add the atomic masses of all the atoms in the $Ca(NO_3)_2$ formula unit. Remember that the subscript applies to the entire polyatomic ion.

1 Ca atom	$1 \times 40 = 40$ u
2 N atoms	$2 \times 14 = 28$ u
6 O atoms	$6 \times 16 = \underline{96 \text{ u}}$
formula mass of $Ca(NO_3)_2$	164 u

Use atomic masses that will ensure three significant digits in the result. Thus, to obtain the formula mass of NaCl, use values rounded to tenths: $23.0 + 35.5 = 58.5$. For H_2, use values rounded to hundredths: $1.01 + 1.01 = 2.02$.

PROBLEM

1. a. 30.1 u   h. 110 u
   b. 136 u   i. 380 u
   c. 193 u   j. 58.1 u
   d. 424 u   k. 899 u
   e. 310 u   l. 32.0 u
   f. 484 u   m. 342 u
   g. 266 u   n. 60.1 u

1. Calculate the molecular or formula masses of the following compounds.

   a. C_2H_6
   b. KH_2PO_4
   c. TaC
   d. $Th(SO_4)_2$
   e. $Ca_3(PO_4)_2$
   f. $Na_2Al_2(SO_4)_4$
   g. $TlNO_3$

   h. K_2S
   i. $CeBr_3$
   j. CH_2CHCH_2OH *(propenol)*
   k. $Pb_3(AsO_4)_2$
   l. CH_3OH *(methanol)*
   m. $C_{12}H_{22}O_{11}$ *(sucrose)*
   n. $CH_3CH_2CH_2OH$ *(propanol)*

5:2 AVOGADRO'S NUMBER

Chemists do not deal with amounts of substances by counting out atoms or molecules. Rather, they mass quantities of substances. Thus, it is important to obtain a relation between mass and number of particles.

$7 \times 4 = 28$ $2 \times 14 = 28$

FIGURE 5-1. If it were possible to mass single atoms, the mass of two nitrogen atoms would equal the mass of seven helium atoms. Thus, the mass ratio of nitrogen to helium is 7 to 2.

There is a problem in using the molecular masses of substances. Molecular masses are in atomic mass units. An atomic mass unit is only 1.66×10^{-24} gram. The mass of a single molecule is so small that it is impossible to measure in the laboratory. For everyday use in chemistry, a larger unit, such as a gram, is needed.

One helium atom has a mass of 4 u, and one nitrogen atom has a mass of 14 u. The ratio of the mass of one helium atom to one nitrogen atom is 4 to 14, or 2 to 7. Let us compare the mass of two helium atoms to that of two nitrogen atoms. The ratio would be 2×4 to 2×14, or 2 to 7. If we compare the mass of 10 atoms of each element, we will still get a 2 to 7 ratio. No matter what number of atoms we compare, equal numbers of helium and nitrogen atoms will have a mass ratio of 2 to 7. In other words, the numbers in the atomic mass table give us the relative masses of the atoms of the elements.

The laboratory unit of mass you will use is the gram. We would like to choose a number of atoms that would have a mass in grams equivalent to the mass of one atom in atomic mass units. The same number would fit all elements, because equal numbers of different atoms always have the same mass ratio. Chemists have found that 6.02×10^{23} atoms of an element have a mass in grams equivalent to the mass of one atom in u. For example, one atom of hydrogen has a mass of 1.0079 u; 6.02×10^{23} atoms of hydrogen have a mass of 1.0079 g. This number, **6.02×10^{23}** is called **Avogadro's number** in honor of a 19th century Italian scientist.

The mass of one atom of H is 1.0079 u. The mass of 6.02×10^{23} atoms of H is 1.0079 g.

5:3 THE MOLE

Avogadro's number is an accepted SI standard. We may add it to the others we have studied: the kilogram, the meter, the second, and the kelvin. The symbol used to represent Avogadro's number is N_A. This quantity can be expressed as $6.022\ 05 \times 10^{23}$ to be more precise. This number of things is called one **mole (mol)** of the things. Recall that the mole is an SI base unit representing the chemical quantity of substance.

SUGGESTION: The concept of a mole is central in chemistry. Emphasize its importance and give sufficient time for the students to comprehend fully the idea.

Sulfur
(element)

Potassium dichromate
(compound)

Graphite
(macromolecule)

a

b

c

32 grams

294 grams

12 grams

FIGURE 5-2. One mole of sulfur (a), potassium dichromate (b), and graphite (c) has a mass in grams which equals the mass of a single particle of each substance. Each amount shown here contains 6.02×10^{23} particles for that substance.

One mole of particles (atoms, ions, molecules) has a mass in grams equivalent to that of one particle in atomic mass units. Thus, if a mole of any particle has a mass of 4.02 grams, then a single particle has a mass of 4.02 u. In the same manner, if a single particle has a mass of 54.03 u, then a mole of particles will have a mass of 54.03 grams.

N_A is a number that has been experimentally determined. If a mole of iodine molecules is inspected by X-ray diffraction, the actual number of I_2 molecules can be determined. This number has been found to be 6.02×10^{23} molecules. Avogadro's number has also been determined by the scattering of light, by use of radioactive materials, and by Millikan's oil drop experiment which is covered in Chapter 7.

For our purposes, Avogadro's number (N_A) = 6.02×10^{23}.

It is important to note that *one mole of atoms contains 6.02×10^{23} atoms. One mole of molecules contains 6.02×10^{23} molecules. One mole of formula units contains 6.02×10^{23} formula units. One mole of ions contains 6.02×10^{23} ions.* N_A, therefore, can have any of these units.

Avogadro's number (N_A) of anything is a mole of those things.

$$\frac{molecules}{mole} \quad or \quad \frac{atoms}{mole} \quad or \quad \frac{ions}{mole} \quad or \quad \frac{formula\ units}{mole}$$

EXAMPLE: Conversion to Moles

How many moles are represented by 11.5 g of C_2H_5OH? Use the factor-label method.

Solving Process:
We have grams, we wish to convert to moles. Using the atomic mass table on the inside back cover, we see that one mole of C_2H_5OH has a mass of 46.1 g. Therefore,

$$1\ mol = 46.1\ g \quad or \quad \frac{1\ mol}{46.1\ g} = 1$$

$$\frac{11.5\ \cancel{g\ C_2H_5OH}}{} \left| \frac{1\ mol\ C_2H_5OH}{46.1\ \cancel{g\ C_2H_5OH}} \right. = 0.249\ mol\ C_2H_5OH$$

EXAMPLE: Conversion to Moles and Grams

1.20×10^{25} molecules of NH_3 will be how many moles? What mass is this number of molecules?

Solving Process:

(a) We have molecules and wish to convert to moles. One mole equals 6.02×10^{23} molecules. Use the ratio

$$\frac{1 \text{ mol}}{6.02 \times 10^{23} \text{ molecules}}$$

$$\frac{1.20 \times 10^{25} \text{ molecules } NH_3}{} \quad \left| \quad \frac{1 \text{ mol}}{6.02 \times 10^{23} \text{ molecules}} \right. = 1.99 \times 10^2 \text{ mol}$$

$$= 19.9 \text{ mol}$$

(b) Using the table on the inside back cover, the molecular mass of NH_3 is calculated to be 17.0 g. Use

$$\frac{17.0 \text{ g } NH_3}{1 \text{ mol } NH_3}$$

$$\frac{19.9 \text{ mol } NH_3}{} \quad \left| \quad \frac{17.0 \text{ g } NH_3}{1 \text{ mol } NH_3} \right. = 338 \text{ g of } NH_3$$

EXAMPLE: Conversion to Atoms

How many atoms are in a 10.0 g sample of calcium metal?

Solving Process:

1 formula mass of calcium is 40.1. Therefore, use the ratios

$$\frac{1 \text{ mol Ca}}{40.1 \text{ g Ca}} \quad \text{and} \quad \frac{6.02 \times 10^{23} \text{ atoms}}{1 \text{ mol}}$$

$$\frac{10.0 \text{ g Ca}}{} \quad \left| \quad \frac{1 \text{ mol Ca}}{40.1 \text{ g Ca}} \quad \right| \quad \frac{6.02 \times 10^{23} \text{ atoms}}{1 \text{ mol}} = 1.50 \times 10^{23} \text{ atoms}$$

PROBLEMS

Make the following conversions.

2. 7.74×10^{26} formula units of TlI to moles

3. 0.943 mole H_2O to molecules

4. 50.4 g $CaBr_2$ to moles

5. 91.9 g Ag_2Te to formula units

6. 6.63×10^{23} formula units of $Mg(CH_3COO)_2$ to grams

7. 0.638 moles $Ce_2(CO_3)_3$ to grams

8. 6.77×10^{24} formula units $Ca(ClO_4)_2$ to moles

9. 53.1 g HBr to moles

10. 4.06 moles SiH_4 to molecules

2. 1.29×10^3 mol TlI
3. 5.68×10^{23} molecules H_2O
4. 0.252 mol $CaBr_2$
5. 1.61×10^{23} formula units
6. 156 g
7. 293 g
8. 11.2 mol
9. 0.656 mol
10. 2.44×10^{24} molecules

The SI unit of volume is the cubic meter (m^3). Although liquid volume is often expressed in liters this unit is not SI. 1 L = 1 dm. Thus, cubic decimeter (dm^3) is used throughout the text.

$$M = \frac{\text{mol of solute}}{dm^3 \text{ of solution}}$$

For a known molarity, a measurement of volume is a measure of the number of particles.

BACKGROUND: A 1 formal (1F) solution contains one gram-formula mass of solute per dm^3 of solution. Some references reserve the term molar for solutions of substances which actually occur as molecules (sugar). We will not use the term formal.

a

36.2% O   33.3% Ni

27.1% C

3.4% H

b

64.1% Pb

19.8% O

16.1% Cr

FIGURE 5-3. The graph shows the percentages of each element present in the compounds nickel(II) acetate (a) and lead(II) chromate (b).

5:4 MOLES IN SOLUTION

Most chemical reactions take place in solution. There are several methods of expressing the relationship between the dissolved substance and the solution. The method most often used by chemists is molarity (M). **Molarity** is the ratio between the moles of dissolved substance and the volume of solution in cubic decimeters. Remember that 1 dm^3 = 1 L = 1000 cm^3. A one-molar (1M) solution of nitric acid contains one mole of nitric acid molecules in one dm^3 of solution. A 0.372M solution of $Ba(NO_3)_2$ contains 0.372 moles of $Ba(NO_3)_2$ in 1 dm^3 of solution.

Assume that you wish to try a reaction using 0.1 mole of glucose ($C_6H_{12}O_6$). If the solution of glucose in your laboratory is 1M, then 0.1 mole would be contained in 0.1 dm^3, or 100 cm^3 of solution. You can see that expressing the composition of solutions in units of molarity is a convenient way of measuring a number of particles.

It is important to be able to compute the molarity of solutions if you are given their composition. It is also important to be able to compute the amount of substance you need to produce a specific solution. You will be using these calculations in your laboratory work and later in solving problems in this book.

EXAMPLE: Molarity

What is the molarity of 2.50×10^2 cm^3 of solution containing 9.46 g CsBr, cesium bromide?

Solving Process:
The units of molarity are moles of substance per (divided by) dm^3 of solution. Thus, to obtain molarity we must divide the substance, expressed in moles, by the solution, expressed in dm^3. The table on the inside back cover can be used to determine the formula mass of cesium bromide.

$$\frac{9.46 \text{ g CsBr}}{} \; \left| \; \frac{1 \text{ mol CsBr}}{213 \text{ g CsBr}} \right. = 0.0444 \text{ mol CsBr}$$

$$\frac{2.50 \times 10^2 \text{ cm}^3}{} \; \left| \; \frac{1 \text{ dm}^3}{1000 \text{ cm}^3} \right. = 0.250 \text{ dm}^3$$

$$\frac{0.0444 \text{ mol CsBr}}{0.250 \text{ dm}^3} = 0.178M \text{ CsBr}$$

To save time and to reduce the chance for error, these calculations can be combined in one continuous chain. Note that the factors are arranged to yield an answer in mol/dm^3, which is molarity.

$$\frac{9.46 \text{ g CsBr}}{2.50 \times 10^2 \text{ cm}^3} \; \left| \; \frac{1 \text{ mol CsBr}}{213 \text{ g CsBr}} \right. \; \left| \; \frac{1000 \text{ cm}^3}{1 \text{ dm}^3} \right. = 0.178M \text{ CsBr}$$

EXAMPLE: Making a Solution

How would you make 5.00×10^2 cm^3 of a 0.133M solution of MnSeO$_4$, manganese(II) selenate?

Solving Process:
First, use the given quantity of solution, 5.00×10^2 cm^3, to find the part of a dm^3 desired. Then use the molarity to convert from solution to moles of substance. Finally, convert the moles of substance to grams.

$$\frac{5.00 \times 10^2 \text{ cm}^3}{} \left| \frac{1 \text{ dm}^3}{1000 \text{ cm}^3} \right| \frac{0.133 \text{ mol MnSeO}_4}{1 \text{ dm}^3} \left| \frac{198 \text{ g MnSeO}_4}{1 \text{ mol MnSeO}_4} \right. = 13.2 \text{ g MnSeO}_4$$

To make the solution, then, you would dissolve 13.2 g MnSeO$_4$ in sufficient water to make 5.00×10^2 cm^3 of solution.

PROBLEMS

Compute the molarity of the following solutions.
11. 89.7 g (NH$_4$)$_2$C$_4$H$_4$O$_6$ in 5.00×10^2 cm^3 of solution
12. 9.94 g CoSO$_4$ in 2.50×10^2 cm^3 of solution
13. 5.23 g Fe(NO$_3$)$_2$ in 100.0 cm^3 of solution
14. 44.3 g Pb(ClO$_4$)$_2$ in 200.0 cm^3 of solution
15. 8.55 g MnSiF$_6$ in 50.0 cm^3 of solution

Describe the preparation of the following solutions.
16. 1.000×10^3 cm^3 of 3.00M NiCl$_2$
17. 2.50×10^2 cm^3 of 4.00M RbOH
18. 5.00×10^2 cm^3 of 1.50M AgF
19. 2.50×10^2 cm^3 of 0.500M SrSiF$_6$
20. 2.50×10^2 cm^3 of 0.002 00M Tl$_2$CO$_3$

11. 0.975M
12. 0.257M
13. 0.291M
14. 0.546M
15. 0.868M
16. Dissolve 390 g NiCl$_2$ in enough water to make 1000 cm^3 of solution.
17. Dissolve 103 g RbOH in enough H$_2$O to make 250 cm^3 of solution.
18. Dissolve 95.3 g
19. Dissolve 28.8 g
20. Dissolve 0.234 g

5:5   PERCENTAGE COMPOSITION

A chemist often compares the percentage composition of an unknown compound with the percentage composition calculated from an assumed formula. If the percentages agree it will help confirm the identity of the unknown. *The percentage of the total mass of a compound contributed by an element is the percentage of that element in the compound.* Consider the percentage composition of the following substances: copper, sodium chloride, and ethanol. For copper, the percentage composition is 100 percent Cu because it is composed of a single element. Salt is composed of two elements, sodium and chlorine. We know they are always present in the same ratio by mass. The ratio in which they are present is the ratio of their atomic masses. Therefore, the percentage of

Percentage composition may be used in the identification of some compounds.

Total percent of all elements in a compound equals 100%.

sodium in any sample of sodium chloride would be the atomic mass of the element divided by the formula mass and multiplied by 100.

$$\frac{\text{mass Na}}{\text{mass NaCl}} \times 100 = \frac{23.0 \text{ u}}{(23.0 + 35.5) \text{ u}} \times 100 = 39.4\%$$

Consider a compound such as ethanol where more than one atom of an element appears. The formula for ethanol is C_2H_5OH and its molecular mass is 46.1 u. It can be seen that one ethanol molecule contains two carbon atoms with a combined atomic mass of 24.0 u. Therefore, the percentage of carbon in the compound is

$$\frac{\text{mass 2C}}{\text{mass C}_2\text{H}_5\text{OH}} \times 100 = \frac{24.0 \text{ u}}{46.1 \text{u}} \times 100 = 52.1\%$$

The percentage of hydrogen is $(6.05 \text{ u}/46.1 \text{ u}) \times 100$, and that of oxygen is $(16.0 \text{ u}/46.1 \text{ u}) \times 100$. The three percentages should add to 100%. Often, because we round off answers, we may find that the percentages total one or two-tenths more or less than 100%.

EXAMPLE: Percentage Composition

Find the percentage composition of aluminum sulfate.

Solving Process:
The formula for aluminum sulfate is $Al_2(SO_4)_3$. The formula mass is

2 Al atoms	$2 \times 27.0 =$	54.0 u
3 S atoms	$3 \times 32.0 =$	96.3 u
12 O atoms	$12 \times 16 =$	192 u
		342 u

The percentage of Al is $\dfrac{\text{mass 2Al}}{\text{mass Al}_2(\text{SO}_4)_3} \times 100 = \dfrac{54.0 \text{ u}}{342 \text{ u}} \times 100 = 15.8\%$

The percentage of S is $\dfrac{\text{mass 3S}}{\text{mass Al}_2(\text{SO}_4)_3} \times 100 = \dfrac{96.3 \text{ u}}{342 \text{ u}} \times 100 = 28.2\%$

The percentage of O is $\dfrac{\text{mass 12O}}{\text{mass Al}_2(\text{SO}_4)_3} \times 100 = \dfrac{192 \text{ u}}{342 \text{ u}} \times 100 = 56.1\%$

PROBLEMS

Find the percentage composition of the following.

21. CsF
22. NiI_2
23. Bi_2O_3
24. CuC_2O_4
25. $TlIO_3$
26. ThO_2
27. $Co_3(AsO_4)_2$
28. BaTe
29. $ZnSiO_3$
30. CdF_2
31. LaF_3
32. $Sc(NO_3)_3$

21. Cs = 87.5%
    F = 12.5%
22. Ni = 18.8%
    I = 81.2%
23. Bi = 89.7%
    O = 10.3%
24. 41.8%, 15.8%, 42.1%
25. 53.8%, 33.5%, 12.7%
26. 87.9%, 12.1%
27. 38.9%, 33.0%, 28.1%
28. 51.7%, 48.3%
29. 46.1%, 19.8%, 33.8%
30. 74.7%, 25.3%
31. 70.9%, 29.1%
32. 19.5%, 18.2%, 62.3%

5:6 EMPIRICAL FORMULAS

Using experimental data we can find the empirical formula for a substance. We need know only the mass of each element in the laboratory sample. Elements are made of atoms, and compounds are made of elements. Half an atom does not exist. Therefore, we can state that the elements in a compound combine in simple whole-number ratios, such as 1 to 1, 1 to 2, 2 to 3, and so on. If the atoms of the elements are present in simple ratios, then the moles of atoms for each element in the substance will also be in small whole number ratios.

Consider the following example. We find a 2.50 gram sample of a certain substance contains 0.900 gram of calcium and 1.60 grams of chlorine. The substance is composed of only two elements. We can calculate the number of moles of calcium and the number of moles of chlorine in the compound. Then, we can find the ratio of the number of moles of calcium atoms to the number of moles of chlorine atoms. From this ratio, we can find the **empirical formula,** which is the simplest ratio of atoms in a compound.

Elements in compounds combine in simple whole-number ratios.

An empirical formula is the simplest ratio of the atoms in a compound.

EXAMPLE: Empirical Formula

What is the empirical formula for a compound if a 2.50-g sample contains 0.900 g of calcium and 1.60 g of chlorine?

Solving Process:

(a) We must determine the number of moles of each element in the compound. Calcium in the sample has a mass of 0.900 g, and the atomic mass of Ca is 40.1 g. Chlorine in the sample has a mass of 1.60 g, and the atomic mass of Cl is 35.5 g. The sample contains

$$\frac{0.900 \text{ g Ca}}{} \left| \frac{1 \text{ mol Ca}}{40.1 \text{ g Ca}} \right. = 0.0224 \text{ mol of Ca}$$

$$\frac{1.60 \text{ g Cl}}{} \left| \frac{1 \text{ mol Cl}}{35.5 \text{ g Cl}} \right. = 0.0451 \text{ mol of Cl}$$

(b) To obtain the simplest ratio, divide both numbers of moles by the smaller one (0.0224). We get 1.00 and 2.01. Since we know the ratio must be in whole numbers, we round off to 1 to 2. This calculation shows that for each mole of calcium, there are 2 moles of chlorine. The empirical formula is $CaCl_2$. We can also calculate empirical formulas from percentage composition.

EXAMPLE: Empirical Formula from Percentage Composition

A compound has a percentage composition of 40.0% carbon, 6.71% hydrogen, and 53.3% oxygen. What is the empirical formula?

The ratio of moles is the same as the ratio of atoms for a given formula unit because there are exactly N_A atoms in one mole of any element.

SUGGESTION: Point out that any mass could be used: 45 g, 93.7 g, or any other. We use 100 g to simplify arithmetic.

Solving Process:

We know that every sample of the compound, no matter how small or how large, will have this composition. To calculate the ratio of moles of these elements, we assume a convenient amount of compound, usually 100 g. Then the percentages of the elements have the same numerical value in grams. In the present example, we would find 40.0 g of carbon, 6.71 g of hydrogen, and 53.3 g of oxygen in a 100-g sample. We then change the quantities to moles.

$$\frac{40.0 \text{ g C}}{} \left| \frac{1 \text{ mol C}}{12.0 \text{ g C}} \right. = 3.33 \text{ mol of carbon}$$

$$\frac{6.71 \text{ g H}}{} \left| \frac{1 \text{ mol H}}{1.01 \text{ g H}} \right. = 6.64 \text{ mol of hydrogen}$$

$$\frac{53.3 \text{ g O}}{} \left| \frac{1 \text{ mol O}}{16.0 \text{ g O}} \right. = 3.33 \text{ mol of oxygen}$$

Dividing each result by 3.33, we get 1 to 1.99 to 1. We round off to 1 to 2 to 1. Thus, the empirical formula is CH_2O.

Sometimes dividing by the smallest number of moles does not yield a ratio close to a whole number. In these cases another step is needed, as shown in the following example.

EXAMPLE: Empirical Formula

To determine an empirical formula, change grams to moles and find the ratio of the moles.

What is the empirical formula of a compound that is 66.0% Ca and 34.0% P?

Solving Process:

Assume a 100-g sample so that we have 66.0 g Ca and 34.0 g P. Convert these quantities to moles of atoms.

$$\frac{66.0 \text{ g Ca}}{} \left| \frac{1 \text{ mol Ca}}{40.1 \text{ g Ca}} \right. = 1.65 \text{ mol Ca}$$

$$\frac{34.0 \text{ g P}}{} \left| \frac{1 \text{ mol P}}{31.0 \text{ g P}} \right. = 1.10 \text{ mol P}$$

Dividing both results by 1.10, we obtain 1.50 to 1. This result is not close to a whole number. Substituting the fractional form of 1.5, we get ½. That ratio is 3 to 2. Thus, the ratio of Ca atoms to P atoms is 3 to 2 and the empirical formula is Ca_3P_2.

Suppose we have an empirical formula problem that produces a ratio of 2.33 to 1. What is the correct whole number ratio? We can say 2.33 ≈ 2⅓. Since 2⅓ is ⅞, the ratio is 7 to 3.

PROBLEMS

33. CeI₃
34. Al₂S₃

Find the empirical formulas of the following compounds.

33. 1.67 g Ce, 4.54 g I   **34.** 77.9 g Al, 139 g S

35. 4.04 g Cs, 1.08 g Cl   **37.** 4.73 g Sc, 2.52 g O

36. 9.11 g Ni, 5.89 g F

35. CsCl
36. NiF$_2$
37. Sc$_2$O$_3$

5:7 MOLECULAR FORMULAS

We have, thus far, calculated empirical formulas from experimental data. In order to calculate a molecular formula, we need one additional piece of data, the molecular mass. In one of the examples in the previous section, the empirical formula calculated was CH_2O. If we know that the molecular mass of the compound is 180, how can we find the molecular formula? The **molecular formula** shows the actual number of atoms of each element in a molecule, as well as the ratio of atoms. Knowing that the elements will always be present in the ratio 1:2:1, we can calculate the mass of the empirical formula. Then we can find the number of these empirical units present in one molecular formula. In the substance CH_2O, the empirical unit has a formula mass of

Molecular mass is a whole number multiple of the empirical formula mass.

$$12.0 + 2(1.01) + 16.0 = 30.0$$

It will, therefore, take six of these units to equal 180 or one molecular formula. Thus, the molecular formula is $C_6H_{12}O_6$.

PROBLEMS

38. The molecular mass of benzene is 78.0 and its empirical formula is CH. What is the molecular formula for benzene?

39. What is the molecular formula of dichloroacetic acid, if the empirical formula is CHOCl and the molecular mass is 129?

40. What is the molecular formula of cyanuric chloride, if the empirical formula is CClN and the molecular mass is 184.5?

41. Find the molecular formula for a compound with percentage composition 85.6% C, 14.5% H, and molecular mass 42.1.

42. Aspirin contains 60.0% carbon, 4.48% hydrogen, and 35.5% oxygen. It has a molecular mass of 180. What are its empirical and molecular formulas?

38. C$_6$H$_6$
39. C$_2$H$_2$O$_2$Cl$_2$
40. C$_3$Cl$_3$N$_3$
41. C$_3$H$_6$
42. C$_9$H$_8$O$_4$; C$_9$H$_8$O$_4$

5:8 HYDRATES

There are many compounds that crystallize from a water solution with water molecules adhering to the particles of the crystal. These **hydrates,** as they are called, usually contain a specific ratio of water to compound. Chemists use heat to dry these compounds and then calculate the ratio of compound to water. An example of a hydrate is $NiSO_3 \cdot 6H_2O$. The dot shows that 6 molecules of water adhere to 1 formula unit. To calculate the formula mass, we add the formula mass of the compound and water. For $NiSO_3$ we obtain 139. We multiply the 18.0 for water by 6 and add to the 139. The formula mass of $NiSO_3 \cdot 6H_2O$ is then 139 + 6(18.0), or 247.

Hydrates are crystals which contain water molecules.

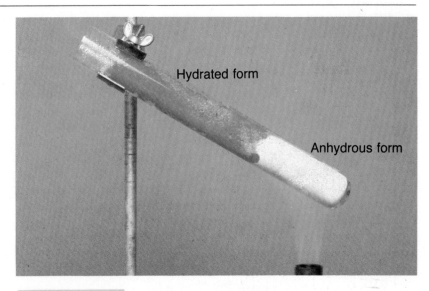

Hydrated form

Anhydrous form

FIGURE 5-4. The difference in color between the anhydrous and hydrated forms of a compound is shown. Heating drives off water molecules which causes the color change.

EXAMPLE: Hydrate Calculation

We have a 10.407 g sample of hydrated barium iodide. The sample is heated to drive off the water. The dry sample has a mass of 9.520 g. What is the ratio between barium iodide, BaI_2, and water, H_2O? What is the formula of the hydrate?

Solving Process:

The difference between the initial mass and that of the dry sample is the mass of water that was driven off.

$$10.407 - 9.520 = 0.887 \text{ g}$$

The mass of water and mass of dry BaI_2 are converted to moles.

$$\frac{9.520 \text{ g } BaI_2}{} \left| \frac{1 \text{ mol } BaI_2}{391 \text{ g } BaI_2} \right. = 0.0243 \text{ mol } BaI_2$$

$$\frac{0.887 \text{ g } H_2O}{} \left| \frac{1 \text{ mol } H_2O}{18.0 \text{ g } H_2O} \right. = 0.0493 \text{ mol } H_2O$$

The ratio between BaI_2 and H_2O is seen to be 1 to 2. The formula for the hydrate is written as $BaI_2 \cdot 2H_2O$.

PROBLEMS

Find the formulas for the following hydrates.

43. 0.391 g Li_2SiF_6, 0.0903 g H_2O

44. 0.737 g $MgSO_3$, 0.763 g H_2O

45. 95.3 g $LiNO_3$, 74.7 g H_2O

46. 76.9% $CaSO_3$, 23.1% H_2O

47. 89.2% $BaBr_2$, 10.8% H_2O

43. $Li_2SiF_6 \cdot 2H_2O$
44. $MgSO_3 \cdot 6H_2O$
45. $LiNO_3 \cdot 3H_2O$
46. $CaSO_3 \cdot 2H_2O$
47. $BaBr_2 \cdot 2H_2O$

BIOGRAPHY   *Stanislao Cannizzaro (1826-1910)*

As a pioneer in the development of modern atomic theory, Stanislao Cannizzaro insisted on the distinction between molecular and atomic masses. He determined atomic masses of elements in volatile compounds from the molecular masses of those compounds. He also found atomic masses of elements from a knowledge of their specific heat capacities.

Cannizzaro was devoted to organic chemistry, particularly the study of compounds containing a benzene ring. Cannizzaro's investigations were interrupted many times because of his political interests. In 1848, he became involved in a Sicilian revolution and was forced to flee to Paris. He returned to Italy and was eventually elected vice president of the senate.

TECHNOLOGY AND CHEMISTRY

5:9   Computers in Chemistry

The chemical laboratory has been revolutionized by the computer, as have many other areas of our lives. Not long ago, the analytical laboratory looked similar to your school chemistry lab. Analytical chemists used much of the same equipment that you use in lab. Today, much of the apparatus in an analytical laboratory is electronically operated and controlled by microprocessors. A microprocessor is similar to the "works" of your hand-held calculator. However, the microprocessor has been programmed to do a specific job: run an analytical instrument and record and process data.

Some microprocessors have been programmed to perform certain calculations from the results obtained by an analytical instrument. The microprocessor is, in effect, acting as a microcomputer. The chemist is relieved of the job of performing routine calculations on the analytical results.

Computers are used by theoretical chemists to do complex and lengthy calculations that test ideas about molecular structure, stability of compounds, and possible reaction pathways.

The use of a computer in the laboratory can be applied to safety as well as analysis. Sensors can be placed in reaction vessels and other sensitive locations. The sensor output is then directed to a computer. If temperatures or pressures exceed safe limits, the computer will decide what action is necessary and carry out that action. Remember that the

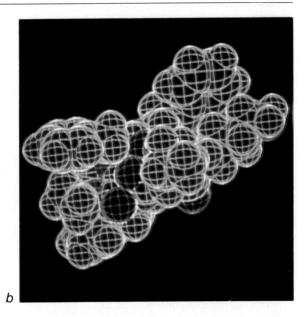

a

b

FIGURE 5-5. Computers are used to collect and process data from analytical testing equipment as in this gas chromatograph (a). The compound shown in (b) is a drug that was designed by chemists using a computer.

FIGURE 5-6. The action of a substrate and enzyme can be shown on a computer. Chemists can then work on synthesizing this enzyme for people who do not naturally produce it.

computer must already have been programmed to make the appropriate decision and take the appropriate action. Typical actions include sounding alarms, turning off heaters, opening sprinkler or other safety valves, or starting cooling fans.

Chemists also use computers for instructional purposes. Many laboratory experiments can be simulated on a computer equipped with a cathode-ray tube terminal (CRT). By viewing a simulated experiment before entering the laboratory, students can work more effectively once the experiment is actually performed.

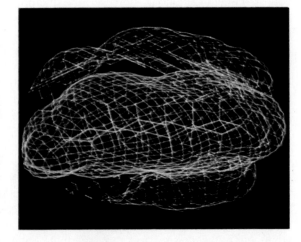

SUMMARY

1. The symbol for an element represents one atom of the element or one mole of the element. **Intro**

2. The formula for a compound can represent one molecule or formula unit. It can also represent one mole of the compound. **Intro**

3. Masses of atoms are based on the atomic mass unit (u). An atom of the element hydrogen has a mass of approximately 1 u, or 1.660×10^{-24} g. **5:1, 5:2**

4. The molecular mass of a molecule is found by adding the atomic masses of all the atoms in one molecule. **5:1**

5. Not all substances exist normally as molecules. Therefore, the term molecular mass is not used for all substances. The mass of the empirical formula unit of an ionic substance such as sodium chloride is called the formula mass. **5:1**

6. There are 6.02×10^{23} particles in 1 mole. This quantity is known as Avogadro's number. **5:2**

7. The number of moles in a given mass of substance can be found by dividing the total mass by the formula mass expressed in units of g/mol. **5:3**

8. Molarity is the ratio of moles of solute to cubic decimeters of solution. **5:4**

9. The percentage of the total mass of a compound contributed by an element is the percentage of that element in the compound. **5:5**

10. The empirical formula indicates the simplest whole-number ratio of atoms present in a compound. **5:6**

11. The molecular formula of a compound is some whole-number multiple of the empirical formula. **5:7**

12. Many crystalline compounds called hydrates contain water molecules attached to the particles of the compound. **5:8**

2. This number of particles has a mass in g equal to the mass of one particle in u.

VOCABULARY

atomic mass **5:1**	molarity **5:4**
molecular mass **5:1**	empirical formula **5:6**
formula mass **5:1**	molecular formula **5:7**
Avogadro's number **5:2**	hydrate **5:8**
mole **5:3**	

3. mole = certain number of objects
molarity = unit of concentration
4. molecular formula describes the contents of a molecule; empirical for-

PROBLEMS

1. To what substances does the term formula mass refer?   **1. ionic**

2. Why do chemists use 6.02×10^{23} as the number of things in a mole?

3. Explain the difference between the terms mole and molarity.

4. Explain the difference between an empirical formula and a molecular formula.

5. Why do we not make Avogadro's number some convenient round number such as 10^{25}?

mula describes the simplest whole-number ratio between the different atoms in a compound
5. Rounding would not permit the chemist to readily convert ratios of compounds or elements from macroscopic to microscopic levels without error.

Find the empirical formula of each of the following compounds.

6. Rb_2O
7. UCl_5
8. $Ni(NO_3)_2$
9. Na_3AsO_4
10. $(NH_4)_2SeO_4$
11. $CrCl_3$
12. $CoSe$
13. $LaCl_3$
14. Tl_2O
15. $RbNO_3$
16. $Rh_2(SO_3)_3$
17. $Cd(CH_3COO)_2$
18. FeF_3
19. $NiSe$
20. $Al(ClO_4)_3$

6. 63.0 g Rb, 5.90 g O
7. 0.159 g U, 0.119 g Cl
8. 5.13 g Ni, 2.45 g N, 8.39 g O
9. 2.13 g Na, 2.32 g As, 1.98 g O
10. 30.0 g N, 8.65 g H, 84.7 g Se, 68.6 g O
11. 32.8% Cr, 67.2% Cl
12. 42.7% Co, 57.3% Se
13. 56.6% La, 43.4% Cl
14. 96.2% Tl, 3.77% O
15. 58.0% Rb, 9.50% N, 32.5% O
16. 46.1% Rh, 21.6% S, 32.3% O
17. 48.8% Cd, 20.8% C, 2.62% H, 27.8% O
18. 49.5% Fe, 50.5% F
19. 42.6% Ni, 57.4% Se
20. 8.29% Al, 32.7% Cl, 59.0% O

21. Calculate the formula mass of each of the following.
    a. K_2SO_4
    b. CuO
    c. $CsClO_4$
    d. Tl_2SiF_6
    e. $Mg_3(AsO_4)_2$
    f. $Pb(CH_3COO)_2$

21. a. 174
    b. 79.5
    c. 233
    d. 550.
    e. 351
    f. 325

22. Calculate the molecular or formula mass of each of the following.
    a. $CuCl_2$
    b. $Hg(CH_3COO)_2$
    c. NiF_2
    d. $MnSeO_4$
    e. $PbSeO_4$
    f. $Ca(BO_3)_2$

22. a. 135
    b. 319
    c. 96.7
    d. 198
    e. 350.
    f. 158

23. Convert.
    a. 64.3 g of Rb_2SeO_4 to moles
    b. 3.33×10^{25} molecules of I_2 to grams
    c. 0.846 mole of HF to molecules
    d. 39.8 moles of CO_2 to molecules
    e. 308 formula units of MnC_2O_4 to moles

23. a. 0.205 mol
    b. 1.41×10^4 g
    c. 5.09×10^{23} molecules
    d. 2.40×10^{25} molecules
    e. 5.12×10^{-22} mol

Compute the molarity of each of the following solutions.

24. 5.70 g ZrF_4 in 5.00×10^2 cm³ of solution
25. 7.90 g NH_4Br in 2.50×10^2 cm³ of solution
26. 6.44 g CuF_2 in 1.00×10^3 cm³ of solution
27. 13.1 g $CdCl_2$ in 1.00×10^3 cm³ of solution
28. 38.3 g $Ce(CH_3COO)_3$ in 2.50×10^2 cm³ of solution

24. 0.683M
25. 0.323M
26. 0.0631M
27. 0.0716M
28. 0.483M

Describe the preparation of each of the following solutions.

29. 1.00×10^3 cm³ of 4.00M CsCl
30. 1.00×10^3 cm³ of 6.00M LiBr
31. 5.00×10^2 cm³ of 2.00M $MgBr_2$
32. 1.00×10^3 cm³ of 1.50M $MnSO_4$
33. 1.00×10^3 cm³ of 0.750M $NiSO_4$

29. 676 g
30. 521 g
31. 184 g
32. 227 g
33. 116 g

Find the percentage composition of each element in the following.

34. NaBr

35. CH_3COOH (*acetic acid*)

36. $U(SO_4)_2$

37. ZnS

38. $Sn(CrO_4)_2$

39. CH_3CH_2OH (*ethanol*)

40. Find the empirical formula for a compound containing 33.3% calcium, 40.0% oxygen, and 26.7% sulfur.

41. The percentage composition of a compound is 92.3% C and 7.7% H. If the molecular mass is 78, what is the molecular formula?

42. Find the molecular formula of a compound with percentage composition 26.7% P, 12.1% N, and 61.2% Cl and molecular mass 695.

43. What is the formula for a hydrate that consists of 90.7% SrC_2O_4 and 9.30% H_2O?

44. What is the formula for a hydrate that consists of 76.9% $La_2(CO_3)_3$ and 23.9% H_2O?

45. What is the formula for a hydrate that consists of 86.7% Mo_2S_5 and 13.3% H_2O?

34. 22.3%, 77.6%
35. 40.0%, 6.73%, 53.3%
36. 55.3%, 14.9%, 29.8%
37. 67.1%, 32.9%
38. 33.9%, 29.6%, 36.5%
39. 52.1%, 13.1%, 34.7%
40. $CaSO_3$
41. C_6H_6
42. $P_6H_6Cl_{12}$
43. $SrC_2O_4 \cdot H_2O$
44. $La_2(CO_3)_3 \cdot 8H_2O$
45. $Mo_2S_5 \cdot 3H_2O$

REVIEW

1. Convert 81.2 g to mg.

2. How many significant digits are in the measurement 41.02 m?

3. What is the relative error of a measurement of 12.0 seconds if the stop watch is precise to ±0.5 second?

4. Classify the following properties as physical or chemical.

    a. flammability

    b. electrical conductivity

    c. displaces hydrogen from water

    d. reacts with acids

5. Classify the following changes as physical or chemical.

    a. distillation

    b. fermentation

    c. crystallization

    d. dissolving

1. 81 200 mg
2. 4
3. 0.04
4. a. chemical
   b. physical
   c. chemical
   d. chemical
5. a. physical
   b. chemical
   c. physical
   d. physical

ONE MORE STEP

1. Investigate the report of a new compound as reported in the *Journal of the American Chemical Society*. Duplicate the calculations of the researcher in computing the theoretical percent composition of the compound. Do you think the experimental percentages reported are close enough to the theoretical to justify the proposed formula for the new compound?

2. Investigate the various methods scientists have used in determining Avogadro's number.

Answers are in the Teacher Guide in the front of this book.

READINGS

Shugar, Gershon J., et al., *Chemical Technician's Ready Reference Handbook*, 2nd Ed., Chapter 19, NY: McGraw-Hill Book Company, 1981.

When you think of chemical reactions you usually picture an occurrence that happens immediately. However the chemical reactions involved in making this petrified wood have taken place over a very long period of time. The decaying wood cells are displaced by minerals so that the wood eventually turns to stone. In this chapter, you will study the characteristics of displacement reactions. What system is used to classify reactions? How can you determine the amount of product your reaction will yield?

CHEMICAL REACTIONS

Chapter 6 covers using chemical formulas to write and balance chemical equations. Mass-mass calculations are also presented.

DEMONSTRATION: Mix 25 cm^3 glycerine with 25 cm^3 liquid dish soap. Connect rubber tubing to natural gas outlet and other end to a small funnel. Invert funnel into beaker of soap mixture. Make a bubble using the gas. Dislodge bubble by turning funnel upright and shaking gently. As bubble rises, ignite with candle taped to meter stick. Discuss how equations are used to represent observations in a concise form. $CH_4(g) + 2O_2(g) \rightarrow CO_2(g) + 2H_2O(g)$

GOALS:
• You will demonstrate a proficiency in writing and balancing chemical equations.
• You will differentiate between four general types of chemical reactions.
• You will demonstrate your understanding of mass relationships in chemical reactions by performing mass-mass calculations.

You have already seen that chemists have a shorthand method for writing the formulas of substances. They also use this shorthand for describing the changes which substances undergo. Consider the following statement: "Two molecules of acetylene gas will react with five molecules of oxygen gas to produce four molecules of carbon dioxide gas and two molecules of liquid water." How much easier it is to write

$$2C_2H_2(g) + 5O_2(g) \rightarrow 4CO_2(g) + 2H_2O(l)$$

to express the burning of acetylene in a welder's torch.

6:1 REPRESENTING CHEMICAL CHANGES

The formulas of compounds are used to represent the chemical changes that occur in a chemical reaction. A **chemical reaction** is the process by which one or more substances are changed into one or more different substances. A chemical reaction may be represented by an equation. A correct chemical equation shows what changes take place. It also shows the relative amounts of the various elements and compounds that take part in these changes. The starting substances in a chemical reaction are called **reactants.** The substances that are formed by the chemical reaction are called **products.**

Chemical equations are used to represent chemical reactions.

Reactants are the starting substances and products are the substances formed in chemical reactions.

$$2C_2H_2(g) + 5O_2(g) \rightarrow 4CO_2(g) + 2H_2O(l)$$
$$\text{reactants} \qquad\qquad \text{products}$$

The letters in parentheses indicate the physical state of each substance involved. The symbol (g) after a formula means that the substance is a gas. Liquids are indicated by the symbol (l), and solids by the symbol (cr). The symbol (cr) for solid indicates that the solid is crystalline. We can see that in the reaction described above C_2H_2, O_2, and CO_2 are gases. The H_2O is a liquid.

Physical state symbols in an equation:
(g) gas
(l) liquid
(cr) crystalline solid

The symbol (aq) indicates a water solution of the substance.

BACKGROUND: The symbol (cr) is recommended by IUPAC for indicating that a substance is a crystalline solid.

Since many chemical reactions take place in water solution, a substance dissolved in water is shown by the symbol (aq). This symbol comes from the word aqueous (Latin *aqua* = water). For example, if a water solution of sulfurous acid is warmed, it decomposes. The products of this reaction are water and sulfur dioxide, a gas.

$$H_2SO_3(aq) \rightarrow H_2O(l) + SO_2(g)$$

6:2   BALANCING EQUATIONS

A chemical reaction can be represented by a chemical equation. To write an equation that accurately represents the reaction, we must perform correctly three steps.

Step 1. *Determine exactly what are the reactants and the products.* For example, when propane gas burns in air, the reactants are propane (C_3H_8) and oxygen (O_2). The products formed are carbon dioxide (CO_2) and water (H_2O).

Reactants are written on the left side of chemical equations; products are written on the right.

Step 2. *Assemble the parts of the chemical equation.* Write the formulas for the reactants on one side of the equation, usually on the left, and connect them with plus signs. Write the formulas for the products on the right side of the equation. Connect the two sides using an arrow to show the direction of the reaction. Thus,

$$C_3H_8 \quad + \quad O_2 \quad \rightarrow \quad CO_2 \quad + H_2O$$
propane + oxygen yield carbon dioxide + water
reactants   yield   products

The symbols and formulas must be correct. If not, Step 3 will be useless.

FIGURE 6-1. The reaction of propane with oxygen produces carbon dioxide, water, and a tremendous amount of energy. Thus, propane is used as a fuel in torches, lanterns, and camping stoves.

Use the oxidation tables in Chapter 4 when trying to write correct formulas. We will omit the symbols that indicate physical state while we learn to balance equations.

Step 3. *Balance the equation.* Balancing means showing an equal number of atoms for each element on both sides of the equation. Remember that the law of conservation of mass states that the same amount of matter must be present both before and after all chemical reactions. So, the same number and kinds of atoms must be present on both sides of the equation. Check the preceding equation. It is not balanced. There are three carbon atoms on the left, but only one carbon atom on the right. To put the carbon in balance, we place the coefficient 3 before the carbon dioxide on the right. In balancing an equation, *change only the coefficients. Never change the subscripts.* To do so would change the substance represented. Our equation is now

Balanced equations have the same kind and number of atoms on each side.

Coefficients, not subscripts, may be changed to balance an equation.

$$C_3H_8 + O_2 \rightarrow 3CO_2 + H_2O$$

The carbon atoms are balanced, but the hydrogen atoms are not. There are eight hydrogen atoms on the left and only two on the right. By placing the coefficient 4 in front of the water, both the carbon and hydrogen atoms will be in balance. The equation is now

$$C_3H_8 + O_2 \rightarrow 3CO_2 + 4H_2O$$

Only the oxygen remains to be balanced. There are two oxygen atoms on the left and ten oxygen atoms on the right. To balance the oxygen, place the coefficient 5 in front of the oxygen. The equation is now balanced.

$$C_3H_8 + 5O_2 \rightarrow 3CO_2 + 4H_2O$$

Reactants		Products
3 carbon atoms		3 carbon atoms
8 hydrogen atoms	yield	8 hydrogen atoms
10 oxygen atoms		10 oxygen atoms

In another reaction, the commercial production of hydrogen, steam reacts with carbon in the form of coke to produce hydrogen and carbon monoxide. The equation is

$$H_2O + C \rightarrow H_2 + CO$$

2 hydrogen atoms		2 hydrogen atoms
1 carbon atom	yield	1 carbon atom
1 oxygen atom		1 oxygen atom

Because we have equal numbers of each kind of atom on both sides of the equation, the equation is balanced.

Be careful not to confuse subscripts and coefficients in balancing equations. *Never change the subscript in a formula in an attempt to balance an equation.* Changing a subscript changes the substance that is

Never change a subscript to balance an equation.

taking part in the reaction. The resulting equation will not represent the chemical change that actually takes place.

PROBLEMS

Balance each of the following equations.

1. $Te + H_2O \rightarrow TeO + H_2$

2. $La(NO_3)_3 + NaOH \rightarrow La(OH)_3 + NaNO_3$

3. $RhO_3 \rightarrow RhO + O_2$

4. $Hf + N_2 \rightarrow Hf_3N_4$

5. $Ga + H_2SO_4 \rightarrow Ga_2(SO_4)_3 + H_2$

6. $PdCl_2 + HNO_3 \rightarrow Pd(NO_3)_2 + HCl$

7. $RbBr + AgCl \rightarrow AgBr + RbCl$

8. $PaI_5 \rightarrow Pa + I_2$

9. $O_2 + Sb_2S_3 \rightarrow Sb_2O_4 + SO_2$

10. $Cu + Cl_2 \rightarrow CuCl_2$

1. balanced
2. $La(NO_3)_3 + 3NaOH \rightarrow La(OH)_3 + 3NaNO_3$

3. balanced
4. $3Hf + 2N_2 \rightarrow Hf_3N_4$
5. $2Ga + 3H_2SO_4 \rightarrow Ga_2(SO_4)_3 + 3H_2$
6. $PdCl_2 + 2HNO_3 \rightarrow Pd(NO_3)_2 + 2HCl$
7. balanced
8. $2PaI_5 \rightarrow 2Pa + 5I_2$
9. $5O_2 + Sb_2S_3 \rightarrow Sb_2O_4 + 3SO_2$
10. balanced

a

b

FIGURE 6-2. The hydrogen gas bubbles in this tube were produced by the single displacement reaction of magnesium and hydrochloric acid (a). The silver bromide precipitate shown was produced by the double displacement reaction of silver nitrate and zinc bromide (b).

6:3   CLASSIFYING CHEMICAL CHANGES

There are hundreds of different kinds of chemical reactions. For now, we will consider only four general types. Of these four, three are often used to make, or synthesize, new compounds.

Single Displacement. In this type of reaction, one element displaces another in a compound. For example, in the reaction

$$Cl_2(g) + 2KBr(aq) \rightarrow 2KCl(aq) + Br_2(l)$$

chlorine displaces bromine from potassium bromide. In the reaction

$$3Li(cr) + CmF_3(cr) \rightarrow 3LiF(cr) + Cm(cr)$$

lithium displaces curium from curium(III) fluoride. This type of reaction is recognized and predicted by its general form:

element + compound → element + compound

Double Displacement. There are hundreds of reactions in which the positive and negative portions of two compounds are interchanged.

$$PbCl_2(cr) + Li_2SO_4(aq) \rightarrow 2LiCl(aq) + PbSO_4(cr)$$
$$ZnBr_2(aq) + 2AgNO_3(aq) \rightarrow Zn(NO_3)_2(aq) + 2AgBr(cr)$$
$$BaCl_2(aq) + 2KIO_3(aq) \rightarrow Ba(IO_3)_2(cr) + 2KCl(aq)$$

The form of these reactions is easy to recognize,

compound + compound → compound + compound

FIGURE 6-3. Hydrogen peroxide decomposes on standing to form water and oxygen. This reaction proceeds slowly, therefore a catalyst (MnO_2) is used to speed the process.

Decomposition. Many substances will break up into simpler substances when energy is supplied.

Products of a decomposition are not necessarily elements.

$$CdCO_3(cr) \rightarrow CdO(cr) + CO_2(g)$$
$$Pb(OH)_2(cr) \rightarrow PbO(cr) + H_2O(g)$$
$$N_2O_4(g) \rightarrow 2NO_2(g)$$
$$PCl_5(cr) \rightarrow PCl_3(cr) + Cl_2(g)$$
$$H_2CO_3(aq) \rightarrow H_2O(l) + CO_2(g)$$
$$2KClO_3(cr) \rightarrow 2KCl(cr) + 3O_2(g)$$
$$2Ag_2O(cr) \rightarrow 4Ag(cr) + O_2(g)$$

Energy may be supplied in the form of heat, light, mechanical shock, or electricity. The general form for this type of reaction is,

compound → two or more elements or compounds

Synthesis. In synthesis reactions two or more substances combine to form one new substance.

Reactants of a synthesis are not necessarily elements.

$$NH_3(g) + HCl(g) \rightarrow NH_4Cl(cr)$$
$$CaO(cr) + SiO_2(cr) \rightarrow CaSiO_3(cr)$$
$$2H_2(g) + O_2(g) \rightarrow 2H_2O(g)$$

From the name, one might expect that synthesis reactions would be the most common method of preparing new compounds. However, these reactions are rarely as practical as one of the three preceding methods. Here the general form is,

element or compound + element or compound → compound

Not all reactions take one of the general forms we have described. Other classes of reactions will be considered later. Until then, we will deal chiefly with displacement (single or double), decomposition, or synthesis reactions.

Four simple chemical reactions are: single displacement, double displacement, decomposition, synthesis.

SUGGESTION: Remind students about the diatomic gases. Acid formulas can be found on page 69.

11. balanced
    single displacement
12. $2Sb + 3H_2O \rightarrow$
    $Sb_2O_3 + 3H_2$
    single displacement
13. $2Re + 3Br_2 \rightarrow 2ReBr_3$
    synthesis
14. $2Ac(OH)_3 \rightarrow Ac_2O_3 +$
    $3H_2O$ decomposition
15. $Ra + 2C \rightarrow RaC_2$ synthesis
16. $3HfCl_3 + Al \rightarrow 3HfCl_2 +$
    $AlCl_3$
17. $Zn + 2CrCl_3 \rightarrow 2CrCl_2 +$
    $ZnCl_2$
18. $Ca(AlO_2)_2 + 8HCl \rightarrow 2AlCl_3$
    $+ CaCl_2 + 4H_2O$
19. $BaCO_3 + C + H_2O \rightarrow 2CO$
    $+ Ba(OH)_2$
20. $2CeO_2 + 2KI + 8HCl \rightarrow$
    $2KCl + 2CeCl_3 + 4H_2O +$
    I_2
21. $CuCO_3(cr) \rightarrow CuO(cr) +$
    $CO_2(g)$
22. $2Na(cr) + 2H_2O(l) \rightarrow$
    $2NaOH(aq) + H_2(g)$
23. $NH_4NO_2(cr) \rightarrow 2H_2O(l) +$
    $N_2(g)$
24. $2Cu(cr) + S(cr) \rightarrow Cu_2S(cr)$
25. $2AgNO_3(aq) + H_2SO_4(aq)$
    $\rightarrow Ag_2SO_4(cr) +$
    $2HNO_3(aq)$
26. $H_2SO_4(l) \rightarrow H_2O(l) +$
    $SO_3(g)$
27. $CaCO_3(cr) + 2HCl(aq) \rightarrow$
    $CaCl_2(aq) + H_2O(l) +$
    $CO_2(g)$
28. $NH_4NO_3(cr) \rightarrow 2H_2O(l) +$
    $N_2O(g)$

> The coefficients of a balanced equation give the relative amounts (in moles) of reactants and products.

PROBLEMS

Balance each of the following. Then classify 11-15 as single or double displacement, decomposition, or synthesis.

11. $CuO + H_2 \rightarrow Cu + H_2O$

12. $Sb + H_2O \rightarrow Sb_2O_3 + H_2$

13. $Re + Br_2 \rightarrow ReBr_3$

14. $Ac(OH)_3 \rightarrow Ac_2O_3 + H_2O$

15. $Ra + C \rightarrow RaC_2$

16. $HfCl_3 + Al \rightarrow HfCl_2 + AlCl_3$

17. $Zn + CrCl_3 \rightarrow CrCl_2 + ZnCl_2$

18. $Ca(AlO_2)_2 + HCl \rightarrow AlCl_3 + CaCl_2 + H_2O$

19. $BaCO_3 + C + H_2O \rightarrow CO + Ba(OH)_2$

20. $CeO_2 + KI + HCl \rightarrow KCl + CeCl_3 + H_2O + I_2$

Substitute symbols for names, then balance the following equations.

21. copper(II) carbonate decomposes to copper(II) oxide and carbon dioxide gas

22. sodium reacts with water to produce sodium hydroxide and hydrogen gas

23. ammonium nitrite decomposes to nitrogen gas and water

24. copper combines with sulfur to form copper(I) sulfide

25. silver nitrate reacts with sulfuric acid to produce silver sulfate and nitric acid

26. sulfuric acid decomposes to water and sulfur trioxide

27. calcium carbonate reacts with hydrochloric acid to produce calcium chloride, water, and carbon dioxide gas

28. ammonium nitrate decomposes to water and nitrogen(I) oxide

6:4   MASS-MASS RELATIONSHIPS

Equations provide both qualitative and quantitative information. Each symbol and formula in an equation represents a specific amount of element and compound.

The mass relationships between reactants and products in chemical changes are an important concern to chemists. Several questions arise here. How much of one reactant is needed to combine with a given amount of another reactant? How much product is produced from a specific amount of reactant? For instance, how much silver chloride can be produced from 17.0 g of silver nitrate? There are other, similar, questions. Fortunately, all these questions can be answered using the same procedure. The coefficients of a balanced equation give the relative amounts (in moles) of reactants and products. Calculations to find the masses of materials involved in reactions are called **mass-mass problems.**

EXAMPLE: Mass-Mass

How many grams of silver chloride can be produced from the reaction of 17.0 g of silver nitrate with excess sodium chloride solution?

Solving Process:

Step 1. We are given silver nitrate and requested to find silver chloride. What do we know that would connect two different substances? A chemical equation would relate them in a quantitative way. Therefore, we write a balanced equation to represent the reaction that occurs. Silver nitrate is reacting with sodium chloride. Since we have compound plus compound, we predict that a double displacement reaction will occur.

First step.
Write the balanced equation.

$$AgNO_3(aq) + NaCl(aq) \rightarrow AgCl(cr) + NaNO_3(aq)$$

Step 2. We have thought of equations as written in terms of individual atoms and formula units. We can also consider the coefficients in the equation as indicating the number of *moles* of formula units that take part in the reaction. The equation above indicates that one formula unit of silver nitrate will produce one formula unit of silver chloride. It also indicates that one mole of silver nitrate formula units will produce one mole of silver chloride formula units. The problem states that an excess of sodium chloride is used, which means that all the silver nitrate will react.

Second Step.
Find the number of moles of reactant and product.

Let us review where we are. We are given grams of silver nitrate. We are asked to find grams of silver chloride. Silver nitrate and silver chloride are related by the equation. The equation is read in units of moles.

Step 3. Our solution begins by converting the grams of silver nitrate to moles. We use the table on the inside back cover to determine the formula mass of $AgNO_3$, which is 1.70×10^2 g.

Third Step.
Convert the grams of given to moles.

$$\frac{17.0 \text{ g AgNO}_3}{} \left| \frac{1 \text{ mol AgNO}_3}{1.70 \times 10^2 \text{ g AgNO}_3} \right. \cdots$$

Step 4. We have now converted the silver nitrate to units that will enable us to relate it to the silver chloride. We use the equation to find the conversion factor to use in going from silver nitrate to silver chloride. The equation tells us that one mole of silver nitrate will produce one mole of silver chloride. Using this fact gives us a partial solution which appears as:

Fourth Step.
Determine mole ratio from the balanced equation.

$$\frac{17.0 \text{ g AgNO}_3}{} \left| \frac{1 \text{ mol AgNO}_3}{1.70 \times 10^2 \text{ g AgNO}_3} \right| \left. \frac{1 \text{ mol AgCl}}{1 \text{ mol AgNO}_3} \right. \cdots$$

Step 5. We have now arrived at silver chloride which is the substance we were asked to find. However, we were to find the answer in grams. To complete the problem, we must convert the moles of silver chloride to grams. The final solution then appears as:

Fifth Step.
Express the moles of required substance in terms of grams.

$$\frac{17.0 \text{ g AgNO}_3}{} \left| \frac{1 \text{ mol AgNO}_3}{1.70 \times 10^2 \text{ g AgNO}_3} \right| \left| \frac{1 \text{ mol AgCl}}{1 \text{ mol AgNO}_3} \right| \frac{144 \text{ g AgCl}}{1 \text{ mol AgCl}} = 14.4 \text{ g AgCl}$$

This problem involved finding the mass of one substance from a given mass of another substance. Problems of this type are called mass-mass problems. All mass-mass problems can be solved in this way. This example and other quantitative studies of chemical reactions are called **stoichiometry** (stoy kee AHM uh tree). Let us review the process.

Step 1. *Write the balanced equation.*
The first step in the solution of any mass-mass problem is to write a balanced equation for the correct reaction. In this section, we will always assume that only one reaction occurs and that all of one reactant is used. In practice, several reactions may occur, the actual reaction may not be known, or all the reactant may not react.

Step 2. *Find the number of moles of the given substance.*
Express the mass of the given substance in moles by dividing the mass of the given substance by its formula mass.

$$\frac{grams\ of\ given\ substance}{} \left| \frac{1\ mole}{\substack{formula\ mass \\ of\ given\ substance}} \right. \ldots$$

Step 3. *Inspect the balanced equation to determine the ratio of moles of required substance to moles of given substance.*
For example, look at the following equation.

$$2H_2(g) + O_2(g) \rightarrow 2H_2O(g)$$

In this reaction, 1 mole of oxygen reacts with 2 moles of hydrogen. From the same equation, 1 mole of oxygen will produce 2 moles of water. Also, 2 moles of water are produced by 2 moles of hydrogen. Once the equation is balanced, only the reactants and products directly involved in the problem should be in your calculations. Multiply the moles of given substance by the ratio:

$$\ldots \frac{moles\ of\ required\ substance}{moles\ of\ given\ substance} \ldots$$

Step 4. *Express the moles of required substance in terms of grams.*

$$\ldots \frac{formula\ mass\ of\ required\ substance}{1\ mole} = grams\ of\ required\ substance$$

Step 5. *Convert moles to grams.*
Notice that, as you work through a problem of this kind, you first convert grams of given substance to moles, and then convert moles of required substance back to grams.

$$\left(\substack{start\ with \\ grams\ given}\right) \rightarrow \left(\substack{grams \\ to\ moles}\right) \rightarrow \left(\substack{use \\ mole\ ratio}\right) \rightarrow \left(\substack{moles \\ to\ grams}\right) \rightarrow \left(\substack{end\ with \\ grams\ required}\right)$$

This method is used because the balanced equation relates the number of moles of given substance to the number of moles of required substance. Now try the following two problems.

Use the unit in your solution as a check on the answer.

FIGURE 6-4. Mass must be measured carefully so that accurate data will be available for solving mass-mass problems.

EXAMPLE: Mass-Mass

How many grams of Cu_2S could be produced from 9.90 g of CuCl reacting with an excess of H_2S gas?

Solving Process:

(a) We must write the balanced equation. CuCl and H_2S are reactants, Cu_2S is one product.

$$2CuCl(aq) + H_2S(g) \rightarrow Cu_2S(cr) + 2HCl(aq)$$

If we use the wrong reaction or do not balance the equation properly, we cannot get a correct answer.

(b) Find the number of moles of the given substance.

1 mole of CuCl has mass: $\quad$ 1Cu $\quad$ 1 × 63.5 = 63.5 g
$\qquad\qquad\qquad\qquad\qquad$ 1Cl $\quad$ 1 × 35.5 = 35.5 g
$\qquad\qquad\qquad\qquad\qquad$ formula mass = 99.0 g

$$\frac{9.90 \text{ g CuCl}}{} \left| \frac{1 \text{ mol CuCl}}{99.0 \text{ g CuCl}} \cdots \right.$$

(c) Determine the mole ratio of the required substance to the given substance. Notice that, although H_2S and HCl are part of the reaction, we do not consider them in this problem.

$$2CuCl + H_2S \rightarrow Cu_2S + 2HCl$$

$$\frac{9.90 \text{ g CuCl}}{} \left| \frac{1 \text{ mol CuCl}}{99.0 \text{ g CuCl}} \right| \frac{1 \text{ mol Cu}_2S}{2 \text{ mol CuCl}} \cdots$$

(d) We must convert moles of Cu_2S into grams of Cu_2S.

$$1 \text{ mole of } Cu_2S \text{ has mass:} \quad \begin{array}{ll} 2Cu & 2 \times 63.5 = 127 \text{ g} \\ 1S & 1 \times 32 = \underline{32 \text{ g}} \\ & \text{formula mass} = 159 \text{ g} \end{array}$$

$$\frac{9.90 \text{ g } CuCl}{} \left| \frac{1 \text{ mol } CuCl}{99.0 \text{ g } CuCl} \right| \frac{1 \text{ mol } Cu_2S}{2 \text{ mol } CuCl} \left| \frac{159 \text{ g } Cu_2S}{1 \text{ mol } Cu_2S} \right. = 7.95 \text{ g of } Cu_2S$$

Thus, we predict 9.90 g of CuCl will react to produce 7.95 g of Cu_2S. If the problem is set up correctly, all the factor units will divide out except the final result. The final result should be the correct units for the answer.

EXAMPLE: Mass-Mass

How many grams of calcium hydroxide will be needed to react completely with 10.0 g of phosphoric acid? Note that we are asked to find the mass of one reactant that will react with a given mass of another reactant.

Solving Process:
(a) Write a balanced equation.

$$3Ca(OH)_2 + 2H_3PO_4 \rightarrow Ca_3(PO_4)_2 + 6H_2O$$

(b) Change 10.0 g phosphoric acid to moles of phosphoric acid.

$$\frac{10.0 \text{ g } H_3PO_4}{} \left| \frac{1 \text{ mol } H_3PO_4}{98.0 \text{ g } H_3PO_4} \right. \cdots$$

(c) From the equation, 2 moles of H_3PO_4 will require 3 moles $Ca(OH)_2$.

$$\frac{10.0 \text{ g } H_3PO_4}{} \left| \frac{1 \text{ mol } H_3PO_4}{98.0 \text{ g } H_3PO_4} \right| \frac{3 \text{ mol } Ca(OH)_2}{2 \text{ mol } H_3PO_4} \cdots$$

(d) Change moles of calcium hydroxide into grams (mass) of calcium hydroxide.

$$\frac{10.0 \text{ g } H_3PO_4}{} \left| \frac{1 \text{ mol } H_3PO_4}{98.0 \text{ g } H_3PO_4} \right| \frac{3 \text{ mol } Ca(OH)_2}{2 \text{ mol } H_3PO_4} \left| \frac{74.1 \text{ g } Ca(OH)_2}{1 \text{ mol } Ca(OH)_2} \right. = 11.3 \text{ g } Ca(OH)_2$$

PROBLEMS

29. 3.16 g
30. 36.9 g

29. How many grams of H_2 can be produced from the reaction of 72.0 g of sodium with an excess of water?

30. An excess of nitrogen reacts with 6.57 g of hydrogen. How many grams of ammonia are produced?

31. How many grams of oxygen are required to burn completely 84.9 g of carbon?

32. In Problem 31, how many grams of CO_2 will be formed?

33. In the decomposition of potassium chlorate, 82.6 g of O_2 are formed. How many grams of potassium chloride are produced?

34. The action of carbon monoxide on iron(III) oxide can be represented by the equation, $Fe_2O_3(cr) + 3CO(g) \rightarrow 2Fe(cr) + 3CO_2(g)$. What would be the minimum amount of carbon monoxide used if 80.3 grams of iron were produced?

35. How many grams of hydrochloric acid are required to react completely with 44.7 grams of calcium hydroxide?

36. How many grams of hydrogen are produced when 4.77 grams of aluminum react with excess hydrochloric acid?

31. 226 g
32. 311 g
33. 128 g
34. 60.4 g
35. 44.1 g
36. 0.535 g

6:5   ENERGY AND CHEMICAL CHANGE

Chemical changes are always accompanied by a change in energy. If energy is absorbed in a reaction, the reaction is **endothermic.** The products, therefore, are higher in energy than the reactants. On the other hand, if energy is given off by a reaction, the reaction is **exothermic.** In this case, the products are lower in energy than the reactants. For example, the calcium hydroxide-phosphoric acid reaction is exothermic. When a thermometer is placed in the reaction vessel, we find that the temperature rises as the reaction occurs. Energy is given off. In our example reaction, the products, calcium phosphate and water, are at a lower energy state than the reactants.

Both endothermic and exothermic reactions require a certain minimum amount of energy to get started. This minimum amount of energy is called the **activation energy.** Without it, the reactant atoms or molecules will not unite to form the product and the reaction does not occur.

Chemical changes are accompanied by a change in energy.

If energy is absorbed, the reaction is endothermic.

If energy is released, the reaction is exothermic.

FIGURE 6-5. A skin irritant, steam, and heat are the products of an exothermic reaction used by the bombardier beetle as ''artillery'' against enemies. The beetle is named for the cracking sound and smoke it emits when attacked.

Chemical reactions have many possible sources for their activation energy. When a match is struck, friction produces enough heat to activate the reactants on the match head. As a result the match ignites. In photography, light is the source of the activation energy. You will study activation energy again in Chapter 23.

BIOGRAPHY   James Prescott Joule (1818-1889)

James Joule was a self-educated scientist. His only formal education consisted of a somewhat brief tutorship under John Dalton. Most of Joule's experiments were conducted as a hobby. As the owner of an English brewery, he did not have to concern himself with financial support and was free to experiment at leisure.

Throughout his life, Joule aimed at precise, quantitative measurements. After establishing that heat was a form of energy transfer, he proceeded to investigate the quantitative relationships between electricity and heat, and between mechanical work and heat.

Joule discovered the mathematical relationship between the amount of current passed in a conductor and the amount of heat generated by its passage. He also determined the relationship between the amount of mechanical work performed and the amount of heat generated. The First Law of Thermodynamics is credited to Joule.

CAREERS AND CHEMISTRY

6:6 Health and Safety Inspectors

We often take for granted that food we purchase is safe to eat. Most of the time it is because people and companies handling food are subject to many laws and regulations designed to protect the public. Federal, state, and local governments all employ investigators and inspectors to see that laws and regulations regarding health and safety are obeyed.

Much of the food we eat contains a number of additives used to enhance flavor, color, and prolong shelf life. Before any additive is approved for use by the Food and Drug Administration, a food processor must submit the results of a number of biochemical and analytical tests on the additive. Inspectors obtain samples from the field so the FDA can run their own set of tests to be sure the industry test data is accurate and complete. Inspectors must have a background in analytical procedures in that they are also responsible for on-site inspections of food processors' laboratories to be sure they are run in an appropriate manner. Thus, the FDA can rely on the industry data as being accurately determined.

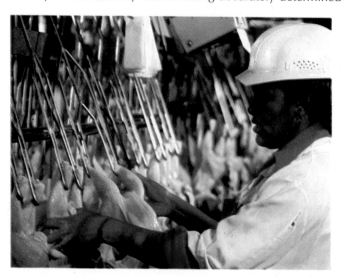

FIGURE 6-6. FDA inspectors routinely check food processing plants to ensure health standards are enforced.

Restaurants are frequently visited by health inspectors. The inspector looks for proper storage of food to make sure no insect pests or rodents can contaminate it. The inspector also observes the employees at work to ensure that the food is being handled in a clean and sanitary manner.

Food processing plants are also subject to on-site inspections of their facilities. Labeling of products is also examined to be sure a label complies with government standards. Inspectors have the power to seize and destroy any products that are improperly labeled, spoiled, contaminated, or processed under unsanitary conditions. The agency may take court action that could result in fines as well as an injunction prohibiting a business from resuming operations.

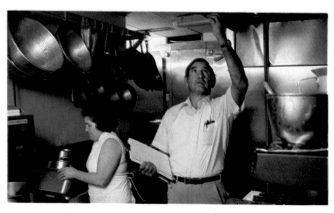

FIGURE 6-7. OSHA inspectors check for safe working conditions.

The Occupational Safety and Health Administration has many inspectors who visit industrial and commercial establishments. OSHA inspectors check for the observance of accepted procedures and safe physical arrangements of equipment and personnel. One of their major tasks is to check for fire hazards and the availability and maintenance of fire-fighting equipment.

These people are also concerned with many aspects of the workplace which may not appear potentially dangerous. For instance, they will check sound levels in a factory to see if the workers' hearing could be damaged. They check air quality inside the plant to ensure the prevention of occupational respiratory diseases. They also check radiation levels and worker exposure around nuclear power plants and medical facilities.

SUMMARY

1. Chemists use equations to describe the changes that substances undergo. **6:1**
2. The physical state of substances in equations is shown by (g) for gas, (l) for liquid, (cr) for solid, and (aq) for a water solution. **6:1**
3. Reactants are the starting substances in a reaction. Products are the substances resulting from a reaction. **6:1**
4. A chemical equation represents changes that take place in a reaction. It also shows relative amounts of reactants and products. **6:2**
5. Balancing an equation means adjusting coefficients so that there are the same number of atoms of each element on both sides of the equation. **6:2**
6. Four general types of reactions are the single displacement, double displacement, synthesis, and decomposition reactions. **6:3**
7. The balanced equation indicates the ratio of moles of reactants and products in the reaction and is used as the basis for solving mass-mass problems. **6:4**
8. A chemical change is always accompanied by an energy change. Energy is absorbed in an endothermic reaction and given off in an exothermic reaction. **6:5**

VOCABULARY

chemical reaction **6:1**
reactants **6:1**
products **6:1**
single displacement **6:3**
double displacement **6:3**
decomposition **6:3**

synthesis **6:3**
mass-mass problem **6:4**
stoichiometry **6:4**
endothermic **6:5**
exothermic **6:5**
activation energy **6:5**

PROBLEMS

Substitute symbols for names and balance.

1. chromium displaces hydrogen from hydrochloric acid, with chromium(II) chloride as the other product 1. $Cr(cr) + 2HCl(aq) \rightarrow H_2(g) + CrCl_2(aq)$

2. barium hydroxide reacts with carbon dioxide to form barium carbonate and water 2. $Ba(OH)_2(aq) + CO_2(g) \rightarrow BaCO_3(cr) + H_2O(l)$

3. Why is it that subscripts never change when balancing an equation?

4. Why is it necessary to balance equations? 4. **Matter is conserved in chemical reactions.**

Balance each of the following equations.

5. $Na(cr) + O_2(g) \rightarrow Na_2O(cr)$

6. $AsCl_3 + H_2O(l) \rightarrow HCl(aq) + As(OH)_3(aq)$

7. $Ho(cr) + H_2O(l) \rightarrow Ho(OH)_3(aq) + H_2(g)$

8. $IrCl_3(aq) + NaOH(aq) \rightarrow Ir_2O_3(cr) + HCl(aq) + NaCl(aq)$

9. $MoO_3(cr) + Zn(cr) + H_2SO_4(l) \rightarrow Mo_2O_3(cr) + ZnSO_4(aq) + H_2O(l)$

10. $NbI_3(cr) + I_2(cr) \rightarrow NbI_5(cr)$

11. $Pb(CH_3COO)_2(aq) + K_2CrO_4(aq) \rightarrow PbCrO_4(cr) + KCH_3COO(aq)$

12. $RbCl(cr) + O_2(g) \rightarrow RbClO_4(cr)$

13. $SiF_4(cr) + H_2O(l) \rightarrow H_2SiF_6(aq) + H_2SiO_3(cr)$

14. $Sn(cr) + KOH(aq) \rightarrow K_2SnO_2(cr) + H_2(g)$

Balance each of the following reactions after predicting the products.

15. silver oxide decomposes

16. copper plus silver nitrate (displacement; copper(II) compound is formed)

17. magnesium plus oxygen (synthesis)

18. hydrochloric acid plus silver nitrate (double displacement)

19. magnesium plus hydrochloric acid (displacement)

20. iron plus oxygen (synthesis; iron(III) compound is formed)

21. iron plus sulfur (synthesis; iron(II) compound is formed)

22. calcium hydroxide plus sulfuric acid (double displacement)

23. magnesium plus nitrogen (synthesis)

24. zinc plus sulfuric acid (single displacement)

25. Why is it necessary to use a balanced equation in solving a mass-mass problem?

26. How many grams of $NaAlO_2$ can be obtained from 7.71 g of $AlCl_3$ according to the reaction: $AlCl_3(aq) + 4NaOH(aq) \rightarrow NaAlO_2(aq) + 3NaCl(aq) + 2H_2O(l)$?

27. How many grams of CO_2 are obtained when 2.96 g of $Ce_2(C_2O_4)_3$ are formed according to the reaction:
$2Ce(IO_3)_4(aq) + 24H_2C_2O_4(aq) \rightarrow Ce_2(C_2O_4)_3(aq) + 4I_2(aq) + 42CO_2(aq) + 24H_2O(l)$?

28. What is the difference between endothermic reactions and exothermic reactions? **endothermic: take in energy, exothermic: give off energy**

3. It would change the type of substances present in the reaction.

8. $2IrCl_3(aq) + 3NaOH(aq) \rightarrow Ir_2O_3(cr) + 3HCl(aq) + 3NaCl(aq)$

9. $2MoO_3(cr) + 3Zn(cr) + 3H_2SO_4(l) \rightarrow Mo_2O_3(cr) + 3ZnSO_4(aq) + 3H_2O(l)$

10. Balanced. $NbI_3(cr) + I_2(cr) \rightarrow NbI_5(cr)$

11. $Pb(CH_3COO)_2(aq) + K_2CrO_4(aq) \rightarrow PbCrO_4(cr) + 2KCH_3COO(aq)$

12. $RbCl(cr) + 2O_2(g) \rightarrow RbClO_4(cr)$

13. $3SiF_4(cr) + 3H_2O(l) \rightarrow 2H_2SiF_6(aq) + H_2SiO_3(cr)$

14. $Sn(cr) + 2KOH(aq) \rightarrow K_2SnO_2(cr) + H_2(g)$

15. $2Ag_2O(cr) \rightarrow 4Ag(cr) + O_2(g)$

16. $Cu(cr) + 2AgNO_3(aq) \rightarrow Cu(NO_3)_2(aq) + 2Ag(cr)$

17. $2Mg(cr) + O_2(g) \rightarrow 2MgO(cr)$

18. $HCl(aq) + AgNO_3(aq) \rightarrow HNO_3(aq) + AgCl(cr)$

19. $Mg(cr) + 2HCl(aq) \rightarrow MgCl_2(aq) + H_2(g)$

20. $4Fe(cr) + 3O_2(g) \rightarrow 2Fe_2O_3(cr)$

21. $Fe(cr) + S(cr) \rightarrow FeS(cr)$

22. $Ca(OH)_2(aq) + H_2SO_4(aq) \rightarrow CaSO_4(cr) + 2H_2O(l)$

23. $3Mg(cr) + N_2(g) \rightarrow Mg_3N_2(cr)$

24. $Zn(cr) + H_2SO_4(aq) \rightarrow ZnSO_4(aq) + H_2(g)$

25. to obtain the ratio of moles of required substance to moles of given substance

26. 4.72 g

27. 10.1 g

29. striking a match
   a. exothermic
   b. released
   c. lower
30. 0.213 g O_2

29. In an experiment, two clear liquids are combined. A white precipitate forms and the temperature of the substances in the beaker rises.

   a. Is this reaction endothermic or exothermic?
   b. Is heat released or absorbed?
   c. Are the products higher or lower in energy than the reactants?

30. In manned space vehicles, air purification is partly accomplished with the use of lithium peroxide, Li_2O_2. It reacts with waste CO_2 in the air according to the reaction $2Li_2O_2 + 2CO_2 \rightarrow 2Li_2CO_3 + O_2$. How many grams of oxygen are released by the reaction of 0.611 g CO_2?

REVIEW

1. a. 0.004 19 mol
   b. 4270 g
   c. 0.0152 mol
   d. 0.286 mol
   e. 0.187 g
2. 0.001 34*M*
3. 0.265 g
4. 25.6%, 74.3%
5. ZnSe
6. Zr(NO$_3$)$_4$·5H$_2$O

1. Make the following conversions.
   a. 2.52×10^{21} formula units of ZrS_2 to moles.
   b. 1.26×10^{25} formula units of $Al(CH_3COO)_3$ to grams.
   c. 6.06 grams $Fe_2(SO_4)_3$ to moles.
   d. 88.4 grams MnI_2 to moles.
   e. 0.002 02 mole $Ni(OH)_2$ to grams.

2. What is the molarity of a 1.000×10^3-cm^3 solution containing 0.550 g $Ni(IO_3)_2$?

3. How would you prepare a 0.003 64*M* solution of $Ag_2C_4H_4O_6$? Assume you need 2.00×10^2 cm^3 of solution.

4. Find the percentage composition of each element in SrI_2.

5. Find the empirical formula for a substance with the following composition: 45.3% Zn and 54.7% Se.

6. Find the formula for the hydrate with the composition 79.0% $Zr(NO_3)_4$ and 21.0% H_2O.

ONE MORE STEP

See Teacher Guide for detailed answers.

1. Try balancing each of the following equations.
   a. $Cu(cr) + H_2SO_4(aq) \rightarrow CuSO_4(aq) + SO_2(g) + H_2O(l)$
   b. $Cu_2S(cr) + HNO_3(aq) \rightarrow Cu(NO_3)_2(aq) + CuSO_4(aq) + NO_2(g) + H_2O(l)$
   c. $CH_4(g) + O_2(g) \rightarrow CO_2(g) + H_2O(l)$
   d. $Ce(IO_3)_4(aq) + H_2C_2O_4(aq) \rightarrow Ce_2(C_2O_4)_3(aq) + I_2(aq) + CO_2(g) + H_2O(l)$
   e. $KBr(cr) + H_2SO_4(aq) + MnO_2(cr) \rightarrow KHSO_4(aq) + MnSO_4(aq) + H_2O(l) + Br_2(l)$

2. What kind of reaction is a metathesis reaction?

3. There are a number of general rules for predicting the products of decomposition reactions. Try to find at least four of these rules.

4. Why are some foods and beverages stored in brown bottles?

5. Find out how light affects the emulsion on a photographic film. Obtain a book on photography to determine what chemical reactions are involved in developing film.

6. If neither matter nor energy is created or destroyed in an ordinary chemical reaction before the reaction occurs, where is the energy that is given off or absorbed by the reaction?

READINGS

Shugar, Gershon J., et al., *Chemical Technician's Ready Reference Handbook,* 2nd Ed., NY: McGraw-Hill Book Company, 1981.

Webb, Michael J., et al., ''Let's Stress Chemistry,'' *The Science Teacher,* Vol. 50,. No. 7(October 1983), pp. 27-30.

The building can be thought of as a simple model for the atom. A scientific model is a verbal description or visual representation for something that cannot be observed directly. You may already have the idea that atoms consist of hard spheres. However, like the building, the atom is much more complex on the inside than originally appears. How did early chemists describe the atom? What advances in technology caused scientists to change the model? What evidence do we have that atoms actually exist?

ATOMIC STRUCTURE

Chapter 7 contains a short historical summary of the development of atomic theory, introduces subatomic particles, and presents Bohr's atomic model.

DEMONSTRATION: To help students relate to how small an atom or molecule is, have each one inflate a small balloon. Release the air from it. Place one or two drops of vanilla flavoring into the balloon using a dropper. Have the student re-inflate the balloon, and tie it closed. Why do they smell the vanilla flavoring through the balloon wall?

GOALS:
• You will gain an understanding of the historical development for our present day model of the atom.
• You will learn how spectroscopy is used to identify substances.
• You will calculate the average atomic mass of a mixture of isotopes of an element.

The first six chapters have been devoted to learning the language of chemistry. We will now look at the structure and properties of matter.

Much of the world depends on electricity. Most of our electricity travels from place to place along wires made of the element copper. Let us take a closer look at some copper. Suppose that we take a piece of copper wire and cut it into very small pieces. Would these pieces still be copper? How many times could we continue to divide a piece of copper and still have particles of copper? What do we have when we have divided the copper into the smallest possible pieces? We found earlier that the smallest piece of matter that would still be copper is called an atom. This atom, in turn, is made of smaller particles such as electrons, protons, and neutrons. Why do we believe that such small particles actually exist? What evidence do we have that they exist? Our modern concept of the atom is a result of generations of work. Even today, our knowledge of the atom is not yet complete.

Yes. Until one atom is left.

We will devote this chapter to the study of atoms and their parts. In learning about the structure of the atom we will gain a better understanding of the properties of atoms. This knowledge will be useful when we study chemical reactions. We will follow the historical development of ideas about atoms. This approach will enable you to see how concepts about atomic structure changed as we accumulated more experimental evidence.

7:1 EARLY ATOMIC THEORY

Democritus proposed the first atomic theory.

Early thoughts concerning atoms were proposed by the Greek philosopher, Democritus, about 400 B.C. He suggested that the world was made of two things—empty space and tiny particles he called "atoms." This word comes from the Greek word *atomos*, meaning indivisible. Thus, he thought of atoms as the smallest possible particles of matter. He also thought there were different types of atoms for each material in the world. His theory was very general and was not supported by experimental evidence.

CAREERS: Historians, who write about the advances and discoveries in chemistry, relate them to the political and cultural activities of the times.

The belief in the existence of atoms was not accepted for centuries because it contradicted the teachings of Aristotle. Aristotle believed that matter was continuous and made of only one substance called hyle. Aristotle's teachings were accepted until the 17th century. Then, many people began to express doubts and objections to his theory.

Two of these individuals were Isaac Newton and Robert Boyle. They published articles stating their belief in the atomic nature of elements. Their works offered no proof. They were explanations of the known, with no predictions of the unknown. It was up to an English chemist, John Dalton, to offer a logical hypothesis about the existence of atoms.

During the early 1800's, Dalton studied certain experimental observations made by others concerning chemical reactions. Antoine Lavoisier, a French chemist, had made one of these discoveries. He found that when a chemical change occurred in a closed system, the mass of the reactants before a chemical change equaled the mass of the products after the change. In all tests of chemical changes in a closed system, he found that mass remained constant. He proposed that, *in ordinary chemical reactions, matter can be changed in many ways, but it cannot be created or destroyed.* Today this law is called the **law of conservation of mass.**

Proust stated that the elements in substances have definite proportion by mass.

FIGURE 7-1. The research of Newton (a), Lavoisier (b), and Dalton (c) was important to the development of modern atomic theory.

The work of another French chemist, Joseph Proust, also came to the attention of Dalton. Proust had observed that *specific substances always contain elements in the same ratio by mass.* For example, table salt is made of sodium and chlorine. The ratio of the mass of sodium to the mass of chlorine in any sample of pure salt is always the same. No matter where the sample is obtained, how it is obtained, or how large it is, the ratio of the mass of sodium to the mass of chlorine never changes. This principle is known as the **law of definite proportions.**

a

b

c

7:2   DALTON'S HYPOTHESIS

Dalton was trying to explain the findings of Lavoisier and Proust when he formed the basis of our present atomic theory. He stated that all matter is composed of very small particles called atoms, and that these atoms cannot be broken apart. Dalton's ideas were like those of Democritus. However, Dalton believed that atoms were simpler than particles of air or rock, and that atoms of different elements were quite unlike. He also believed that all atoms of an element were exactly alike. He stated that atoms can unite with other atoms in simple ratios to form compounds.

These last three sentences are the key to the atomic theory. We can see how Dalton's ideas explain the two laws of Lavoisier and Proust. If atoms cannot be destroyed, then they must simply be rearranged in a chemical change. The total number and kind of atoms must remain the same. Therefore, the mass before a reaction must equal the mass after a reaction. If the atoms of an element are always alike, then all atoms of a particular element must have the same mass.

According to Dalton, all sodium atoms have the same mass and all chlorine atoms have the same mass. When a sodium atom combines with a chlorine atom, salt is formed. The same is true of any pair of these atoms. Therefore, the ratio of the mass of sodium to the mass of chlorine must be the same for any sample of salt. He believed this reasoning would hold true for any given material. Experiments have shown that Dalton's ideas are not entirely correct. As we will see later, not all atoms of the same element have exactly the same mass. However, by changing the word "mass" to "average mass," we can use Dalton's ideas today.

Dalton stated a second law based on his own atomic theory but not based on experimental data. *The ratio of masses of one element that combine with a constant mass of another element can be expressed in small whole numbers.* This statement is the **law of multiple proportions.** Look at Table 7-1. Do you see why these numbers cannot be fractions? Atoms cannot be divided. A fraction of an atom does not exist.

Dalton believed that each element is composed of like atoms.

Atoms unite in simple whole number ratios to form compounds.

Dalton's atomic theory:
1. All matter is composed of atoms.
2. All atoms of the same element are identical.
3. Atoms of different elements are different.
4. Atoms unite in definite ratios to form compounds.

Atoms of the same element may differ in mass. Thus we use "average mass" rather than "mass."

The law of multiple proportions states that the combining masses of one element with a constant amount of another element are in the ratio of small whole numbers.

Table 7-1

Proportions of Tin to Oxygen		
	Mass of Sn in 1 mole	Mass of O in 1 mole	Ratio of O masses combined with constant mass (119 g) of tin.
tin(II) oxide, SnO	119 g	16 g	1
tin(IV) oxide, SnO$_2$	119 g	32 g	2

At about the same time that Dalton formed his atomic theory, J. L. Gay-Lussac, a French chemist, made an interesting observation. He was working with gas reactions at constant temperature and pressure. He noted that, under constant conditions, the volumes of reacting gases and gaseous products were in the ratio of small whole numbers.

Under constant temperature and pressure combining volumes of gases are related by small whole numbers.

A few years later, Amadeo Avogadro, an Italian physicist, explained Gay-Lussac's work using Dalton's theory. Avogadro's hypothesis also concerned gases at the same temperature and pressure. He stated that *equal volumes of gases, under the same conditions, have the same number of molecules.* These observations sped the acceptance of Dalton's theory.

The atomic theory and the law of multiple proportions, as stated by Dalton, have been tested and are accepted as correct. There are, however, major exceptions to some of Dalton's statements. These differences will be considered as we form our modern model of the atom in the sections that follow.

7:3 EARLY RESEARCH ON ATOMIC PARTICLES

Experiments by several scientists in the middle of the 19th century led to the conclusion that the atom consisted of smaller particles. Using a tube such as the one in Figure 7-2, it was possible to learn a great deal about atoms. In each end of the tube, there is a metal piece called an electrode. The positive terminal is called the **anode.** The negative terminal is called the **cathode.** Careful observation revealed rays in the tube. Since these rays appeared to begin at the cathode and travel toward the anode, they were called **cathode rays.**

DEMONSTRATION: Borrow this equipment from the physics lab to demonstrate the various discharge tubes.

BACKGROUND: The same principles apply to both the cathode ray tube and the TV tube.

FIGURE 7-2. Thomson used a cathode ray tube to determine the properties of electrons. Note how the path of the ray is affected by the magnet.

BACKGROUND: Joseph John Thomson (1856-1940) received the Nobel Prize in physics in 1906 for his discovery of the electron.

Cathode rays are streams of electrons.

Thomson measured the ratio of charge to mass of the electron.

In 1897, J. J. Thomson, an English scientist, did some skillful research on the cathode rays. As a result, Thomson is generally credited with the discovery that the rays consist of electrons. Thomson built a cathode ray tube to subject the rays to both a magnetic field and an electric field. He measured the bending of the path of the cathode rays and was then able to determine the ratio of the electron's charge to its mass.

FIGURE 7-3. This illustration shows a cross-sectional view of an apparatus similar to the one used by Millikan to determine the charge on an electron.

Robert Millikan, an American, obtained the first accurate measurement of an electron's charge. He used a device like the one in Figure 7-3. Electrons were transferred from the brass atomizer to oil droplets. These negatively charged droplets, under the influence of gravity, fell through a vacuum chamber. The charge on the plates was adjusted to just offset the gravitational force on the droplet. Millikan calculated the charge on the droplet. He found that the charges on the droplets varied. However, each charge was a multiple of one small charge. He concluded (correctly) that this small charge must be the charge on a single electron. This charge is now the standard unit of negative charge (1−). The electron and charge on the electron may be represented by the symbol e^-

Using the data of Thomson and Millikan, it was possible to calculate the actual mass of the electron. Its mass was only $\frac{1}{1837}$ the mass of the lightest atom known, the hydrogen atom.

Protons were also discovered in an experiment involving a cathode ray tube modified such as the one in Figure 7-4 on the next page. Rays were discovered traveling in the direction opposite to that traveled by the cathode rays. Later it was shown that these rays possessed a positive charge. J. J. Thomson showed they consisted of particles. The particles he found have the same amount of electric charge as an electron. However, the charge is opposite in sign to that on the electron. These particles are now called protons. The atoms of hydrogen gas he used in the tube consist of a single proton and a single electron. Thomson calculated that the mass of the proton was just about 1836 times that of the electron. The proton is now the standard unit of positive charge (1+).

A third particle remained unobserved for a long time. However, its existence had been predicted by Lord Rutherford, an English physicist, in 1920. The first evidence of the particle was obtained by Walter Bothe in 1930. Another English scientist, James Chadwick, repeated Bothe's work

Millikan determined the charge of an electron.

e^- is the symbol for an electron, which has a charge of 1−.

BACKGROUND: The mass of the electron is 9.1×10^{-31} kg. The charge on a single electron is 1.6×10^{-19} C. The SI unit of electrical charge is the coulomb, C.

A proton has a charge equal in size but opposite in sign to that of an electron.

A proton has a mass 1836 times that of an electron.

BACKGROUND: To obtain protons, the gas discharge tube must be charged with hydrogen.

Chadwick discovered the neutron.

A neutron has no charge and has approximately the same mass as a proton.

in 1932. He found high energy particles with no charge and with essentially the same mass as the proton. These particles are now known as neutrons. We now know of a number of other subatomic particles. Scientists have predicted the existence of still others. Subatomic particles will be studied in greater detail in Chapter 28.

Dalton had assumed that atoms could not be broken into smaller particles. The discovery of subatomic particles led to a major revision of Dalton's atomic theory to include this new information.

FIGURE 7-4. Using a modified cathode-ray tube, Goldstein discovered rays that traveled in a direction opposite to that of cathode rays.

7:4   ISOTOPES AND ATOMIC NUMBER

While working with neon, J. J. Thomson observed what seemed to be two kinds of neon atoms. They were exactly alike chemically, but slightly different in mass. We call these different atoms of the same element **isotopes.** Isotopes possess the same number of protons but a different number of neutrons.

Isotopes contain the same number of protons but a different number of neutrons.

In 1913 another English scientist, Henry Moseley, found the wavelength of X rays produced in an X-ray tube was characteristic of the metal used as the anode. The wavelength depended on the number of protons in the nucleus of the atom and was always the same for a given element. This number of protons is known as the **atomic number** of the element and is represented by the symbol Z. Since an atom is electrically neutral, the number of electrons must equal the number of protons. The mass difference of isotopes is due to the different numbers of neutrons in the nucleus. Thus, *the number of protons determines the identity of the element* and *the number of neutrons determines the particular isotope of the element.*

The atomic number (Z) of an element equals the number of protons in the nucleus.

Dalton's atomic theory was again changed. It now states that all atoms of an element contain the same number of protons but they can contain different numbers of neutrons. The particles that make up the nucleus (protons and neutrons) are called **nucleons.** The total number of nucleons in an atom is called the **mass number** of that atom. The symbol

High voltage cathode

X rays

−

+

Electrons

Metal target anode

a

b

for the mass number is *A*. A particular kind of atom containing a definite number of protons and neutrons is called a **nuclide.** The number of neutrons for any nuclide may be found by subtracting the atomic number from the mass number.

number of neutrons = A − Z

FIGURE 7-5. This tube is similar to that used by Moseley in studying X rays (a). The metal target in the X ray tube can be changed to produce X rays of different wavelengths (b).

The mass number (*A*) of an atom is the sum of the nucleons.

Table 7-2

Isotopes of Hydrogen			
Name	**Protons**	**Neutrons**	**Mass Number**
protium	1	0	1
deuterium	1	1	2
tritium	1	2	3

PROBLEM

1. Use Table 7-3 on page 129 to compute the number of electrons, neutrons, and protons in the nuclide of (a) carbon with *A* = 13 and (b) americium with *A* = 243.

1. (a) C = 6 electrons, 7 neutrons, 6 protrons; (b) Am = 95 electrons, 148 neutrons, 95 protons

7:5 RUTHERFORD-BOHR ATOM

During the period 1912-1913, Lord Rutherford brought together a brilliant team of physicists. Included in this group was Niels Bohr, a young Dane. The beginnings of our modern concept of atomic structure were developed by this group through experiment and hypothesis. Experiments designed to reveal the structure of atoms were performed under Rutherford's direction. These experiments showed that the atom consists of a central, positively charged nucleus surrounded in some manner by electrons. Hans Geiger and Ernest Marsden subjected a very thin sheet of gold foil to a stream of subatomic particles. They found that most of the

Lord Rutherford's experiments showed that the atom has a central positive nucleus surrounded by electrons.

FIGURE 7-6. Most alpha particles pass through the gold foil. The deflections of particles indicate a collision has occurred between an alpha particle and a gold nucleus.

particles passed right through the sheet. From this observation Rutherford concluded that the atom is mostly empty space. They also found that a few particles (about 1 in 8000) bounced back in almost the opposite direction from which they started. Rutherford explained this observation as meaning that there was a very small "core" to the atom. The core contained all the positive charge and almost all the mass of the atom. This core is now called the nucleus.

Geiger and Marsden found that most of the atom is empty space. Most atoms have a diameter between 0.1 and 0.5 nm. However, the radii of the nuclei of atoms vary between 1.2×10^{-6} and 7.5×10^{-6} nm. The radius of the electron is about 2.82×10^{-6} nm. In small atoms, the distance between the nucleus and the nearest electron is about 0.05 nm. Thus, the nucleus occupies only about one trillionth (10^{-12}) of the volume of an atom. To help you think about this relationship, imagine the

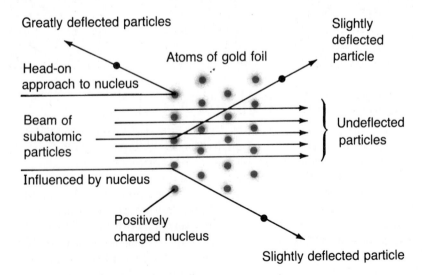

FIGURE 7-7. The gold foil experiment indicates that the gold atom consists of a central positively charged nucleus surrounded by electrons.

hydrogen nucleus as the size of a ping-pong ball. The electron is roughly the size of a tennis ball, and about 1.35 km away.

Electrons are negatively charged and attracted to the positive nucleus. What prevents the electrons from being pulled into the nucleus? The discussion of this question, led by Rutherford and Bohr, resulted in a new idea. They thought of electrons in "orbit" around the nucleus in much the same manner as the earth is in orbit around the sun. They suggested that the relationship between the electrons and the nucleus is similar to that between the planets and the sun. The Rutherford-Bohr model of the atom is sometimes called the planetary atomic model. Thus, according to the **planetary model,** the hydrogen atom should be similar to a solar system consisting of a sun and one planet.

Rutherford and Bohr thought the electrons "orbit" the nucleus.

The Rutherford-Bohr atom is a planetary model.

7:6 SPECTROSCOPY

In order to improve his description of atomic structure, Bohr used the experimental evidence of atoms exposed to radiant energy. When a substance is exposed to a certain intensity of light or some other form of energy, the atoms absorb some of the energy. Such atoms are said to be excited. When atoms and molecules are in an excited state, energy changes occur. Each excited atom or molecule produces unique energy changes that can be used to identify it. Radiant energy of several different types can be emitted (given off) or absorbed (taken up) by excited atoms and molecules. The methods of studying substances that are exposed to some sort of continuous exciting energy are called **spectroscopy.**

Flame tests illustrate emission of light as excited electrons return to lower energy states.

Element	Color
Na	Yellow
K	Violet
Ca	Yellow-red
Sr	Deep red
Li	Crimson
Ba	Green-yellow
Cu	Blue-green

Atoms are said to be excited when they absorb energy. Spectroscopy depends on continuous exciting energy.

Sodium Copper Calcium Strontium

a   b   c   d

Light is one form of radiant, or electromagnetic energy. Other forms of **electromagnetic energy** are radio, infrared, ultraviolet, and X ray. This energy consists of variation in electric and magnetic fields. The variation takes place in a regular, repeating fashion. If we plot the strength of the variation against time, our graph shows the "waves" of energy. The number of wave peaks that occur in a unit of time is called the **frequency** of the wave. Frequency is represented by the Greek letter *nu* (ν) and is measured in units of **hertz** (Hz). A hertz is one peak, or cycle, per second. All electromagnetic energy travels at the speed of light. The speed of light is 3.00×10^8 m/s in a vacuum and is represented by the symbol c. A third important characteristic of waves is the physical distance between peaks.

FIGURE 7-8. When exposed to a flame, these compounds emit colored light which is characteristic of the metal element in the compound. The flame tests for (a) sodium, (b) copper, (c) calcium, and (d) strontium can be used to identify each.

Frequency (ν) is the number of cycles per unit of time.

Hertz (Hz), the frequency unit, is one cycle per second.

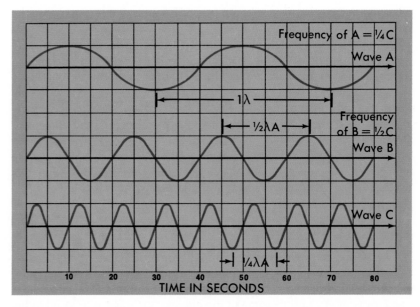

FIGURE 7-9. Wave *A* has the longest wavelength, however wave *C* has the largest frequency. Short electromagnetic waves have higher frequencies than long electromagnetic waves.

Wavelength (λ) is the physical distance between peaks.

This characteristic is called the **wavelength** and is represented by *lambda* (λ). These characteristics of waves are related by the statement, $c = \lambda \nu$. In spectroscopy, the wavelength of light absorbed is characteristic of the substance being excited. The unique set of wavelengths absorbed by a substance is called the **spectrum** of that substance. This set would be emitted by all excited particles of the same substance. We will work with absorption spectra, although emission spectra are also useful.

The spectrum of a substance is the set of wavelengths absorbed or emitted by that substance.

Another wave property that is of importance is the amplitude of a wave, or its maximum displacement from zero. In Figure 7-10, two waves are plotted on the same axes. Note that the amplitude of wave *A* is twice that of wave *B*, even though they have the same wavelength.

Amplitude of a wave is its maximum displacement from a base line.

FIGURE 7-10. Waves having different amplitudes can have the same wavelength.

Absorption and emission spectra are the fingerprints of the elements. Each element has its own unique set of wavelengths that it absorbs or emits. Electromagnetic energy with a wavelength between 700 and 400 nanometers lies in the visible spectrum. This small band of visible radiation has given chemists and physicists much information about the elements. Some elements (rubidium, cesium, helium, and hafnium) were actually discovered through its use. The visible spectrum may also be used for finding the concentration of substances, and for analyzing mixtures and complex ions. Almost any change involving color can be measured using visible spectroscopy.

Each element has a characteristic spectrum.

CAREER: Spectroscopy is used to find the concentration and identity of substances in crime labs.

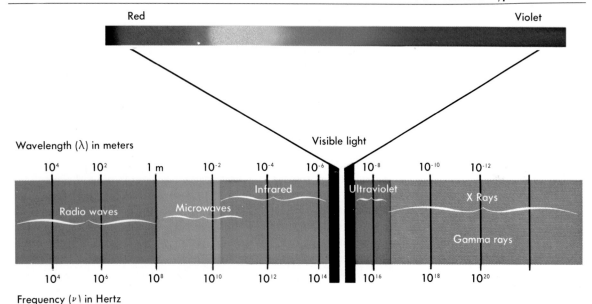

Wavelength (λ) in meters

| 10^4 | 10^2 | 1 m | 10^{-2} | 10^{-4} | 10^{-6} | | 10^{-8} | 10^{-10} | 10^{-12} |

Visible light

Radio waves   Microwaves   Infrared   Ultraviolet   X Rays   Gamma rays

| 10^4 | 10^6 | 10^8 | 10^{10} | 10^{12} | 10^{14} | | 10^{16} | 10^{18} | 10^{20} |

Frequency (ν) in Hertz

Ultraviolet radiation (400-200 nm) can also be used to study atomic and molecular structure. Both ultraviolet spectra and visible spectra are produced by electron changes. The ultraviolet spectrum of an element or compound consists of bands rather than lines. Ultraviolet radiation has such high energy, it violently excites the electrons. The transition of the electrons from the normal state to such highly excited states causes changes in the molecule being studied. Bonds between atoms may even be broken. Visible radiations are not as destructive because they have less energy than UV radiation. Ultraviolet and visible spectroscopy are used for the same types of analyses. In order to describe completely the electronic structure of a substance, both types of analysis must be used.

FIGURE 7-11. Visible light is only a small part of the electromagnetic spectrum. Note that the high frequency waves have short wavelengths.

CAREER: The ink pigments used to print the color photos in this text are matched by using spectral analysis. This process assures good quality control during printing.

a

b

FIGURE 7-12. The emission (a) and absorption (b) spectrum of sodium are used to identify the presence of sodium in a substance.

7:7   PLANCK'S HYPOTHESIS

In his attempt to explain the hydrogen spectrum, Bohr developed his planetary model of the atom. Bohr used the **quantum theory** that had been stated by a German, Max Planck. Planck assumed that energy, instead of being given off continuously, is given off in little packets, or **quanta**. Quanta of radiant energy are often called **photons**. He further

Planck proposed that light was radiated in little packets called quanta or photons.

Energy of a quantum:
$E = h\nu$

Planck's constant (h) = 6.6262
$\times 10^{-34}$ J/Hz

Each wavelength corresponds
to a definite change in the energy of an electron.

Electrons absorb or emit only
whole numbers of quanta.

An electron moves farther from
the nucleus as it absorbs energy.

The ground state of an electron
is the level of least energy.

Modern atomic theory differs
from Bohr's in describing the
path of the electron.

**FIGURE 7-13. The actual hydro-
gen spectrum consists of many
closely spaced lines. Bohr used
quantum theory to calculate the
frequencies for four of these
lines.**

stated that the amount of energy given off is directly related to the frequency of the light emitted.

Planck's idea was that one quantum of energy (light) was related to
the frequency by the equation $E = h\nu$, where h is a constant. The constant
is known as Planck's constant. Its value is 6.6262×10^{-34} joules per
hertz.

7:8 THE HYDROGEN ATOM AND QUANTUM THEORY

Planck's hypothesis stated that energy is given off in quanta instead of
continuously. Bohr pointed out that the absorption of light by hydrogen at
definite wavelengths means definite changes in the energy of the electron.
He reasoned that the orbits of the electrons surrounding a nucleus must
have a definite diameter. According to Bohr, electrons could occupy only
certain orbits. The only orbits allowed were those whose differences in
energy equaled the energy absorbed when the atom was excited. Bohr
thought that the electrons in an atom could absorb or emit energy only in
whole numbers of photons. In other words, an electron could emit energy
in one quantum or two quanta, but not in 1¼ or 3½ quanta.

Bohr pictured the hydrogen atom as an electron circling a nucleus at
a distance of about 0.053 nm. He also imagined that this electron could
absorb a quantum of energy and move to a larger orbit. Since a quantum
represents a certain amount of energy, the next orbit must be some definite distance away from the first. If still more energy is added to the
electron, it moves into a still larger orbit, and so on.

When an electron drops from a larger orbit to a smaller one, energy is
emitted. Since these orbits represent definite energy levels, a definite
amount of energy is radiated.

The size of the smallest orbit an electron can occupy, the one closest
to the nucleus, can be calculated. This smallest orbit is called the **ground
state** of the electron. Bohr calculated the ground state of the hydrogen
electron. Using quantum theory, he calculated the frequencies for the
lines that should appear in the hydrogen spectrum. His results agreed
almost perfectly with the actual hydrogen spectrum. Although today we
use a model of the atom that differs from the Bohr model, many aspects of
his theory are still retained. The major difference is that electrons do not
move around the nucleus as the planets orbit the sun. We will explore this
difference in the next chapter. However, the idea of energy levels is still
the basis of atomic theory. The energy level values calculated by Bohr for
the hydrogen atom are still basically correct.

We can summarize as follows: A wave of a certain frequency has only one possible wavelength, given by $\lambda = c/\nu$. It has only one possible amount of energy, given by $E = h\nu$. Since both c and h are constants, if any one of the three quantities, frequency, wavelength, or energy, is known, we can calculate the other two.

The visible and ultraviolet spectra produced by a compound can be used to determine the elements in the compound. Each line in a spectrum represents one frequency of light. Because the velocity of light is always constant, each frequency means a certain energy. This energy is determined by the movement of electrons between energy levels that are specific for each element. The same set of energy levels will always produce the same spectrum.

7:9 PHOTOELECTRIC EFFECT

Before leaving quantum theory, we will consider another observation explained by this theory. Recall that quanta of light energy are referred to as photons. It had been known for some time that light falling on the surface of certain substances would cause electrons to be emitted. There was, however, a puzzling fact about this change. When the intensity of light (the number of photons per unit time) was reduced, the electrons had the same energy. However, there were fewer electrons emitted. Einstein pointed out that Planck's hypothesis explained this observation.

A certain amount of energy is needed to remove an electron from the surface of a substance. If a photon of greater energy strikes the electron, the electron will move away from the surface. Since it is in motion, the electron has some kinetic energy. Some of the energy of the photon is used to free the electron from the surface. The remainder of the energy becomes the kinetic energy of the electron. If light of one frequency is used, then the electrons escaping from the surface of the substance will all have the same energy. This emission of electrons is called the **photoelectric effect.** If the light intensity is increased, but the frequency remains the

Photoelectric effect refers to emission of electrons from certain substances when exposed to light of suitable frequency.

FIGURE 7-14. This diagram of a photocell circuit shows light causing the ejection of electrons from a metal's surface. The circuit is completed as electrons move toward the opposite plate.

The photoelectric effect lends strong support to the quantum theory.

same, the number of electrons being emitted will increase. If the frequency of the light is increased, the energy of the photon is increased. The amount of energy that must be used to free the electron from the atom is constant for a given substance. Thus, the electrons now leave the surface with a higher kinetic energy than they did with the lower frequency. Planck's hypothesis, together with Einstein's explanation, confirmed the particle nature of light.

Einstein received the Nobel prize in 1921 for his explanation of the photoelectric effect, not for his theory of relativity.

7:10 ATOMIC MASS

The proton and neutron are essentially equal in mass. The mass of the electron is extremely small, so almost all of the mass of an atom is located in the nucleus. Even the simplest atom, which contains only one proton and one electron, has 1836/1837 of its mass in the nucleus. In other atoms that have neutrons in the nucleus, an even higher fraction of the total mass of the atom is in the nucleus.

Nearly all the mass of an atom is in the nucleus.

It is possible to discuss the mass of a single atom. However, chemists have continued to use the masses of large groups of atoms. They do so because of the very small size of the particles in the atom. Chemists have chosen one mole, which is Avogadro's number of atoms (N_A), as a standard unit for large numbers of atoms. Chemists chose this number so that the mass of N_A atoms in grams is equivalent to the mass of one atom in atomic mass units. We know that the unit gram was defined as $1/1000$ the mass of the International Prototype Kilogram. What is an atomic mass unit? To measure atomic masses, an atom of one element was chosen as a standard, and the other elements were compared with it. Scientists used a carbon nuclide, carbon-12, as the standard for the atomic mass scale. The carbon-12 atom is the nuclide of carbon with 6 protons and 6 neutrons in the nucleus. *One carbon-12 atom is defined as having a mass of 12 atomic mass units.* An atomic mass unit is defined to be $1/12$ the mass of the carbon-12 nuclide.

Chemists generally deal in moles of atoms rather than in individual atoms.

The particles that make atoms are called **subatomic particles.** The subatomic particles that we have studied thus far have the following masses.

BACKGROUND: Carbon-12 was selected for its isotopic purity.

One u is defined as $1/12$ the mass of one carbon-12 atom.

$$\text{electron} = 9.10953 \times 10^{-28} \text{ g} = 0.000\,549 \text{ u}$$
$$\text{proton} = 1.67265 \times 10^{-24} \text{ g} = 1.0073 \text{ u}$$
$$\text{neutron} = 1.67495 \times 10^{-24} \text{ g} = 1.0087 \text{ u}$$

Avogadro's number (N_A) of atoms is contained in 12 grams of carbon-12.

If it were possible to take exactly 12 grams of carbon-12 atoms and count them, we would have Avogadro's number of atoms. Look carefully at Table 7-3. Notice that many of the elements have a mass in atomic mass units that is close to the total number of protons and neutrons in their nuclei. However, some do not. What causes the mass of chlorine or copper, for example, to be about halfway between whole numbers? The numbers in the table are based on the "average atom" of an element.

Table 7-3

International Atomic Masses							
Element	Symbol	Atomic number	Atomic mass	Element	Symbol	Atomic number	Atomic mass
Actinium	Ac	89	227.0278*	Neon	Ne	10	20.179
Aluminum	Al	13	26.98154	Neptunium	Np	93	237.0482
Americium	Am	95	243.0614*	Nickel	Ni	28	58.69
Antimony	Sb	51	121.75	Niobium	Nb	41	92.9064
Argon	Ar	18	39.948	Nitrogen	N	7	14.0067
Arsenic	As	33	74.9216	Nobelium	No	102	259.1009*
Astatine	At	85	209.9871*	Osmium	Os	76	190.2
Barium	Ba	56	137.33	Oxygen	O	8	15.9994
Berkelium	Bk	97	247.0703*	Palladium	Pd	46	106.42
Beryllium	Be	4	9.01218	Phosphorus	P	15	30.97376
Bismuth	Bi	83	208.9804	Platinum	Pt	78	195.08
Boron	B	5	10.811	Plutonium	Pu	94	244.0642*
Bromine	Br	35	79.904	Polonium	Po	84	208.9824*
Cadmium	Cd	48	112.41	Potassium	K	19	39.0983
Calcium	Ca	20	40.078	Praseodymium	Pr	59	140.9077
Californium	Cf	98	251.0796*	Promethium	Pm	61	144.9128*
Carbon	C	6	12.011	Protactinium	Pa	91	231.0359*
Cerium	Ce	58	140.12	Radium	Ra	88	226.0254
Cesium	Cs	55	132.9054	Radon	Rn	86	222.0176*
Chlorine	Cl	17	35.453	Rhenium	Re	75	186.207
Chromium	Cr	24	51.9961	Rhodium	Rh	45	102.9055
Cobalt	Co	27	58.9332	Rubidium	Rb	37	85.4678
Copper	Cu	29	63.546	Ruthenium	Ru	44	101.07
Curium	Cm	96	247.0703*	Samarium	Sm	62	150.36
Dysprosium	Dy	66	162.50	Scandium	Sc	21	44.95591
Einsteinium	Es	99	252.0828*	Selenium	Se	34	78.96
Erbium	Er	68	167.26	Silicon	Si	14	28.0855
Europium	Eu	63	151.96	Silver	Ag	47	107.8682
Fermium	Fm	100	257.0951*	Sodium	Na	11	22.98977
Fluorine	F	9	18.998403	Strontium	Sr	38	87.62
Francium	Fr	87	223.0197*	Sulfur	S	16	32.066
Gadolinium	Gd	64	157.25	Tantalum	Ta	73	180.9479
Gallium	Ga	31	69.723	Technetium	Tc	43	97.9072*
Germanium	Ge	32	72.59	Tellurium	Te	52	127.60
Gold	Au	79	196.9665	Terbium	Tb	65	158.9254
Hafnium	Hf	72	178.49	Thallium	Tl	81	204.383
Helium	He	2	4.002602	Thorium	Th	90	232.0381
Holmium	Ho	67	164.9304	Thulium	Tm	69	168.9342
Hydrogen	H	1	1.00794	Tin	Sn	50	118.710
Indium	In	49	114.82	Titanium	Ti	22	47.88
Iodine	I	53	126.9045	Tungsten	W	74	183.85
Iridium	Ir	77	192.22	Unnilennium†	Une	109	266*
Iron	Fe	26	55.847	Unnilhexium†	Unh	106	263*
Krypton	Kr	36	83.80	Unniloctium†	Uno	108	265*
Lanthanum	La	57	138.9055	Unnilpentium†	Unp	105	262*
Lawrencium	Lr	103	260.1054*	Unnilquadium†	Unq	104	261*
Lead	Pb	82	207.2	Unnilseptium†	Uns	107	262*
Lithium	Li	3	6.941	Uranium	U	92	238.0289
Lutetium	Lu	71	174.967	Vanadium	V	23	50.9415
Magnesium	Mg	12	24.305	Xenon	Xe	54	131.29
Manganese	Mn	25	54.9380	Ytterbium	Yb	70	173.04
Mendelevium	Md	101	258.0986*	Yttrium	Y	39	88.9059
Mercury	Hg	80	200.59	Zinc	Zn	30	65.39
Molybdenum	Mo	42	95.94	Zirconium	Zr	40	91.224
Neodymium	Nd	60	144.24				

*The mass of the isotope with the longest known half-life.

†Names for elements 104-109 have been approved for temporary use by the IUPAC. The USSR has proposed Kurchatovium (Ku) for element 104, and Bohrium (Bh) for element 105. The United States has proposed Rutherfordium (Rf) for element 104, and Hahnium (Ha) for element 105.

Most elements have many isotopic forms that occur naturally. It is difficult and costly to collect a large amount of a single nuclide of an element. Thus, for most calculations, the average atomic mass of the element is used.

The average atomic mass of an element is used in calculations.

7:11   AVERAGE ATOMIC MASS

Using a standard nuclide, there are two ways of determining masses for atoms of other elements. One method is by reacting the standard element with the element to be determined. Using accurate masses of the two elements and a known mole ratio, the atomic mass of the second element may be calculated as a mass-mass problem.

A mass spectrometer measures the masses and amounts of isotopes.

Greater accuracy can be obtained by using a physical method of measurement in a device called a **mass spectrometer.** Its development was based on the early tubes of J. J. Thomson. It is similar in design to the tube used by Thomson to find the charge/mass ratio of the electron. Using a mass spectrometer, we can determine the relative amounts and masses of the nuclides for all isotopes of an element.

Average atomic mass can be determined from relative amounts of each isotope.

The element sample, which is in the form of a gas, enters a chamber where it is ionized by hitting it with electrons. These ions are then propelled by electric and magnetic fields. As in the Thomson tube, the fields bend the path of the charged particles as shown in Figure 7-15. The paths of the heavy particles are bent slightly as they pass through the fields. The paths of the lighter particles are curved more. Thus, the paths of the particles are separated by relative mass. The particles are caught and recorded electronically. One drawback of the instrument is that the ionization chamber, field tube, and detection device must all be in a vacuum. The vacuum containing these devices must be equal to about one hundred-millionth (1/100 000 000) of normal atmospheric pressure.

Since the strength of the fields and the speed and paths of the particles are known, the mass of the particles can be calculated. Once the

FIGURE 7-15. In a mass spectrometer, the ion beam is subjected to a magnetic field. Massive ions are affected less by the magnetic field than lighter ions.

masses of the isotopes and their relative amounts have been found, the average atomic mass can be calculated.

EXAMPLE: Average Atomic Mass

Neon has two isotopes. Neon-20 has a mass of 19.992 u and neon-22 has a mass of 21.991 u. In any sample of 100 neon atoms, 90 will be neon-20 and ten will be neon-22. Calculate the average atomic mass of neon.

Solving Process:
Each of the isotopic masses is multiplied by its fractional abundance. Then the products are added.

$$\frac{90}{100}(19.992 \text{ u}) + \frac{10}{100}(21.991 \text{ u}) = 17.993 \text{ u} + 2.1991 \text{ u}$$

$$= 20.192 \text{ u}$$

This average mass is called the **atomic mass** of an element. It is represented by the symbol U. The mass spectrometer has other uses. Geologists, biologists, petroleum chemists, and many other research workers use the mass spectrometer as an analytical tool.

FIGURE 7-16. A chemist uses the data obtained from a mass spectrometer in chemical analysis.

PROBLEMS

2. What is the atomic mass of silicon if 92.21% of its atoms have mass 27.977 u, 4.70% have mass 28.976 u, and 3.09% have mass 29.974 u?

2. 28.1 u

3. What is the atomic mass of hafnium if, out of every 100 atoms, 5 have mass 176, 19 have mass 177, 27 have mass 178, 14 have mass 179, and 35 have mass 180.0?

3. 179 u

BIOGRAPHY

Ernest Rutherford (1871-1937)

Ernest Rutherford was one of the most brilliant scientists involved in the investigation of atomic structure. He won the Nobel Prize in chemistry for his study of radioactivity. The theories he proposed in this area serve as a basis for our modern theory of radioactivity.

In his principle of atomic transmutation, Rutherford contended a radioactive atom emits electrically charged particles and forms a new atom of a different chemical element.

In 1911, Rutherford worked out the nuclear theory of the atom which led him to be known as the "father of nuclear science." From his experiments, he constructed a model for the atom in which the electrons were outside a positively charged center or nucleus. This model is the basis of our modern view of atomic structure.

CAREERS AND CHEMISTRY

7:12   Laboratory Technicians

FIGURE 7-17. Chemical technicians run a variety of tests on cosmetics and related substances to ensure their safety for consumer use.

Not all workers in chemical laboratories are professional chemists. Most companies having one or more chemical laboratories employ laboratory technicians or assistants.

Laboratory technicians are involved with a number of aspects of laboratory operation. However, some of their principal work consists of carrying out routine analyses of materials. These procedures are tied to maintaining or improving product quality. If a company should receive a shipment of returned goods due to poor quality or shipment damage, the technicians will run tests to determine the source of any manufacturing or packaging problems. They may measure the concentration of solutions using the titration process. They may separate mixtures using various analytical techniques such as distillation and chromatography.

In running an analytical procedure, the technician usually employs a number of delicate instruments designed to give very precise measurements. The maintenance and repair of those instruments is usually the responsibility of the technician. It may also be his or her responsibility to calibrate the instrument periodically, that is, to check its accuracy.

Some technicians spend considerable time preparing solutions or other materials for use by a professional chemist. Grinding coarse solids, obtaining samples from large batches of raw materials throughout the

FIGURE 7-18. Biological enzyme studies are being carried out in these flasks. The technician will interpret the resulting data.

stages of production, and thorough testing of the final product are all routine tasks for a technician.

The technician must have sufficient background knowledge to read and interpret technical manuals. In addition, he or she may be called upon to write reports based on the work or to assist a chemist in writing a report on a project on which they have worked jointly.

Technicians employed by drug manufacturers must also master some biological techniques. They monitor incubators, use microscopes, and run sterilizers, all of which require a knowledge of the equipment and analytical procedure being performed.

FIGURE 7-19. Some technicians run simple analytical procedures with equipment similar to that in your chemistry lab.

A laboratory technician in a petroleum refinery may move throughout the plant reading temperatures and pressures from meters and gauges. The data gathered in the plant may be an important part of his or her report on the analytical sample taken at a particular time.

Laboratory technicians can be involved in a wide variety of jobs. An experienced technician could well move into a position as an important part of a research and development team.

To prepare to be a laboratory technician, at least two years of college training in a science is required. Most technicians receive further on-the-job training in procedures and equipment specific to their particular job.

SUMMARY

1. Democritus proposed the earliest recorded atomic theory. **7:1**

2. Modern atomic theory dates from John Dalton's hypothesis. He made use of the law of conservation of mass and the law of definite proportions to state that all matter is formed of indivisible particles called atoms; all atoms of one element are the same; atoms of different elements are unlike; and atoms can unite with one another in simple whole-number ratios. **7:1-7:2**

3. Modern atomic theory differs from Dalton's atomic theory due to the discovery of subatomic particles and isotopes. 7:3-7:4

4. An electron is a negatively charged particle with a very small mass. A proton is a positively charged particle with a mass 1836 times the mass of an electron. A neutron is an uncharged particle with a mass about the same as the mass of a proton. 7:3

5. All atoms of an element contain the same number of protons in their nuclei. Atoms containing the same number of protons but different numbers of neutrons are isotopes of the same element. The atomic number (Z) of an element is the number of protons in its nucleus. The mass number (A) of an atom is the number of particles in its nucleus. 7:3-7:4

6. Atoms are extremely small and consist mostly of space. Rutherford and Bohr pictured the atom as consisting of a central nucleus surrounded by electrons in orbits. 7:5

7. Substances excited by an energy source emit light in definite wavelengths called a spectrum. Visible and ultraviolet spectroscopy are used to study the wavelengths of light absorbed and emitted by electrons in atoms. 7:6

8. Planck stated that energy is radiated in discrete units called quanta. A photon is a quantum of light energy. The energy of a quantum of radiation varies directly as the frequency of the radiation ($E = h\nu$). 7:7

9. Quantum theory helped Bohr explain the hydrogen spectrum, and thus, to calculate the orbits for the hydrogen atom. 7:8

10. The photoelectric effect is the loss of electrons from a substance, caused by photons striking its surface. 7:9

11. The atomic mass of an element is the weighted average mass, (U) of all the natural isotopes of the element. It is the mass of an average individual atom of the element compared with $\frac{1}{12}$ the mass of the carbon-12 atom. Atomic mass can be measured with the mass spectrometer. 7:10-7:11

VOCABULARY

law of conservation of mass 7:1
law of definite proportions 7:1
law of multiple proportions 7:2
anode 7:3
cathode 7:3
isotopes 7:4
atomic number 7:4
nucleons 7:4
mass number 7:4
planetary model 7:5
spectroscopy 7:6
electromagnetic energy 7:6

frequency 7:6
hertz 7:6
wavelength 7:6
spectrum 7:6
quantum theory 7:7
quanta 7:7
photon 7:7
ground state 7:8
photoelectric effect 7:9
subatomic particles 7:10
atomic mass 7:11

PROBLEMS

1. What did each of the following contribute in forming the atomic theory?
   a. Dalton
   b. Thomson
   c. Rutherford
   d. Chadwick
   e. Moseley
   f. Bohr
   g. Planck
   h. Avogadro

See the Teacher Guide for detailed answers to all problems.

2. List the major points in Dalton's atomic theory.

3. What element is used as the reference standard in defining atomic mass units?

   3. carbon-12

4. How would you show the law of conservation of mass with a burning candle?

5. Design an experiment to demonstrate the law of definite proportions.

6. State Avogadro's hypothesis.

7. A particular atom of potassium contains 19 protons, 19 electrons, and 20 neutrons. What is the atomic number of this atom? What is its mass number?

   7. 19; 39 u
   8. 107.9 u
   9. 83.8 u

8. Compute the average atomic mass of silver, if 51.82% of the silver atoms occurring in nature have mass 106.905 and 48.18% of the atoms have mass 108.905.

9. Compute the average atomic mass of krypton if the relative amounts are as follows.

isotopic mass	percentage
77.920	0.350
79.916	2.27
81.913	11.56
82.914	11.55
83.912	56.90
85.911	17.37

10. How many nm are in 4.23 cm?

    10. 4.23×10^7 nm

11. How did the discovery of subatomic particles and isotopes affect Dalton's theories?

12. What are the differences in charge and mass among protons, neutrons, and electrons?

13. How many electrons, neutrons, and protons are in the isotope of chlorine with mass number 35? How many of each are in the isotope of thorium with mass number 232?

    13. Cl=17 electrons; 17 protons; 18 neutrons
    Th=90 electrons; 90 protons; 142 neutrons

14. What was Rutherford's role in the Geiger-Marsden experiment?

15. How did Bohr use spectroscopic data to formulate his model of the atom?

16. Why is it necessary to ionize an element sample before it can be separated into its isotopic components?

17. How does quantum theory explain the photoelectric effect?

REVIEW

1. Write names for the following compounds.

a. $Sr(CH_3COO)_2$ c. CdC_2O_4 e. Th_3N_4
b. $Mn(OH)_2$ d. Li_3AsO_4 f. $Ce_2(CO_3)_3$

2. Find the formula for the hydrate that has a composition of 84.2% $(NH_4)_2CO_3$ and 15.8% H_2O.

3. Balance the following equations.

a. $Na + H_2O \rightarrow NaOH + H_2$ c. $Sb + Cl_2 \rightarrow SbCl_3$
b. $Mg + HCl \rightarrow MgCl_2 + H_2$ d. $Cl_2 + KBr \rightarrow KCl + Br_2$

4. Write formulas for the following compounds.

a. sodium nitride   d. hydrogen telluride
b. cerium(III) sulfide   e. silver sulfate
c. barium hexafluorosilicate   f. cesium hexafluorosilicate

5. Balance the following equations.

a. $K + H_2O \rightarrow KOH + H_2$ c. $Cl_2 + KI \rightarrow KCl + I_2$
b. $Ca + HCl \rightarrow CaCl_2 + H_2$ d. $Na_2O_2 + H_2O \rightarrow NaOH + O_2$

6. Convert 0.633 mole $Th(SeO_4)_2$ to formula units.

7. Convert 0.0731 mole $Sr(CN)_2$ to grams.

8. Find the percentage composition of each element in $BaSO_4$.

9. Find the empirical formula for a compound with composition: 44.2% Cd, 44.8% F, and 11.0% Si.

10. Find the formula for a hydrate with composition: 76.0% SrI_2 and 24.0% H_2O.

11. What mass of magnesium hydroxide is obtained from 84.1 grams of magnesium oxide in accordance with the reaction:

$$MgO + H_2O \rightarrow Mg(OH)_2?$$

12. How much heat is required to raise the temperature of 91.0 grams ZnS from 8.9°C to 35.7°C?

Answer key (left margin):

1. a. strontium acetate
   b. manganese(II) hydroxide
   c. cadmium oxalate
   d. lithium arsenate
   e. thorium(IV) nitride
   f. cerium(III) carbonate
2. $(NH_4)_2CO_3 \cdot H_2O$
3. a. $2Na + 2H_2O \rightarrow 2NaOH + H_2$
   b. $Mg + 2HCl \rightarrow MgCl_2 + H_2$
   c. $2Sb + 3Cl_2 \rightarrow 2SbCl_3$
   d. $Cl_2 + 2KBr \rightarrow 2KCl + Br_2$
4. a. Na_3N
   b. Ce_2S_3
   c. $BaSiF_6$
   d. H_2Te
   e. Ag_2SO_4
   f. Cs_2SiF_6
5. a. $2K + 2H_2O \rightarrow 2KOH + H_2$
   b. $Ca + 2HCl \rightarrow CaCl_2 + H_2$
   c. $Cl_2 + 2KI \rightarrow 2KCl + I_2$
   d. $2Na_2O_2 + 2H_2O \rightarrow 4NaOH + O_2$
6. 3.81×10^{23} formula units
7. 10.2 g
8. Ba 58.8%, S 13.8%, O 27.5%
9. $CdSiF_6$
10. $SrI_2 \cdot 6H_2O$
11. 122 g
12. 1140 J

See the Teacher Guide for detailed solutions to all problems.

ONE MORE STEP

1. The mass spectrometer is used to separate isotopes for use as nuclear fuel. Investigate this process and see how it differs from other processes used for the same purpose.

2. James Franck and Gustav Hertz performed an experiment to test the quantum theory. Prepare a report on their experiment and its results.

3. Make a table listing as many subatomic particles as you can. For each particle, list its mass, charge, and lifetime.

4. Use a handbook to make a list of the mass numbers of all known isotopes of the first twenty elements. Show those that are unstable (radioactive) in red.

5. Although Bohr was the first to use experimental evidence to support his hypothesis, he was not the first person to propose a planetary model for the atom. Look into the history of this idea prior to Bohr.

6. Find a description of an experiment used for determining the size of a proton or a neutron.

7. What is the energy of a quantum of light of frequency 4.31×10^{14} Hz?

8. What is the energy of light with wavelength 662 nm?

9. What would be the wavelength of light necessary to cause electrons to leave the surface of a substance with an energy of 1.20×10^{-19} J? Assume the energy necessary to release the electron from the surface is 3.60×10^{-19} J.

10. In considering the photoelectric effect, what is the relationship between the frequency of a photon striking the metal surface and the number and energy of the electrons leaving that surface?

11. A certain violet light has a wavelength of 413 nm. What is its frequency? The velocity of light is equal to 3.00×10^8 m/s.

12. A certain green light has a frequency of 6.26×10^{14} Hz. What is its wavelength?

13. What is the energy content of one quantum of the light in Problem 11?

14. What is the energy content of one quantum of the light in Problem 12?

15. Three techniques for analysis which are closely allied with spectroscopy are colorimetry, fluorimetry, and nephelometry (nef uh LAHM ih tree). Investigate the uses of these procedures.

16. Prepare a report for your class on the topic of electron paramagnetic resonance (EPR), one of the newer methods in analysis.

7. 2.86×10^{-19} J
8. 3.00×10^{-19} J
9. 414 nm

11. 7.26×10^{14} Hz
12. 479 nm
13. 4.81×10^{-19} J
14. 4.15×10^{-19} J

READINGS

"Educated Guess," *SciQuest*, Vol. 54, No. 4(April 1981), p. 25.

Ekstrom, Philip, and David Wineland, "The Isolated Electron," *Scientific American*, Vol. 242, No. 8(August 1980), p. 104.

Shugar, Gershon J., et al., *Chemical Technician's Ready Reference Handbook*, 2nd Ed., New York: McGraw-Hill Book Co., 1981.

The structure and behavior of atoms could not be fully explained by the solar system model. Therefore, it became necessary
to formulate a new model for the atom. In some ways the galaxy
shown is a more accurate representation of an atom. Think of this
cloudlike mass as the volume occupied by electrons. Note that the
edges of the galaxy are not clearly defined. Some areas appear more
dense than others. In what other ways is the galaxy similar to an
electron cloud? What are the other characteristics of the modern
model of the atom?

ELECTRON CLOUDS AND PROBABILITY

Chapter 8 develops the wave mechanical model of the atom by introducing Schrödinger's probability equation and Heisenberg's uncertainty principle.

DEMONSTRATION: Using five evaporating dishes, dissolve small amounts of Sr, Li, Ba, Cu, and Na salts separately in each dish by adding a few cm^3 of water and then a few cm^3 of methanol. Ignite the alcohol solutions and observe the colors in a dark room. Discuss how improved spectral data have advanced the modern atomic theory. See additional information in front of text.

GOALS:
* You will gain an understanding of the electron structure of the quantum mechanical model of the atom.
* You will define the four quantum numbers.
* You will use the diagonal rule to write electron configurations.
* You will write electron dot diagrams for the elements.

The properties of matter are a consequence of its structure. Therefore, we need to improve our ideas of atomic structure. In the attempts to refine our model of the atom, we see the division between matter and energy has become less clear. Radiant energy is found to have many properties of particles. Small particles of matter are found to display the characteristics of wave motion. The purpose of this chapter is to look more closely at this wave-particle problem.

We have seen in Chapter 7 that the frequencies predicted by Bohr for the hydrogen spectrum are "essentially" correct. Note that we did not use the word "exactly." Improved equipment has shown that the hydrogen spectrum lines predicted by Bohr are not single lines. If we were to reexamine the hydrogen spectrum with a better spectroscope, we would see that what seemed to be single lines are really several lines closely spaced. Scientists have had to change many of their ideas about the behavior of the particles in an atom. They have done so because of the discovery of the "fine structure" of spectral lines. Bohr's use of quantum theory in the study of atomic structure has been revised to include the fine structure.

Bohr's theory of the atom was revised to include the fine lines of the hydrogen spectrum.

8:1 DE BROGLIE'S HYPOTHESIS

In 1923, a French physicist, Louis de Broglie, proposed a hypothesis that led the way to the present theory of atomic structure. De Broglie knew of Planck's ideas concerning radiation being made of discrete amounts of energy called quanta. This theory seemed to give waves the properties of particles. De Broglie thought if Planck were correct, then it might be possible for particles to have some of the properties of waves.

De Broglie suggested that particles have characteristics of waves.

Recall the Law of Conservation of Mass-Energy from Section 1:6.

DeBroglie made use of Einstein's relationship between matter and energy

$$E = mc^2$$

and Planck's quantum theory

$$E = h\nu$$

De Broglie equated the two expressions for energy

$$mc^2 = h\nu$$

He then substituted **v**, a general velocity, for c, the velocity of light

$$m\nu^2 = h\nu$$

and **v**/λ for ν because the frequency of a wave is equal to its velocity divided by its wavelength.

$$m\nu^2 = \frac{h\nu}{\lambda}$$

$$\lambda = \frac{h\nu}{m\nu^2} = \frac{h}{m\nu}$$

BACKGROUND: The first demonstration of an electron's wave nature occurred in 1927 in the United States. Germer and Davisson diffracted an electron beam using a crystal.

The final expression was de Broglie's prediction of the wavelength of a particle of mass m and velocity **v**. Within two years, de Broglie's hypothesis was proven correct. Scientists found by experiment that, in some ways, an electron stream acted in the same way as a ray of light. They further showed that the wavelength of the electrons was exactly that predicted by de Broglie.

PROBLEM

1. 0.332 nm

1. What is the wavelength of an electron of mass 9.11×10^{-28} g traveling at 2.19×10^6 m/s? (Planck's constant = 6.6262×10^{-34} J/Hz, 1 Hz = 1/s, 1 J = N·m, 1 N = 1 kg·m/s^2)

8:2   THE APPARENT CONTRADICTION

BACKGROUND: 2.19×10^6 m/s is the speed of the ground state electron in hydrogen.

Waves can act as particles, and particles can act as waves. We saw how the photoelectric effect and Bohr's atom model explained light in terms of particle properties. Now let us look at a light property that can be explained by wave behavior.

Refraction occurs when light strikes a surface and changes direction.

Light waves travel at different speeds in different substances. When a light wave passes from one substance into another it changes speed. If a light wave strikes a surface at an angle, it also changes direction (is bent or refracted).

*Symbols in boldface are vector quantities. Vectors have both magnitude and direction.

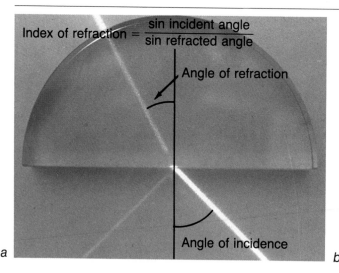

Index of refraction = $\dfrac{\text{sin incident angle}}{\text{sin refracted angle}}$

Angle of refraction

Angle of incidence

a

b

FIGURE 8-1. Light is refracted as it passes through this piece of glass (a). Due to refraction, the thermometer appears bent (b).

The **index of refraction** of a substance is determined by the bending of a light wave as it passes from a vacuum into that substance. We measure the angle between the ray and the surface both before and after the ray passes through the surface. Each substance has a characteristic index of refraction, Figure 8-1. We can identify a substance by its index of refraction. The instrument used to measure index of refraction is called a refractometer (ree frak TOM uh tuhr).

Like light, electrons also have properties of both waves and particles. However, one cannot observe both the particle and wave properties of an electron by the same experiment. If an experiment is done to show an electron's wave properties, the electron exhibits the behavior of a wave. Another experiment, carried out to show the electron as a particle, will show that the electron exhibits the behavior of a particle. The whole idea of the two-sided nature of waves and particles is referred to as the **wave-particle duality of nature.** The duality applies to all waves and all particles. Scientists are not always interested in duality. For example, when scientists study the motion of a space shuttle, wave characteristics do not enter into their study. They are only interested in the shuttle as a particle. However, with very small particles we cannot ignore wave properties. For an electron, a study of its wave characteristics can tell as much about its behavior as a study of its particle characteristics.

Index of refraction is a characteristic of all transparent materials. (Section 3:4)

Light has properties of both particles and waves.

Electrons have wave-particle duality.

BACKGROUND: Index of refraction is measured with respect to a vacuum. However, the index with respect to air will be negligibly different in most cases.

8:3 MOMENTUM

The product of the mass and velocity of an object is called the **momentum** of the object. In equation form, $m\mathbf{v} = \mathbf{p},$ where m is the mass, $\mathbf{v}$ is the velocity, and $\mathbf{p}$ is the symbol for momentum. You should

Momentum is a vector quantity which consists of mass and velocity.

Momentum (**p**):

$mv = p$

As momentum of an object increases, its wavelength decreases.

BACKGROUND: Newton's laws of motion:
1. Every object remains at rest or in uniform motion until an external force acts to change its motion.
2. The change in motion of an object produced by an external force varies directly with the force exerted.
3. For every action, there is an equal and opposite reaction.

note that velocity includes not only the speed but also the direction of motion. Substituting momentum (**p**) for mv in the de Broglie equation, we can then write

$$\lambda = \frac{h}{p}$$

Note that the wavelength varies inversely as the momentum. The wave properties of all objects in motion are not always of interest to the scientist. There is a basic difference between Newtonian and quantum mechanics. **Newtonian mechanics** (or classical mechanics) describes the behavior of visible objects traveling at ordinary velocities. **Quantum mechanics** describes the behavior of extremely small particles traveling at velocities near that of light.

To the chemist, the behavior of the electrons in an atom is of greatest interest. To be able to give a full description of an electron, we must know two things: where it is, and where it is going. In other words, we must know the electron's present position and its momentum. From the velocity and position of an electron at one time, we can calculate where the electron will be some time later.

8:4 MEASURING POSITION AND MOMENTUM

Werner Heisenberg further improved the ideas about atomic structure. He pointed out that *it is impossible to know both the exact position and the exact momentum of an object at the same time.* Let us take a closer look at Heisenberg's ideas. To locate the exact position of an electron, we must be able to "look" at it. When we look at an object large enough to see with our eyes, we actually see the light waves which the object has reflected. When radar detects an object, the radar receiver is actually "seeing" the radar waves reflected by the object. In other words, for us to see an object, it must be hit by a photon of radiant energy. A collision between a photon and an electron results in a large change in the energy of the electron. Let us assume we have "seen" an electron, using some sort of radiant energy as "illumination." We have found the exact position of the electron. However, we would have little idea of the electron's velocity. The collision between it and the photons used to see it has caused its velocity to change. Thus, we would know the position of the electron, but not its velocity. On the other hand, if we measure an electron's velocity, we will change the electron's position. We would know the velocity fairly well, but not the position. Heisenberg stated that there is always some uncertainty about the position and momentum of an electron. This statement is known as **Heisenberg's uncertainty principle.**

Heisenberg's uncertainty principle: The exact position and momentum of an object can not be determined at the same time.

FIGURE 8-2. Radar is used in detecting weather patterns. The reflections of radar waves are picked up by a detector to form the image on the screen.

The uncertainty of the position and the uncertainty of the momentum of an electron are related by Planck's constant. If Δp* is the uncertainty in the momentum and Δx is the uncertainty in the location, then

$$\Delta p \Delta x \geq h$$

Thus, since h is constant, the more certain we are of the position of the electron, the less certain we are of its momentum. The more certain we are of its momentum, the less certain we are of its position.

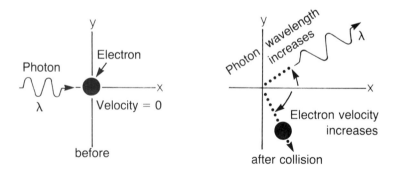

FIGURE 8-3. If an electron were in a fixed position and a photon collided with it, the velocity of the electron would change. Thus, there is always some uncertainty as to the position and momentum of the electron.

8:5 SCHRÖDINGER'S WORK

Chemists and physicists now found themselves unable to describe the exact structure of the atom. Heisenberg had, in effect, stated that the exact motion of an electron was unknown and could never be determined. Notice, however, that Heisenberg's principle of uncertainty treats

*Recall the Greek letter delta (Δ) means *change in*.

the electron as a particle. What happens if the electron is treated as a wave? The wave nature of the electron was investigated by the Austrian physicist, Erwin Schrödinger.

Schrödinger treated the electron as a wave and developed a mathematical equation to describe its wave-like behavior. Schrödinger's equation related the amplitude of the electron-wave ψ (psi) to any point in space around the nucleus. He pointed out that there is no physical meaning to the values of ψ. You should avoid trying to assume one. Terms for the total energy and for the potential energy of the electron are also part of this equation. In computing the total energy and the potential energy, certain numbers must be used. For example, the term for the total energy

BACKGROUND:

$$\frac{\partial^2 \psi}{\partial x^2} + \frac{\partial^2 \psi}{\partial y^2} + \frac{\partial^2 \psi}{\partial z^2} + \frac{8\pi^2 m}{h^2}(E - V)\psi = 0$$

is

$$2\pi^2 m e^4 / h^2 n^2$$

Here, m is the mass of the electron, e is the charge on the electron, h is Planck's constant, and n can take positive whole number values. The symbol n represents the first of four quantum numbers. These four **quantum numbers** are used in describing electron behavior. They will be studied in detail in later sections. The actual wave equation involves mathematics with which you are probably not familiar and so it will not be given.

The four quantum numbers in Schrödinger's equation are used in describing electron behavior.

CAREER: Biologists use the wave property of an electron beam in electron microscopes. Electric and magnetic fields are used to focus the electrons. This device results in very high magnification and resolution.

The physical significance of all this mathematics was pointed out by Max Born. He worked with the square of the absolute value of the amplitude, $|\psi|^2$. He showed that $|\psi|^2$ gave the probability of finding the electron at the point in space for which the equation was solved. By **probability,** we mean the ratio between the number of times the electron is in that position divided by the total number of times it is at all possible positions. The higher the probability, the more likely the electron will be found in a given position.

Probability =

No. of times in position X
Σ times in all positions

8:6 WAVE-MECHANICAL VIEW OF THE HYDROGEN ATOM

Schrödinger's equation can be used to describe the most probable positions of the hydrogen electron.

Schrödinger's wave equation is used to determine the probability of finding the hydrogen electron in any given place. The probabilities can be computed for finding the electron at different points along a given line away from the nucleus. One point will have a higher probability than any other, Figure 8-4. To carry the process even further, computers can be used to calculate the probabilities for thousands of points in space. There will be many points of equal probability. If all the points of highest probability are connected, some three dimensional shape is formed. These shapes will be shown later in the chapter. The most probable place to find the electron will be some place on the surface of this calculated shape. Remember that this shape is only a "mental model" and does not actually

BACKGROUND: The 1933 Nobel Prize in Physics was awarded to Schrödinger for his development of quantum mechanics.

a

b

FIGURE 8-4. Probability plots for a hydrogen electron are shown in (a). Note the area represented by 90% probability. The point of highest probability for a hydrogen electron occurs at about 0.053 nm from the nucleus (b).

exist. It is something we use in our minds to help locate the most probable position of the electron.

There is another way of looking at probability. The electron moves about the nucleus in such a way as to pass through the points of high probability more often than through any other points. The electron is traveling at a high rate of speed. If the electron were visible to the eye, its rapid motion would cause it to appear as a cloud. Think of an electric fan as shown in Figure 8-5. When the fan is turning, it appears to fill the complete circle through which it turns. We cannot place an object between the blades while the fan is turning. If we do, the result will show that the fan is effectively filling the entire circle. So it is with the electron. It effectively fills all the space. At any given time, it is more likely to be somewhere on the surface of the shape described by the points of highest probability. The probability of finding the blade outside its volume is

An electron effectively occupies all the space around a nucleus.

FIGURE 8-5. The fan blades (a) appear to occupy the total volume through which they turn. An electron occupies a 3-dimensional volume to form a cloud of negative charge (b).

a

b   Electron cloud

zero. However, it is possible to find the electron outside of its high probability surface. Therefore, since the volume occupied by an electron is somewhat vague, it is better to refer to it as an **electron cloud.** Let us now look more closely at this electron cloud to learn more about its size and shape.

The position of an electron can best be represented by a cloud.

8:7 SOLVING SCHRÖDINGER'S EQUATION

Prior to the use of computers, solutions to the Schrödinger equation proved difficult for even the best mathematicians. It had been solved exactly only for simple cases involving the hydrogen atom. The use of quantum numbers in the solution of the wave equation was mentioned in Section 8:5. These numbers represent different energy states of the electron. In Schrödinger's atomic model, changes between energy states must take place by emission or absorption of whole numbers of photons. For the simple hydrogen atom, solution of the wave equation gives us accurate energy states. The differences between these energy states correspond to the lines observed in the hydrogen spectrum. With more complex atoms, however, the interaction of electrons makes solution of the equation impossible. Recall that electrons all have the same charge, which causes them to repel each other. In spite of this difficulty, scientists can come close to finding the electronic structure of atoms by making an assumption. They first calculate the various single energy states in the simple hydrogen atom. A different quantum number is used to arrive at a value for each state. They then assume that the various electrons in a multielectron atom occupy these same energy states without affecting each other. There are four quantum numbers, n, l, m, and s. Each electron within an atom can be described by a unique set of four quantum numbers. We will discuss each quantum number separately starting with n.

Quantum numbers represent different electron energy states.

Each electron within an atom can be described by a unique set of four quantum numbers.

8:8 PRINCIPAL QUANTUM NUMBER

An electron can occupy only specific energy levels. These energy levels are numbered, starting with 1 and proceeding to the higher integers. The **principal quantum number** (n) corresponds to the energy levels (1, 2, 3, . . . n) calculated for the hydrogen atom. The number of the energy level, referred to as n, is called the principal quantum number.

Electrons may be found in each energy level of an atom. The greatest number of electrons possible in any one level is $2n^2$. Thus, in the first level ($n = 1$) there may be at most two electrons (2×1^2). In the fourth energy level, there can be no more than 32 electrons (2×4^2). Figure 8-6 shows the relative energies of the various levels. It also indicates the maximum number of electrons possible in each level.

Principal quantum number, n, describes energy level. Maximum number of electrons in energy level = $2n^2$.

n determines effective volume

FIGURE 8-6. The relationship between energy and principal quantum number is shown in (a). The relationship between size of the charge cloud and principal quantum number is shown in (b).

PROBLEM

2. Calculate the maximum number of electrons that can occupy the levels when $n = 2, 3, 5,$ and 7.

2. 8, 18, 50, 98

8:9   ENERGY SUBLEVELS AND ORBITALS

The second quantum number is l. In a hydrogen atom, all electrons in one level have the same energy. This statement is not true for any other atom. Spectrum studies have shown that an energy level is actually made of many energy states closely grouped together. We refer to these states as **sublevels.**

Each level has a number of sublevels equal to the value of the principal quantum number. You can expect to find one sublevel in the first level, two sublevels in the second level, and three sublevels in the third level. The lowest sublevel in each level has been named s; the second, p; the third, d; and the fourth, f. Thus, the first level has only an s sublevel. The second energy level has s and p sublevels, while the third energy level has s, p, and d sublevels.

As an example, consider the $n = 4$ level. Instead of the single energy line as was shown in Figure 8-6, the $n = 4$ level should show all sublevels, as in Figure 8-7.

Second quantum number, l, describes sublevels.

The number of sublevels in an energy level equals the value of n, the principal quantum number.

Sublevels are named s, p, d, and f.

BACKGROUND: The letters s, p, d, and f stand for sharp, principal, diffuse, and fundamental. These terms were originally spectroscopy labels for different series of spectral lines emitted by the elements.

FIGURE 8-7. The relationship between energy and the sublevels in $n = 4$ is shown.

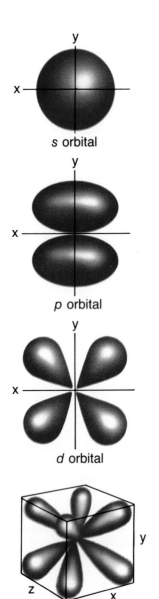

s orbital

p orbital

d orbital

f orbital

FIGURE 8-8. The relationship between sublevel number and orbital shape is shown.

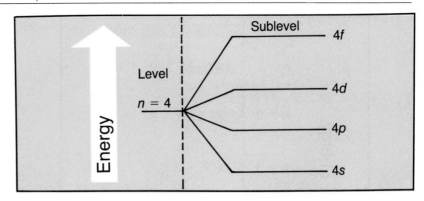

We can now rework the energy level diagram. Figure 8-9 shows the various sublevels for each of the energy levels. Notice the overlapping in the third and fourth levels. There is even more overlapping in the fourth and fifth, fifth and sixth, and so on. The effect is that the atom is more stable if the 4s sublevel is of lower energy than the 3d sublevel. The reason for the overlap will be considered in Section 8:10. In Section 8:11 we will explain why the overlap is so important in understanding atomic structure.

Calculation has shown that any s sublevel may contain one pair of electrons; any p sublevel, three pairs; any d sublevel, five pairs; and any f sublevel, seven pairs. Each pair in a given sublevel has a different place in space. This space occupied by one pair of electrons is called an **orbital.** Orbitals are designated by the third quantum number, m.

We can now redraw the energy level diagram with the orbitals shown. Each short line in Figure 8-10 represents an orbital that can hold a pair of electrons. For example, a p sublevel has three orbitals.

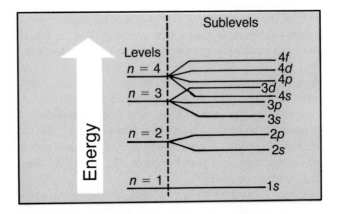

FIGURE 8-9. This energy level diagram shows the overlapping of orbitals that occurs between $n = 3$ and $n = 4$.

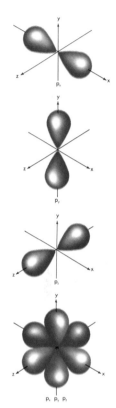

FIGURE 8-10. This energy level diagram shows the distribution of orbitals for each sublevel.

8:10 SHAPE OF THE CHARGE CLOUD

We now want to see how these various energy levels and sublevels affect the electron charge cloud described in Section 8:6. In general, the size of the charge cloud is related to n, the principal quantum number. The larger the value of n, the larger the cloud. However, there are also other factors which govern the size of the cloud. Electrons are repelled by each other; they are also attracted by the positively charged nucleus. At the same time, other electrons serve to screen the effect of the nucleus. Picture an electron A between the nucleus and electron B. Electron A reduces the attraction of the nucleus for electron B. Thus, the size of the charge cloud is not controlled by any single factor.

The sum of all electron clouds in any sublevel (or energy level) is a spherical cloud. However, orbitals have characteristic probability shapes of their own. For example, look at Figure 8-11. The three p orbitals can be directed along the three mutually perpendicular x, y, and z axes. They are sometimes labeled as p_x, p_y, and p_z.

As shown in Figures 8-12 and 8-13, the five d and seven f orbitals also have characteristic probability shapes. Notice that these, as well as the p orbitals, when filled and combined, form a spherical charge cloud.

FIGURE 8-11. The probability shapes for each p orbital with a composite of their orientation in space.

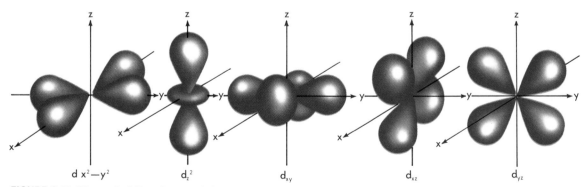

FIGURE 8-12. The probability shapes of the d orbitals.

A large, simple shape (such as $4s$) represents a lower energy state in an atom than a small, complex shape (such as $3d$).

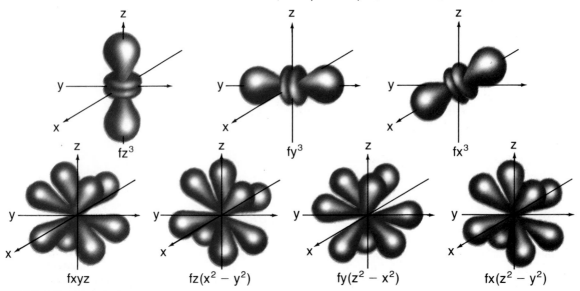

FIGURE 8-13. One set of probability shapes for the *f* orbitals.

The third quantum number, *m*, defines each orbital more precisely by indicating its direction in space. For a *p* sublevel there are three possible values for *m*. The numbers designate orbitals aligned along the *x*, *y*, and *z* axes. There are five values for *m* in a *d* sublevel and seven values for *m* in an *f* sublevel. Orbitals that are alike in size and shape and differ only in direction have the same energy. Orbitals of the same energy are said to be **degenerate**. When atoms react, degenerate orbitals may change energy by different amounts. If this energy change occurs, the orbitals will no longer be degenerate.

The direction of the orbital in space depends on *m*.

Degenerate orbitals are occupied by electrons having the same energy.

PROBLEM

3. a. 1
   b. 3
   c. 5
   d. 7

3. How many orbitals are in a(n)
   a. *s* sublevel   c. *d* sublevel
   b. *p* sublevel   d. *f* sublevel

8:11 DISTRIBUTION OF ELECTRONS

How are electrons of a particular atom arranged among the energy levels? The atom is electrically neutral. For each proton in the nucleus, there is one electron in the charge cloud. Thus, as the atomic number increases, the number of electrons increases.

The energy levels in an atom can be thought of as a rooming house in which the choice double rooms are on the ground level. Electrons, as tenants, will tend to fill the better (lower) rooms first, one at a time. Then, they double up in these better rooms before going to the next level. In other words, electrons occupy the energy level and sublevel that produces the arrangement with the lowest energy. Let us consider as the first "tenant," the electron from the hydrogen atom. It will occupy the position of least energy, the $1s$ orbital. What about a different set of room tenants, the two electrons of the helium atom?

Before we can answer this question, we must consider a principle that helps to explain the arrangement of electrons. It has been found that *no two electrons in an atom have the same set of quantum numbers.* This behavior was first observed and stated by Wolfgang Pauli and is called the **Pauli exclusion principle.** The quantum numbers n, l, and m describe relative cloud size (n), shape of the cloud (l), and direction of the cloud (m). The fourth quantum number, s, describes the spin of the electron, clockwise or counterclockwise. If two electrons occupy the same orbital, they have opposite spins. Otherwise their quantum numbers would be identical, Figure 8-14.

Each orbital may contain a pair of electrons.

Pauli's exclusion principle: No two electrons in an atom can have the same set of four quantum numbers.

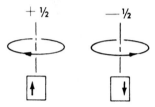

FIGURE 8-14. The fourth quantum number depicts the difference in spin for two electrons occupying the same orbital.

Table 8-1

| \multicolumn{8}{c|}{**Quantum States for the Hydrogen Atom**} |

n	l	m	s		n	l	m	s	
1	0	0	$\pm\frac{1}{2}$	1s	4	0	0	$\pm\frac{1}{2}$	4s
2	0	0	$\pm\frac{1}{2}$	2s	4	1	-1	$\pm\frac{1}{2}$	
2	1	-1	$\pm\frac{1}{2}$				0	$\pm\frac{1}{2}$	4p
		0	$\pm\frac{1}{2}$	2p			1	$\pm\frac{1}{2}$	
		1	$\pm\frac{1}{2}$		4	2	-2	$\pm\frac{1}{2}$	
3	0	0	$\pm\frac{1}{2}$	3s			-1	$\pm\frac{1}{2}$	
3	1	-1	$\pm\frac{1}{2}$				0	$\pm\frac{1}{2}$	4d
		0	$\pm\frac{1}{2}$	3p			1	$\pm\frac{1}{2}$	
		1	$\pm\frac{1}{2}$				2	$\pm\frac{1}{2}$	
3	2	-2	$\pm\frac{1}{2}$		4	3	-3	$\pm\frac{1}{2}$	
		-1	$\pm\frac{1}{2}$				-2	$\pm\frac{1}{2}$	
		0	$\pm\frac{1}{2}$	3d			-1	$\pm\frac{1}{2}$	
		1	$\pm\frac{1}{2}$				0	$\pm\frac{1}{2}$	4f
		2	$\pm\frac{1}{2}$				1	$\pm\frac{1}{2}$	
							2	$\pm\frac{1}{2}$	
							3	$\pm\frac{1}{2}$	

BACKGROUND: Two electrons can occupy the same orbital only if they have opposite spins. The magnetic fields of force produced by a moving charge can be used to explain the pairing.

Now consider the helium atom. Both electrons of a helium atom take positions in the $1s$ orbital, and thus have opposing spins. We call this arrangement a $1s^2$ (read as *one-s-two*) electron configuration. We can represent the electron configuration by a diagram like that in Figure 8-15. In the diagram, each box stands for an orbital. Arrows are used to indicate the direction of the spin of the electrons in the orbital.

The electron configuration of lithium ($Z = 3$) shows both positions in the $1s$ orbital and one position in the $2s$ orbital filled. We designate this arrangement as $1s^22s^1$, Figure 8-15.

FIGURE 8-15. The orbital filling diagram and electron configuration for hydrogen, helium, and lithium.

Let's move on to the nitrogen atom and see how the seven electrons are distributed. We would expect two electrons in the $1s$ orbital, two in the $2s$, and three in the $2p$. This arrangement can be indicated as in Figure 8-16, where each arrow represents an electron. The opposing arrows indicate opposite spins. Notice that each electron takes an empty orbital within a sublevel, if possible, rather than pair with another. This arrangement is reasonable because the negative electrons repel each other. It requires no more energy because all orbitals in a sublevel of an atom are degenerate. Since each orbital has a different orientation in space, electrons in different orbitals are farther apart than electrons in the same orbital. The electrons in the oxygen atom are arranged as shown in Figure 8-16. The eighth electron enters the partially filled $2p$ orbital.

Electrons in the same sublevel tend to occupy empty orbitals rather than pair with another electron.

BACKGROUND: Hund's Rule: Show a maximum number of unpaired electrons in a sublevel.

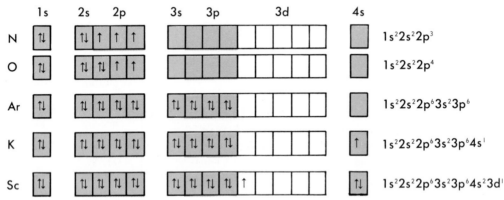

FIGURE 8-16. The orbital filling diagram and configuration for some representative elements.

8:12   DIAGONAL RULE

Everything works well until we finish the electron configuration of argon: $1s^2 2s^2 2p^6 3s^2 3p^6$. Where will the electrons of the next element, potassium ($Z = 19$), go? You may remember that in the first energy level diagram, Figure 8-9, the $4s$ level was shown below the $3d$ level. Thus, in this case, the $4s$ level fills first, because that order produces an atom with lower energy. The potassium configuration, therefore, is $1s^2 2s^2 2p^6 3s^2 3p^6 4s^1$. Calcium ($Z = 20$) has the configuration $1s^2 2s^2 2p^6 3s^2 3p^6 4s^2$. Scandium, however, begins filling the $3d$ orbitals, and has a configuration of $1s^2 2s^2 2p^6 3s^2 3p^6 4s^2 3d^1$.

The 4s sublevel fills before the 3d sublevel.

In many atoms with higher atomic numbers, the sublevels are not regularly filled. It is of little value to memorize each configuration. However, there is a rule of thumb that gives a correct configuration for most atoms in the ground state. It is a rule of thumb because we make an assumption that is not always true. The order of increasing energy sublevels is figured for the one-electron hydrogen atom. In a multielectron atom, each electron affects the energy of the others. Consequently, there are a number of exceptions to the rule of thumb. We will explore these exceptions more fully in the next chapter. This rule of thumb is called the **diagonal rule** and is shown in Figure 8-17. *If you follow the diagonals,*

Sublevels are not regularly filled in atoms with higher atomic numbers.

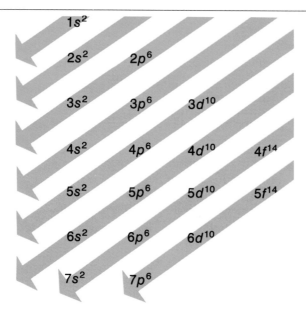

FIGURE 8-17. Use this model for the diagonal rule in writing electron configurations.

listing the orbitals passed, you can find the electron configuration of most atoms. As an example, suppose you are to find the electron configuration of zirconium ($Z = 40$). Begin with the $1s$ level, drop to the $2s$, and move back to the $2p$. Follow the diagonal to $3s$ and move to $3p$. Follow the diagonal to $4s$. Move back up to the tail of the next diagonal at $3d$ and follow it through $4p$ and $5s$. Move back to the tail of the next diagonal, $4d$, and place the remaining two electrons there. Thus, the electron configuration is

SUGGESTION: To make clear that this rule is only an approximation, cite some exceptions: Cr, Cu, Nb, Mo, Tc, Ru, Rh, Pd, Ag, La, Ir, Pt, Au, Ac.

$$1s^2 2s^2 2p^6 3s^2 3p^6 4s^2 3d^{10} 4p^6 5s^2 4d^2$$

A quick addition of the superscripts gives a total of 40, which is the atomic number.

The atomic number (Z) is equal to the sum of the superscripts in the electron configuration.

Levels n	Sublevels l	Orbitals m	Spin $+$ $-$
3	d	5	
	p	3	
	s	1	
2	p	3	
	s	1	
1	s	1	

FIGURE 8-18. This complete energy level diagram depicts the relationships among the four quantum numbers.

4. $Z = 1$, $1s^1$
  $Z = 10$, $1s^2 2s^2 2p^6$
  $Z = 20$,
  $1s^2 2s^2 2p^6 3s^2 3p^6 4s^2$

Usually only the electrons in the outer level of atoms are involved in chemical change.

In the electron dot diagram, the symbol represents the nucleus and all electrons except those in the outer level.

In the electron dot diagram, dots indicate outer level paired or unpaired electrons.

PROBLEM

4. Write the electron configurations of the elements with $Z = 1$ through $Z = 20$.

8:13 ELECTRON DOT DIAGRAMS

In studying electrons in atoms in the following chapters, our primary concern will be the electrons in the outer energy level. It is often useful to draw these outer electrons around the symbol of an element. This notation is referred to as a **Lewis electron dot diagram.**
The procedure for drawing electron dot diagrams follows.

Step 1. We let the symbol of the element represent the nucleus and all electrons except those in the outer level.

Step 2. We write the electron configuration of the element. From the configuration we select the electrons that are in the outer energy level. Those in the outer level are the ones with the largest principal quantum number. Remember that n represents electron cloud size.

Step 3. Each "side" (top, bottom, left, right) of the symbol represents an orbital. We draw dots on the appropriate sides to represent the electrons in that orbital. It is important to remember which electrons are paired and which are not. *It is not important which side represents which orbital.*

EXAMPLE: Electron Dot Diagrams

Write the electron dot diagrams for hydrogen, helium, oxygen, calcium, and cadmium.

Solving Process:
(a) Begin with the symbols for the elements required.

$$\text{H, He, O, Ca, and Cd}$$

(b) Write the electron configurations for each and determine the number of outer electrons.

$\text{H} = 1s^1$	(outer electron $= 1s^1$)
$\text{He} = 1s^2$	(outer electrons $= 1s^2$)
$\text{O} = 1s^2 2s^2 2p^4$	(outer electrons $= 2s^2 2p^4$)
$\text{Ca} = 1s^2 2s^2 2p^6 3s^2 3p^6 4s^2$	(outer electrons $= 4s^2$)
$\text{Cd} = 1s^2 2s^2 2p^6 3s^2 3p^6 4s^2 3d^{10} 4p^6 5s^2 4d^{10}$	(outer electrons $= 5s^2$)

(c) Use the outer configuration to determine the number of dots required for each element.

$$\text{H}^\bullet,\ \text{He}\colon,\ \colon\ddot{\text{O}}^\bullet,\ \text{Ca}\colon,\ \text{and Cd}\colon$$

Note the following special considerations. First, when choosing the outer electrons for cadmium, we ignored the $4d$ electrons. These $4d$

electrons are the highest energy electrons in the atom, but they are not in the outermost energy level. Their principal quantum number is less than that of the $5s$ electrons. Second, note that the s electrons are always shown as paired, that is, on the same side of the symbol. Note that in oxygen the four p electrons are distributed as one pair and two single electrons. Remember from Section 8:12 that electrons, being negative, will occupy an empty degenerate orbital before pairing with other electrons. For oxygen, no pairing takes place until the fourth electron in the p sublevel enters.

Table 8-2

Electron Dot Diagrams for Some Elements					
Element	Configuration Ending	Dot Diagram	Element	Configuration Ending	Dot Diagram
carbon	$2s^2 2p^2$	$\cdot \overset{\cdot}{\underset{}{C}} :$	bromine	$4s^2 3d^{10} 4p^5$	$: \overset{\cdot\cdot}{Br} :$
sodium	$3s^1$	$Na \cdot$	xenon	$5s^2 4d^{10} 5p^6$	$: \overset{\cdot\cdot}{Xe} :$
magnesium	$3s^2$	$Mg :$	cerium	$6s^2 4f^2$	$Ce :$
aluminum	$3s^2 3p^1$	$\overset{\cdot}{Al} :$	tungsten	$6s^2 4f^{14} 5d^4$	$W :$
phosphorus	$3s^2 3p^3$	$\cdot \overset{\cdot}{P} :$	osmium	$6s^2 4f^{14} 5d^6$	$Os :$
zinc	$4s^2 3d^{10}$	$Zn :$	uranium	$7s^2 5f^3 6d^1$	$U :$

PROBLEM

5. Predict electron configurations using the diagonal rule and draw electron dot diagrams for the following elements.
   a. $Z = 28$ **c.** $Z = 16$ **e.** $Z = 19$
   b. $Z = 18$ **d.** $Z = 47$ **f.** $Z = 32$

8:14   ELECTRON SUMMARY

We have treated the electron as particle, wave, and cloud of negative charge. Which is right? They all are. As pointed out in Section 8-2, electrons can behave as particles or as waves. There are times when chemists consider the electron as a particle. At that time, the electron is exhibiting its particle characteristics. At other times, chemists will be working on an experiment where the wave properties of the electron are of the greatest importance. At still other times, chemists will consider the electrons in an atom as a cloud of negative charge. Scientists do not have a single, completely satisfactory description of the structure of atoms. Consequently, they make use of more than one explanation for the properties they observe. The particular explanation that best fits each situation is the one applied in that situation.

We are now able to describe the electron configurations of the atoms of the elements. Our next study will be of a system of arranging elements based on their electronic structure—the periodic table.

5. a. $1s^2 2s^2 2p^6 3s^2 3p^6 4s^2$ $3d^8$ $Ni :$
   b. $1s^2 2s^2 2p^6 3s^2 3p^6$ $: \overset{\cdot\cdot}{Ar} :$
   c. $1s^2 2s^2 2p^6 3s^2 3p^4$ $\cdot \overset{\cdot\cdot}{S} :$
   d. $1s^2 2s^2 2p^6 3s^2 3p^6 4s^2$ $3d^{10} 4p^6 5s^2 4d^9$ $Ag :$
   e. $1s^2 2s^2 2p^6 3s^2 3p^6 4s^1$ $K \cdot$
   f. $1s^2 2s^2 2p^6 3s^2 3p^6 4s^2$ $3d^{10} 4p^2$ $\cdot Ge :$

The electron can be thought of as a particle, a wave, or a negatively charged cloud.

Scientists do not have a single, completely satisfactory description of the structure of atoms.

BIOGRAPHY   Wolfgang Pauli (1900-1958)

As theorists, few physicists could match Vienna-born Wolfgang Pauli. As a young man he had the opportunity to study with Max Born and Niels Bohr.

In 1945, Pauli was awarded the Nobel Prize for his exclusion principle which enabled physicists to prepare a more useful description of the electronic structure of atoms. His interest in the electron and statistics led him to the study of other elementary particles. Some of his work concerned the theory of mesons and he predicted the existence of the neutrino.

Some of his other theories helped explain atomic spectra, the behavior of electrons in metals, and how metals are affected by magnetic fields.

In 1940, he was appointed to the chair of theoretical physics at the Institute for Advanced Studies in Princeton, New Jersey. He became a naturalized citizen of the United States in 1946, but later he returned to Zurich, Switzerland, to live.

CAREERS AND CHEMISTRY

8:15   Perfumers

Everybody likes to smell nice. Consequently, there is a large market for scented products.

The manufacture of perfume is part science and part creative art. One phase of perfume development is the evaluation of the odors from various sources as well as those from different mixtures. Such evaluations are subjective and comprise the creative art aspect of perfumery and the job of a perfumer.

One component of perfumes is the vehicle, or solvent. It usually contains ethanol or another similar alcohol. The solvent vaporizes readily and acts as the vehicle for transporting the scent. However, solvents have odors of their own. Perfumers are constantly looking for substances that will reduce any objectionable odors in the solvent without interfering with its other desirable properties.

Most perfumes are mixtures of many different compounds. The particular odor desired is achieved by blending several substances. Each of these substances tends to evaporate at a different rate. As a result, the odor of the perfume tends to change with time after being applied to the skin.

Perfumers add a material called a fixative to perfumes. A fixative, such as musk, tends to even out evaporation rates and therefore, maintains the quality of the scent.

The odorous substances are the most important parts of perfumes. Perfumers are constantly searching for new scents. Many odorous substances are extracts from plant parts (flowers, bark, leaves, fruits). Perfumers not only look for new plant extracts, but, using chemical analysis, they try to duplicate synthetically the particular substance or substances providing the odor. These substances can then be used directly in compounding perfumes, in place of the extracts, at much lower cost. Perfumers, in conjunction with chemists, also work to develop new odorous substances. A thorough knowledge of solutions and organic chemistry is an important part of a perfumer's training.

The development of new fragrances is a highly competitive business. Consequently, the research and development function of a perfumer is quite important. An experienced perfumer may also be involved in the supervision of perfume production, quality control, marketing, and personnel administration.

Perfumers may be involved in more than the production of substances used in perfumes. Many are also employed by soap and cosmetic industries. The scent associated with a soap or cosmetic product is a critical factor in its marketability. The plastics industry also employs perfumers whose job is to deodorize plastics and other synthetic polymers. Once again the marketability of a product is at stake. You may have stored food in a plastic container and later detected the odor of the container in the food. Such a product has little appeal to the consumer at any price.

FIGURE 8-19. A perfumer combines a knowledge of chemistry with an acute sense of smell to produce pleasing fragrances.

SUMMARY

1. De Broglie first pointed out the wave-particle duality of nature. His idea was that all particles exhibit some wave characteristics, and vice versa. 8:1

2. Heisenberg's uncertainty principle concerns the process of observing an electron's position or its velocity. It is impossible to know accurately both the position and the momentum of an electron at the same time. 8:4

3. Schrödinger developed a mathematical equation which describes the behavior of the electron as a wave. The solution set of the wave equation can be used to calculate the probability of finding an electron at a particular point. 8:5

4. Because of the electron's high velocity, it effectively occupies all the volume defined by the path through which it moves. This volume is called the electron cloud. 8:6

5. The principle quantum number ($n = 1, 2, 3, \ldots$) is the number of the energy level and describes the relative electron cloud size. 8:8

6. Each energy level has as many sublevels as the principal quantum number. The second quantum number ($l = s, p, d, f \ldots$) describes the shape of the cloud. 8:9

7. The third quantum number, m, describes the orientation in space of each orbital. 8:9, 8:10

8. The fourth quantum number, s, describes the spin direction of the electron. 8:11

1. $\lambda = \dfrac{h}{mv}$

2. $\lambda = \dfrac{h}{p}$

3. 32

4. +1/2, −1/2

5. $Z = 92$
   e^- in each level
   $n = 1, 2$
   $n = 2, 8$
   $n = 3, 18$
   $n = 4, 32$
   $n = 5, 22$
   $n = 6, 8$
   $n = 7, 2$
   Levels 5, 6, and 7 are not full.

6. a. Mn manganese
   b. Mo molybdenum

7. Zr $Z = 40$
   $1s^2 2s^2 2p^6 3s^2 3p^6$
   $4s^2 3d^{10} 4p^6 5s^2 4d^2$
   Ga $Z = 31$ $1s^2 2s^2$
   $2p^6 3s^2 3p^6 4s^2 3d^{10}$
   $4p^1$

8. Bi $Z = 83$ $1s^2 2s^2$
   $2p^6 3s^2 3p^6 4s^2 3d^{10}$
   $4p^6 5s^2 4d^{10} 5p^6 6s^2$
   $4f^{14} 5d^{10} 6p^3$
   Ru $Z = 44$
   $1s^2 2s^2 2p^6$
   $3s^2 3p^6 4s^2 3d^{10} 4p^6$
   $5s^2 4d^6$

9. $Z = 7$, ·N̈:
   $Z = 15$, ·P̈:
   $Z = 33$, ·Äs:
   $Z = 51$, ·S̈b:
   $Z = 83$, ·B̈i:

10. B   2 pairs
    S   7 pairs
    F   4 pairs

11. 2 electrons
Actual   configurations may differ from those predicted by the diagonal rule.

9. Pauli's exclusion principle states that no two electrons in an atom can have the same set of quantum numbers. Each orbital may contain a maximum of one pair of electrons. Electrons in the same orbital have opposite spins. 8:11

10. Electrons occupy first the empty orbital giving the atom the lowest energy. 8:11

11. The diagonal rule can be used to provide the correct electron configuration for most atoms. 8:12

12. The chemist is primarily concerned with the electrons in the outer energy level. Electron dot diagrams are useful in representing these outer level electrons. 8:13

VOCABULARY

index of refraction 8:2	quantum numbers 8:5	degenerate 8:10
wave-particle duality of nature 8:2	probability 8:5	Pauli exclusion principle 8:11
Newtonian mechanics 8:3	electron cloud 8:6	diagonal rule 8:12
quantum mechanics. 8:3	principal quantum number 8:8	electron dot diagram 8:13
Heisenberg uncertainty principle 8:4	sublevel 8:9	
	orbital 8:9	

PROBLEMS

1. How did de Broglie show the relationship between waves and particles?

2. What is the relationship between momentum and wavelength?

3. How many electrons can exist in the fourth energy level?

4. What are the actual values for the fourth quantum number (s)?

5. Write the electron configuration for uranium. Compute the number of electrons in each level. Calculate the levels which are not full of electrons.

6. What elements are composed of atoms having the following electron configurations:
   a. $1s^2 2s^2 2p^6 3s^2 3p^6 4s^2 3d^5$
   b. $1s^2 2s^2 2p^6 3s^2 3p^6 4s^2 3d^{10} 4p^6 5s^2 4d^4$

7. Write the electron configurations for zirconium and gallium.

8. Write the electron configurations for bismuth and ruthenium.

9. Draw electron dot diagrams for the elements with Z equal to 7, 15, 33, 51, and 83.

10. How many pairs of electrons are there in an atom of boron? an atom of sulfur? an atom of fluorine?

11. How many electrons are not shown in the electron dot diagrams of the elements from $Z = 3$ to $Z = 10$?

REVIEW

1. What observations led John Dalton to formulate his atomic theory?
2. What is a nuclide? What are isotopes?
3. What is the difference between atomic number and atomic mass?
4. How much energy is needed to heat 10.0 g of tin from 25°C to 225°C? (Use Table A-3 in the Appendix.)
5. What data led Bohr to formulate the planetary model of the atom?
6. What is Planck's contribution to the development of atomic theory?
7. What is the average atomic mass of molybdenum if it has the following isotopic composition?

isotope	mass	abundance
92	91.906808	15.84%
94	93.905090	9.04%
95	94.905837	15.72%
96	95.904674	16.53%
97	96.906023	9.46%
98	97.905409	23.78%
100	99.907478	9.63%

8. How many electrons, neutrons, and protons are in mendelevium of mass number 256?
9. What is the photoelectric effect?

See the Teacher Guide for detailed solutions to all problems.

4. 4.40×10^2 J

7. 95.9 u

8. 101 electrons, 155 neutrons, 101 protons

ONE MORE STEP

1. What is the uncertainty in the momentum of an electron if its position has been determined to an accuracy of ±0.01 nm?
2. Classical physics would predict that only the three quantum numbers should be necessary to describe the motion of the electron in three-dimensional space. What necessitates a fourth?
3. Look up experiments which have been performed with the electron. Select one demonstrating its properties as a wave, and one demonstrating its properties as a particle. Prepare a report to your class on the procedure and results of these experiments.

1. 6.63×10^{-23} kg·m/s

READINGS

Bouchiat, Marie-Anne, and Lionel Potter, "An Atomic Preference Between Left and Right," *Scientific American*, Vol. 250, No. 6(June 1984), pp. 100-111.

David, Carl W., "On Orbital Drawings," *Journal of Chemical Education*, Vol. 58, No. 5(May 1981), p. 377.

Greenberger, Daniel M., and Albert W. Overhauser, "The Role of Gravity in Quantum Theory," *Scientific American*, Vol. 242, No. 5(May 1980), p. 66.

Hofstadter, Douglas R., "Mathematical Themas," *Scientific American*, Vol. 245, No. 1(July 1981), pp. 18-30.

The colored lights in this picture are produced using different noble gas elements. The noble gases have filled outer energy levels. This similar configuration causes them to have similar properties. How are the elements arranged in the periodic table? Why are the noble gases placed in the last column? What are some properties of noble gases?

PERIODIC TABLE 9

Chapter 9 introduces the periodic table and reveals some of the periodic characteristics of the elements based upon their electronic structures.

DEMONSTRATION: Place a petri dish that is ½ full of water on an overhead projector. Add 2 drops of phenolphthalein to the H_2O. Drop a pea-sized piece of Li metal into the dish. Repeat the same procedure using Na metal in a second dish. The reactions are best viewed in a darkened room. See Teacher Guide for discussion suggestions.

The element sodium reacts violently with water. Potassium reacts still more violently with water. An experienced chemist can predict that the elements rubidium, cesium, and francium will react in a similar manner. How can this prediction be made? Such predictions can be made because all of these elements have the same electron configuration in their outer energy levels. They have been placed in the same column of the periodic table because they have a similar structure.

GOALS:
• You will gain an understanding of how the periodic table is organized.
• You will learn to predict the stability of atoms using the octet rule.
• You will examine the relationship between an element's electron configuration and its placement on the periodic table.

9:1 EARLY ATTEMPTS AT CLASSIFICATION: DOBEREINER AND NEWLANDS

Early in the 19th century, scientists began to seek ways to classify the elements. One attempt at classification was by Johann Dobereiner, a German chemist, in 1817. Dobereiner found that the properties of the metals calcium, barium, and strontium were very similar. He also noted that the atomic mass of strontium was about midway between those of calcium and barium. He formed what he termed a **triad** of these three elements. Later, Dobereiner found several other groups of three elements with similar properties.

Properties of elements are in Appendix A, Table A-3.

Dobereiner discovered groups of three related elements which he termed a triad.

Table 9-1

Some of Dobereiner's Triads					
Name	**Atomic Mass**	**Name**	**Atomic Mass**	**Name**	**Atomic Mass**
Calcium	40	Chlorine	35.5	Sulfur	32
Barium	137	Iodine	127	Tellurium	127.5
Average	88.5	**Average**	81.3	**Average**	79.8
Strontium	87.6	Bromine	79.9	Selenium	79.2

161

Newlands' law of octaves was proposed to explain the property similarities which occurred with every eighth element when the elements were arranged in order of increasing atomic mass.

In 1863, John Newlands, an English chemist, suggested another classification. He arranged the elements in order of their increasing atomic masses. He noted that there appeared to be a repetition of similar properties every eighth element. Therefore, he arranged the elements known at that time into seven groups of seven each.* Newlands referred to his arrangement as the **law of octaves.**

Table 9-2

Newlands' Law of Octaves						
1	2	3	4	5	6	7
Li	Be	B	C	N	O	F
Na	Mg	Al	Si	P	S	Cl
K						

9:2 MENDELEEV'S PERIODIC TABLE

Just six years after Newlands' proposal, Dmitri Mendeleev, a Russian chemist, proposed a similar idea. He suggested, as had Newlands, that the properties of the elements were a function of their atomic masses. However, Mendeleev felt that similar properties occurred after periods (horizontal rows) of varying length. Although he placed seven elements each in his first two periods, he placed seventeen elements in the next two.

Mendeleev suggested periods of varying lengths based on atomic masses.

Table 9-3

Mendeleev's Predictions	
Ekasilicon* *Predicted properties*	**Germanium** *Actual properties*
1. Atomic mass = 72	1. Atomic mass = 72.60
2. High melting point	2. Melting point = 958°C
3. Density = 5.5 g/cm^3	3. Density = 5.36 g/cm^3
4. Dark gray metal	4. Gray metal
5. Will obtain from K_2EsF_6	5. Obtain from K_2GeF_6
6. Slightly dissolved by HCl	6. Not dissolved by HCl
7. Will form EsO_2	7. Forms oxide (GeO_2)
8. Density of EsO_2 = 4.7 g/cm^3	8. Density of GeO_2 = 4.70 g/cm^3

*One of the blank spaces in Mendeleev's table was below silicon. Mendeleev assumed such an element existed but had not yet been discovered. He called this element (later named germanium) ekasilicon and predicted some of its properties.

BACKGROUND: Mendeleev predicted the existence of six undiscovered elements: ekaboron (scandium) ekaaluminum (gallium) ekasilicon (germanium) ekamanganese (technetium) dvimanganese (rhenium) ekatantalum (polonium)

In the 1860s, Mendeleev and the German chemist Lothar Meyer, each working alone, made an eight-column table of the elements. How-

*Note: Noble gases were not known at this time.

			Ti = 50	Zr = 90	? = 180
			V = 51	Nb = 94	Ta = 182
			Cr = 52	Mo = 96	W = 186
			Mn = 55	Rh = 104,$_4$ (103)	*Pt = 197,$_4$
			Fe = 56	Ru = 104,$_4$ (101)	*Ir = 198 (193)
			Ni, Co = 59*	Pd = 106,$_6$	*Os = 199 (191)
H = 1			Cu = 63,$_4$	Ag = 108	*Hg = 200
	Be = 9,$_4$	Mg = 24	Zn = 65,$_2$	Cd = 112	
	B = 11	Al = 27,$_4$	? = 68	*Ur = 116 (238)	*Au = 197?
	C = 12	Si = 28	? = 70	Sn = 118	
	N = 14	P = 31	As = 75	Sb = 122	Bi = 210
	O = 16	S = 32	Se = 79,$_4$	Te = 128?	
	F = 19	Cl = 35,$_5$	Br = 80	I = 127	
Li = 7	Na = 23	K = 39	Rb = 85,$_4$	Cs = 133	*Tl = 204
		Ca = 40	Sr = 87,$_6$	Ba = 137	*Pb = 207
		? = 45	*Ce = 92 (138)		
		*Er = 56 (166)	*La = 94 (137)		
		*Yt = 60 (88)	*Di = 95 (140)		
		*In = 75,$_6$ (113)	*Th = 118 (231)		

Sovfoto

Таблица I. *Elements added after original publication in 1869.

Первая попытка Менделѣева найти естественную систему элементовъ. Перепечатана изъ „Журнала Химическаго Общества", т. I, стр. 70 (1869г.). Жирнымъ шрифтомъ и звѣздочками я обозначилъ элементы, попавшіе не на свое мѣсто, по причинѣ неточнаго опредѣленія ихъ атомнаго вѣса, а въ скобкахъ я привелъ ихъ дѣйствительные вѣса. У Менделѣева жирнаго трифта и звѣздочекъ не было совсѣмъ. Все было однимъ шрифтомъ.

FIGURE 9-1. Mendeleev's arrangement of the elements as published in 1869.

ever, Mendeleev had to leave some blank spots in order to group all the elements with similar properties in the same column. To explain these blank spots, Mendeleev suggested there must be other elements that had not yet been discovered. On the basis of his arrangement, Mendeleev predicted the properties and atomic masses of several elements that were unknown at the time. One of the blank spaces in Mendeleev's table was below silicon. Mendeleev assumed such an element existed but had not yet been discovered. Table 9-3 shows Mendeleev's predictions for the properties of ekasilicon (later named germanium). Today, the other elements have been discovered, and Mendeleev's predictions have been found to be very nearly correct.

In Mendeleev's table, the elements were arranged in order of their increasing atomic masses. The table showed that the properties of the elements are repeated in an orderly way. Mendeleev regarded the properties of the elements as a periodic function of their atomic masses. This statement was called the periodic law.

Mendeleev left blanks in his table for undiscovered elements.

Mendeleev predicted properties and masses of unknown elements correctly.
BACKGROUND: Mendeleev's predictions made his proposal seem superior to Meyer's.
Mendeleev's periodic law: Properties of elements are periodic functions of their atomic masses.

Periodic Table
(Based on Carbon 12 = 12.000)

	1* IA*	2 IIA	3 IIIB	4 IVB	5 VB	6 VIB	7 VIIB	8	9 VIIIB
1	1 **H** Hydrogen 1.00794						Metals		
2	3 **Li** Lithium 6.941	4 **Be** Beryllium 9.01218				Transition Elements			
3	11 **Na** Sodium 22.98977	12 **Mg** Magnesium 24.305							
4	19 **K** Potassium 39.0983	20 **Ca** Calcium 40.078	21 **Sc** Scandium 44.95591	22 **Ti** Titanium 47.88	23 **V** Vanadium 50.9415	24 **Cr** Chromium 51.9961	25 **Mn** Manganese 54.9380	26 **Fe** Iron 55.847	27 **Co** Cobalt 58.9332
5	37 **Rb** Rubidium 85.4678	38 **Sr** Strontium 87.62	39 **Y** Yttrium 88.9059	40 **Zr** Zirconium 91.224	41 **Nb** Niobium 92.9064	42 **Mo** Molybdenum 95.94	43 **Tc** Technetium 97.9072*	44 **Ru** Ruthenium 101.07	45 **Rh** Rhodium 102.9055
6	55 **Cs** Cesium 132.9054	56 **Ba** Barium 137.33	71 **Lu** Lutetium 174.967	72 **Hf** Hafnium 178.49	73 **Ta** Tantalum 180.9479	74 **W** Tungsten 183.85	75 **Re** Rhenium 186.207	76 **Os** Osmium 190.2	77 **Ir** Iridium 192.22
7	87 **Fr** Francium 223.0197*	88 **Ra** Radium 226.0254	103 **Lr** Lawrencium 260.1054*	104 **Unq** 261*	105 **Unp** 262*	106 **Unh** 263*	107 **Uns** 262*	108 **Uno** 265*	109 **Une** 266*

LANTHANIDE SERIES	57 **La** Lanthanum 138.9055	58 **Ce** Cerium 140.12	59 **Pr** Praseodymium 140.9077	60 **Nd** Neodymium 144.24	61 **Pm** Promethium 144.9128*	62 **Sm** Samarium 150.36
ACTINIDE SERIES	89 **Ac** Actinium 227.0278*	90 **Th** Thorium 232.0381	91 **Pa** Protactinium 231.0359*	92 **U** Uranium 238.0289	93 **Np** Neptunium 237.0482	94 **Pu** Plutonium 244.0642*

Gases—green, Liquids—blue, Solids—yellow, Synthetics—orange

Noble Gases

18

VIIIA

Nonmetals

13 IIIA	14 IVA	15 VA	16 VIA	17 VIIA	2 **He** Helium 4.002602
5 **B** Boron 10.811	6 **C** Carbon 12.011	7 **N** Nitrogen 14.0067	8 **O** Oxygen 15.9994	9 **F** Fluorine 18.998403	10 **Ne** Neon 20.179
13 **Al** Aluminum 26.98154	14 **Si** Silicon 28.0855	15 **P** Phosphorus 30.97376	16 **S** Sulfur 32.066	17 **Cl** Chlorine 35.453	18 **Ar** Argon 39.948

10

11 IB	12 IIB				
28 **Ni** Nickel 58.69	29 **Cu** Copper 63.546	30 **Zn** Zinc 65.39	31 **Ga** Gallium 69.723	32 **Ge** Germanium 72.59	33 **As** Arsenic 74.9216

28 **Ni** Nickel 58.69	29 **Cu** Copper 63.546	30 **Zn** Zinc 65.39	31 **Ga** Gallium 69.723	32 **Ge** Germanium 72.59	33 **As** Arsenic 74.9216	34 **Se** Selenium 78.96	35 **Br** Bromine 79.904	36 **Kr** Krypton 83.80
46 **Pd** Palladium 106.42	47 **Ag** Silver 107.8682	48 **Cd** Cadmium 112.41	49 **In** Indium 114.82	50 **Sn** Tin 118.710	51 **Sb** Antimony 121.75	52 **Te** Tellurium 127.60	53 **I** Iodine 126.9045	54 **Xe** Xenon 131.29
78 **Pt** Platinum 195.08	79 **Au** Gold 196.9665	80 **Hg** Mercury 200.59	81 **Tl** Thallium 204.383	82 **Pb** Lead 207.2	83 **Bi** Bismuth 208.9804	84 **Po** Polonium 208.9824*	85 **At** Astatine 209.9871*	86 **Rn** Radon 222.0176*

Rare Earth Elements

63 **Eu** Europium 151.96	64 **Gd** Gadolinium 157.25	65 **Tb** Terbium 158.9254	66 **Dy** Dysprosium 162.50	67 **Ho** Holmium 164.9304	68 **Er** Erbium 167.26	69 **Tm** Thulium 168.9342	70 **Yb** Ytterbium 173.04
95 **Am** Americium 243.0614*	96 **Cm** Curium 247.0703*	97 **Bk** Berkelium 247.0703*	98 **Cf** Californium 251.0796*	99 **Es** Einsteinium 252.0828*	100 **Fm** Fermium 257.0951*	101 **Md** Mendelevium 258.0986*	102 **No** Nobelium 259.1009*

*Currently there are two systems of labeling groups on the periodic table. A traditional system uses Roman numerals I through VIII with letters A and B. A more current system uses Arabic numerals 1 through 18, with no A and B designations. Throughout this text the traditional system will be used with the other heading following in parenthesis, for example, Group IA(1).

$*Pt = 197,_4$

$*Ir = 198 \ (193)$

$*Os = 199 \ (191)$

$*Hg = 200$

$*Au = 197?$

$Te = 128?$

$I = 127$

FIGURE 9-2. Discrepencies in Mendeleev's arrangement of some elements resulted in the revision of Mendeleev's periodic law.

Moseley's revision: Properties of the elements are periodic functions of their atomic numbers.

SUGGESTION: Obtain blank periodic tables and have the students fill them in as this section is discussed.

Elements with similar electron configurations are listed in columns.

9:3 MODERN PERIODIC LAW

There was a problem with Mendeleev's table. If the elements were arranged according to increasing atomic masses, tellurium and iodine seemed to be in the wrong columns. Their properties were different from those of other elements in the same column. However, they were next to each other. Switching their positions put them in the columns where they belonged according to their properties. If the switch were made, Mendeleev's basic assumption that the properties of the elements were a periodic function of their atomic masses would be wrong. Mendeleev assumed that the atomic masses of these two elements had been poorly measured. He thought that new mass measurements would prove his hypothesis to be correct. However, new measurements simply confirmed the original masses.

Soon, new elements were discovered, and two other pairs showed the same kind of reversal. Cobalt and nickel were known by Mendeleev, but their atomic masses had not been accurately measured. When such a determination was made, it was found that their positions in the table were also reversed. When argon was discovered, the masses of argon and potassium were reversed.

Henry Moseley found the reason for these apparent exceptions to the rule. Moseley's x-ray experiments showed that the nucleus of each element has an integral positive charge, the atomic number. Iodine, nickel, and potassium have greater atomic numbers than tellurium, cobalt, and argon, respectively. As a result of Moseley's work, the periodic law was revised. It now has as its basis the atomic numbers of the elements instead of the atomic masses. Today's statement of the **periodic law** is *the properties of the elements are a periodic function of their atomic numbers.*

9:4 MODERN PERIODIC TABLE

The atomic number of an element indicates the number of protons in the nucleus of each atom of the element. Because the atom is electrically neutral, the atomic number also indicates the number of electrons surrounding the nucleus.

Certain electron arrangements are periodically repeated. (See Section 8:13). We can place elements with similar electron configurations in the same column. We can also list the elements in the column in order of their increasing principal quantum numbers. Thus, we can form a table of the elements similar to that on pages 164 and 165. This table is called the **periodic table** of the elements.

We construct our periodic table in this manner. We will use the diagonal rule (Section 8:12) to determine the order of filling the sublevels. Each s sublevel contains two electrons. Each p sublevel contains six electrons arranged in three pairs, or orbitals. Each d sublevel contains ten electrons in five orbitals. Each f sublevel contains fourteen electrons in seven orbitals. We then align the elements with similar outer electron configurations.

sublevel	e^- capacity
s	2
p	6
d	10
f	14

Table 9-4

		1	2	
Elements 1-10				
Z	Element	s	s	p
1	H	1		
2	He	2		
3	Li	2	1	
4	Be	2	2	
5	B	2	2	1
6	C	2	2	2
7	N	2	2	3
8	O	2	2	4
9	F	2	2	5
10	Ne	2	2	6

Hydrogen: $1s^1$

Helium: $1s^2$

Lithium: $1s^2 2s^1$

Beryllium: $1s^2 2s^2$

Carbon: $1s^2 2s^2 2p^2$
Boron: $1s^2 2s^2 2p^1$

Nitrogen: $1s^2 2s^2 2p^3$
Oxygen: $1s^2 2s^2 2p^4$
Fluorine: $1s^2 2s^2 2p^5$
Neon: $1s^2 2s^2 2p^6$

The first configuration in Table 9-4, hydrogen ($Z = 1$), consists of one electron in the $1s$ sublevel. The second configuration, helium ($Z = 2$), consists of two electrons in the $1s$ sublevel. These two electrons completely fill the $1s$ sublevel. The third element, lithium ($Z = 3$), has two electrons in the $1s$ sublevel and one electron in the $2s$ sublevel. Lithium is similar to hydrogen in that it has only one electron in its outermost sublevel. Therefore, we will place it in the same column as hydrogen. The next element, beryllium ($Z = 4$), has two electrons in the $1s$ sublevel and two electrons in the $2s$ sublevel. It might seem to belong in the column with helium. However, the two electrons in helium's outermost level fill that level.

The two electrons in the $2s$ sublevel of beryllium do not fill the second level. Recall that the $n = 2$ level has a p sublevel, as well as its s sublevel. Even though the beryllium and helium configurations are similar, beryllium starts a new column next to lithium. Boron ($Z = 5$) has a configuration composed of two $1s$ electrons, two $2s$ electrons, and one $2p$ electron. It heads a new column. Carbon ($Z = 6$), nitrogen ($Z = 7$), oxygen ($Z = 8$), and fluorine ($Z = 9$) atoms come next. They have structures containing two, three, four, and five electrons, respectively, in the $2p$ sublevel. Each of these elements heads a new column. The atoms of neon ($Z = 10$), the tenth element, contain six $2p$ electrons. The second level ($n = 2$) is now full. Therefore, neon is placed in the same column as helium.

Sodium: $1s^2 2s^2 2p^6 3s^1$

Calcium: $1s^2 2s^2 2p^6 3s^2 3p^6 4s^2$
Potassium: $1s^2 2s^2 2p^6 3s^2 3p^6 4s^1$

Scandium: $1s^2 2s^2 2p^6 3s^2 3p^6 4s^2 3d^1$

This text uses the traditional headings for group numbers followed by the more current heading in parentheses.

The transition elements fill the B columns.

Table 9-5

		Elements 11-20						
		1	2		3			4
Z	Element	s	s	p	s	p	d	s
11	Na	2	2	6	1			
12	Mg	2	2	6	2			
13	Al	2	2	6	2	1		
14	Si	2	2	6	2	2		
15	P	2	2	6	2	3		
16	S	2	2	6	2	4		
17	Cl	2	2	6	2	5		
18	Ar	2	2	6	2	6		
19	K	2	2	6	2	6		1
20	Ca	2	2	6	2	6		2

Sodium atoms ($Z = 11$) have the same outer level configuration as lithium atoms, one s electron ($3s^1$). Thus, sodium is placed under lithium. The elements magnesium ($Z = 12$) through argon ($Z = 18$) have the same outer structures as the elements beryllium through neon. They are also placed in the appropriate columns. Atoms of potassium ($Z = 19$) and calcium ($Z = 20$) have outer structures that are similar to the atoms of sodium and magnesium.

9:5 TRANSITION ELEMENTS

The scandium ($Z = 21$) configuration introduces a new factor into the arrangement. It has two electrons in the outer level ($4s^2$) and is similar to the calcium configuration. However, the scandium atom has, in addition to a filled $4s$ sublevel, one electron in the $3d$ sublevel. It is, therefore, placed in a new column, which is labeled IIIB (3). For the atoms of elements titanium ($Z = 22$) through nickel ($Z = 28$), additional electrons are added in the $3d$ sublevel. For all these elements, however, the outer level is the 4th level so they are placed in the fourth row. Each of these elements heads a new column, columns IIIB to VIIIB (3-10). Note that the atoms of copper and zinc have filled inner levels. All structures in column IB (11) have filled inner levels and one electron in the outer level. All structures in column IIB (12) have filled inner levels and two electrons in the outer level. In columns IIIA (13) through VIIIA (18) electrons are added to the p sublevel until there are a total of eight electrons in the outer level. The next electron is added to the next s sublevel whether the inner level is filled or not. The process is continued until all of the elements are placed in the main part of the table.

Table 9-6

		1	2		3			4				5				6			7
Transition Elements																			
Z	Element	s	s	p	s	p	d	s	p	d	f	s	p	d	f	s	p	d	s
21	Sc	2	2	6	2	6	1	2											
22	Ti	2	2	6	2	6	2	2											
23	V	2	2	6	2	6	3	2											
24	Cr	2	2	6	2	6	5	1											
25	Mn	2	2	6	2	6	5	2											
26	Fe	2	2	6	2	6	6	2											
27	Co	2	2	6	2	6	7	2											
28	Ni	2	2	6	2	6	8	2											
29	Cu	2	2	6	2	6	10	1											
30	Zn	2	2	6	2	6	10	2											
39	Y	2	2	6	2	6	10	2	6	1		2							
40	Zr	2	2	6	2	6	10	2	6	2		2							
41	Nb	2	2	6	2	6	10	2	6	4		1							
42	Mo	2	2	6	2	6	10	2	6	5		1							
43	Tc	2	2	6	2	6	10	2	6	5		2							
44	Ru	2	2	6	2	6	10	2	6	7		1							
45	Rh	2	2	6	2	6	10	2	6	8		1							
46	Pd	2	2	6	2	6	10	2	6	10									
47	Ag	2	2	6	2	6	10	2	6	10		1							
48	Cd	2	2	6	2	6	10	2	6	10		2							
71	Lu	2	2	6	2	6	10	2	6	10	14	2	6	1		2			
72	Hf	2	2	6	2	6	10	2	6	10	14	2	6	2		2			
73	Ta	2	2	6	2	6	10	2	6	10	14	2	6	3		2			
74	W	2	2	6	2	6	10	2	6	10	14	2	6	4		2			
75	Re	2	2	6	2	6	10	2	6	10	14	2	6	5		2			
76	Os	2	2	6	2	6	10	2	6	10	14	2	6	6		2			
77	Ir	2	2	6	2	6	10	2	6	10	14	2	6	7		2			
78	Pt	2	2	6	2	6	10	2	6	10	14	2	6	9		1			
79	Au	2	2	6	2	6	10	2	6	10	14	2	6	10		1			
80	Hg	2	2	6	2	6	10	2	6	10	14	2	6	10		2			
103	Lr	2	2	6	2	6	10	2	6	10	14	2	6	10	14	2	6	1	2
104	Unq	2	2	6	2	6	10	2	6	10	14	2	6	10	14	2	6	2	2?
105	Unp	2	2	6	2	6	10	2	6	10	14	2	6	10	14	2	6	3	2?

BACKGROUND: The elements in both columns IA (1) & IB (11) contain only one e^- in the outer level. However, column IA (1) metals contain 8 e^- in the next to outer level and column IB (11) metals contain 18 e^- in this level. The column IA (1) metals (alkali metals) easily lose the single outer electron and form extremely stable ions which have a stable noble gas configuration. Column IB (11) metals (coinage metals) are noncorrosive and relatively unreactive because loss of the single outer level electron does not result in the formation of an appreciably more stable ion.

9:6   THE LANTHANIDES AND ACTINIDES

The **lanthanide** series contains the elements lanthanum ($Z = 57$) through ytterbium ($Z = 70$). All of these elements have a predicted structure with two electrons in the outer level. In this series, electrons are being added to the $4f$ sublevel instead of to a sublevel of the sixth or outer level as shown in Table 9-7.

Lanthanides add electrons to the 4*f* sublevels.

Table 9-7

Z	Element	1	2		3			4				5			6
		s	s	p	s	p	d	s	p	d	f	s	p	d	s
57	La	2	2	6	2	6	10	2	6	10		2	6	1	2
58	Ce	2	2	6	2	6	10	2	6	10	1	2	6	1	2
59	Pr	2	2	6	2	6	10	2	6	10	3	2	6		2
60	Nd	2	2	6	2	6	10	2	6	10	4	2	6		2
61	Pm	2	2	6	2	6	10	2	6	10	5	2	6		2
62	Sm	2	2	6	2	6	10	2	6	10	6	2	6		2
63	Eu	2	2	6	2	6	10	2	6	10	7	2	6		2
64	Gd	2	2	6	2	6	10	2	6	10	7	2	6	1	2
65	Tb	2	2	6	2	6	10	2	6	10	9	2	6		2
66	Dy	2	2	6	2	6	10	2	6	10	10	2	6		2
67	Ho	2	2	6	2	6	10	2	6	10	11	2	6		2
68	Er	2	2	6	2	6	10	2	6	10	12	2	6		2
69	Tm	2	2	6	2	6	10	2	6	10	13	2	6		2
70	Yb	2	2	6	2	6	10	2	6	10	14	2	6		2

Actinides add electrons to the 5*f* sublevels.

The **actinide series** contains actinium (*Z* = 89) through nobelium (*Z* = 102). In this series, the 5 *f* sublevel is being filled as shown in Table 9-8.

The atoms of some elements do not have the exact electron configurations predicted for them. However, the differences involve only one or two electrons. Note the configuration for gadolinium (*Z* = 64). For purposes of constructing the table, we will assume that all elements have the predicted configurations.

Table 9-8

Z	Element	1	2		3			4				5				6			7
		s	s	p	s	p	d	s	p	d	f	s	p	d	f	s	p	d	s
89	Ac	2	2	6	2	6	10	2	6	10	14	2	6	10		2	6	1	2
90	Th	2	2	6	2	6	10	2	6	10	14	2	6	10		2	6	2	2
91	Pa	2	2	6	2	6	10	2	6	10	14	2	6	10	2	2	6	1	2
92	U	2	2	6	2	6	10	2	6	10	14	2	6	10	3	2	6	1	2
93	Np	2	2	6	2	6	10	2	6	10	14	2	6	10	4	2	6	1	2
94	Pu	2	2	6	2	6	10	2	6	10	14	2	6	10	6	2	6		2
95	Am	2	2	6	2	6	10	2	6	10	14	2	6	10	7	2	6		2
96	Cm	2	2	6	2	6	10	2	6	10	14	2	6	10	7	2	6	1	2
97	Bk	2	2	6	2	6	10	2	6	10	14	2	6	10	8	2	6	1	2?
98	Cf	2	2	6	2	6	10	2	6	10	14	2	6	10	10	2	6		2
99	Es	2	2	6	2	6	10	2	6	10	14	2	6	10	11	2	6		2
100	Fm	2	2	6	2	6	10	2	6	10	14	2	6	10	12	2	6		2
101	Md	2	2	6	2	6	10	2	6	10	14	2	6	10	13	2	6		2
102	No	2	2	6	2	6	10	2	6	10	14	2	6	10	14	2	6		2

The blocks representing these elements are shown below the main table. Their proper position would be between 56 and 71 and 88 and 103. If we were to split the table there and insert the lanthanides and actinides the table would be too wide to print reasonably.

All elements in a horizontal line are referred to as a **period.** All elements in the same vertical column are referred to as a **group** and are labeled IA through VIIIA and IB through VIIIB (1-18).

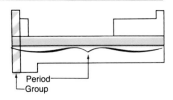

Period
Group

Periods are horizontal rows of elements.

Groups are vertical columns of elements.

9:7 OCTET RULE

When an *s* electron is the highest energy level electron in an atom, it is in the outer level. The same is true of a *p* electron. However, *d* and *f* electrons, theoretically, can never be in the outer level of a neutral atom (see diagonal rule, page 152). Since *s* sublevels hold two electrons and *p* sublevels hold six, the largest number of electrons normally in an outer level is eight **(octet).** *We will consider an atom with eight electrons in the outer level to have a full outer level. One of the basic rules in chemistry is that an atom with eight electrons in its outer level is particularly stable.* This rule is called the **octet rule.** Although the helium atom has only two electrons in its outer level, it, too, is one of these stable elements. Its outer level is the first level and can hold only two electrons. Thus, it has a full outer level. We will then consider the octet rule to include helium. Under exceptional circumstances it is sometimes possible to force the outer level of an element in the third or higher period to hold more than eight electrons. For example, noble gas compounds (Section 11:11) have been formed.

SUGGESTION: The octet rule should be learned as "four pairs" of electrons.

Eight electrons in the outer level of an atom represent a stable arrangement.

Helium is included in the octet rule.

9:8 SURVEYING THE TABLE: ELECTRON CONFIGURATIONS

The periodic table was originally constructed by placing elements with similar properties in a column. We now know that an atom's chemical properties are determined by its electron configuration. Therefore, we have constructed the table on the basis of electron configurations. By reversing the procedure in which the table was constructed, the table may be used to "read" the configuration of an element. Remember that elements in columns headed by "A" have their highest energy electron in an outer *s* or *p* sublevel. Those elements in columns headed "B" have their highest energy electron in a *d* sublevel one level below the outer level.

Thus, the written configuration of any element in Group IA (1) will end in s^1. This configuration means that the outer level of each atom of Group IA (1) elements contains one electron. The coefficient of s^1 is easily found from the table because the number of the period indicates the outer energy level. For example, potassium is in the fourth period of Group IA (1). Thus, the written electron configuration for the outer level of potassium is $4s^1$. The superscript in s^1 indicates the group number. The coefficient, in $4s^1$, indicates the period number. Find lithium in the periodic table. How does its written electron configuration end? Find Group IIA (2)

The periodic table can be used to determine the electron configuration of an element.

IA	IIA	IIIB	IVB	VB	VIB	VIIB	VIII	VIII	VIII	IB	IIB	IIIA	IVA	VA	VIA	VIIA	VIIIA
ns^1																	$1s^2$
																	ns^2np^6
ns^1	ns^2	$ns^2(n-1)d^1$	$ns^2(n-1)d^2$	$ns^2(n-1)d^3$	$ns^1(n-1)d^5$	$ns^2(n-1)d^5$	$ns^2(n-1)d^6$	$ns^2(n-1)d^7$	$ns^2(n-1)d^8$	$ns^1(n-1)d^{10}$	$ns^2(n-1)d^{10}$	ns^2np^1	ns^2np^2	ns^2np^3	ns^2np^4	ns^2np^5	ns^2np^6
	ns^2	$ns^2(n-1)d^1(n-2)f^{14}$															
	ns^2	$ns^2(n-1)d^1(n-2)f^{14}$															

f-block:

$ns^2(n-1)d^1$	$ns^2(n-1)d^1(n-2)f^1$	$ns^2(n-2)f^3$	$ns^2(n-2)f^4$	$ns^2(n-2)f^5$	$ns^2(n-2)f^6$	$ns^2(n-2)f^7$	$ns^2(n-1)d^1(n-2)f^7$	$ns^2(n-2)f^9$	$ns^2(n-2)f^{10}$	$ns^2(n-2)f^{11}$	$ns^2(n-2)f^{12}$	$ns^2(n-2)f^{13}$	$ns^2(n-2)f^{14}$
$ns^2(n-1)d^1$	$ns^2(n-1)d^2$	$ns^2(n-1)d^1(n-2)f^2$	$ns^2(n-1)d^1(n-2)f^3$	$ns^2(n-1)d^1(n-2)f^4$	$ns^2(n-2)f^6$	$ns^2(n-2)f^7$	$ns^2(n-1)d^1(n-2)f^7$	$ns^2(n-1)d^1(n-2)f^8$	$ns^2(n-2)f^{10}$	$ns^2(n-2)f^{11}$	$ns^2(n-2)f^{12}$	$ns^2(n-2)f^{13}$	$ns^2(n-2)f^{14}$

FIGURE 9-3. An element's position in the table can be used to determine its electron configuration.

Atoms in the same period have the same principal quantum number (n).

Some deviations from the diagonal rule are periodic and explainable.

Full or half-full sublevels are particularly stable.

in the periodic table. How does the written electron configuration for all elements in this group end? The same procedure can be used for Groups IIIA through VIIIA (13-18). There the endings, instead of s^1 or s^2, are p^1 through p^6 preceded by a coefficient which is the same as the number of the period.

For Groups IIIB through IIB (3-12), the endings are d^1 through d^{10} preceded by a coefficient which is one less than the period number. For transition elements, remember that the d sublevel is always preceded by an s sublevel that is one quantum number higher. For the lanthanides, the endings are f^1 through f^{14} preceded by a coefficient that is two less than the period number.

To understand some of the exceptions to the diagonal rule, it is necessary to know that there is a special stability associated with certain electron configurations in an atom. You already know that an atom with eight electrons in the outer level has this stability. *An atom having a filled or half filled sublevel is slightly more stable than an atom with no special arrangement.* Thus, chromium is predicted to have two electrons in its $4s$ sublevel and four electrons in its $3d$ sublevel. Actually, it has one electron in its $4s$ sublevel and five electrons in its $3d$ sublevel. Note that one electron is shifted between two very closely spaced sublevels. The atom thus has two half-full sublevels instead of one full sublevel and one with no special arrangement. Copper has a similar change. Copper is predicted to have two $4s$ electrons and nine $3d$ electrons. Actually, it has one electron in its $4s$ sublevel and ten electrons in its $3d$ sublevel. One full and one half-full sublevel make an atom more stable than one full sublevel and one with no special arrangement as predicted. Most of the exceptions from predicted configurations can be explained in this way.

9:9 METALS AND NONMETALS

Groups IA (1) and IIA (2) of the periodic table contain the most active metals. Many of the columns in the table have family names. Group IA (1), except hydrogen, is called the *alkali metal family*. Group IIA (2) is called the *alkaline earth metal family*.

On the other side of the table are the nonmetals, in Groups VIA (16), VIIA (17), and VIIIA (18). Group VIA (16) is called the *chalcogen* (KAL kuh juhn) *family*. Group VIIA (17) is known as the *halogen family*. The elements of Group VIIIA (18) are called the *noble gases*.

We are all familiar with typical metallic properties. **Metals** are hard and shiny. They conduct heat and electricity well. **Nonmetals** are generally gases or brittle solids at room temperature. Their surfaces are dull and they are insulators. Chemists use the electron structure of elements to classify them as metals or nonmetals.

One characteristic of metals is that they have only a few electrons in the outer level. Nonmetals have more electrons in the outer level. As a general rule, *elements with three or less electrons in the outer level are considered to be metals. Elements with five or more electrons in the outer*

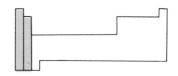

Most active metals: groups IA and IIA.

SUGGESTION: Ask students to list typical metallic and nonmetallic properties with which they are familiar, such as: electrical conductivity, hardness, and metallic lustre. This will set the stage for later development of these properties in terms of bonding and electrons.

Metals generally have fewer electrons in the outer level than nonmetals.

- Alkali Metals
- Alkaline Earth Metals
- Lanthanides
- Actinides
- Chalcogens
- Halogens
- Noble Gases
- Transition Metals

FIGURE 9-4. Groups of elements are often referred to as families.

Metalloids are elements which
have both metallic and nonmetallic properties.

level are considered to be nonmetals. There are exceptions. Some elements have properties of both metals and nonmetals. These elements are called the **metalloids.** Silicon, an element used in the manufacture of microcomputer chips, is a metalloid. On the periodic table, you will note a heavy, stairstep line on the right side. This line is a rough dividing line between metals and nonmetals. As you might expect, the elements along the line are generally metalloids.

The elements of Groups IB through VIIIB (3-12) are called the *transition elements.* Since all atoms of transition elements have one or two electrons in the outer level, they all show metallic properties. The elements 57 through 70, and 89 through 102 have a similar characteristic.

a

b

c

FIGURE 9-5. Sulfur (a) has properties characteristic of nonmetals. Silicon (b) is a metalloid. Calcium (c) is a metal.

Metallic character increases
down the table.

These atoms have two electrons in the outer level as predicted and are therefore classified as metals.

The elements of Groups IIIA (13) through VA (15) include both metals and nonmetals. At the top of the table, each of these groups contains nonmetallic elements. The metallic character of the elements increases toward the bottom of the table, and the last member of each family is distinctly metallic.

We can now look at the periodic table as a whole. Metals are located on the left and nonmetals on the right. Note again that most of the elements are metallic; that is, their atoms contain one, two, or three electrons in the outer energy level. The most stable atoms are those of the noble gases. This stability is explained by the octet rule.

PROBLEMS

1. a. nonmetal
   b. metal
   c. metalloid
   d. metal
   e. metal
   f. metal
   g. metal
2. more metals

1. Classify the following elements as metals, metalloids, or nonmetals.

a. oxygen   **e.** europium
b. scandium   **f.** cerium
c. silicon   **g.** mercury
d. lithium

2. Are there more metals or nonmetals in the periodic table?

BIOGRAPHY   Henry Gwyn-Jeffreys Moseley (1887-1915)

Henry Moseley was the first to discover a definite way of determining the atomic numbers of the elements. He accomplished this task by using different metals as targets in an X-ray tube. His research enabled scientists to determine the atomic number of elements, numbers which were unknown at the time and to correct the order in Mendeleev's periodic table.

As a teacher at the University of Manchester, Moseley also spent time investigating radioactivity. His efforts in this field were halted, however, when the British government sent him to serve as an ordinary foot soldier in the First World War. He was killed in the fighting in Gallipoli at the age of 28. Because of this loss, the British government later restricted its scientists to noncombatant duties during World War II.

CAREERS AND CHEMISTRY

9:10 Analytical Chemists

Analytical chemists are concerned chiefly with identifying the type and quantity of substances present in a material. Quality control in such fields as foods, pharmaceuticals, and safe water is one of the jobs performed by analytical chemists. Analytical chemists may be responsible for coordinating and conducting laboratory or field tests in order to maintain quality control. Chemical processes must be checked each step of the way to ensure that the process is proceeding properly. The product must be analyzed to see that governmental and industrial standards are met.

Some analytical chemists devote their efforts to research in one of two areas. One area is the characterization of substances never before analyzed. The second is the development of new techniques, methods, and procedures in analysis. This area also includes the development of new instrumentation for analysis. One problem that arises in setting standards of purity for commercial products is the result of recent improvements in analytical procedures and equipment. Analytical chemists can now detect the presence of substances at extremely low concentrations. Unfortunately, no one knows the actual effects of some substances. Consequently, it is difficult to decide whether a substance should be banned at the 0.000 000 1% level if it is toxic at 1%. Analytical chemists can

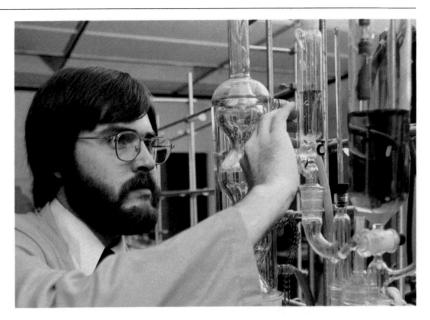

FIGURE 9-6. The analytical chemist must have an in-depth knowledge of analytical methods to interpret data.

detect many elements at levels equivalent to one gram of salt in a cube of water ten kilometers on an edge.

Analytical chemists may also investigate the chemical and physical properties of substances. These investigations may involve the determination of the molecular or ionic structure of a substance. Structure and property determinations usually require the use of many instruments. You will study some of these instruments in this book. Many analytical devices are controlled by microcomputer. The analytical chemist must have a knowledge of computer programming and operation to use these devices effectively.

SUMMARY

1. There have been many attempts to classify the elements in a systematic manner. These attempts include Dobereiner's triads, Newlands' law of octaves, and Mendeleev's and Meyer's tables. 9:1-9:2

2. The modern periodic law states: The properties of the elements are a periodic function of their atomic numbers. 9:3

3. Today's periodic table is based on the electron configurations of atoms. All elements in a horizontal line of the table are called a period. All elements in a vertical line are called a group or family. 9:4-9:8

4. The most stable atoms, the noble gases, have eight electrons in the outer level. Helium atoms are stable with two electrons in the outer level. 9:7

5. Full and half-full sublevels represent atoms in states of special stability. 9:8

6. Elements with one, two, or three electrons in the outer level tend to be metals. Elements with five, six, seven, or eight outer electrons tend to be nonmetals. 9:9

VOCABULARY

triad 9:1
law of octaves 9:1
periodic law 9:3
periodic table 9:4
lanthanide series 9:6

actinide series 9:6
period 9:6
group 9:6
octet 9:7

octet rule 9:7
metal 9:9
nonmetal 9:9
metalloid 9:9

PROBLEMS

1. Classify the following elements as metals or nonmetals.

   a. manganese
   b. fluorine
   c. silver
   d. neon

   e. cobalt
   f. praeseodymium
   g. nitrogen
   h. niobium

   i. hydrogen
   j. lithium
   k. radon
   l. carbon

Element X has the following electron configuration $1s^2 2s^2 2p^6 3s^2 3p^6 4s^2 3d^{10} 4p^4$.

Use this information to answer the following questions.

2. Locate the position of Element *X* on the periodic table.

3. To what group and to what period does this element belong?

4. Classify the element as a metal, nonmetal, or metalloid.

5. List the properties associated with the classification you chose.

6. Draw the electron dot diagram for an atom of Element *X*.

The positions of some elements are highlighted on the periodic table Figure 9-7 below. For each element highlighted answer the following.

7. To what group and what period does this element belong?

8. Classify the element as a metal, nonmetal, or metalloid.

9. List the properties this element should exhibit based on the classification you chose in 8.

10. Write the electron configuration of the element.

11. Draw the electron dot diagram for an atom of this element.

1. a. metal
   b. nonmetal
   c. metal
   d. nonmetal
   e. metal
   f. metal
   g. nonmetal
   h. metal
   i. nonmetal
   j. metal
   k. nonmetal
   l. nonmetal
2. $Z = 34$, selenium
3. 4th period, Group VIA (16)
4. nometal
5. tends to gain electrons, hard, brittle
6. ·Se:

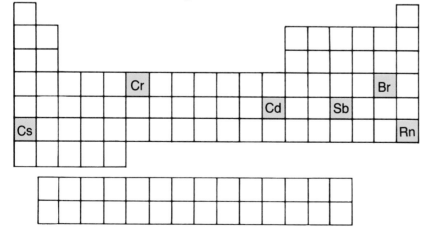

FIGURE 9-7. Use with Problems 7-11.

REVIEW

1. frequency, wave-length, velocity, amplitude

2. Schrödinger considered the electron as a wave; Bohr considered it a particle.

3. n, l, m, s
n represents energy level, l sublevel, m and s have no effect on energy
n = cloud size,
l = cloud shape,
m = cloud spatial orientation,
s = electron spin

4. a. $1s^2 2s^2 2p^6 3s^2$
$3p^1$ Al:

b. $1s^2 2s^2 2p^6 3s^2$
$3p^4$ ·S̈:

c. $1s^2 2s^2 2p^6 3s^2$
$3p^6 4s^2$ Ca:

d. $1s^2 2s^2 2p^6 3s^2$
$3p^6 4s^2 3d^2$ Ti:

e. $1s^2 2s^2 2p^6 3s^2$
$3p^6 4s^2 3d^3$ V:

f. $1s^2 2s^2 2p^6 3s^2$
$3p^6 4s^2 3d^5$ Mn:

g. $1s^2 2s^2 2p^6 3s^2$
$3p^6 4s^2 3d^7$ Co:

h. $1s^2 2s^2 2p^6 3s^2$
$3p^6 4s^2 3d^{10} 4p^2$
·Ge:

i. $1s^2 2s^2 2p^6 3s^2$
$3p^6 4s^2 3d^{10} 4p^5$
:B̈r:

5. h = Planck's constant
m = mass
v = velocity
λ = wavelength

14. dissolve 0.233 g in enough H_2O to make 10 cm³ of solution

19. $Cr(NO_3)_3 + 3NaOH \rightarrow$ $Cr(OH)_3 + 3NaNO_3$

20. 10.1 g $AgNO_3$

21. 2490 J

1. What are the four characteristics of waves that we have studied?

2. How does Schrödinger's analysis of the atom differ from that of Bohr?

3. What are the four quantum numbers associated with each electron in an atom? What does each represent in terms of energy? In terms of the electron cloud?

4. Write the electron configurations and draw electron dot diagrams for the following elements.
   a. Al ($Z = 13$)   d. Ti ($Z = 22$)   g. Co ($Z = 27$)
   b. S ($Z = 16$)   e. V ($Z = 23$)   h. Ge ($Z = 32$)
   c. Ca ($Z = 20$)   f. Mn ($Z = 25$)   i. Br ($Z = 35$)

5. Explain the meaning of each symbol in the de Broglie equation.

6. Compute the atomic mass of tungsten if its isotopes occur as follows.
   1.140%   179.9467;   26.41%   181.948 25;   14.40%   182.950 27;   30.64%   183.950 97;   and 28.41%   185.954 40   6. 185.6 u

7. How many significant digits are in the measurement 26°C?   7. 2

8. What is the percent uncertainty of the measurement 10.14 g if the balance is accurate to ±0.01 g?   8. ±0.09%

9. What volume is occupied by 42.5 g of a substance of density 3.15 g/cm³?   9. 13.5 cm³

10. Write formulas for the following compounds.
    a. zinc phosphide   c. aluminum fluoride
    b. zirconium(IV) selenate   d. bismuth(III) chloride

10. a. Zn_3P_2
    b. $Zr(SeO_4)_2$
    c. AlF_3
    d. $BiCl_3$

11. Write names for the following compounds.
    a. $ZnC_4H_4O_6$ c. $Cr(CH_3COO)_3$
    b. $PbSe$ d. Mn_3P_2

11. a. zinc tartrate
    b. lead(II) selenic
    c. chromium(III) acetate
    d. manganese(II) phosphide

12. Compute the formula mass of Sr_3N_2.   12. 291 u

13. What is the mass of 3.00 mol $Zn_3(PO_4)_2$?   13. 1160 g

14. How would you prepare 10.0 cm³ of a 0.100M solution of $ZrCl_4$?

15. Find the percentage composition of $Co(CH_3COO)_2$.   15. 33.3%, 27.1%, 3.42%, 36.2%

16. What is the empirical formula for a compound with the following composition: 40.1% Co, 16.3% C, and 43.5% O?   16. CoC_2O_4

17. What is the molecular formula for a compound with empirical formula BiC_3O_6 and molecular mass 682?   17. $Bi_2C_6O_{12}$

18. What is the formula for a hydrate which is 66.3% $Ga_2(SeO_4)_3$ and 33.7% H_2O?   18. $Ga_2(SeO_4)_3 \cdot 16H_2O$

19. Balance the following equation.
$$Cr(NO_3)_3 + NaOH \rightarrow Cr(OH)_3 + NaNO_3$$

20. What mass of silver nitrate will react with 2.37 g NaOH?
$$2AgNO_3 + 2NaOH \rightarrow Ag_2O + 2NaNO_3 + H_2O$$

21. How much energy is needed to heat 5.24 g of Ru from 25°C to 2020°C? (Refer to Table A-5 in the Appendix.)

22. How many electrons, neutrons, and protons are found in an isotope of oxygen with a mass number 16?

ONE MORE STEP

1. Make a chart showing the history of the classification of elements. Include date, person, and contribution.

2. Mendeleev made predictions about five elements in addition to germanium. Find out what these elements were and how accurate his predictions were.

3. Explain why the following elements do not follow the diagonal rule for electron configurations: molybdenum, palladium, and gadolinium.

4. Explain the deviations from the diagonal rule for the electron configurations of gold, curium, and thorium.

5. The names of the elements have an interesting history. Develop a table showing how each name was derived.

6. What property of metalloids has led to their use in transistors and computer chips?

READINGS

Seaborg, Glenn T., "Charting the New Elements," *SciQuest,* Vol. 53, No. 8(October 1980), pp. 7-11.

The elements copper, silver, and gold are often referred to as the coinage metals. Throughout history these elements have been valued for their properties, such as luster and malleability. These three elements are listed in the same group on the periodic table. By knowing the properties of any one of the elements we can predict the properties of the other two. This ability is due to the periodic nature of the properties of the elements. What are some periodic properties of the elements?

PERIODIC PROPERTIES

Chapter 10 focuses on the relationship between atomic and ionic radii by introducing ionization energy and electron affinity. Oxidation number, as it relates to electron configuration, is also presented.

GOALS:
• You will explain the periodic nature of the properties of the elements.
• You will learn how atomic and ionic size changes in groups and periods.
• You will define ionization energy and electron affinity and describe the factors affecting these properties.

DEMONSTRATION: Obtain a battery operated smoke detector. Burn a piece of paper in a pan near the detector. The detector circuit senses a current when smoke is introduced into the ionization chamber. A radioactive source in the chamber is used to ionize the invisible gas which then conducts electricity. Use this demonstration to introduce ionization energy.

The periodic table is a powerful tool of the chemist. The table is organized on the basis of the atomic structures of the elements. We know that atoms of elements in the same column have similar outer level electron configurations. We also know that the change in structure from one column to the next as we scan across the table varies in a set way. Since the properties of the elements are determined by their electron configurations, we should be able to predict properties of most elements based on our knowledge of the behavior of a few.

We have already seen that as we scan across the table from left to right, we proceed from metallic elements, through metalloids, to nonmetals. When we drop down to the next period, the same pattern repeats. In other words, the properties are **periodic.** Similar properties occur at certain intervals of atomic number, as is stated in the modern periodic law. In this chapter, we will examine some properties whose variation depends upon electron configurations. These properties should be closely related to elements' positions in the periodic table. Remember, the elements do not have the properties *because* of their positions in the table. Rather, *both the position and the properties arise from the electron configurations of the atoms.*

An element's position on the periodic table, and its properties are a result of the electron configuration.

SUGGESTION: Covalent and ionic bonds are discussed in Chapter 12. It would probably be advisable to avoid consideration of bond formation in this chapter. Concentrate instead on the properties of atoms as a function of their structure.

10:1   RADII OF ATOMS

As you look at the periodic table from top to bottom each period represents a new, higher principal quantum number. *As the principal quantum number increases, the size of the electron cloud increases.* Therefore, the size of atoms in each group increases as you look down the table. Chemists discuss the size of atoms by referring to their radii. As you look across the periodic table, all the atoms in a period have the same principal quantum number. However, the positive charge on the nucleus increases by one proton for each element. As a result, the outer electron cloud is pulled in a little tighter. Consequently, one periodic property of atoms is that they generally decrease slightly in size from left to right across a period of the table. In summary, *atomic radii increase top to bottom and right to left in the periodic table.* If you look at Table 10-1 you can see the general trends and the few exceptions to the rule.

Sodium and chlorine are located at opposite ends of the third period. Sodium is found at the left side of the table and is a metal. Chlorine is on the right side of the table in Column VIIA (17) and is a nonmetal.

Atomic size increases down a group.

In general, atomic size decreases from left to right across a period.

FIGURE 10-1. The orbital filling diagrams for sodium and chlorine show they have partially filled outer levels.

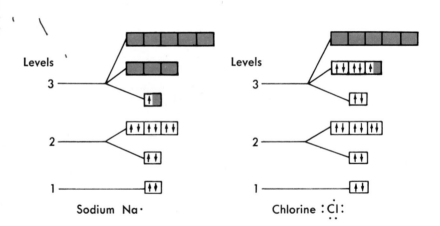

BACKGROUND: The variation in atomic and ionic radii can be explained in terms of:
1. *shielding effect*
2. *distance of outer electrons from the nucleus*
3. *size of nuclear charge*

The chlorine atom is smaller than the sodium atom.

Both sodium and chlorine have partially filled third levels. The outer electrons that take part in reactions are separated from the positively charged nucleus by two inner energy levels. These two inner levels are filled (ten electrons). The chlorine nucleus contains seventeen protons; the sodium nucleus contains only eleven protons. The outer electrons of the chlorine atom are attracted by six more protons than are the outer electrons of the sodium atom. Therefore, the chlorine electrons are held more tightly, and the chlorine atom is smaller than the sodium atom. These two atoms follow the general pattern discussed in the first paragraph of this section.

Table 10-1

Atomic and Ionic Radii (in nanometers)

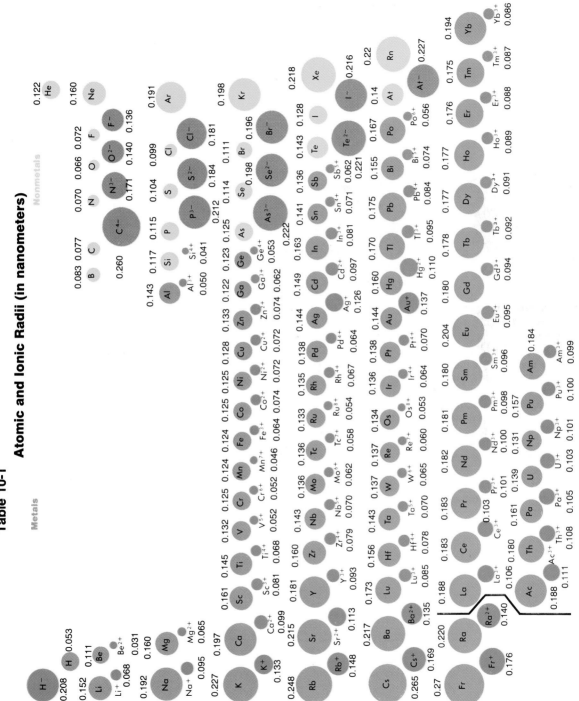

10:2   RADII OF IONS

In general, when atoms unite to form molecules or compounds, their structures become more stable. Sodium and chlorine form the compound sodium chloride, or common table salt. The sodium atom holds its single outer $3s$ electron loosely. When chlorine and sodium atoms react, the chlorine removes the outer electron from the sodium atom. The sodium ion has eleven protons, but only ten electrons, so it has a 1+ charge. There are two main reasons why the sodium ion is smaller than the sodium atom. First, the positively charged nucleus is now attracting fewer electrons. Second, with the loss of the $3s^1$ electron, the ion now has two energy levels while the atom had three levels. The sodium ion is stable because its new outer level ($2s^2 2p^6$) is the same as the outer level of the noble gas, neon. It is important to remember that **noble gas configurations** are particularly stable because the noble gases have filled outer energy levels.

The chlorine atom has gained an electron. The seventeen protons in its nucleus are now attracting eighteen electrons. The chloride ion thus has a 1− charge. Also, the chloride ion is larger than the chlorine atom. The ion is stable because it has the same outer level configuration as the noble gas, argon.

The sodium ion is smaller than the sodium atom.

The configuration of Na$^+$ is similar to neon.

The chlorine ion is larger than the chlorine atom.

The configuration of Cl$^-$ is similar to argon.

FIGURE 10-2. The sodium ion is smaller than the sodium atom because 11 protons are attracting only 10 electrons in the ion. The chlorine ion is larger than the chlorine atom because 17 protons are attracting 18 electrons in the ion. The chlorine atom is smaller than the sodium atom because the electrons in the outer energy level of chlorine are attracted by 6 more protons than in sodium.

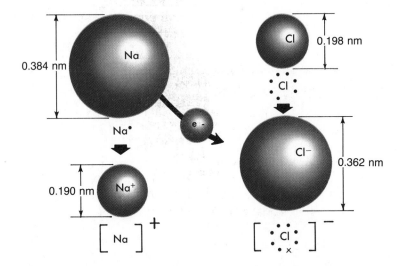

The compound formed from sodium ions and chloride ions does not consist of sodium chloride molecules. Instead, each cube of sodium chloride is a collection of equal numbers of Na$^+$ and Cl$^-$ ions. When salt is dissolved or melted, it will carry a current since the ions are free to move. However, a solid salt crystal will not carry an electric current because the individual ions are tightly bound in the crystal structure. The mobility of electric charge completes a circuit. Thus, the solution or molten substance is able to conduct a current.

Ions which are free to move can conduct an electric current.

We have noted that the sodium ion is smaller than the sodium atom. The magnesium ion is even smaller than its atom. In losing two outer electrons, the unbalanced nuclear positive charge is larger than the negative charge on the electron cloud. The cloud shrinks in size. The nonmetals, sulfur and chlorine, form ions that are larger than their respective atoms. These elements gain electrons to form ions. The elements silicon and phosphorus do not gain or lose electrons readily. They tend to form compounds by sharing their outer electrons.

We can now look at some trends that will apply to any row of the periodic table. In general, *metallic ions, on the left and in the center of the table, are formed by the loss of electrons. They are smaller than the atoms from which they are formed. Nonmetallic ions are located on the right side of the table. They are formed by the gain of electrons and are larger than the atoms from which they are formed.* The metallic ions have a stable outer level that resembles the noble gas at the end of the preceding period. Nonmetallic ions have an outer level resembling the noble gas to the right in the same period.

Metallic atoms lose electrons to form smaller ions.

Nonmetallic atoms gain electrons to form larger ions.

PROBLEMS

1. From each of the following pairs of particles, select the particle that is larger in radius.

a. Ar, Ne

b. B, C

c. O, O^{2-}

d. Mg, Mg^{2+}

e. N, P

f. Cl, O

g. Ca, Sc

h. Te, Te^{2-}

i. Ti, Ti^{4+}

2. State the reasons for your answers to Problem 1.

1. a. Ar   f. Cl
   b. B   g. Ca
   c. O^{2-} h. Te^{2-}
   d. Mg   i. Ti
   e. P

2. See Teacher Guide

10:3   PREDICTING OXIDATION NUMBERS

Those electrons that are involved in the reaction of atoms with each other are the outer and highest energy electrons. You now know about electron configurations and the stability of atoms with noble gas structures. Thus, it is possible for you to predict what oxidation numbers atoms will have.

Consider the metals in Group IA (1). Each atom has one electron in its outer level. The loss of this one electron will give these metals the same configuration as a noble gas. Group IA (1) metals have an oxidation number of 1+. Note that the hydrogen atom could attain the helium configuration by gaining one electron. If this change occurred, we would say that hydrogen has a 1− oxidation number. Hydrogen does indeed exhibit a 1− oxidation number in some compounds. In Group IIA (2) we expect the loss of the two s electrons for the atom to achieve the same configuration as the prior noble gas element. That loss leads to a prediction of 2+

Oxidation numbers can be predicted from electron configurations.

Hydrides contain hydrogen with a 1− oxidation state.

FIGURE 10-3. The oxidation numbers of the elements can be predicted if one knows the element's location in the periodic table.

Trends in Oxidation Numbers of the Elements

SUGGESTION: Inform students that our knowledge about scandium and other elements comes from actual observation and does not always follow patterns or rules.

Metals	
Group	Oxidation Number
IA(1)	1+
IIA(2)	2+
Transition (B Groups)	tend to have more than one
IIIA(13)	3+
IVA(14)	2+ or 4+

Nonmetals	
Group	Oxidation Number
VA(15)	3−
VIA(16)	2−
VIIA(17)	1−

oxidation number for the alkaline earth metals. The elements in these two columns exhibit the oxidation numbers predicted for them.

Beginning with Group IIIB (3) we have atoms in which the highest energy electrons are not in the outer level. For instance, scandium has the configuration $1s^2 2s^2 2p^6 3s^2 3p^6 4s^2 3d^1$. Scandium's outer level is the fourth level containing two electrons. Its highest energy electron, however, is the one in the $3d$ sublevel. For the transition elements, it is possible to lose not only the outer level electrons but also some lower level electrons. Further, these d electrons may be lost one at a time. The transition elements exhibit oxidation numbers varying from $2+$ (representing loss of the two outer s electrons) up to $7+$. We would predict scandium to show only $2+$ and $3+$ oxidation numbers. In actual practice, the element shows only the $3+$ oxidation number. Titanium, which has one more $3d$ electron than scandium, should show $2+$, $3+$, and $4+$, and it does. As we continue across the fourth row, vanadium has a maximum oxidation number of $5+$, chromium $6+$, and manganese $7+$. Iron, which has the configuration $1s^2 2s^2 2p^6 3s^2 3p^6 4s^2 3d^6$, has only $2+$ and $3+$ oxidation numbers. Recall that an atom with a half-full sublevel represents a particularly stable configuration. To take iron higher than $3+$ would mean removing electrons from a half-full $3d$ sublevel.

Group IIIA (13) elements lose three electrons and have an oxidation number of $3+$. Thallium, in addition to the $3+$ oxidation number, exhibits a $1+$ oxidation number. If we look at its configuration, we can understand why. The thallium configuration ends $6s^2 4f^{14} 5d^{10} 6p^1$. The large energy difference between the $6s$ and the $6p$ electrons makes it possible to lose only the $6p$ electron. That loss leads to an oxidation number of $1+$. If stronger reaction methods are used, thallium also has an oxidation number of $3+$. For the same reason, tin and lead in Group IVA (14) may have a $2+$ or $4+$ oxidation number.

In Groups VA (15), VIA (16), and VIIA (17), there is a general tendency to gain electrons to complete the octet. The outside level is already more than half filled. These elements show oxidation numbers of 3– (Group VA), 2– (Group VIA), and 1– (Group VIIA). It is also possible for these elements to lose electrons and have positive oxidation numbers. The tendency to lose electrons increases as we move down a column. This tendency will be discussed in more detail later.

The pattern that emerges from the behavior described above is as follows. For the "A" group elements, the column number represents the maximum positive oxidation number of the elements in that column. Alternatively, the column number minus 8 represents the lowest possible oxidation number. For the "B" group elements, on the other hand, we would predict oxidation numbers of 2 through the column number. For example, consider the element vanadium. It is in column VB(5), period 4. The electron configuration of vanadium is then: $1s^2 2s^2 2p^6 3s^2 3p^6 4s^2 3d^3$. If an atom of vanadium loses the two, outer level, $4s$ electrons, its oxidation number would be 2+. Its *new* outer level would then be $3s^2 3p^6 3d^3$. Each of the $3d$ electrons can now be lost, one at a time. Such changes would lead to 3+, 4+, and 5+ oxidation states. The maximum, 5+, oxidation state is the source of the column V.

PROBLEMS

3. Predict the oxidation numbers for terbium, barium, and molybdenum.

4. Would you predict iron to be more stable at the 2+ or 3+ oxidation state? Provide a reason for your answer.

3. Tb 2+
Ba 2+
Mo 2+, 3+, 4+, 5+, 6+
4. 3+, *d* sublevel is half-filled

10:4 FIRST IONIZATION ENERGY

We know that some atoms tend to give up electrons and become positive ions, while other atoms tend to gain electrons and become negative ions. We now want to examine the periodic nature of these atomic tendencies. Atoms react with each other to form compounds. The path of reactions and the properties of the products are largely dependent upon the tendencies of the reacting atoms to gain or lose electrons. In later chapters, we will be examining the manner in which atoms are bonded to each other in compounds. Again, the attraction of an atom for electrons is the determining factor in the type of bond formed.

Our model of the atom was developed partly from determining the energy needed to remove the most loosely held electron from an atom. This energy is called the **first ionization energy** of that element. It is measured in kilojoules per mole (kJ/mol).

The first ionization energies of the first ninety-five elements are graphed in Figure 10-4. Note that the **ionization energies,** like many other properties of the elements, are periodic. In fact, the relative ionization

BACKGROUND: Ionization energy is also measured in electron volts. 1 *eV* = 96.5 kJ/mol.

BACKGROUND: Ionization energy is determined by bombardment of a vapor by electrons.

First ionization energy: Energy needed to remove the most loosely held electron in an atom.

The energies shown on the graph are first ionization energies. Subsequent ionization energies give experimental evidence for the existence of energy levels and sublevels.

BACKGROUND: Note that the ionization energy falls off immediately as each maximum node is passed and gradually builds up to the next maximum. This corresponds to the formation and filling of each new level.

FIGURE 10-4. The peaks in the graph indicate that ionization energy is a periodic property.

energies of two elements can be predicted by referring to their positions in the periodic table.

The ionization energy tends to increase as atomic number increases in any horizontal row or period. In any column or group, there is a gradual decrease in ionization energy as atomic number increases. Note, for example, the gradual decrease in ionization energy in the alkali metal series, lithium through cesium. The same trend is seen in the noble gas series, helium through radon.

Ionization energies *increase* across rows or periods. Ionization energies *decrease* down columns or groups.

Table 10-2

First Ionization Energies (in kilojoules per mole)							
H 1312.1							He 2372.5
Li 520.3	Be 899.5	B 800.7	C 1086.5	N 1402.4	O 1314.0	F 1681.1	Ne 2080.8
Na 495.9	Mg 737.8	Al 577.6	Si 786.5	P 1011.8	S 999.7	Cl 1251.2	Ar 1520.6
K 418.9	Ca 589.9	Ga 578.6	Ge 761.2	As 946.5	Se 940.7	Br 1142.7	Kr 1350.8
Rb 402.9	Sr 549.2	In 558.2	Sn 708.4	Sb 833.8	Te 869.0	I 1008.7	Xe 1170.3

A metal is characterized by a low ionization energy. Metals are located at the left side of the table. *An element with a high ionization energy is nonmetal.* Nonmetals are found at the right side of the table.

These ionization energies provide strong evidence for the existence of energy levels in the atom. Our theories of structure are based on experimental results such as ionization energies and atomic spectra. The experimental evidence came first, then the model of structure.

Look at Table 10-2. Notice that the ionization energies decrease as you go down a column of the periodic table (for instance, lithium, sodium, potassium). The increased distance of the outer electrons from the nucleus and the **shielding effect** of the inner electrons tend to lower the ionization energy. Though it appears that the increased nuclear charge of an element with a greater atomic number tends to increase ionization energy, the lowering tendency is greater. Remember that the number of electrons in the outermost sublevel is the same for all elements in a column or group.

In moving across a period of the periodic table, we see some deviations from the expected trend of increasing ionization energy. This increase in ionization energy in going from left to right across the table is a result of the increasing nuclear charge. Look at the second row. There is a small decrease from beryllium ($1s^2 2s^2$) to boron ($1s^2 2s^2 2p^1$). In beryllium, the first ionization energy is determined by removing an *s* electron from a full *s* sublevel. In boron, it is determined by removing the lone *p* electron.

There is another slight decrease from nitrogen ($1s^2 2s^2 2p^3$) to oxygen ($1s^2 2s^2 2p^4$). The nitrogen *p* sublevel is half-full (a state of special stability) and a large amount of energy is needed to remove an electron from the sublevel. Thus, oxygen has a lower ionization energy than nitrogen.

The patterns in ionization energy values can be explained by the same factors we discussed in detail in Chapter 9 in connection with the periodic table.

Metals have *low* ionization energy; nonmetals have *high* ionization energy.

This experimental data gives evidence for:
1. effect of increasing nuclear charge
2. stability of octet
3. effect of increased radius
4. *s* & *p* sublevel in outer level

The fourth factor, the effect of *s* & *p* sublevels, causes the slight drop from beryllium to boron and from magnesium to aluminum. Electrons in the *p* sublevel have slightly more energy and therefore require less additional energy to be removed from the atom.

SUGGESTION: Emphasize that the theories came from experimental evidence.

Table 10-3

Factors Affecting Ionization Energy
1. **Nuclear charge**—the larger the nuclear charge, the greater the ionization energy.
2. **Shielding effect**—the greater the shielding effect, the less the ionization energy.
3. **Radius**—the greater the distance between the nucleus and the outer electrons of an atom, the less the ionization energy.
4. **Sublevel**—an electron from a full or half-full sublevel requires additional energy to be removed.

FIGURE 10-5. The second, third, and fourth ionization energies of aluminum are higher than the first because the inner electrons are more tightly held by the nucleus.

10:5 MULTIPLE IONIZATION ENERGIES

It is possible to measure other (second, third, and so on) ionization energies of an atom. These measurements give us the same evidence for atomic structure as first ionization energies. For example, the second ionization energy of aluminum is about three times as large as the first, as shown in Table 10-4. The difference can be explained by the fact that the

Table 10-4

Ionization Energies (in kilojoules per mole)					
Element	1st	2nd	3rd	4th	5th	6th
H	1312.1					
He	2372.5	5250.7				
Li	520.3	7298.5	11 815.6			
Be	899.5	1752.2	14 849.5	21 007.6		
B	800.7	2427.2	3 660.0	25 027.0	32 828.3	
C	1086.5	2352.8	4 620.7	6 223.0	37 832.4	47 279.4
Al	577.6	1816.7	2 744.8	11 577.5	14 831.0	18 377.9

Ionization energy increases with the removal of each additional electron.

first ionization removes a p electron and the second removes an s electron from a full s sublevel. The third ionization energy is about one and one-half times as large as the second. The second and third electrons are in the same sublevel. Yet, the third electron's ionization energy is greater because the nuclear charge remains constant as we remove electrons. As a result, the remaining electrons are more tightly held. The fourth ionization energy is about four times as large as the third. Why is the jump so large between the third and fourth ionization energies? Let us look at the electron configuration. Aluminum has the configuration $1s^2 2s^2 2p^6 3s^2 3p^1$. The fourth electron would come from the full second energy level that is closer to the nucleus. The $2s^2 2p^6$ level with eight electrons is stable. Thus, a large amount of energy will be required to remove that fourth electron.

We have looked only at the aluminum atom, but the same reasoning can be used to explain similar data for other elements. This information can be applied as evidence for our theories of atomic structure.

10:6   ELECTRON AFFINITIES

Now consider an atom's attraction for additional electrons. The attraction of an atom for an electron is called **electron affinity.** The same factors that affect ionization energy will also affect electron affinity. In general, as electron affinity increases, an increase in ionization energy can be expected. *Metals have low electron affinities. Nonmetals have the high electron affinities* as shown in Table 10-5. Although not as regular as ionization energies, electron affinities still show periodic trends. Look at the column headed by hydrogen. The general trend as we go down the column is a decreasing tendency to gain electrons. We should expect this trend since the atoms further down the column are larger. As a consequence, the nucleus is further from the surface and attracts electrons less strongly.

Look at the period beginning with lithium. The general trend as we go across is a greater attraction for electrons. The increased nuclear charge contained in each successive nucleus accounts for the trend.

How do we account for the exceptions of beryllium, nitrogen, and neon in the lithium period? The high negative value for beryllium is taken as evidence of the stability of the full 2s sublevel. The failure of nitrogen to attract electrons more strongly is evidence of the stability of the half-full 2p sublevel. Neon, of course, has a stable, full octet of electrons in the outer level.

All of these properties are involved when atoms react with each other to form compounds. The properties of the compounds, in turn, also depend on the structures of the atoms they contain.

Electron affinity: attraction of an atom for an additional electron expressed as the energy needed to remove an electron from the 1− ion.

Metals have low electron affinities: nonmetals have high electron affinities.

Table 10-5

Electron Affinities (in kilojoules per mole)							
H 72.8							He (−21.2)
Li 59.8	Be (−241)	B 23.2	C 123	N 0	O 141	F 322	Ne (−28.9)
Na 52.9	Mg (−232)	Al 44.4	Si 120	P 74.3	S 200	Cl 349	Ar (−34.7)
K 48.3	Ca (−156)	Ga (36)	Ge 120	As 77	Se 195	Br 324	
Rb 46.9	Sr (−168)	In 39	Sn 125	Sb 101	Te 190	I 295	

( ) indicates a calculated rather than an experimental value.

BIOGRAPHY   Dmitri Ivanovich Mendeleev (1834-1907)

The "Father of The Periodic Table" was the youngest of 14 children in Tobolsk, Siberia. When he was in high school, his father died. His mother took him on a thousand mile trip to Moscow to college. He was refused admittance to the University and so they journeyed to St. Petersburg (now Leningrad) where Mendeleev was allowed to attend college. He became an honor student and a distinguished professor.

As a professor of chemistry, Mendeleev was intrigued by the then known 63 elements. He arranged them and rearranged them finally coming up with the idea of the periodic table. Through his arrangement he was able to predict the existence of previously unknown elements and to predict their properties. Although he was not exactly right in the method he used to arrange the elements (atomic mass), it pointed the way to the correct arrangement by atomic number years later.

CAREERS AND CHEMISTRY

10:7 Pharmacology

All of us are aware of the important role modern medicine plays in our lives. One of the major tools physicians have at their disposal is the array of modern drugs. The science of drugs is pharmacology.

Pharmacologists must master a number of chemistry and chemistry-related fields of knowledge. The most important aspect of their work is knowing the effect substances have on living organisms. In order to interpret drug effects, pharmacologists must have a thorough knowledge of the normal functioning of the body, known as physiology. They must also be prepared to recognize alteration of the normal physiology due to injury or disease. Pathology is the study of such changes in the structure and function of the body.

When drugs are introduced into the body, they are often changed chemically before reaching the target organ. The reactivity of compounds being considered as drugs can often be predicted on the basis of the similarity of their structure to other compounds whose behavior is already understood. Thus, pharmacologists need an intimate knowledge of chemistry, particularly organic chemistry.

When physicians prescribe drugs, they specify certain dosages at definite time intervals. These amounts and times are determined by the concentration of the substances needed in tissues, and by the rate at which the body metabolizes (breaks down) or eliminates the drug. Much pharmacological research is devoted to testing methods that will establish proper dosages.

Pharmacology should not be confused with the profession of pharmacy, which is the dispensing of drugs and the preparation of drug mixtures in accordance with physicians' prescriptions.

FIGURE 10-6. Pharmacologists research the effects of chemicals on body functions.

SUMMARY

1. Within a group of elements, the atomic radii of the atoms increases with increasing atomic number. **10:1**

2. Within a series, the atomic radii of the atoms increase with increasing atomic number. **10:1**

3. Positive ions are smaller than the atoms from which they are produced. **10:2**

4. Negative ions are larger than the atoms from which they are produced. **10:2**

5. Metals are found on the left side of the periodic table and their atoms tend to lose electrons. **10:3**

6. Nonmetals are found on the right side of the periodic table and tend to gain electrons. **10:3**

7. Oxidation numbers can be predicted from electron configurations by making use of the special stability of the outer octet as well as full and half-full sublevels. **10:3**

8. First ionization energy is the energy necessary to remove the first electron from an atom, leaving a positive ion. Ionization energies provide evidence for our theories of atomic structure. **10:4**

9. Electron affinity is the attraction of an atom for electrons. **10:6**

10. Metals have low ionization energies and electron affinities. Nonmetals have high ionization energies and electron affinities. **10:6**

VOCABULARY

periodic intro.
noble gas configuration 10:2
first ionization energies 10:4

ionization energy 10:4
shielding effect 10:4
electron affinity 10:6

PROBLEMS

1. Ar 0, Eu 2+, Al 3+, Sb 3+, 5+, Br 1−
2. U 2+, Na 1+, Si 4+, 4−, Ce 2+, Co 2+
3. decrease
4. increase
5. smaller
6. larger
7. a. 3+
   b. 2+, 3+
   c. 3+, 5+, 3−
   d. 2−, 4+, 6+
   e. 1+, 2+
   f. 2+, 3+, 4+
   g. 2+
   h. 1+
   i. 2+
8. a. Al
   b. Tl
   c. N
   d. Na
   e. K
   f. Br

1. Predict possible oxidation numbers for the following elements and state your evidence: argon, europium, aluminum, antimony, and bromine. Check the actual oxidation numbers and explain any deviations from your predictions.

2. Predict possible oxidation numbers for the following and state your evidence: uranium, sodium, silicon, cerium, and cobalt. Check the actual oxidation numbers and explain any deviations.

3. Explain the change in the size of the atoms as you move from left to right across a horizontal row of the periodic table.

4. Explain the change in the size of the atoms as you move from the top to the bottom of a column of the periodic table.

5. How does the size of a positive ion compare to the size of the atom from which it was formed?

6. How does the size of a negative ion compare to the size of the atom from which it was formed?

7. Predict the oxidation numbers for the following elements.
   a. aluminum
   b. samarium
   c. arsenic
   d. polonium
   e. mercury
   f. titanium
   g. barium
   h. rubidium
   i. silver

8. Which atom in each of the following pairs of atoms would have the lower first ionization energy?
   a. Al, B
   b. B, Tl
   c. F, N
   d. Mg, Na
   e. K, Ca
   f. Br, Cl

9. Using the data in Table 10-4, explain why the ionization energy changes so much for the fourth boron electron and the fifth carbon electron.

10. Explain the differences in the six ionization energies of carbon (Table 10-4).

11. The electron affinities of magnesium and zinc are both negative. What structural features which they possess would lead to values less than zero for their electron affinities?

REVIEW

1. Predict electron configurations using the diagonal rule for niobium, radon, and tin.
2. Find the atomic mass of magnesium if the natural element has the following isotopic composition:

$$78.70\% \quad 23.985\ 044$$
$$10.13\% \quad 24.985\ 839$$
$$11.17\% \quad 25.982\ 593$$

3. How many grams of $NaMnO_4$ can be prepared from 1.27 grams of $NaBiO_3$ according to the reaction

$$2Mn(NO_3)_2 + 5NaBiO_3 + 14HNO_3 \rightarrow$$
$$2NaMnO_4 + 5Bi(NO_3)_3 + 3NaNO_3 + 7H_2O$$

4. Balance: $SnCl_2 + I_2 + HCl \rightarrow SnCl_4 + HI$
5. What is the empirical formula of a compound which is 63.9% Cd, 11.8% P, and 24.3% O?
6. Name each of the following compounds.
   a. Be_3N_2
   b. $CeCl_3$
   c. $Hg_3(AsO_4)_2$
   d. Ca_3P_2
   e. $CuSeO_4$
7. Write formulas for each of the following compounds.
   a. silicon(IV) fluoride
   b. thallium(I) perchlorate
   c. nickel(II) cyanide
   d. calcium pyrophosphate
   e. beryllium hydride

1. [Kr] $4d^3\ 5s^2$
   [Xe] $4f^{14}\ 5d^{10}\ 6s^2\ 6p^6$
   [Kr] $4d^{10}\ 5s^2\ 5p^2$
2. 24.31 u
3. 0.258 g $NaMnO_4$
4. $2HCl + SnCl_2 + I_2 \rightarrow 2HI + SnCl_4$
5. $Cd_3P_2O_8$ or $Cd_3(PO_4)_2$
6. a. beryllium nitride
   b. cerium(III) chloride
   c. mercury(II) arsenate
   d. calcium phosphide
   e. copper(II) selenate
7. a. SiF_4
   b. $TlClO_4$
   c. $Ni(CN)_2$
   d. $Ca_2P_4O_7$
   e. BeH_2

ONE MORE STEP

1. Ionization energies are often reported in the literature in units of electron volts per molecule. Find a conversion factor for kJ/mol to eV/molecule and prepare a table similar to Table 10-2 with values in electron volts.
2. Investigate the experimental method of determining electron affinities.

READINGS

Porterfield, William W., *Inorganic Chemistry: A Unified Approach*, Reading, MA: Addison-Wesley, 1984.

Colorful displays of fireworks have been enjoyed for centuries. Compounds containing the alkaline earth metals are used to produce the brilliant colors. What group on the periodic table is formed by the alkaline earth metals? What elements compose this group? What are some other uses for these elements?

TYPICAL ELEMENTS

Chapter 11 concerns how properties can be predicted after looking at the periodic nature of the elements in groups and periods.

GOALS:
- You will associate families of elements with columns of the periodic table.
- You will differentiate among the properties of the families of elements.
- You will be able to explain the reasons for similarities and differences of properties within the same family.

DEMONSTRATION: Show the trend in solubility for Group IIA (2) by dissolving 1 g of $MgSO_4$, $CaSO_4$, and $BaSO_4$ each in 50 cm^3 of water in separate graduated cylinders. Allow to stand for a few minutes. Ask students how trends in properties such as solubility can be used to predict the solubility of other elements in Group IIA. See Teacher Guide for other information.

We can see the periodic nature of the elements in groups as well as in periods of the table. The elements in the first group, hydrogen through francium, all contain one *s* electron in the outer level. A group is often called a **family** because of the similarity of the elements within it. The members of a family have a similar arrangement of outer electrons and thus tend to react similarly. For instance, lithium, sodium, and potassium all lose one electron to chlorine and form chlorides (LiCl, NaCl, KCl). Hydrogen is also found in this group. It forms a chloride, hydrogen chloride. Let us take a closer look at some elements. From studying the properties of a few, we can predict the properties of many more.

Members of a chemical family (group) react similarly.

11:1 HYDROGEN

Hydrogen, like the alkali metals, has only one outer electron. Because of its unique properties, it is usually considered as a family by itself. There are four ways in which the hydrogen atom can react. It may lose its one electron to become a positive hydrogen ion. A **hydrogen ion,** H^+, is simply a bare proton. Remember from Section 7:5 that a proton is about one trillionth the size of an atom. Because of its small size, the hydrogen ion is not stable. This characteristic will be considered in studying hydrogen bonding and acids later in this text.

Hydrogen is generally considered a "family" by itself.

a

b

FIGURE 11-1. This experimental vehicle is powered by hydrogen released from a storage battery (a). The metal hydride fuel (b) contains a number of cracks where the metal surface has reacted with hydrogen.

● Boron
○ Hydrogen

B_4H_{10}

FIGURE 11-2. Hydrogen acts as a bridge between boron atoms. Compounds, such as the one shown, are discussed in detail on page 257.

The second way a hydrogen atom can react is by sharing its single outer electron. Most nonmetals react with hydrogen to form compounds involving shared electrons. Examples of these compounds are HCl and H_2O. These compounds and their formation will be studied in more detail in Chapter 13.

The third way hydrogen can react is to gain an electron. When this change occurs, the atom becomes a **hydride ion,** H^-. Such a reaction can take place only between hydrogen and atoms of elements that give up electrons easily. The most reactive metals, Groups IA (1) and IIA (2), form ionic hydrides. In these compounds, the radius of the hydride ion averages about 0.208 nm. From Table 10-1 we can see that the hydride ion is larger than the fluoride ion. Such a radius indicates that the single proton of the hydride ion has a very weak hold on the two electrons. We would expect, then, that the ionic hydrides would not be highly stable. Research confirms this conclusion. Ionic hydrides are found to be quite reactive compounds.

By sharing or gaining electrons, hydrogen attains the stable outer level configuration of helium. Hydrogen gas is used in the manufacture of other chemicals such as ammonia and methanol. One interesting use is the conversion of a vegetable oil such as corn oil into shortening, or oleomargarine. The reaction which takes place involves the addition (Chapter 30) of hydrogen atoms to double bonds (Chapter 13) in the oil molecules.

A fourth type of bonding involves the formation of bridges between two atoms by hydrogen atoms. The best examples of these compounds are found with the element boron and some of the transition metals. A study of such compounds is beyond the scope of this book. Since they are not common compounds, their behavior is only a small fraction of the chemistry of hydrogen. (See Chemistry and Technology, Section 13:13.)

Hydrogen reacts in four differ-ent ways.
1. by losing an electron
2. by sharing an electron
3. by gaining an electron
4. by forming bridges

11:2 ALKALI METALS

The metals in Group IA (1) are reactive. If one member of a family forms a compound with an element or ion, we can predict that the other members will do the same. However, the members of a family are not the same in every way. The outer electron of lithium occupies a volume closer to the nucleus than the outer electron of sodium. The sodium atom has many more electrons between the outer electron and the nucleus than lithium. An increasing number of electrons between the outer level and the nucleus has a **shielding effect.** This effect blocks the attraction of the nucleus for the outer electrons. Larger atoms tend to lose their outer elec-trons more readily. This tendency is due to the increased distance of the electrons from the nucleus as well as the shielding effect.

As the atoms of the alkali metals increase in size, the nucleus increases in positive charge. However, the force of the increased positive charge is more than offset by the outer electron's distance from the nu-cleus and the shielding effect. As a result, we find that the alkali metals lose their outer electrons more readily as we proceed down the group. This trend indicates that the most active metal would be francium in the lower left corner of the periodic table.

Alkali metals are the Group IA (1) elements.

As the atomic numbers of the alkali metals increase
1. the atoms become larger
2. the outer electron is farther from the nucleus
3. the lower level electrons shield the effect of the larg-er nucleus
4. the outer electrons are held less tightly
5. the atoms become more ac-tive.

FIGURE 11-3. The peaks in the graph show that atomic radius is a periodic property.

Sodium and potassium ions are important biologically. The ratio of their concentrations in the body is vital to the transmission of nerve impulses.

Na^+ and K^+ ion concentrations are vital to nerve impulse trans-mission.

Table 11-1

Distribution of Sodium and Potassium Ions in the Body (mg/100 g)		
	K$^+$	Na$^+$
Whole blood	200	160
Plasma	20	330
Cells	440	85
Muscle tissue	250-400	6-160
Nerve tissue	530	312

Sodium compounds are used as catalysts and in the production of paper, glass, detergents, soaps, pigments, and petroleum products.

Sodium compounds are among the most important in the chemical industry. Millions of tons of sodium hydroxide are consumed each year in producing other chemicals, paper, and petroleum products. Sodium carbonate is also produced in millions of tons and used in manufacturing glass and other chemicals. Sodium sulfate is another substance used in manufacturing glass as well as paper and detergents. Sodium silicate is widely used as a catalyst in addition to being consumed in making soaps, detergents, paper, and pigments. A **catalyst** speeds up a reaction. Sodium tripolyphosphate ($Na_5P_3O_{10}$) is used as a food additive, in softening water, and in making detergents.

There are two other 1+ ions that, because of their size, behave in a similar fashion to the alkali ions. These ions are the ammonium ion (NH_4^+) and the thallium(I) ion (Tl^+). Their compounds follow much the same patterns as the alkali metal compounds.

FIGURE 11-4. Many sodium and potassium compounds are used as food additives (a). Sodium hydrogen carbonate has a variety of everyday uses (b).

INGREDIENTS

EGG NOODLES, MODIFIED FOOD STARCH, CULTURED NONFAT MILK SOLIDS, SALT, PARTIALLY HYDROGENATED SOYBEAN OIL, SOUR CREAM SOLIDS, SUGAR, BUTTERFAT SOLIDS, CHEDDAR CHEESE SOLIDS, WHEY SOLIDS, HYDROLYZED VEGETABLE PROTEIN, DEHYDRATED ONION, LACTOSE, MONOSODIUM GLUTAMATE, DEHYDRATED GARLIC, SODIUM CASEINATE, SODIUM CITRATE, DIPOTASSIUM PHOSPHATE, SODIUM SILICO ALUMINATE, CITRIC ACID, ARTIFICIAL COLOR, BHA, (PRESERVATIVE).

a

Used in the manufacture of many sodium salts and as a source of CO_2.

Major ingredient in baking powder, effervescent salts and beverages.

99.8% pure

Used in fire extinguishers, cleaning compounds, as an antacid, and deodorizer.

b

11:3   LITHIUM

The reactions of the alkali metals involve mainly the formation of 1+ ions. In general, the reactivity increases with increasing atomic number, with one exception. Lithium reacts more vigorously with nitrogen than any other alkali metal. Lithium is exceptional in other ways, too. Its ion has the same charge as the other alkali metals, but the unusual behavior is due to its smaller size. The ratio of charge to radius is often a good indication of the behavior of an ion. The charge/radius ratio of lithium more closely resembles the magnesium ion (Mg^{2+}) of Group IIA (2). Its behavior resembles Mg^{2+} more closely than the next member of its own family, sodium (Na^+). This diagonal relationship is not unusual among the lighter elements. One example of this relationship is that lithium burns in air to form the oxide, Li_2O, as does magnesium to form MgO. The other alkali metals burn in oxygen to form the peroxide, M_2O_2, or the superoxide, MO_2 (where M = Na, K, Rb, or Cs). Another example of this relationship concerns the solubilities of compounds. The solubility of lithium compounds is similar to that of magnesium compounds, but not to that of sodium compounds.

> Charge to radius ratio is a good indicator of ion behavior.

> Lithium exhibits a diagonal relationship. The lithium ion reacts similarly to the Mg^{2+} ion.

> Solubility of Li compounds is similar to that of Mg compounds.

The lithium atom also differs from the other alkali metal atoms in some physical properties. Unlike the other alkali metals that dissolve in each other in any proportion, lithium is insoluble in all but sodium. It will dissolve in sodium only above 380°C. In other respects, lithium metal is like the other members of its family. For example, it is a soft, silvery metal with a low melting point, as are the other alkali metals except cesium, which is yellow. All of the alkali metals will dissolve in liquid ammonia to give faintly blue solutions. These solutions conduct electricity.

The alkali metals form binary compounds with almost all nonmetals. In these compounds, nonmetals are in the form of negative ions. In solution, the lithium ion, because of its high charge/radius ratio, attracts water molecules more strongly than any other alkali ion.

> Alkali metals form binary compounds with most nonmetals.

11:4 ALKALINE EARTH METALS

The alkaline earth metals are quite similar to the alkali metals except that they form the 2+ ion. Most of their compounds exist as ions and are soluble in water except for some hydroxides, carbonates, and sulfates. Beryllium is used in making nonsparking tools and magnesium is widely used in lightweight alloys. The other metals are too reactive to be used as free elements.

Two calcium compounds find large markets. Lime (calcium oxide) is used to make steel, cement, and heat-resistant bricks. It is also applied to soils that are too acidic to farm without treatment. Some lakes that have become too acidic to support aquatic life have been treated with lime. Calcium chloride is used in a wide range of applications. One interesting use is in controlling road conditions through de-icing in the winter and keeping down dust in the summer. It is also used in the paper and pulp industry.

FIGURE 11-5. Calcium hydroxide is used to make steel.

> Alkaline earth metals are reactive and form the 2+ ion. Most group IIA (2) compounds are soluble.

11:5   ALUMINUM

Aluminum is the only metal of practical importance in Group IIIA (13). With three electrons in the outer level, it is less metallic than the elements of Group IA (1) and IIA (2). For instance, in forming compounds it tends to share electrons rather than form ions. It is also less reactive than Group IA (1) and IIA (2) metals. Large quantities of aluminum are consumed each year in producing lightweight alloys to make everything from soda cans to aircraft. Aluminum sulfate finds applications in water purification, paper manufacture, and fabric dyeing.

Aluminum has 3 outer electrons which it tends to share.

a   b

FIGURE 11-6. Aluminum products are being recycled as a conservation measure (a). "Aluminum lake" compounds are complex organic substances used extensively as colorants in the food industry (b).

11:6   GROUP IVA (14)

The elements of Group IVA (14) have atoms with four electrons in the outer level. These elements generally react by sharing electrons. However, the tendency to lose electrons increases as the atomic number of Group IVA (14) elements increases. There are a few compounds in which carbon in the form of a **carbide ion** (C^{4-}) can be considered to exist. Silicon and germanium, the next members of this family, are metalloids. They do not form 4− ions under any conditions. However, there are compounds in which silicon and germanium exist as a 4+ ion.

Group IVA (14) members generally react by sharing electrons.

The major part of carbon chemistry is classed as organic chemistry. Most **organic compounds** involve sharing electrons between a carbon atom and one or more other carbon atoms. The tendency to form "chains" of similar atoms is called **catenation** (kat uh NAY shuhn). Only carbon exhibits catenation to any great extent. In general, those compounds that do not contain carbon are called **inorganic compounds.** Exceptions to this general rule are carbon itself, carbonic acid and its

Organic chemistry is the chemistry of carbon.

Catenation is the tendency to form "chains" of similar atoms.

$$CH_3-CH_2-CH_2-CH_2-CH_2-CH_2-CH_2-CH_2-CH=CH-CH_2-CH_2-CH_2-CH_2-CH_2-CH_2-CH_2-C\overset{\displaystyle O}{\underset{\displaystyle OH}{}}$$

Oleic acid

$$\cdots-\underset{\underset{CH_3}{|}}{\overset{\overset{CH_3}{|}}{Si}}-O-\underset{\underset{CH_3}{|}}{\overset{\overset{CH_3}{|}}{Si}}-O-\underset{\underset{CH_3}{|}}{\overset{\overset{CH_3}{|}}{Si}}-O-\underset{\underset{CH_3}{|}}{\overset{\overset{CH_3}{|}}{Si}}-O-\underset{\underset{CH_3}{|}}{\overset{\overset{CH_3}{|}}{Si}}-\underset{\underset{CH_3}{|}}{\overset{\overset{CH_3}{|}}{C}}-\cdots$$

Methyl silicon polymer chain

FIGURE 11-7. Carbon compounds exhibit catenation as shown by the structure for oleic acid. Silicon also exhibits this property as shown by the structure of this methyl silicon polymer.

Different forms of the same element are called allotropes.

salts, carbides, cyanides, and the oxides and sulfides of carbon which are also considered inorganic.

Carbon is found in nature in two different molecular forms—diamond and graphite. In diamond, each carbon atom shares electrons with the four nearest carbon atoms. In graphite, the sharing is to the nearest three carbon atoms. The difference in structure results in different properties for these two forms of carbon. We will study these differences in Chapter 16. Different forms of the same element are called **allotropes.**

Industrially, carbon is used in a form called "carbon black" made by burning natural gas or other fuel. Carbon black is often referred to as soot when it has accumulated in a place where it is unwanted. It is actually a microcrystalline form of graphite, and is used as a black pigment and wear-resistant additive in rubber tires. Carbon dioxide gas is a by-product of several chemical processes. It is collected, compressed, and sold as a liquid in steel cylinders. Customers use it for refrigeration, carbonating beverages, and producing other chemicals.

Silicon shows only a slight tendency toward catenation, much less so than carbon. However, the chemistry of silicon, like that of carbon, is characterized by electron sharing. Silicon is the second most plentiful

FIGURE 11-8. Natural latex is a white liquid (a). Graphite is added as a colorant to rubber in making tires (b). Carbonated beverages are solutions of CO_2 gas in liquid. The CO_2 tanks in a vending machine must be replaced periodically (c).

a   b   c

element in the Earth's crust. (Oxygen is the most plentiful.) It is found in a large number of minerals.

Transistors are discussed more fully in Section 16:9.

Carbon and silicon differ more than other vertically neighboring elements.

Silicon is bound to oxygen atoms in a variety of ways. In these compounds, called **silicates,** each silicon atom is surrounded by four oxygen atoms with which it shares electrons. Transistors, computer chips, and synthetic motor oils are three developments of silicon chemistry. Carbon and silicon differ more than any other two vertically neighboring elements in the periodic table.

a   b

FIGURE 11-9. Silicon is a component of the mineral quartz (a). Since it is a semiconductor, silicon is used extensively in the manufacture of computer chips (b).

Tin and lead are common components of alloys which are mixtures of metals.

Tin and lead are distinctly metallic members of Group IVA (14). They are quite similar except that for tin the 4+ state is more stable than the 2+, while the reverse is true for lead. These two metals are easily produced from their ores and have both been known since early times. In general, their uses are based on their lack of chemical reactivity. They are common components of alloys that are mixtures of metals. Examples of alloys are solder, which contains lead and tin, and bronze, which contains copper and tin.

11:7 NITROGEN AND PHOSPHORUS

Nitrogen and phosphorus differ greatly for being adjacent members of Group VA(15).

N₂ gas is one of the most stable substances known but many nitrogen compounds are relatively unstable.

Nitrogen and phosphorus differ considerably for adjacent members of the same family. Nitrogen occurs in all oxidation states ranging from 3− through 5+; phosphorus shows only 3−, 0, 3+, and 5+. Liquid nitrogen is used to maintain very low temperatures. The unreactive gas is used to surround reactive materials that would otherwise react with oxygen in the air. Elemental nitrogen, N_2 gas, is one of the most stable substances known. Most nitrogen compounds are relatively unstable, tending to decompose to N_2. Conventional high explosives, for example, trinitrotoluene (TNT) and dynamite, utilize nitrogen compounds. Nitrogen compounds are produced naturally from atmospheric nitrogen by nitrogen-fixing bacteria. These bacteria convert molecular nitrogen to a form that can be used readily by plants. This process is essential to plant life. Nitrogen compounds serve a vital function in living systems in amino acids, essential components of proteins.

Nitrogen compounds are important to living systems.

O_2N—⬡—NO_2 (with CH_3 at top vertex and NO_2 at bottom vertex)

$$CH_3 \diagdown CH—CH—COOH$$
$$CH_3 \diagup \qquad NH_2$$

2,4,6-Trinitrotoluene
TNT

Valine
An amino acid

FIGURE 11-10. Nitrogen compounds have a variety of functions. TNT is used as an explosive. Each vertex in the TNT hexagon represents a carbon atom. Valine, an amino acid, is an essential component of protein.

However, most nitrogen compounds are produced from atmospheric nitrogen by synthetic processes. Huge quantities of liquid N_2, obtained from the air, are used in the Haber Process, Section 23:9, or other similar processes to produce ammonia. The most common use of ammonia is as a fertilizer. Much of the ammonia not used directly as a fertilizer is converted to other nitrogen compounds which are themselves fertilizers. An example is ammonium nitrate, which is also used in explosives. Some ammonia is converted to nitric acid. Nitric acid itself is widely used in the manufacture of fertilizer and explosives. Large quantities of ammonium sulfate are obtained from the steel industry's conversion of coal to coke. The $(NH_4)_2SO_4$ by-product is then used as a fertilizer.

Ammonia, a nitrogen compound, is used most commonly as a fertilizer.

Elemental phosphorus occurs as P_4 molecules and is solid at room temperature. The P_4 molecules "stack" in different ways to form several allotropes. One allotrope, white phosphorus, is so reactive that it ignites spontaneously on contacting air. Red phosphorus must be exposed to a flame to ignite. The principal source for phosphorus in nature is phosphate rock, $Ca_3(PO_4)_2$. Most phosphate rock is used in producing $Ca(H_2PO_4)_2$ and $CaHPO_4$ for use as fertilizer. Some phosphate rock is

Elemental phosphorus occurs as P_4 molecules, which form several allotropes.

FIGURE 11-11. White and black phosphorus are allotropes. Note the difference in the geometric arrangement of the phosphorus atoms.

White phosphorus

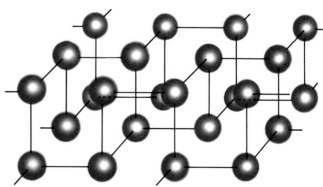

Black phosphorus

converted to phosphoric acid which is also used primarily in making fertilizer, but has other applications in industry.

Organic compounds of phosphorus are vital to living organisms. Utilization of energy by living systems involves a compound called adenosine triphosphate (ATP). The transfer of genetic information from generation to generation involves deoxyribonucleic acid (DNA). Each DNA molecule contains hundreds of phosphate groups. Ribonucleic acid (RNA), used by cells in metabolism, also contains phosphate groups.

ATP, DNA, and RNA are biologically important compounds which contain phosphate groups.

Portion of a DNA molecule

FIGURE 11-12. The structures for DNA and ATP are shown. Note that the unlabeled vertices in each ring are occupied by carbon atoms.

SUGGESTION: Consider familiarizing students with the shorthand method of writing organic ring compounds at this point. It will be covered further in Chapter 13 in the section on benzene.

11:8 OXYGEN

Oxygen is the most plentiful element in the Earth's crust.

Oxygen is the most plentiful element in the earth's crust. It combines with all other elements except helium, neon, and argon. Since the atom has six electrons in its outer level, it can gain two electrons to achieve the stable octet configuration of neon. In so doing, it becomes the oxide ion, O^{2-}. It can also react by sharing electrons. With metals, which tend to lose electrons readily, oxygen forms ionic oxides. With nonmetals, oxygen tends to share electrons. The behavior of these oxides when dissolved in water depends on their structure. Ionic oxides generally react with water to produce basic solutions. However, oxides formed by the sharing of electrons tend to react with water to form acidic solutions. There are some oxides that can produce either acidic or basic solutions, depending on the other substances present. Such oxides are called **amphoteric** (am foh TER ik) oxides.

Like carbon, oxygen has allotropes. Oxygen usually occurs in the form of diatomic oxygen molecules, O_2. The free oxygen you breathe from air is O_2. There is another allotrope of oxygen called ozone. Ozone is the triatomic form of oxygen, O_3, and is highly reactive. Ozone can be synthesized by subjecting O_2 to a silent electric discharge. It is formed naturally in small amounts by lightning and, in the upper atmosphere, by ultraviolet radiation from the sun. That layer of ozone protects living things on the earth from the sun's harmful ultraviolet radiation. In Europe, ozone is the main chemical used in water purification.

Pure oxygen is extracted from air, compressed, and sold in cylinders. Its largest uses are in the production of steel, artificial breathing atmospheres, rocket engines, and welding torches.

The chemistry of sulfur is similar to the chemistry of oxygen, especially in the behavior of the $2-$ ion. The S^{2-} ion shows characteristics

Oxygen reacts by gaining 2 electrons or sharing electrons.

Amphoteric oxides produce either acidic or basic solutions.

O_3 is ozone, a highly reactive allotrope of oxygen.

The chemistry of sulfur is similar to the chemistry of oxygen.

FIGURE 11-13. Rockets are fueled with liquid oxygen, LOX.

similar to the oxide ion in solubility and acid-base behavior. Unlike oxygen whose longest chain is O_3, sulfur can form long chains of atoms attached to the S^{2-} ion. These ions, for example $S_6{}^{2-}$, are called polysulfide ions. Sulfur exhibits two important positive oxidation states represented by the oxides SO_2 and SO_3. When sulfur or sulfur compounds are burned in an ample supply of air, SO_2 is produced. Using a catalyst, SO_2 can be converted to SO_3. When SO_2 is dissolved in water, sulfurous acid (H_2SO_3) is produced. If SO_3 is combined with water, sulfuric acid (H_2SO_4) is produced. The combination of SO_3 and water is done by dissolving the SO_3 in H_2SO_4 and then adding water. Sulfuric acid is produced in huge quantities. Twice as much H_2SO_4 (by mass) is produced as the next most common chemical. The principal sulfuric acid-consuming industries in the United States are fertilizer, petroleum refining, steel, paints, and pigments.

11:9 HALOGENS

Group VIIA (17) contains fluorine, chlorine, bromine, iodine, and astatine. The elements of this group are called the halogen (salt forming) family. In many chemical reactions, halogen atoms gain one electron. They become negatively charged ions with a stable outer level of eight electrons. As in other families already discussed, three factors determine the reactivity of the halogens. They are the distance between the nucleus and the outer electrons, the shielding effect of inner level electrons, and the size of the positive charge on the nucleus. Fluorine atoms contain fewer inner level electrons than the other halogens, so the shielding effect is the least. The distance between the fluorine nucleus and its outer electrons is less than the other halogens. Thus, the fluorine atom has the greatest tendency to attract other electrons. This attraction makes fluorine the most reactive nonmetal.

The astatine nucleus has the largest number of protons and the largest positive charge. However, the increased charge on the nucleus is not enough to offset the distance and shielding effects. Thus, of all halogen atoms, the astatine nucleus has the least attraction for outer electrons.

Notice that fluorine is active because the atoms of fluorine have a great tendency to gain one electron and become negative ions. The active metals are active because they hold the single outer electron loosely and it is easily removed. The groups between IA (1), and VIIA (17) vary between these two extremes. In general, *on the right side of the table, the non-metallic elements become more active as we move from the bottom to the top. On the left-hand side of the table, the metals become more active as we move from the top to the bottom.* The most active elements are located at the upper right-hand and lower left-hand corners of the periodic table.

11:10   FLUORINE AND CHLORINE

The halogens are the most reactive nonmetallic family. They usually react by forming negative ions or sharing electrons. Fluorine is the most reactive of all the chemical elements. It reacts with all other elements except helium, neon, and argon. Fluorine is obtained from the mineral fluorspar, CaF_2. Like hydrogen, halogen atoms can form bridges between two other atoms. An example of such a compound is BeF_2. The halogens also form a large number of compounds among themselves. Examples are ClF, ClF_5, BrF_5, IF_5, IF_7, $BrCl$, and ICl_3.

Chlorine, though less abundant than fluorine in the Earth's crust, is more commonly found in both the laboratory and industry. Chlorides of most elements are available commercially. These compounds are quite often used in the laboratory as a source of positive metal ions bound with the chloride ions.

Chlorine is produced primarily to make other chemicals, but some is consumed in paper manufacture. Hydrochloric acid is a by-product of many industrial processes. Its uses include steel manufacture, dye production, food processing, and oil well drilling.

The commercial preparation of chlorine led to one of the major water pollution crises of the early 1970s. The chlorine was produced by running an electric current through a solution of sodium chloride in water. One of the substances used to conduct current in the apparatus was mercury. The leakage of mercury into nearby water sources caused a public outcry. Industries had to remove the mercury from their waste before dumping or switch to another method of producing chlorine. Chemists solved the problem by designing new cells.

11:11   NOBLE GASES

For many years after their discovery, the noble gases, Group VIIIA (18), were believed to be chemically unreactive or inert. However, in 1962, the first "inert" gas compound was synthesized. Since these gases are not inert, we will refer to them as the noble gases. The first compound made was xenon hexafluoroplatinate ($XePtF_6$).

Other compounds of xenon were soon produced. Once the techniques were known, the compounds could be made with increasing ease. Xenon difluoride (XeF_2) was first made by combining xenon and oxygen difluoride (OF_2) in a nickel tube at 300°C under pressure. The same compound can now be made from xenon and fluorine. An evacuated glass container of fluorine and xenon is exposed to daylight. Compounds of xenon with oxygen and nitrogen have also been synthesized. Krypton and radon compounds have also been produced.

Argon and helium are used to protect active metals during welding. Aluminum, for example, must be welded in an atmosphere of argon or

Halogens are the most reactive nonmetallic family.
Fluorine is the most reactive chemical element.

The primary use of chlorine is to make other chemicals.

Noble gases are not chemically inert.

Xenon, krypton, and radon compounds have been made.

helium. Argon is also used to fill light bulbs. Neon, krypton, and xenon are used to fill brightly colored gas discharge tubes for advertising.

11:12   TRANSITION METALS

Transition elements have electrons filling *d* sublevels.

The transition metals ("B" groups) are those elements whose highest energy electrons are in the *d* sublevels. In all groups except IIB (12), the *d* orbitals are only partially filled. These partially filled *d* orbitals make the chemical properties of the transition metals different from the "A" group metals. Remember that *d* electrons may be lost, one at a time, after the outer *s* electrons have been lost.

The major uses of the transition metals are as structural elements. The fourth period elements, titanium through zinc, are our principal structural

FIGURE 11-14. The map shows major concentrations of high technology materials throughout the world. Note most of these materials are transition metals.

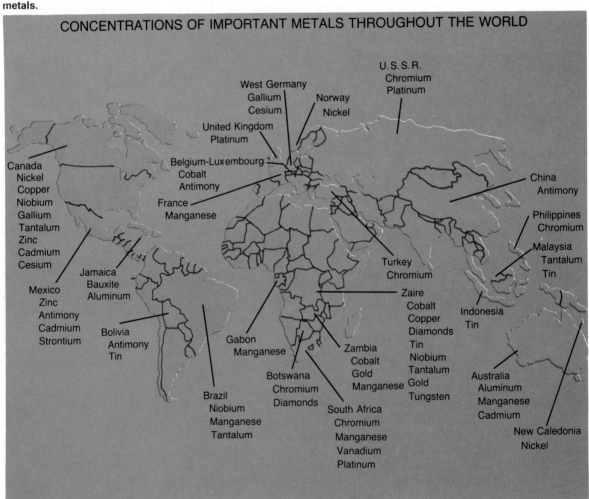

CONCENTRATIONS OF IMPORTANT METALS THROUGHOUT THE WORLD

metals. These metals are used either alone or as alloys. The only important transition metal compound produced commercially is titanium(IV) oxide, TiO_2. The TiO_2 is used extensively as a white paint pigment.

Transition metals, used alone or as alloys, are our principal

11:13 CHROMIUM

Chromium exhibits the typical properties of a transition metal. One property of chromium important to industry is its resistance to corrosion. Large quantities are used to make stainless steel and to "chromeplate" regular steel. In both cases, the chromium protects the iron in steel from corrosion.

Chromium usually reacts by losing three electrons to form the Cr^{3+} ion. Also of importance is the 6+ oxidation state. Recall that the outer electron configuration of chromium is $4s^1 3d^5$. This state is formed when chromium loses all five of its $3d$ electrons, as well as its outer level $4s$ electron. Two polyatomic ions are important examples of the 6+ state. These ions are the chromate ion, CrO_4^{2-}, and the dichromate ion, $Cr_2O_7^{2-}$. Chromium also forms a Cr^{2+} ion. However, this ion is easily converted by oxygen in air to Cr^{3+}. Consequently, the 2+ state is not of great importance. The 4+ and 5+ states are so unstable, they are just laboratory curiosities.

SUGGESTION: You can begin a discussion of how political issues and relations can affect our supply of these materials. Many industries such as electronics, aerospace, and nuclear power depend on the supply of high technology materials.

Chromium resists corrosion.

Chromium forms polyatomic ions like CrO_4^{2-} and $Cr_2O_7^{2-}$. Chromium has multiple oxidation numbers.

a

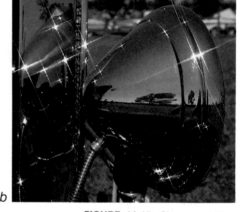

b

FIGURE 11-15. Chrome plating is a chemical process whereby chromium ions in solution are changed to chromium metal, which is deposited on the object to be plated (a). The chrome detailing on cars is produced by this process.

11:14 ZINC

Although zinc is classed as a transition element, its behavior differs slightly due to a full d sublevel. It exhibits only one oxidation state, 2+. The special stability of the full d sublevel leaves only the two outer $4s$ electrons available for reacting. Zinc is the second most important transition element (after iron) in biological systems. As an example, lack of zinc in the diet prevents the pancreas from producing some digestive enzymes. Over 25 zinc-containing proteins have been discovered.

Zinc's behavior differs slightly from the other transition elements due to a full d sublevel ($3d^{10}$).

Iodine: Essential for the synthesis of thyroid hormones

Iron: Metallic center of hemoglobin; needed for the formation of vitamin A; component of some enzymes

Copper: Essential for hemoglobin synthesis; needed for bone formation and the production of melanin and myelin

Potassium: Maintains intracellular osmotic pressure and pH; needed for proper transmission of nerve impulses and muscle contraction

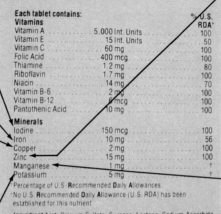

Each tablet contains:		% U.S. RDA*
Vitamins		
Vitamin A	5,000 Int. Units	100
Vitamin E	15 Int. Units	50
Vitamin C	60 mg	100
Folic Acid	400 mcg	100
Thiamine	1.2 mg	80
Riboflavin	1.7 mg	100
Niacin	14 mg	70
Vitamin B-6	2 mg	100
Vitamin B-12	6 mcg	100
Pantothenic Acid	10 mg	100
Minerals		
Iodine	150 mcg	100
Iron	10 mg	56
Copper	2 mg	100
Zinc	15 mg	100
Manganese	1 mg	†
Potassium	5 mg	†

*Percentage of U.S. Recommended Daily Allowances.
†No U.S. Recommended Daily Allowance (U.S. RDA) has been established for this nutrient.

Ingredient List: Calcium Sulfate, Sucrose, Lactose, Sodium Ascorbate (Vit. C), Ferrous Sulfate, Zinc Oxide, Vitamin E Acetate, Niacinamide, Calcium Pantothenate, Potassium Sulfate, Cupric Sulfate, Artificial Color, Lacca, Gelatin, Povidone, Magnesium Stearate, Manganese Sulfate, Pyridoxine HCl (B-6), Vitamin A Acetate, Silica, Riboflavin (B-2), Thiamine Mononitrate (B-1), Folic Acid, Sodium Benzoate, Potassium Iodide, Carnauba and White Wax, Sesame Oil, Cyanocobalamin (B-12).

Zinc: Component of several enzymes involved in digestion, respiration, bone formation, liver metabolism; needed for a normal healing process and good skin tone

Manganese: Component of enzymes involved in the synthesis of fatty acids and cholesterol; needed for the formation of urea and the normal functioning of the nervous system

FIGURE 11-16. Zinc is one of many elements essential to proper body function. Vitamin tablets act as a supplement in the event that one does not receive adequate amounts from the daily diet.

Zinc is corrosion resistant.

FIGURE 11-17. Zinc discs are used on the underside of ships to prevent corrosion.

Metallic zinc, like chromium, is corrosion resistant. It is used extensively as a coating to protect iron. The coating can be applied in three ways. When the iron is dipped in molten zinc, the process is called **galvanizing.** The coating is also applied electrically. The third method is to allow gaseous zinc to condense on the surface of iron. Another major use for metallic zinc is in the production of alloys. Especially important is its combination with copper to form brass.

11:15   NEODYMIUM, A LANTHANIDE

The electron configuration of neodymium (knee o DIM ee um) ends $6s^2 4f^4$. From that configuration we would predict a 2+ oxidation state.

However, Nd, as all the lanthanides, shows 3+ as its most stable state. The 3+ ion is pale violet in solution. The metal itself is soft and quite reactive. It tarnishes when exposed to air. The element itself is used in some alloys with unusual conductivity and magnetic properties. The compound Nd_2O_3, is used in glass filters and in some lasers. Neodymium is the second most abundant lanthanide metal. Its compounds are separated from the other lanthanides by a chromatographic technique (Chapter 14). The metal is obtained from the fluoride by a single displacement reaction.

The lanthanides show 3+ as the most stable oxidation state.

$$3Ca + 2NdF_3 \rightarrow 3CaF_2 + 2Nd$$

11:16 CURIUM, AN ACTINIDE

Curium's predicted electron configuration ends $7s^2 5f^8$. However, its actual configuration is $7s^2 5f^7 6d^1$. Plainly, the stability of the half-full f sublevel more than offsets the promotion of one electron to the $6d$. The element exhibits a 3+ oxidation state in its compounds and the ion is pale yellow in solution. The element itself is a silvery, hard metal of medium density and high melting point. It does not occur in nature. All curium (multigram quantities) has been produced by the slow neutron bombardment of the artificial element plutonium. It is reactive and highly toxic to the human organism. This metal is used as the energy source in nuclear generators in satellites. Curium also has potential use as an energy source by converting the heat generated by its nuclear decay to electric energy.

Curium has a half-full f sublevel which is very stable.

BIOGRAPHY

Lise Meitner (1878-1968)

Lise Meitner was able to overcome the discriminatory practices against women and Jewish people in Europe in the early 1900's to become an honored scientist. After receiving her doctorate at the University of Vienna, she worked as an assistant to Otto Hahn in the field of radioactivity. Together, they researched the concept of isotopes until their study was interrupted by World War I. At the end of the war, Meitner and Hahn were responsible for the discovery of the radioactive element protactinium ($^{231}_{91}Pa$).

Later Meitner worked on Ida Noddack's presumptions (page 231), and was credited with predicting the products of a fission reaction. She was the major author of the first published work on fission in 1939.

CAREERS AND CHEMISTRY

11:17   Sanitary Engineers

Water is one of the most precious resources we have on Earth. Some areas are already faced with water shortages. Water is used by industry as a solvent, raw material, and as a coolant. However, water used for drinking is the most important use and the most critical problem.

The sanitary engineer is involved in two phases of the process of providing good water to the public. One phase is the treatment of water supplies to ensure that the water is safe to drink. The first step is to analyze the water to find out what contaminants, if any, are present. The engineer must then decide what treatment is necessary. Chemicals may have to be added to precipitate minerals and neutralize acidic or basic compounds. Other substances might be added to cause suspended impurities to settle so they can be removed easily. The water may then be filtered through sand and gravel. Finally, it is treated with chlorine to destroy harmful organisms. Analyses are continued at each stage to ensure a consumable water supply.

Sanitary engineers are also concerned with preventing the introduction of pollutants into the water supply. This important task covers the treatment of industrial and domestic wastes. Garbage and trash are often disposed of in land fills. It is the sanitary engineer's job to control the operation of such a site. This job may include supervising an incinerator that burns all flammable wastes. The design, construction, and supervision of sewage disposal plants becomes even more important as the population grows and government regulations become more stringent.

Sewage treatment is divided into three stages. Primary treatment consists of the separation of solids and liquid waste. The solid material, or sludge, usually goes to a land fill, while the liquid is treated with chlorine and dumped in a nearby river or stream. Unfortunately, primary treatment is the only treatment used in many locations. Qualified sanitary engineers are needed to upgrade inadequate treatment plants.

Secondary treatment consists of using the liquid from the primary stage and treating it with bacteria that consume almost all the organic

FIGURE 11-18. Sanitary engineers are primarily involved in the processes necessary to maintain a safe water supply.

matter. The liquid is then treated with chlorine and released to a stream or river. The best plants provide tertiary treatment that subjects the water from secondary treatment to filtration through activated charcoal and oxidation using ozone. Sanitary engineers are steadily improving the treatment methods used to preserve the purity of our water.

SUMMARY

1. Hydrogen is often considered a family by itself because of the unique ways in which it reacts. **11:1**

2. The most active metals are listed toward the lower left-hand corner of the table. The alkali metals, Group IA (1), are the most active metals. They react by losing one electron to form 1+ ions. **11:2**

3. The alkaline earth metals, Group IIA (2), are second only to alkali metals in terms of reactivity. They form 2+ ions. **11:4**

4. Aluminum, Group IIIA (13), is less reactive than the alkaline earth metals and forms 3+ ions. **11:5**

5. The elements in Group IVA (14) have four electrons in the outer level. Carbon is a nonmetal, while silicon and germanium are metalloids. Tin and lead, in the same family, are distinctly metallic. **11:6**

6. Nitrogen and phosphorus, Group VA (15), form compounds by sharing electrons, but differ from each other considerably. **11:7**

7. In Group VIA (16), oxygen is distinctly nonmetallic and reacts by gaining two electrons or by sharing electrons. Sulfur is similar to oxygen but also exhibits positive oxidation states. **11:8**

8. The most active nonmetals are listed toward the upper right-hand corner. The halogens, Group VIIA (17), are the most active nonmetallic elements and usually react by gaining one electron. **11:9**

9. The noble gases, Group VIIIA (18), have very stable outer electron configurations and are much less reactive than most of the other elements. **11:11**

10. Chromium is a typical, corrosion-resistant transition metal exhibiting more than one oxidation number. **11:12-11:13**

11. Zinc is corrosion-resistant. However, because of its full *d* sublevel, it does not exhibit more than one oxidation state as do most transition metals. **11:14**

12. Lanthanides exhibit the 3+ oxidation state. Curium, an actinide, also exhibits the 3+ oxidation state. **11:15-11:16**

VOCABULARY

family **Intro**
hydrogen ion **11:1**
hydride ion **11:1**
shielding effect **11:2**
catalyst **11:2**
carbide ion **11:6**
inorganic compounds **11:6**

organic compounds **11:6**
catenation **11:6**
allotropes **11:6**
silicates **11:6**
amphoteric **11:8**
galvanizing **11:14**

PROBLEMS

1. Describe the four ways hydrogen can react.
2. What is the shielding effect? How does it explain the difference in reactivity between calcium and barium?
3. Why does thallium(I), a member of Group IIIA (13), have characteristics similar to those of the alkali ions?
4. What properties of lithium account for the differences in behavior that it exhibits in relation to the other alkali metals?
5. Why is aluminum considered less metallic than sodium and magnesium?
6. What is catenation? Why is it important to the study of carbon?
7. What chemical property accounts for the use of tin and lead as alloys?
8. What are allotropes? What elements discussed in this chapter exist in allotropic forms?
9. What is the importance of phosphorus to body systems?
10. What elements are particularly important in producing fertilizers?
11. How does the chemical behavior of oxygen differ when it combines with a metal rather than a nonmetal?
12. How does the chemical behavior of an amphoteric oxide differ from that of a nonmetal oxide?
13. Is the compound SO_3 produced by the transfer or sharing of electrons?
14. Why is Group VIIA (17) labeled as the halogens?
15. Which element on the periodic table would you predict to have the least attraction for its outer level electrons?
16. Why would you predict the noble gases to be inert?
17. How does the electronic structure of the transition elements differ from the elements in the "A" groups of the periodic table?
18. What properties are typical of transition metals?
19. Why is zinc important in the production of materials made from iron?
20. What oxidation state is common to all of the lanthanides?
21. What is the importance of plutonium to the production of curium?
22. Which element in each of the following pairs would you predict to be more active?

   a. cobalt, nickel   **f.** titanium, zirconium
   b. copper, gallium   **g.** sodium, potassium
   c. mendelevium, nobelium   **h.** arsenic, cobalt
   d. chlorine, fluorine   **i.** beryllium, lithium
   e. barium, radium   **j.** oxygen, phosphorus

23. From their relative positions in the periodic table, predict which element from each of the following pairs is more active.

   a. actinium, thorium   **c.** erbium, fermium
   b. americium, europium   **d.** arsenic, gallium

22. a. cobalt
    b. copper
    c. mendelevium
    d. fluorine
    e. radium
    f. zirconium
    g. potassium
    h. arsenic
    i. lithium
    j. oxygen

23. a. actinium
    b. americium
    c. fermium
    d. gallium

e. berkelium, californium
f. carbon, lithium
g. bromine, iodine

h. boron, carbon
i. potassium, rubidium
j. iodine, tellurium

e. berkelium
f. lithium
g. bromine
h. boron
i. rubidium
j. iodine

REVIEW

1. Balance the following equations.

a. $Cr + H_2SO_4 \rightarrow$
b. $Mn + H_2O \rightarrow$

c. $CuSO_4 + NaOH \rightarrow$
d. $BaCrO_4 + HCl \rightarrow$

2. How many grams of $AgNO_3$ are required to produce 38.7 grams of AgCNS?

$$AgNO_3 + KCNS \rightarrow AgCNS + KNO_3$$

3. Compute the atomic mass of bromine from the following data.

isotopic mass	abundance
78.918 332	50.54%
80.916 292	49.46%

4. Draw electron dot diagrams for yttrium, dysprosium, and indium.
5. Predict oxidation numbers for sulfur and germanium.

1. a. $Cr + H_2SO_4 \rightarrow$
   $CrSO_4 + H_2$ or
   $2Cr + 3H_2SO_4 \rightarrow$
   $Cr_2(SO_4)_3 + 3H_2$
   b. $Mn + 2H_2O \rightarrow$
   $Mn(OH)_2 + H_2$ or
   $Mn + H_2O \rightarrow$
   $MnO + H_2$
   c. $CuSO_4 + 2NaOH$
   $\rightarrow Cu(OH)_2 +$
   Na_2SO_4
   d. $BaCrO_4 + 2HCl \rightarrow$
   $BaCl_2 + H_2CrO_4$
2. 39.6 g $AgNO_3$
3. 79.91 u
4. Y:, Dy:, İn:
5. $S = 2-$, $Ge = 4\pm$

ONE MORE STEP

1. Since 1962, research has been done on compounds of the noble gases. Find an article about one of these projects and report on it to the class.
2. Lithium is often listed as more reactive than sodium, contrary to predictions. See if you can find out why.
3. Investigate the lanthanide contraction and see what effect it has on the behavior of the elements exhibiting it.

READINGS

Birchall, J. D., and Anthony Kelly, "New Inorganic Materials," *Scientific American,* Volume 248, No. 5(May 1983), pp. 104-115.

Firsching, F. H., "Anomalies in the Periodic Table," *Journal of Chemical Education,* Vol. 58, No. 6(June 1981), pp. 478-479.

Reilly, J. J., and G. D. Sandrock, "Hydrogen Storage in Metal Hydrides," *Scientific American,* Vol. 242, No. 2(February 1980), p. 118.

Robinson, Paul R., "A Gas for When the Oil is Gone," *SciQuest,* Vol. 54, No. 2(February 1981), pp. 10-14.

Tosteson, Daniel C., "Lithium and Mania," *Scientific American,* Vol. 244, No. 4(April 1981), pp. 164-174.

Young, Gordon, "Platinum," *National Geographic,* Volume 164, No. 5(November 1983), pp. 686-706.

Zurer, Pamela S., "Volcanoes," *Chemical and Engineering News,* Volume 62, No. 39(September 24, 1984), pp. 26-40.

An electron microscope was used to photograph this sample of uranyl acetate. The colored spots with the red-orange centers are individual uranium atoms. The atoms and ions in compounds have measurable bond lengths and bond angles. The separation between the uranium atoms in this compound is 0.34 nm. How are atoms and ions bonded in substances?

CHEMICAL BONDING

Chapter 12 introduces chemical bonding and examines the factors which help determine the nature of the bond, and the properties characteristic of ionic, covalent, and metallic bonds.

DEMONSTRATION: Burn magnesium in air, burn sulfur in O_2. See the Teacher Guide for preparation details and discussion ideas. Use your demonstration as an introduction to the process of ionic and covalent bonding.

GOALS:
• You will explain the relationship between electronegativity and type of bond character.
• You will differentiate among the four types of radii.
• You will understand the special nature of metals and metallic bonding.

Now that we have examined the structure and properties of atoms in some detail, we are prepared to study how atoms bond to each other to form compounds. The bonds formed between atoms depend on the electron configurations of those atoms and, also, the attraction the atoms have for electrons. Since configuration and attraction for electrons are periodic properties, we can expect bonding of atoms to vary in a systematic way also.

12:1 ELECTRONEGATIVITY

Both electron affinity and ionization energy deal with isolated atoms. Chemists need a comparative scale relating the abilities of elements to attract electrons when their atoms are combined. The relative tendency of an atom to attract electrons to itself when bound with another atom is called its **electronegativity.** The elements are assigned electronegativities on the basis of many experimental tests.

Many chemical properties of the elements can be organized in terms of electronegativities. For example, the greater the strength of the bond between two atoms, the greater the difference in electronegativities.

Bond strength increases as the electronegativity difference increases.

Table 12-1

Bonds between Hydrogen and Halogens		
Bond	Bond Strength (kJ/mol)	Electronegativity Difference
H—F	569	1.80
H—Cl	432	0.80
H—Br	366	0.62
H—I	299	0.28

Most active metals have low electronegativities; most active nonmetals have high electronegativities.

FIGURE 12-1. The general trends for ionization energy, electron affinity, and electronegativity are shown.

Electronegativities of elements are influenced by the same factors affecting ionization energies and electron affinities. It is possible to construct an electronegativity scale using first ionization energies and electron affinities of the elements. Examine Table 12-2, which represents average values from several calculations. It shows that the variation in electronegativity follows the same trends as the ionization energies and the electron affinities. *The most active metals* (lower left) *have the lowest electronegativities.* Fluorine has the highest electronegativity of all the elements (4.00). Consider a reaction between two elements. Their relative attraction for electrons determines how they react. We can use the electronegativity scale to determine this attraction. Since electronegativity represents a comparison of the same property for each element, it is a dimensionless number.

Table 12-2

Electronegativities																
H 2.20																
Li 0.96	Be 1.50											B 2.02	C 2.56	N 2.81	O 3.37	F 4.00
Na 0.96	Mg 1.29											Al 1.63	Si 1.94	P 2.04	S 2.46	Cl 3.00
K 0.84	Ca 1.02	Sc 1.28	Ti 1.44	V 1.54	Cr 1.61	Mn 1.57	Fe 1.74	Co 1.79	Ni 1.83	Cu 1.67	Zn 1.60	Ga 1.86	Ge 1.93	As 2.12	Se 2.45	Br 2.82
Rb 0.85	Sr 0.97	Y 1.16	Zr 1.27	Nb 1.23	Mo 1.73	Tc 1.36	Ru 1.42	Rh 1.87	Pd 1.78	Ag 1.57	Cd 1.52	In 1.69	Sn 1.84	Sb 1.83	Te 2.03	I 2.48
Cs 0.82	Ba 0.93	*Lu 1.20	Hf 1.23	Ta 1.33	W 1.88	Re 1.46	Os 1.52	Ir 1.88	Pt 1.86	Au 1.98	Hg 1.72	Tl 1.74	Pb 1.87	Bi 1.76	Po 1.76	At 1.96
Fr 0.86	Ra 0.97	**														

*La 1.09	Ce 1.09	Pr 1.10	Nd 1.10	Pm 1.07	Sm 1.12	Eu 1.01	Gd 1.15	Tb 1.10	Dy 1.16	Ho 1.16	Er 1.17	Tm 1.18	Yb 1.06
**Ac 1.00	Th 1.11	Pa 1.14	U 1.30	Np 1.29	Pu 1.25	Am 1.2 ←	Cm	Bk	Cf estimated	Es	Fm	Md → 1.2	

PROBLEMS

Arrange the following elements in order of increasing force of attraction for electrons in a bond.

1. antimony, fluorine, helium, indium, selenium

2. francium, gallium, germanium, phosphorus, zinc

1. He, In, Sb, Se, F
2. Fr, Zn, Ga, Ge, P

12:2 BOND CHARACTER

Electrons are transferred between atoms when the difference in electronegativity between the atoms is quite high. If the electronegativity difference between two reacting atoms is small, we might expect a sharing of electrons. At what point in electronegativity difference does the change-over occur? The answer is not simple. For one thing, the electronegativity of an atom varies slightly depending upon the atom with which it is combining. Another factor is the number of other atoms with which the atom is combining. Therefore a scale showing the percent of transfer of electrons (percent ionic character) has been constructed, Table 12-3. The amount of transfer depends on the electronegativity difference between two atoms.

Bond character between atoms depends upon electronegativity differences.

Table 12-3

Character of Bonds										
Electronegativity Difference	0.00	0.65	0.94	1.19	1.43	1.67	1.91	2.19	2.54	3.03
Percent Ionic Character	0%	10%	20%	30%	40%	50%	60%	70%	80%	90%
Percent Covalent Character	100%	90%	80%	70%	60%	50%	40%	30%	20%	10%

When two atoms combine by transfer of electrons, ions are produced. The opposite charges of the ions hold them together. When two elements combine by electron transfer, they are said to form an ionic bond. If two elements combine by sharing electrons, they are said to form a covalent bond.

Ionic bonds: Transfer of electrons. Covalent bonds: Sharing of electrons.

From Table 12-3 we see that two atoms with electronegativity difference of about 1.67 would form a bond that is 50% ionic 50% covalent. For our purposes, we will consider an electronegativity difference of less than 1.67 as indicating a covalent bond. A difference of 1.67 or greater indicates an ionic bond. However, almost all bonds have some of both sets of characteristics.

Think of magnesium reacting with oxygen. Magnesium has an electronegativity of 1.29 and oxygen is 3.37. The difference is 2.08. We would predict the formation of an ionic bond between these two elements. On the other hand, consider boron and nitrogen. Boron has an electronegativity of 2.02 and nitrogen is 2.81. The difference is 0.79. We would predict boron and nitrogen to form a covalent bond.

Nearly all bonds have both covalent and ionic characteristics.
SUGGESTION: Emphasize that the character of the bonds—ionic to covalent—is on a continuum. The use of 1.67 as the breaking point is simply a convenience for working with compounds. Most covalent bonds will have some ionic character and vice versa.

PROBLEMS

3. Classify the bonds between the following pairs of atoms as principally ionic or covalent.

a. Al—Si
b. Ba—O
c. C—H
d. Li—S
e. Ca—P
f. B—Na
g. Ca—Cl
h. F—S
i. Br—Rb

*3. ionic b,g,i
   covalent a,c,d,e,f,h*

4. ionic c,e,f
   covalent a,b,d

4. For each atom pair listed below, decide whether an ionic or a covalent bond would form between the elements.

    a. hydrogen-iodine   **d.** chlorine-tellurium
    b. astatine-beryllium   **e.** bromine-cerium
    c. cobalt-fluorine   **f.** calcium-fluorine

FIGURE 12-2. Covalent molecules, such as HCl, are held together by a mutual sharing of electrons. Note there is an overlap of the electron clouds. Ionic substances, such as MgO, are held together by the attractive force between oppositely-charged ions.

HCl
Covalent

MgO
Ionic

12:3 IONIC BONDS

We have discussed sodium chloride, an excellent example of a compound with an ionic bond (an ionic compound). Most of the properties of ionic compounds are best explained by assuming a complete transfer of electrons.

$$2Na^{\cdot} + \;:\!\ddot{C}l\!:\!\ddot{C}l\!: \;\rightarrow 2Na^{+} + 2\!:\!\ddot{C}l\!:^{-}$$

If a chloride ion and a sodium ion are brought together, there will be an attractive force between them. If the ions are brought almost into contact, the force will be great enough to hold the two ions together. The electrostatic force that holds two ions together due to their differing charges is the **ionic bond.**

Elements are assigned oxidation numbers for ionic bonding based on the number of electrons they must gain or lose in order to obtain a stable octet. Characteristics of compounds with ionic bonds.
  1. high melting point
  2. soluble in water
  3. well-defined crystals
  4. molten form conducts electricity

Elements can be assigned oxidation numbers for ionic bonding. Sulfur, for example, with six electrons in the outer level, will tend to gain two electrons. Thus, it attains the stable octet configuration. The oxidation number of sulfur for ionic bonding is 2−. The negative two is its electric charge after gaining two electrons.

Ionic compounds are characterized by high melting points and the ability to conduct electricity in the molten state. They tend to be soluble in water and usually crystallize as sharply defined particles.

12:4 IONIC RADII

We saw in Chapter 10 that a sodium ion is smaller than a sodium atom. We also found that a chloride ion is larger than a chlorine atom. Values for the radii of many ions have been determined, Table 10-1. These values are found from a combination of experimental data and simplifying assumptions. By adding the radii of two ions in a compound we may find their **internuclear distance** in a crystal. Remember that the radii are not fixed values. One reason for their variability is the "fuzziness" of the electron cloud. Another reason is the effect each ion has on its neighbor ions.

a   *b*

12:5 COVALENT BONDS

Atoms with the same or nearly the same electronegativities tend to react by sharing electrons. The shared pair or pairs of electrons constitute a **covalent bond.** Covalent compounds typically have low melting points, do not conduct electricity, and are brittle.

When two or more atoms bond covalently, the resulting particle is called a **molecule.** The line joining the nuclei of two bonded atoms in a molecule is called the **bond axis** as shown in Figure 12-9. If one atom is bonded to each of two other atoms, the angle between the two bond axes is called the **bond angle.** The distance between nuclei along the bond axis is called the **bond length.** This length is not really fixed, because the bond acts much as if it were a stiff spring. The atoms vibrate as though the bond were alternately stretching and shrinking as shown in Figure 12-4.

Bonds also undergo bending, wagging, and rotational vibrations. These movements cause the bond angles and length to vary. The amplitudes of these vibrations are not large and the bond lengths and bond angles that we measure are average values. We may think of them as the values for a molecule completely at rest. However, molecular motion never entirely ceases.

We have learned much of what we know about the structure of molecules from infrared spectroscopy. Recall from Figure 7-11 that infrared wavelengths lie in a region of the electromagnetic spectrum between radio waves and visible light waves. The wavelengths vary from 700 nm to over 50 000 nm. A molecular compound can be identified by the infrared radiation it absorbs or transmits. Each molecular compound has

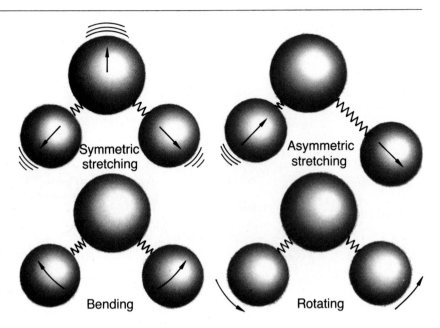

FIGURE 12-4. Molecules exhibit a variety of motions. Therefore, bond lengths and bond angles should be considered as average values.

its own infrared spectrum, which is different from that of any other compound.

The infrared (IR) spectrum indicates energy changes in the bonding between the particles of the molecule. At specific frequencies the atoms of the molecule stretch, twist, wag, and bend around the bonds joining them. Radiation of the wavelengths corresponding to those frequencies will be absorbed. The energy absorbed must agree in frequency with the natural frequency of vibration of the molecule.

The IR spectrum indicates energy changes in the bonding between particles of the molecule.

SUGGESTION: Point out IR spectroscopy as one more experimental process available to help understand the structure of the molecule. Stress its usefulness as an identification process.

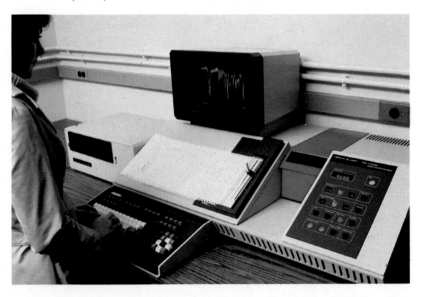

FIGURE 12-5. Most infrared spectrophotometers now provide video readouts. Hard copies of peak values can be obtained by computer. A chemist uses this information in comparing the spectra of an unknown substance to those of known substances to determine the identity of the unknown.

In using the IR spectrophotometer, a sample of the compound is subjected to varied wavelengths of IR radiation. The various wavelengths absorbed by the compound are measured and recorded graphically. A unique continuous absorption spectrum can be plotted for each molecular compound. Comparison with known spectra will reveal the identity of the compound, just as fingerprints reveal the identity of a person.

12:6 COVALENT RADII

It is possible, by experiment, to determine the internuclear distance between two bonded atoms. For example, consider iodine (I) chloride, ICl. What are the radii of the iodine and chlorine atoms in this molecule? The internuclear distance in ICl is found to be 0.230 nm. The internuclear distance in Cl_2 is 0.198 nm, and in I_2 it is 0.266 nm as shown in Figure 12-7. One half of each of these values might be taken as the radii of the chlorine and iodine atoms in a covalent bond: 0.099 nm and 0.133 nm. The sum of the iodine and chlorine radii would then be 0.232 nm. This

FIGURE 12-6. For the infrared spectra shown, note that the composition of both compounds is similar. However, the difference in the way the atoms are arranged causes different stretching motions in each molecule. Characteristic peaks in each graph can be used to identify the compound.

FIGURE 12-7. The internuclear distance is the sum of the covalent radii for each atom. Recall that bond distances are not fixed values.

Approximate bond length can be determined by adding the radii of 2 bonded atoms.

These radii are averages obtained from a number of different compounds.

sum is in good agreement with the observed bond distance in ICl. Covalent radii are only approximate. The value for hydrogen is less reliable than that for other atoms. Nevertheless, these radii are very useful in predicting bond lengths in molecules. Table 12-4 gives the covalent radii for some common atoms; Table 12-5 gives the bond lengths for some molecules. See for yourself how well the predicted bond lengths agree with the measured ones.

Remember that covalent radii are used to find the internuclear distance between atoms bonded to each other. Like electronegativities covalent radii are average values. The radius of a particular atom is not constant. Its size is influenced by the other atom or atoms to which it is bonded.

Table 12-4

Covalent Radii (in nanometers)			
Atom	**Radius**	**Atom**	**Radius**
Al	0.125	Li	0.134
As	0.121	Mg	0.130
B	0.088	N	0.070
Be	0.089	Na	0.154
Bi	0.152	O	0.066
Br	0.114	P	0.110
C	0.077	Pb	0.144
Ca	0.174	S	0.104
Cl	0.099	Sb	0.141
F	0.064	Sc	0.144
Ga	0.125	Se	0.117
Ge	0.122	Si	0.117
H	0.037	Sn	0.140
I	0.133	Te	0.140
K	0.196	Ti	0.132

Table 12-5

Experimental Bond Lengths (in nanometers)		
Molecule	**Bond**	**Length**
BCl_3	B—Cl	0.174
B_2H_6	B—H	0.132
$BeCl_2$	Be—Cl	0.177
Diamond	C—C	0.154
CH_4	C—H	0.110
CH_3I	C—H	0.110
	C—I	0.221
ClBr	Cl—Br	0.214
HF	H—F	0.092
H_2O	H—O	0.096
$LiCl_2(C_4H_8O_2)_2$	Li—O	0.195
NH_3	N—H	0.101
$OBe_4(CH_3COO)_6$	Be—O	0.162
OF_2	O—F	0.141
O_3	O—O	0.128
H_2SAlBr_3	S—Al	0.243
$(H_3Si)_2NN(SiH_3)_2$	Si—N	0.173

12:7 POLYATOMIC IONS

There are a large number of ionic compounds made of more than two elements. In these compounds, one ion consists of two or more atoms covalently bonded. However, the particle as a whole possesses an overall charge.

For example, consider the hydroxide ion (OH^-). The oxygen atom is bonded covalently to the hydrogen atom. The hydrogen atom is stable with two electrons in its outer level. The hydrogen atom contributes only one electron to the octet of oxygen. The other electron required for oxygen to have a stable octet is the one that gives the $1-$ charge to the ion. Although the two atoms are bonded covalently, the combination still possesses charge. Such a group is called a polyatomic ion. Polyatomic ions form ionic bonds just as other ions do. Table 4-4 gives some of the more common polyatomic ions with their charges. Note that most polyatomic ions are negative. The important positive polyatomic ion is the ammonium ion, NH_4^+

12:8 VAN DER WAALS RADII

A certain minimum distance is maintained between atoms that are not bonded to each other. This limitation exists because the electron cloud of one atom repels the electron cloud of other atoms.

In effect, colliding free atoms and molecules act as if they had a rigid outer shell. This shell limits the closeness with which they may approach other atoms or molecules. Since the covalent bond consists of shared electrons, bonded atoms can come closer than atoms that are not bonded as shown in Figure 12-9. The radius of this imaginary rigid shell of an atom is called the **van der Waals radius.** It is named for the Dutch physicist Johannes van der Waals.

Sulfate ion

FIGURE 12-8. The sulfate ion contains S—O covalent bonds. The electron dot structure shows a stable octet for each atom. However, the particle as a whole has a net negative charge.

van der Waals radius: Distance of closest approach of non-bonded atoms.

BACKGROUND: The term *polyatomic ion* is used throughout this text in place of the term *radical*. We reserve the term radical for the free radical of organic chemistry.

van der Waals radius
0.100 nm

van der Waals radius
0.140 nm

Covalent radii

FIGURE 12-9. The van der Waals radius is the minimum distance between nuclei for atoms on adjacent molecules. Note that the van der Waals radius will be larger than the covalent radius of a bonded atom.

Table 12-6

van der Waals Radii (in nanometers)			
Atom	Radius	Atom	Radius
As	0.200	O	0.140
Br	0.195	P	0.190
C	0.185	S	0.185
Cl	0.181	Sb	0.220
F	0.135	Se	0.200
H*	0.120	Si	0.200
I	0.215	Te	0.220
N	0.154		

*The van der Waals radius for hydrogen when it is hydrogen-bonded (Section 17:10) is 0.100 nm.

12:9 SUMMARY OF RADII

Thus far, we have studied four radii—atomic, ionic, covalent, and van der Waals. How do these various measurements differ? How are they the same? Atomic radii are measured in one of two ways. First, they may be measured on individual atoms in the gaseous state. On the other hand, they may be measured on atoms in metallic crystals. These atoms have special characteristics that will be discussed in Section 12:10. Note that in the first method, the atoms are unaffected by neighboring atoms. In the second case, neighboring atoms have a major effect. Measurements made on the same atom by the two methods will not give exactly the same results. The values given in Figure 12-9 are drawn from both methods and adjusted to give a consistent set of values.

Ionic radii differ from atomic radii because of the loss or gain of electrons. This difference was discussed in Section 10:2. Since most ionic radii are determined from ionic crystals, their values are consistent with the data. Covalent radii and van der Waals radii are quite variable due to the wide range of atoms to which the subject atom may be bonded. We

Bond distance equals the sum of the covalent radii

Nonbonded distance equals the sum of the van der Waals radii

FIGURE 12-10. The relationships among covalent radii, internuclear distances, and van der Waals radii are shown for an iodine crystal.

would expect covalent radii to be less than an atomic radius. However, if an atom is bonded to more than one other atom, its electron cloud may be distorted. The distortion may make its covalent radius larger than the atomic radius. The same situation occurs with van der Waals radii. For both of these radii the data given in the tables in this chapter represent average values for the atom bonded to its usual number of neighboring atoms. In every case, we can use the radii to predict the internuclear distance between atoms.

Radii are used to predict internuclear distances between atoms.

12:10   SPECIAL PROPERTIES OF METALS

The properties of metals are not explained by any of the bonding properties already considered. One of these properties is the ability to conduct electricity quite readily. Good electric conductivity indicates a ready source of electrons in metals.

We can use the following model to describe a piece of metal. Imagine metal atoms without their outer level electrons. These positive ions are packed together and their empty outer-level orbitals interact with each other. Each outer level is split into several closely-spaced energy levels. These splits are so small that we actually have bands of possible energies. These energy bands are separated from each other by small energy gaps called **forbidden zones** as shown in Figure 12-11.

In metal atoms, empty outer-level orbitals split into closely spaced energy bands.

Gaps between energy bands are called forbidden zones.

FIGURE 12-11. Metals are excellent conductors in that electrons can move easily to the conduction band. Insulators block the passage of current in that the forbidden zone represents too large an energy gap. Semiconductors can conduct if electrons receive enough energy to move past the forbidden zone to the conduction band.

Let us now replace the outer level electrons in the metal. These electrons enter the lowest available energy band. However, there is another band representing a slightly higher energy. This higher energy band is called the **conduction band.** If an outside energy source is applied, the electrons could jump to the conduction band. An electric field is such an energy source. The orbitals of the atoms in the conduction band overlap. Once the electrons are in this conduction band, they can travel anywhere in the piece of metal. Under the influence of the electric field they will

The high energy band closest to the ground state is called the conduction band.

Electrons in the conduction band are free to travel and are referred to as delocalized electrons.

flow from one end of the piece of metal to the other. In other words, the metal is now conducting electrically. Since these electrons can travel anywhere, they are referred to as free or **delocalized electrons.** The electrons are called delocalized because they are not held in one "locality" as part of a specific atom or bond. The delocalized electrons act as a negative cloud surrounding and holding the positive ions. It is this negative cloud that constitutes the metallic bond. If the forbidden zone of a substance represents a large energy gap, this substance cannot conduct and is an insulator. Semiconductors have a moderate forbidden zone, and will conduct under certain conditions.

Metals bond through sharing delocalized electrons.

Semiconductors have a small forbidden zone.

The properties of metals are determined by the number of outer electrons available. Group IA (1) metals have only one outer electron per atom. These metals are soft. Group IIA (2) metals have two outer electrons and are harder than Group IA (1) metals. In the transition elements however, electrons from the partially filled *d* orbitals may take part in the metallic bond. Many of these metals are very hard.

The number of electrons available for metallic bonding determines the properties of metals.

Groups IIIB (3) through VIB (6) elements have three through six delocalized electrons. In the elements of Groups VIIB (7) through VIIIB (10) the number of delocalized electrons remains at six because all of the *d* sublevel electrons of these elements are not involved in the metallic bond. The number of delocalized electrons per atom begins to decrease with the metals of Groups IB (11) and IIB (12). Going from Groups IIIA (13) through VIIIA (18), the nonmetals, the metallic properties decrease more rapidly.

Nonmetals are insulators since they block the passage of electricity.

The strong metallic bond of our structural metals, such as iron, chromium, and nickel, makes them hard and strong. In general, the transition elements are the hardest and strongest elements. It is possible to strengthen some of the elements with fewer delocalized electrons by combining them with other metals to form alloys. These alloys have properties different from those of pure elements.

Alloys have properties different from those of pure metals.

FIGURE 12-12. Strong, lightweight alloys are needed for aircraft construction. These alloys can be made by combining metals with few delocalized electrons with other metals.

Table 12-7

		Chemical Bond Summary			
	Bond Type	**Generally Formed between**	**Bond Formed by**	**Properties of Bond Type**	**Substances Utilizing Bond Type**
INTERATOMIC BONDS	Covalent	Atoms of nonmetallic elements of similar electronegativity	Sharing of electron pairs	Stable nonionizing molecules–not conductors of electricity in any phase.	OF_2, C_2H_6, $AsCl_3$, $GeCl_4$, C, SiC, Si
	Ionic	Atoms of metallic and nonmetallic elements of widely different electronegativities	Electrostatic attraction between ions resulting from transfer of electrons	Charged ions in gas, liquid, and solid. Solid is electrically non-conducting. Gas and liquid are conductors. High melting points.	NaCl, K_2O, BaS, LiH, CdF_2, $BaBr_2$, $ErCl_3$, CdO, Ca_3N_2
	Metallic	Atoms of metallic elements	Delocalized electron cloud around atoms of low electronegativity	Electrical conductors in all phases, lustrous, very high melting points.	Na, Au, Cu, Zn, Ac, Be, Gd, Fe, Dy

BIOGRAPHY   Ida Tacke Noddack (1896-   )

Ida Tacke Noddack was intensely interested in the structure and organization of the periodic table. This interest led to two important discoveries. A gap in the table under manganese had led most researchers to assume that the new element would have properties similar to manganese.

Ida and Walter Noddack investigated the properties of the elements surrounding manganese. In 1925, using X-ray spectra, they were able to identify the element rhenium. This element was discovered in a sample of the mineral columbite. Further research allowed them to determine the properties of rhenium.

In 1934, Ida proposed that heavy nuclei bombarded by neutrons break down into isotopes of known elements but not neighboring elements or transuranium elements. This proposal was in direct opposition to the beliefs commonly held at that time. However, five years later Ida's proposal was confirmed by others in the scientific community.

TECHNOLOGY AND CHEMISTRY

12:11   Ceramics

Your home or school may be a brick building. Brick is classified as a ceramic. Ceramics are materials formed by heating nonmetallic matter to a high temperature. Chinaware, porcelain, firebrick, cement, tile, abrasives, pottery, and glass are also classified as ceramics.

Pottery has been made for thousands of years. However, the field of ceramic chemistry is growing rapidly as a result of new technological advancements and applications. Some of our most recently developed materials are ceramics. In attempting to harness the energy produced by fusion reactions, scientists are having problems developing reaction containers that will withstand the extremely high temperatures involved. Zirconium oxide and silicon carbide ceramics have properties that may make them useful for this application. Lasers are being used to reach the high temperatures necessary for fusion reactions to occur. New glasses containing fluorine compounds such as beryllium fluoride have been developed for these lasers. These materials operate at high power levels, absorb less energy, and show less distortion of the laser beam than current laser materials.

Engineers have been trying to develop nonmetallic rotors for engines as an energy conservation measure. Silicon nitride and silicon carbide rotors are now close to the production stage. These rotors are lighter, cheaper to produce, and made of readily available materials.

The practical transmission of information through glass fibers has been achieved by coating the fibers with a resin augmenting their strength. Incorporating glass fibers and graphite fibers in plastics has allowed the use of these reinforced plastics to replace metal parts on automobiles. Thus, lighter automobiles can be produced resulting in lower fuel consumption.

FIGURE 12-13. Ceramic materials are used in the manufacture of bricks.

Medical scientists are constantly searching for new materials that can be implanted in the human body without causing biological problems. The materials must be compatible with existing tissue to prevent rejection by the body's immune system. A calcium phosphate ceramic has been developed for repairing bones. As the body heals, the ceramic is gradually replaced by new, natural bone.

One drawback to the use of nuclear fission as a power source is the disposal of radioactive waste materials. A solution to this problem is the incorporation of radioactive wastes into special, stable glass pellets. The glass can then be stored underground in deep abandoned mines for thousands of years.

The tiles covering the Space Shuttle are another ceramic development of interest. These tiles protect the craft from the tremendous heat generated by friction between the returning Shuttle and the atmosphere. These tiles are strong, tough, and have a low heat conductivity.

SUMMARY

1. The relative tendency of a bonded atom to attract shared electrons to itself is called its electronegativity. **12:1**

2. Ionic bonds are formed by transfer of electrons between atoms with a large difference in electronegativity. **12:2**

3. Ionic compounds are characterized by high melting points, solubility in water, and crystal formation. **12:3**

4. The ionic radius is the best estimate chemists can make of the effective size of an ion. **12:4**

5. Covalent bonds are formed by sharing electrons between atoms with either no difference or slight differences in electronegativity. **12:5**

6. The bond axis is a line joining the nuclei of two bonded atoms. The length of the bond axis is called the bond length. The angle between two bond axes is called the bond angle. **12:5**

7. The infrared (IR) spectrophotometer can be used to determine molecular structure. Radiation is absorbed in characteristic patterns by molecular bonds. **12:5**

8. Covalent radii can be used to predict the distance between bonded atoms. **12:6**

9. Polyatomic ions are composed of groups of atoms bonded covalently and possess an overall charge just as other ions. **12:7**

10. Compounds containing polyatomic ions are bonded ionically. **12:7**

11. Electron clouds repel each other strongly when two nonbonded atoms approach each other. The distance of closest approach for an atom is called the van der Waals radius of the atom. **12:8**

12. A metallic bond is formed between atoms with few electrons in the outer level. These electrons circulate as delocalized electrons and allow metals to carry an electric current. **12:10**

13. The high number of delocalized electrons of such metals as iron, chromium, and nickel makes these metals very hard and strong. In general, the transition elements are the hardest and strongest elements. **12:10**

VOCABULARY

electronegativity **12:1**
ionic bond **12:3**
internuclear distance **12:4**
covalent bond **12:5**
molecule **12:5**
bond axis **12:5**

bond angle **12:5**
bond length **12:5**
van der Waals radius **12:8**
forbidden zones **12:10**
conduction band **12:10**
delocalized electrons **12:10**

PROBLEMS

1. Why are most ionic compounds brittle?

2. What type of bond would you expect to find between xenon and fluorine in XeF_4?

3. Using Table 12-4, predict the bond lengths indicated for the following substances.

  a. F-F in F_2
  b. C-Pb in $Pb(C_2H_5)_4$
  c. Li-P in Li_3P

  d. Rb-Si in Rb_4Si
  e. C-C in CH_3CH_3
  f. N-O in N_2O_4

4. Construct a graph of the number of delocalized electrons versus the atomic number for the elements $Z = 21$ through $Z = 30$.

5. What four factors affect the values obtained for ionization energies of an element?

6. How does van der Waals radius differ from covalent radius?

7. Why is it difficult to give exact values for bond lengths and bond angles?

8. List three characteristics of metals.

9. How does the number of delocalized electrons in a metal affect its properties?

(margin answers)
2. covalent
3. a. 0.128 nm
   b. 0.221 nm
   c. 0.244 nm
   d. 0.315 nm
   e. 0.154 nm
   f. 0.136 nm

5. nuclear charge, shielding effect, radius, sublevel

8. conductors, malleable, ductile

REVIEW

1. Make a list of ten elements having more than two possible oxidation states.

2. Briefly describe the development of classification for elements from Dobereiner to the modern periodic table.

3. Predict the oxidation number of the following elements, using only the periodic table as a guide.

  a. astatine, germanium, mercury, polonium, tin
  b. francium, hafnium, neodymium, rubidium, tellurium.

4. Describe the structure of the modern periodic table.

5. Predict oxidation numbers for the following elements using only the periodic table as a guide.

   a. rubidium   **d.** tellurium

   b. zirconium   **e.** iodine

   c. niobium   **f.** boron

6. Classify each of the elements in Problem 5 as a metal, metalloid, or nonmetal.

7. What are the family names of the elements in the following groups?

   a. IA (1)   **d.** VIIA (17)

   b. IIA (2)   **e.** VIIIA (18)

   c. IB through VIIIB (3-12)

8. Write electron configurations for the following elements.

   a. molybdenum   **d.** technetium

   b. antimony   **e.** tin

   c. lanthanum   **f.** calcium

5.-6. **a.** metal 1+
      b. metal 2+
      c. metal 2+
      d. metalloid 6+, 2−
      e. nonmetal 1−
      f. metalloid 3+

7. **a.** alkali metals
   b. alkaline earth metals
   c. transition metals
   d. halogens
   e. noble gases

ONE MORE STEP

1. Find an equation used to calculate electronegativities and try it on several elements.

2. Investigate the methods used by chemists for determining bond lengths.

3. What experimental data are used in determining covalent, ionic, and van der Waals radii? What assumptions are made in each case?

4. One factor affecting ionic radius, bond energy, and electronegativity of an atom is the coordination number of the atom. Prepare a report on this concept.

READINGS

Levy, Donald H., "The Spectroscopy of Supercooled Gases," *Scientific American,* Volume 250, No. 2(February 1984), pp. 96-109.

McMinn, Dennis, "Introductory Use of Infrared Spectra," *Journal of Chemical Education,* Volume 61, No. 8(August 1984), p. 708.

Pauling, Linus, and Zelek S. Herman, "Valence-Bond Concepts in Coordination Chemistry and the Nature of Metal-Metal Bonds," *Journal of Chemical Education,* Volume 61, No. 7(July 1984), pp. 582-587.

Sanders, Howard J., "High-Tech Ceramics," *Chemical and Engineering News,* Volume 62, No. 28(9 July 1984), pp. 26-40.

Silvera, Isaac F., and Jook Walreven, "The Stabilization of Atomic Hydrogen," *Scientific American,* Volume 246, No. 1(January 1982), pp. 66-74.

The properties and uses of a material are dependent on its structure. The internal atomic structure of materials is an important part of the design of this amusement park ride. The external design is based on chemical structure and geometric principles. What aspects of geometry are used in studying molecular structure? What theories are used to explain molecular structure? How does the geometry of a molecule determine its properties?

MOLECULAR STRUCTURE

GOALS:
• You will study several hypotheses regarding the structure of molecules.
• You will predict the structures of isomers from molecular formulas.
• You will use one or more hypotheses to explain the structure of given organic and inorganic molecules.

Chapter 13 focuses on the relationship between chemical bonding and molecular structure in introducing four ways of explaining the apparent structural features of molecules. Valence shell electron pair repulsion (VSEPR), hybridization, resonance, and molecular orbital theory are presented.

DEMONSTRATION: Large and small balloons can be used to represent shared and unshared electron pairs. Inflate 10 small (S = shared pair) and 6 large (U = unshared pair). Attach a rubber band to each balloon. Form the following molecules by connecting the balloons. Discuss the shapes found due to the interaction of S and U electron pairs. See 13:1.

HF (3U, 1S) H_2O (2U, 2S) NH_3 (1U, 3S) CH_4 (4S)

There are several ways of looking at the structure of molecules in order to describe their shape. We will consider four of these hypotheses. The first of these ideas takes into account the repulsive forces of electron pairs surrounding an atom. The second method considers different ways in which atomic orbitals can combine to form orbitals surrounding more than one nucleus. The electrons occupying these combined orbitals then serve to bind the atoms together. The third method considers molecules with more than one possible structure. The fourth method considers orbitals for molecules as a whole instead of atoms.

In order to describe the shape of a molecule or polyatomic ion, it is useful to draw an electron dot diagram for it. Consider the water molecule. It is composed of one oxygen and two hydrogen atoms. The electron dot diagrams are $\cdot \ddot{O}\!:$ and H$^{\times}$ for these elements. All electrons are identical. We use different symbols here only to help us understand how we arrive at the final structure. By combining an oxygen and two hydrogens, we obtain the following electron dot diagram.

$$H \!:\! \overset{\cdot\cdot}{\underset{\overset{\times\times}{H}}{O}} \!:$$

It is the only arrangement of electrons in which all three atoms can achieve a full outer level. Note that two pairs of electrons in the outer level of oxygen are involved in bonding the hydrogens. They are called **shared pairs.** The other two pairs of electrons are not involved in bonding. They are called **unshared pairs.**

Outer electron pairs attracted by two nuclei are called shared pairs.
Outer electron pairs attracted to one nucleus are called unshared pairs.

13:1   METHOD 1: PAIR REPULSION

One way of looking at molecules is to consider electron repulsion. Each bond and each unshared pair in the outer level of an atom form a charge cloud that repels all other charge clouds. In part, this repulsion is due to all electrons having the same charge. Another more important factor is the Pauli exclusion principle. Although electrons of opposite spin may occupy the same volume of space, electrons of the same spin may not do so. The repulsions resulting from the Pauli principle are much greater than the electrostatic ones at small distances. Because of these repulsions, atoms cannot be compressed.

The repulsions between the charge clouds in the outer level of atoms determine the arrangement of the orbitals. The orbital arrangement, in turn, determines the shape of molecules. As a result, the following rule may be stated: *Electron pairs spread as far apart as possible to minimize repulsive forces.* If there are only two electron pairs in the outer level, they will be on opposite sides of the nucleus. The arrangement is called linear. If there are three electron pairs, the axes of their charge clouds will be 120° apart. This arrangement is called trigonal planar and the electron pairs lie in the same plane as the nucleus. If there are four electron pairs, the axes of the charge clouds will be farthest apart when they intersect at an angle of 109.5°. Of course, these axes will not all lie in the same plane. The easiest way to see them is to imagine a regular tetrahedron. A tetrahedron is a figure having four faces, each of which is an equilateral triangle. The nucleus is at the center and the axes extend out to the corners.

Electron pairs spread as far apart as possible to minimize repulsions.

FIGURE 13-1. Electron pairs spread as far apart as possible resulting in linear, trigonal planar, and tetrahedral arrangements for molecules containing two, three, and four bonding pairs.

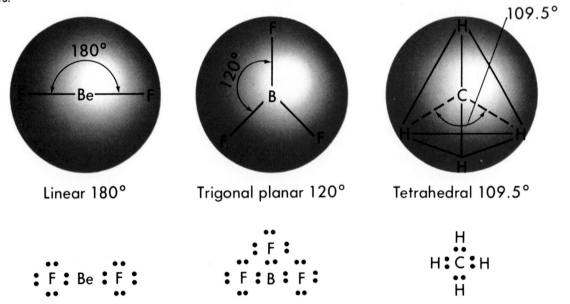

Linear 180°   Trigonal planar 120°   Tetrahedral 109.5°

Figure 13-1 shows some examples in which each electron pair in the outer level is used in bonding to another atom.

The bonds and unshared electron pairs determine the shape of a molecule. An unshared pair is acted upon by only one nucleus. Its charge cloud is shaped like a very blunt pear, Figure 13-2, with its stem end at the nucleus. A shared pair of electrons moves within the field of two nuclei. The cloud is more slender.

The electron pair repulsions in a molecule may not all be equal. The repulsion between two unshared pairs is greatest because they occupy the most space. The repulsion between two shared pairs is least because they occupy the least space. The repulsion between an unshared pair and a shared pair is an intermediate case.

unshared-unshared > unshared-shared > shared-shared
repulsion   repulsion   repulsion

Let us look at the molecular shapes of the compounds CH_4, NH_3, H_2O, and HF to illustrate this repulsion. In each of these compounds, the central atom has four clouds around it. We expect the axes of all four charge clouds to point approximately in the direction of the corners of a tetrahedron.

In methane (CH_4) molecules, all clouds are shared pairs, so their sizes are equal and each bond angle is in fact 109.5°. The CH_4 molecule is a perfect tetrahedron. In NH_3 molecules, there are one unshared pair and three bonded pairs. The unshared pair occupies more space than the other three, so the bonding clouds are at an angle of 107° to each other. Although the electron clouds form a tetrahedron, the atoms composing the molecule form a trigonal pyramid. In H_2O molecules, two unshared pairs are present, both of these clouds are larger than the bonds. This additional cloud size results in a still greater reduction in the bond angle which is, in fact, 104.5°. Again, the electron clouds are tetrahedral but the molecule is "V" shaped, or bent. In the HF molecule, there is only one bond axis and consequently no bond angle. Note that in the four molecules discussed, each has four electron clouds. The differences in molecular shape result from the unequal space occupied by the unshared pairs and the bonds. The shapes for different numbers of clouds can be predicted in the same way and are listed in Table 13-1.

Bonding charge clouds

FIGURE 13-2. The charge clouds occupied by shared and unshared electron pairs are different shapes.

Electron pair repulsion strengths may not be equal.

CH_4 4 shared pairs 109.5°
NH_3 3 shared pairs, 1 unshared 107°
H_2O 2 shared pairs, 2 unshared 104.5°
HF 1 shared pair, 3 unshared

Tetrahedron

Trigonal pyramid

Angular

FIGURE 13-3. The central atom in each molecule is surrounded by four electron pairs. The influence of shared and unshared pairs accounts for the different shapes.

Table 13-1

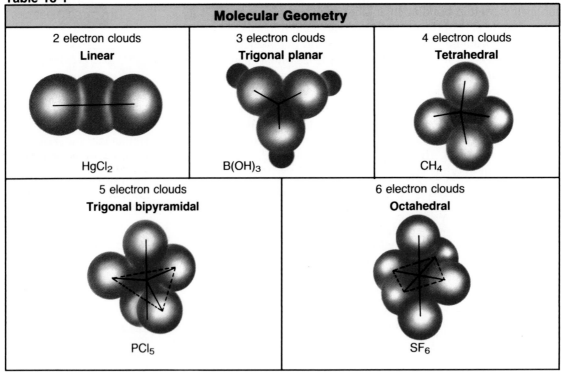

13:2 MULTIPLE BOND REPULSIONS

Two atoms can form covalent bonds by sharing more than one pair of electrons.

When two atoms combine by forming a covalent bond, it is sometimes possible for them to share more than one pair of electrons. For example, the organic compound formaldehyde (methanal) contains a double bond. The carbon atom and the oxygen atom share two pairs of electrons. The electron dot diagram for formaldehyde (methanal) is

$$\begin{array}{c} \text{H} \\ \text{H} \!:\! \overset{..}{\text{C}} \!:\! \overset{\times\!\times}{\underset{..}{\text{O}}} \!:\! \end{array}$$

In the diatomic molecule, N_2, the two nitrogen atoms share three pairs of electrons. They are bound to each other by a triple bond. The electron dot diagram for the nitrogen molecule is

$$:\text{N} \!:\!:\!: \text{N}:$$

How does the electron-pair repulsion theory predict the shapes of molecules containing multiple bonds?

A **double bond** can be considered as a single electron cloud made of two orbitals. However, because the bond consists of four electrons occupying the space, the cloud will occupy more space than a single bond.

Three orbitals forming a single bonding electron cloud constitute a **triple bond.** The triple bond would occupy still more space than the double bond. In the case of formaldehyde (methanal), there are three clouds around the carbon atom, two single bonds and one double bond. We anticipate that the clouds will assume a trigonal planar shape. The double bond will occupy somewhat more space. As a result, the H—C—H bond angle should be a little less than 120°, and the H—C=O bond angle a little more. Experiment shows a H—C—H bond angle of 116° and a H—C=O angle of 122°.

BACKGROUND: It is also possible to have three pairs in the outer level arranged as a double bond and a single bond with another atom. The three pairs form two bonds and we get a linear molecule. This arrangement is found in some unstable organic molecules.

FIGURE 13-4. The methanal molecule contains a double bond. Thus the H—C—H bond angle is smaller than predicted, since a double bond occupies more space than a single bond.

With two double bonds, each to a separate atom, we get a linear molecule. The organic compound, ketene, illustrates two double bonds as well as a double bond with two singles. The structure of the ketene molecule is

$$\begin{array}{c} H \\ \diagdown \\ C{=}C{=}O \\ \diagup \\ H \end{array}$$

The C=C=O bond angle is 180°, while the H—C=C bond angle is slightly greater than 120°.

The one remaining case is that of eight electrons shared as a triple bond and a single bond. As you might expect, such an arrangement gives rise to a linear shape. Another organic compound, acetylene (ethyne), illustrates this arrangement. Acetylene (ethyne) has the structure

$$H—C{\equiv}C—H$$

The H—C≡C bond angles are 180°. When individual molecules are investigated in detail, the experimental bond angles are not always exactly as we would predict. There are other factors influencing bond angles that we will not study in this course.

In most compounds, the outer level is considered full with four pairs or eight electrons. The outer level in some atoms can contain more than

Some atoms can have ex-
panded outer levels containing
more than eight electrons.

BACKGROUND: The concept
of expanded octet is important
in the study of complex ions
(Chapter 14).

eight electrons (if the outer level is the third or higher). A number of
nonmetals, mainly the halogens, form compounds in which the outer
level is expanded to 10, 12, or 14 electrons. Such an arrangement would
also explain noble gas compounds. An example is xenon tetrafluoride,
XeF_4. The structure for this compound is shown in Figure 13-5. Xenon has
eight electrons of its own in its outer level together with four from the
fluorine atoms (one from each).

**FIGURE 13-5. XeF_2 and XeF_4 are
two examples of compounds
where the central atom has an
expanded octet of electrons.**

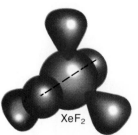

XeF₂

Trigonal bipyramidal shape
Linear molecule

XeF₄

Octahedral shape
Square planar molecule

Table 13-2

Experimental Molecular Shapes		
Cl—B(—Cl)—Cl 120°	I—C(—H)(—H)—H 107°, 112°	H—C(—H)(—H)—H 109.5°
H,H—C=C—F,F 109°, 125°	:O: F—O—F 103°	NH₂—C=S—NH₂ 116°, 122°
C C C C C C C C C 109.5°	:O: H—O—H 104.5°	H H, H H Si 130° N—N 130° Si H H, H H
	·N· H—N—H 107°	
	Ö O=O—O 117°	

13:3 METHOD 2: HYBRID ORBITALS

A second way of looking at molecular shape is by considering the different ways *s* and *p* orbitals can overlap when electrons are shared. This method can best be seen by looking at the element carbon. However, the same principles can be applied to any atom forming covalent bonds.

We would expect the carbon atom with four outer electrons to have two *p* orbitals available for bonding. However, it has been discovered that carbon does not usually form two *p* orbital bonds. Instead, according to theory, the *s* and *p* orbitals of carbon merge to form four equivalent **hybrid orbitals.** If one *s* and three *p* orbitals merge, four sp^3 hybrid orbitals are formed. The sp^3 orbitals are arranged in tetrahedral fashion.

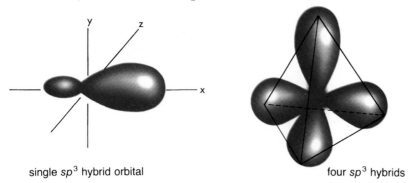

single sp^3 hybrid orbital   four sp^3 hybrids

FIGURE 13-6. Carbon can form four equivalent sp^3 hybrid orbitals which are arranged in a tetrahedral shape.

A carbon atom can form four equivalent bonds. Carbon atoms can link covalently to other carbon atoms. Carbon atoms can also link covalently to atoms of many other elements. However, it is the linking of carbon atom to carbon atom that gives rise to the large number of carbon compounds. There are more carbon compounds than the total of non-carbon compounds. As a result of the almost unlimited number of possible carbon compounds, a large part of chemical research is devoted to producing new carbon compounds, including drugs, plastics, synthetic fibers, and other consumer goods.

13:4 SIGMA AND PI BONDS

A covalent bond is formed when an orbital of one atom overlaps an orbital of another atom and they share the electron pair in the bond. For example, a bond may be formed by the overlap of two *s* orbitals. A bond formed by the direct overlap of two orbitals is called a **sigma bond** and is designated σ. A sigma bond is also formed by the overlap of an *s* orbital of one atom with a *p* orbital of another atom.

When two *p* orbitals overlap, there are two possibilities since *p* orbitals are not spherical. If two *p* orbitals overlap along an axis in an end-to-end fashion a sigma type (σ) bond is formed as shown in Figure 13-8. If,

A sigma bond is formed by the direct overlap of two *s* orbitals or the direct overlap of an *s* and *p* orbital.

A sigma bond is also formed by direct overlap of two *p* orbitals.

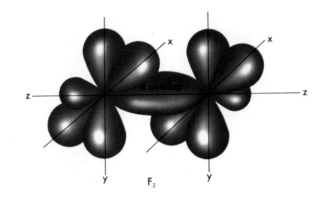

FIGURE 13-7. The overlap of two *s* orbitals is a sigma bond. The H—H bond in hydrogen gas is a sigma bond.

1*s*   1*s*   σ bond

Two *p* orbitals with parallel overlap is a pi bond.

however, the two *p* orbitals overlap sideways with their axes parallel, as in Figure 13-9, they form what is called a **pi (π) bond.** Ethylene (ethene)

FIGURE 13-8. The direct overlap of two *p* orbitals is also a sigma bond.

The orbitals are distorted to form pi bonds.

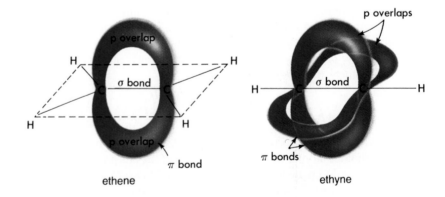

contains one sigma and one pi bond. Acetylene (ethyne) has one sigma and two pi bonds.

FIGURE 13-9. The C=C double bond in ethene consists of one sigma and one pi bond. The C≡C triple bond in ethyne is one sigma and two pi bonds.

ethene   ethyne

13:5   GEOMETRY OF CARBON COMPOUNDS

The bonding of four hydrogen atoms to one carbon atom forms methane. The bonds involve the overlap of the *s* orbital of each hydrogen atom with one of the *sp*³ hybrid orbitals of a carbon atom.

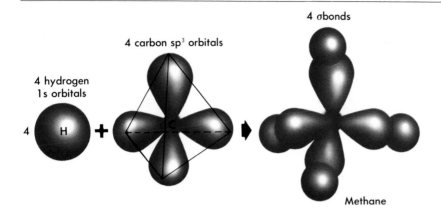

4 σbonds

4 carbon sp³ orbitals

4 hydrogen
1s orbitals

4

H

+

C

Methane

FIGURE 13-10. The methane structure can be explained by combining a hydrogen's orbital with each of the sp³ hybrid orbitals of carbon.

A three dimensional representation of the formula of methane is shown in Figure 13-10. There is an angle of 109.5° between each carbon—hydrogen bond axis.

Carbon atoms may bond to each other by the overlap of an orbital of one carbon atom with an orbital of another carbon atom. The carbon—carbon single bond is a sigma type bond. Many carbon atoms may bond in this manner to form a chain or ring. Recall from Chapter 11 that carbon exhibits catenation. Plastics, synthetic fibers, and synthetic rubber all contain molecules with hundreds or thousands of carbon atoms joined in chains and rings.

The other three sp^3 orbitals of each carbon atom may bond with hydrogen s orbitals. The compound C_2H_6 is called ethane. A three dimensional structure of ethane is shown below.

Carbon can form four single sp^3 hybrid bonds. The bond angle between the bond axes is 109.5°.

FIGURE 13-11. The shape of ethane is explained by combining two sp³ hybrid carbon atoms. The single bond is a direct overlap of one hybrid orbital from each carbon atom.

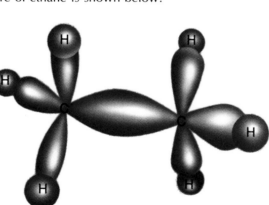

13:6 MULTIPLE BONDS

Carbon can also form compounds where one s orbital and two p orbitals merge to form sp^2 hybrid orbitals as in ethylene (ethene). The

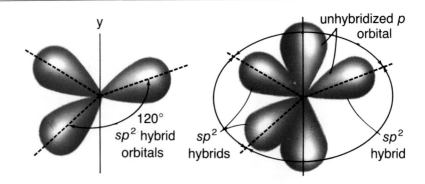

unhybridized *p* orbital

$120°$

sp^2 hybrid orbitals

sp^2 hybrids

sp^2 hybrid

FIGURE 13-12. Carbon can form three equivalent *sp²* hybrid orbitals. The remaining *p* orbital is not hybridized and its lobes are perpendicular to the plane of the *sp²* hybrids. Note the hybrid orbitals are smaller than the *p* orbital.

The *sp²* hybrid orbitals are in a plane with 120° bond angles.

three sp^2 hybrid orbitals are arranged in a plane with 120° bond angles. The third *p* orbital is not hybridized. It is perpendicular to the plane of the sp^2 hybrids.

A double bond consists of one sigma bond and one pi bond.

There is a double bond in ethylene (ethene), $H_2C{=}CH_2$. It is formed by the σ overlap of two sp^2 orbitals and the π overlap of two pure *p* orbitals. Thus, the two carbon atoms are sharing two pairs of electrons. The six atoms of ethene lie in one plane. The structural formula shows the bond angles in the plane.

FIGURE 13-13. The shape of ethene is explained by combining two *sp²* hybrid carbon atoms. The C—H sigma bonds all lie in the same plane. The unhybridized *p* orbitals of the carbon atoms combine to form the pi bond.

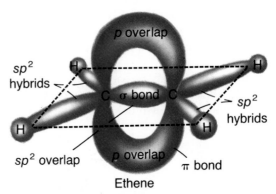

p overlap

sp^2 hybrids

H

H

C σ bond C

sp^2 hybrids

H

H

sp^2 overlap

p overlap

π bond

Ethene

A triple bond consists of one sigma bond and two pi bonds.

The triple bond in acetylene (ethyne) HC≡CH consists of one σ bond and two π bonds. The σ bond is formed when one *s* orbital and one *p* orbital merge to form an *sp* hybrid. The change leaves two pure *p* orbitals perpendicular to each other and the hybrids. Two of the *sp* hybrid

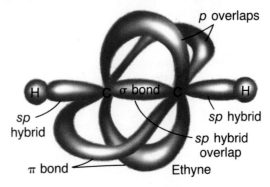

p overlaps

H

C σ bond C

H

sp hybrid

sp hybrid

sp hybrid overlap

FIGURE 13-14. The shape of ethyne is explained by combining two *sp* hybrid carbon atoms. The two pi bonds are formed from the unhybridized *p* orbitals of both carbon atoms.

π bond

Ethyne

orbitals, one from each carbon atom, overlap head on to form a σ type bond. The two *p* orbitals in each atom overlap sideways to form π type bonds.

Double and triple bonds are less flexible than single bonds. Also, a multiple bond between two atoms is stronger than a single bond between them. It holds the atoms closer than a single bond would. However, pi bonds are more easily broken than sigma bonds. As a result, molecules containing multiple bonds are usually more reactive than molecules containing only single bonds.

A multiple bond has a shorter bond length and is stronger than a single bond.

Molecules containing multiple bonds are usually more reactive than similar molecules containing only single bonds.

13:7   BENZENE

One of the top 20 industrial chemicals in the United States is benzene, C_6H_6. It is used extensively in making drugs, dyes, and coatings, as well as solvents. It is also highly toxic and can cause cancer. Each of the six carbon atoms in a benzene ring has three sp^2 hybrid orbitals and one *p* orbital. Sigma bonds are formed by the overlap of the sp^2 orbitals of six carbon atoms forming a ring of single bonds. The π bonds of the benzene ring are formed by the sideways overlap of the *p* orbitals of the carbon atoms.

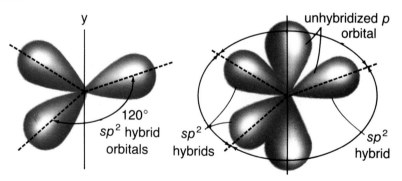

FIGURE 13-15. Each atom in a benzene ring is an sp^2 hybrid. The unhybridized *p* orbitals will form pi bonds.

However, one of the characteristics of benzene is that the π electrons can be shared all around the ring. Since the π electrons are shared equally among all the carbon atoms and not confined to one atom or bond, they are delocalized. This **delocalization** of π electrons among the carbon atoms in benzene results in greater stability of the compound.

Benzene is such an important compound it has been given the structural symbol shown at the right. The inner circle indicates the unsaturated character of all the carbon atoms of the benzene ring. **Unsaturated compounds** are those containing double or triple bonds between carbon atoms.

Whenever multiple *p* orbital overlap can occur, the molecule is said to contain a **conjugated system.** Conjugated systems can occur in chains as well as in rings of atoms. 1,3-butadiene, $CH_2{=}CH{-}CH{=}CH_2$, is an example. Again, the conjugated system imparts a special stability to the molecule.

Benzene has delocalized π electrons.

benzene

A conjugated system stablizes a molecule.

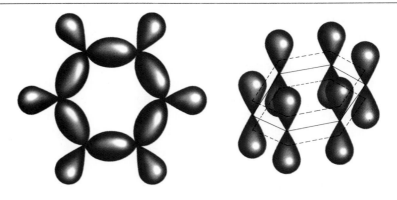

FIGURE 13-16. The benzene ring results from the overlap of six sp^2 hybrid carbon atoms. The unhybridized p orbitals form two pi clouds allowing electrons to be shared around the ring.

σ bonds with sp^2 hybrid orbitals   unhybridized p orbitals

13:8 ISOMERS

The existence of two or more substances with the same molecular formula, but different structures, is called **isomerism** (i sOHM eh rihz uhm). The different structures are called **isomers** (i sOH muhrs). Since isomerism is so common in organic chemistry, we will study the isomers of carbon compounds.

Consider the compound with the formula C_4H_{10}. There are two structures that can be written for this formula. Butane and methylpropane are examples of **structural isomers** or skeleton isomers, since it is the carbon chain that is altered. Methylpropane was at one time called iso-butane since it is made of the same atoms as butane.

Isomers have the same molecular formula but different structures.

butane   methylpropane

A double bond prevents free rotation of the atoms on each end of the bond.

Cis- and *trans*- are two forms of geometric isomerism.
Cis form: Like atoms are on the same side of the double bond.

Trans form: Like atoms are on opposite sides of the double bond.

Look at the two structures shown for butene. Note that the formation of a π bond prevents the atoms on each end of the bond from rotating with respect to each other. Some compounds containing double bonds exhibit a kind of isomerism called **geometric isomerism.** Geometric isomers are composed of the same atoms bonded in the same order, but with a different arrangement of atoms around a double bond. We will use the compound 2-butene (C_4H_8) to illustrate geometric isomers. Note that in the *cis* form of 2-butene, the CH_3 groups and the hydrogen atoms are on the same side of the double bond. In the *trans* form, the CH_3 groups and the hydrogen atoms are on opposite sides.

$$CH_3 \diagdown C{=}C \diagup CH_3$$

(cis-2-butene structure: CH₃ and CH₃ on same side, H and H on other)

(trans-2-butene structure: CH₃ and H top, H and CH₃ bottom)

cis-2-butene

trans-2-butene

If we introduce another element into a hydrocarbon molecule, we find two more kinds of isomers, positional and functional. **Positional isomers** are formed when the newly introduced particle may occupy two or more positions in the molecule. Each different position produces a positional isomer. The positional isomers for propanol are shown. Note both compounds have the same molecular formula but differ in the position of the OH group.

Positional isomers are formed in hydrocarbon molecules where particles can occupy 2 or more different positions.

(1-propanol structure: H—C—C—C—OH with H's)

(2-propanol structure: H—C—C—C—H with OH on middle carbon)

1-propanol

2-propanol

Functional isomers have a new element being bonded in two different ways. Ethanol is a liquid while methoxymethane is a gas at room temperature.

Functional isomers are formed when the new element can be bonded in two different ways.

(ethanol structure: H—C—C—OH)

(methoxymethane structure: H—C—O—C—H)

ethanol

methoxymethane

$$CH_3{-}CH_2{-}CH_2{-}CH_2{-}CH_2{-}CH_3$$

$$CH_3{-}\overset{\displaystyle CH_3}{\underset{\displaystyle CH_3}{C}}{-}CH_2{-}CH_3$$

FIGURE 13-17. The mass spectrograms for hexane (a) and 2,2-dimethylbutane (b) show the same number of peaks. However, the differences in *m/e* values for each peak can be used to identify each compound.

The mass spectrometer can be used to distinguish between isomers that have very similar properties. During the analysis, the sample being studied is ionized and divided into ion fragments. Each fragment has an *m/e* value (mass to charge ratio). In Figure 13-17, the mass spectrogram for hexane shows peaks at 17 different *m/e* values. The hexane molecule can be broken into 17 fragments that each have a different mass. Note the spectrogram for 2,2-dimethylbutane also shows 17 fragments. However, you can see that the relative intensities for 2,2-dimethylbutane are significantly different from those shown for hexane.

13:9   INORGANIC COMPOUNDS

The ground state electron configuration of carbon ends in $2s^2 2p^2$. In Section 13:3 we saw that each of the four electrons was placed in a separate orbital. We treated the carbon atom as if it were in the state $2s^1 2p^3$. We assumed that this was the configuration in order that hybridization of orbitals could occur.

What about other atoms? For example, beryllium has two outer electrons, $2s^2$. Only two orbitals need be hybridized. We would expect *sp* hybridization to lead to linear bonding orbitals. Analysis bears out this prediction with molecules having a central atom ending in an s^2 configuration. For boron, $2s^2 2p^1$, and other atoms with three outer electrons, we would predict sp^2 hybridization. Again, analysis bears out the prediction of trigonal planar bond arrangements.

H—Be—H	F | B / \\ F F
beryllium hydride	boron trifluoride

Atoms other than carbon atoms may have hydridized orbitals.

SUGGESTION: Point out to students that the electron dot structures for Be and B do not follow the octet rule.

We can, in fact, apply all our principles of molecular geometry and isomerism to inorganic compounds as well.

13:10   METHOD 3: RESONANCE

We have been looking at compounds that can be represented by a single structural formula. However, analysis shows that many molecules and polyatomic ions cannot be described by one formula. We will now consider another way of looking at molecules.

Consider the nitrate ion (NO_3^-). The theory of electron cloud spacing would predict 120° O—N—O bond angles and a trigonal planar ion. Experiments have shown this prediction to be true.

Now, suppose we attempt to draw an electron dot diagram for the nitrate ion. If we let electrons originally associated with oxygen atoms be

Compounds cannot always be represented by a single structural formula.

represented by (x), the electron dot structure for an oxygen atom would be

$$\overset{\times\times}{\underset{\times}{\vdots}} \overset{}{O} \times$$

Likewise, if nitrogen electrons are represented by (o), the electron dot structure for nitrogen would be

$$\underset{\circ}{\overset{\circ}{\circ}} N \circ$$

A possible electron dot diagram for the nitrate ion shows an ion with a 1⁻ charge. The extra electron is shown by the symbol (·).

$$\overset{\times\times}{\underset{\times\times}{\vdots O \vdots}} \quad -$$
$$\overset{\times\times\;\;\circ\circ\;\;\times\times}{\underset{\times\times\;\;\;\;\;\;\times\times}{\vdots O \vdots N \vdots O \vdots}}$$

Note that the nitrogen atom has only six electrons in its outer level. We know that most atoms tend to satisfy the octet rule in compound formation. How, then, can we properly explain the structure of the nitrate ion?

Another electron dot diagram can be shown that satisfies our requirements. One of the oxygen atoms shares two pairs of electrons with the nitrogen. Suppose this nitrate ion was actually constructed. Then we would expect the doubly-bonded oxygen atom to be a little closer to the nitrogen than the other two oxygen atoms. However, analysis has shown that all three N—O bonds are the same length.

In NO_3^-, all bond lengths are equal.

$$\overset{\times}{\underset{\times}{\vdots O \vdots}} \quad -$$
$$\overset{\times\times\;\;\circ\times\;\;\times\times}{\underset{\times\times\;\;\;\;\;\;\times\times}{\vdots O \vdots N \vdots O \vdots}}$$

To account for this observation, chemists have formulated a concept called resonance. Using the idea of **resonance,** we can draw several equivalent diagrams for the distribution of electrons in a molecule or ion. In fact, we draw all possible diagrams that obey the rules about full outer levels and the number of bonds an atom can form. We then consider the actual structure of the particle to be the average of all these possibilities. Thus, the following structures can be drawn for the nitrate ion.

Resonance: Equivalent alternative structures for a molecule or polyatomic ion which lead to "average" bond lengths.

$$
\begin{array}{ccccc}
\overset{\cdot\cdot}{O} & & \overset{\cdot\cdot}{O} & & \overset{\cdot\cdot}{O} \\
\quad\quad\; - & & \quad\quad\; - & & \quad\quad\; - \\
N\;O & \longleftrightarrow & N\;O & \longleftrightarrow & N\;O \\
\overset{\cdot\cdot}{O} & & \overset{\cdot\cdot}{O} & & \overset{\cdot\cdot}{O}
\end{array}
$$

If we "average" these three structures in our minds, we can see that we will end up with three equal N—O bonds. Each of these bonds will be about one and one third times the normal single bond strength. Because each bond is slightly stronger than a single bond, each bond length is slightly shorter than a single N—O bond. Since they are equivalent, the bond lengths will be the same, and the bond angles will be equal, 120°. Note that the different forms are shown to be equivalent by the double-ended arrows between them.

13:11   METHOD 4: MOLECULAR ORBITAL THEORY

The structure and properties of some molecules and ions cannot be explained by any of the methods we have studied. Another approach to structure makes use of **molecular orbitals.** These orbitals belong to the molecule as a whole, not to a particular atom. By combining atomic orbitals from the outer levels of bonding atoms, we get an equal number of molecular orbitals.

Molecular orbitals belong to the molecule as a whole, not to a particular atom.

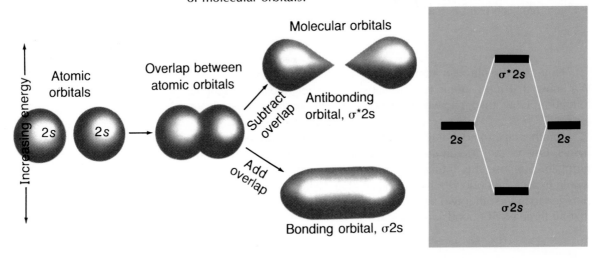

FIGURE 13-18. Two molecular orbitals are formed from two *s* atomic orbitals. The low energy molecular orbital is more stable than both atomic orbitals.

Consider the bonding of two atoms whose outer level is the second energy level. Each atom has four orbitals in its outer level, one *s* and three

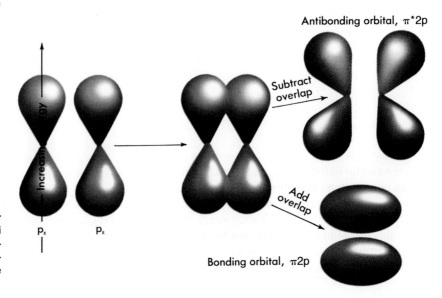

FIGURE 13-19. Four molecular orbitals are formed from the pi overlap of four atomic *p* orbitals. Two of these molecular orbitals are more stable than the four atomic orbitals.

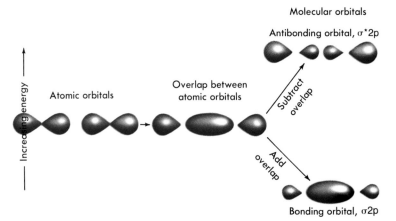

Molecular orbitals

Antibonding orbital, σ*2p

Overlap between
atomic orbitals

Atomic orbitals

Subtract overlap

Add overlap

Bonding orbital, σ2p

Increasing energy

FIGURE 13-20. Two molecular orbitals are formed from the sigma overlap of two atomic p orbitals. The low energy molecular orbital is more stable than the atomic orbitals.

p orbitals. By combining the two atomic $2s$ orbitals we get two molecular orbitals. One of these two molecular orbitals represents less energy and is therefore more stable than the two atomic orbitals from which it was made. The other molecular orbital represents more energy and is less stable than its atomic orbitals. The more stable orbital is designated σ_{2s} (sigma two ess) and the less stable σ^*_{2s} (sigma star two ess). Electrons in the σ_{2s} orbital bond the two atoms together. As a result the σ_{2s} is called a bonding orbital. Electrons in the σ^*_{2s} repel each other and the σ^*_{2s} is called an antibonding orbital.

Molecular orbitals result from combining outer atomic orbitals.

Two atomic orbitals combine to form two molecular orbitals; one is more stable, and one is less stable than the atomic orbital.

The more stable molecular orbital is a bonding orbital.

The less stable molecular orbital is an antibonding orbital.

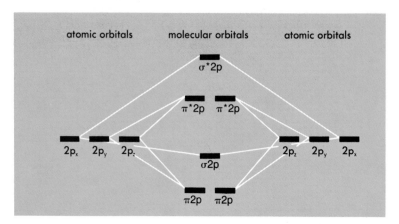

atomic orbitals   molecular orbitals   atomic orbitals

σ*2p

π*2p   π*2p

2p$_x$ 2p$_y$ 2p$_z$ 2p$_z$ 2p$_y$ 2p$_x$

σ2p

π2p   π2p

FIGURE 13-21. The energy diagram for the formation of molecular orbitals shows the lowest energy orbitals to be the bonding molecular orbitals. The highest energy and least stable orbitals are the antibonding molecular orbitals.

In a similar fashion, the $2p$ atomic orbitals are combined to form six molecular orbitals. The lowest energy molecular orbitals formed from the $2p$ atomic orbitals are two π_{2p} orbitals. At a slightly higher energy, one σ_{2p} orbital is formed. At still higher energy, two π^*_{2p} orbitals are formed. At the highest energy, one σ^*_{2p} orbital is formed. Again the starred orbitals represent antibonding orbitals.

Electrons in the outer level of the atoms enter newly formed molecular orbitals. These electrons obey the same rules of filling molecular

Electrons enter the lowest-energy molecular orbital available first. (aufbau principle)

If two or more orbitals of the same energy are available, one electron will enter each before pairing. (Hund's Rule)

orbitals that they obeyed for atomic orbitals. Specifically, electrons enter the lowest-energy available orbital first. If two or more orbitals of the same energy are available, one electron will enter each before any pairing is done. Electron configurations for molecules can be written just as we write configurations for atoms, for example, $(\sigma_{2s})^2$, $(\sigma_{2s}^{\star})^2$, $(\pi_{2p})^4$, and so on. The bond order between atoms is found by subtracting antibonding electrons from bonding electrons and dividing by two. Bond order indicates whether a bond is single, double, or triple. We divide by two because a bond consists of a shared pair of electrons.

One molecule that is successfully treated by molecular orbital theory is the oxygen molecule. Let us first consider the O_2 molecule by another method. Each oxygen atom has six electrons in its outer level. To satisfy the octet rule, the electron dot diagram for oxygen would be

$$:\ddot{O}::\ddot{O}:$$

SUGGESTION: You may wish to introduce the terms para-magnetic (unpaired e^-) and diamagnetic (all e^-'s are paired).

That diagram indicates a double bond between oxygen atoms, with all electrons paired. Study of the oxygen molecule indicates that there is a double bond present (bond order = 2). However, behavior of the oxygen molecule in the magnetic field indicates two unpaired electrons.

How does molecular orbital theory describe the oxygen molecule? Molecular orbital theory predicts the formation of the molecular orbitals as mentioned earlier in this section. We then position the twelve outer

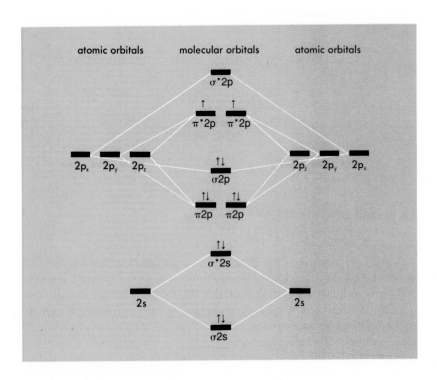

FIGURE 13-22. In filling the molecular orbital diagram for oxygen, electrons are placed in the lowest energy orbitals first.

electrons (six from each O atom). The first two enter the two σ_{2s} orbital and the next two enter the σ_{2s}^{*} orbital as shown in Figure 13-22. Four electrons enter the two π_{2p} orbitals and two enter the σ_{2p} orbital. The last two electrons enter the π_{2p}^{*} orbitals. Since there are two of these orbitals, one electron enters each. Thus, there are the two unpaired electrons as observed by experiment. Eight electrons have entered bonding orbitals, $(\sigma_{2s})^2$, $(\pi_{2p})^4$, $(\sigma_{2p})^2$. Four electrons have entered antibonding orbitals, $(\sigma_{2s}^{*})^2$, (π_{2p}^{*2}). We calculate the bond order as

$$\frac{8 - 4}{2} = 2$$

In agreement with experiment, molecular orbital theory shows the two oxygen atoms to be doubly bonded.

$$\text{Bond order} = \frac{\text{bonding electrons} - \text{anti-bonding electrons}}{2}$$

Again experimental evidence backs up or precedes theory.

EXAMPLE: **Molecular Orbitals**

Is the Be_2 molecule stable as described by molecular orbital theory?
Solving Process:
If the two beryllium atoms were to combine, their atomic orbitals would form the molecular orbitals shown in Figure 13-23. Each beryllium atom

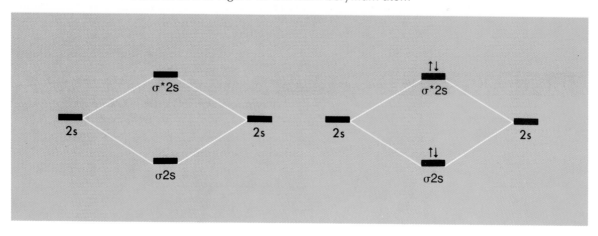

has two electrons in the outer level. Therefore, there would be four electrons to place in molecular orbitals. The first two electrons would enter the σ_{2s} orbital and the second two would enter the σ_{2s}^{*} orbital. The bond order is

$$\frac{2 - 2}{2} = 0$$

No bond forms. Therefore, the Be_2 molecule would be unstable, and, in fact, does not exist.

FIGURE 13-23. The molecular orbital model for Be_2 contains two molecular orbitals formed from two **2s** atomic orbitals. Filling the diagram shows two electrons in the antibonding orbital resulting in a bond order of zero.

The band structure of metals, the delocalized electrons of benzene, and "averaged" resonance structures are all ideas that can be explained by molecular orbital theory. We will not go into the details of any of these derivations. They have, however, proved to be very useful concepts in understanding how properties are a consequence of structure.

13:12   BOND SUMMARY

In studying atomic structure we treated the electron as particle, wave, and negative cloud. In studying bonding we have also studied several different approaches to explain what we observe. It is plain that chemists do not have a complete understanding of all factors in bonding. Therefore, more than one explanation is often needed to account for observations.

When faced with multiple explanations, scientists follow a basic rule. That rule is to try the simplest explanation first. If that method does not suffice, then the more complex ideas are applied until one is found to fit. The various ideas on structure presented in this chapter are arranged roughly in order of increasing complexity. Consequently, electron-pair repulsion is the simplest and should be applied first.

Chemists use several different approaches to explain bonding.
1. electron pair repulsion theory
2. hybrid orbital theory
3. resonance
4. molecular orbital theory

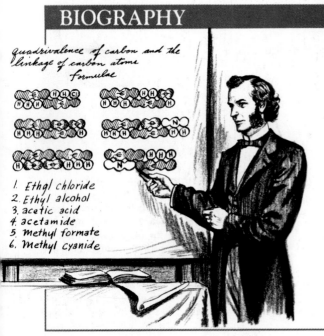

BIOGRAPHY

Friedrich August Kekulé (1829-1896)

German chemist Friedrich Kekulé was considered by many as the most brilliant of his day. His work centered around ideas on the linking of atoms and the structure of molecules. He was the first to speculate on the existence of bonds between atoms and he drew structural diagrams similar to those we use now.

Kekulé explained that in substances containing several carbon atoms, it must be assumed that some of the bonds of each carbon atom are bonded to other carbon atoms.

This concept led Kekulé to propose a ring structure as the logical arrangement for the atoms composing benzene. At this time, many scientists felt that this proposal was the "most brilliant piece of prediction in all of organic chemistry."

Many of our present theories on the structures of compounds were formulated by Kekulé.

TECHNOLOGY AND CHEMISTRY

13:13 The Boranes

Boron and hydrogen form several compounds with unusual bonding arrangements. From the electron configurations of boron and hydrogen, we would predict boron hydride, BH_3, to be a planar molecule with 120° H—B—H bond angles. Instead, the two elements form a whole series of compounds called boranes. The simplest compound in the series is diborane (6), B_2H_6.

In naming boranes, a prefix is used to indicate the number of boron atoms in the molecule. The number of hydrogen atoms is shown by Arabic numerals in parentheses after the name. In addition to diborane (6), some other boranes are tetraborane (10), pentaborane (9), pentaborane (11), hexaborane (10), and decaborane (14).

All of these compounds are said to be electron deficient. That is, there are not enough electrons in the outer levels of the atoms to form any electron dot diagram to satisfy the octet rule.

Boron $1s^2 2s^1$ Ḃ:

Hydrogen $1s^1$ H·

As a result, chemists have developed a three-center, two-electron bond model. In this model, a pair of electrons occupies an orbital spread over three atoms, so that the middle atom acts as a bridge between the other two atoms.

Diborane, B_2H_6

FIGURE 13-24. The structure of diborane shows four hydrogen atoms in the same plane. The two bridging hydrogen atoms are at a 90° angle to this plane.

FIGURE 13-25. The structures of more complex diboranes are shown.

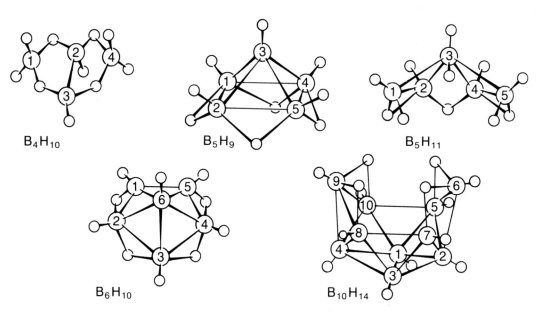

B_4H_{10} B_5H_9 B_5H_{11}

B_6H_{10} $B_{10}H_{14}$

In the structural diagrams shown, note that each contains bridging hydrogen atoms in three-center, two-electron bonds. In addition, all boranes having five or more boron atoms have at least one boron atom acting as a bridge between other boron atoms.

Most boranes are unstable. Several, including diborane (6), are spontaneously flammable. Diborane (6) is used as a reactant in making other chemicals since it is an excellent Lewis acid. (Lewis acids will be covered in Chapter 24.) Diborane (6) has also been used on an experimental basis as a rocket fuel. The best rocket fuels are composed of low atomic mass elements. Lighter atoms travel faster than heavy atoms at the same temperature. The combustion of boranes produces higher velocity gases in the rocket motor nozzle. In addition, these compounds produce more energy than similar molecular mass organic fuels. For example, the energy produced by burning a mole of diborane (6), B_2H_6, is 2010 J, while ethane, C_2H_6, produces only 970 J/mol.

It is possible to produce similar compounds in which one or more boron atoms have been replaced by carbon atoms. These compounds are called carboranes. Their chemistry has been studied extensively in the hope that they too can be used as rocket fuels. Carborane polyesters have been used as ablative materials. An ablative material has the ability to carry away heat by gradually peeling away in layers. Space capsules use ablative materials in their heat shields. The peeling occurs when the capsule reenters the earth's atmosphere.

SUMMARY

1. The shape of molecules can be approximated by assuming the mutual repulsion of electron pairs due to the same electrostatic charge and the Pauli exclusion principle. Electron pairs spread as far apart as possible. **13:1**

2. The shape of a molecule containing three or more atoms is determined by the number of electron clouds in the outer level. **13:1**

3. If the central atom has two bonds and no unshared pairs, the molecule is linear. **13:1**

4. If there are three bonds and no unshared pairs, the molecule is trigonal planar. **13:1**

5. If there are four bonds, the molecule is tetrahedral. **13:1**

6. The actual bond angles may vary from predicted angles. Unshared electron pairs occupy the most space. Shared pairs occupy the least space. **13:1**

7. Two atoms sometimes share more than one pair of electrons forming double and triple bonds. This possibility must be considered when discussing molecular geometry. **13:2**

8. Molecular covalent bonds are formed by overlap of atomic orbitals: s-s, s-p, and p-p. **13:3**

9. If two s orbitals or s and p orbitals overlap, a sigma (σ) bond is formed. If two p orbitals overlap end-to-end, a sigma (σ) bond is formed. If two p orbitals overlap sideways, a pi (π) bond is formed. **13:3**

10. s and p orbitals of the same atom can combine to form hybrid orbitals. One s and three p orbitals merge to form four tetrahedral sp^3 hybrids. One s and two p orbitals merge to form three planar sp^2 hybrid orbitals. One s and one p orbital merge to form two linear sp hybrid orbitals. **13:5**

11. A double bond is formed by the sigma overlap of two sp^2 orbitals and the π overlap of the two p orbitals. **13:6**

12. A triple bond is formed by the sigma overlap of two sp orbitals and the π overlap of four p orbitals. **13:6**

13. Delocalization of π electrons in conjugated chain and ring compounds produces stability. **13:7**

14. Isomers are compounds with the same formula but a different arrangement of atoms and bonds. **13:8**

15. There are several types of isomers: structural, geometric, positional, and functional. **13:8**

16. In the concept of resonance, we consider all correct structures that can be written for that compound. We assume that the actual distribution of electrons in a particle is the average of all these structures. **13:10**

17. Molecular orbital theory combines atomic orbitals to form molecular orbitals. Electrons fill molecular orbitals under the same rules as atomic orbitals. Molecular orbitals can be bonding or antibonding. Bond order is one-half the difference between bonding and antibonding electrons. **13:11**

VOCABULARY

shared pairs **Intro**
unshared pairs **Intro**
double bond **13:2**
triple bond **13:2**
hybrid orbitals **13:3**
sigma bond **13:4**
pi bond **13:4**
delocalization **13:7**
unsaturated compounds **13:7**

conjugated system **13:7**
isomerism **13:8**
isomers **13:8**
structural isomers **13:8**
geometric isomerism **13:8**
positional isomers **13:8**
functional isomers **13:8**
resonance **13:10**
molecular orbitals **13:11**

PROBLEMS

1. Predict the bond angles indicated in the following compounds.
   a. H—Se—H in H_2Se
   b. H—P—H in PH_3
   c. C—N—C in $N(CH_3)_3$
   d. Cl—P—Cl in PCl_3
   e. F—C—F in CF_4
   f. C—Pb—C in $Pb(C_2H_5)_4$

2. What is the major difference between sigma and pi bonds?

See Teacher Guide
1. a. <109.5°
   b. <109.5°
   c. ≈109.5°
   d. <109.5°
   e. 109.5°
   f. 109.5°

3. What is meant by the term "hybridization"?

4. What kinds of orbital arrangements contribute to the bonding in ethene ($H_2C{=}CH_2$)?

5. Why is benzene a particularly stable compound?

6. Predict the shapes of the following molecules:

6. a. trigonal planar
   b. angular or bent
   c. trigonal planar
   d. octahedral
   e. See Teacher Guide
   f. trigonal bipy-ramid

   a. H_2CO
   b. SeO_2
   c. BF_3

   d. SF_6 (see Table 13-1)
   e. S_2Cl_2
   f. SF_4

7. In the HCN molecule, the H—C bond is a single bond and the C≡N bond is a triple bond. Predict the shape of the molecule, the hybridization of the carbon atom, and the type (σ, π) of each bond.

8. The substance H_2Se is a molecular compound. Sketch a cross-sectional view of the molecule and label its various dimensions.

9. Draw the isomers of the compound with the formula C_6H_{14}.

10. Define geometric, positional, and functional isomers.

11. Predict shapes for the following ions.

11. a. tetrahedral
    b. trigonal pyramid
    c. octahedral
    d. tetrahedral
    e. tetrahedral
    f. square planar

    a. IO_4^-
    b. ClO_3^-
    c. SiF_6^{2-} (see Table 13-1)

    d. SO_4^{2-}
    e. PO_4^{3-} (see Table 13-1)
    f. ClF_4^-

12. The substance phosphorus pentachloride occurs as PCl_5 molecules in the gaseous state. As a solid, it is an ionic compound, $PCl_4^+PCl_6^-$. Describe the shape and bonding in each of these species. (see Table 13-1)

13. How does the conjugated bonding arrangement in benzene compare to the bonding in metals?

14. One might expect the bond angle for each C—H bond in methane to be 90°. Why is this prediction incorrect?

15. Why is the bond angle in NH_3 only 107° when the bond angle for BF_3 is 120°?

16. Draw electron dot diagrams to show the resonance structures for the carbonate ion (CO_3^{2-}).

17. Conjugated systems, such as benzene, are often considered as "averages" of resonant forms. Draw the resonance forms for benzene and a related compound, naphthalene $C_{10}H_8$.

18. Write the molecular orbital configurations for the following molecules. Compute the bond order in each molecule and decide whether the molecule would be stable or not.

    a. Li_2 b. B_2 c. C_2 d. N_2 e. F_2

19. When dissimilar atoms combine, the energy level diagram for the molecular orbital interpretation of the bond is much more complex than for two identical atoms. For the molecule CO, however, the two atoms are close enough to assume an energy diagram following Figures 13-18 and 13-21. Describe the bonding in the CO molecule.

REVIEW

1. Arrange the following elements in order of increasing attractive force between nucleus and outer electrons.

   a. boron
   b. francium
   c. manganese
   d. zinc

2. Classify the bonds between the following pairs of atoms as principally ionic or principally covalent.

   a. barium and fluorine
   b. bromine and rubidium
   c. cesium and oxygen
   d. iodine and antimony
   e. nitrogen and sulfur
   f. silicon and carbon

3. Explain briefly why metals conduct electricity.

See Teacher Guide
1. francium, manganese, zinc, boron
2. a. ionic
   b. ionic
   c. ionic
   d. covalent
   e. covalent
   f. covalent

ONE MORE STEP

1. Using library resources, find the following bond angles.

   a. C—C=C in CH_3CHCH_2
   b. F—C—F in CF_3I
   c. H—N—N in HN_3
   d. O—N—O in NO_2
   e. O—N—O in NO_2^-

2. Find out the geometry of d^2sp^3 hybrid orbitals. See if you can discover some compounds or ions containing such hybrids.

3. Predict the shape of cyclohexane (C_6H_{12}). From references, determine the two shapes of cyclohexane. Make models of the two shapes to illustrate why one form is more stable than the other.

4. Predict shapes for the following molecules.

   a. $H_2C=C=CH_2$
   b. $H_2C=C=C=CH_2$

5. Read the story of the development of molecular structure theories.

6. Find out why the molecular orbital theory is difficult to apply to molecules composed of atoms from two different elements.

7. Investigate the molecular orbital structure of the benzene molecule.

See Teacher Guide
1. a. 125°
   b. 108°
   c. 113°
   d. 134°
   e. 115°
2. octahedral

3. puckered ring chair form is more stable

READINGS

Mickey, Charles D., "Molecular Geometry." *Journal of Chemical Education*, Vol. 57, No. 3 (March 1980), pp. 210-212.

These ice crystals are composed of water molecules. Water molecules are polar. The intermolecular forces between polar molecules are stronger than the forces between nonpolar molecules. The principal bonding force between water molecules is hydrogen bonding. What is hydrogen bonding? How do intermolecular forces affect the properties of substances?

POLAR MOLECULES

14

Chapter 14 describes the interrelationship of the attractive forces between molecules, molecular structure, and physical and chemical properties. The structures and properties of complex ions are introduced. The discussion of polarity is carried further in describing chromatography as an analytical process.

DEMONSTRATION: Fill two burets, one with a polar liquid (H_2O) and the other with a nonpolar liquid (cyclohexane). Allow the liquids to run out of the burets in a thin stream. Use a charged rod (lucite rubbed with silk) to deflect the polar stream. Use this demonstration as an introduction to the differences between polar and nonpolar molecules.

GOALS:
• You will gain an understanding of the relationship between molecular structure and the properties of molecular compounds.
• You will explain the formation of coordination compounds and complex ions.
• You will gain an understanding of how chromatography is used to indentify compounds.

Think for a moment about the salt and sugar on your dinner table. They look alike. They both dissolve in water. Yet, to a chemist, they are quite different. Salt is made of ions. The sodium ions and chloride ions are oppositely charged and attract each other. Knowing the properties of ionic substances, we know why salt is a solid. Sugar, on the other hand, is made of molecules. Each molecule of sugar contains twelve atoms of carbon, twenty-two atoms of hydrogen, and eleven atoms of oxygen. These atoms are bonded to each other covalently. However, since a sugar molecule is neutral, what holds sugar molecules together? Why don't the sugar molecules just float away from each other and become a gas?

Substances composed of molecules exhibit a wide range of melting and boiling points. There must be, therefore, a wide range in the strength of forces holding molecules to each other. These forces are determined by the internal structure of a molecule. In this chapter we will take a closer look at the aspects of internal structure that affect the forces holding molecules to each other.

There is a wide range of forces holding molecules together.

14:1 POLARITY

Recall that electronegativity is an atom's ability to attract the electrons involved in bonding. Since the electronegativity of each element differs, we should consider that in a covalent bond one of the atoms attracts the shared pair more strongly than the other. The resulting bond is said to be **polar covalent.** Since one atom in the bond attracts the electrons more strongly, there will be a partial negative charge near that end of the bond. In the bond, the atom with the higher electronegativity will have a partial negative charge. The other atom will have a partial positive charge. Polar bonds, unless symmetrically arranged, produce polar molecules. In CCl_4, the four C—Cl bonds are polar but their symmetrical arrangement (tetrahedral) produces a nonpolar molecule. In contrast, the chloromethane molecule, CH_3Cl, is polar, because the polarity of the C—Cl bond is not offset by the three C—H bonds.

A polar covalent bond occurs when a shared pair of electrons is attracted more strongly to one of the atoms.

Polar bonds, unless symmetrically arranged, produce polar molecules.

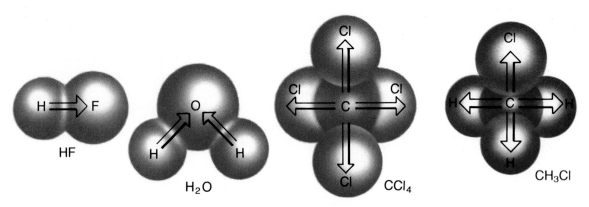

FIGURE 14-1. CH₃Cl, HF, and H₂O are polar molecules because the arrangement of polar bonds is not symmetrical. The CCl₄ molecule is nonpolar in spite of the fact that it contains four polar bonds.

Dipole: A polar molecule.

Dipole moment, μ, describes the strength of the dipole.

SUGGESTION: You may wish to introduce vectors and vector addition to show why a nonsymmetrical molecule has a dipole moment.

Melting point and freezing point are directly related to dipole moment.

A polar molecule is sometimes called a dipole. A **dipole** has asymmetrical charge distribution. Partial charges within a molecule are indicated by δ (delta). A water molecule would be represented as follows:

$$\delta^+H\!:\!\overset{\cdot\cdot}{\underset{\cdot\cdot}{O}}\!:\!\delta^- \qquad \text{bond angle } 104.5°$$
$$\overset{\displaystyle H}{\underset{\displaystyle \delta^+}{}}$$

Dipole moment, μ, is used to describe the strength of a dipole. The dipole moment depends upon the size of the partial charges and the distance between them. In symbols

$$\mu = Qd$$

where Q is the size of the partial charge in coulombs and d is the distance in meters. Dipole moment is then expressed in coulomb·meters.* The higher the dipole moment, the stronger the intermolecular forces; and, consequently, the higher the melting point and boiling point. Table 14-1

*Older tables of dipole moments may be expressed in debyes (D) where $1 \text{ D} = 3.338 \times 10^{-30}$ C·m.

lists a number of common solvents in order of increasing polarity. (The first three are nonpolar.)

Table 14-1

Polarity of Solvents		
Name	**Formula**	**$\mu \times 10^{30}$**
Cyclohexane	C_6H_{12}	0
Carbon tetrachloride	CCl_4	0
Benzene	C_6H_6	0
Toluene	$C_6H_5CH_3$	1.20
Ethoxyethane	$CH_3CH_2OCH_2CH_3$	3.84
1-Butanol	$CH_3CH_2CH_2CH_2OH$	5.54
1-Propanol	$CH_3CH_2CH_2OH$	5.61
Ethanol	CH_3CH_2OH	5.64
Methanol	CH_3OH	5.67
Ethyl acetate	$CH_3CH_2OOCCH_3$	5.94
Water	HOH	6.14
Propanone	CH_3COCH_3	9.61

PROBLEM

1. The following pairs of atoms are all covalently bonded. Arrange the pairs in order of decreasing polarity of the bonds. (See Table of Electronegativities, Chapter 12.)

   a. aluminum and phosphorus
   b. chlorine and nitrogen
   c. hydrogen and sulfur
   d. molybdenum and tellurium
   e. phosphorus and sulfur
   f. chlorine and silicon

1. f, e, a, d, c, b

14:2   WEAK FORCES

Covalent compounds show a melting point range of over 3000 C°. How can we account for such a wide variation? The forces involved in some of these cases are called **van der Waals forces.** Johannes van der Waals was the first to account for these forces in calculations concerning gases. These forces are sometimes referred to as weak forces because they are much weaker than chemical bonds. Weak forces involve the attraction of the electrons of one atom for the protons of another.

It is important to note the difference between intramolecular forces and intermolecular forces. **Intramolecular forces** are those holding atoms together in molecules, that is, covalent bonds. **Intermolecular forces** are those forces holding molecules to each other, that is, van der Waals forces.

Weak attractive forces between the nucleus of one atom and the electrons of another atom are van der Waals forces.

Dipole-dipole attractions occur between two permanent polar molecules.

The first source of van der Waals attraction that we will consider is **dipole-dipole forces.** With dipole-dipole forces two molecules, of the same or different substances, that are both permanent dipoles will be attracted to each other, Figure 14-2. Such would be the case between two trichloromethane molecules, $CHCl_3$, or between a trichloromethane and an ammonia molecule.

FIGURE 14-2. Dipole-dipole attraction exists between molecules which are permanent dipoles.

We can also have the attraction of a dipole for a molecule that is not ordinarily a dipole. When a dipole approaches a nonpolar molecule, its partial charge either attracts or repels the electrons of the other particle. For instance, if the negative end of the dipole approaches a nonpolar molecule, the electrons of the nonpolar molecule are repelled by the negative charge. The electron cloud of the nonpolar molecule is distorted by bulging away from the approaching dipole as shown in Figure 14-3. As a result, the nonpolar molecule is itself transformed into a dipole. We say it has become an **induced dipole.** Since it is now a dipole, it can be attracted to the permanent dipole. Interactions such as these are called **dipole-induced dipole forces.** An example of this force occurs in a water solution of iodine. The I_2 molecules are nonpolar while the water molecules are highly polar.

A nonpolar molecule may become an induced dipole.

FIGURE 14-3. Dipole-induced dipole attraction occurs when a molecule which is a dipole causes a nonpolar molecule to become an induced dipole.

Two nonpolar molecules may be attracted to each other.

The case of two nonpolar molecules being attracted must also be taken into account. For instance, there must be some force between hydrogen molecules; otherwise it would be impossible to form liquid hydrogen. Consider a hydrogen molecule with its molecular orbital including both nuclei. We know intuitively that the electrons occupying that orbital must have a specific location. If they are both away from one end of the molecule for an instant, then the nucleus is exposed for a short time. That end of the molecule has a partial positive charge for an instant; a temporary dipole is set up. For that time, the **temporary dipole** can induce a dipole in the molecule next to it and an attractive force results, as shown in Figure 14-4. The forces generated in this way are called **dispersion forces** or London forces after the scientist who first investigated them.

Dispersion forces result from temporary dipoles.

FIGURE 14-4. Dispersion forces exist between nonpolar- molecules and are the result of the formation of temporary dipoles.

Many molecules will exhibit two of these dipole/dispersion interactions, or even all three. However, we are only interested in the net result. The liquid and solid states of many compounds exist because of these intermolecular forces. Substances composed of nonpolar molecules are generally gases or low-boiling liquids. Substances composed of polar molecules generally have higher boiling points than nonpolar compounds. Many polar molecules are solids under normal conditions.

These forces are effective only over very short distances. They vary roughly as the inverse of the sixth power of distance, $1/d^6$. In other words, if the distance is doubled, the attractive force is only $1/64$ as large.

Of the three contributing factors to van der Waals forces, dispersion forces are the most important. They are the only attractive forces that exist between nonpolar molecules. Even for most polar molecules, dispersion forces account for 85% or more of the van der Waals forces. Only in some special cases, such as NH_3 and H_2O, do dipole-dipole interactions become more important than dispersion forces. We will examine these special cases in Chapter 17.

van der Waals attraction can result from
1. dipole-dipole forces
2. dipole-induced dipole forces
3. dispersion forces

The van der Waals forces are effective only over very short distances.

While chemical bonds range from about 200 to 800 kJ/mol, dipole-dipole forces are < 125 kJ/mol.

Table 14-2

Weak Forces Summary		
Type of Force	Dispersion Forces	Dipole
Substances Exhibiting Force	Nonpolar molecules	Polar covalent molecules
Source of the Force	Weak electric fluctuations which destroy spherical symmetry of electronic fields about atoms	Electric attraction between dipoles resulting from polar bonds
Properties Due to the Force	Substances have low melting and boiling points	Substances have higher boiling and melting points than nonpolar molecules of similar size $100° <$ mp $< 600°$
Example	Cl_2, CH_4, N_2, O_2, F_2, Br_2, He, Ar	ICl, SO_2, $BiBr_3$, AlI_3, SeO_3

14:3   LIGANDS

One of the most important properties of polar molecules is their behavior toward positive ions in solution. As an ionic compound dissolves in water, its ions become hydrated. The surface ions of the crystal become surrounded by polar H_2O molecules that adhere to the surface. The water molecule-ion clusters formed enter solution. The stability of these clusters is greatest when they have at their center a small ion of high charge. Since positive ions are usually smaller than negative ions, the clusters with which we are concerned have a positive ion at the center. When polar molecules or negative ions cluster around a central positive ion, a **complex ion** is formed. Complex ions are widely used in analytical chemistry.

FIGURE 14-5. When an ionic substance dissolves in water, the molecules cluster around the ions forming complex ions.

FIGURE 14-6. PtCl$_6{}^{2-}$ is a complex ion having an octahedral shape. Chloride ions are the ligands. Complexes with a coordination number of four may be square planar or tetrahedral.

The polar molecules or negative ions that are attached to the central positive ion are known as **ligands.** The number of ligands around a central positive ion in a complex is called the **coordination number.** By far, the most common coordination number found in complexes is 6. These complex ions are described as octahedral. The ligands may be thought of as lying at the vertices of a regular octahedron with the central positive ion in the middle. PtCl$_6{}^{2-}$ is an example of an octahedral complex.

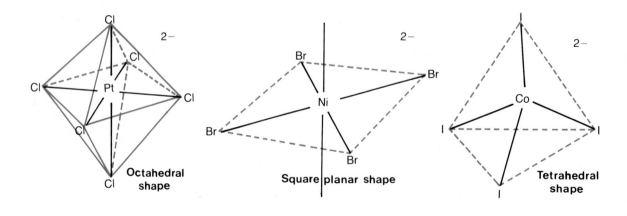

The coordination number 4 is also common. These complexes may be square-planar, with the ligands at the corners of a square and the central positive ion in the center. Others may be tetrahedral, with the ligands at the vertices of a regular tetrahedron and the central positive ion in the middle. Complexes of Ni^{2+}, Pd^{2+}, and Pt^{2+} are usually planar if the coordination number is four. These elements all have electron configurations ending in d^8. They should have five orbitals available: one s, three p, and one d. However, the d orbital turns out to be an antibonding orbital and is oriented perpendicular to the plane of the other four orbitals. An example of a square planar complex is $NiBr_4^{2-}$. A typical tetrahedral complex is CoI_4^{2-}, Figure 14-6.

> The number of coordinated groups is determined in part by the size and charge of the central ion. However, coordination numbers cannot at present be predicted from purely theoretical considerations.

The coordination number 2 is found in complexes of Ag^+, Au^+, and Hg^{2+}. Complex ions with coordination number 2 are always linear. The ligands are always located at the ends and the positive ion in the middle of a straight line. An example is $Ag(CN)_2^-$.

> Complexes with a coordination number of 2 are always linear.

$$NC—Ag—CN^-$$

Ligands can be either molecules or negative ions. Molecular ligands are always polar and always have an unshared pair of electrons that can be shared with the central ion. The most common ligand is water. The hydrated compounds mentioned in Chapter 5 are composed of positive ions surrounded by water ligands and the negative ions. Ammonia, NH_3, is also a common ligand. Many negative ions can also act as ligands in complexes. Some of the most important are the following: fluoride, F^-; chloride, Cl^-; bromide, Br^-; iodide, I^-; cyanide, CN^-; thiocyanate, CNS^-; and oxalate $C_2O_4^{2-}$.

> Water is the most common ligand.

Oxalate ion as bidentate ligand.

Three oxalate ions in octahedral complex.

FIGURE 14-7. The oxalate ion is a bidentate ligand. Three oxalate ions surrounding a central ion form an octahedral complex.

The oxalate ion has two of its oxygen atoms attached to the positive ion. Such a ligand is called bidentate ("two-toothed"). A bidentate ligand attaches at two points. Therefore, two bidentate ligands can form a tetrahedral complex. Three bidentate ligands can form an octahedral complex. Tridentate and quadridentate ligands are also known.

> A bidentate ligand attaches at two points.

FIGURE 14-8. The EDTA ion (ethylenediamminetetraacetate) is hexadentate. When added to hard water, EDTA forms a complex with Ca^{2+}. This procedure is used as a test for hard water.

Ca(EDTA)$^{2-}$

EDTA ion

14:4   ISOMERS OF COMPLEXES

Complex ions can exhibit isomerism because different ligands can have uniquely different arrangements.

It is possible to have more than one kind of ligand in the same complex. For example, platinum(IV) may form an octahedral complex with four ammonia molecules and two chloride ions. This complex ion has the formula $[Pt(NH_3)_4Cl_2]^{2+}$. The coordination number is 6. Since two ligands are of one kind and four are of another kind, there are two uniquely different ways of arranging the ligands. These arrangments are shown in Figure 14-9. Note that in one structure, the chloride ions are at opposite corners of the octahedron, while in the other they are at adjacent corners. Thus, there are *cis* and *trans* isomers of $[Pt(NH_3)_4Cl_2]^{2+}$. The two complexes differ slightly in color and solubility.

Another example of isomerism in complexes is Co(NH$_3$)$_4$Cl$_2$.

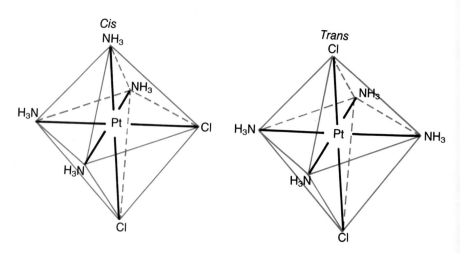

FIGURE 14-9. The [Pt(NH$_3$)$_4$Cl$_2$]$^{2+}$ complex exhibits *cis-trans* isomerism.

14:5 NAMING COMPLEXES

In naming a complex ion, the ligands are named first, followed by the name of the central ion. Each type of ligand is preceded by a prefix designating the number of molecules or ions of that particular ligand present in the complex. The prefixes used are *di-*, *tri-*, *tetra-*, *penta-*, and *hexa-*. The names of some of the common ligands are given in Table 14-3.

Complex ions are named in the following order.
1. negative ligands
2. molecular ligands
3. central ion
4. *-ate* ending, if the ion is negative
5. Roman numeral, if needed

Table 14-3

Some Common Ligands			
Ligand	**Name**	**Ligand**	**Name**
OH^-	hydroxo	$S_2O_3^{2-}$	thiosulfato
Br^-	bromo	$C_2O_4^{2-}$	oxalato
Cl^-	chloro	H_2O	aquo
F^-	fluoro	NH_3	ammine
I^-	iodo	CO	carbonyl
S^{2-}	thio	NO	nitrosyl
CN^-	cyano		

BACKGROUND: A more extensive list may be found in the IUPAC report, *Nomenclature of Inorganic Chemistry.*

The order given in the table represents the order in which the ligands appear in a name. Note that negative ions are named before molecules. The name of the complex ion ends in -ate if the complex as a whole possesses a negative charge. If the central ion has more than one possible oxidation number, a Roman numeral in parentheses must follow the name of the central ion.

EXAMPLE: Naming Complex Ions

Name the complex ion with the formula $Cr(NH_3)_5Cl^{2+}$.

Solving Process:
The two ligands are the chloride ion and ammonia molecules. The negative ion is named first.

one negative ion: chloro-
five molecules: -pentaammine-

Chromium, the central ion, has more than one oxidation number. Write its oxidation number in parentheses after its name. The ending on the word chromium remains unchanged because the ion as a whole has positive charge.

central ion: -chromium(III)

The name of the complex ion is written as one word.

chloropentaamminechromium(III) ion

Table 14-4

Latin Stems Used in Metal Complexes	
Metal	**Latin Stem**
copper	cuprate
gold	aurate
iron	ferrate
lead	plumbate
silver	argentate
tin	stannate

Note that it is possible to have a complex with a net charge of zero in a coordination compound.

If two more chloride ions are added to the ion named in the example we obtain a compound with the formula $[Cr(NH_3)_5Cl]Cl_2$. Note that when a question about composition could arise, the whole complex is placed in brackets. This compound would be named chloropentamminechromium(III) chloride. The following examples further illustrate this method.

SiF_6^{2-}	hexafluorosilicate(IV) ion
$PtCl_6^{2-}$	hexachloroplatinate(IV) ion
$Ni(NH_3)_6Br_2$	hexaamminenickel(II) bromide
$Na_2Sn(OH)_6$	sodium hexahydroxostannate(IV)
$Ag_3Fe(CN)_6$	silver hexacyanoferrate(III)

Note that Latin stems are used for some metals. Some of these Latin stems are given in Table 14-4.

PROBLEMS

2. Name the following complex ions.

a. PtI_6^{2-}
b. $Cd(NH_3)_2^{2+}$
c. GeF_6^{2-}
d. $Cr(H_2O)_4^{2+}$
e. $Fe(CN)_6^{3-}$
f. $Fe(CN)_6^{4-}$
g. $Co(NH_3)_6^{2+}$
h. $PtCl_6^{2-}$
i. $Ni(NH_3)_6^{2+}$
j. $IrCl_6^{2-}$

3. Write formulas for the following complex ions.

a. tetraiodoaurate(III)
b. tetraammineplatinum(II)
c. tetracyanoaurate(III)
d. hexachloropalladate(IV)
e. hexaaquoiridium(III)
f. octocyanotungstate(V)
g. hexaamminecobalt(III)
h. hexafluoroaluminate
i. dichlorodiamminepalladium(II)
j. tetraamminecadmium

4. Name the following complex ions.

a. $Ir(NH_3)_5Cl^{2+}$
b. $Pd(NH_3)_4^{2+}$
c. $Sb(OH)_6$
d. $PdCl_4^{2-}$
e. $Fe(C_2O_4)_3^{3-}$
f. $Cu(NH_3)_6^{2+}$

5. Write formulas for the following complex ions.

a. pentacyanocarbonylferrate(II)
b. pentacarbonylruthenium(0)
c. tetrabromodiammineplatinate(IV)
d. dicyanocuprate(I)
e. chloroaquotetraamminecobalt(III)
f. hexaamminechromium(III)

6. Write formulas for the following complex ions.

a. tetrabromogallate(III)
b. hexafluorogallate(III)
c. trithiosulfatomercurate(II)
d. hexachloroosmate(IV)
e. hexabromoiridate(III)
f. pentaaquonitrosyliron(II)

2. a. hexiodoplatinate(IV) ion
   b. diamminecadmium ion
   c. hexafluorogermanate(IV) ion
   d. tetraquochromium(II) ion
   e. hexacyanoferrate(III) ion
   f. hexacyanoferrate(II) ion
   g. hexamminecobalt(II) ion
   h. hexachloroplatinate(IV) ion
   i. hexamminenickel(II) ion
   j. hexachloroiridate(IV) ion

3. a. AuI_4^-
   b. $Pt(NH_3)_4^{2+}$
   c. $Au(CN)_4^-$
   d. $PdCl_6^{2-}$
   e. $Ir(H_2O)_6^{3+}$
   f. $W(CN)_8^{3-}$
   g. $Co(NH_3)_6^{3+}$
   h. AlF_6^{3-}
   i. $Pd(NH_3)_2Cl_2$
   j. $Cd(NH_3)_4^{2+}$

4. a. chloropentamineiridium(III) ion
   b. tetraamminepalladium(II) ion
   c. hexahydroxoantimonate(V) ion
   d. tetrachloropalladate(II) ion
   e. trioxalatoferrate(III) ion
   f. hexamminecopper(II) ion

5. a. $FeCO(CN)_5^{3-}$
   b. $Ru(CO)_5$
   c. $Pt(NH_3)_2Br_4$
   d. $Cu(CN)_2^-$
   e. $Co(NH_3)_4(H_2O)Cl^{2+}$
   f. $Cr(NH_3)_6^{3+}$

6. a. $GaBr_4^-$
   b. GaF_6^{3-}
   c. $Hg(S_2O_3)_3^{4-}$
   d. $OsCl_6^{2-}$
   e. $IrBr_6^{3-}$
   f. $Fe(NO)(H_2O)_5^{2+}$

14:6 BONDING IN COMPLEXES

Almost any positive ion might be expected to form complexes. In practice, the complexes of the metals of the first two groups in the periodic table have little stability. By far the most important and most interesting complexes are those of the transition metals. The transition metals have partially filled *d* orbitals that can become involved in bonding. These positive ions are small because of the strong attractive force of the nucleus for the inner electrons. They also have high oxidation numbers. The combination of small size and high charge results in a high charge density on the central ion. Such a high charge density is particularly favorable to complex ion formation.

Transition metals have partially filled *d* orbitals and high charge density.

Transition metals form complex ions.

FIGURE 14-10. The colors of many gemstones are due to small quantities of transition metal ions.

In an isolated ion of one of the metals of the first transition series, the five 3*d* orbitals are degenerate (have the same energy). No energy is absorbed if an electron is transferred from one of the 3*d* orbitals to another. However, in the complex, the ligands affect the energies of the different 3*d* orbitals. In an octahedral complex, the *d* orbitals are split into

FIGURE 14-11. The copper tetrammine complex is highly colored as the result of the splitting of the *d* orbitals. Light energy is absorbed as electrons move from the lower to higher energy orbitals.

high energy orbitals

ENERGY

degenerate *d* orbitals
of a free metal ion

Δ Energy

low energy orbitals

a higher energy group of two orbitals and a lower energy group of three orbitals. Many complex ions have intense colors. The blue color that is typical of solutions of copper(II) compounds is an example. This blue color is due to the $Cu(H_2O)_6^{2+}$ ion. The colors of complexes arise from electron transitions between the split d orbitals. The split represents only a small energy gap. As the electrons move from the lower to the higher energy group, they absorb light energy.

Ligands are either negative ions or polar molecules, while the central atom is a positive ion. These facts suggest that the bonding forces in a complex are electrostatic, just as they are in a salt crystal. In fact, there are strong similarities between the structures of salts and the structures of complex ions. On the other hand, the ligands have an unshared pair of electrons that they are capable of donating. The central ion always has unoccupied orbitals into which electron pairs might be placed. This combination suggests that the bonds are covalent. The name **coordinate covalent bond** has been given to covalent bonds in which both of the electrons in the shared pair come from the same atom. The chemistry of coordinate covalent bonds is exactly like any other covalent bond. The bonds of most complex ions have characteristics of both covalent and ionic bonding types. The covalent character dominates.

Zinc, as a central ion, does not have available orbitals due to d^{10} configuration. Thus, it is colorless.

Coordinate covalent bond forms when both electrons in the shared pair come from the same atom.

Complex ions form predominantly through covalent bonding but have ionic character also.

Results from microwave spectroscopy show that all 4 bonds in NH_4^+ are the same. Thus, there is really no difference between a covalent bond and a coordinate covalent bond.

FIGURE 14-12. The color change for the reaction is caused by the replacement of water ligands by chloride ions according to the equation: $[Co(H_2O)_6]^{2+} + 4Cl^- \rightarrow [CoCl_4]^{2-} + 6H_2O$.

14:7 REACTIONS OF COMPLEXES

Complex ions undergo many different kinds of reactions. One of the most common reactions is an exchange of ligands. In water, the cadmium ion exists as the tetraaquo complex, $Cd(H_2O)_4^{2+}$. If a large amount of ammonia is added to the solution, the following reaction occurs.

$$Cd(H_2O)_4^{2+} + 4NH_3 \rightleftharpoons Cd(NH_3)_4^{2+} + 4H_2O$$

The reaction takes place in four steps.

One common reaction that complex ions undergo is ligand replacement.
Multiple step reaction mechanisms and equilibrium constants will be studied in Chapter 23.

$$Cd(H_2O)_4{}^{2+} + NH_3 \rightleftarrows Cd(NH_3)(H_2O)_3{}^{2+} + H_2O$$
$$Cd(NH_3)(H_2O)_3{}^{2+} + NH_3 \rightleftarrows Cd(NH_3)_2(H_2O)_2{}^{2+} + H_2O$$
$$Cd(NH_3)_2(H_2O)_2{}^{2+} + NH_3 \rightleftarrows Cd(NH_3)_3(H_2O)^{2+} + H_2O$$
$$Cd(NH_3)_3(H_2O)^{2+} + NH_3 \rightleftarrows Cd(NH_3)_4{}^{2+} + H_2O$$

The double arrow indicates the reaction is reversible.

Since each step can go in either direction, a measurement for the tendency for each step can be made. However, the tendency for the reaction to occur, called an equilibrium constant (Section 23:8) is usually given for the overall reaction. For example, the equilibrium constant for the reaction

$$Cd^{2+} + 4CN^- \rightleftarrows Cd(CN)_4{}^{2-}$$

is 1.23×10^{50}. This number indicates that there is a strong attraction between Cd^{2+} and CN^-. There is a great tendency for the reaction to occur.

Chromatography is a separation method which depends on polarity of substances.

14:8 FRACTIONATION

Sometimes it is necessary to separate several materials from a mixture and identify them individually. These separations are called fractions because they are parts of the whole. The overall separation of parts from a whole by any process may be called **fractionation.** A convenient method of separation based on the polarity of substances is a process called chromatography (kroh muh TAHG ruh fee). The name **chromatography** (writing for color) comes from the fact that the fractions are often different colors. Gas chromatography does not involve color. However, since it also depends upon fractionation, the name chromatography is still applied.

In chromatography, a mobile phase containing a mixture of substances is allowed to pass over a stationary phase that has an attraction for polar materials. The **mobile phase** consists of the mixture to be separated dissolved in a fluid (liquid or gas). The **stationary phase** consists of a solid or liquid adhering to the surface of a solid. The different substances in the mixture will travel at different rates due to their varying polarity. There are several polarity considerations in determining the rate at which each component of the mixture will migrate. A polar substance will have some attraction for the solvent as well as an attraction for the stationary phase. The stationary phase will attract some of the substances more strongly than others. The slowest migrating substance will be the one with the greatest attraction for the stationary phase. The fastest migrating substance will be the one with the least attraction for the stationary phase. Thus, they can be separated.

FIGURE 14-13. The packing components for a typical chromatography column are shown.

14:9   COLUMN CHROMATOGRAPHY

BACKGROUND: Suggestions for adsorbents: Aluminum oxide, Fuller's earth, calcium oxide, calcium carbonate, calcium phosphate, talc, and starch. Suggested solvents, beginning with the least polar: Petroleum ether, cyclohexane, CS_2, ether, acetone, chloroform, alcohol, water, pyridine, and acid.

Column chromatography is used for extremely delicate separations. Complex substances such as vitamins, proteins, and hormones, not easily separated by other methods, can be separated by chromatography. In column chromatography, a glass or plastic column is used to carry out the separation. The column is packed with a stationary phase such as calcium carbonate. Other packings used are magnesium or sodium carbonate, activated charcoal, ion exchange resins, clays, gels, and many organic compounds.

FIGURE 14-14. The chemist in (a) is using column chromatography to separate the components of a cosmetic. The column chromatogram in (b) shows the separation of plant pigments into chlorophylls and xanthophylls.

b

FIGURE 14-15. A mixture of dichromate and permanganate ions can be separated by column chromatography.

The mobile phase with the material to be fractionated is added to the top of the column. Then fresh solvent is poured onto the top of the column and allowed to percolate through the column. The solvent may be water, ammonia, an acid, an alcohol, or some other organic or inorganic substance.

Each substance in the mobile phase migrates down the tube at a different rate and the substances are separated. The rate of travel depends upon the attraction of each substance for the stationary phase, its attraction for the solvent, and the solvent concentration. If the substance has a high attraction for the stationary phase, only a high concentration of solvent will dislodge it. As the solvent moves down the tube, it becomes less concentrated, and the solute becomes more attracted to the stationary phase again. Those substances with less attraction for the stationary phase are carried farther, even by the less concentrated solvent. By constant percolation, the substances are separated into zones. A sample chromatogram is shown in Figure 14-15. In the column shown, dichromate ions and permanganate ions are being separated on a packing of aluminum oxide. The solvent being used is dilute nitric acid. As you can see, the dichromate is more strongly attracted to the stationary phase so it moves down the column more slowly.

After separation, it may be necessary to recover the material in each separate zone for identification. One method involves forcing the zones out the bottom of the tube, one at a time. The substance in each zone is dissolved and then recovered by evaporation. A second method uses solvents of increasing polarity until each zone comes out the bottom along with the solvent. Identification is then made by any number of methods.

14:10 SURFACE CHROMATOGRAPHY

Paper chromatography is a form of chromatography in which the separations are carried out on paper rather than in glass columns. Strips of paper are placed in a box or bell jar in which the atmosphere is saturated with water vapor or solvent vapor. A drop of the solution to be separated is placed at the top of the paper. The paper is then overlapped into solvent at the top of the box. The solvent moves down the paper by capillary action, separating the constituents of the drop. The paper may be placed in solvent at the bottom of the box. In this case, the drop of the solution would be placed at the bottom of the paper and the solvent would ascend the paper. In either case, the separations are seen as a series of colored spots on the paper strip. If the separated fractions are colorless, they can be sprayed with solutions that will produce colored compounds. Some of these compounds may fluoresce under ultraviolet light.

For example, consider the separation of Ag^+, Pb^{2+}, and Hg_2^{2+}. Let us see how it might be done with a paper chromatogram. The chromatogram is prepared, using 1-butanol and H_2O at a ratio of $^{85}/_{15}$ solvent and a drop of the solution to be separated. The solvent will move to within 1 or 2 cm of the end of the paper. Then the chromatogram is sprayed with

Paper chromatography uses strips of paper rather than columns.

DEMONSTRATION: Obtain a large test tube and a cork. Attach a strip of filter paper to the cork. Place a little water and isopropyl alcohol in the bottom of the test tube. Arrange the filter paper so the bottom tip is immersed in the solution at the bottom of the test tube when the cork is inserted. Place a drop of ink on the filter paper just above the solution level and let the tube stand upright. Observe.

FIGURE 14-16. The chromatography equipment shown includes a drying rack, chromatogram chamber, and dipping tank.

potassium chromate. A brick-red spot (Ag_2CrO_4) that fades to a pale yellow when held over ammonia indicates Ag^+. A bright yellow spot ($PbCrO_4$) that becomes orange with ammonia indicates Pb^{2+}. An orange or brown spot that blackens with ammonia indicates Hg_2^{2+}.

If further separation between spots is needed, the paper can be turned 90°. Each spot is then used as an originating spot. The same solvent, or a second solvent, may be used. For example, a solution containing Ba, Pb, Cu, U, and Fe ions could be resolved by the use of 1-butanol/water first. Then the paper may be turned and ethanol/6M HCl at a solvent ratio of $^{90}/_{10}$ used as the second solvent.

Paper chromatography is simple, fast, and has a high resolving power. This method can be used to separate the constituents of blood, urine, and antibiotics. One great difficulty with paper chromatography separation arises out of its extremely small scale. Quantitative determinations are difficult. In addition, a control is needed to determine which spots belong to which compound. Even with these difficulties, the method is still extremely useful. One way of extending the usefulness of paper chromatography is to combine it, when possible, with an electric field. By using both solvent and electric field, it is possible to separate substances that are inseparable by either method alone.

BACKGROUND: The development of specially treated papers such as cellulose phosphate has made this method even more valuable.

FIGURE 14-17. Paper chromatograms show the following separations: (a) Zn^{2+}, Co^{2+}, Mn^{2+}, Ni^{2+}, (b) Co^{2+}, Cu^{2+}, Ni^{2+}, (c) and (d) both show Co^{2+}, Cu^{2+} Fe^{3+}, Mn^{2+}, Ni^{2+}, Zn^{2+} using different locating reagents.

a   b   c   d

Thin layer chromatography combines some of the techniques of both column and paper chromatography. A glass or plastic plate is coated with a very thin layer of stationary phase, as is used in column chromatography. A spot of an unknown mixture is applied as in paper chromatography. The glass plate is placed in an atmosphere of solvent vapor and solvent. The procedure from this point is just the same as that for paper chromatography. The thin layer technique is used frequently in separating biological materials.

SUGGESTION: A number of reagent manufacturers presently produce excellent demonstration kits for thin layer chromatography.

TYPICAL CHROMATOGRAPHS

Synthesized Spearmint 0:1 600   Natural Spearmint (Midwest Origin)

FIGURE 14-18. These drawings of gas chromatograms show how closely synthetic spearmint flavoring matches natural spearmint oil.

14:11 GAS CHROMATOGRAPHY

Volatile liquids and mixtures of gases or vapors can also be analyzed by a chromatographic process. The gases to be analyzed are carried along by an inert gas such as helium in the mobile phase. The gases are fractionated on a stationary phase by a method similar to column chromatography. They are then carried by the inert helium through a tube fitted with an electrocouple. The varying amounts of contamination in the helium produce varying amounts of current. These variations are recorded by a needle on a moving sheet of graph paper. The amount of gas present in each fraction can be determined from the area under the curve.

A common test performed by environmental scientists is analysis of agricultural run-off for pesticide residues (organic compounds). Figure 14-19 shows such a chromatogram.

Gas chromatography is used to analyze volatile liquids and mixtures of gases.

Gas chromatography has been used mostly in organic chemistry because inorganic substances only vaporize at higher temperatures.

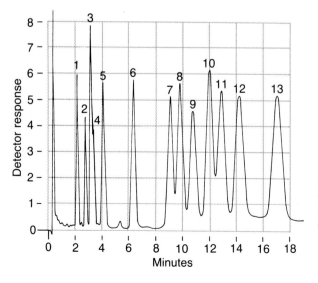

1. α-BHC
2. Lindane
3. β-BHC
4. Heptachlor
5. Aldrin
6. Heptachlor epoxide
7. p,p'-DDE
8. Dieldrin
9. o,p'-DDD (TDE)
10. Endrin
11. o,p'-DDT
12. p,p-DDD (TDE)
13. p,p-DDT

FIGURE 14-19. This drawing shows the pesticides present in a sample of run-off water.

BIOGRAPHY   Jokichi Takamine (1854-1922)

It is not often that industrial chemists receive the same fame that research chemists do. However, Jokichi Takamine, a Japanese industrial chemist, had many "firsts" in the field of chemistry. He was the first to make a successful separation of the starch-hydrolyzing enzyme called diastase. As a result of this accomplishment, he made enzyme production commercially feasible.

At the age of 30, while in the United States, he learned of the use of superphosphate as a fertilizer. He returned to his native country and soon started an artificial fertilizer company to use the process in Japan. In 1901, he was the first to isolate pure adrenalin, which he added to the product line of his manufacturing laboratory.

Eleven years later, as a tribute both to his native country and his adopted country, the United States, he convinced the mayor of Tokyo to send the first cherry trees as a gift to the United States. Each year when these trees bloom along the Potomac, they reflect the social consciousness of a chemist who loved both countries.

TECHNOLOGY AND CHEMISTRY

14:12 Salt

When we use the word salt in normal conversation, we generally mean sodium chloride. In addition to its use with food, salt is used for a variety of purposes by nearly all chemical industries. Its physical and chemical properties, as well as its availability, make it suitable for a variety of uses.

When salt is scattered on an icy sidewalk, the salt lowers the freezing point of water. Thus, ice melts as long as the air temperature is not too low. Salt is not effective at extremely low temperatures. (See Chapter 22.)

Water softening involves replacing hard water ions such as Ca^{2+} and Fe^{2+} with Na^+ ions. When the sodium ions in the softening agent are depleted, they may be restored by soaking the material in a concentrated brine or NaCl solution.

Salt is applied to the flesh side of animal skins as the first step in making leather. The salt destroys any bacteria that could rot the skins.

Salt is an essential component of the diet. Most body fluids contain sodium ions, although the concentration inside cells is low. The ratio between sodium ions and potassium ions must be maintained within fairly narrow limits for good health. The ratio between these two ions is considerably different inside and outside nerve cells. See Table 11-1. Nerve impulses are transmitted in part by varying these ratios.

During competition, athletes tend to perspire freely. That process is a normal function that cools the body. Perspiration consists of salt as well as water. A perspiring athlete will often drink water to replace lost fluid. Failure to replace lost salt causes an upset in the Na^+/K^+ ratio. As a result, the nerve impulses are disrupted and the athlete suffers muscle spasms or cramps. Many athletes now consume specially prepared drinks designed to maintain the ion balance and restore lost fluids.

Though most salt is mined, about 12% comes from the evaporation of salt water. Mines in Louisiana and Texas produce about half the total salt mined in the United States. Though some salt is mined as a solid, most is obtained by pumping water into the mine. The water dissolves the salt and the solution is piped to the surface. The salt solution, called brine, is then evaporated to recover the solid. The recovery process typically produces 98-99% pure sodium chloride.

The abundance of sodium chloride makes it a readily available raw material for the production of many other chemicals, such as sodium carbonate, sodium hydroxide, sodium sulfate, chlorine, and hydrochloric acid.

SUMMARY

1. A polar bond is one in which a shared pair of electrons is attracted more strongly to one of the atoms. **14:1**

2. van der Waals forces are the net result of dipole-dipole, dipole-induced dipole, and dispersion effects. **14:2**

3. A complex ion is composed of a central positive ion and molecular or negative ion ligands. **14:3**

4. The number of ligands surrounding the central ion is the coordination number of a complex. **14:3**

5. Complex ions that contain more than one type of ligand may exhibit geometric isomerism. **14:4**

6. Small positive ions with a large nuclear attractive force form excellent central ions. The transition metal ions are good examples of these. **14:6**

7. The bonds of complex ions have both ionic and covalent bonding characteristics. **14:6**

8. Chromatography is a method of separating substances into identifiable chemical fractions by differences in their polarity. **14:8-14:11**

VOCABULARY

polar covalent **14:1**
dipole **14:1**
van der Waals forces **14:2**
intramolecular forces **14:2**
intermolecular forces **14:2**
dipole-dipole forces **14:2**
induced dipole **14:2**
dipole-induced dipole forces **14:2**
temporary dipole **14:2**
dispersion forces **14:2**
complex ion **14:3**

ligands **14:3**
coordination number **14:3**
coordinate covalent bond **14:6**
fractionation **14:8**
chromatography **14:8**
mobile phase **14:8**
stationary phase **14:8**
column chromatography **14:9**
paper chromatography **14:10**
thin layer chromatography **14:10**

PROBLEMS

1. b, a, e, f, c, d
2. van der Waals forces
3. octahedral

5. size and charge
6. empty d orbitals to accept e⁻, large charge-to-radius ratio
7. a. pentafluorogallate(III) ion
   b. tetrathioantimonate(V) ion
   c. dicyanoaurate(I) ion
   d. tetracyanoaurate(III) ion
   e. dichlorotetraaquochromium(III) ion

9. X₂A, X₂A

1. The following pairs of atoms are all covalently bonded. Arrange the pairs in order of decreasing polarity of the bonds using Table 11-6.
   a. phosphorus and sodium
   b. fluorine and nitrogen
   c. nitrogen and oxygen
   d. arsenic and iodine
   e. chlorine and tellurium
   f. antimony and sulfur

2. What forces hold molecular substances in the liquid and solid states?

3. What shape would you expect the $[Al(H_2O)_6]^{3+}$ complex to have? Sketch it.

4. Define: central ion, ligand, coordination number.

5. What factors determine coordination number?

6. Why do transition metals make good central ions?

7. Name the following complex ions.
   a. GaF_5^{2-} **b.** SbS_4^{3-} **c.** $Au(CN)_2^-$ **d.** $Au(CN)_4^-$ **e.** $Cr(H_2O)_4Cl_2^+$

8. How are column and paper chromatography similar? How are they different?

9. The dipole moment of compound X_2A equals 1.84×10^{-30} C·m. Compound X_3D has a dipole moment of 1.50×10^{-30} C·m. Which compound is more polar? If they have approximately the same formula mass, which compound would you predict to have the higher melting point?

10. Considering what you know about forces between molecules, why do all of the elements in Group VIIIA (18) exist as gases at room temperature?

11. Carbon dioxide has a dipole moment of 0. The dipole moment of sulfur dioxide is 1.6×10^{-30} C·m. Draw structural diagrams for both molecules and use them to explain the difference in polarity.

1. pyramidal, tetrahedral
2. s-spherical p-dumbbell

REVIEW

1. What shape would you predict for the NI_3 molecule? For CCl_4?
2. Describe the shapes of s and p orbitals.

3. Explain why carbon with a predicted outer configuration of $2s^2 2p^2$ can form four equivalent bonds.

4. Why is benzene more stable than a compound with three single and three double bonds?

5. What shape would you predict for H_2Se? Why?

6. From molecular orbital theory, predict the stability of the He_2^+ ion.

7. Draw as many isomers of C_5H_{10} as you can. Hint: There are 12 isomers and the compound contains one $C{=}C$ double bond.

8. Predict the $N{-}C{=}O$ bond angle in $(NH_2)_2CO$.

9. Draw isomers for compounds with the formula C_6H_6.

10. Draw resonance structures for SO_3.

3. The s and three p orbitals hybridize to four orbitals of equivalent energy, containing one electron each.

4. The π electrons are delocalized among the carbon atoms.

5. bent, the two unshared pairs of electrons push the shared pairs toward each other.

8. 120°

ONE MORE STEP

1. In preparing paper chromatograms, identification of unknowns is aided by the measurement of R_f values. These values concern the distance an unknown has advanced compared to the distance the solvent has advanced. Research the chromatographic process to determine how these values are useful in identification.

2. Look up the structure of chlorophyll and hemoglobin. Determine the central ion and its coordination number. What is the coordinated group, and what is its spatial orientation about the central ion?

3. Medicine and industry use certain materials called chelating agents. What are they and how are they related to complexes?

4. A number of organic compounds are used in the analysis of inorganic ions because they form complex ions. Investigate the substances used in detecting nickel, aluminum, and zirconium by such a method.

5. Try to separate the pigments of spinach leaves using paper chromatography.

READINGS

Nassau, Kurt, "The Causes of Color," *Scientific American*, Vol. 243, No. 4(October 1980), pp. 124-154.

A particle of a solid, liquid, or gas can be compared to a tennis ball in constant motion. A particle of matter constantly collides with other particles and the walls of its container just as the tennis ball collides with the court surface and rackets. The velocity of a tennis ball can be changed if a player increases the force on the ball. How can the velocity of a particle be increased? How does a change in velocity affect a particle?

KINETIC THEORY

GOALS:
• You will gain an under-
standing of kinetic theory.
• You will use the kinetic
theory to describe the effects of energy and pres-
sure on matter.
• You will differentiate
among the four states of
matter.

Chapter 15 uses the kinetic theory to describe the effects of energy and pressure on the four states of matter.

DEMONSTRATION: Place 5 to 10 glass beads in a petri dish on the overhead projector. Cover the dish and move it back and forth to show the activity of molecules. Also open a bottle of HCl and place it near an open bottle of NH_3(aq). The formation of the NH_4Cl smoke further demonstrates the kinetic theory. **CAUTION:** *Handle HCl and NH_3(aq) with care. Perform demonstration in a well-ventilated room.*

The **kinetic theory** explains the effect of temperature and pressure on matter. First, let us consider some basic assumptions of the theory. *All matter is composed of small particles* (atoms, ions, or molecules). *These small particles are in constant motion.* Finally, *all collisions between particles are perfectly elastic.* Perfectly elastic means that there is no change in the total kinetic energy of two particles before and after their collision. It may be difficult to imagine that all particles in a great structure such as the Golden Gate Bridge are in constant motion. However, as we shall see, many of the properties of matter are the result of such motion. As early as the mid-seventeenth century, the English inventor Robert Hooke proposed a kinetic theory. He predicted that there were particles in nature that were in constant motion. In order to have some concept of size for the quantities involved, we will first discuss oxygen.

The kinetic theory is based on three assumptions.
1. All matter is composed of particles.
2. The particles of matter are in constant motion.
3. All collisions are perfectly elastic.

15:1 OXYGEN MOLECULES IN MOTION

At room temperature (25°C), the average speed of an oxygen molecule is 443 m/s. This speed is equivalent to just over 1700 kilometers per hour. At this speed, the molecules collide with each other frequently. We can determine the average number of collisions a molecule undergoes in a unit of time. We do so by finding the average distance a molecule travels before colliding with another molecule. This distance is called the **mean free path** of the molecule. For oxygen at 25°C, the mean free path is 106 nm. The diameter of the oxygen molecule is about 0.339 nm. Thus, an oxygen molecule at 25°C will travel, on the average, about 314 times its own diameter before colliding with another molecule.

Even at room temperature molecules are moving extremely fast.

The mean free path of a molecule is the average distance a molecule travels between collisions.

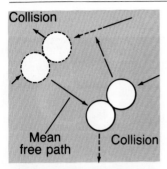

FIGURE 15-1. The mean free path of a molecule is the distance it travels between collisions.

Gas pressure results from collision of molecules with the walls of a container.

SUGGESTION: Emphasize that air pressure is equal in all directions in a container.

101.325 kPa is the average normal air pressure at sea level.

1 newton (N) = 1 kg·m/s^2

Each molecule will have a little over four and a half billion collisions per second. We give these figures for oxygen as examples of the speed, the distance of travel, and the number of molecular collisions in a gas. These factors vary with the temperature and the mass of the particles composing the gas.

15:2   PRESSURE

Besides colliding with each other, gas molecules collide with the walls of the container in which the gas is confined. When a gas molecule collides with the wall of a container, it exerts a force on the container. It is the force of collision and the number of collisions with the walls of a container that cause gas **pressure,** Figure 15-2. This pressure is measured in terms of the force per unit area.

The molecules and atoms of the gases present in the air are constantly hitting the surface of the Earth and everything on it. As a result, you and everything surrounding you are subject to a certain pressure from the molecules of the air. Air pressure has been used as a scientific standard of pressure. The standard is defined as the average pressure of the air at sea level under normal conditions. Since conditions in the air depend upon many weather factors, it is difficult to define "normal" conditions at sea level. Therefore, the standard has been defined in terms of a system that can be reproduced in the laboratory. It is 101.325 kilopascals (kPa). One **pascal** is a pressure of one newton per square meter (N/m^2). We will generally employ units of kilopascals.

Volume (a) = 2 Volume (b)
Pressure (a) = ½ Pressure (b)

FIGURE 15-2. If the volume of a gas is halved, the number of collisions with the walls of the container doubles. Thus, the pressure in container (b) is twice that of container (a).

15:3 MEASURING PRESSURE

In measuring gas pressure, an instrument called a **manometer** (mah NAHM uh tuhr) is used. Two types of manometers are shown in Figure 15-3. In the "open" type, air exerts pressure on the column of liquid in one arm of the U-tube. The gas being studied exerts pressure on the other arm. The difference in liquid level between the two arms is a measure of the gas pressure relative to the air pressure. If you know the density of the liquid in the manometer, you can calculate the pressure difference between the gas and the air.

A manometer is an instrument used to measure pressure.

$P_{gas} = 105$ mm $= 14.0$ kPa

Valve closed

Valve closed

Vacuum

Gas sample

$P_{atm} = 101.3$ kPa

Gas sample

$P_{gas} = 655$ mm $= 87.3$ kPa

105 mm

655 mm

Hg

Hg

101.3 kPa
$-$ 87.3 kPa
14.0 kPa = Pressure of the gas

a

b

FIGURE 15-3. Closed (a) and open arm (b) manometers are used to measure gas pressure.

The "closed" type of manometer has a vacuum above the liquid in one arm. The operation of a closed-arm manometer is independent of air pressure. A closed-arm manometer used to measure atmospheric pressure is called a **barometer.** Most barometers are manufactured with a scale calibrated to read the height of a column of mercury in millimeters. Average air pressure will support a column of mercury 760 mm high. Since average air pressure is defined as 101.325 kPa, then 101.325 kPa = 760

FIGURE 15-4. This barometer (a) is used to measure air pressure in the laboratory. This gauge (b) measures air pressure in tires. A sphygmomanometer (c) is used to measure blood pressure.

a

b

c

mm. By dividing both sides of the equation by 101.325 we find that 1 kPa = 7.50 mm Hg.

Closed-arm manometers can be used to measure actual or "absolute" gas pressure. It is also possible to calculate the absolute pressure of a gas using an open manometer. However, a barometer must be available to measure the atmospheric pressure on the outside arm of the open manometer. The following examples show some typical calculations involving gas pressure.

EXAMPLE: Pressure

The open manometer in Figure 15-3 is filled with mercury. The difference between mercury levels in the two arms is 6 mm. What is the total pressure, in kilopascals, of the gas in the container? The air pressure is 101.3 kPa.

Solving Process:
The mercury is higher in the arm connected to the gas. Thus, the pressure exerted by the gas must be less than that of the air. As a result, we must subtract the pressure of the mercury from the air pressure to get the gas pressure. Before subtracting, however, we must convert the 6 mm difference in height to kilopascals.

$$\frac{6 \text{ mm}}{} \left| \frac{1 \text{ kPa}}{7.50 \text{ mm}} \right. = 0.8 \text{ kPa}$$

Now we can subtract the two pressures.

$$101.3 - 0.8 = 100.5 \text{ kPa}$$

EXAMPLE: Pressure

Suppose the difference in height of the two mercury levels in the closed manometer in Figure 15-3 is 238 mm. What is the pressure in kilopascals of the gas in the container?

Solving Process:
Since the column of mercury is 238 mm high and 7.50 mm of mercury equals 1 kPa, the pressure is

$$\frac{238 \text{ mm}}{} \left| \frac{1 \text{ kPa}}{7.50 \text{ mm}} \right. = 31.7 \text{ kPa}$$

PROBLEMS

1. An open manometer, such as the one in Figure 15-3, is filled with mercury and connected to a container of hydrogen. The mercury level is 62 mm higher in the arm of the tube connected to the gas.

Air pressure is 97.7 kPa. What is the pressure of the hydrogen in kilopascals?

2. A closed manometer like the one in Figure 15-3 is filled with mercury and connected to a container of nitrogen. The difference in the height of mercury in the two arms is 691 mm. What is the pressure of the nitrogen in kilopascals?

3. An open manometer is filled with mercury and connected to a container of oxygen. The level of mercury is 6 mm higher in the arm of the tube connected to the container of oxygen. Air pressure is 100.0 kPa. What is the pressure, in kilopascals, of the oxygen?

4. An open manometer connected to a tank of argon has a mercury level 38 mm higher in the atmospheric arm. If atmospheric pressure is 96.3 kPa, what is the pressure of the argon?

5. A closed manometer is filled with mercury and connected to a container of helium. The difference in the height of mercury in the two arms is 86.0 mm. What is the pressure, in kilopascals, of the helium?

1 kPa = 7.50 mm
1. 89.4 kPa
2. 92.1 kPa
3. 99.2 kPa
4. 101.4 kPa
5. 11.5 kPa

15:4   KINETIC ENERGY AND TEMPERATURE

The average speed of the particles in a gas depends only on the temperature and the mass of the particles. How are temperature and particle mass related?

Kinetic energy is the energy an object possesses because of its motion. Temperature is a measure of that kinetic energy. The average kinetic energy of molecules or atoms in a gas is the same for all particles at a particular temperature. In other words, if two gases are at the same temperature, the average kinetic energies of their particles are equal. The kinetic energy of a particle is equal to $mv^2/2$, where m is its mass and v its velocity. Therefore, at a given temperature, a particle with small mass will

SUGGESTION: Stress that kinetic energy relates to *average* speed of molecules in a sample.

FIGURE 15-5. The cotton on one end of the tube is saturated with concentrated HCl. The cotton at the other end is saturated with $NH_3(aq)$. The formation of NH_4Cl is shown by the white ring in the tube. By noting the position of the ring, can you determine which end of the tube contains HCl?

Particles of samples of gases at the same temperature have the same average kinetic energy.

$$K.E. = \frac{1}{2} mv^2$$

FIGURE 15-6. The first two graphs show the relationships among mass, velocity, and kinetic energy. The third graph shows that in any given sample some particles will have more or less energy than the average particle.

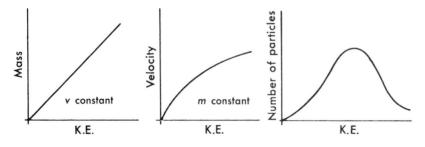

move faster than a particle with large mass. A decrease in the temperature of a substance means the particles of the substance are moving more slowly. An increase in temperature means the particles are moving faster.

In theory, it should be possible to lower the temperature to a point where all molecular motion ceases. The temperature at which all molecular motion should cease is known as **absolute zero.** It is −273.15°C. This value is usually rounded to −273°C.

To make a temperature scale based on absolute zero, scientists have agreed on a system known as the absolute, or **kelvin scale.** The zero point of the kelvin scale is absolute zero. The divisions, or degrees, are the same size as those of the Celsius scale. Therefore,

$$K = °C + 273$$

The kelvin is the SI unit of temperature.

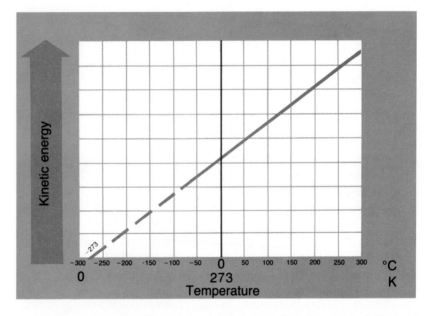

Temperature can be used to determine the direction of flow of energy. Energy always flows from a warmer object to a cooler one. Kinetic theory explains the flow of energy in terms of particle collisions. The particles of the warmer object and the cooler object have unequal kinetic energy. The excess kinetic energy of the particles in the warmer object is passed on to the particles of the cooler object as they collide, Figure 15-8. The particles of the cooler object gradually receive more kinetic energy until the average kinetic energy of both objects is the same. For example, you can feel the air warm near a bowl of hot soup. If left undisturbed the soup and bowl will eventually reach room temperature. Heat is the amount of energy transferred. Heat, like energy, is measured in joules.

FIGURE 15-8. Heat flows from hot objects to cooler ones through a transfer of kinetic energy when particles collide.

PROBLEMS

6. Convert the following temperatures from Celsius to kelvin.

    a. 65°   **b.** 16°   **c.** 48°   **d.** −36°   **e.** −73°

7. Convert the following temperatures from kelvin to Celsius.

    a. 86   **b.** 191   **c.** 533   **d.** 321   **e.** 894

8. Convert the following temperatures from Celsius to kelvin.

    a. 23°   **b.** 58°   **c.** −90°   **d.** 18°   **e.** 25°

9. Convert the following temperatures from kelvin to Celsius.

    a. 872   **b.** 690   **c.** 384   **d.** 20   **e.** 60

10. At 25°C, which of the following gas molecules move fastest?

    a. N_2 **b.** F_2 **c.** CO   **d.** O_2

6. a. 338 K		d. 237 K	
b. 289 K		e. 346 K	
c. 321 K			
7. a. −187°C		d. 48°C	
b. −82°C		e. 621°C	
c. 260°C			
8. a. 296 K		d. 291 K	
b. 331 K		e. 298 K	
c. 183 K			
9. a. 599°C		d. −253°C	
b. 417°C		e. −213°C	
c. 111°C			
10. N_2			

15:5   STATES OF MATTER

Matter exists in four states—solid, liquid, gas, and plasma. Thus far, our discussion of the kinetic theory has been limited to gases. However, kinetic theory can also be used to explain the behavior of solids and liquids. Plasmas are treated as a special case.

Gas particles are independent of each other and move in a straight line. Change of direction occurs only when one particle collides with another, or when a particle collides with the walls of the container. Gas particles, then, travel in a completely random manner. Since they travel until they collide with a neighbor or with the walls of their container, gases assume the shape and volume of their container.

The particles of a liquid have what appears to be a vibratory type of motion. Actually, they are traveling a straight-line path between collisions with near neighbors. The point about which the seeming vibration occurs often shifts as one particle slips past another. These differences in the amount of space between particles allow the particles to change their relative positions continually. Thus, liquids, although they have a definite volume, assume the shape of their container.

In solids, a particle occupies a relatively fixed position in relation to the surrounding particles. A particle of a solid appears to vibrate about a fixed point. Again, the particle is actually traveling a straight-line path between collisions with very near neighbors. For example, a molecule of oxygen gas at 25°C travels an average distance equal to 314 times its own diameter before colliding with another molecule. In a solid, however, the particles are closely packed and travel a distance equal to only a fraction of their diameters before colliding. Unlike liquids, solids have their particles arranged in a definite pattern. Solids, therefore, have both a definite shape and a definite volume.

The physical state of a substance at room temperature and standard atmospheric pressure depends mostly on the bonding in the substance.

Four states of matter: solid, liquid, gas, plasma.

Gas particles travel in random paths.

Gases assume the shape and volume of their container.

Liquid particles travel in straight-line paths between collisions, but appear to vibrate about moving points.

Liquids have definite volume but assume the shape of their container.

Solid particles appear to vibrate about fixed points.

Solid particles are arranged in a definite pattern.

Solids have both definite shape and definite volume.

The physical state of a substance depends mostly on its bonding structure.

Ionic compounds have strong electric charges holding the ions together and exist as solids. Molecular substances are attracted to each other by van der Waals forces. Molecular compounds of high molecular mass tend to be solids. Nonpolar molecules of low molecular mass tend to be gases. Greater molecular mass and greater polarity both tend to make substances form a condensed state, either liquid or solid.

The arrangement of particles is important to the chemist. In the following chapters we will discuss some of the special characteristics of solids, liquids, and gases.

FIGURE 15-9. The particles of a solid vibrate about fixed points. The particles of a liquid vibrate about moving points. The particles of a gas travel in straight lines between collisions.

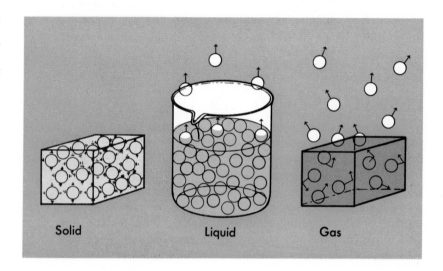

Solid   Liquid   Gas

15:6 PLASMA

When matter is heated to very high temperatures ($> 5000°C$), the collisions between particles are so violent that electrons are knocked away from atoms. Such a state of matter, composed of electrons and positive ions, is called a plasma.

A plasma state is composed of electrons and positive ions at very high temperatures.

Most of the universe is made of plasma. Stars are in a plasma state. Outer space is not really empty. It is composed of extremely thin plasma. The Van Allen radiation belts that surround the Earth are made of plasma. Matter in a neon tube or in a cyclotron is in the form of plasma. Scientists are working on the character of plasmas because a nuclear reaction, called fusion, occurs only in plasmas. If the fusion reaction can be controlled, it promises to be an energy source second only to the sun.

Electric and magnetic fields affect the plasma state.

Since plasma consists of charged particles traveling at high speeds, it is greatly affected by electric and magnetic fields. The study of plasma is called magnetohydrodynamics (mag NET oh hy droh dy NAM iks). Magne-

The study of plasma is called magnetohydrodynamics, MHD.

tohydrodynamics (MHD) involves confining the plasma that scientists hope can be used as an energy source through nuclear fusion reactions. It is also concerned with designing an advanced propulsion unit for space vehicles.

Plasma can be contained in a "magnetic bottle". (It is contained by magnetic fields.)

BIOGRAPHY   George Washington Carver   (1864-1943)

George Washington Carver was born in slavery in the United States. However, before he died he became one of the foremost agricultural chemists in the world. Largely self-educated, Carver was 35 years old when he received his masters degree from Iowa State University.

Carver is probably best known for his work with sweet potatoes and peanuts. However, he also made use of other agricultural products to develop building materials and household goods. For example, he prepared imitation marble from sawdust, and rugs from vegetable stalks. He was probably the forerunner of today's recycling movement. In addition to being an accomplished scientist, Carver was also a pianist and an artist. Although many of his contemporaries scoffed because he failed to produce any scholarly papers, his experiments and practical contributions have benefited people all over the world.

TECHNOLOGY AND CHEMISTRY

15:7 Artificial Body Parts

Fifty years ago, a person with a leaky heart valve had little chance of living a normal life. Today, replacing a malfunctioning natural valve with an artificial one is a common procedure.

Biomedical engineers have made and continue to build replacements for various parts of the human body. Artificial heart valves have been under development for a long time. However, other artificial body parts, such as eyes, ears, and livers, have only been attempted recently. One problem to be overcome by the design engineer is the tendency of the body to reject foreign substances. The body treats an artificial organ as an invader and reacts as if the organ were a bacterium or germ. Good materials for artificial organs must not trigger any of the body's defense systems.

The biggest problem in using biomaterials concerns the formation of bonds between natural tissue and the replacement part. Many of the substances used cause the growth of fibrous tissue that separates the natural tissue from the implant. This fibrous tissue may harden, causing inflammation, pain, and the destruction of normal tissue.

Most biomaterials research concerns controlling any chemical reactions that may occur at the interface between the biomaterial and natural tissue.

One material that has found wide usage in medicine is silicone rubber (Silastic®). It contains very long molecules made of repeating units. Such molecules are called polymers. A simple structure for a silicone could be represented as

$$\left[-O-\underset{\underset{CH_3}{|}}{\overset{\overset{CH_3}{|}}{Si}}-\right]_n$$

Many other tissue-compatible materials are polymers. Their molecular shapes are such that they imitate safe biological materials. Some polymers are almost shapeless, that is, their surfaces are relatively smooth. Thus, they are ignored by the body's defenses.

Polyethylene terephthalate (Dacron®)

Polymethyl methacrylate (Plexiglass®)

Polytetrafluoroethylene (Teflon®)

Polyurethane

Currently, researchers are attempting to produce materials by imitating or reusing natural body materials. One example is collagen, a protein material that makes up tendons and cartilage in the body. The collagen structure consists of three strands of protein twisted together to form a material called tropocollagen. These strands are then aligned to form collagen fibers. To align correctly, the third amino acid in each protein must be glycine. Collagen is also known to have a high content of hydroxyproline.

Table 15-1

Some Biomaterials and Their Uses	
Material	**Use**
Aluminum oxide	vertebrae spacers, dental reconstruction, tooth replacement
Co-Cr alloys	heart valves; joint reconstruction; plates, pins, and screws used in fracture repairs
Collagen	tumorous tissue replacement, artificial skin, internal shunts for dialysis
Dacron®	breast prosthesis, tissue patches
Polyethylene	artificial catheters and shunts, filling in bone defects
Polymethyl methacrylate	corneas used in correcting cataracts, replacing bones in the middle ear
Polyurethane	vessel replacements, artificial cartilage
Silicone rubber	artificial eustachian tubes, pacemakers, vessel replacements, tumorous tissue replacements
Stainless steel	filling in bone defects; joint reconstruction; tooth replacement; plates, pins, and screws used in fracture repair
Teflon®	artificial eustachian tubes; vessel replacements; artificial ureters, bladders, and intestinal walls
Ti alloy/Silastic®	heart valves

SUMMARY

1. The kinetic theory explains the effects of temperature and pressure on matter. This theory assumes that (1) all matter is composed of small particles; (2) these particles are in constant motion; (3) collisions between these particles are perfectly elastic. **Intro.**

2. At 25°C, an oxygen molecule travels at just over 1700 kilometers per hour in straight lines. At this temperature it has more than four and a half billion collisions per second. **15:1**

3. A gas exerts pressure on its container because the gas molecules are constantly colliding with the walls of the container. **15:2**

4. The average pressure of the atmosphere at sea level is 101.325 kilopascals under normal conditions. **15:2**

5. The pressure necessary to support a column of mercury 760 mm high is 101.325 kilopascals. Therefore 7.50 mm Hg = 1 kPa. **15:3**

6. A manometer is an instrument used to measure gas pressure. **15:3**

7. Kinetic energy is the energy an object possesses because of its motion. It is related to the mass and the velocity of the object ($KE = mv^2/2$). **15:4**

8. Temperature is a measure of the average kinetic energy of the particles of a substance. **15:4**

9. The kelvin scale is based on absolute zero. It has the same unit as the Celsius scale degree, but a zero point at absolute zero (K = °C + 273). **15:4**

10. Energy flows from an object of higher temperature to one of lower temperature until both reach the same temperature. **15:4**

11. The particles of a gas travel at random in a straight-line manner. **15:5**

12. The particles of a liquid appear to be vibrating about a point that is moving with respect to neighboring particles. **15:5**

13. The particles of a solid appear to be vibrating about a point that is fixed with respect to neighboring particles. **15:5**

14. A plasma consists of electrons and positive ions in random motion. It is strongly affected by electric and magnetic fields. **15:6**

VOCABULARY

kinetic theory **Intro**
mean free path **15:1**
pressure **15:2**
pascal **15:2**

manometer **15:3**
barometer **15:3**
absolute zero **15:4**
kelvin scale **15:4**

PROBLEMS

1. 97.1 kPa
2. 69.6 kPa
3. a. 333°C
   b. 1024 K
   c. 291 K
   d. −270°C
   e. 335 K
   f. 259 K
4. ammonia
5. average   distance
   traveled   between
   collisions
7. 103.5 kPa
8. temperature and kinetic energy are directly related
9. all molecular motion ceases
10. kinetic energy is conserved

1. The open manometer in Figure 15-3 is filled with mercury. The mercury level is 12 mm higher in the gas sample arm. What is the pressure, in kilopascals, of the gas in the container if the air pressure is 98.7 kilopascals?

2. In the closed manometer in Figure 15-3, assume that the height of the levels differs by 522 mm Hg. What is the pressure in kPa of the gas in the container?

3. Convert the following temperatures from one temperature scale to another as indicated.
   a. 606 K to °C   c. 18°C to K   e. 62°C to K
   b. 751°C to K   d. 3 K to °C   f. −14°C to K

4. Suppose you have two vials, one containing ammonia and the other containing chlorine. When they are opened across the room from you, which would you expect to smell first?

5. What is the mean free path of a particle?

6. With regard to particle motion, what are the differences in the states of matter?

7. An open manometer is connected to a container of carbon dioxide. The mercury level is 24 mm higher in the atmosphere arm. If the pressure of the atmosphere is 100.3 kPa, what is the pressure of the carbon dioxide?

8. How does temperature affect the kinetic energy of a particle?

9. In terms of the kinetic theory, what is the significance of absolute zero?

10. What is an elastic collision? How does it differ from an inelastic collision?

REVIEW

1. Which of the following bonds has a greater polarity?
   a. Ru—F   **b.** Be—Br
2. What advantage does surface chromatography have over column chromatography? What disadvantage?
3. What is the most common ligand?
4. Predict the shape of the molecule ICl_3.
5. What is the difference between a sigma bond and a pi bond?
6. What spatial orientation is taken by *sp* hybrid orbitals?
7. What properties are associated with multiple bonds?
8. Draw resonance structures for the SO_2 molecule.
9. Which element is more reactive, At or Po?
10. Arrange in order of increasing force of attraction on the outer electrons: Ni, F, Ti, C, Sc.
11. Label each of the following as ionic or covalent.
    a. Au—Cl   **c.** B—C   **e.** Bi—F
    b. Li—Cl   **d.** Pb—Cl
12. Predict the shape of CS_2.
13. Describe the electronic structure of NO^+ using molecular orbital theory.
14. Name the following complexes.
    a. $Co(NH_3)_6{}^{2+}$ **c.** $Ni(NH_3)_4(H_2O)_2{}^{2+}$ **e.** $Ag(NH_3)_2{}^+$
    b. $Cu(NH_3)_2{}^{2+}$ **d.** $Pt(NH_3)_2Cl_4$
15. Write formulas for the following complex ions.
    a. hexachlororhodate(III)   **c.** hexacarbonyliron(0)
    b. tetrafluoroberyllate   **d.** tetracarbonylnickel(0)

1. RuF
2. advantage—rapid, disadvantage—not quantitative
3. H_2O
4. trigonal bipyramidal
5. A sigma bond involves end-to-end overlap of orbitals. Pi bonds involve sideways overlap of *p* orbitals.
6. linear
7. rigid with respect to rotation of the bonded atoms; more reactive than single bonds and always formed from *p* orbitals
9. At
10. Sc, Ti, Ni, C, F
11. ionic b, e
    covalent a, c, d
12. linear
13. $(\sigma_{2s})^2$, $(\sigma_{2s}^*)^2$, $(\pi_{2p})^4$, $(\sigma_{2p})^2$
14. **a.** hexamminecobalt(II) ion
    b. diamminecopper(II) ion
    c. diaquotetramminenickel(II) ion
    d. diammineplatinum(IV) chloride
    e. diamminesilver ion

ONE MORE STEP

1. Compute the kinetic energy of an oxygen molecule at 25°C, and of an automobile with a mass of 1500 kg traveling at 50 km/h.
2. Calculate the velocity of a hydrogen molecule at 25°C.
3. Investigate the workings of an aneroid barometer. Are there other instruments used to measure pressures in addition to manometers?
4. Prepare a report for your class on the topic of plasmas.
5. The SI unit of pressure is the pascal. Find out who Pascal was. Also investigate the relationship between the millibar and the pascal.

15. **a.** $RhCl_6{}^{3-}$
    b. $BeF_4{}^{2-}$
    c. $Fe(CO)_6$
    d. $Ni(CO)_4$

1. oxygen molecule – 5.22×10^{-21} J
   automobile – 1.45×10^5 J
2. 1.76×10^3 m/s
5. 1 mbar = 0.750 mm = 0.1 kPa

READINGS

Waite, Boyd A., "A Gas Kinetic Explanation of Simple Thermodynamic Processes," *Journal of Chemical Education*, Vol. 62, No. 3(March 1985), pp. 224-227.

A study of the solid state is the study of the structure and properties of cystalline substances. When we think of a solid, we imagine an orderly arrangement of particles. However, as the photograph shows most crystals are not perfectly ordered structures. There are advantages to having defective arrangements in crystals. What are the types of crystal defects? Why are defects added purposely to some crystals? How do these defects affect the properties of the crystal?

SOLIDS

Chapter 16 introduces crystals through a study of unit cells. The relationship between packing arrangement and properties is covered for various substances. The distinction between crystalline solids and amorphous materials is emphasized.

DEMONSTRATION: Place a shallow glass dish on the overhead projector. Add 10 cm^3 of H_2O and 10–15 drops of liquid dishwashing detergent to the dish. Gently blow bubbles with a straw or glass tube. The bubbles will arrange themselves like the unit cells in a crystal. Emphasize the definition of a crystal as having particles arranged in a repeating fashion. See Teacher Guide.

GOALS:
- You will gain an understanding of crystal structure.
- You will use the concepts of bonding to explain melting point of crystals.
- You will study crystal aberrations such as defects, transistors, liquid crystals, hydrated crystals, and amorphous solids.

Have you ever examined table salt under a magnifying glass? If so, you would have seen that the crystals appear to be little cubes. The lengths of the edges may vary, but the angles between the surfaces are always exactly 90°.

The systematic study of crystals began with Nicolaus Steno, in 1669. He observed that corresponding angles between faces on different crystals of the same substance were always the same. This fact was true regardless of the size or source of the crystals.

Steno's observation has been extended to all intensive properties (density, refractive index, face angles, and other similar properties). For example, a single crystal of the mineral beryl, $Be_3Al_2Si_6O_{18}$, with a mass of more than 40 tons was unearthed in New Hampshire. This huge crystal was found to be identical in intensive properties to all other beryl crystals. The size or mass of the crystal is not important. It can now be stated that *the extensive properties of crystals vary while the intensive properties remain the same*. (See Section 3:4 to refresh your memory on the difference between intensive and extensive properties.)

16:1 CRYSTALS

The study of the solid state is really a study of crystals. All true solid substances are crystalline. Apparent exceptions to this statement can be explained in either of two ways. In some cases, substances we think of as solids are not solids at all. In other cases, the crystals are so small that the solid does not appear crystalline to the unaided eye. The relationship of properties to structure is important to chemists in the study of crystals as in other aspects of chemistry. Once the relationship is established, the chemist can use that knowledge to predict properties of new substances.

SUGGESTION: Wooden models of the various crystal structures are available and can be helpful in the study of this chapter. It is also possible to have one or more students construct such models from foam spheres.

All crystals of the same substance have the same angles between faces.

Extensive properties of crystals of the same substance may vary, but intensive properties remain the same.

No exceptions have been found to Steno's Law.

A study of crystals is a study of the solid state.

SUGGESTION: Obtain a microscope and allow students to observe salt crystals under low power, or use a microprojector.

299

a

b

c

FIGURE 16-1. True crystalline substances such as beryl (a), sugar (b), and celestite (c) are made of regular repeating units.

A crystal is a rigid body in which the particles are arranged in a repeating pattern.

Properties of crystals are partially determined by the bonding.

Repeating patterns of atoms, molecules, or ions are caused by bonding.

All crystals of a certain substance must be made of similar small units. These units are then repeated over and over again as the crystal grows. Thus, a **crystal** is defined as a rigid body in which the particles are arranged in a repeating pattern. The arrangement of these units is determined by the bonds between the particles. Therefore, the bonding in the crystal partially determines the properties of the crystal.

The units that compose a crystal are too small to be seen. Yet before any methods existed for studying crystal structure, scientists suggested that crystals form by repetition of identical units. Consider the patterns on wallpaper or drapery fabrics. These patterns are applied by rollers that repeat the design with each revolution. In a crystal, the forces of chemical bonding play the same role that the roller does in printing. They cause the basic pattern to be repeated. However, the "design" of a crystal must be composed of atoms, molecules, or ions instead of ink. A major difference between crystals and wallpaper is that the units in crystals are three-dimensional. The units on wallpaper are only two-dimensional.

There is a relationship between the repeating units and the external shape of the crystal. Long ago, crystallographers (kris tuh LAHG ruh fuhrs)

FIGURE 16-2. Crystal structures exhibit a repeating pattern just as that shown for the wallpaper and honeycomb.

classified crystals on the basis of their external shapes into seven "crystal systems," Table 16-1.

Crystal structure is often determined by studying X-ray and electron diffraction patterns.

Table 16-1

	Seven Crystal Systems		
	Lengths of the Unit Cell Axes	**Angles Between the Unit Cell Axes**	**Crystal System**
	all equal	all = 90°	cubic
	2 equal 1 unequal	all = 90°	tetragonal
	3 equal 1 unequal	1 = 90° 3 = 60°	hexagonal
	all equal	all ≠ 90°	rhombohedral
	all unequal	all = 90°	orthorhombic
	all unequal	2 = 90°, 1 ≠ 90°	monoclinic
	all unequal	all ≠ 90°	triclinic

16:2   UNIT CELLS

Each substance that crystallizes does so according to a particular geometric arrangement. The simplest repeating unit in this arrangement is called the **unit cell.** It is possible to have more than one kind of unit cell with the same shape.

Consider the different kinds of three-dimensional unit cells. Fourteen such cells are possible, Table 16-2.

Table 16-2

Unit Cells	
Crystal System	**Unit Cell**
Cubic	simple, body-centered, face-centered
Tetragonal	simple, body-centered
Orthorhombic	simple, single face-centered, body-centered, face-centered
Monoclinic	simple, single face-centered
Triclinic	simple
Trigonal	simple
Hexagonal	simple

Three of the simplest unit cells are **cubic, face-centered cubic (FCC),** and **body-centered cubic (BCC).** Note the packing arrangement of the particles in each unit cell. In the simple cubic cell, each particle has six immediate neighbors. In the face-centered cell, each has twelve; and in the body-centered, each has eight. The three-dimensional arrangement of unit cells repeated over and over in a definite geometric arrangement is called a **space lattice.**

Keep in mind that the particles in the cells are not as far apart as indicated in the diagrams. They are represented as dots simply for clarity in those diagrams. Actually, the particles are extremely close.

It should also be pointed out that space lattices and unit cells have no real physical existence. The crystal is built of atoms, ions, or molecules. The space lattice is a mental model, or frame of reference, that helps us understand the facts of crystal structure.

Cubic   Face-centered cubic   Body-centered cubic

FIGURE 16-3. The three unit cells of the cubic system have the same shape.

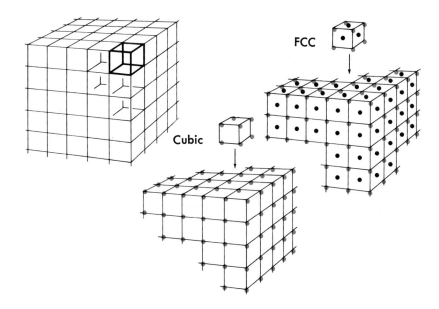

FIGURE 16-4. The space lattice is a regular arrangement of unit cells. Space lattices and unit cells are mental models.

16:3 COMPOUND UNIT CELLS

Sodium chloride crystallizes in a structure similar to that pictured in Figure 16-5. If you study the illustration, you can see that the Na^+ and Cl^- ions occupy different positions relative to each other. How would you classify this unit cell? It apparently is some form of cubic, but which one? Look more closely. Each Cl^- ion is surrounded by six Na^+ ions. Each Na^+ ion in turn is surrounded by six Cl^- ions. If you consider either alone, you can see that the unit of repetition is face-centered cubic. Thus, the unit

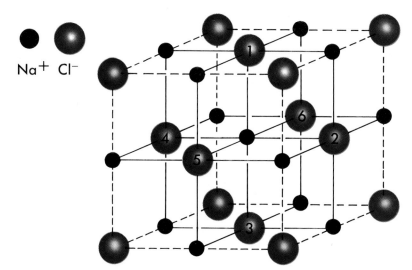

Na^+ Cl^-

Sodium chloride crystals are face-centered cubic.

FIGURE 16-5. The sodium chloride unit cell is face-centered cubic. Each ion is surrounded by six ions of opposite charge.

The particles of matter in the unit cell are arranged symmetrically.

A crystal is symmetric if the parts of the crystal can be interchanged in an orderly way to produce a resulting crystal which looks just like the original crystal. To check for symmetry, observe the following planes:
in a square,
in an equilateral triangle.

cell can be considered FCC, even though more than one kind of particle is present.

The particles of matter lying within the cells are arranged in a symmetrical fashion. This symmetry is related to the symmetry of the cell itself. When the combinations of space lattices and symmetry arrangements are analyzed mathematically, it turns out that there are only 230 different kinds of internal arrangements in crystals. Crystals can have axes, planes, or points of symmetry.

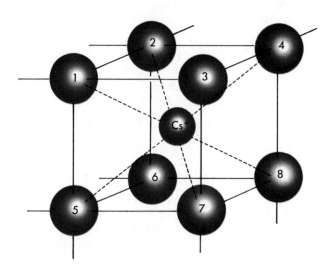

FIGURE 16-6. The cesium chloride unit cell is body-centered cubic. Each ion is surrounded by eight ions of opposite charge.

Ionic crystal structure is determined mainly by the ratio of the radii of the ions.

The particular crystal structure of an ionic compound such as salt is determined principally by the ratio of the radii of the ions. Since negative ions are generally larger than positive ions, the positive ions must be large enough to keep the negative ions from coming into contact with each other, but small enough not to come into contact with neighboring positive ions.

FIGURE 16-7. The size difference between the sodium ion and cesium ion accounts for the difference in unit cell arrangement.

DEMONSTRATION: Take seven spheres of equal size and arrange six of them around a central sphere. Repeat this process with another set of seven spheres, which differs in size from the first set. This can be demonstrated on the overhead projector using seven pennies and seven quarters.

Simple salts are those formed by the elements of Group IA (1) and the elements of Group VIIA (17) (the halogens). These salts, except for Cs, always have structures based on the FCC lattice. Figure 16-5 shows a model of the sodium chloride structure, which is typical of this class of compounds. The same model would serve for other members of the group and also for many other binary compounds, like MgO and CaO. Note that it is impossible to distinguish a molecule of NaCl.

Figure 16-6 shows a body-centered cubic arrangement for CsCl. The Cs ion is too large to assume a face-centered cubic arrangement.

16:4   CLOSEST PACKING

Let us examine in detail some of the various types of arrangement in crystals. The elements usually have rather simple structures. Imagine placing a group of spheres as close as possible on a table and holding them so that they cannot roll apart. Then place another layer on top of the first one in an equally close arrangement. If we continue with more layers, a close-packed structure results. This structure is the kind found in the majority of metals. It is difficult to visualize the lattice in such a structure, since the lattice is really only a system of imaginary lines. However, the experienced eye will detect that the lattice is either hexagonal or face-centered cubic in the close-packed arrangement. They are often called **hexagonal closest packing** (HCP) and **cubic closest packing,** Figure 16-8. Note that cubic closest packing and face-centered cubic are two names for the same arrangement. HCP is the one most frequently found in metals

The closest packed arrangements are hexagonal and FCC. Cubic closest packing and face-centered cubic are the same arrangement.

FIGURE 16-8. The similarity in arrangement for the first two layers of a HCP and FCC lattice are shown. The dots represent the positions of particles in the second layer of the FCC arrangement. Differences in the arrangement are more apparent as subsequent layers are added as shown by the top and side views.

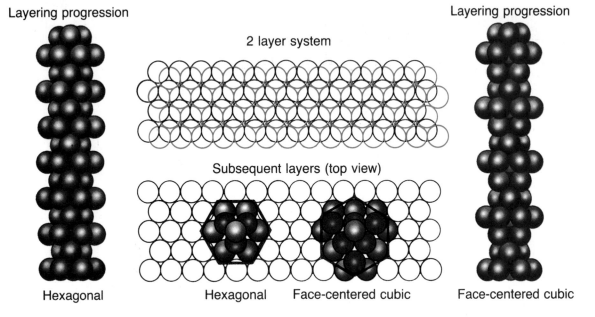

Layering progression

2 layer system

Subsequent layers (top view)

Hexagonal   Hexagonal   Face-centered cubic

Layering progression

Face-centered cubic

a

b

FIGURE 16-9. A salt crystal model is based on the FCC lattice (a). This structure gives salt its cubic shape as shown in the microscopic view of the crystal (b).

at room temperature. Another structure, found particularly in the metals of Group IA (1) of the periodic table, is based on a body-centered cubic lattice. This structure is not quite so closely packed as the other two. In BCC, while the openings between the atoms are smaller, there are more openings.

Iron has a body-centered structure at ordinary temperatures. At higher temperatures, it has a face-centered cubic structure. This fact is of great practical importance. Iron, in the form of steel, always contains a small amount of carbon. Carbon atoms are smaller than iron atoms, and at high temperatures they fit into the open spaces in the face-centered structure. When the iron cools, it changes to the body-centered cubic form. In that form, the carbon atoms cannot fit into the smaller spaces. Either the iron lattice is distorted by the oversize carbon atoms, or the carbon separates out of the iron as iron carbide, Fe_3C.

Iron and Fe_3C crystals exist in many sizes and shapes. The final structure of the crystal is determined by the percentage of iron and the rate of cooling. These differences in crystal structure result in the great versatility of steel as an industrial material. They also account for the fact that the properties of steel can be changed greatly by heat treatment.

CRYSTALLINE FORMS OF METALS

IA																	VIIIA
H	IIA														VIAVIIA		He
Li	Be											B	C	N	O	F	Ne
Na	Mg				"B" groups							Al	Si	P	S	Cl	Ar
K	Ca	Sc	Ti	V	Cr	Mn	Fe	Co	Ni	Cu	Zn	Ga	Ge	As	Se	Br	Kr
Rb	Sr	Y	Zr	Nb	Mo	Tc	Ru	Rh	Pd	Ag	Cd	In	Sn	Sb	Te	I	Xe
Cs	Ba	Lu	Hf	Ta	W	Re	Os	Ir	Pt	Au	Hg	Tl	Pb	Bi	Po	At	Rn
Fr	Ra	Lr	Rf	Ha													

La	Ce	Pr	Nd	Pm	Sm	Eu	Gd	Tb	Dy	Ho	Er	Tm	Yb
Ac	Th	Pa	U	Np	Pu	Am	Cm	Bk	Cf	Es	Fm	Md	No

◻ Body-centered cubic

◼ Face-centered cubic

▨ Hexagonal closest packed

FIGURE 16-10. Stable unit cell packing arrangements for metals are shown on this coded periodic table.

16:5 ELEMENTARY CRYSTALS

In Chapter 12 we discussed the metallic bond. At that point, we just "packed together" the positive metal ions before adding the electrons. How are the metal ions packed? Almost all metals are packed in one of three kinds of unit cells. These three are body-centered cubic (BCC), face-centered cubic (FCC), or hexagonal closest packed (HCP). Figure 16-10 lists the most stable unit cell arrangements for metals at room temperature. Many metals, like iron, change their packing as the temperature rises. The general, though not universal, trend is toward the HCP arrangement.

There are two crystal forms of carbon—diamond and graphite. Their structures are illustrated in Figure 16-11. You can see that in graphite, the atoms within each layer have a hexagonal arrangement. The atoms within each layer are held close by strong covalent bonds. The layers themselves are relatively far apart and are held together only by weak van der Waals forces.

Most metals are packed in one of three kinds of unit cells: BCC, FCC, or HCP.

Many metals change their packing as the temperature rises.

Diamond and graphite are different crystalline forms of carbon.

Molecules are held in crystal lattices by van der Waals forces.

FIGURE 16-11. The difference in crystalline structure of diamond and graphite accounts for the differences in physical properties.

DIAMOND   GRAPHITE

In diamond, each carbon atom is bonded covalently to four other carbon atoms. The four atoms are at the vertices of a tetrahedron. This arrangement forms a face-centered cubic lattice.

Nonmetallic elements have relatively low melting points. Elements like sulfur or iodine form crystals in which the lattice positions are occupied by molecules. The atoms within the molecules are held together by covalent bonds. The molecules are attached to each other by weak van der Waals forces.

DEMONSTRATION: Take three hair pins and heat two of them until they turn red. Cool one quickly in H_2O. Allow the other one to cool slowly in air. Compare the flexibility of the three hair pins. Count the number of bends before it breaks. Discuss the effect of heat treatment and tempering on metals.

FIGURE 16-12. The sulfur molecule is a puckered ring of eight atoms.

The repulsion of bonding and nonbonding electron pairs makes the sulfur ring pucker.

In sulfur crystals, the S_8 molecule contains eight atoms arranged in a ring as shown in Figure 16-12. The atoms within the molecule are much closer to each other (0.208 nm) than they are to the atoms of neighboring molecules (0.37 nm). This lattice is orthorhombic.

16:6   MACROMOLECULES OR NETWORK CRYSTALS

To melt diamond or other compounds having a covalent lattice crystalline structure, the individual covalent bonds must be broken. This process requires energy and such compounds melt at high temperatures.

In order to melt most molecular solids, we need to overcome only the van der Waals forces. Observations in the laboratory show that discrete molecular compounds have very low melting points. They range from −272°C to about 400°C. There are some very large molecules that melt at even higher temperatures, but here we are concerned with the rule, not the exception. Still, we have not accounted for covalently bound substances with melting points in the range 1000°C to 3000°C. An example is silicon carbide which melts at about 2700°C. In silicon carbide, each carbon atom is surrounded by four silicon atoms to which it is covalently bonded. Each of these silicon atoms, in turn, is surrounded by four carbon atoms to which it is covalently bonded.

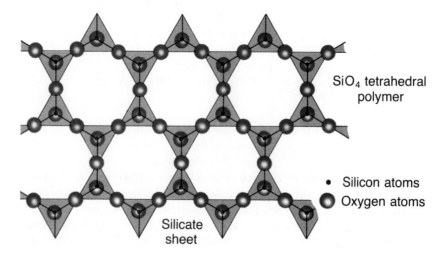

SiO_4 tetrahedral polymer

• Silicon atoms
◉ Oxygen atoms

Silicate sheet

FIGURE 16-13. Silicate compounds generally have high melting points. The macromolecule shown consists of repeating SiO_4 units. This substance melts at a high temperature because covalent bonds must be broken to liquefy the crystal.

Thus, each atom in the crystal network is bonded to its four nearest neighbors. Silicon carbide has the same structure as diamond except every other atom is silicon. We may think of the entire crystal as one giant molecule. In fact, this type of structure is often called a **network crystal** or a **macromolecule.** There are many substances composed of macromolecules. All of these substances have very high melting points. In order to melt the substance, you must break covalent bonds. These bonds are, on the average, about ten times stronger than van der Waals forces.

A macromolecule or network crystal consists of a single molecule with all component atoms bonded in a network fashion.

Table 16-3

Characteristics of Crystals			
Crystal Type	**Bonding**	**Melting Points**	**Examples**
Ionic	Electrostatic forces	300-1000°C	NaCl, LiBr
Metallic	Delocalized electrons	100-3500°C	Na, W
Macromolecular	Covalent	2000-3800°C	C, Si
Molecular	van der Waals forces	−260-400°C	He, C_6H_6

16:7   ISOMORPHISM AND POLYMORPHISM

There are many solid compounds and only a few ways they may crystallize. Therefore, it is not surprising that many substances have the same crystalline structure. Crystals of different solids with the same structure and shape are **isomorphous.**

Crystals of different substances with the same structure and shape are isomorphous.

It is also possible that the same substance may crystallize into two or more different patterns. A single substance having two or more crystalline shapes is said to be **polymorphous.** Calcium carbonate, $CaCO_3$, has two crystalline forms: calcite, which is rhombohedral; and aragonite, which is orthorhombic. Surprisingly, calcite is isomorphous with crystalline $NaNO_3$, while aragonite is isomorphous with crystalline KNO_3. Aragonite is the normal form for $CaCO_3$. If aragonite is subjected to a high temperature, it rearranges to calcite.

A polymorphous substance has two or more crystalline shapes.

16:8   CRYSTAL DEFECTS

The repetition of the unit cell arrangement is not perfect in all crystals. Actually, a perfect crystal is rare. Most crystals contain defects of one or more types. We will cover two basic types of defects.

Defects in crystals are common.

The first type of defect occurs within the unit cell structure. Look at a plane of a simple crystal such as sodium chloride. The positive and

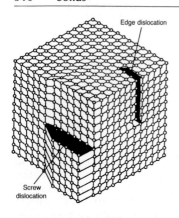

Edge dislocation

Screw dislocation

FIGURE 16-14. Edge and screw dislocations are defects in the way unit cells are joined.

negative ions alternate in such a crystal lattice. However, it is entirely possible that one of the ions may be missing from its proper position and occupy a space where no ion usually occurs. This change causes an imperfect crystal. Another possibility is that an ion may be missing completely from its position in the lattice. If a defect of this type occurs, for every positive ion missing there must be a negative ion missing. This arrangement preserves the electrical neutrality of the crystal. It is sometimes possible for foreign ions, atoms, electrons, or molecules to occupy these spaces vacated by the normal ions of the crystal.

The second basic type of defect concerns the manner in which the unit cells are joined. These defects are called **dislocations.** In some crystals, an extra layer of atoms extends part of the way into a crystal. The resulting crystal is said to have an edge dislocation as shown in Figure 16-14. It is also possible for the particles to be slightly out of position. This defect is due to unequal growth while the crystal forms. Such a defect is termed a screw dislocation.

16:9 SEMICONDUCTORS

Sometimes defects in crystals are valuable. For example, in the manufacture of semiconductor material for transistors, almost perfect crystals are **"doped."** That is, impurities are added deliberately. Silicon and germanium, Group IVA (14), are the most common elements used in transistors. A pure crystal of either of these elements will not conduct electricity. However, if a small amount of another element is added, current will readily flow through the resulting "doped" crystal.

A closer look at the bonding of silicon and germanium reveals why they behave as semiconductors. Silicon and germanium, each with four electrons in the outer level, crystallize in a structure similar to that of the diamond. Thus, all four electrons are involved in bonding. Substances such as silicon and germanium have a small forbidden zone. Under the proper circumstances an electron can be excited to the conduction band. Thus, these substances are called semiconductors.

Arsenic atoms have five electrons available for bonding and gallium atoms have three. If arsenic atoms are introduced into a crystal of germanium, extra electrons are present. When a voltage is applied, the extra electrons in the lattice will move, Figure 16-15. If on the other hand, gallium atoms are introduced, the crystal will be short of electrons. The resulting electron deficient lattice, however, will also conduct electricity. It does so by moving electrons into the "holes" created by the gallium atom. Note that in both types of doping, the crystal is still electrically neutral.

After their development in the late 1940's, transistors were used in place of vacuum tubes in electronic circuits. Because of their small size, long life, and resistance to shock, they revolutionized the communica-

Doping is important in the production of transistors. For instance, arsenic- and gallium-doped germanium crystals can be made which have the correct structure for developing semiconducting (transistor) properties.

Transistors are crystals which are deliberately "doped", causing imperfections.

Transistors depend upon an excess or shortage of electrons in the crystal lattice.

tions industry. Today's integrated circuits, such as silicon microprocessors, contain thousands of transistors. Computers, radios, heart pacemakers, space probes, and microwave ovens are only a few of the many products that semiconductor devices have either made possible or improved.

In order to produce an integrated circuit module ("chip"), a thin wafer of silicon is cut from a very pure crystal. Extremely pure silicon is produced by the process of zone refining. A cylindrical crystal of silicon is fixed vertically and a heating coil placed around it. The coil melts a narrow band of the crystal. As the coil is passed down the crystal, the impurities remain in the moving liquid zone, leaving behind a more pure crystal. After several passes of the heating coil, a crystal of silicon with not

FIGURE 16-15. Doped crystals are good electric conductors due to the fact that they contain an extra electron or an electron hole. Both arrangements allow electrons to move through the crystal.

(a) Normal Ge crystal

(b) Arsenic-doped Ge crystal

(c) Arsenic-doped Ge crystal after application of electrical field has caused the extra electron to move one atom

(d) Gallium-doped Ge crystal

(e) Gallium-doped Ge crystal after application of an electrical field has caused the "hole" to move two bonds more than one alien atom per ten billion silicon atoms can be produced. A wafer of this pure silicon is exposed to oxygen or water vapor at about 1000°C. The surface layers of silicon atoms are oxidized to silicon dioxide which forms a protective layer. The oxide surface is coated with a photosensitive material called a photoresist. The coated wafer is then exposed to ultraviolet light through a "mask" containing the desired pattern of doped areas. The exposed areas of photoresist are removed by solvent and the oxide coating is then removed by hydrofluoric acid. After removing the remainder of the photoresist, the chip is exposed to vapor of the appropriate Group IIIA (13) or Group VA (15) element for doping. These gaseous atoms diffuse into the surface only where unprotected by oxide, that is, in the pattern of the mask. By repeating this process several times, complex circuits can be built on one silicon surface.

CAREER: Chemical engineers work to improve computer chips by designing new processes that allow faster, cheaper production.

16:10 HYDRATED CRYSTALS

If solids crystallize from water solutions, molecules of water may be incorporated into the crystal structure. For some ionic substances, the attraction for water molecules is so high that the water molecules become chemically bonded to the ions. Ions that are chemically bonded to water atoms are called **hydrated ions.** Crystals containing hydrated ions are called hydrated crystals. As we saw in Chapter 14, it is also possible for ions to be surrounded by, or coordinated with, solvent molecules other than water.

Hydrated ions are chemically bonded to water molecules. Hydrated crystals contain hydrated ions.

Many common chemical compounds are normally hydrated. It is possible to remove the water molecules from some hydrated crystals. It can be done by raising the temperature or lowering the pressure, or both. The resulting compound, without the water molecules, is said to be anhydrous. **Anhydrous** means without water. Some anhydrous compounds gain water molecules so easily that they can be used to remove water from other substances. They are called drying agents. Chemists refer to drying agents as dehydrating agents or **desiccants** (DES ih kants). Silica gel [silicon(IV) oxide] and concentrated sulfuric acid are typical desiccants.

Common drying agents: calcium chloride, conc. H_2SO_4, sodium hydroxide, magnesium chloride.

Formulas for hydrated compounds place the water of hydration following a dot after the regular formula. For example, $CuSO_4 \cdot 5H_2O$ is the formula for a hydrate of copper(II) sulfate that contains 5 moles of water for each mole of copper(II) sulfate. The name of the compound is copper(II) sulfate pentahydrate. Such compounds are named just as regular compounds except that the water is included. The regular name is followed by the word hydrate to which a prefix has been added to indicate the relative molar proportions of water and compound. The prefixes are listed in Table 16-4.

The ions of some anhydrous substances have such a strong attraction for water molecules that the dehydrated crystal will recapture and hold

Table 16-4

Prefixes Used in Naming Hydrates			
Prefix	**Moles of Water**	**Name**	**Formula**
mono-	1	monohydrate	$XY \cdot H_2O$
di-	2	dihydrate	$XY \cdot 2H_2O$
tri-	3	trihydrate	$XY \cdot 3H_2O$
tetra-	4	tetrahydrate	$XY \cdot 4H_2O$
penta-	5	pentahydrate	$XY \cdot 5H_2O$
hexa-	6	hexahydrate	$XY \cdot 6H_2O$
hepta-	7	heptahydrate	$XY \cdot 7H_2O$
octa-	8	octahydrate	$XY \cdot 8H_2O$
nona-	9	nonahydrate	$XY \cdot 9H_2O$
deca-	10	decahydrate	$XY \cdot 10H_2O$

water molecules from the air. Such a substance is called a **hygroscopic** (hi gruh SKAHP ihk) substance. Desiccants are examples of hygroscopic substances. Some substances are so hygroscopic that they take up enough water from the air to dissolve and form a liquid solution. These substances are said to be **deliquescent** (del ih KWES uhnt). Sodium hydroxide is deliquescent. The opposite process can also occur. Water of hydration may be spontaneously released to the air. A crystal that releases water molecules to the air is said to be **efflorescent** (ef luh RES uhnt). Sodium sulfate decahydrate ($Na_2SO_4 \cdot 10H_2O$) is efflorescent.

Special care is required in storing hygroscopic substances. You may have noticed that some reagents in the laboratory stockroom have formed a liquid or hardened in the bottle. This action can be reduced by making sure bottles are closed tightly.

Hygroscopic substances pick up water from the air.

Deliquescent substances take up enough water to form a liquid solution.

Efflorescent substances release water of hydration to the air.

DEMONSTRATION: NaOH pellets are hygroscopic. Place a few on a watch glass and have students observe them for a few minutes. Discuss the effect on a quantitative lab experiment if NaOH were allowed to remain uncovered for a long period of time.

a b

FIGURE 16-16. Sodium hydroxide (a) has a strong attraction for water molecules. Thus, it will begin to dissolve (b) if left exposed to the air.

16:11   LIQUID CRYSTALS

A crystalline solid is highly ordered.

As we have seen, true solids are crystalline. Their constituent particles are arranged in a highly ordered manner. The arrangement is called "ordered" because the particles are spaced in a regular, repeating fashion in all three dimensions.

In Chapter 15, we saw that the structure of liquids was much less regular. Particles can actually change their positions in a liquid. The structure of a liquid is less ordered than the structure of a solid. The disorder of the liquid extends to all three dimensions. In general, when a pure solid is heated, it has a sharp melting point at a specific temperature. At that temperature the solid changes to a liquid and the order in all three dimensions is destroyed.

A liquid has disorder in all three dimensions.

However, some solid materials can lose their crystalline order in only one or two dimensions at the melting point. At a specific higher temperature, the remaining order will also be destroyed. Between these two transition temperatures, these materials retain some degree of order. These substances are called **liquid crystals.** If they retain two-dimensional order, they are usually called smectic substances. If they retain only one-dimensional order, they are called nematic substances. There is a third class of liquid crystals (with two-dimensional order) that will not be considered here.

Solids which lose their crystalline order in only 1 or 2 dimensions at the melting point form liquid crystals.

Smectic substances retain two dimensional order.

Nematic substances retain order in only one dimension.

The structure leading to such properties has been determined. Liquid crystals are formed by long, rodlike molecules arranged in a parallel manner. When the attractive force between layers of the molecules is overcome by energy, a smectic material results, with the layers remaining intact. If energy overcomes both layer attraction and end-to-end attraction, only parallel orientation remains. We then have a nematic material because only one-dimensional order remains.

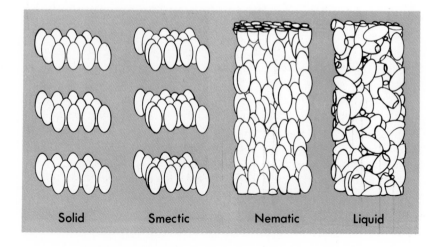

FIGURE 16-17. This diagram shows the differences in the degree of order for a solid, liquid crystal, and liquid.

Solid   Smectic   Nematic   Liquid

Substances in liquid crystal form are said to be mesomorphic; that is, between solid and liquid. Mesomorphic materials exhibit anisotropy. Anisotropic materials show different properties in different directions. We have already seen that graphite is anisotropic because of its bonding structure. Liquid crystals have optical and electrical anisotropy. Interestingly, along with several other biological systems, both muscle fibers and nerve fibers exhibit liquid crystal properties.

Some liquid crystals become transparent when subjected to a pulse of high-frequency current. Then, if subjected to a low-frequency pulse, they become opaque. This property has led to the widespread use of liquid crystals for digital displays in watches and calculators.

Off (bright)   On (dark)

16:12 AMORPHOUS MATERIALS

There are many substances that appear to be solids, but are not crystalline. Examination of their structure reveals a disordered arrangement of particles. These materials are said to be **amorphous,** or without crystalline form.

Glass is an excellent example of an amorphous material. When glass is heated, it does not reach a point at which it suddenly becomes liquid. Glass does not have a sharply defined melting point as ice has. Rather, as glass is heated, it softens more and more and melts gradually over a wide temperature range. The hotter it gets, the more easily the glass flows. The resistance of a liquid to flow is called its **viscosity** (vis KAHS uh tee). Glass and cold molasses are good examples of viscous materials. Water and alcohol are good examples of liquids with low viscosities, or nonviscous

FIGURE 16-18. When a voltage is applied to a liquid crystal, the arrangement of particles prevents the passage of light through the crystal. The watch display will be dark. In the absence of the voltage, light passes through the crystal to light the display.

An amorphous solid has a disordered arrangement of particles.

Viscosity is the resistance of a liquid to flow.
SUGGESTION: Emphasize that viscosity should not be confused with either density or volatility.

BACKGROUND: Crystals are said to undergo cleavage. Glasses are said to fracture.

Often the amorphous form will change into the more stable crystalline form.

The long-lasting amorphous form of a substance is the metastable form.

liquids. Upon cooling, glass does not reach a specific temperature at which it turns into a solid. As it cools, it becomes more viscous and it flows more slowly. Thus, amorphous materials are called super-cooled liquids. Butter is another example of an amorphous material, or super-cooled liquid. For equations in the chapters that follow, true crystalline solids will retain the symbol (cr), and amorphous materials will be designated by (amor).

One form of sulfur contains long chains. It is an amorphous form and is called plastic sulfur. A few hours after it is prepared it changes back into the stable orthorhombic form. This change is characteristic of most amorphous substances. In these substances the amorphous form is unstable. Some substances, such as glass, remain in the amorphous form for long periods instead of changing to a more stable crystalline form as sulfur does. Substances that can occur in a long-lasting amorphous form are said to be **metastable.** Although a metastable form is not the most stable form, a substance in this form is not likely to change unless subjected to some outside disturbance. Glass is a metastable substance. It normally occurs in the amorphous form, but even glass may be crystallized under the proper conditions. The crystallizing times for many metastable substances have been calculated. These times range from centuries to millions of years.

BIOGRAPHY

Dorothy Crowfoot Hodgkin (1910-   )

In the early 1930's, X-ray analysis of crystal structure was a new and limited field of study. Yet in 1933, a young British chemist and crystallographer, Dorothy Crowfoot, made the first X-ray diffraction photograph of a protein molecule. The application of this technique set the stage for her later work.

By 1948, Hodgkin, in working with other scientists, had determined the structure of penicillin. Her work in finding the crystalline structure of vitamin B_{12} won her the 1964 Nobel Prize for Chemistry and the British Order of Merit in 1965. Later, in 1969, she determined the three-dimensional structure of insulin.

A recipient of more than a dozen honorary doctorate degrees, Dorothy Hodgkin currently lives in England. Her husband is a noted authority on Africa.

Technology and Chemistry

16:13 Inside Crystals

Light waves can be spread into a spectrum using a diffraction grating. The grating consists of a transparent or reflective plate containing a pattern of closely spaced lines. When a spectrum is produced by a grating, the process is called diffraction. You can see light diffraction by looking at a distant, bright light through a fine fabric or the narrow space between two fingers. The diffraction pattern that forms will be a multitude of little rainbows.

In 1912, Max von Laue got the idea that if the current theories concerning X rays and crystal structure were correct, a crystal ought to behave toward X rays in much the same way a diffraction grating behaves toward light. An experiment was performed whereby a narrow beam of X rays was passed through a crystal and a photographic record made of the scattered X rays. Von Laue was interested in the diffraction experiment primarily because of its application to the measurement of X-ray wavelengths. However, W. E. Bragg and his son, W. L. Bragg immediately recognized the value of this technique as a powerful tool for studying the solid state.

We now know that each unit cell in a crystal diffracts an X ray just as a slit in a grating diffracts light. A crystal is more complex and the resulting diffraction pattern is 2-dimensional. The greatest part of the radiation

FIGURE 16-19. Using the proper orientation, X rays will be deflected by unit cells in a crystal (a). The resulting diffraction pattern can be used to determine the distances between layers of a crystal (b).

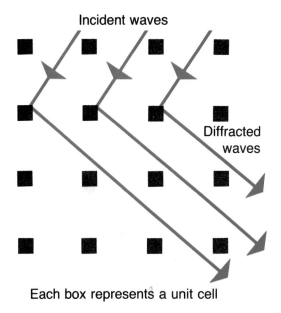

Incident waves

Diffracted waves

a   Each box represents a unit cell

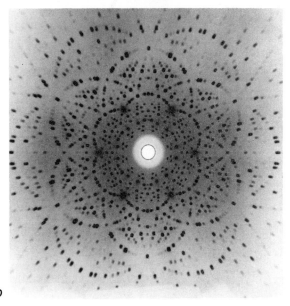

b

passes through undeflected. However, some of the X rays are diffracted. The diffraction pattern obtained possesses a symmetry related to the symmetry of the external faces of the crystal. The exact pattern of diffraction is determined by the dimensions of the unit cell. For crystals possessing a highly symmetrical arrangement, the interpretation of the data requires only a basic knowledge of physics and geometry. For less symmetrical arrangements, the calculations to determine the distances between cell layers may require the use of a computer.

The determination of the structure of biologically important molecules is a current application of X-ray analysis. The structure of hemoglobin was determined by combining X-ray diffraction with several other analytical techniques.

Present commercial methods of reacting atmospheric nitrogen require large amounts of energy. The molecules used by nitrogen-fixing bacteria are currently being investigated by X-ray diffraction. If a chemical process using a plant-like molecule could be developed, energy and money could be saved.

X-ray diffraction is also being used in determining the structure of new ceramic materials. By gaining a better understanding of the relationship between structure and properties in ceramics, even better products may be developed.

SUMMARY

1. Steno's law states that the corresponding angles between faces on different crystals of the same substance are always the same. **Intro.**

2. A crystal is a rigid body in which particles are arranged in a repeating pattern. The smallest unit of the repeating pattern in a crystal is called the unit cell. **16:1, 16:2**

3. The repetition of the unit cell in a crystal forms an imaginary lattice of particles called a space lattice. **16:2**

4. Molecular substances form crystals in which the molecules are held together by weak van der Waals forces. These substances have low melting points and low boiling points. **16:5**

5. Some substances form macromolecular crystals that are characterized by very high melting points. **16:6**

6. Crystal defects are lapses in the regular repetition of the unit cell arrangement. Defects can be a result of either missing particles that leave a hole or extraneous particles. Other defects are edge dislocations and screw dislocations. **16:8**

7. Semiconductors are an example of a practical application of a crystal defect. **16:9**

8. Crystals having the same structure and shape but different components are said to be isomorphous. A single substance which has two or more crystalline shapes is said to be polymorphous. **16:7**

9. Anhydrous compounds that gain water molecules easily are called dessicants because they remove water from other substances. **16:10**

10. A hygroscopic substance has such a strong attraction for water molecules that it will capture water molecules from the air. A deliquescent substance is so hygroscopic that it takes enough water from the air to dissolve itself. **16:10**

11. A substance that spontaneously releases water of hydration to the air from a crystal is called an efflorescent substance. **16:10**

12. Liquid crystals are substances that retain some degree of order at their melting point. If they retain two-dimensional order they are called smectic. If they retain order in only one dimension they are called nematic. **16:11**

13. Substances that seem to be solids but do not have a crystalline form are called amorphous substances. **16:12**

14. The resistance of a liquid to flow is called its viscosity. The viscosity of substances usually decreases as the temperature increases. **16:12**

VOCABULARY

crystal **16:1**
unit cell **16:2**
cubic **16:2**
face-centered cubic **16:2**
body-centered cubic **16:2**
space lattice **16:2**
hexagonal closest packing **16:4**
cubic closest packing **16:4**
network crystal/macromolecule **16:6**
isomorphous **16:7**
polymorphous **16:7**
dislocations **16:8**

doped **16:9**
hydrated ions **16:10**
anhydrous **16:10**
desiccants **16:10**
hygroscopic **16:10**
deliquescent **16:10**
efflorescent **16:10**
liquid crystals **16:11**
amorphous **16:12**
viscosity **16:12**
metastable **16:12**

PROBLEMS

1. From the photo of the NaCl lattice, show why NaCl is the simplest formula.

2. From a table of ionic radii, determine the distance between the Na^+ ion and the Cl^- ion in the NaCl crystal.

3. In Section 16:7, calcium carbonate is shown to have two crystalline forms, each isomorphous with different compounds. What explanation could you offer for this situation?

See Teacher Guide

1. There is a 1:1 correspondence between Na^+ and Cl^- ions

2. 0.276 nm

4. Find the percentage of water in a crystal of $CuSO_4 \cdot 5H_2O$.

5. For $NiSO_4 \cdot 7H_2O$, determine the following information.
   a. the name of the compound
   b. the percentage of water
   c. the percentage of oxygen

6. Answer parts a, b, and c in Problem 5 for $Ba(OH)_2 \cdot 8H_2O$.

7. Answer parts a, b, and c in Problem 5 for $Na_2CO_3 \cdot 10H_2O$.

8. A hydrate of nickel(II) chlorate having a mass of 9.88 g was heated to drive off the water. The anhydrous material had a mass of 6.68 g. What is the empirical formula of the hydrate?

9. Use diamond and graphite to explain how bonding affects the properties of a crystal.

10. Simple cubic, body-centered cubic, and face-centered cubic unit cells all have the same shape. How are they different?

11. What determines the crystal structure of an ionic compound?

12. Explain why NaCl has a face-centered cubic unit cell, while CsCl is body-centered cubic.

13. Cite reasons why nonmetallic elements have low melting points.

14. What are the characteristics of macromolecules?

15. How do the properties of a defective crystal differ from a perfect crystal?

16. How does doping change the properties of silicon and germanium?

17. Write formulas for the following hydrates
   a. magnesium nitrate hexahydrate
   b. iron(II) sulfate heptahydrate
   c. copper(II) nitrate trihydrate
   d. tin(II) chloride dihydrate

18. How do isomorphs differ from isomers?

19. How do amorphous substances differ from crystalline substances?

REVIEW

1. If an open manometer shows a mercury level 64 mm higher in the arm connected to the confined gas, what is the pressure of that gas? The pressure of the air is 92.7 kPa.

2. If a closed manometer shows a mercury level difference of 421 mm, what is the pressure of the gas in kilopascals?

3. How does plasma differ from the other three states of matter?

4. Why is gas chromatography called a chromatographic method even though it does not involve color?

ONE MORE STEP

1. Read about the lives of W. E. Bragg and W. L. Bragg. Write a report on the processes they used to determine crystal structure.

See Teacher Guide

2. Write a report on how transistors work.

3. In this chapter it was mentioned that there is another class of liquid crystals with two-dimensional order in addition to smectic. This other class consists of cholesteric compounds. Find out the source of the name for the class and how smectic and cholesteric compounds differ.

READINGS

Allcock, Harry R., "Inorganic Macromolecules," *Chemical and Engineering News,* Vol. 63, No. 11(March 18, 1985), pp. 22-36.

Bardeen, John, "To a Solid State," *Science 84,* Vol. 5, No. 9(November 1984), pp. 143-145.

Brown, Glenn H., and Peter P. Crooker, "Liquid Crystals," *Chemical and Engineering News,* Vol. 61, No. 5(January 31, 1983), pp. 24-37.

Chaudhari, Praveen, et al., "Metallic Glasses," *Scientific American,* Vol. 242, No. 4(April 1980), pp. 98-117.

Hazen, Robert M., and Larry W. Finger, "Crystals at High Pressure," *Scientific American,* Vol. 252, No. 5(May 1985), pp. 110-117.

Huggins, Maurice L., "The Hydrogen Bond and Other Reminiscences," *ChemTech,* Vol. 10, No. 7(July 1980), pp. 422-429.

Kolata, Gina, "The Great Crystal Caper," *Science,* Vol. 229, No. 4711(July 26, 1985), pp. 370-371.

Sherby, Oleg D., and Jeffrey Wadsworth, "Damascus Steels," *Scientific American,* Vol. 252, No. 2(February 1985), pp. 112-120.

Shriver, Duward F., and Gregory C. Farrington, "Solid Ionic Conductors," *Chemical and Engineering News,* Vol. 63, No. 20(May 20, 1985), pp. 42-57.

Townes, Charles H., "Harnessing Light," *Science 84,* Vol. 5, No. 9(November 1984), pp. 153-155.

One property of liquids is their ability to flow. Water is a liquid that flows easily. This property is based on the internal structure of the liquid and the forces between molecules. What are some liquids that do not flow easily? What term is used to describe the ability to flow? What are some other properties that are characteristic of the liquid state?

LIQUIDS

17

Chapter 17 introduces liquids by developing the concept of vapor pressure through the use of phase diagrams. Students will be expected to calculate the energy associated with changes of physical state.

DEMONSTRATION: Water can be boiled at less than 100°C in a Florence flask at reduced pressure. See the Teacher Guide in the front of this text for complete preparation details. This demonstration can be used to begin a discussion of constant temperature during a change of state, vapor pressure, and boiling. 17:6

According to the kinetic theory, if the temperature of a solid is raised, the velocity of the particles should increase. As the temperature increases, the particles collide with each other with a greater force. Thus, they are forced farther apart. Almost all solids and liquids expand when their temperature is raised because of this increase in velocity. If the temperature of a solid is raised sufficiently, the particles will move far enough apart to slip over one another. The ordered arrangement of the solid state breaks down. When such a change takes place, we say the solid has melted.

If particles are in the liquid state, there will be a certain temperature (and pressure) at which the particles travel so slowly that they can no longer slip past one another. All pure liquids have a definite freezing point and all pure solids have a definite melting point. The freezing point of the liquid form of a substance is the same temperature as the melting point of the solid form.

For a substance, the freezing point of the liquid state = melting point of solid state.

17:1 VAPOR EQUILIBRIUM

The average kinetic energy of atoms or molecules in a gas is a constant for all substances at a given temperature. This average kinetic energy can be calculated for any particular temperature. If we were to measure the kinetic energy of individual atoms or molecules in a gas, we would find that few had the predicted kinetic energy. Some molecules would have more and some would have less kinetic energy than the average. Most would have a kinetic energy close to the calculated amount.

Average K.E. of particles is constant for a given temperature.

Boltzmann distribution law.

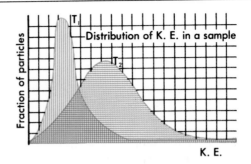

FIGURE 17-1. If it were possible to measure the kinetic energy of every gas particle in a sample at T_1, most would have a kinetic energy corresponding to T_1. Some particles would have more or less than the average kinetic energy. The particle distribution covers a wider range at T_2.

Few gas molecules have the average K.E. Most have a K.E. close to the calculated average.

Molecules having enough kinetic energy to overcome the attractive forces of neighboring molecules escape from the surface to form a vapor.

In a closed container, the vapor phase is in dynamic equilibrium with its solid or liquid phase.

However, we would sometimes find a molecule with a kinetic energy considerably above or below the average.

All that has been said about the collisions of particles in a gas is also true of particles in a solid or a liquid. A molecule in a liquid, because of several rapid collisions with other molecules, might gain kinetic energy considerably above the average value. Imagine that molecule on the surface of the liquid. If it has enough kinetic energy to overcome the attractive force of nearby molecules, it may escape from the liquid surface. The same process may also occur at the surface of a solid. The molecules that escape from the surface of a solid or a liquid form a vapor. This vapor is made of molecules or atoms of the substance in the gaseous state. A gas and a vapor are the same. We usually use the word gas for those substances that are gaseous at room temperature. **Vapor** is used for the gaseous state of substances that are liquids or solids at room temperature.

A molecule of a solid or liquid that has escaped the surface behaves as a gaseous molecule. It is possible for this molecule to collide with the surface of the liquid it left. If its kinetic energy is sufficiently low at the time of such a collision, the molecule may be captured and again be a part of the liquid. However, in an open container, there is little chance of the molecule returning to the surface it left.

If the solid or liquid is in a closed container, then there is an increased chance of the molecule returning to the surface. In fact, a point will be reached where just as many molecules return to the surface as leave the surface. There will be a constant number of molecules in the solid or liquid phase, and a constant number of molecules in the vapor phase. Such a situation is known as an **equilibrium** condition. It is a special kind of equilibrium, called **dynamic equilibrium.** It is called dynamic because molecules are continuously escaping from and returning to the surface. However, the overall result remains constant. When a substance is in equilibrium with its vapor, the gaseous phase of the system is said to be **saturated** with the vapor of that substance.

The physical change from liquid to vapor is represented in equation form as

$$X_{(l)} \rightarrow X_{(g)}$$

where X represents any vaporizable substance, such as water. The opposite process can be represented by

$$X_{(l)} \leftarrow X_{(g)}$$

The two equations can be combined

$$X_{(l)} \rightleftharpoons X_{(g)}$$

This kind of change is called a **reversible change.** The reversible change has reached equilibrium when the change is occurring at the same rate in both directions.

17:2   LE CHATELIER'S PRINCIPLE

The vapor phase exerts a pressure that is dependent on the temperature. The higher the temperature, the higher the vapor pressure. In a closed container a liquid and its vapor will reach equilibrium at a specific pressure for any particular temperature. This shifting of the equilibrium was observed and described by the Frenchman Le Chatelier in 1884.

Le Chatelier's principle is expressed as: *If stress is applied to a system at equilibrium, the system readjusts so that the stress is reduced.* The stress may be a change in temperature, pressure, concentration, or other external force.

For example, an ice skater can skim over the ice with little effort. The skate blades are not really touching the ice but are traveling on a thin film of liquid water. The presence of this water can be explained by Le Chatelier's principle.

Both pressure and temperature must be considered in this example. We will discuss pressure first. The entire weight of the skater is directed onto the ice through the blades on the skates. The surface area of the blades in contact with the ice is probably less than 15 cm². Thus, the blades exert a great pressure on the ice at the points of contact. A piece of

Stress: increased pressure
ice → water
greater volume → less volume

Stress: increased temperature
ice → water
melting uses heat

ice (solid) occupies a greater volume than an equal mass of water (liquid). Therefore, the change of ice to water will tend to reduce the pressure (stress) caused by the blades. Increased pressure causes a reduction in volume. As a result the blades travel on a film of liquid water.

Temperature also plays an important role in skating. Friction between the ice and the blades of the skates warms the blades. This increased temperature (stress) will be relieved by the flow of heat into the ice. Increased temperature causes an increase in molecular motion. The low energy ice molecules are changed into more energetic water molecules. The blades will be cooled by this change. Both the increased pressure and the increased temperature enable the skater to glide over the ice with very little friction. However, the effect of pressure is much more important.

FIGURE 17-3. A skater glides across the ice due to the formation of a thin film of water on the ice.

SUGGESTION: Have students think in the following pattern.
What is the stress? How can the stress be relieved? How does the equilibrium shift so as to accomplish the relief of stress?

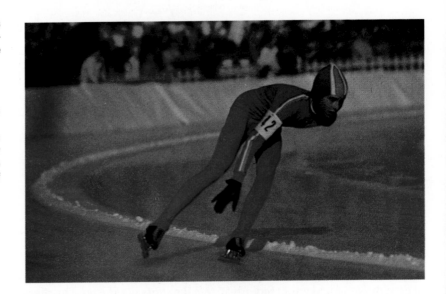

17:3 MEASURING VAPOR PRESSURE

Many techniques are available to measure vapor pressure. Figure 17-4 shows two methods of finding the vapor pressures of substances. The apparatus in Figure 17-4 is especially useful for finding the vapor pressure of solids at elevated temperatures. Table 17-1 gives the vapor pressures of some substances near room temperature. *Substances with low vapor pressure have strong intermolecular forces. Those with high vapor pressures have weak intermolecular forces.*

High vapor pressures are the result of weak intermolecular forces.

Table 17-1

Vapor Pressures of Some Liquids at 25°C			
Substance	**Vapor Pressure (kPa)**	**Substance**	**Vapor Pressure (kPa)**
Mercury (Hg)	0.000 247	Bromine (Br_2)	30.10
Turpentine ($C_{10}H_{16}$)	0.679	Acetone (CH_3COCH_3)	30.70
Water (H_2O)	3.17	Carbon disulfide (CS_2)	48.10
Carbon tetrachloride (CCl_4)	15.30	Sulfur dioxide (SO_2)	392.00

a

Closed mercury manometer

Thermometer

Vacuum

Vapor

Temp. = 8°C

Vapor pressure = 84.5 (kPa)

Flask

Constant temperature bath

b

Vapor pressure of water

Water vapor

Air pressure of 101.3 kPa

Column of Hg 760 mm high

Drop of Water

FIGURE 17-4. Two devices used for measuring vapor pressure are shown. In each, the vaporized liquid exerts a force (pressure) on the mercury in the tube.

BACKGROUND: Section 17:4 is the first of several sections which lead toward the development of the phase diagram.

17:4 MELTING POINT

Consider the phenomenon of melting in a closed container. In a mixture of solid and liquid states, there will be a dynamic equilibrium between the molecules of the solid and liquid. Remember, though, that each state is also in equilibrium with its vapor. Since there is only one vapor, the solid and liquid have the same vapor pressure, Figure 17-5a. In

FIGURE 17-5. The graph (a) shows the melting point of a substance to be that temperature where the vapor pressures of the solid and liquid phases are equal. The apparatus in (b) is used for melting point determinations.

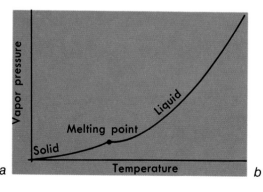

a

Vapor pressure

Melting point

Solid

Liquid

Temperature

b

The temperature at which the vapor pressure of the solid and vapor pressure of the liquid are equal is the melting point.

fact, **melting point** is defined as the temperature at which the vapor pressure of the solid and the vapor pressure of the liquid are equal.

17:5 SUBLIMATION

Some solids have a vapor pressure large enough at room temperature to vaporize rapidly if not kept in a closed container. Such substances will change directly from a solid to a gas, without passing through the liquid state. This process is known as **sublimation.** Dry ice (solid CO_2) and moth crystals are two examples of substances that sublime.

Sublimation: Change directly from solid to gas.

FIGURE 17-6. Dry ice (a) and iodine (b) are two substances which sublime.

Examples of sublimation: Snow disappears from ground on a cold day without melting. Frozen clothes gradually become soft and flexible as ice sublimes. Dry ice sublimes to CO_2 gas.

a

b

17:6 BOILING POINT

A liquid and its vapor can be at equilibrium only in a closed container. The molecules leaving the surface of a liquid have little chance of returning if the liquid container is open to the air. When a liquid is exposed to the air, it may gradually disappear. The disappearance is due to the constant escape of molecules from its surface. The liquid is said to evaporate.

Evaporation is the escape of molecules from the surface of a liquid.

As the temperature of a liquid is increased, the vapor pressure of that liquid increases, because the kinetic energy of the molecules increases. Eventually, the kinetic energy of the molecules becomes large enough to overcome the internal pressure of the liquid. The internal pressure is due to the air pressing on the liquid surface. When this pressure is overcome, the molecules are colliding violently enough to push each other apart. They are pushed far enough apart, in fact, to form bubbles of gas within the body of the liquid. These bubbles rise to the surface of the liquid because the vapor of which they are composed is less dense than the surrounding liquid. At this point, the liquid is boiling. The **normal boiling point** is the temperature at which the vapor pressure is equal to standard atmospheric pressure, or 101.325 kPa. Boiling point is a function of pressure. At lower pressures, the boiling point is lower.

Note carefully the difference between evaporation and boiling. Evaporation occurs only at the surface. Boiling, on the other hand, takes place throughout the body of a liquid.

Adding energy to a liquid at its boiling point will cause it to change to a gas rapidly by boiling. In a like manner, if we remove energy from a gas at the boiling point of the substance, the gas will change to a liquid. The boiling point of a liquid is also the condensation point of the vapor state of the liquid.

Different liquids boil at different temperatures. A liquid that boils at a low temperature and evaporates rapidly at room temperature is said to be **volatile** (VAHL uht uhl). Examples of volatile liquids are alcohol and ether. Liquids that boil at high temperatures and evaporate slowly at room temperature are said to be nonvolatile. Two such liquids are molasses and glycerol. Volatile substances have high vapor pressures; nonvolatile substances have low vapor pressures at room temperature.

Boiling occurs when the vapor pressure of a liquid is equal to atmospheric pressure.

FIGURE 17-7. The boiling point of a substance is lowered when atmospheric pressure is lowered. At any temperature, the vapor pressure of $CHCl_3$ is greater than that of H_2O.

PROBLEM

1. Using Figure 17-7, determine boiling points of the following under the conditions listed.
   a. $CHCl_3$ at 70.0 kPa
   b. H_2O at 100.0 kPa
   c. CCl_4 at 80.0 kPa
   d. H_2O at 11.0 kPa

1. a. 50°C   c. 70°C
   b. 99°C   d. 48°C

17:7   LIQUEFACTION OF GASES

We have considered the condensation of gases to liquids only for substances that are normally solids or liquids at room temperature. What about substances that are normally gases at room temperature? Can they be condensed? Yes, under the correct conditions. The condensation of substances that are normally gases is called **liquefaction** (lik wuh FAK shuhn). A gas must be below a certain temperature before it can be liquefied. Cooling reduces the kinetic energy of the molecules to the point where the van der Waals attraction is sufficient to bind the molecules together. It is also necessary to compress some gases. The van der Waals forces are effective for only short distances. Compression forces the molecules of these gases close enough for the van der Waals forces to take effect.

For every gas, there is a temperature above which no amount of pressure will result in liquefying the gas. This point is called the critical temperature (T_c) of the gas. The critical pressure (P_c) is the pressure that will cause the gas to liquefy at the critical temperature.

Liquefaction is the condensation of gases.

Gases may be liquefied by cooling and/or increased pressure.

T_c = Temperature above which no pressure will liquefy the gas.
P_c = Pressure needed to liquefy a gas at T_c.

SUGGESTION: Have students attempt to explain why the attractive forces differ (as indicated by the varying T_c and P_c) on the basis of the structure of these molecules. Note that this is fairly complicated; the higher T_c for SO_2 is due to both van der Waals attraction and polarity.

Table 17-2

Critical Temperature and Pressure		
Substance	Critical temperature (K)	Critical pressure (kPa)
Water (H_2O)	647.3	22.10×10^3
Sulfur dioxide (SO_2)	430.6	7.89×10^3
Carbon dioxide (CO_2)	304.4	7.39×10^3
Oxygen (O_2)	154.2	5.08×10^3
Nitrogen (N_2)	126.0	3.39×10^3
Hydrogen (H_2)	33.2	1.30×10^3

Many gases have critical temperatures above normal room temperature. Sulfur dioxide, for example, has a critical temperature of 430.6 K. It can be liquefied by increased pressure alone, if the temperature is not allowed to exceed 430.6 K. The critical temperature of a gas is an indication of the strength of the attractive forces between its atoms or molecules. The low critical temperature of hydrogen indicates weak forces between its molecules. The high critical temperature of water indicates the existence of strong attractive forces between molecules.

T_c indicates the relative strength of attractive forces between particles.

Low T_c indicates weak attractive forces between gas particles.

17:8   PHASE DIAGRAMS

Much of the information we have discussed can be shown in a graphic form called a phase diagram. The phase diagram shows the

Phase diagrams graphically represent changes of state at varying temperatures and pressures.

relationship among temperature, pressure, and physical state. Figure 17-8 is a phase diagram for water. The line labeled Solid-Vapor represents the vapor pressure of ice at temperatures from −100°C to point Y. The line labeled Liquid-Vapor represents the vapor pressure of the liquid at temperatures from point Y to 374°C. Point Y is called the **triple point.** All three states are in equilibrium at this temperature and pressure (0.01°C and 0.611 kPa). Above the critical point, X, there is no vapor pressure curve. Only a single state, the gaseous state, exists at pressures and temperatures above this point.

The triple point is the temperature and pressure at which all three phases of a substance are in equilibrium.

T_b is the normal boiling point and T_m is the normal melting point. The melting point occurs where the Solid-Liquid equilibrium line is cut by the standard atmospheric pressure line. It is important to realize that the vapor pressure of the liquid and solid (see point T_m in Figure 17-8) is not equal to atmospheric pressure at this point. The line YZ simply indicates the pressure-temperature conditions under which the solid and liquid can be in equilibrium. Only the Solid-Vapor and Liquid-Vapor lines represent vapor pressure information. The normal boiling point is that temperature at which the liquid-vapor equilibrium curve is cut by the pressure line of 101.325 kPa (see dotted lines crossing at T_b in Figure 17-8).

Note that the Solid-Liquid equilibrium line for water has a negative slope. A negative slope indicates that a rise in pressure will lower the freezing point. As was pointed out in Section 17:2, water expands when it freezes. Such a change is unusual. Most substances contract when they freeze and their solid-liquid equilibrium line has a positive slope. Figure 17-9 shows the phase diagram for hydrogen. Note the positive slope for the Solid-Liquid equilibrium line.

Note: The slope of the solid-liquid line is exaggerated slightly to emphasize that the triple point is slightly above 0°C.

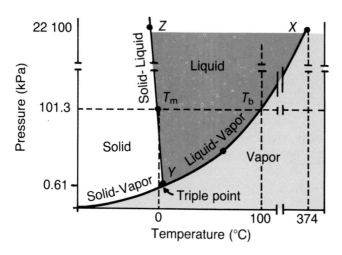

FIGURE 17-8. The phase diagram for water shows the relationships among pressure, temperature, and physical state.

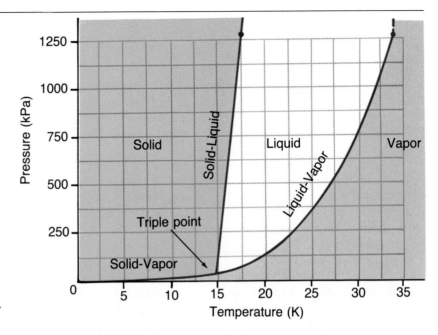

FIGURE 17-9. The phase diagram for hydrogen is shown.

PROBLEMS

2. Using Figure 17-9, determine the following for hydrogen.

a. critical temperature

b. critical pressure

c. triple point temperature

d. triple point pressure

e. normal melting point

f. normal boiling point

3. Using Figure 17-8, determine the state of matter that exists for water under the following conditions.

a. 50°C and 0.1 kPa

b. −30°C and 50.0 kPa

c. 105°C and 1000 kPa

d. 30°C and 100 kPa

2. a. T_c = 33 K
   b. P_c = 1290 kPa
   c. T_t = 13.8 K
   d. P_t = 5 kPa
   e. T_m = 14 K
   f. T_b = 18 K

3. a. gas   c. liquid
   b. solid   d. liquid

17:9 ENERGY AND CHANGE OF STATE

We have seen that the loss or gain of energy from a system has an effect upon the equilibrium that exists between states. it is important for the chemist to be able to treat these energy changes quantitatively in order to describe completely a change that has taken place in a system.

When energy is added to a solid substance, the temperature of the object increases until the melting point of the substance is reached. Upon the addition of more energy, the substance begins to melt. The temperature, however, remains the same until all of the substance has melted. Before the melting point is reached, the added energy increases the kinetic energy of the molecules. In other words, the temperature is raised. At the actual melting point, the position of the particles is changed. In other words, the physical state is changed and the potential energy is increased. The energy required to melt one gram of a specific substance at its melting point is called the energy of melting or **enthalpy of fusion** (H_{fus}) of that substance. A similar phenomenon takes place at the boiling point. The energy required to vaporize one gram of a substance at its boiling point is called the **enthalpy of vaporization** (H_{vap}) of the substance.

H_{fus} is the heat required to melt one gram of a substance at its melting point.

H_{vap} is the heat required to vaporize one gram of a substance at its boiling point.

EXAMPLE: Enthalpy of Fusion and Vaporization

How much energy is necessary to convert 10.0 g of ice at $-10.0°C$ to steam at 150°C?

Solving Process:
It is often helpful in problems of this type to draw a graph to indicate the steps in changing the ice to steam.

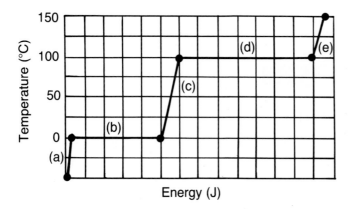

FIGURE 17-10. The graph shows the energy changes involved in heating ice at $-10°C$ to 150°C.

There is no increase in kinetic energy during melting and boiling because the temperature remains constant. Any additional energy is changed to potential energy which causes the particles to move farther apart and become more disorganized.

(a) The ice must be warmed to its melting point, 0.0°C. The energy that must be absorbed for the ice to reach 0.0°C is calculated by

$$q = m(\Delta T)C_p$$

The specific heat, C_p, of ice is 2.06 J/g·C°.

$$q = \frac{10.0\ g}{} \left| \frac{10.0\ C°}{} \right| \frac{2.06\ J}{g \cdot C°} = 206\ J$$

Refer to Section 3:9 for a discussion of specific heat. Tables A-3 and A-5 of the Appendix contain C_p values for the elements and several compounds.

(b) The ice must be melted. The enthalpy of fusion of ice is 334 J/g. The change of state energy is calculated as follows:

$$q = mass \times enthalpy\ of\ fusion = m(H_{fus})$$

$$q = \frac{10.0\ g}{} \left| \frac{334\ J}{g} \right. = 3340\ J$$

(c) The water must now be heated from 0.0°C to its boiling point, 100.0°C. The C_p of water is 4.18 J/g·C°.

$$q = \frac{10.0\ g}{} \left| \frac{100.0\ C°}{} \right| \frac{4.18\ J}{g \cdot C°} = 4180\ J$$

DEMONSTRATION: Have a student give you a piece of notebook paper. Fold it into a box and staple the corners. Place it on a wire screen above a bunsen burner. Fill the paper container with water to a depth of 1 cm. Light the burner. The water will boil but the paper will not burn. Ask the students why?

(d) The water must now be vaporized. The enthalpy of vaporization of water is 2260 J/g. The change of state energy is calculated as follows:

$$q = mass \times enthalpy\ of\ vaporization = m(H_{vap})$$

$$q = \frac{10.0\ g \mid 2260\ J}{g} = 22\ 600\ J$$

(e) Finally, the steam must be heated from 100.0°C to 150.0°C. The C_p of steam is 2.02 J/g·C°.

$$q = \frac{10.0\ g \mid 50.0\ C° \mid 2.02\ J}{g·C°} = 1010\ J$$

The total heat that must be absorbed is the sum of each of the five steps.

$$206\ J + 3340\ J + 4180\ J + 22\ 600\ J + 1010\ J = 31\ 300\ J$$

SUGGESTION: Remind students to express answers to the proper number of significant digits.

4. a. 5.50×10^3 J
   b. 15 400 J
   c. 19 200 J
   d. 104 000 J
   e. 1300 J
5. 1570 J
6. 687 J
7. 32 600 J

SUGGESTION: Introduce molar heat of fusion and vaporization before assigning these problems.

8. 2450 kJ

9. 2.80×10^5 J

10. 1.18×10^4 J

PROBLEMS

4. You have a sample of H_2O with mass 46.0 g at a temperature of −58.0°C. How many joules of energy are necessary to:
   a. heat the ice to 0°C?
   b. melt the ice?
   c. heat the water from 0.0°C to 100.0°C?
   d. boil the water?
   e. heat the steam from 100.0°C to 114°C?

5. How much energy is needed to melt 25.4 g of I_2 ($H_{fus} = 61.7$ J/g)?

6. How much energy is needed to melt 4.24 g of Pd ($H_{fus} = 162$ J/g)?

7. From the following data and that of Table A-3 of the Appendix, calculate the heat required to raise 45.0 g of cesium metal from room temperature (24.0°C) to 880.0°C. Specific heat of solid Cs = 0.246 J/g·C°; specific heat of liquid Cs = 0.252 J/g·C°; specific heat of gaseous Cs = 0.156 J/g·C°; enthalpy of fusion = 15.7 J/g; enthalpy of vaporization = 514 J/g.

8. Using data from Table A-3 of the Appendix, calculate the heat needed to raise the temperature of 5.58 kg of iron from 20.0°C to 1000.0°C.

9. Using information from the Example problem in Section 17:9, calculate the heat required to change 70.0 g of ice at −64°C to steam at 522°C.

10. Using data from Table A-3 of the Appendix, calculate the energy released when a 28.9 g piece of copper is cooled from its melting point to 25.0°C.

17:10   HYDROGEN BONDING

In a number of substances the predicted melting and boiling points differ from the observed ones. Remember that these changes of state can be predicted from a knowledge of atomic and molecular structure. It is the structure that affects interatomic and intermolecular forces. Many of the substances that do not behave as predicted have two things in common. First, their molecules contain hydrogen, and second, the hydrogen is covalently bonded to a highly electronegative atom. Under these conditions, the electronegative atom has almost complete possession of the electron pair shared with the hydrogen atom. The molecule is therefore highly polar. This polarity leaves the hydrogen atom with a strong partial positive charge. In fact, at the point of attachment of the hydrogen atom, there is a nearly bare hydrogen nucleus, or proton. The only elements electronegative enough to cause bonded hydrogen to behave in this manner are nitrogen, oxygen, and fluorine.

If an actual H^+ ion existed, it would consist of a bare proton. Consider the size of a proton compared to the size of the next largest ion with a 1^+ charge, Li^+. The H^+ ion would have a full positive charge in about one trillionth of the space! It simply will not exist near other particles without interacting with them. Consequently, hydrogen is always covalently bonded, even with the most electronegative elements. We will discuss this phenomenon again when we study the hydronium ion in Chapter 24.

FIGURE 17-11. Molecules containing hydrogen bonded to an atom with a high electronegativity have boiling points which are higher than would be predicted.

FIGURE 17-12. The high electronegativity of fluorine leaves hydrogen with a partial positive charge in HF. As a result, the HF molecules form chains linked by hydrogen bonds.

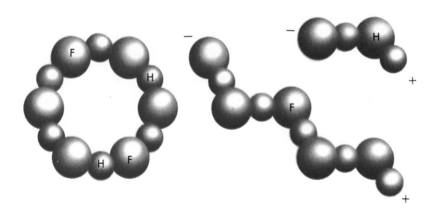

DEMONSTRATION: See Teacher Guide for details on a hydrogen bonding demonstration.

In a molecule containing hydrogen bonded to a highly electronegative element, the proton is not completely bare. However, the partial charge on the hydrogen end of the molecule is much more concentrated than that at the positive end of an average dipole. Hydrogen is the only element to exhibit this property. All other positive ions have inner levels

Hydrogen bonded to a strongly electronegative element causes some substances to differ from predicted behavior.

of electrons shielding their nuclei. In a substance composed of polar molecules containing hydrogen, the hydrogen atom is attracted to the negative portion of other molecules. Since the hydrogen atom has been reduced to a proton with almost no electron cloud density, the attractive force is strong. However, it is not nearly as strong as an actual chemical bond. The attractive force in such substances is called the hydrogen bond. The result of the hydrogen bond is that the hydrogen atom tends to hold the two molecules firmly to each other.

> The hydrogen bond is weaker than an actual chemical bond.

> Hydrogen "bonds" have energies in the range of 8 to 36 kJ/mol.

> A hydrogen bond is a dipole attraction.

Because of its special properties, the hydrogen bond has a greater effect than another dipole with the same electronegativity difference. **Hydrogen bonding** is really just a subdivision of the large class of interactions called dipole attractions. It is considered apart from other dipole attractions because it has a greater effect on the properties of substances.

FIGURE 17-13. Hydrogen bonding occurs between the nitrogen bases in DNA.

Guanine   Cytosine   Adenine   Thymine

17:11 HYDROGEN BONDING IN WATER

The effects of hydrogen bonding can be seen in water. For example, when water is frozen, a molecule of water is hydrogen bonded to four other water molecules, Figure 17-14. The two hydrogen atoms that are part of the central water molecule are attracted to the oxygen atoms of two other water molecules. Hydrogen atoms from two other water molecules are attracted to the oxygen atom of the central water molecule. This open crystalline structure occupies a large amount of space.

When ice melts, many, but not all, of the hydrogen bonds are broken. As some of the bonds are broken, the lattice collapses. The water molecules move closer. The same number of molecules occupy less space. Thus, water is more dense than ice. As water is heated above 0°C, more hydrogen bonds are broken, and the molecules continue to move closer. At 3.98°C, most of the hydrogen bonds have been broken. Above 3.98°C, the water expands with increased temperature. Above this temperature, the density of water starts to decrease. Now, we can understand why water has its maximum density at 3.98°C.

> **SUGGESTION:** Ask What would happen if ice were more dense than water?
> Ans. Ice would sink to the bottom of oceans and lakes. It would freeze from the bottom up.

> Water is the most dense at 3.98°C.

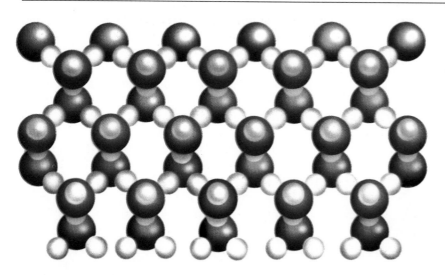

The energy due to hydrogen bonding in water is about 50 kJ per mol of water (or 25 kJ/mole of bonds since each water molecule forms 2 bonds).

FIGURE 17-14. Hydrogen bonding causes water to expand as the temperature falls below 3.98°C. This expansion is seen in the model for ice.

a

b

FIGURE 17-15. The temperature at which water reaches its minimum volume in graph (a) corresponds to the maximum density of water in graph (b).

17:12   SURFACE TENSION AND CAPILLARY RISE

Obtain a needle and a glass of water. With tweezers, place the needle carefully on the surface of the water. Be sure there is no soap on your hands, the tweezers, or the needle. With a little practice, you will be able to float the needle on the surface of the water. Why does the needle float?

Have you ever poured a drink into a glass so that the surface of the liquid was higher than the rim of the glass?

The particles at the surface have special properties because they are subjected to unbalanced forces, as shown in Figure 17-16. These unbalanced forces help explain the **surface tension,** or apparent elasticity of the surface. You know that jarring the overfilled glass destroys the forces at the surface and the liquid overflows.

Surface tension of liquids is due to unbalanced forces on surface particles.

FIGURE 17-16. Differences in surface tension can be seen in the drops of these four liquids. From left to right the liquids are mercury, water, acetone and mineral spirits.

The net force not only accounts for the surface tension, but also helps explain why liquids form spheres when dropped. The net force acting on a surface particle is directed perpendicularly into the liquid. Thus, the body of a liquid is pulling the surface molecules inward. Since a sphere has the least surface area for any given bulk, liquids tend to assume a spherical shape when dropped.

The unbalanced force also accounts for the phenomenon known as capillary rise. If there is an attractive force between a liquid and the solid

FIGURE 17-17. Surface tension causes the needle to float (a) and the splashing liquid to form spherical drops (b).

a

b

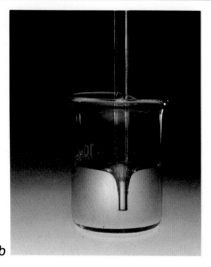

a
b

DEMONSTRATION: Demonstrate this capillary rise by the use of a number of capillary tubes in liquids with various surface tensions, such as alcohol, water, glycerol, and concentrated salt solution.

FIGURE 17-18. Water has a very high surface tension as seen by the fact that it rises in the capillary tube (a). The low surface tension of mercury is shown by the fact that it is depressed in the tube (b).

wall of the capillary tube, the liquid will rise in the tube. Capillary rise for water is shown in Figure 17-18. The attractive force relieves the unbalanced force on the surface molecules. Capillary rise is one method used for measuring surface tension. For example, water has a high surface tension at room temperature. It will rise quite readily in a capillary tube. Mercury, on the other hand, is depressed in a capillary tube as shown in Figure 17-18. It does not "wet" the glass of the tube. That is, there is not enough attractive force between the mercury and the glass to overcome the surface tension of mercury. Compare the meniscus of water and the meniscus of mercury in Figure 17-19. Can you think of an explanation for the difference in behavior?

Capillary rise is one method for measuring surface tension.

Surface tension causes the inverted meniscus of Hg and the almost spherical shape of liquid drops in a vacuum.

FIGURE 17-19. Compare the meniscus of water (a) with that of mercury (b).

a
b

BIOGRAPHY   Norbert Rillieux (1806-1894)

Norbert Rillieux was born in the United States; however he received his education in Paris, France. At the age of 24, he was teaching applied engineering at École Centrale. It was his interest in chemistry and steam engineering which returned him to the United States and led him to a process that revolutionized the sugar industry.

The crystallization of sugar from cane syrup had been done by ladling the cane syrup from vat to vat until the liquid evaporated. In 1846, Rillieux made use of the reduced boiling point of a liquid under a vacuum evaporator. This process produced a cheaper, better, and more automated method of crystallizing sugar. The same concept is now used in the manufacture of condensed milk, soap, and glue. It is also useful in the recovery of wastes from distilleries and paper factories.

TECHNOLOGY AND CHEMISTRY

17:13 Herbicides

As the population of the world increases, it becomes more and more difficult to feed everyone. Scientists are constantly searching for ways to increase crop yields from farmland. One method of improving farm productivity is to remove weeds that crowd cash crops. Herbicides are chemicals that kill weeds without harming the cash crop. Over 200 different herbicides are available commercially in the United States.

Two widely used herbicides are alachlor and atrazine. Another herbicide, one which has caused much controversy is 2,4,5-T (2,4,5-trichlorophenoxyacetic acid). This substance tends to accumulate in the ground and in water run-off from fields where it has been used. Most herbicides used today are decomposed by bacteria in the soil within a year. Persistent herbicides, such as 2,4,5-T, can be a problem if they accumulate to levels that are harmful to animals and humans.

Scientists are constantly searching for microorganisms that can degrade these persistent herbicides. It is sometimes possible to control the evolution of such organisms over a long period of time by gradually changing their diets. Thus, organisms can be bred to naturally degrade some of these materials. There are many problems to be overcome in such research. For instance, a microorganism that thrives on a certain chemical in the laboratory may not be able to survive in the wild.

There are a number of mechanisms by which herbicides kill weeds. Some cause the weed to grow very rapidly so the plant's cells never mature, as is the case with 2,4,5-T. Others inhibit the reactions associated with photosynthesis. For example, atrazine prevents the activation of water molecules by sunlight. Alachlor inhibits protein synthesis. Plants unaffected by a herbicide usually contain enzymes that render the chemical ineffective. The altered molecules are then metabolized quickly to eliminate them from the plant.

Herbicides are developed to protect cash crops. Farmers must choose their herbicides carefully to see that the product selected kills weeds only.

SUMMARY

1. The vapor pressure of a substance is the pressure exerted by the gaseous phase in equilibrium with the liquid or solid phase. 17:1

2. In a gas-liquid dynamic equilibrium, the number of molecules in both the liquid and gaseous phases remains constant. 17:1

3. If stress is applied to a system at equilibrium, the system tends to readjust so that the stress is reduced (Le Chatelier's principle). 17:2

4. At the melting or freezing point of any substance, the vapor pressure of the liquid and the vapor pressure of the solid are equal. 17:4

5. Sublimation is the change of state in which a substance passes directly from the solid to the gaseous state. 17:5

6. The boiling point of a liquid is the temperature at which the vapor pressure of the liquid is equal to the atmospheric pressure. 17:6

7. Evaporation is the process whereby molecules escape from the surface of a liquid or solid. 17:6

8. For every gas there is a critical temperature (T_c) above which no amount of pressure will result in liquefying the gas. The critical pressure (P_c) is the pressure that will produce liquefaction at T_c. A low critical temperature indicates weak van der Waals forces between molecules. 17:7

9. A phase diagram is a graph showing the relationship between temperature, pressure, and physical state. 17:8

10. The triple point is the temperature and pressure at which all three states of a substance are in equilibrium. 17:8

11. Adding energy to a substance may change its kinetic energy or its potential energy. If the kinetic energy is increased, the temperature of the substance will rise. If the potential energy is raised, the substance will change state (melt or boil). 17:9

12. The enthalpy of fusion is the amount of energy required to melt one gram of a solid substance at its melting point. The enthalpy of vaporization is the amount of energy required to vaporize one gram of a liquid at its boiling point. 17:9

13. Compounds containing hydrogen bonded to fluorine, oxygen, or nitrogen have unusual properties. These properties occur because of the formation of hydrogen bonds. **17:10**

14. Ice is less dense than water, which is most dense at 3.98°C. The expansion of ice upon freezing occurs because of hydrogen bonding between the highly polar water molecules. **17:11**

15. Unbalanced forces account for the surface tension of liquids. Capillary rise of liquids in tubes with small diameters is due to surface tension. **17:12**

VOCABULARY

vapor **17:1**
equilibrium **17:1**
dynamic equilibrium **17:1**
saturated **17:1**
reversible change **17:1**
melting point **17:4**
sublimation **17:5**
normal boiling point **17:6**

volatile **17:6**
liquefaction **17:7**
triple point **17:8**
enthalpy of fusion **17:9**
enthalpy of vaporization **17:9**
hydrogen bonding **17:10**
surface tension **17:12**

PROBLEMS

See Teacher Guide

1. What is critical temperature? What is critical pressure?

2. What is a triple point? Look at the phase diagram in Figure 17-8. Determine the triple point.

3. What is Le Chatelier's principle? How does pressing on a partially filled balloon demonstrate this principle?

4. Describe how a molecule could leave the surface of a solid. (How do solids evaporate?)

5. What is sublimation? List three examples of a substance that sublimes.

6. Define boiling point and melting point in terms of vapor pressure.

7. Why would you expect the boiling point of HF to be higher than that of HBr?

8. Describe what happens to the crystal lattice as ice melts.

9. What is the difference between volatile and nonvolatile substances? Give a solid and a liquid example of each.

10. A well-stirred mixture of ice and water is at equilibrium. If a small amount of warm water or ice is added, the temperature does not change. Why?

11.	x	y
B.P.	249 K	699 K
M.P.	133 K	300 K
T.P.	124 K	300 K
T_c	255 K	710 K
P_c	120 kPa	120 kPa

12. 6.93 kJ
13. 302 000 J

11. Using the two phase diagrams shown in Figure 17-20, determine the boiling point, melting point, triple point, and the critical temperature and pressure for substances x and y.

12. Calculate the energy in joules required to melt 86.4 g of gallium. (Use Table A-3.)

13. Calculate the energy in joules required to change 59.5 g of ice at −95.4°C to steam at 1024°C.

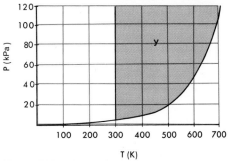

FIGURE 17-20. Use the phase diagrams with problem 11.

REVIEW

1. What is a crystal?
2. How many particles are found in a simple cubic unit cell?
3. What are the most common crystal structures found in metals?
4. What is a macromolecule? Name one substance that has a macromolecular crystal.
5. How does doping affect the physical properties of some crystals?
6. How many kinds of unit cells have been identified?
7. What is the usual unit cell for the simplest salts?
8. Why does a gas exert a pressure?
9. Compare the distance between molecules in a gas at room temperature with the size of the molecules themselves.
10. An open manometer shows a mercury level 97.1 mm higher in the arm connected to the confined gas. The air pressure is 98.5 kPa. What is the pressure of the confined gas?
11. A closed manometer shows a mercury level difference of 409 mm. What is the pressure of the gas in kilopascals?

1. A rigid body in which the constituent particles are arranged in a repeating pattern.
2. 1
3. FCC, BCC, HCP
4. A macromolecule is a network crystal in which each atom is bonded to its nearest neighbors throughout the entire crystal. diamond, graphite
5. The doped crystal will conduct electricity.
6. 14
7. FCC
8. because of its collisions with the walls of its container
9. 360 times greater than molecular size
10. 85.6 kPa   11. 54.5 kPa

ONE MORE STEP

1. A particular physics experiment consists of a block of ice and two heavy weights at the ends of a thin wire. The ice is placed on a table and the wire is placed over the ice so that the weights hang over the edges of the table. Eventually, the wire moves through the ice but the block of ice is still whole. Explain.
2. Find out how Michael Faraday (1791-1867) liquefied chlorine.
3. Why does carbon dioxide "snow" form when a CO_2 fire extinguisher is used?

See Teacher Guide

READINGS

Able, Robert B., "The Chemical Oceanographer," *Journal of Chemical Education*, Vol. 60, No. 3(March 1983), pp. 221-223.

Filling a hot air balloon requires a thorough knowledge of the properties of gases. The temperature and density of the gas in the balloon are critical in getting the balloon off the ground. Once in the air, changing atmospheric pressures must be considered or the balloon could burst. What are the effects of pressure on a gas? How does changing the temperature of a gas affect its volume? How can the laws governing gases be applied to the flight of a balloon?

GASES

Chapter 18 introduces the characteristics of an ideal gas. Gas behavior is covered through a discussion of Boyle's law, Charles' law, and the combined gas law.

DEMONSTRATION: Place a small amount of H_2O in an empty cola can. Heat it until the H_2O boils and steam comes from the opening on top. Using a hot pad, remove the can from the heat and immediately invert the open top into a large container of ice water. The air pressure will crush the can.

GOALS:
• You will use the kinetic theory to gain an understanding of the behavior of ideal gases.
• You will demonstrate a proficiency in the use of Boyle's and Charles' laws to solve temperature/pressure/volume problems.
• You will differentiate between ideal and real gas behavior.

You already know many characteristics of gases because air is composed of gases. When we speak of a cubic centimeter of a solid or a hundred cubic centimeters of a liquid, we are referring to a definite amount of matter. Both solids and liquids expand and contract with temperature changes. However, the change is usually small enough to ignore. This statement is not true for gases. The kinetic theory, as well as common experience, shows that a given amount of gas will occupy the entire volume of its container. When the temperature of a gas is raised or lowered, the change in its volume is large. Most solids and liquids subjected to the same temperature change would change very little in comparison.

Changes in temperature have a greater effect on the volume of a gas than on the volume of a liquid or solid.

18:1 KINETIC THEORY OF GASES

According to the kinetic theory, a gas is made of very small particles that are in constant random motion. Gas particles are not held in a fixed position by the attraction of other particles as are those in a solid. These particles do not behave like those found in a liquid either. In a liquid, particles may change their relative position easily, but their motion is restricted. This restriction occurs because particles of a liquid are held relatively close by van der Waals forces.

Gas particles are in constant random motion.

The size of a gas molecule is insignificant when compared with the distance between molecules. Thus, we assume that the particles of a gas have no attraction for each other. They are called **point masses** since they are considered to have no volume or diameter.

A gas composed of point masses does not actually exist. This imaginary gas, composed of molecules with mass but with no volume and no mutual attraction, is called an **ideal gas.** In the latter part of this chapter, you will study about real gases, and how they differ in behavior from ideal gases.

An ideal gas is composed of point masses with no volume and no mutual attraction.

SUGGESTION: Molecules of an ideal gas are considered to be points with no attractive or repulsive force. Emphasize that this is not actually true of real gases.

STP = 101.325 kPa and 0°C

Pressure exerted by a gas depends on
1. number of particles/unit volume
2. average kinetic energy of particles

FIGURE 18-1. The number of molecules in flask (a) equals that in (b) and (c). The average kinetic energy of the molecules in (b) and (c) is increased by the warm water bath. Note the difference in pressure between the three flasks.

The number of gas particles in a volume of gas depends upon the pressure and temperature of the gas. Therefore, in discussing quantities of gas, it is necessary to specify not only the volume but also the pressure and the temperature. Scientists agreed that standards of pressure and temperature were needed in order to compare volumes of gas. **Standard pressure** is 101.325 kilopascals and **standard temperature** is 0°C. We indicate that a gas has been measured at standard conditions by the capital letters **STP** (standard temperature and pressure). Gas volumes are reported in the scientific literature as so many m^3 or dm^3 at STP. The system is convenient, but what can we do if we must actually measure a gas in the laboratory when the pressure is 98.7 kilopascals and the temperature is 22°C? In this chapter, we will describe how a measured gas volume can be adjusted mathematically to the volume the gas would occupy at STP.

18:2 BOYLE'S LAW

We have seen that a gas exerts pressure on the walls of its container because gas molecules collide with the walls. The pressure exerted by a gas will then depend on two factors. The two factors are the number of molecules per unit of volume and the average kinetic energy of the molecules. A change in either of these factors will change the pressure exerted by the gas. If the number of molecules in a constant volume increases, the pressure increases. If the number of molecules and the

a 0°C	b 50°C	c 100°C
4.6 mm = 0.61 (kPa)	92.5 mm = 12.3 kPa	760.0 mm = 101.3 kPa

Water

T_1 P_1 $T_2 = T_1$ $P_2 = 2P_1$

V_2 contains twice as many molecules per unit volume as V_1

N = number of molecules

$N_1 = N_2$

FIGURE 18-2. At constant temperature, an increase in pressure decreases the volume.

volume remain constant but the kinetic energy of the molecules increases, the pressure increases.

Consider a container of gas with a movable piston in the top, as shown in Figure 18-2. Now imagine that the piston is lowered (without change in the number of molecules) and the temperature is kept constant. If the piston is lowered until it is half the original distance from the bottom, there will be only half as much space as before. The same number of molecules will occupy half the volume. The molecules will hit the walls of the container twice as often and with the same force per collision. Since the same number of molecules in half the space is equivalent to twice as many in the same space, the pressure is doubled. We conclude that, at constant temperature, pressure varies inversely as volume. The product of pressure and volume is then a constant.

The British chemist, Robert Boyle, arrived at this principle by experiment 300 years ago. This relationship is called Boyle's law. **Boyle's law** states: *If the temperature of a gas remains constant, the pressure exerted by the gas varies inversely as the volume.* By putting the relationships into mathematical form, we obtain the following relationship:

$$P = k' \frac{n}{V} \text{ and if } k'n = k \text{ } (n \text{ is constant}),$$

$$\text{then } P = \frac{k}{V} \text{ or } PV = k$$

In this equation, P is the pressure, V the volume, and n is the number of molecules. The k is a constant, which takes into account the number of molecules and the temperature. Thus, pressure varies directly as the number of molecules, and inversely as the volume.

FIGURE 18-3. These graphs show the relationships among pressure, temperature, kinetic energy, and the number of molecules per unit volume.

18:3 APPLYING BOYLE'S LAW

It usually is not convenient to experiment with gases under standard conditions. Experiments are often carried out at room temperature and pressure. Since the temperature and pressure vary from day to day, experimental results cannot be compared easily. It is desirable, therefore, to adjust all results mathematically to standard conditions. If P_1 = measured pressure and V_1 = measured volume, P_2 is standard pressure and V_2 is volume at standard pressure, then:

Boyle's Law: At constant temperature, $PV = k$. (Volume varies inversely with pressure.)

$$V_1 = \frac{k}{P_1} \text{ and } V_2 = \frac{k}{P_2}$$

In the first equation $k = V_1P_1$. Since k is a constant, we may substitute $k = V_1P_1$ into the second equation:

$$V_2 = \frac{V_1P_1}{P_2} \quad \text{or} \quad V_2 = V_1 \ \left| \ \frac{P_1}{P_2} \right.$$

Note that the original volume is simply multiplied by the ratio of the two pressures to find the new volume. We have derived this relationship by using Boyle's law.

SUGGESTION: These problems can be solved by simply plugging values into the Boyle's law equation. However, students should be encouraged to reason their way to solutions.

EXAMPLE: Pressure Correction

A gas is collected in a 242-cm³ container. The pressure of the gas in the container is measured and determined to be 87.6 kPa. What is the volume of this gas at standard pressure? (Assume that the temperature remains constant.)

Solving Process:
Standard pressure is 101.325 kPa. Thus, a change to standard pressure would compress the gas. Therefore, the gas would occupy a smaller volume. If the volume is to decrease, then the ratio of pressures by which the original volume is to be multiplied must be less than 1. The two possible ratios by which the original volume could be multiplied are

Use the pressure ratio which will provide the desired volume change.

$$\frac{101.3 \text{ kPa}}{87.6 \text{ kPa}} \quad \text{and} \quad \frac{87.6 \text{ kPa}}{101.3 \text{ kPa}}$$

The latter value is the proper one in this case because it is less than 1 and will decrease the volume. The corrected volume is

$$242 \text{ cm}^3 \ \left| \ \frac{87.6 \text{ kPa}}{101.3 \text{ kPa}} \right. = 209 \text{ cm}^3$$

$$V_2 = V_1 \left(\frac{P_1}{P_2}\right)$$

The same process can be used to change the volume of a gas to correspond to a pressure other than standard. For instance, if we wish to compare the volume of a gas measured at 16.0 kPa with another gas measured at 8.8 kPa, the mathematical operations would be as follows. Correcting for a pressure change from 16.0 kPa to 8.8 kPa is equivalent to expanding the gas. The new volume would be greater, and the ratio of pressures must be greater than 1. The proper ratio is 16.0 kPa/8.8 kPa. Do not fall into the habit of "plugging" numbers into equations. Visualize the change to be made in the volume, and then multiply by the appropriate ratio.

$$V_2 = V_1 \ \left| \ \frac{16.0 \text{ kPa}}{8.8 \text{ kPa}} \right.$$
$$V_2 = (1.8)V_1$$

PROBLEMS

1. Correct the following volumes of gas from the indicated pressures to standard pressure. (Use 101.3 kPa.)

   a. 844 cm^3 at 98.5 kPa   d. 598 cm^3 at 94.4 kPa

   b. 273 cm^3 at 59.4 kPa   e. 77.0 m^3 at 105.9 kPa

   c. 116 m^3 at 90.0 kPa

2. Correct the following volumes of gas from the indicated pressures to standard pressure.

   a. 817 cm^3 at 80.8 kPa   d. 641 cm^3 at 93.1 kPa

   b. 50.0 m^3 at 55.1 kPa   e. 231 cm^3 at 80.7 kPa

   c. 13.7 m^3 at 87.1 kPa

3. Make the indicated corrections in the following gas volumes.

   a. 0.600 m^3 at 110.0 kPa to 62.4 kPa

   b. 380.0 cm^3 at 66.0 kPa to 42.1 kPa

   c. 0.338 m^3 at 102.4 kPa to 47.3 kPa

   d. 248 cm^3 at 94.1 kPa to 46.3 kPa

   e. 0.123 m^3 at 104.1 kPa to 117.7 kPa

4. Make the indicated corrections in the following gas volumes.

   a. 338 cm^3 at 86.1 kPa to 104.0 kPa

   b. 0.873 m^3 at 94.3 kPa to 102.3 kPa

   c. 31.5 cm^3 at 97.8 kPa to 82.3 kPa

   d. 524 cm^3 at 110.0 kPa to 104.5 kPa

   e. 171 cm^3 at 122.5 kPa to 104.3 kPa

1. a. 821 cm^3 2. a. 652 cm^3
   b. 160 cm^3 b. 27.2 m^3
   c. 103 m^3 c. 11.8 m^3
   d. 557 cm^3 d. 589 cm^3
   e. 80.5 m^3 e. 184 cm^3

3. a. 1.06 m^3 4. a. 321 cm^3
   b. 596 cm^3 b. 0.805 m^3
   c. 0.732 m^3 c. 37.4 cm^3
   d. 504 cm^3 d. 552 cm^3
   e. 0.109 m^3 e. 201 cm^3

SUGGESTION: Remind students to answer the problems using the proper number of significant digits.

SUGGESTION: See Teacher Guide for suggested presentation for students having difficulty with math.

18:4   DALTON'S LAW OF PARTIAL PRESSURE

Chemists often obtain samples of gases by bubbling the gas through water. This procedure is known as collecting a gas by water displacement. It is a useful system for collecting many gases, but the gas must be practically insoluble in water. Also, water vapor will be present in the gas sample and the pressure it exerts must be accounted for.

How much pressure is exerted by a particular gas in a mixture of gases? John Dalton was the first to form a hypothesis about partial pressures. After experimenting with gases, he concluded that: *The total pressure in a container is the sum of the partial pressures of the gases in the container.* This statement is called **Dalton's Law** of partial pressure. In other words, each gas exerts the same pressure it would if it alone were present at the same temperature. When a gas is one of a mixture, the pressure it exerts is called its partial pressure. Gases in a single container are all at the same temperature and have the same volume. Therefore, the difference in their partial pressures is due only to the difference in the numbers of molecules present.

FIGURE 18-4. The total pressure of a gas collected over water is the sum of the pressure exerted by the gas and the pressure exerted by water vapor.

Dalton's Law: The sum of the partial pressures equals the total pressure in the container.

For example, we add 1000 cm³ of O_2 and 1000 cm³ of N_2, both at room temperature and 101.325 kilopascals. The volume of the mixture is then adjusted to 1000 cm³ with no change in temperature. The pressure exerted by this mixture will be 202.650 kilopascals. However, the pressure exerted by the oxygen will still be 101.325 kilopascals (one half the pressure). Also, the pressure exerted by the nitrogen will be 101.325 kilopascals (one half of the pressure). Air is an example of such a mixture. The air contains nitrogen, oxygen, argon, carbon dioxide, and other gases in small amounts. The total pressure of the atmosphere at standard conditions is 101.325 kilopascals. If 78% of the molecules present are nitrogen molecules, then 78% of the pressure is due to nitrogen. The partial pressure of nitrogen in the air at standard conditions is, then, 0.78 × 101.325 kilopascals or 79 kilopascals.

Table 18-1

Composition of Air (dry)	
Gas	Partial pressure (kPa)
nitrogen	79.119
oxygen	21.224
argon	0.946
carbon dioxide	0.030
neon	0.002
Traces of helium, krypton, hydrogen, and xenon	

If a gas is collected over water, the pressure in the container actually includes the sum of the partial pressures of the gas and the water vapor. We know that each of the gases exerts the same pressure it would if it alone were present in the container. Therefore, if we subtract the value for water vapor pressure from the total pressure, the result will be the pressure of the gas alone. The vapor pressure of water at various temperatures has been measured. We need only to consult Table 18-2 to determine the partial pressure of water.

Table 18-2

Vapor Pressure of Water					
Temperature (°C)	Pressure (kPa)	Temperature (°C)	Pressure (kPa)	Temperature (°C)	Pressure (kPa)
0	0.6	21	2.5	30	4.2
5	0.9	22	2.6	35	5.6
8	1.1	23	2.8	40	7.4
10	1.2	24	3.0	50	12.3
12	1.4	25	3.2	60	19.9
14	1.6	26	3.4	70	31.2
16	1.8	27	3.6	80	47.3
18	2.1	28	3.8	90	70.1
20	2.3	29	4.0	100	101.3

EXAMPLE: Volume of a Dry Gas

A quantity of gas is collected over water at 8°C in a 353-cm³ vessel. The manometer indicates a pressure of 84.5 kPa. What volume would the dry gas occupy at standard pressure and 8°C?

Solving Process:

(a) We must determine what part of the total pressure is due to water vapor. Table 18-2 indicates that at 8°C, water has a vapor pressure of 1.1 kPa. To find the pressure of the collected gas:

$$P_{gas} = P_{total} - P_{water}$$
$$= 84.5 \text{ kPa} - 1.1 \text{ kPa}$$
$$= 83.4 \text{ kPa}$$

(b) Since this pressure is less than standard, the gas would have to be compressed to change it to standard. The pressure ratio by which the volume is to be multiplied must be less than 1. The correct volume is

$$353 \text{ cm}^3 \left| \frac{83.4 \text{ kPa}}{101.3 \text{ kPa}} \right. = 291 \text{ cm}^3$$

$$V_2 = V_1 \left(\frac{P_1}{P_2} \right)$$

Note that the temperature remains constant. See Table 18-2 page 350 for pressure corrections.

PROBLEM

5. The following gas volumes were collected over water under the indicated conditions. Correct each volume to the volume that the dry gas would occupy at standard pressure and the indicated temperature (*T* is constant).

   a. 888 cm³ at 14°C and 93.3 kPa
   b. 30.0 cm³ at 16°C and 77.5 kPa
   c. 34.0 m³ at 18°C and 82.4 kPa
   d. 384 cm³ at 12°C and 78.3 kPa
   e. 8.23 m³ at 27°C and 87.3 kPa

5. a. 804 cm³
   b. 22.4 cm³
   c. 27.0 m³
   d. 292 cm³
   e. 6.80 m³

18:5   CHARLES' LAW

Jacques Charles, a French physicist, noticed a simple relationship between the volume of a gas and the temperature. He found that, starting at 0°C, the volume of any gas would double if the temperature were raised to 273°C (pressure constant). For each Celsius degree increase in temperature, the volume of the gas increased by ¹⁄₂₇₃ of its volume at 0°C. An increase in temperature of 1 C° will result in a new volume of ²⁷⁴⁄₂₇₃, or a ¹⁄₂₇₃ increase in volume. Similarly, Charles found that a gas will decrease by ¹⁄₂₇₃ of its 0°C volume for each Celsius degree decrease in temperature. This finding would suggest that at −273°C, a gas would have no volume,

For each 1 C° change, a gas changes ¹⁄₂₇₃ of its 0°C volume.

or would disappear. This temperature is called absolute zero. However, all gases become liquid before they are cooled to this low temperature, and Charles' relationship does not hold for liquids or solids. *The volume of a quantity of gas, held at a fixed pressure, varies directly with the kelvin temperature.* This relationship is called **Charles' Law.**

This experimental information led to the formation of the absolute or kelvin temperature scale. Thus far, we have always defined the kelvin scale in terms of the Celsius scale. Now we are in a position to define the kelvin scale directly. The zero point of the kelvin scale is absolute zero. The other reference point in defining the kelvin scale is the triple point of water, which is defined as 273.16 K. You must remember that temperatures given in Celsius must be converted to kelvin to work with gases. The relationship is K = °C + 273.

FIGURE 18-5. The volume of a gas at zero kelvin is theoretically zero.

18:6 APPLYING CHARLES' LAW

Charles' law states that volume varies directly as the absolute temperature: $V = k'T$. For any original volume, $V_1 = k'T_1$. A change in volume, with pressure constant, could be indicated at $V_2 = k'T_2$. Since $k' = V_1/T_1$, substituting would give

$$\frac{V_1}{T_1} = \frac{V_2}{T_2} \quad \text{or} \quad V_2 = \frac{V_1}{} \left| \frac{T_2}{T_1} \right.$$

To correct the volume for a change in temperature, you must, as in pressure correction, multiply the original volume by a ratio. For temperature changes, the ratio is expressed in kelvin temperatures.

FIGURE 18-6. Note how the volume of the balloon changes from the ice bath (a) to the hot water bath (b).

EXAMPLE: Temperature Correction

A 225 cm³ volume of gas is collected at 58°C. What volume would this sample of gas occupy at standard temperature? Assume constant pressure.

Solving Process:
The temperature decreases and the pressure remains constant. Charles' law states that if the temperature of a gas decreases at constant pressure, the volume will decrease. Therefore, the original volume must be multiplied by a fraction less than 1. Convert both the initial (58°C) and the final (0°C) temperatures to the kelvin scale (331 K and 273 K). The two possible temperature ratios are the following.

K = °C + 273

$$\frac{331 \text{ K}}{273 \text{ K}} \quad \text{and} \quad \frac{273 \text{ K}}{331 \text{ K}}$$

The correct ratio is 273 K/331 K because it is less than 1. The corrected gas volume is

$$\frac{225 \text{ cm}^3}{} \left| \frac{273 \text{ K}}{331 \text{ K}} \right. = 186 \text{ cm}^3$$

PROBLEMS

6. Correct the following volumes of gases for a change from the temperature indicated to standard temperature (P is constant).

a. 617 cm³ at 9°C
b. 609 cm³ at 83°C

6. a. 597 cm³
   b. 467 cm³

c. 872 cm^3
d. 1.97 m^3
e. 156 m^3
f. 3.29 m^3
g. 2.20 m^3
h. 761 cm^3
i. 4.44 m^3
j. 4.61 m^3

7. a. 3.80 m^3
   b. 321 cm^3
   c. 13.1 m^3
   d. 486 cm^3
   e. 4.97 m^3
   f. 4.32 m^3
   g. 111 cm^3
   h. 4.14 m^3
   i. 1270 cm^3
   j. 991 cm^3

c. 942 cm^3 at 22°C
d. 7.12 m^3 at 988 K
e. 213 m^3 at 99°C
f. 5.93 m^3 at 492 K
g. 2.27 m^3 at 9°C
h. 819 cm^3 at 21°C
i. 4.67 m^3 at 287 K
j. 5.94 m^3 at 79°C

7. Correct the following volumes of gases for the temperature changes indicated (P is constant).
   a. 2.90 m^3 at 226 K to 23°C
   b. 376 cm^3 at 379 K to 51°C
   c. 7.91 m^3 at 52°C to 538 K
   d. 667 cm^3 at 431 K to 41°C
   e. 4.82 m^3 at 22°C to 31°C
   f. 2.97 m^3 at 72°C to 502 K
   g. 19.0 cm^3 at 56.0 K to 53°C
   h. 5.18 m^3 at 76°C to 6°C
   i. 882 cm^3 at 42°C to 455 K
   j. 833 cm^3 at 27°C to 84°C

SUGGESTION: Introduce the combined gas law as a two-step procedure—the second step being a correction of the result of the first step.

A change in volume resulting from a change in both temperature and pressure can be found by combining the temperature and pressure ratios.

BACKGROUND: The common sense approach used here simplifies use of gas laws in mass-volume problems at nonstandard conditions in Chapter 19.

18:7   COMBINED GAS LAW

Laboratory experiments are almost always made at temperatures and pressures other than standard. It is sometimes necessary to correct the laboratory volumes of gases for temperature and pressure. The correction is made by multiplying the original volume by two ratios, one for temperature and the other for pressure.

Since multiplication is commutative, it does not make any difference which ratio is used first. We may think of the process as correcting the volume for a pressure change while the temperature is held constant. Then, we correct for the temperature change while the pressure is held constant. The two changes do not have any effect on each other.

EXAMPLE: Volume Correction to STP

The volume of a gas measured at 75.6 kPa pressure and 60.0°C is to be corrected to correspond to the volume it would occupy at STP. The measured volume of the gas is 10.0 cm^3.

Solving Process:
The pressure must be increased from 75.6 kPa to 101.3 kPa. The volume must decrease, which means the pressure ratio must be less than one. The correct pressure ratio is 75.6 kPa/101.3 kPa.

The temperature must be decreased from 333 K to 273 K. This change would also decrease the volume. Therefore, the correct temperature ratio is 273 K/333 K. The problem then becomes

$$\frac{10.0 \text{ cm}^3}{} \mid \frac{75.6 \text{ kPa}}{101.3 \text{ kPa}} \mid \frac{273 \text{ K}}{333 \text{ K}} = 6.12 \text{ cm}^3 \text{ at STP.}$$

PROBLEMS

8. Correct the volumes of the following gases as indicated.
   a. 7.51 m³ at 5°C and 59.9 kPa to STP
   b. 351 cm³ at 19°C and 82.5 kPa to 36°C and 94.5 kPa
   c. 7.03 m³ at 31°C and 111 kPa to STP
   d. 955 cm³ at 58°C and 108.0 kPa to 76°C and 123.0 kPa
   e. 960.0 cm³ at 71°C and 107.2 kPa to 13°C and 59.3 kPa

9. Correct the volumes of the following gases as indicated.
   a. 654 cm³ at 6°C and 65.3 kPa to 4°C and 108.7 kPa
   b. 2.13 m³ at 95°C and 103 kPa to STP
   c. 4.76 m³ at 6°C and 124.5 kPa to STP
   d. 61.4 cm³ at 67°C and 96.8 kPa to STP
   e. 164 cm³ at STP to 21°C and 98.0 kPa

8. a. 4.36 m³
   b. 324 cm³
   c. 6.92 m³
   d. 884 cm³
   e. 1440 cm³

9. a. 3.90×10^2 cm³
   b. 1.61 m³
   c. 5.72 m³
   d. 47.1 cm³
   e. 183 cm³

18:8 DIFFUSION AND GRAHAM'S LAW

One of the basic ideas of the kinetic theory is that gas molecules travel in straight lines. However, a molecule is always colliding with other molecules. Therefore, its actual path is a series of straight lines connected end to end in no particular pattern. If a bottle of a substance with a strong odor is opened on one side of the room, its odor can later be detected on the other side of the room. The molecules of the substance have traveled across the room by traveling in straight lines between collisions. However, they did not necessarily travel straight across the room. It took some time for them to reach the other side because they were colliding with air molecules. This random scattering of the gas molecules is called **diffusion**. As the gas molecules diffuse, they become more and more evenly distributed throughout the room.

All gases do not diffuse at the same rate. We will assume that the rate of diffusion varies directly as the velocity of the molecules. This assumption is supported by experimental evidence. At the same temperature, molecules of low mass diffuse faster than molecules of large mass because they travel faster. They also will pass through a small hole (effuse) more rapidly than the molecules of higher mass.

DEMONSTRATION: Stuff two cotton plugs that are saturated with HCl and NH3(aq) respectively into the ends of a large glass tube. Discuss why the NH4Cl forms where it does. (Graham's Law)

BACKGROUND: Emphasize that the rate of diffusion of gases varies directly with the velocity of the molecules. In two samples of the same gas, the rate of diffusion will be higher for the one having a higher temperature because the velocity of the molecules will be higher.

Diffusion is the random scattering of gas particles.

Molecules of large mass diffuse more slowly than molecules of small mass.

Effusion is the passage of gas molecules through small openings.

a   b   c

FIGURE 18-7. This series of photos shows the diffusion of bromine vapor.

Particles of samples of gases at the same temperature have the same average kinetic energy.

$$K.E. = \frac{1}{2}mv^2$$

SUGGESTION: Stress that kinetic energy relates to *average* speed of molecules in a sample.

SUGGESTION: Stress that at equal temperatures the average kinetic energies of different kinds of molecules are equal; however, their velocities may be different depending upon the molecular mass of each.

Graham's Law: The relative rates of diffusion of two gases under identical conditions vary inversely as the square roots of their molecular masses.

In Section 15:4 we found that if two substances are at the same temperature their kinetic energies must be the same. Thus,

$$KE_1 = KE_2$$
$$\tfrac{1}{2}\, m_1 v_1{}^2 = \tfrac{1}{2}\, m_2 v_2{}^2$$

$$m_1 v_1{}^2 = m_2 v_2{}^2 \quad \text{or} \quad \frac{v_1{}^2}{v_2{}^2} = \frac{m_2}{m_1}$$

which is equivalent to

$$\frac{v_1}{v_2} = \sqrt{\frac{m_2}{m_1}}$$

From this equation, we see that the relative rates of diffusion of two gases vary inversely as the square roots of their molecular masses. This relationship is true only when the temperature is the same for each. This principle was first formulated by a Scottish chemist, Thomas Graham, and is known as Graham's law. **Graham's Law** states: *The relative rates at which two gases under identical conditions of temperature and pressure will pass through a small hole vary inversely as the square roots of the molecular masses of the gases.*

PROBLEMS

10. What is the ratio of the speed of hydrogen molecules to that of oxygen molecules when both gases are at the same temperature? Remember that both elements are diatomic.

10. 3.98

11. What is the ratio of the speed of helium atoms to the speed of radon atoms when both gases are at the same temperature?

12. At a certain temperature, the velocity of oxygen molecules is 0.0760 m/s. What is the velocity of helium atoms at the same temperature?

13. Compute the relative rate of diffusion of helium to argon.

14. Compute the relative rate of diffusion of argon to radon.

11. 7.45

12. 0.215 m/s

13. 3.16

14. 2.36

18:9   GAS DENSITY

The density of gases and vapors is most often expressed in grams per cubic decimeter. We express it in these units because the usual density units, g/cm^3, lead to very small numbers for gases. It is possible to calculate the density of a gas at any temperature and pressure from data collected at any other temperature and pressure. Assuming that the number of particles remains the same, a decrease in temperature would decrease the volume and increase the density. An increase of pressure would decrease the volume and increase the density. The following problem illustrates this calculation. (Remember 1000 cm^3 equals 1 dm^3.)

density = mass per unit volume

If the number of particles remains the same:
1. density increases as pressure increases
2. density decreases as temperature increases

DEMONSTRATION: Set a short, lighted candle in the center of a 400 cm^3 beaker. Fill a 1000 cm^3 beaker with CO_2 gas and proceed to pour it into the one with the lighted candle. Discuss gas densities. Relate to CO_2 fire extinguisher.

EXAMPLE: Density at STP

It is found that 981 cm^3 of a gas collected at 48°C and 98.1 kPa has mass 3.40 g. What is its density at STP?

Use a logical approach. Do not merely "plug" values into an equation.

Solving Process:

(a) The temperature is decreased from 48°C (321 K) to 0°C (273 K). This change decreases the volume and increases the density. We would use

$$\frac{321 \text{ K}}{273 \text{ K}}$$

(b) The pressure is increased from 98.1 kPa to 101.3 kPa. This change decreases the volume and increases the density. Thus, we would use

$$\frac{101.3 \text{ kPa}}{98.1 \text{ kPa}}$$

The solution therefore, is

$$\frac{3.40 \text{ g}}{981 \text{ cm}^3} \left| \frac{1000 \text{ cm}^3}{1 \text{ dm}^3} \right| \frac{321 \text{ K}}{273 \text{ K}} \left| \frac{101.3 \text{ kPa}}{98.1 \text{ kPa}} \right. = 4.21 \text{ g/dm}^3$$

| Original Density | Unit Correction | T Correction | P Correction |

PROBLEMS

15. a. 2.20 g/dm³
    b. 1.16 g/dm³
    c. 13.4 g/dm³
    d. 4.18 g/dm³
    e. 2.66 g/dm³

16. 2.79 g/dm³

17. 5.65 g/dm³

15. Compute the gas density at STP for the following.

   a. 969 cm³ of gas at 64°C and 96.4 kPa has mass 1.64 g

   b. 498 cm³ of gas at 31°C and 103.5 kPa has mass 0.530 g

   c. 833 cm³ of gas at 99°C and 103 kPa has mass 8.30 g

   d. 883 cm³ of gas at 37°C and 115.0 kPa has mass 3.69 g

   e. 2540 cm³ of gas at 25°C and 80.4 kPa has mass 4.91 g

16. The density of a gas is 3.08 g/dm³ at STP. What would its density be at 28°C and 101.0 kPa?

17. At 325 K and 107.0 kPa, a gas has a density of 5.01 g/dm³. What would be its density at STP?

18:10   DEVIATIONS OF REAL GASES

In Sections 18:1 through 18:9 we made two assumptions. The first was that gas molecules have no volume. The second was that gas molecules have no attraction for each other. These assumptions are true only for ideal gases. However, for many **real gases** at low pressure, the molecules closely approach the behavior of ideal gas molecules.

At low pressures, the molecules of both ideal and real gases are far apart. The volume occupied by the molecules is small when compared to the total gas volume. Most of the total volume is empty space. As the pressure is increased, the gas molecules are forced closer. Ideal gas molecules still remain relatively far apart but real gas molecules begin to occupy a significant portion of the total volume. A further increase in pressure does not always cause the predicted decrease in volume. If the molecules are slowed down enough, the van der Waals forces will have an effect.

Not all gases behave as ideal gases.

When the molecules are slowed down, van der Waals forces have an effect on the behavior of real gases.

FIGURE 18-8. An increase in pressure increases the number of molecules per unit volume. Thus, the density of the gas increases.

Roughly, you reduce only the space not occupied by gas molecules.

For most common gases, the ideal gas laws are accurate to 1% at normal laboratory temperatures and pressure. It will be assumed, for convenience, that these gases have ideal gas properties. Generally, the lower the critical temperature of a gas the more closely the gas obeys the ideal gas laws. Using this knowledge, we can estimate that helium more nearly approaches ideal behavior than any of the other gases listed in Table 18-3.

Table 18-3

Critical Temperature	
Gas	Critical Temperature (K)
He	5.19
H_2	33.2
N_2	126.0
O_2	154.2
CO_2	304.4
SO_2	430.6
H_2O	647.3

Critical temperature is the temperature above which no amount of pressure will liquefy a gas.

Gases with low critical temperatures approximate ideal gases.

The ideal gas would have $T_c = 0$ K.

There is a property of real gases that depends upon the attractive forces existing between molecules. If a highly compressed gas is allowed to escape through a small opening, its temperature decreases. This phenomenon is known as the Joule-Thomson effect, after the two scientists who first investigated it. In order to expand, the molecules of the gas must do some work in order to overcome the attractive forces between them. The energy used to do this work comes from their kinetic energy. As their kinetic energy decreases, the temperature falls. Consider the apparatus shown in Figure 18-9. The system shown is completely insulated so that no heat exchange can take place with the surroundings. Such a system is known as an **adiabatic** (ayd ee uh BAT ik) **system.** The temperature of the gas in (b) will be less than its temperature in (a) before the expansion.

(a) Before   Vacuum

(b) After

FIGURE 18-9. For an adiabatic system, the temperature of the gas in (a) is higher than that in (b).

FIGURE 18-10. The temperature of the material released from an aerosol can decreases as the material is forced through the nozzle.

Push button

Valve held closed by can pressure and coil spring, opened by applying pressure to the push button

Gaseous propellant occupies this volume

Gas pressure

Temperature of can decreases as product and propellant are released

Dip tube

Curved bottom to resist pressure

Product and propellant

BIOGRAPHY

Robert Boyle (1627-1691)

One of seven sons of the Earl of Cork, Robert Boyle distinguished his family by entering Eton at the age of eight. His chief contribution to science is his law concerning the behavior of a quantity of gas subjected to a change in pressure when the temperature is held constant.

Boyle also distinguished between a chemical element and a compound and was the first to define chemical reaction and analysis.

An intensely religious man, Boyle also pursued studies and responsibilities in this area. As a director of the East India Company, he worked for the propagation of Christianity in the East and circulated, at his own expense, translations of the Scriptures.

In the scientific realm, he helped found the Royal Society in England. Membership in this society became the ultimate honor for a British scientist.

TECHNOLOGY AND CHEMISTRY

18:11   Photochemical Smog

The word smog was coined in 1905 as a combination of smoke and fog. Today, it is often used as a synonym for air pollution of any kind. To a chemist, photochemical smog means those air pollutants produced by chemical reaction induced by sunlight.

Some of the reactants producing photochemical smog are natural components of the air, such as oxygen and water vapor. The principal source of other reactants is automobile engine exhaust. Industrial factories and electric power generating stations also contribute a significant amount.

Gasoline consists almost entirely of saturated hydrocarbons. Saturated hydrocarbons are chain compounds in which all the carbon-carbon bonds are single bonds. In the combustion of gasoline in the engine cylinder, some hydrocarbons do not react completely and are expelled in the exhaust as unsaturated hydrocarbons. Unsaturated hydrocarbons contain double and triple bonds between carbon atoms. The compound ethene, $CH_2{=}CH_2$ is produced in this way. In addition, some of the nitrogen in the air combines with oxygen to form oxides of nitrogen, such as NO and NO_2.

Small quantities of ozone, O_3, occur naturally in the air as a result of the action of sunlight on oxygen molecules.

$$O_2 + h\nu \rightarrow 2O \qquad O + O_2 \rightarrow O_3$$

The ozone is split by a quantum of sunlight into an oxygen molecule and a free oxygen atom which is highly reactive. The oxygen atom reacts with water vapor to form the highly reactive hydroxyl radical. The ozone oxidizes NO to NO_2.

$$O + H_2O \rightarrow 2OH \qquad O_3 + NO \rightarrow NO_2 + O_2$$

The hydroxyl radical* reacts with the unsaturated hydrocarbons to produce a number of products. These products are eventually oxidized to CO_2 if they do not react with other compounds in the meantime. However, some intermediate products react with NO_2 to produce peroxyacetyl nitrate, PAN, which is poisonous to plants and animals alike. It is especially irritating to the eyes.

$$CH_3-\overset{\overset{\textstyle O}{\|}}{C}-O-O-NO_2$$
$$\text{PAN}$$

There are also other smog products that can irritate and poison cells. Sunlight provides the activation energy for reactions of oxygen, unsaturated hydrocarbons, and nitrogen oxides to produce pernitric acid, carbon monoxide, ozone, organic peroxycompounds, and aldehydes.

The long term effects of photochemical smog on humans are unknown. However, research seems to indicate an increased susceptibility to bronchitis, emphysema, and lung cancer for people living in high smog areas.

The introduction of catalytic converters to automobile exhaust systems has helped reduce photochemical smog in some areas. The converter causes the hydrocarbons to be oxidized to CO_2 and H_2O before they leave the automobile.

Photochemical smog is a significant problem in areas which experience a phenomenon known as temperature inversion. This effect is said to occur when air temperature increases with altitude. The density of the air at ground level is greater than that at higher elevations. The pollutants then tend to remain at ground level rather than be dispersed into the upper air. As a result of temperature inversion, the concentration of pollutants increases.

*A radical is a part of a molecule which lacks a complete octet of electrons.

SUMMARY

1. An ideal gas is an imaginary gas whose particles have no diameter and no mutual attraction. **18:1**

2. The volume of a gas depends not only on the number of particles but also on temperature and pressure. **18:1**

3. Standard temperature and pressure (STP) are 0°C and 101.325 kilopascals. Gas volumes are usually reported in m^3 or dm^3 at STP. **18:1**

4. Gas pressure depends on the number of molecules per unit volume and the average kinetic energy of the molecules. **18:1**

5. Boyle's law states that, at constant temperature, the volume of a gas varies inversely as its pressure ($V = k/P$). **18:2-18:3**

6. Dalton's law states that the total pressure in a container is the sum of the partial pressures of the individual gases in the container. **18:4**

7. Charles' law states that, at constant pressure, the volume of a gas varies directly with the absolute temperature ($V = k'T$). **18:5-18:6**

8. The absolute temperature scale is defined by two points. One point is absolute zero (0 K). The other point is the triple point of water (273.16 K). **18:5**

9. When applying the combined gas laws, the correction for temperature and pressure have no effect upon each other. **18:7**

10. Diffusion is the process by which gases spread to become evenly distributed throughout the entire space in which they are confined. All gases do not diffuse or effuse at the same rate. **18:8**

11. Graham's law states that, under constant temperature and pressure, the relative diffusion rates of two gases vary inversely as the square roots of their molecular masses. **18:8**

12. Gas density varies directly as pressure and inversely as temperature. It is usually expressed in grams per cubic decimeter (g/dm^3). **18:9**

13. The particles of real gases, as opposed to ideal gases, have both volume and mutual attraction. At high pressures and low temperatures, these two factors take effect. **18:10**

14. At normal laboratory temperatures and pressures, most common gases behave nearly as ideal gases. The lower the critical temperature of a gas, the more nearly it behaves as an ideal gas. **18:10**

VOCABULARY

point masses **18:1**	Dalton's Law **18:4**
ideal gas **18:1**	Charles' Law **18:5**
standard pressure **18:1**	diffusion **18:8**
standard temperature **18:1**	Graham's Law **18:8**
STP **18:1**	real gases **18:10**
Boyle's Law **18:2**	adiabatic system **18:10**

PROBLEMS

2. low pressure, high temperature

1. What are the characteristics of an ideal gas?
2. Under what conditions do real gases behave in a manner similar to ideal gases?
3. Theoretically, what would happen to a gas that is cooled to absolute zero? In reality, what occurs?
4. Why is it that if the kinetic energies of two different gases at the same temperature are equal, their rates of diffusion are not equal?
5. What is the Joule-Thomson effect?

6. Find the volume of a dry gas at STP if it measures 806 cm^3 at 26°C and 103.0 kPa.

7. A chemist collects 96.0 cm^3 of gas over water at 27°C and 122.0 kPa. What volume would the dry gas occupy at 70°C and 127.0 kPa?

8. A chemist collects 372 cm^3 of gas over water at 90°C and 111.0 kPa. What volume would the dry gas occupy at 2°C and 98.0 kPa?

9. A chemist collects 7.29 cm^3 of gas at 6°C and 100.8 kPa over water. What volume would the dry gas occupy at 22°C and 114.3 kPa?

10. 30.0 cm^3 of a gas are collected over water at 20°C and 93.0 kPa. What volume would the dry gas occupy at STP?

11. The following gas volumes were collected over water under the indicated conditions. Correct each volume to the volume that the dry gas would occupy at standard pressure and the indicated temperature (T is constant).

   a. 871 cm^3 at 12°C and 84.1 kPa   **c.** 7.83 m^3 at 20°C and 107 kPa
   b. 317 cm^3 at 26°C and 115.7 kPa   **d.** 964 cm^3 at 29°C and 111.5 kPa

12. At STP, a gas measures 325 cm^3. What will it measure at 20°C and 93.3 kPa?

13. A chemist collects 8.00 cm^3 of gas over water at STP. What volume would the dry gas occupy at STP?

6. 748 cm^3
7. 102 cm^3
8. 118 cm^3
9. 6.74 cm^3
10. 25.0 cm^3
11. a. 711 cm^3
   b. 351 cm^3
   c. 8.09 m^3
   d. 1020 cm^3
12. 379 cm^3
13. 7.95 cm^3

See Teacher Guide for detailed solutions.

REVIEW

1. What requirements must be met by the escaping molecules when a liquid at room temperature evaporates?

2. State Le Chatelier's principle.

3. What is meant by sublimation?

4. What requirements must be met to liquify a gas?

5. Sketch a sample phase diagram, labeling all parts.

6. What is meant by the word "dynamic" in the phrase, "dynamic equilibrium"?

7. Define melting point in terms of vapor pressure.

8. How much energy is needed to change 1.70 g of ice at −12°C to steam at 140°C?

9. How many moles of CaCl$_2$ are found in 146 g CaCl$_2$?

2. A system at equilibrium will shift so as to relieve an outside stress.

3. direct solid to vapor phase change

4. high pressure, low temperature

6. Changes that are the reverse of each other are occurring at the same rate.

7. The temperature at which the vapor pressures of the solid and liquid phases are equal.

8. 5300 J

9. 1.32 mol CaCl$_2$

ONE MORE STEP

1. Using a bicycle tire pump or a football inflating pump and an air pressure gauge such as a tire gauge, see if you can demonstrate Boyle's law. Don't forget that the air in the pump is already at atmospheric pressure before you depress the plunger.

2. There are a number of approximate equations that deal with the behavior of real gases. Using one of these equations, calculate the percent deviation from ideal nitrogen gas at 0°C and 40 000 kPa pressure.

READINGS

Scott, Arthur F., "The Invention of the Balloon and the Birth of Modern Chemistry," *Scientific American*, Vol. 250, No. 1 (January 1984), pp. 126-137.

The steam from this geothermal field produces mechanical energy. The mechanical energy is converted to electrical energy that is used by area residents and industries. How can the amount of steam available be determined? How are gases used to do work? Is steam the only gas produced in a geothermal field?

GASES AND THE MOLE

Chapter 19 continues the study of gases focusing on the ideal gas law and gas reaction calculations in conjunction with varying conditions studied in the previous chapter.

DEMONSTRATION: Put 15 cm^3 of concentrated HCl in a 100 cm^3 graduated cylinder. Add enough water to fill the cylinder completely. Place a 7 cm piece of magnesium ribbon in the cylinder. Stopper the cylinder with a 1-hole rubber stopper and immediately invert the cylinder into a beaker of water. Ask students why only a specific amount of hydrogen gas was produced. Discuss the mole relationship between magnesium and hydrogen gas. **CAUTION:** *HCl is corrosive.*

In Chapter 18, we examined the effect of temperature and pressure on the volume of a constant mass of gas. The principles hold true for any gas exhibiting ideal behavior. Different gases, however, have molecules and atoms of different masses. In this chapter, we will look at the effect of the number of particles on the other gas variables, particularly volume. We will also find out how to obtain mass measurements of gases at various temperatures and pressures.

GOALS:
• You will gain an understanding of the relationship between the mole and gas volumes.
• You will use the concept of molar gas volumes to solve gas reaction problems.
• You will learn the relationship between gases and work.

19:1 DEVELOPING AVOGADRO'S PRINCIPLE

Suppose we place two different gases at exactly the same temperature and pressure in separate containers that have exactly the same volume. At a given temperature, all gas molecules will have the same average kinetic energy regardless of size or mass. Massive molecules will travel slowly, lighter molecules will travel more rapidly. However, the average kinetic energy, $mv^2/2$, will be the same for all. If the kinetic energies are equal, any difference in pressure exerted by the gases is determined by the number of molecules of each gas. Since we have already said the two gases are at the same pressure, there must be an equal number of molecules in the two containers. *At equal temperatures and equal pressures, equal volumes of gases contain the same number of molecules.* This statement is called **Avogadro's principle,** after Amadeo Avogadro. When he proposed the principle, in 1811, the kinetic theory had not been developed. As we read in Section 5:2, Avogadro developed his principle to explain some of the observations made by Gay-Lussac. Gay-Lussac had observed that two gases always react in such a way that the combining volumes can be expressed in small whole numbers.

The number of gas molecules in a container determines the pressure at a given temperature.

Avogadro's principle states that under similar conditions, equal volumes of gases contain the same number of molecules.

FIGURE 19-1. The research of Gay-Lussac was used by Avogadro in developing his principle dealing with gas volumes.

Proust had previously stated his law of definite proportions. Avogadro knew that one molecule of chlorine always united with one molecule of hydrogen. He also knew that two molecules of hydrogen chloride were formed. He therefore concluded that equal volumes of gases must contain equal numbers of molecules. Avogadro's principle has been verified so often that it is sometimes called a law. One consequence of Avogadro's principle is that the value of the constant k, in

$$V = \frac{k}{P}$$

The values of the constants in the gas laws are the same for all gases.

is the same for all gases. Similarly, the value of the constant in $V = kT$ does not change. It is the same for all gases.

19:2 MOLAR VOLUME

Let n represent the number of moles of a gas, and let V represent the volume. Then, for two gases under similar conditions, Avogadro's principle states: If $V_1 = V_2$, then $n_1 = n_2$. Conversely, if the number of moles of two gases under similar conditions is equal, then their volumes are equal. Thus, we can conclude that 1 mole of any gas at STP will occupy the same volume as 1 mole of any other gas at STP. For example, 1 mole of oxygen has mass 32.0 g and 1000 cm³ of oxygen has mass 1.43 g. Therefore, a mole of oxygen will occupy

$$\frac{32.0 \text{ g}}{1 \text{ mol}} \left| \frac{1000 \text{ cm}^3}{1.43 \text{ g}} \right| \frac{1 \text{ dm}^3}{1000 \text{ cm}^3} = 22.4 \text{ dm}^3/\text{mol}$$

One mole of hydrogen gas has mass 2.016 g and 1000 cm³ of hydrogen has mass 0.0899 g. We find that 1 mole of hydrogen occupies

One mole of any gas at STP occupies 22.4 dm³.

$$\frac{2.016 \text{ g}}{1 \text{ mol}} \left| \frac{1000 \text{ cm}^3}{0.0899 \text{ g}} \right| \frac{1 \text{ dm}^3}{1000 \text{ cm}^3} = 22.4 \text{ dm}^3/\text{mol}$$

The molar volume of a gas is the volume of 1 mole of the gas at STP.

The volume occupied by 1 mole of any gas under standard conditions is 22.4 dm³. This volume is called the **molar volume** of the gas at STP.

$$\frac{1.43 \text{ g}}{1 \text{ dm}^3} = \frac{32.0 \text{ g}}{x(V \text{ of 1 mol at STP})}$$

Molar volume of O_2 = 22.4 dm³ at STP

FIGURE 19-2. One mole of oxygen gas occupies 22.4 dm³ at STP.

19:3 IDEAL GAS EQUATION

We are now in a position to combine all four variables concerned with the physical characteristics of gases. These variables are pressure, temperature, volume, and number of particles. Charles' law states that volume varies directly as the absolute temperature. Boyle's law states that volume varies inversely as the pressure. We have combined the two as

$$V = k''\left(\frac{T}{P}\right), \text{ or } PV = k''T$$

The constant, k'', depends upon the number of particles present. Therefore, it will change if we add or remove molecules (if n is increased or decreased). We can write the equation using two constants, n and R, to replace the k''.

$$k'' = nR$$

therefore,

$$PV = nRT$$

The equation $PV = nRT$ is called the **ideal gas equation.** The value of the new constant R can be obtained by substituting into the equation a set of known values of n, P, V, and T. We know that standard pressure P is 101.325 kPa, molar volume V is 22.4 dm³, standard temperature T is 273 K, and the number of moles n is 1.

$$(101.325 \text{ kPa})(22.4 \text{ dm}^3) = (1 \text{ mol})(R)(273 \text{ K})$$

$$R = \frac{(101.325 \text{ kPa})(22.4 \text{ dm}^3)}{(1 \text{ mol})(273 \text{ K})}$$

$$R = 8.31 \text{ dm}^3 \cdot \text{kPa/mol} \cdot \text{K}$$

This value for R is constant and can always be used if the units of the other quantities are not changed. We can determine the number of moles in a quantity of a substance by dividing its mass by its formula mass. Any problem that can be solved by this equation can also be solved by direct application of the gas laws.

The ideal gas equation is $PV = nRT$.

R is a constant = 8.31 dm³·kPa/mol·K

PROBLEMS

1. 162 kPa
2. 0.0138 mol
3. 16.2 dm^3
4. 85.8 K or −187°C
5. 277 kPa

1. What pressure will be exerted by 0.622 mol of gas contained in a 9.22 dm^3 vessel at 16°C?

2. How many moles of gas will occupy a 486 cm^3 flask at 10°C and 66.7 kPa pressure?

3. What volume will be occupied by 0.684 mol of gas at 99.1 kPa and 9°C?

4. At what temperature is a gas if 0.0851 mol of it are found in a 604 cm^3 vessel at 100.4 kPa?

5. What pressure is exerted by 0.00306 mol of gas in a 25.9 cm^3 container at 9°C?

19:4   MOLECULAR MASS DETERMINATION

Molecular mass of a gas can be found from laboratory measurements.

The ideal gas equation can be used to solve a variety of problems. One type, which we will illustrate here, is the calculation of the molecular mass of a gas from laboratory measurements. Such calculations are of importance to the chemist in determining the formulas and structures of unknown compounds.

EXAMPLE: Molecular Mass from Gas Measurements

BACKGROUND: Note that this simple procedure includes an application of
Boyle's law
Charles' law
Avogadro's hypothesis
The kinetic-molecular theory
and—if the gas is collected over water—Dalton's law.

Suppose we measure the mass of the vapor of an unknown compound contained in a 273 cm^3 gas bulb. We find that the bulb contains 0.750 g of gas at 97.2 kPa pressure and 61°C. What is the molecular mass of the gas?

Solving Process:
The number of moles n of a substance is equal to mass m divided by the molecular mass M. Therefore, the ideal gas equation may be written

This equation should be memorized.
$$M = \frac{mRT}{PV}$$

$$PV = \frac{mRT}{M}, \text{ or } M = \frac{mRT}{PV}$$

Before we can substitute the known values into the ideal gas equation, °C must be converted to K. We get the following expression

The correct unit on an answer is a good check that the correct answer has been found.

$$\frac{\underset{m}{0.750 \text{ g}}}{\underset{P}{97.2 \text{ kPa}}} \left| \frac{\underset{R}{8.31 \text{ dm}^3 \cdot \text{kPa}}}{\text{mol} \cdot \text{K}} \right| \frac{\underset{T}{334 \text{ K}}}{\underset{V}{273 \text{ cm}^3}} \left| \frac{1000 \text{ cm}^3}{1 \text{ dm}^3} \right. = 78.4 \text{ g/mol}$$

conversion to dm^3

The solution is, therefore, 78.4 g/mol. Note that all other units in the problem divide out. The units remaining at the end of the problem serve as a check on the answer itself. In this problem, an answer with units of °C/kPa, or any other except g/mol, would be wrong. If we solve a problem and the units of our answer are not the units of the quantity which we set out to determine, we have made an error. The wrong units can often serve as a starting point in locating an error.

This modified form of the ideal gas equation

$$PV = \frac{mRT}{M}$$

may be used in many other types of problems.

PROBLEMS

6. What is the molecular mass of a gas if 150.0 cm³ have mass 0.922 g at 99°C and 107.0 kPa?

7. What will be the density of oxygen at 100.5 kPa and 23°C?

8. What is the molecular mass of a gas if 3.59 g of it occupy 4.34 dm³ at 99.2 kPa and 31°C?

9. What is the molecular mass of a gas if 0.858 g of it occupies 150.0 cm³ at 106.3 kPa and 2°C?

10. What is the molecular mass of a gas if 8.11 g of it occupy 2.38 dm³ at 109.1 kPa and 10.0°C?

6. 178 g/mol
7. 1.31 g/dm³
8. 21.1 g/mol
9. 123 g/mol
10. 73.5 g/mol

19:5 MASS-GAS VOLUME RELATIONSHIPS

In Section 6:4, we discussed a method of finding the mass of one substance produced by a specific mass of another substance. It is usually awkward to measure the mass of a gas. It is easier to measure the volume under existing conditions and convert to the volume under standard conditions. One mole of gas molecules occupies 22.4 dm³ (STP). This knowledge enables us to determine the volume of gas in a reaction by using the balanced equation for the reaction.

Stoichiometry is the quantitative study of chemical reactions.

EXAMPLE: Mass-Gas Volume

What volume of hydrogen at STP can be produced from the reaction of 6.54 g of zinc with hydrochloric acid?

Solving Process:

(a) Write a balanced equation for the reaction.

$$2HCl(aq) + Zn(cr) \rightarrow H_2(g) + ZnCl_2(aq)$$

A balanced equation is necessary for obtaining correct answers to chemical problems.

(b) Remember that the coefficients in chemical equations express mole ratios. Therefore, express the mass (6.54 g) of zinc in moles.

$$\frac{6.54 \text{ g Zn}}{} \left| \frac{1 \text{ mol Zn}}{65.4 \text{ g Zn}} \right. \cdots$$

Find the number of moles of reactant and product.

(c) Determine the mole ratio. Note that 1 mole of zinc yields 1 mole of hydrogen gas.

$$2HCl(aq) + Zn(cr) \rightarrow H_2(g) + ZnCl_2(aq)$$
$$1 \text{ mole} \rightarrow 1 \text{ mole}$$

Find the moles of hydrogen produced.

$$\frac{6.54 \text{ g Zn}}{} \left| \frac{1 \text{ mol Zn}}{65.4 \text{ g Zn}} \right| \frac{1 \text{ mol } H_2}{1 \text{ mol Zn}} \cdots$$

One mole of gas occupies 22.4 dm^3 at STP.

(d) Express the volume of hydrogen in terms of dm^3 of hydrogen, since 1 mole of hydrogen occupies 22.4 dm^3.

$$\frac{6.54 \text{ g Zn}}{} \left| \frac{1 \text{ mol Zn}}{65.4 \text{ g Zn}} \right| \frac{1 \text{ mol } H_2}{1 \text{ mol Zn}} \left| \frac{22.4 \text{ dm}^3 H_2}{1 \text{ mol } H_2} \right. = 2.24 \text{ dm}^3 H_2$$

We conclude that 2.24 dm^3 of hydrogen will be produced when 6.54 g of zinc react completely with hydrochloric acid.

All mass-gas volume problems in this book can be solved in a manner similar to that shown in the example. Try to keep in mind the following four steps.

Step 1. *Write a balanced equation.*
Step 2. *Find the number of moles of the given substance.*
Step 3. *Find the ratio of the moles of given substance to the moles of required substance.*
Step 4. *Express moles of gas in terms of volume of gas.*

Remember that 1 mole of gas occupies 22.4 dm^3 at STP.

19:6   GAS VOLUME-MASS RELATIONSHIPS

It is also possible to determine the mass of one substance formed in a reaction when the volume of a gaseous substance is known.

EXAMPLE: Gas Volume-Mass

How many grams of NaCl can be produced by the reaction of 112 cm^3 of chlorine at STP with an excess of sodium?

Solving Process:
(a) Determine the balanced equation.

$$2Na(cr) + Cl_2(g) \rightarrow 2NaCl(cr)$$

(b) Express the volume of chlorine as moles of chlorine at STP.

$$\frac{112 \text{ cm}^3 Cl_2}{} \left| \frac{1 \text{ dm}^3}{1000 \text{ cm}^3} \right| \frac{1 \text{ mol } Cl_2}{22.4 \text{ dm}^3} \cdots$$

(c) Determine the mole ratio.

$$2Na(cr) + Cl_2 \rightarrow 2NaCl(cr)$$
$$1 \text{ mole} \rightarrow 2 \text{ moles}$$

$$\frac{112 \text{ cm}^3 \text{ Cl}_2}{} \left| \frac{1 \text{ dm}^3}{1000 \text{ cm}^3} \right| \frac{1 \text{ mol}}{22.4 \text{ dm}^3} \left| \frac{2 \text{ mol NaCl}}{1 \text{ mol Cl}_2} \right. \ldots$$

(d) Convert moles of NaCl to grams of NaCl.

$$1 \text{ mole of NaCl has mass: Na } 1(23.0 \text{ g}) = 23.0 \text{ g}$$
$$\text{Cl } 1(35.5 \text{ g}) = 35.5 \text{ g}$$
$$\text{formula mass of NaCl} = \overline{58.5 \text{ g}}$$

Place the conversion factor so a previous unit divides out.

$$\frac{112 \text{ cm}^3 \text{ Cl}_2}{} \left| \frac{1 \text{ dm}^3}{1000 \text{ cm}^3} \right| \frac{1 \text{ mol Cl}_2}{22.4 \text{ dm}^3} \left| \frac{2 \text{ mol NaCl}}{1 \text{ mol Cl}_2} \right| \frac{58.5 \text{ g NaCl}}{1 \text{ mol NaCl}} = 0.585 \text{ g NaCl}$$

We conclude that 112 cm^3 of Cl$_2$, plus enough sodium to react completely with the Cl$_2$, will yield 0.585 g of NaCl.

Note that the solution varied from the steps given in our mass-gas volume procedure. We began with gas volume and found the mass of solid produced. In the first example, we started with the mass of solid and found the volume of gas produced. However, we are still concerned with the mole relationships. The procedure followed in the second example is as follows.

Step 1. *Write a balanced equation.*
Step 2. *Change volume of gas to moles of gas.*
Step 3. *Determine the ratio of moles of given to moles of required substance.*
Step 4. *Express moles of reacting substance as grams of reacting substance.*

After you have worked enough problems to become familiar with these procedures, you should be able to vary your approach to suit the problem.

PROBLEMS

11. An excess of hydrogen reacts with 14.0 grams of nitrogen. How many cm^3 of ammonia will be produced at STP?

12. How many cm^3 of hydrogen at STP will be produced from 28.0 grams of zinc reacting with an excess of sulfuric acid?

13. Bromine will react with 5.60×10^3 cm^3 of hydrogen to yield what mass of hydrogen bromide at STP?

14. How many grams of antimony(III) chloride can be produced from 3570 cm^3 of chlorine at STP reacting with an excess of antimony?

SUGGESTION: You may wish to give the students the equations so that they can concentrate on the stoichiometry.

11. 22 400 cm^3 NH$_3$
12. 9590 cm^3 H$_2$
13. 41 g HBr
14. 24.3 SbCl$_3$

19:7   VOLUME-VOLUME RELATIONSHIPS

The equation for the complete burning of methane is

$$CH_4(g) + 2O_2(g) \rightarrow CO_2(g) + 2H_2O(g)$$

Gas is more easily measured by volume than by mass.

Notice that all reactants and all products are gases. Gas is more easily measured by volume than by mass. Therefore, we will solve problems involving gases by converting moles to dm^3, instead of converting moles to grams.

EXAMPLE: Volume-Volume

How many dm^3 of oxygen are required to burn 1.00 dm^3 of methane? (All of these substances are gases measured at the same temperature and pressure.)

Solving Process:
(a) Write a balanced equation.

$$CH_4(g) + 2O_2(g) \rightarrow CO_2(g) + 2H_2O(g)$$

(b) Change to moles.

$$\frac{1.00 \text{ dm}^3 \text{ CH}_4}{} \left| \frac{1 \text{ mol}}{22.4 \text{ dm}^3} \cdots \right.$$

In volume-volume problems, the coefficients of the balanced equation are used to determine the ratio of combining gas volumes.

(c) Determine the ratio of moles from the equation.

$$CH_4 + 2O_2 \quad \rightarrow (\underline{\hspace{2cm}}) + (\underline{\hspace{2cm}})$$
1 mole + 2 moles

$$\frac{1.00 \text{ dm}^3 \text{ CH}_4}{} \left| \frac{1 \text{ mol}}{22.4 \text{ dm}^3} \right| \frac{2 \text{ mol O}_2}{1 \text{ mol CH}_4} \cdots$$

(d) Change moles to dm^3.

$$\frac{1.00 \text{ dm}^3 \text{ CH}_4}{} \left| \frac{1 \text{ mol}}{22.4 \text{ dm}^3} \right| \frac{2 \text{ mol O}_2}{1 \text{ mol CH}_4} \left| \frac{22.4 \text{ dm}^3}{1 \text{ mol}} \right| = 2.00 \text{ dm}^3 \text{ O}_2$$

We conclude that 1.00 dm^3 of methane will be completely burned by 2.00 dm^3 of O_2. This problem is no different from the gas volume-mass problems we discussed in the previous section, except that we start and end with volume.

There is an easier way to solve volume-volume problems. The volume of one mole of a solid or liquid may be larger or smaller than the volume of 1 mole of a different solid or liquid. One mole of any gas, however, occupies the same volume, 22.4 dm^3. It is, therefore, possible to eliminate the second and third steps of our procedure. We can find the ratio of moles of given to moles of required by inspecting the balanced equation.

EXAMPLE: Volume-Volume

We will solve the preceding example by a different method called inspection.

Solving Process:

(a) Write a balanced equation.

$$CH_4(g) + 2O_2(g) \rightarrow CO_2(g) + 2H_2O(g)$$

(b) One mole of CH_4 unites with 2 moles of O_2, or 1 dm^3 of CH_4 unites with 2 dm^3 of O_2, or 22.4 dm^3 of CH_4 unites with 44.8 dm^3 of O_2.

The ratio of combining gas volumes is the same as the ratio of combining moles.

$$\frac{1.00 \text{ dm}^3 \text{ CH}_4}{} \left| \frac{2 \text{ dm}^3 \text{ O}_2}{1 \text{ dm}^3 \text{ CH}_4} = 2.00 \text{ dm}^3 \text{ O}_2 \right.$$

Note that the ratio of CH_4 to O_2 is $\frac{1}{2}$, or of O_2 to CH_4 is $\frac{2}{1}$. Both 2 and 1 are whole numbers. A fractional coefficient would indicate a fractional atom or molecule, and these do not exist.

The ratio of the combining volumes is the same as the ratio of the combining moles. Thus, you can make use of the coefficients of the balanced equation as the ratios of the combining volumes.

EXAMPLE: Volume-Volume

How many dm^3 of CO_2 will be produced by burning completely 5.00 dm^3 of ethane C_2H_6? (All of these substances are gases measured at the same temperature and pressure.)

Solving Process:

(a) Write a balanced equation.

$$2C_2H_6(g) + 7O_2(g) \rightarrow 4CO_2(g) + 6H_2O(g)$$

(b) Note that 2 moles or 2 dm^3 of ethane yield 4 moles or 4 dm^3 of CO_2. Therefore,

$$\frac{5.00 \text{ dm}^3 \text{ C}_2\text{H}_6}{} \left| \frac{4 \text{ dm}^3 \text{ CO}_2}{2 \text{ dm}^3 \text{ C}_2\text{H}_6} = 10.0 \text{ dm}^3 \text{ CO}_2 \right.$$

We conclude that 5.00 dm^3 of ethane will yield 10.0 dm^3 of CO_2.

PROBLEMS

15. What volume of oxygen is required to burn completely 401 cm^3 of butane, C_4H_{10}? (All substances are gases measured at the same temperature and pressure.)

16. What volume of bromine gas is produced if 75.2 dm^3 of Cl_2 react with excess HBr? (All substances are gases measured at the same temperature and pressure.) $Cl_2(g) + 2HBr(g) \rightarrow Br_2(g) + 2HCl(g)$

15. 2610 cm^3 O_2
16. 75.2 dm^3 Br_2

17. 2.50×10^2 cm^3 O$_2$
18. 3760 m^3 H$_2$

17. What volume of O$_2$ is required to oxidize 499 cm^3 of NO to NO$_2$? (Assume STP.)

18. C$_6$H$_{14}$(g) → C$_6$H$_6$(g) + 4H$_2$(g). What volume of hydrogen is produced when 941 m^3 of C$_6$H$_6$ are produced? (All substances are gases measured at the same temperature and pressure.)

19:8 LIMITING REACTANTS

DEMONSTRATION: See Teacher Guide.

Suppose 4.00 dm^3 of hydrogen and 1.00 dm^3 of oxygen are placed in a container and ignited by means of a spark. An explosion occurs and water is formed.

$$2H_2(g) + O_2(g) \rightarrow 2H_2O(g)$$

We know that two volumes of hydrogen are all that can combine with one volume of oxygen, so 2.00 dm^3 of hydrogen are left unreacted. To take another example, let us drop nine moles of sodium into a vessel containing four moles of chlorine. If we warm the container slightly, the sodium will burn with a bright yellow flame, and crystals of sodium chloride will be formed.

$$2Na(cr) + Cl_2(g) \rightarrow 2NaCl(cr)$$

A "limiting reactant" is completely used in a reaction.

SUGGESTION: Emphasize that the number of moles is the basis on which judgment is made.

We know that one mole of Cl$_2$ will react completely with two moles of Na, so it is clear that one mole of sodium will remain unreacted. For these two reactions we say that the hydrogen and sodium are in "excess" and that the oxygen and chlorine are "limiting reactants." In a chemical reaction, the **limiting reactant** is the one which is completely consumed in the reaction. It is not present in sufficient quantity to react with all of the other reactant(s). The reactants that are left are said to be in **excess.** The amount of product is therefore determined by the limiting reactant.

EXAMPLE: Limiting Reactants

How many grams of CO$_2$ are formed if 10.0 g of carbon are burned in 20.0 dm^3 of oxygen? (Assume STP.)

Solving Process:
(a) Write a balanced equation.

$$C(cr) + O_2(g) \rightarrow CO_2(g)$$

(b) Change both quantities to moles.

$$\frac{10.0 \text{ g\!\!\!/C} \mid 1 \text{ mol C}}{\mid 12.0 \text{ g\!\!\!/}} = 0.833 \text{ mol C}$$

$$\frac{20.0 \text{ dm}^3 \text{ O}_2 \mid 1 \text{ mol O}_2}{\mid 22.4 \text{ dm}^3 \text{ O}_2} = 0.893 \text{ mol O}_2$$

(c) The equation indicates that

$$1 \text{ mole C} + 1 \text{ mole O}_2 \rightarrow 1 \text{ mole CO}_2$$

Because there are fewer moles of carbon, the carbon limits the reaction. Some oxygen (0.060 mole) is left unreacted. We call carbon the limiting reactant.

(d) Complete the problem on the basis of the limiting reactant.

$$\frac{0.833 \text{ mol C}}{} \left| \frac{1 \text{ mol CO}_2}{1 \text{ mol C}} \right| \frac{44.0 \text{ g}}{1 \text{ mol CO}_2} = 36.7 \text{ g CO}_2$$

We conclude that 10.0 g of carbon will react with excess O_2 to form 36.7 g of CO_2. Notice that in the example, all coefficients are 1. When coefficients other than 1 are introduced, as in the following example, an additional calculation is necessary.

EXAMPLE: Limiting Reactants

How many grams of aluminum sulfide are formed if 9.00 g of aluminum react with 8.00 g of sulfur?

Solving Process:

(a)
$$2Al(cr) + 3S(cr) \rightarrow Al_2S_3(cr)$$

(b)
$$\frac{9.00 \text{ g Al}}{} \left| \frac{1 \text{ mol Al}}{27.0 \text{ g Al}} \right. = 0.333 \text{ mol Al}$$

2 moles Al yield 1 mole Al_2S_3.

$$\frac{0.333 \text{ mol Al}}{} \left| \frac{1 \text{ mol Al}_2S_3}{2 \text{ mol Al}} \right. = 0.167 \text{ mol Al}_2S_3$$

$$\frac{8.00 \text{ g S}}{} \left| \frac{1 \text{ mol S}}{32.1 \text{ g S}} \right. = 0.249 \text{ mol S}$$

3 moles S yield 1 mole Al_2S_3

$$\frac{0.249 \text{ mol S}}{} \left| \frac{1 \text{ mol Al}_2S_3}{3 \text{ mol S}} \right. = 0.0830 \text{ mol Al}_2S_3$$

(c) 0.0830 mole of Al_2S_3 is less than 0.167 mole of Al_2S_3. Using all of the sulfur would produce less product than using all of the aluminum. Therefore, sulfur is the limiting reactant and aluminum is in excess. Complete the problem on the basis of the limiting reactant.

⅓ mol of Al requires ½ mol of S. Since only ¼ mol of S is available, S is the limiting reactant.

$$\frac{0.0830 \text{ mol Al}_2S_3}{} \left| \frac{150 \text{ g Al}_2S_3}{1 \text{ mol Al}_2S_3} \right. = 12.5 \text{ g Al}_2S_3$$

12.5 g of Al_2S_3 will be produced from 8.00 g sulfur and an excess of aluminum.

Thus, using sulfur as the limiting reactant, 0.0830 times the formula mass of aluminum sulfide will give the mass of aluminum sulfide produced. An alternate method for determining the limiting reactant is as follows.

EXAMPLE: Alternate Method

How many grams of aluminum sulfide are formed if 9.00 g of aluminum react with 8.00 g of sulfur?

Solving Process:

(a) $$2Al(cr) + 3S(cr) \rightarrow Al_2S_3(cr)$$

(b) According to the equation, 2 moles Al require 3 moles S.

$$\frac{9.00 \text{ g Al}}{} \left| \frac{1 \text{ mol Al}}{27.0 \text{ g Al}} \right| \frac{3 \text{ mol S}}{2 \text{ mol Al}} = 0.500 \text{ mol S}$$

Since we have only

$$\frac{8.00 \text{ g S}}{} \left| \frac{1 \text{ mol S}}{32.1 \text{ g S}} \right. = 0.249 \text{ mol S}$$

sulfur is the limiting reactant. If we had more than 0.500 mole of sulfur, aluminum would have been the limiting reactant.

PROBLEMS

19. 1.63 g Br_2
20. 0.746 dm^3 CO
21. 0.456 g S
22. 58.0 cm^3 Cl_2O

19. $2NaBr(aq) + 2H_2SO_4(aq) + MnO_2(cr) \rightarrow Br_2(l) + MnSO_4(aq) + 2H_2O(l) + Na_2SO_4(aq)$. What mass of bromine could be produced from 2.10 g of NaBr and 9.42 g of H_2SO_4?

20. $2Ca_3(PO_4)_2(cr) + 6SiO_2(cr) + 10C(cr) \rightarrow P_4(g) + 6CaSiO_3(cr) + 10CO(g)$. What volume in dm^3 of carbon monoxide gas is produced from 4.14 g $Ca_3(PO_4)_2$ and 1.20 g SiO_2? (Assume STP.)

21. $H_2S(g) + I_2(aq) \rightarrow 2HI(aq) + S(cr)$. What mass of sulfur is produced by 4.11 g of I_2 and 317 cm^3 of H_2S at STP?

22. $2Cl_2(g) + HgO(cr) \rightarrow HgCl_2(cr) + Cl_2O(g)$. What volume in cm^3 of Cl_2O can be produced from 116 cm^3 of Cl_2 at STP and 7.62 g HgO?

19:9 NONSTANDARD CONDITIONS

It is important to keep in mind when working problems of the type described in Sections 19:5 through 19:8 that pressure and temperature affect the volume of a gas. Thus, the equality 22.4 dm^3 = 1 mol is true only at STP. If a problem involves a gas under conditions other than standard conditions, it is necessary, before changing gas volume to moles of gas, to calculate the gas volume under standard conditions. The secret to success in these problems is to remember that the central step (moles of given to moles of requested) must take place at STP. Thus, if you are given a volume of gas at other than STP, you must convert to STP before performing the moles to moles step in the solving process. On the other hand, if you are requested to find the volume of a gas at conditions other than STP, you must convert the volume after the moles to moles step. Let us look at some examples.

EXAMPLE: Mass-Gas Volume

What volume of chlorine gas at 24°C and 99.2 kPa would be required to react with 2.51 g of silver according to the equation

$$2Ag(cr) + Cl_2(g) \rightarrow 2AgCl(cr)$$

Solving Process:
In order to solve this problem, we calculate the volume needed at STP, then we convert to the conditions stated. The solution is

$$\frac{2.51 \text{ g Ag}}{} \left| \frac{1 \text{ mol Ag}}{108 \text{ g Ag}} \right| \frac{1 \text{ mol Cl}_2}{2 \text{ mol Ag}} \left| \frac{22.4 \text{ dm}^3 \text{ Cl}_2}{1 \text{ mol Cl}_2} \right| \frac{297 \text{ K}}{273 \text{ K}} \left| \frac{101.3 \text{ kPa}}{99.2 \text{ kPa}} \right. = 0.289 \text{ dm}^3 \text{ Cl}_2$$

EXAMPLE: Gas Volume-Mass

What mass of mercury(II) chloride will react with 0.567 dm^3 of ammonia at 27°C and 102.7 kPa according to the equation

$$HgCl_2(aq) + 2NH_3(ag) \rightarrow Hg(NH_2)Cl(cr) + NH_4Cl(aq)?$$

Solving Process:
In this problem, we must change the volume of ammonia to standard conditions before converting it to moles. The solution is

$$\frac{0.567 \text{ dm}^3 \text{ NH}_3}{} \left| \frac{273 \text{ K}}{300 \text{ K}} \right| \frac{102.7 \text{ kPa}}{101.3 \text{ kPa}} \left| \frac{1 \text{ mol NH}_3}{22.4 \text{ dm}^3 \text{ NH}_3} \right| \frac{1 \text{ mol HgCl}_2}{2 \text{ mol NH}_3} \left| \frac{271 \text{ g HgCl}_2}{1 \text{ mol HgCl}_2} \right.$$
$$= 3.16 \text{ g HgCl}_2$$

The same procedure can be used to solve limiting reactant problems. If one of the given materials is a gas at other than STP, its volume must be converted to STP before computing the number of moles in the sample. If the answer to the problem is the volume of a gas at other than STP, the volume must be computed at STP and then converted to the required conditions.

In solving volume-volume problems, the situation is changed slightly. Suppose both original and final gas volumes are measured at the same temperature and pressure. We would first correct the volumes to STP and then convert back to the original conditions. The corrections would all divide out. Thus, as long as the temperature and pressure remain the same, a volume-volume problem need not be worked at STP.

EXAMPLE: Volume-Volume (nonstandard conditions)

What volume of oxygen at 100°C and 105.5 kPa is required to burn 684 m³ of methane at the same temperature and pressure according to the equation $CH_4(g) + 2O_2(g) \rightarrow CO_2(g) + 2H_2O(g)$?

Solving Process:

$$\frac{684 \ m^3 \ \cancel{CH_4}}{} \ \left| \ \frac{2 \ m^3 \ O_2}{1 \ m^3 \ \cancel{CH_4}} \right. = 1370 \ m^3 \ O_2$$

What happens if the given substance in a volume-volume problem is at a different temperature and pressure from the required substance? The volume of the given substance must then be changed to correspond to the conditions of the required substance. The problem may now be solved as a regular volume-volume problem.

EXAMPLE: Volume-Volume

What volume of oxygen at 26°C and 102.5 kPa is required to burn 684 m³ of methane at 101°C and 107.5 kPa?

Solving Process:

$$\frac{684 \ m^3 \ \cancel{CH_4}}{} \ \left| \ \frac{299 \ K}{374 \ K} \right. \ \left| \ \frac{107.5 \ \cancel{kPa}}{102.5 \ \cancel{kPa}} \right. \ \left| \ \frac{2 \ m^3 \ O_2}{1 \ m^3 \ \cancel{CH_4}} \right. = 1150 \ m^3 \ O_2$$

Cylinder

Piston

Steam inlet

Inlet valve

Expansion

Exhaust

Compression

Exhaust valve

FIGURE 19-3. The compression or expansion of the gas depends on the external pressure on the piston.

$w < 0$ when gas does work on its surroundings (expansion).
$w > 0$ when work is done on the gas (compression).

19:10   GASES AND WORK

Consider a gas confined in a cylinder containing a frictionless piston, as shown in Figure 19-3. If the external pressure (P_{ex}) on the piston is greater than the gas pressure, the gas will be compressed. Compression will cease when the internal gas pressure has risen enough to equal the external pressure. When such a change occurs, work has been done on the confined gas. In the same way, if the internal pressure exceeds the external pressure, the gas will expand. In that case, the gas has done work on its surroundings.

This work is represented by w which is a symbol for the work done on the gas. Thus, if the gas does work on its surroundings, w will be a negative quantity. On the other hand, if work is done on the gas (as in the first example), w will be a positive quantity.

The actual amount of work done by or on a gas depends on the conditions under which expansion or contraction takes place. Specifically, w depends upon whether the volume change occurred in an adiabatic system or an **isothermal** (constant temperature) system. It also depends upon the difference between the external and internal pressures during the change.

Chemists define a reversible expansion or contraction of a gas as an ideal change. Specifically, the change takes place because of an infinitesimal pressure difference between the internal and external pressure. If the pressure difference is infinitesimal, then the process would take infinitely long! Reversible changes do not occur in practice, but they are convenient to use to find the maximum amount of work in a change. In actual practice we deal with irreversible changes that always involve less than the ideal maximum work.

Consider an isothermal reversible change in pressure or volume. Such a change represents the maximum work attainable from a system (or the mimimum work to be done on a system). This work may be found from

FIGURE 19-4. Steam catapults are used to launch planes from aircraft carriers. The internal energy of the steam is used to launch the planes.

$$w = -2.303nRT \log \frac{V_2}{V_1} = -2.303nRT \log \frac{P_1}{P_2}$$

A type of ideal change often approached in the laboratory is an adiabatic reversible change where

use $R = 8.31$ J/mol·K

$$w = C_v \, \Delta T$$

where C_v is the heat capacity at constant volume. For an ideal gas C_v does not vary with temperature.

The most practical change is the irreversible change against a constant pressure, for example, the atmosphere. In this case

DEMONSTRATION: See Teacher Guide.

$$w = -P_{ex} \, \Delta V.$$

The important factor to keep in mind about gases and work is that the work done by or on a gas will change the total energy of the gas. Only when a chemist takes into consideration this energy change can a change in a gas be completely described.

Work done by or on a gas will change the total energy of the gas.

SUGGESTION: You may have to review the use of logarithms before assigning these problems. See Appendix B.

PROBLEMS

23. One mole of gas at 25°C expands from 9.92 dm³ to 44.5 dm³. What work does the gas do on the surroundings if the expansion takes place

   a. as an isothermal reversible change?
   b. against a constant external pressure of 10.0 kPa?

23. a. −3720 J
    b. −346 J
    Note: kPa·dm³ = J

24. A gas expands by an adiabatic reversible change. The heat capacity (constant volume) of the gas is 12.5 J/mol·K. The change causes a decrease in temperature of 8.48 K. What work is done by the gas?

24. 106 J/mol
25. 6560 J
26. 2740 J/mol

25. At 98°C and 30.0 kPa, 1.80 mol of gas expands from 0.492 m³ to 0.151 m³. What work does the gas do on the surroundings?

26. A gas expands by an adiabatic reversible change. The heat capacity of the gas is 34.2 J/mol·K. This change causes a temperature change of 80.0 K. What work is done by the gas?

BIOGRAPHY   Amadeo Avogadro (1776-1856)

The theories of Amadeo Avogadro were over-looked for many years due to the short-sightedness of his compatriots. He is best known for his hypothesis that equal volumes of gases, under identical conditions of pressure and temperature, contain the same number of molecules. However, this hypothesis was discounted by the scientific community until very late in his lifetime.

He also carried out investigations in other areas of science. Avogadro was particularly interested in electricity and heat. He investigated the effects of varying amounts of heat on the temperature of a substance. These experiments led him to measure the expansion of substances when heated and the pressure of the vapor of mercury at various temperatures.

TECHNOLOGY AND CHEMISTRY

19:11   Chemicals from the Sea

Commercial production of chemicals from seawater is currently limited to bromine, magnesium, salt, natural gas, petroleum, and sulfur. The ocean and its underlying crust contain a wealth of minerals as well. Obtaining most of these substances, however, has not been economically feasible. Now that we face exhaustion of some land resources, scientists are seeking ways of recovering the wealth of the sea and its basins.

Seafloor sand and gravel are being dredged in coastal regions. These materials are used in the building industry, highway construction, and railroad track maintenance.

Ocean mining involves some formidable problems. The average depth of the ocean is 4400 meters! Many of the rich deposit areas exist along the ocean floor rather than near the coasts. Special equipment must be designed to withstand corrosion as well as the tremendous pressures that exist at these depths. In spite of these problems, there is great interest in ocean mining.

A particularly rich mineral area exists on the eastern Pacific Ocean floor, just north of the equator. Mining in this area concerns a scattering of potato-sized lumps of metal oxides. The principal elements present are manganese and iron, and the lumps are usually referred to as manganese nodules. Not only is manganese a valuable product itself, but the nodules also contain cobalt, copper, and nickel in quantities sufficient to recover.

A number of companies and countries have developed undersea mining capabilities to recover these nodules. The costs are enormous. Mineral recovery from beneath the sea costs two to three hundred times as much as recovery of the same mineral on land. A political issue may develop in deciding to whom these ocean floor deposits belong.

One method for mining the nodules uses a long cable lined with huge buckets. The cable looks like a huge necklace suspended from the ore ship. The ship dredges the ocean floor as nodules and other sediment fill the buckets. The cable is cycled continuously through the ship to unload the mined materials. Newer methods, such as using hydraulic pumps, are also being investigated.

The near future will probably show a significant increase in coastal mining for minerals that have washed down rivers to the sea. Such operations are being used to mine diamonds, tin ore, gold, and other dense minerals. These deposits are easier to recover because they can be obtained by dredging shallow coastal areas.

Obtaining petroleum from the sea is now an essential industry. The first offshore oil drilling occurred off the Louisiana coast in 1945. Now over one hundred companies are engaged in exploration and drilling in all parts of the world. As with mineral mining, the construction costs are enormous. However, due to foreign political instability and the need to develop domestic sources, offshore drilling is economically feasible, even though it may take some time to reach the break-even point.

Most early exploration and drilling occurred in shallow waters adjacent to onshore fields. Drilling operations were conducted from platforms built up from the sea floor. As petroleum demand further increased, open sea drilling became more common.

A new technology has developed to cope with the problems associated with deep ocean work. Various platform designs have been developed to maintain stability under hazardous weather conditions. The condition of the ocean floor as well as the depth of the well are also important considerations in design. Special diving equipment has been developed to allow divers to work at various depths when completing and maintaining a well. If the composition of the gas mixture divers breathe is carefully controlled, they can remain submerged in special pressure chambers for up to a week.

Engineers are experimenting with designs for undersea drilling stations. These stations would be totally enclosed and contain living quarters for personnel.

It is obvious that the ocean contains a number of important resources that will be a significant part of resource utilization and technological development in the future.

SUMMARY

1. **Avogadro's principle:** *At equal temperatures and pressures, equal volumes of gases contain equal numbers of molecules.* **19:1**
2. The molar volume of a gas is the volume occupied by 1 mole of the gas; at STP, its value is 22.4 dm^3 for all gases. **19:2**
3. The ideal gas equation is $PV = nRT$, where P = pressure, V = volume, n = number of moles, R = a constant, and T = kelvin temperature. **19:3**
4. The molecular mass of a gas may be determined by using a modified form of the ideal gas equation. **19:4**
5. A limiting reactant is a reactant that is completely consumed in a reaction and thereby limits the amount of product. Any remaining reactants are said to be in excess. **19:8**
6. In solving problems involving gas volumes, consideration must be given to the change of gas volume with change in pressure and temperature. **19:9**
7. A gas that expands or is compressed does work or has work done on it. **19:10**

VOCABULARY

Avogadro's principle **19:1**
molar volume **19:2**
ideal gas equation **19:3**

limiting reactant **19:8**
excess reactant **19:8**
isothermal **19:10**

PROBLEMS

1. 99.7 kPa
2. 39.6 g/mol
3. 14.1 dm^3 CO_2
4. 24.7 dm^3 O_2
5. 4.44 dm^3 SO_2
6. 0.0991 mol CO_2
7. 8.90 g NiS
8. 5.86 g $Ca(OH)_2$
9. 58.5 g NaCl
10. 6.59 dm^3 CO_2

1. What pressure will be exerted by 0.400 mole of a gas in a 10.0 dm^3 vessel at 27°C?
2. What is the molecular mass of a gas if 5.00×10^2 cm^3 have a mass of 1.00 g at -23°C and 105.0 kPa?
3. The burning of ethane (C_2H_6) produces CO_2 and water vapor as the only products. 7.07 dm^3 of ethane would produce how many dm^3 of CO_2? (All substances are gases measured at the same temperature and pressure.)
4. How many dm^3 of O_2 would be required for the completion of the reaction described in Problem 3?
5. Carbon disulfide will burn to produce CO_2 and SO_2. How many dm^3 of SO_2 at STP can be produced from 2.22 dm^3 of CS_2 vapor?
6. How many moles of CO_2 would be produced in Problem 5?
7. How many grams of nickel(II) sulfide can be produced by the reaction of 5.75 g of nickel with 5.22 g of sulfur?
8. 4.44 grams of CaO react with 7.77 g of water. How many grams of calcium hydroxide will be formed?
9. How many grams of sodium chloride could be produced from the reaction of 23.0 g of sodium with 22.4 dm^3 of chlorine?
10. Determine how many dm^3 of CO_2 at STP can be produced from 15.7 g of Fe_2O_3 and 11.2 dm^3 of CO, if $Fe_2O_3(cr) + 3CO(g) \rightarrow 2Fe(cr) + 3CO_2(g)$.

11. In Problem 10, if the gas were collected at 27°C and 104.5 kPa pressure, what volume would it occupy?

12. What would be the density of the CO_2 gas collected under the conditions stated in Problem 11?

13. At 17°C and 61.2 kPa, 0.316 mol of gas expands from 11.3 dm^3 to 22.1 dm^3. What work does the gas do on the surroundings?

14. A gas expands by an adiabatic reversible change. The heat capacity of the gas is 20.8 J/mol·K. This change causes a temperature change of 91.1 K. What work is done by the gas?

11. 7.02 dm^3
12. 1.84 g/dm^3
13. −511 J
14. 1890 J/mol

REVIEW

1. If a sample of gas occupies 642 cm^3 at 93.9 kPa, what volume will it occupy at 109.0 kPa if the temperature remains constant?

2. If a sample of gas collected over water at 50°C occupies 62.5 cm^3 at a total pressure of 114.9 kPa, what volume will the dry gas occupy at 50°C and 97.8 kPa?

3. If a sample of gas occupies 286 cm^3 at 98.1 kPa and 42°C, what volume will it occupy at 42.2 kPa and 60.0°C?

4. Compute the relative rates of diffusion for oxygen and argon at the same temperature.

5. What is the density of a gas at STP if 1.34 g of the gas occupy 343 cm^3 at 24°C and 99.9 kPa?

6. Define an ideal gas.

7. If 60.0 dm^3 of gas at 7°C is heated to 312°C, what is the new volume of the gas (pressure is constant)?

1. 553 cm^3
2. 65.6 cm^3
3. 703 cm^3
4. 1.12 O_2/Ar
5. 4.31 g/dm^3
6. The particles of an ideal gas occupy zero volume and have no attractive forces.
7. 125 dm^3

ONE MORE STEP

1. Investigate Cannizzaro's role in gaining acceptance for Avogadro's principle.

See Teacher Guide

2. Molecular masses of materials are often found today by using a mass spectrograph, which we have already discussed (Chapter 8). Find out how a "time-of-flight" spectrometer works.

3. How would knowledge of chemistry help an iron foundry?

4. If a student performs an experiment to determine the molecular mass of a gaseous compound using the modified ideal gas equation, $M = mRT/PV$, and forgets to correct for the fact that the gas was collected over water, would the results be high or low?

5. How much work is done by a gas that expands against zero external pressure?

READINGS

Hakala, Reino W., "The Value of the Critical Compressability Factor for the Redlich-Kwong Equation of State of Gases," *Journal of Chemical Education*, Vol. 62, No. 2(February 1985), pp. 110-111.

A volcanic eruption can be considered an exothermic reaction. This activity is the result of a surplus of energy within the earth. The expulsion of this energy puts the volcano at a lower energy and a higher degree of disorder. When these states are achieved the volcanic activity stops. The occurrence of a chemical reaction depends on the energy and disorder of the reactants and products. What conditions are necessary for a reaction to occur? How can these conditions be altered to obtain products which are higher in energy than the reactants? How does disorder affect a reaction?

ENERGY AND DISORDER

Chapter 20 introduces the student to thermodynamics through a study of state functions.

DEMONSTRATION: The thermite reaction demonstrates the energy associated with a chemical reaction See the Teacher Guide for preparation details.

In the last several chapters, we have been studying macroscopic amounts of matter. We have been interested in physical properties and physical changes. Where chemical reactions were involved, we looked at the quantitative relationships among the reactants and products. Now we will consider what makes reactions occur.

Exothermic reactions generally take place spontaneously (without help). On the other hand, endothermic reactions are generally not spontaneous. In everyday life, we can see that changes in nature are usually "downhill." That is, a system in nature tends to go from a state of higher energy to one of lower energy. A ball will roll down a hill spontaneously, but not up. Also, natural processes tend to go from an orderly state to a disorderly one. Consider a box of twelve marbles arranged in three rows: a row of four red, a row of four blue, and a row of four white. If you empty the box and then return the marbles as a group, shaking the box to allow the marbles to arrange themselves in three rows, the arrangement of colors will be random.

There are some exceptions to these two general rules. How is it possible for products to form that are at a higher energy or in a more ordered state than the reactants? In this chapter we will find the answer to such questions. Keep in mind that unless otherwise stated we will be concerned with reactions taking place at constant temperature and pressure. Reactions taking place at constant temperature are **isothermal processes.** Reactions that take place at constant pressure are **isobaric processes.**

Exothermic reactions generally take place spontaneously.

Natural processes:
High energy → low energy
Order → disorder

Isothermal: Constant temperature
Isobaric: Constant pressure

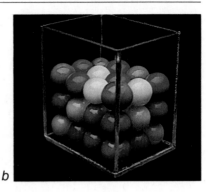

a   *b*

FIGURE 20-1. The marbles in the box are in a highly ordered state (a) until the box is shaken. Then the marbles go to a highly disordered state (b). They do not return to their ordered state.

BACKGROUND: You may wish to introduce the concept of "state functions" here. A state function of a system depends only upon the physical state of the system and not how the system arrived at that state. (ΔU, ΔS, ΔH, and ΔG).

The value of a state function depends only on the initial and final states. It is independent of the pathway used to arrive at that state. q and w are NOT state functions. They depend on the path followed.

20:1 STATE FUNCTIONS

When a system is subjected to a change in temperature, the change is represented by ΔT. No matter how the change is made,

$$\Delta T = T_2 - T_1,$$

where T_2 is the final temperature and T_1 is the initial temperature. The same can be said for volume and pressure.

$$\Delta V = V_2 - V_1 \text{ and } \Delta P = P_2 - P_1$$

Such characteristics as T, V, and P are called **state functions.** The amount of change in a state function depends only on the initial and final states, not on the path followed in getting from state one to state two. In this chapter we will deal with some new properties of systems that are also state functions.

We will also deal with the energy absorbed by the system, q (section 6:5), and the work done on the system, w (section 19:10). Neither q nor w are state functions. These two quantities do depend on the path followed in getting from state one to state two.

20:2 INTERNAL ENERGY

Every system has some internal energy which is designated by U. The **internal energy** is a state function. Since we will be interested only in ΔU, changes in the internal energy of a system, we do not have to know absolute values of U for systems.

The change in energy of a system undergoing a process can be represented by

$\Delta U = q + w.$

$$\Delta U = q + w.$$

Thus we see that there are two ways of transferring energy to a system: by heating it or by doing work on it. Also, the system may transfer energy to its surroundings by giving off heat or doing work on the surroundings. It is interesting to note that although neither q nor w are state functions, their combination, ΔU, is a state function.

ΔU is a state function and is, therefore, path-independent.

Heating or cooling a system is a familiar operation. But how do we do work on a system? There are several ways of doing work on a system, and the most important to a chemist is the expansion or compression of the system (pressure-volume work, see section 19:10). If the system expands it is doing work on the surroundings and energy is being transferred from the system. Examples of other kinds of work besides the pressure-volume work include electric, magnetic, elastic, and surface tension.

EXAMPLE: Change in Internal Energy

A system receives 466 kJ of heat from its surroundings and the surroundings do 56.0 kJ of work on the system. What is the change in the system's internal energy?

Solving Process:
The change in internal energy is represented by

$$\Delta U = q + w.$$

Since heat is received by the system, q is positive. Also, since work is done on the system, w is positive. Therefore,

$$\Delta U = 466 + 56.0 = 522 \text{ kJ}$$

EXAMPLE: Change in Internal Energy

What would be the change in internal energy in the previous example if the work had been done by the system instead of on the system?

Solving Process:
Since the work was done by the system, w is negative.

$$\Delta U = 466 - 56.0 = 4.10 \times 10^2 \text{ kJ}$$

PROBLEMS

1. A system receives 419 kJ of heat from its surroundings and does 389 kJ of work on the surroundings. What is the change in its internal energy?

2. A system gives off 196 kJ of heat to the surroundings and the surroundings do 4.20×10^2 kJ of work on the system. What is the change in the internal energy of the system?

1. 3.0×10^1 kJ
2. 224 kJ

SUGGESTION: Remind students that ΔH values are relative: The free elements are taken to have $\Delta H_f° = 0$

20:3 ENTHALPY

If we rearrange the internal energy equation we get

$$q = \Delta U - w$$

From section 19:10, at constant pressure, we have

$$w = -P_{ext}\Delta V$$

Substituting we obtain

$$q_p = \Delta U + P\Delta V$$

which can be rewritten as

$$q_p = \Delta(U + PV)$$

DEMONSTRATION: A simple demonstration of a change where energy is absorbed can be done by pouring 25 cm^3 of water into a 150 cm^3 beaker half full of NH_4NO_3.

The subscript p represents a constant pressure process. The quantity $U + PV$ occurs frequently in energy considerations and is given the name **enthalpy** and the symbol H. Thus,

$$q_p = \Delta H.$$

Change in enthalpy = ΔH

Enthalpy is a state function, so

$$\Delta H = H_2 - H_1.$$

Exothermic: $\Delta H < 0$
Endothermic: $\Delta H > 0$

In an exothermic reaction the products have less enthalpy than the reactants, so $\Delta H < 0$. In an endothermic reaction $\Delta H > 0$.

The change in enthalpy that occurs when a chemical reaction takes place is due primarily to the energy required to break the chemical bonds in the reactants and the energy produced by forming the chemical bonds in the products. A balanced chemical equation can be used to represent the energy absorbed or released during a chemical reaction.

When carbon (in the form of coal) is burned, energy is released.

$$C(cr) + O_2(g) \rightarrow CO_2(g) + energy \quad (393.5 \text{ kJ})$$

Enthalpy of reaction is the energy absorbed or released during a chemical reaction.

One mole of carbon reacts with one mole of oxygen to produce one mole of carbon dioxide and 393.5 kJ of energy. The energy released is called the enthalpy of reaction and is represented by ΔH. In this case, $\Delta H = -393.5$ kJ.

20:4 STANDARD STATES

We cannot measure enthalpy in absolute terms. We can only measure changes in enthalpy. The height of a hill cannot be measured in absolute terms either. We can describe its level above the surrounding plain or we can say it is a certain number of meters above sea level. The figure we use depends upon the standard of reference used. Our reference will be substances in their standard states. By standard states we mean the enthalpy they have at 298.15 K (25°C) and 101.325 kPa. We specify both

Standard thermodynamic measurement conditions: 298.15 K and 101.325 kPa.

the temperature and the pressure, since a change in either can have an effect on the enthalpy of a substance. In measuring enthalpy, we arbitrarily set the enthalpy of the free elements equal to zero.

20:5   ENTHALPY OF FORMATION

To return to the reaction of carbon and oxygen, then, we know that carbon and oxygen are assigned enthalpies of zero because they are free elements. Therefore, the standard molar enthalpy for the formation of carbon dioxide must be -393.5 kJ/mol. The change in enthalpy when one mole of a compound is produced from the free elements in their standard states is known as the standard **enthalpy of formation.** This quantity is expressed in units of kilojoules per mole. Remember that a negative sign represents an exothermic reaction. Thus the compound has less enthalpy than the elements from which it was formed. By the same reasoning, a compound produced by an endothermic reaction would have a positive enthalpy of formation. Compounds like CO_2 with large negative enthalpies of formation are thermodynamically stable. **Thermodynamics** is the study of the flow of energy, especially heat. **Thermodynamic stability** depends on the amount of energy that would be required to decompose the compound. One mole of CO_2 would require 393.5 kJ of energy to decompose to the elements carbon and oxygen. On the other hand, mercury fulminate, $Hg(OCN)_2$, produces 268 kJ when one mole decomposes. It is explosive and is used in making detonator caps.

Table A-6 of the Appendix lists the enthalpies of formation for some compounds. The symbol used for enthalpy of formation is ΔH°_f. The superscript "°" is used to indicate that the values given are those at standard atmospheric pressure and 25°C. The subscript "f" designates the value as enthalpy of formation.

Enthalpy of formation is the change in enthalpy when one mole of a compound is produced from free elements.

Thermodynamically stable compounds have large negative heats of formation.

FIGURE 20-2. The products of an exothermic reaction (a) are lower in enthalpy than the reactants. The products of an endothermic reaction (b) are higher in enthalpy than the reactants.

20:6   CALCULATION OF ENTHALPY OF REACTION

ΔH°_f = enthalpy of formation at standard pressure and 25°C.

ΔH° = change in enthalpy

A positive ΔH° indicates an endothermic reaction.
A negative ΔH° indicates an exothermic reaction.

Let us apply the law of conservation of energy to a reaction. The enthalpy of the products, $\Sigma\Delta H^\circ_{f(products)}$, must equal the enthalpy of the reactants, $\Sigma\Delta H^\circ_{f(reactants)}$, plus any change in enthalpy (ΔH°_{rxn}) during the reaction. (Sigma, Σ, is the symbol used to indicate summation.)

$$\Sigma\Delta H^\circ_{f(products)} = \Sigma\Delta H^\circ_{f(reactants)} + \Delta H^\circ_{rxn}$$

Solving for ΔH°_{rxn} we get

$$\Delta H^\circ_{rxn} = \Sigma\Delta H^\circ_{f(products)} - \Sigma\Delta H^\circ_{f(reactants)}$$

If the enthalpy of formation of each reactant and product is known, we can calculate the amount of energy produced or absorbed. We can then predict whether a reaction will be exothermic or endothermic.

EXAMPLE: Enthalpy Change

Calculate the enthalpy change in the following chemical reaction.

carbon monoxide + oxygen → carbon dioxide

Solving Process:
First, write a balanced equation. Include all the reactants and products.

$$2CO(g) + O_2(g) \rightarrow 2CO_2(g)$$

When referring to a table of enthalpies of formation, check to determine which convention applies. All tables in this book employ the current convention; that is, a compound produced by an endothermic reaction will have a positive enthalpy of formation.

Each formula unit represents one mole. Remember that free elements have zero enthalpy by definition. Using the table of enthalpies of formation, Table A-6 of the Appendix, the total enthalpy of the reactants (2CO and O_2) is

$$\Sigma\Delta H^\circ_{f(reactants)} = \frac{2 \text{ mol } CO}{} \left| \frac{-111 \text{ kJ}}{\text{mol } CO} \right. + 0 \text{ kJ} = -222 \text{ kJ}$$

The total enthalpy of the product (2CO$_2$) is

$$\Sigma\Delta H^\circ_{f(products)} = \frac{2 \text{ mol } CO_2}{} \left| \frac{-393.5 \text{ kJ}}{\text{mol } CO_2} \right. = -787.0 \text{ kJ}$$

The difference between the enthalpy of the reactants and the enthalpy of the product is

$$\Delta H^\circ_{rxn} = \Sigma\Delta H^\circ_{f(products)} - \Sigma\Delta H^\circ_{f(reactants)}$$

$$\Delta H^\circ_{rxn} = -787.0 \text{ kJ} - (-222 \text{ kJ}) = -565 \text{ kJ}$$

This difference between the enthalpy of the products and the reactants (-565 kJ) is released as the enthalpy of reaction.

$$2CO(g) + O_2(g) \rightarrow 2CO_2(g) + \textit{enthalpy of reaction}$$

PROBLEMS

3. Compute $\Delta H°_{rxn}$ for the following reaction.
   $2NO(g) + O_2(g) \rightarrow 2NO_2(g)$

4. Compute $\Delta H°_{rxn}$ for the following reaction.
   $4FeO(cr) + O_2(g) \rightarrow 2Fe_2O_3(cr)$

3. $\Delta H°_{rxn} = -113$ kJ
4. $\Delta H°_{rxn} = -576$ kJ

20:7 HESS'S LAW

Consider a reaction A → C that can be broken down into two steps:

$$(1)\ A \rightarrow B \quad \text{and} \quad (2)\ B \rightarrow C$$

$$\Delta H_{rxn(1)} = \Delta H°_f B - \Delta H°_f A \qquad \Delta H_{rxn(2)} = \Delta H°_f C - \Delta H°_f B$$

The enthalpy change for the overall change of A to C is $\Delta H = \Delta H_{rxn(1)} + \Delta H_{rxn(2)}$ since enthalpy is a state function. The principle just illustrated is known as **Hess's Law:** *the enthalpy change for a reaction is the sum of the enthalpy changes for a series of reactions that add up to the overall reaction.*

For the reaction in the Example in Section 20:6 we can make the steps

$$C + O_2 \rightarrow CO_2 \qquad \Delta H = -393.5 \text{ kJ}$$
$$2CO \rightarrow CO_2 + C \qquad \Delta H = -171.5 \text{ kJ}$$

Adding, we get $2CO + O_2 \rightarrow 2CO_2$, $\Delta H = -565$ kJ, which is the same result as before.

Hess' Law: enthalpy change for a reaction is the sum of the enthalpy changes for a series of reactions which add to equal the overall reaction.

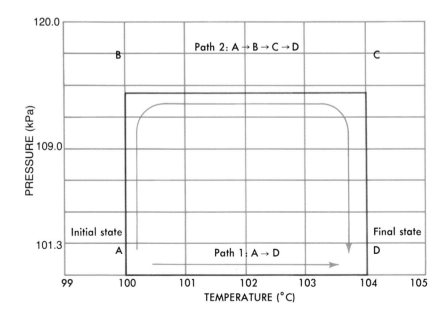

FIGURE 20-3. The overall change in internal energy remains the same when a given amount of water is heated from 100°C to steam at 104°C by two different processes.

SUGGESTION: You may also wish to present the concept of entropy in terms of probability.

20:8 ENTROPY

Highly exothermic reactions tend to take place spontaneously. However, weak exothermic reactions and some endothermic reactions can also occur spontaneously. Sometimes these reactions will proceed under stronger reaction conditions, such as a temperature increase.

Consider the reaction of steam on very hot carbon to form carbon monoxide and hydrogen.

$$C(cr) + H_2O(g) + energy \rightarrow H_2(g) + CO(g)$$

BACKGROUND: Entropy, S, is derived from the second law of thermodynamics by Clausius, in 1850 (places limits on conversion of heat into work, forbids perpetual motion).

The products have a higher enthalpy than the reactants. Therefore, since energy is absorbed in this process, ΔH is positive. It has been determined experimentally that if 1 mole of carbon reacts with 1 mole of steam then $\Delta H = 131$ kJ. We have observed in previous sections that most spontaneous reactions seem to have negative ΔH values. Since ΔH is positive in this reaction, some additional factor must be involved.

Entropy (S) is a measure of disorder in a system.

This additional factor is the degree of disorder or **entropy.** We have seen in Chapter 16 that there is a very orderly arrangement of atoms in crystalline solids. In liquids, there is less order. Gases lack any orderly arrangement. A gas at high temperature is more disorderly than one at a low temperature. Two liquids dissolved in each other make a more disorderly system than the two liquids separated. The degree of disorder, or entropy, is represented by the symbol S. Entropy is a state function.

Increase in disorder:
$$\Delta S > 0$$
Decrease in disorder:
$$\Delta S < 0$$

Change in entropy is symbolized as ΔS. A positive value for ΔS means an increase in the degree of disorder. That is to say, the system becomes less ordered. Such a change (positive ΔS) occurs when a solid is converted to a liquid or a gas. When the opposite reaction occurs (liquid or gas is converted to a solid), ΔS is negative.

PROBLEMS

5. $\Delta H° = -2860$ kJ

5. The equation for the combustion of ethane is:
$$2C_2H_6 + 7O_2 \rightarrow 4CO_2 + 6H_2O$$
Calculate the enthalpy of combustion for ethane, C_2H_6, from these data:

SUGGESTION: Solve problem 5 using the method presented in 20:6. Students will get the same answer. Hess's Law is of little use in modern chemistry.

$C_2H_4(g) + 3O_2(g) \rightarrow 2CO_2(g) + 2H_2O(g)$ $\Delta H_c = -1323$ kJ/mol
$C_2H_4(g) + H_2(g) \rightarrow C_2H_6(g)$ $\Delta H = -137$ kJ/mol
$H_2(g) + \frac{1}{2}O_2(g) \rightarrow H_2O(g)$ $\Delta H_f = -242$ kJ/mol

6. a. positive
   b. negative
   c. negative
   d. positive

6. Will the entropy change for each of the following be positive or negative?

a. Sugar dissolves in tea.
b. Frost forms on a window pane.
c. Air is pumped into a tire.
d. Acetone evaporates from nail polish remover.

7. Will the entropy change for each of the following be positive or negative?

   a. $CaCO_3(cr) \rightarrow CaO(cr) + CO_2(g)$
   b. $N_2(g) + 3H_2(g) \rightarrow 2NH_3(g)$

20:9 FREE ENERGY

The combination of H and S is a state function called **free energy.** It is represented by G. Thus, ΔG represents the change in free energy. These quantities are defined by the following relationships

$$G = H - TS$$
$$\Delta G = \Delta H - T\Delta S$$

where T is the temperature in kelvin (absolute temperature).

It can be shown, both by theory and by experiment, that in a spontaneous change, ΔG is always negative. If $\Delta G < 0$ for a reaction, the reaction is **exergonic.** If $\Delta G > 0$ for a reaction, the reaction is **endergonic.** If a reaction takes place at low temperatures and involves little change in entropy, then the term $T\Delta S$ will be negligible. In such a reaction, ΔG is largely a function of ΔH, the change in enthalpy. Thus, most reactions occurring spontaneously at room temperature have a negative ΔH.

Highly endothermic reactions can occur only if $T\Delta S$ is large. Thus, the temperature is high, or there is a large increase in entropy. In the endothermic reaction of carbon with steam, both of these conditions occur. ΔS is positive because the orderly arrangement of carbon in the solid is converted to the disorderly arrangement in CO gas. T is high because the reaction only takes place at red heat (600–900°C) or higher. If the temperature decreases, the reaction stops and goes into reverse.

If ΔH and ΔS have the same sign, there will be some temperature at which ΔH and $T\Delta S$ will be numerically equal, and ΔG will be exactly zero. This state is the thermodynamic definition of a system in equilibrium. At equilibrium, the value of the free energy G, not ΔG, is at a minimum for the system.

7. a. positive
    b. negative

BACKGROUND: The term ΔG is often called Gibbs free energy. Josiah Gibbs (see page 398) was the first to suggest that any reaction which can do useful work at a constant temperature and pressure is spontaneous.
Change in free energy = ΔG

When $\Delta G < 0$, the reaction is exergonic
When $\Delta G > 0$, the reaction is endergonic

Spontaneous reaction:
$$\Delta G < 0$$
Endothermic reactions occur spontaneously when $T\Delta S$ is large.

FIGURE 20-4. In the formation of CO, the degree of disorder increases resulting in a positive entropy change for the reaction.

Highly ordered state

Graphite

$+$ H_2O Entropy increases   Carbon monoxide gas   Highly disordered state

A spontaneous reaction proceeds toward equilibrium.

Chemical potential energy, G, is
least at equilibrium.

**FIGURE 20-5. The ball in (a) is
supported at a point halfway on
the plank. When the support is
removed (b) the ball rolls down
instead of up.**

The free energy change is the
maximum work that can be obtained from a system.

BACKGROUND: Specifically,
the "chemical potential" of a
species is its partial molar free
energy.

Nitrogen atoms appear in the atmosphere of stars. The body of
the star is plasma.

All spontaneous processes proceed toward equilibrium. For example, a ball rolls down a hill and not up. The bottom of the hill is where the
ball has the least potential energy. Chemical potential energy, technically
called free energy, is least when a system is at equilibrium.

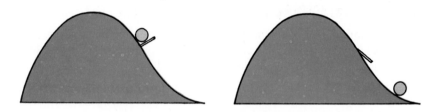

An interesting result of the entropy contribution to the free energy
equation is that molecules like H_2, O_2, and N_2, which are stable on Earth,
do not exist on the sun and stars. To see why they do not, consider the
case of N_2. In order to decompose one mole of N_2 molecules, much
energy must be supplied.

$$N_2 + energy \rightarrow 2N \qquad energy = \Delta H = +941 \text{ kJ}$$

Since ΔH has such a large positive value, at ordinary temperatures N_2 is a
very stable molecule. This stability is a direct result of $T\Delta S$ being small in
comparison to the large positive ΔH (which makes ΔG positive). A gas
composed of separate nitrogen atoms has a greater entropy than one
made of N_2 molecules. The pairing of nitrogen atoms is a kind of order.
Therefore, the decomposition of these molecules represents an increase
in entropy (a positive ΔS). If N_2 molecules are exposed to higher temperatures (like those near the sun), the value of $T\Delta S$ is greater than 941 kJ and
thus ΔG is negative. As a result, nitrogen exists near the sun only as
discrete atoms.

**FIGURE 20-6. Nitrogen exists as
discrete atoms near the stars
rather than as molecules.**

All three quantities, enthalpy, entropy, and free energy, depend on temperature. However, we will work only at 298.15 K and 101.325 kPa. Thus we will always be working with substances in their standard states.

20:10 CALCULATIONS ON FREE ENERGY

Appendix A-6 lists the standard free energies of formation (ΔG_f°), enthalpies of formation (ΔH_f°), and entropies (S°) of some substances. The superscript "$^\circ$" shows these values have been obtained for standard conditions. The subscript "f" shows they are values for the formation of one mole of the compound from the elements. We already know that the enthalpy change for a reaction is found by

$$\Delta H^\circ_{rxn} = \Sigma\Delta H_f^\circ{}_{(products)} - \Sigma\Delta H_f^\circ{}_{(reactants)}$$

In a like manner, we may compute the free energy and entropy changes for a reaction.

$$\Delta G^\circ_{rxn} = \Sigma\Delta G_f^\circ{}_{(products)} - \Sigma\Delta G_f^\circ{}_{(reactants)}$$
$$\Delta S^\circ_{rxn} = \Sigma S^\circ{}_{(products)} - \Sigma S^\circ{}_{(reactants)}$$

EXAMPLE: Entropy Change

What is the change in entropy for the reaction between methane and oxygen under standard measurement conditions? The equation for the reaction is $CH_4(g) + 2O_2(g) \rightarrow CO_2(g) + 2H_2O(l)$.

Solving Process:
(a) It is best to organize the data you will use from Appendix A-6 into a table.

Value	CH_4	O_2	CO_2	H_2O
ΔH_f°(kJ/mol)	−74.8	0	−393.5	−286
ΔG_f°(kJ/mol)	−50.8	0	−394.4	−237
ΔS°(J/mol K)	186	205.0	214	70.0

More extensive tables are available in many reference books, e.g. *The Handbook of Chemistry and Physics.*

(b) To find ΔH°:

$$\Delta H^\circ_{rxn} = \Sigma\Delta H_f^\circ{}_{(products)} - \Sigma\Delta H_f^\circ{}_{(reactants)}$$
$$= [CO_2 + 2H_2O] - [2O_2 + CH_4]$$

Multiply each ΔH_f° by the number of moles from the balanced equation.

$$\frac{1 \text{ mol } CO_2}{} \left| \frac{(-393.5 \text{ kJ})}{\text{mol } CO_2} \right. = -393.5 \text{ kJ}$$

$$\frac{2 \text{ mol } H_2O}{} \left| \frac{(-286 \text{ kJ})}{\text{mol } H_2O} \right. = -572 \text{ kJ}$$

$$\frac{2 \text{ mol } O_2}{} \left| \frac{0 \text{ kJ}}{\text{mol } O_2} \right. = 0$$

$$\frac{1 \text{ mol } CH_4}{} \left| \frac{(-74.8 \text{ kJ})}{\text{mol } CH_4} \right. = -74.8 \text{ kJ}$$

$$\Delta H°_{rxn} = [(-393.5 \text{ kJ}) + (-572 \text{ kJ})] - [(0) + (-74.8 \text{ kJ})]$$

$$\Delta H°_{rxn} = -891 \text{ kJ}$$

Exothermic reaction:
$$\Delta H < 0$$

(c) To find $\Delta G°$ use the following equations. It is important to have a balanced chemical equation.

$$\Delta G°_{rxn} = \Sigma \Delta G_f°_{(products)} - \Sigma \Delta G_f°_{(reactants)}$$
$$= [CO_2 + 2H_2O] - [2O_2 + CH_4]$$

Multiply each $\Delta G_f°$ by the number of moles from the balanced equation. Substitute these values into the equation used to determine $\Delta G°_{rxn}$.

$$\frac{1 \text{ mol } CO_2}{} \left| \frac{(-394.4 \text{ kJ})}{\text{mol } CO_2} \right. = -394.4 \text{ kJ}$$

$$\frac{2 \text{ mol } H_2O}{} \left| \frac{(-237 \text{ kJ})}{\text{mol } H_2O} \right. = -474 \text{ kJ}$$

$$\frac{2 \text{ mol } O_2}{} \left| \frac{0 \text{ kJ}}{\text{mol } O_2} \right. = 0$$

$$\frac{1 \text{ mol } CH_4}{} \left| \frac{(-50.8 \text{ kJ})}{\text{mol } CH_4} \right. = -50.8 \text{ kJ}$$

$$\Delta G°_{rxn} = [(-394.4 \text{ kJ}) + (-474 \text{ kJ})] - [(0) + (-50.8 \text{ kJ})]$$

$$\Delta G°_{rxn} = -818 \text{ kJ}$$

Spontaneous reaction:
$$\Delta G < 0$$

The free energy decreases ($\Delta G < 0$) in a spontaneous reaction because the system is changing to a more stable state.

(d) To find $\Delta S°$:

$$\Delta S°_{rxn} = -\frac{(\Delta G°_{rxn} - \Delta H°_{rxn})}{T}$$

$$T = 25°C + 273 = 298 \text{ K}$$

$$\Delta S°_{rxn} = -\left[\frac{(-818 \text{ kJ}) - (-891 \text{ kJ})}{298 \text{ K}} \right] \left[\frac{(1000 \text{ J})}{1 \text{ kJ}} \right]$$

Decrease in disorder:
$$\Delta S < 0$$

$$\Delta S°_{rxn} = -245 \text{ J/K}$$

(e) We can check the entropy change by using the standard entropies.

$$\Delta S°_{rxn} = \Sigma S°_{(products)} - \Sigma S°_{(reactants)}$$

$$= [CO_2 + 2H_2O] - [2O_2 + CH_4]$$

Multiply each $S°$ by the number of moles from the balanced equation.

$$\frac{1 \text{ mol } CO_2}{} \left| \frac{214 \text{ J}}{\text{mol·K } CO_2} \right. = 214 \text{ J/K}$$

$$\frac{2 \text{ mol } H_2O}{} \left| \frac{70.0 \text{ J}}{\text{mol·K } H_2O} \right. = 140 \text{ J/K}$$

$$\frac{2 \text{ mol } O_2}{} \left| \frac{205.0 \text{ J}}{\text{mol·K } O_2} \right. = 410.0 \text{ J/K}$$

$$\frac{1 \text{ mol } CH_4}{} \left| \frac{186 \text{ J}}{\text{mol·K } CH_4} \right. = 186 \text{ J/K}$$

$\Delta S° = [(214 \text{ J/K}) + (140 \text{ J/K})] - [(410.0 \text{ J/K}) + (186 \text{ J/K})]$

$\Delta S° = -242 \text{ J/K}$

EXAMPLE: Unknown Property

What is the standard entropy of bismuth(III) sulfide? Use the equations: $2Bi(cr) + 3S(cr) \rightarrow Bi_2S_3(cr)$ and $\Delta G = \Delta H - T\Delta S$.

Solving Process:

(a) Organize your data.

Value	Bi	S	Bi$_2$S$_3$
$\Delta H_f°$(kJ/mol)	0	0	−183
$\Delta G_f°$(kJ/mol)	0	0	−164
$S°$(J/mol·K)	56.9	31.9	?

(b) To find $\Delta H°$:

$$\Delta H°_{rxn} = \frac{1 \text{ mol } Bi_2S_3}{} \left| \frac{(-183 \text{ kJ})}{\text{mol } Bi_2S_3} \right. = -183 \text{ kJ}$$

Exothermic reaction: $\Delta H < 0$

(c) To find $\Delta G°$:

$$\Delta G°_{rxn} = \frac{1 \text{ mol } Bi_2S_3}{} \left| \frac{(-164 \text{ kJ})}{\text{mol } Bi_2S_3} \right. = -164 \text{ kJ}$$

(d) To find $\Delta S°_{rxn}$:

$$\Delta S°_{rxn} = - \frac{(\Delta G°_{rxn} - \Delta H°_{rxn})}{T} \text{ where } T = 298 \text{ K}$$

$$\Delta S°_{rxn} = - \left[\frac{(-164 \text{ kJ}) - (-183 \text{ kJ})}{298 \text{ K}} \right] \left[\frac{1000 \text{ J}}{1 \text{ kJ}} \right] = -63.8 \text{ J/K}$$

Decrease in disorder: $\Delta S < 0$

(e) To find $S°$ Bi_2S_3

$$\Delta S°_{rxn} = S°Bi_2S_3 - \left[\left(\frac{2 \text{ mol Bi}}{} \Bigg| \frac{56.9 \text{ J}}{\text{mol·K Bi}}\right) + \left(\frac{3 \text{ mol S}}{} \Bigg| \frac{31.9 \text{ J}}{\text{mol·K S}}\right)\right]$$

$$S° \ Bi_2S_3 = \Delta S°_{rxn} + 114 \text{ J/K} + 95.7 \text{ J/K}$$

$$= (-63.8 \text{ J/K}) + (114 \text{ J/K}) + (95.7 \text{ J/K}) = 146 \text{ J/K}$$

By checking Appendix A-6, we can verify that the answer is correct. For steps (b) and (c) we know that this is a synthesis reaction, so $\Delta G°_{rxn} = \Delta G°_f$ and $\Delta H°_{rxn} = \Delta H_f°$.

PROBLEMS

8. −47 kJ, yes
9. +542 kJ, no
10. 77.4 J/mol·K for Ca(OH)$_2$
11. 203 kJ

8. Compute the free energy change for the following reaction. Is the reaction spontaneous?

$$BaCl_2(aq) + H_2SO_4(aq) \rightarrow BaSO_4(cr) + 2HCl(aq)$$

9. Compute the free energy change for the following reaction. Is the reaction spontaneous?

$$2HF(g) \rightarrow H_2(g) + F_2(g)$$

10. Compute $S°$ for $Ca(OH)_2$ from the following reaction.

$$Ca(cr) + 2H_2O(l) \rightarrow Ca(OH)_2(cr) + H_2(g)$$

11. Compute $\Delta G_f°$ for H from the following reaction.

$$H_2(g) \rightarrow 2H(g)$$

BIOGRAPHY   Josiah Willard Gibbs (1839-1903)

One of the great American theorists, J. Willard Gibbs was born and raised in New Haven, Connecticut. In 1871, he became professor of mathematical physics at Yale, where he remained until his death.

Gibbs's principal contribution to science was his thermodynamic theory. In this work, he related the behavior of systems in equilibrium to the volume, energy, and degree of order present. He extended his theory to heterogeneous systems undergoing reaction, to which no previous theory had been applied.

Although recognized as the work of genius in America, his theories were not really appreciated in Europe.

Gibbs also made contributions in mathematics and electromagnetic theory.

The CARNOT CYCLE

$= 0$ for whole cycle

$= Q_1 - Q_2$ by the first law

TECHNOLOGY AND CHEMISTRY

20:11   Liquefying Air

Several of the gases comprising air have extensive industrial and commercial uses. These gases are obtained from the process of liquefying air.

Before air can be liquefied, it is filtered to remove soot and other small dirt particles that would clog the equipment used later in the process. The filtered air is then compressed to about 10 megapascals (MPa). As a result of being compressed, the temperature of the air rises. This energy is removed in a device called a heat exchanger. A heat exchanger consists of a series of tubes passing through a cylindrical vessel. One fluid passes through the tubes. The other fluid flows through the vessel surrounding the tubes. Heat flows from the hotter fluid to the cooler fluid.

The compressed air is cooled with water, and further compressed to about 15 MPa. This air is cooled once more to room temperature with water in the heat exchanger. The air then goes through a series of heat exchangers using a refrigerant such as Freon or ammonia or some of the cold gas from the end of the process. At an early stage, water vapor and carbon dioxide are condensed and removed.

Some of the cold gas is used to run one or more compressors. In the process of doing that work, the gas uses some of its internal energy. Thus, its temperature drops even further. Most of the cold, compressed gas is allowed to expand through a valve. Recall from Chapter 18 that this expansion results in a temperature decrease. A large part of the gas is liquefied through the Joule-Thomson effect.

FIGURE 20-7. Air is liquefied through a stepwise process similar to that shown here.

The liquid and extremely cold gas then enters a two-stage distillation column. In the column, the air is separated into high-purity nitrogen, oxygen, and other fractions. The high-purity products are sold and low-purity nitrogen gas is used as a coolant in the heat exchangers. The other liquid fraction passes to a specialized distillation unit where neon, argon, krypton, and xenon are produced. During distillation, each component is removed at its boiling point.

SUMMARY

1. Systems in nature go to states of low energy and high disorder. **Intro.**
2. A state function is a quantity that depends only on the conditions of one state compared to another. The change in a state function is independent of the path and depends only on the initial and final states. P, V, and T are examples of state functions. **20:1**
3. The change in internal energy of a system is the sum of the heat absorbed from the surroundings and the work done on the system. $\Delta U = q + w$ **20:2**
4. The change in enthalpy of a reacting system is the energy absorbed or produced during a chemical reaction and is represented by ΔH_{rxn}. **20:3**
5. Since state functions are affected by pressure and temperature, chemists work with substances in their standard states, that is, 298.15 K and 101.325 kPa. **20:4**
6. The standard enthalpy of formation, ΔH°_f, of a compound is the energy absorbed or released when one mole of the compound is formed from its elements. **20:5**
7. A thermodynamically stable compound has a large negative enthalpy of formation. **20:5**
8. The enthalpy change (ΔH°_{rxn}) for a reaction is the difference between the enthalpy of the products and the enthalpy of the reactants. $\Delta H^\circ_{rxn} = \Sigma \Delta H^\circ_{f(products)} - \Sigma \Delta H^\circ_{f(reactants)}$ **20:6**
9. Hess's Law states that the change in enthalpy for a reaction consisting of a series of steps is the sum of the enthalpy changes for all the steps. **20:7**
10. Entropy is the degree of disorder of a system. **20:8**
11. When the enthalpy change and entropy change differ, the net effect is found from the equation $\Delta G = \Delta H - T\Delta S$. In this equation G is free energy, H is enthalpy, T is the absolute temperature, and S is the entropy. **20:9**
12. Spontaneous changes have negative free energy changes. **20:9**
13. When ΔG is zero, the system is at equilibrium. **20:9**

VOCABULARY

isothermal processes **Intro**
isobaric processes **Intro**
state functions **20:1**
internal energy **20:2**
enthalpy **20:3**
enthalpy of formation **20:5**
thermodynamics **20:5**

thermodynamic stability **20:5**
Hess's law **20:7**
entropy **20:8**
free energy **20:9**
exergonic **20:9**
endergonic **20:9**

PROBLEMS

Using Appendix A-6, decide whether the following reactions would occur spontaneously or not. That is, will ΔG_{rxn} be negative?

1. $PbBr_2 + Cl_2 \rightarrow PbCl_2 + Br_2$
2. $H_2O(l) \rightarrow H_2O(g)$
3. $2C_4H_{10} + 13O_2 \rightarrow 8CO_2 + 10H_2O(l)$
4. $Cu_2S + S \rightarrow 2CuS$
5. $CuS + 2O_2 \rightarrow CuSO_4$

Using Appendix A-6, compute the one thermodynamic quantity missing from the table for the following substances.

6. $Hg_2Cl_2 + Cl_2 \rightarrow 2HgCl_2$
7. $3Be + N_2 \rightarrow Be_3N_2$
8. $2H_2O_2 \rightarrow 2H_2O(l) + O_2$
9. $2NO + O_2 \rightarrow 2NO_2$
10. A system received 622 kJ of energy from its surroundings and did 813 kJ of work on the surroundings. What was the change in its internal energy?
11. A system gave off 262 kJ of energy to its surroundings and the surroundings did 160.0 kJ work on the system. What was the change in its internal energy?

1. −54 kJ, spontaneous
2. 8 kJ, nonspontaneous
3. −5490 kJ, spontaneous
4. −21.2 kJ, spontaneous
5. −608 kJ, spontaneous
6. 123 J/mol·K
7. 32.6 J/mol·K
8. −186 kJ/mol
9. 86.4 kJ/mol
10. −191 kJ
11. −102 kJ

REVIEW

1. If a sample of gas occupies 163 cm³ at 52.4 kPa, what volume will it occupy at 68.7 kPa, temperature constant?
2. If a sample of gas occupies 258 cm³ at 97°C, what volume will it occupy at 77°C, pressure constant?
3. If a gas occupies 94.5 dm³ at 46°C, what volume will it occupy at 43°C, pressure constant?
4. Which gas would diffuse faster, CO_2 or UF_6?
5. In what two ways do real gases differ from an ideal gas?
6. What is Avogadro's principle?

1. 124 cm³
2. 244 cm³
3. 93.6 cm³
4. CO₂
5. Real gases occupy a finite volume and exert an attractive force on each other.
6. Equal volumes of gases at the same temperature and pressure contain the same number of molecules.

7. 10 dm³
8. 3.94 g Al
9. 79.6 g NaCl
10. 248 g Na₃AlO₃
11. a. 54.4 K
    b. 0.152 kPa
    c. 90.2 K
    d. 54.8 K
    e. 155 K
    f. 5040 kPa

7. What volume will be occupied by 0.161 mole of gas at 43.3 kPa and 52°C?

8. What mass of aluminum is required to react with 4.90 dm³ of chlorine according to the equation $2Al + 3Cl_2 \rightarrow 2AlCl_3$?

9. What mass of sodium chloride is obtained from the reaction of 49.5 g HCl with 91.8 g NaOH? ($HCl + NaOH \rightarrow NaCl + H_2O$)

10. What mass of sodium aluminate is obtained from the reaction of 134 g Al(OH)₃ with 635 g NaOH?

$$(Al(OH)_3 + 3NaOH \rightarrow Na_3AlO_3 + 3H_2O)$$

11. Use the phase diagram of oxygen to find the following.
    a. triple point temperature   d. normal melting point
    b. triple point pressure   e. critical point temperature
    c. normal boiling point   f. critical pressure

FIGURE 20-8. Use with Review 11.

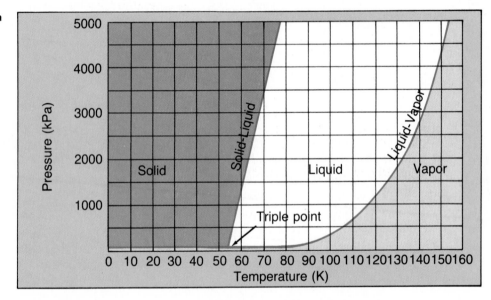

12. 24 800 J
13. 36.1 dm³
14. 576 cm³
15. 6.76 g/dm³
16. 23.5 g/mol

12. How much energy is required to heat 8.16 g of ice at −16°C to steam at 102°C?

13. A gas collected over water at 21°C and 103 kPa is dried. What volume does it occupy when dry if it occupied 37.0 dm³ when wet?

14. If a gas occupies 629 cm³ at 24°C and 101.0 kPa, what volume will it occupy at STP?

15. What is the density of a gas at STP if 8.02 g of it occupy 1.20 dm³ at 103.1 kPa and 8°C?

16. What is the molecular mass of a gas if 2.20 g of it occupy 2.13 dm³ at 20.0°C and 107.1 kPa?

17. How many dm^3 of hydrogen can be obtained from 21.0 g Zn?

$$Zn + 2HCl \rightarrow ZnCl_2 + H_2$$

18. What volume of hydrogen chloride gas can be obtained from 93.0 dm^3 of chlorine?

$$H_2 + Cl_2 \rightarrow 2HCl$$

19. What volume of hydrogen at 6°C and 123.0 kPa can be obtained from 10.1 g Mn?

$$Mn + 2H_2O \rightarrow Mn(OH)_2 + H_2$$

17. 7.19 dm^3
18. 186 dm^3
19. 3.47 dm^3

ONE MORE STEP

1. Prepare a report for the class on the difference between heat capacity and enthalpy.
2. What is meant by the thermodynamic quantity "work function" (Helmholtz free energy)?
3. Under certain conditions, the change in internal energy is equal to the heat absorbed from the surroundings. What are the conditions?
4. Under what conditions is the maximum work attainable from a chemical system?

3. constant volume
4. reversible

READINGS

Spencer, J. N., and E. S. Holmboe, "Entropy and Unavailable Energy," *Journal of Chemical Education,* Vol. 60, No. 12(December 1983), pp. 1018-1021.

The study of the oceans involves a knowledge of the chemistry of solutions. Dissolved solutes in ocean water provide the nutrients necessary for ocean life to exist. These same solutes have changed chemically the materials in the sunken ship. Ocean solutes are now being considered as a source of mineral deposits. Tapping this resource depends on a knowledge of solution chemistry. What causes a solute to dissolve? How can solutes be recovered from a solution? What type of solution is the ocean?

SOLUTIONS

Chapter 21 classifies homogeneous mixtures into nine solutions. The properties of each group are discussed. Molality and mole fraction calculations are introduced along with molarity, which was covered in Chapter 5.

DEMONSTRATION: Prepare a solution of a colored salt such as $KMnO_4$ or $CuSO_4$. Prepare a suspension by mixing some soil and water. Filter both preparations and discuss the results. Ask the students which would be easier to remove from drinking water, chemical pollution or solids such as mud and algae.

GOALS:
- You will gain an understanding of the nine homogeneous mixtures called solutions.
- You will determine the factors that aid or hinder the rate of solution.
- You will solve problems dealing with various means of expressing concentration of solutions.

What do we mean by solution? In Chapter 3, we referred to homogeneous matter as being the same throughout. It is often made of only one substance—a compound or an element—but may also be a mixture of several substances. Such a homogeneous mixture is called a solution. Most solutions consist of a solid dissolved in a liquid. The particles in a true solution are molecules, atoms, or ions that will pass easily through the pores of filter paper. Solutions cannot be separated into their components by filtration.

The substance that occurs to the greater extent in a solution is said to do the dissolving and is called the **solvent.** The less abundant substance is said to be dissolved and is called the **solute.**

A solution is a homogeneous mixture.

The more abundant substance in a solution is called the solvent.

21:1   THE SOLVENT

The most common solvent is water. Using water as a typical solvent, let us look at the mechanism of solvent action. Water molecules are very polar. Because they are polar they are attracted to other polar molecules and to ions. Table salt, NaCl, is an ionic compound made of sodium and chloride ions. If a salt crystal is put in water, the polar water molecules are attracted to ions on the crystal surfaces. The water molecules gradually surround and isolate the surface ions. The ions become hydrated, Figure 21-1. The attraction between the hydrated sodium and chloride ions and the remaining crystal ions becomes so small that the hydrated ions are no longer held by the crystal. They gradually move away from the crystal into solution. This separation of ions from each other is called **dissociation.** The surrounding of solute particles by solvent particles is called **solvation.**

Polar water molecules are attracted to ions and other polar molecules.

Dissociation is the separation of ions from each other.

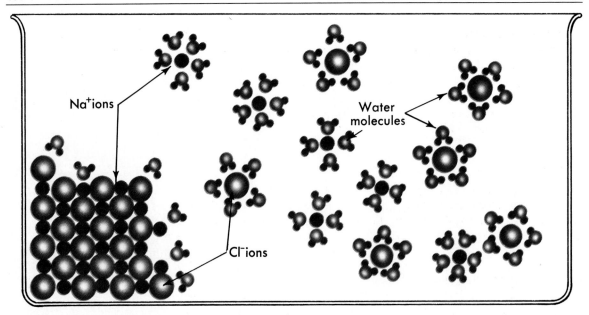

FIGURE 21-1. Table salt dissolves in water because polar water molecules gradually surround and isolate the sodium and chloride ions.

BACKGROUND: The process by which solute particles are surrounded by solvent particles is called solvation, or in the case of water, hydration.

Chemical reaction between solute and solvent is called solvolysis. If water is involved, the reaction is called hydrolysis. Be careful not to confuse the terms solvolysis and hydrolysis, which imply chemical reactions, with solvation and hydration, which imply no chemical change.

The dissociation of ions in solution leads to a factor that is important to keep in mind any time you are working with a solution of an ionic material. When the ions are dissociated, each ion species in the solution acts as though it were present alone. Thus, a solution of sodium chloride acts as a solution of sodium ions and chloride ions. There is no characteristic behavior of "sodium chloride" in solution because there really is no sodium chloride in solution. There is simply a solution containing both sodium ions and chloride ions uniformly mixed.

21:2 SOLVENT-SOLUTE COMBINATIONS

Four simple solution situations can be considered. They are listed in Table 21-1. Not all possible combinations of substances will fit into these four rigid categories. However, we will now consider these four as sample cases for studying solutions.

Table 21-1

Solvent-Solute Combinations		
Solvent Type	**Solute Type**	**Is Solution Likely?**
Polar	Polar	yes
Polar	Nonpolar	no
Nonpolar	Polar	no
Nonpolar	Nonpolar	yes

(1) Polar solvent-Polar solute.

The mechanism of solution involving a polar solvent and a polar solute is the one we have already described for salt and water. The polar solvent particles solvate the polar solute particles. They attach themselves due to the polar attraction. The intracrystalline forces are reduced so much that the surface particles are carried away by the solvent particles. In water, this process is called **hydration.**

(2) Polar solvent-Nonpolar solute.

Because these solvent particles are polar, they are attracted to each other. However, the solute particles in this case are nonpolar and have little attraction for particles of the solvent. Thus, solution to any extent is unlikely, as we see if we try to dissolve wax in water.

(3) Nonpolar solvent-Polar solute.

Reasoning similar to that of the second case applies here. The solvent particles are nonpolar and thus have little attraction for the solute particles. In addition, the solute particles in this case are polar and are attracted to each other. Again, solution to any extent is unlikely, as we see if we try to dissolve salt in hexane.

(4) Nonpolar solvent-Nonpolar solute.

Only van der Waals forces exist among the nonpolar solvent particles. The same is true for the nonpolar solute particles. Thus, all particles in the solution are subject only to van der Waals forces, and solution can occur. Random motion of solute molecules will cause some of them to leave the surface of the solute. There can be solvation in such cases, but the forces are far weaker than those in solutions involving polar compounds. The nonpolar particles are simply randomly dispersed. Thus, wax will dissolve in hexane.

dispersion forces only

Not all nonpolar substances, however, are soluble in each other. Let us consider the most common type of solution: a solid dissolved in a liquid. The solubility of a nonpolar solid in a nonpolar liquid depends upon two factors. These factors are its melting point and its enthalpy of fusion. What do they have to do with solubility? When the solid dissolves, a liquid solution results. The solid is undergoing a phase change. Solids with low melting points and low enthalpies of fusion will be more soluble than those with high melting points and high enthalpies of fusion. This difference is due to stronger attractive forces within the crystal of high melting point substances.

Table 21-2 lists a number of common solvents in order of increasing ability to dissolve highly polar and ionic materials. Compare the order here with that in Table 14-1, page 265.

Table 21-2

Ionic Dissolving Ability	
Name	**Formula**
Cyclohexane	C_6H_{12}
Carbon tetrachloride	CCl_4
Benzene	C_6H_6
Toluene	C_7H_8
Ethoxyethane	$C_4H_{10}O$
Ethyl acetate	$C_4H_8O_2$
1-Butanol	$C_4H_{10}O$
1-Propanol	C_3H_8O
Propanone	C_3H_6O
Ethanol	C_2H_6O
Methanol	CH_4O
Water	H_2O

(arrow labeled "increasing" pointing downward along the list)

21:3 SOLIDS, LIQUIDS, AND GASES IN SOLUTION

Since there are three common physical states of matter (solid, liquid, and gas), there are nine possible combinations of solvent-solute pairs. These combinations are given in Table 21-3.

The property of mutual solubility of two liquids is called **miscibility.** If two liquids are mutually soluble in all proportions, they are said to be completely miscible. Ethylene glycol (automobile antifreeze) and water are two such liquids. Water and carbon tetrachloride, however, do not appreciably dissolve in each other and are, therefore, immiscible. Two liquids such as diethyl ether ($C_4H_{10}O$) and water, which dissolve in each other to some extent but not completely, are referred to as partially miscible.

There are nine possible combinations of solvent-solute pairs.

Miscible: Mutually soluble

Immiscible liquids separate into layers on standing.

Table 21-3

Possible Solution Combinations		
Solvent	**Solute**	**Common Example**
gas	gas	oxygen-helium (deep-sea diver's gas)
gas	liquid	air-water (humidity)
gas	solid	air-naphthalene (mothballs)
liquid	gas	water-carbon dioxide (carbonated beverage)
liquid	liquid	acetic acid-water (vinegar)
liquid	solid	water-salt (seawater)
solid	gas	palladium-hydrogen (gas stove lighter)
solid	liquid	silver-mercury (dental amalgam)
solid	solid	gold-silver (ring)

A number of metals (such as gold and silver) are mutually soluble and form solid—solid solutions. Such solid metal—metal solutions constitute one type of alloy.

Some alloys are solid metal-metal solutions.

a

b

FIGURE 21-2. Not all solutions contain a solid dissolved in a liquid. These mothballs are composed of solid naphthalene which can dissolve in air (a). These divers must use a gaseous solution of oxygen and helium (b).

21:4   SOLUTION EQUILIBRIUM

When crystals are first placed in a solvent, many particles may leave the surface and go into solution. As the number of solute particles in solution increases, some of the dissolved particles return to the surface of the crystal. Eventually the number of particles leaving the crystal surface equals the number returning to the surface. This point is called **solution equilibrium.**

A solution in which an undissolved substance is in equilibrium with the dissolved substance is called a **saturated solution.** A solution containing less than the saturated amount of solute for that temperature is an **unsaturated solution.**

Larger amounts of solute can usually be dissolved in a solvent at a temperature higher than room temperature. If the hot solution is then cooled, an unstable solution is formed. This solution contains more solute than a saturated solution can normally hold. The solution is called a **supersaturated solution.** Supersaturation is possible because solids will not crystallize unless there is a special surface upon which to start crystallization. A container that has a smooth interior and which contains a dust-free solution has no such surfaces. However, a supersaturated solution will crystallize almost instantly if a crystal of the solute is introduced. How could you find out if a solution is saturated, unsaturated, or supersaturated?

At a specific temperature, the amount of solute that will dissolve in a given quantity of solvent at saturation is a fixed amount. For instance, at 20°C, a maximum of 64.2 grams of nickel(II) chloride will dissolve in 100 cm^3 of water. When 64.2 grams $NiCl_2$ dissolve in 100 cm^3 of water, the solution is saturated, and this quantity is called the solubility of the

FIGURE 21-3. This supersaturated solution of sodium thiosulfate (a) can be made to crystallize by the addition of a seed crystal (b).

a

b

substance at 20°C. This solubility can be changed by altering the temperature.

Precipitation reactions are an important tool of the analytical chemist. The differing solubilities of substances can be used to separate them from mixtures. If a solution contains two ionic compounds, they may be separated by choosing a reactant that will precipitate only one ion. For example, consider a mixture of sodium nitrate and barium chloride. A chemist wishes to know what percentage of the mixture is $BaCl_2$, and thus finds the mass of the mixture before dissolving it in water. Once dissolved, the barium ions could be precipitated with sulfate ions from a soluble sulfate such as sulfuric acid. On the other hand, the chloride ions could be precipitated with silver ions from a soluble silver salt such as silver nitrate (see Table A-7 of the Appendix). The product is collected, dried, and massed. By solving a mass-mass problem, the chemist can find the amount, and thereby the percentage of $BaCl_2$ in the original mixture.

The formation of an insoluble solid from a chemical reaction is called precipitation.

DEMONSTRATION: Place a petri dish on the overhead projector. To a small amount of H_2O in the dish, add a crystal of $KMnO_4$ and slowly stir the solution. Discuss what is happening at the particle level when solution equilibrium is reached.

21:5 SOLUTION RATE

The rate of solution of a solid in a liquid is affected by the surface area of the crystal that is exposed to fresh solvent. When the area of an exposed surface is increased, more solute particles are subjected to solvation. The surface area can be increased by breaking the crystal to be dissolved into very small particles. The surface area can also be increased by stirring the mixture as the solute is dissolving. In this way the solvent, which is saturated with solute, is moved away from the surface of the solid solute. Fresh solvent can then come into contact with the solid surface.

Solution rate is also a function of the kinetic energy of both the solute and solvent particles. The kinetic energy of a system is increased by heating the mixture. The faster the solvent particles are moving, the more rapidly they will circulate among the crystal particles. This motion has the same effect as increasing the surface area. If a solute particle's kinetic energy is increased, once it is solvated, it will move away from the solid

Solution rate is affected by
1. surface area exposed to fresh solvent
2. kinetic energy of particles

Kinetic energy can be increased by heating the system.

FIGURE 21-4. Solution rate can be increased by stirring (a), increasing the surface area of the solute (b), or heating (c).

a

b

c

material more rapidly. This motion exposes fresh surface, thus increasing solution rate. Finally, with increased kinetic energy, particles are more easily removed from the crystal.

21:6 ENTHALPY OF SOLUTION

The process involving the solution of most solids in water is endothermic (ΔH positive). Recall from Chapter 20 that the free energy difference (ΔG) for a change is negative if the reaction proceeds spontaneously. For ΔG to be negative in the equation $\Delta G = \Delta H - T\Delta S$, ΔS must be positive if ΔH is positive. The solid has a high degree of order in the crystalline form. When dissolved, the particles are randomly distributed throughout the solution. The random distribution represents more disorder than the crystal. We see, then, that ΔS is positive, as predicted. There are a few solids with a negative ΔH of solution. For these substances the degree of hydration is so high that more order exists in the solution than in the separate solid and liquid.

When gases dissolve in water, the hydrated molecules represent a higher degree of order than the random distribution in the gas. ΔS for the dissolving of a gas is, therefore, negative. Soluble gases, then, must have a negative ΔH. Experiment shows that the dissolving of gases is, in fact, an exothermic process.

Using our knowledge of enthalpy change in solutions, we can predict the effect of temperature on solubility. Most solids having positive enthalpies of solution ($\Delta H > 0$), are more soluble in hot water than in cold. However, gases, with negative enthalpies of solution ($\Delta H < 0$), are more soluble in cold water.

21:7 EFFECTS OF PRESSURE

Pressure has little effect on solutions unless the solute is a gas. The amount of gas that dissolves in a given amount of solvent is greater at high pressure than it is at low pressure. *The mass of a gas that will dissolve in a liquid at a given temperature varies directly with the partial pressure of that gas.* This statement is Henry's Law, named in honor of William Henry, the English chemist who first discovered this relationship.

21:8 MOLAR SOLUTIONS

In Chapter 5 we learned about a precise concentration unit called molarity. We found that a one-molar (1M) solution contains 1 mole of solute in 1 dm³ of solution. If 1 mole of sodium chloride is dissolved in enough water to make 1 dm³ of solution, the solution is a 1-molar solution of sodium chloride. Sodium chloride is in the form of dissociated ions in solution. Therefore, the solution can also be said to be 1-molar in sodium ions and 1-molar in chloride ions.

Molarity is the most common concentration unit in chemistry. Measurement of the volume of solutions is fast and convenient. If the solution

You may wish to review the discussion of ΔH, ΔG, and ΔS in Chapter 20.

The solution of most solids in water is endothermic, ΔH is positive.

DEMONSTRATION: Add 50 cm³ water to a 125 cm³ flask containing 15 g NH_4NO_3. It absorbs 619 J per cm³ of H_2O. Add 50 cm³ water to a flask containing 15 g $CaCl_2$. It gives off 490 J per cm³ of H_2O. Pass the two flasks around the class. Discuss how hot and cold packs used for athletic injuries could be made.

DEMONSTRATION: To demonstrate the effect of temperature on solubility, mass 20 g each of calcium acetate, and KNO_3. Add each solid to 125 cm³ flasks that contain 50 cm³ of H_2O. The calcium acetate dissolves but the KNO_3 is only partially soluble. Place both flasks on a hotplate. Heat with occasional stirring. The calcium acetate comes out of solution while the KNO_3 dissolves. Discuss positive and negative ΔH of solution, and the shape of the solubility curves. (See 3:5)

Henry's Law: More gas will dissolve at high pressure than at low pressure.

A 1 molar (1M) solution contains one mol of solute per dm³ of solution.

$$M = \frac{\text{moles of solute}}{\text{dm}^3 \text{ of solution}}$$

measured has a known molarity, a measurement of volume is also a measurement of a number of particles. Each unit of volume contains a known number of ions or molecules. Multiplying the concentration in molarity (moles per dm^3) by the volume (dm^3) will give you the number of particles (in moles).

Whenever the concentration of solute in a solution is known with a high degree of certainty the solution is called a standard solution. Standard solutions are frequently used in analytical chemistry. For example, a standard solution is used by environmental chemists to determine the dissolved oxygen content of lake, river, and ocean waters.

EXAMPLE: Ion Concentration

What are the concentrations of ions in a 1.00M solution of $Al(NO_3)_3$?
$$Al(NO_3)_3(cr) \rightarrow Al^{3+}(aq) + 3NO_3^-(aq)$$
Solving Process:
A 1.00M solution of $Al(NO_3)_3$ contains a concentration of aluminum ions equal to 1.00M and a concentration of nitrate ions equal to 3.00M.

EXAMPLE: Number of Ions

How many moles of ions of each type are present in 2.00×10^2 cm^3 of 0.100M $MgCl_2$? $MgCl_2(cr) \rightarrow Mg^{2+}(aq) + 2Cl^-(aq)$
Solving Process:

$$\frac{2.00 \times 10^2 \; cm^3 \; soln}{} \left| \frac{0.100 \; mol \; MgCl_2}{1000 \; cm^3 \; soln} \right| \frac{1 \; mol \; Mg^{2+}}{1 \; mol \; MgCl_2} = 0.0200 \; mol \; Mg^{2+}$$

$$\frac{2.00 \times 10^2 \; cm^3 \; soln}{} \left| \frac{0.100 \; mol \; MgCl_2}{1000 \; cm^3 \; soln} \right| \frac{2 \; mol \; Cl^-}{1 \; mol \; MgCl_2} = 0.0400 \; mol \; Cl^-$$

PROBLEMS

Calculate the molarity of the ion designated in the following solutions.
  1. Br^- for 193 g $MgBr_2$ in 5.00×10^2 cm^3 solution
  2. Ca^{2+} for 8.28 g $Ca(C_5H_9O_2)_2$ in 2.50×10^2 cm^3 solution
  3. How many moles of Ca^{2+} are in 2.00 dm^3 of 0.523M $CaCl_2$ solution?

21:9 MOLAL SOLUTIONS

Sometimes, it is convenient to express concentration in terms of moles of solute per kilogram of solvent. A solution that contains 1 mole of solute in each 1000 grams of solvent is called a one-molal (1m) solution. This solution differs from a 1-molar (1M) solution, which contains 1 mole of solute in 1 dm^3 of solution. Molality is most useful in studying the colligative properties of solutions, which will be covered in Chapter 22.

EXAMPLE: Molality

If 52.0 g K_2CO_3 are dissolved in 518 g H_2O, what is the molality of the solution?

Solving Process:
Formula mass of K_2CO_3 = 2(39.1 g) + 12.0 g + 3(16.0 g) = 138 g
Divide solute by solvent and convert to the proper units.

$$\frac{52.0 \text{ g } K_2CO_3}{518 \text{ g } H_2O} \left| \frac{1 \text{ mol } K_2CO_3}{138 \text{ g } K_2CO_3} \right| \frac{1000 \text{ g } H_2O}{1 \text{ kg } H_2O} = 0.727m$$

PROBLEMS

Calculate the molality of the following solutions.
  4. 199 g $NiBr_2$ in 5.00×10^2 g water
  5. 92.3 g KF in 1.00×10^3 g water

4. 1.82m $NiBr_2$
5. 1.59m KF

21:10   MOLE FRACTION

Another method of describing concentration used frequently in organic chemistry is mole fraction. The **mole fraction** shows the comparison of moles of solute to moles of solution.

The mole fraction is a comparison of moles of solute to the total number of moles of solution.

EXAMPLE: Mole Fraction

The mole fraction is most commonly used by organic chemists in fractional distillation calculations.

What is the mole fraction of alcohol in a solution made of 2.00 moles of ethanol and 8.00 moles of water?

Solving Process:
(a) Find the total number of moles.

  2.00 moles ethanol + 8.00 moles water = 10.00 moles solution

(b) The mole fraction of ethanol is

$$\frac{2.00 \text{ mol ethanol}}{10.00 \text{ mol solution}} = 0.200$$

Any size sample of this solution will have an ethanol mole fraction of 0.200. The sum of the mole fractions of all components of a solution must equal 1.

Sum of the mole fractions of all components = 1

PROBLEMS

Calculate the mole fraction for each component in the following solutions.
  6. 12.3 g of C_4H_4O in 1.00×10^2 g of C_2H_6O
  7. 156 g of $C_{12}H_{22}O_{11}$ in 3.00×10^2 g H_2O

6. 0.923 mole fraction C_2H_6O
   0.0770 mole fraction C_4H_4O
7. 0.971 mole fraction H_2O
   0.0265 mole fraction $C_{12}H_{22}O_{11}$

BIOGRAPHY   Agnes Pockels (1862-1935)

Agnes Pockels was the daughter of an Austrian army officer. Although she attended high school for some time, she was largely self-taught. In her late teens, she made her first observations on the changes in surface tension of water contaminated by oil. Her first paper was printed under the sponsorship of Lord Rayleigh nearly ten years later when she was 29.

Most of her experimentation was done at home with homemade apparatus. Among other makeshift devices, she developed the Pockels' trough which was used to measure surface tension.

At 69, she won the Laura-Leonard prize for her work in the properties of surface layers and films. One year later she received her first degree, an honorary doctorate. An extension of her work in surface chemistry led to the Nobel Prize for Irving Langmuir in 1932.

TECHNOLOGY AND CHEMISTRY

21:11   Seawater

From where did the ocean come? Why is there no ocean on the moon? Why is the ocean salty? We know that molecules are constantly in motion. Air molecules, if they are traveling fast enough, may escape Earth's gravitational attraction and fly off into space. The moon, with small gravitational force, has never been able to hold an atmosphere or moisture.

The speed of molecules is determined by their mass and temperature. Scientists have determined that Earth was quite hot at its early stage of formation. Any water present at that time would have vaporized and been lost to space. Our present ocean has accumulated as a result of water emerging from the interior of Earth, principally as a result of volcanic action.

Water vapor was emitted by erupting volcanoes, and as Earth cooled, the water vapor condensed into clouds and eventually fell as rain. The rain dissolved certain minerals as it fell on the original crystalline rocks of Earth's surface. The effects of erosion (weathering) produced a flow of water that contained dissolved minerals, and this solution accumulated to form the ocean. We call the solution seawater or salt water because sodium ions and chloride ions are the main solutes. Small quantities of seawater solute continue to be added from volcanoes as well as rain and stream erosion. Since erosional and volcanic processes continue, why do the concentrations remain relatively constant? Solutes are being removed from the ocean as well as added.

The minerals in the sea are constantly forming sediment on the seafloor. This sediment is the result of chemical reactions within seawater and living organisms in the sea that use the solutes. When these organisms die, their remains sink to the bottom. It is generally assumed by scientists today that seawater represents a state of equilibrium between the addition of new salts and the precipitation of solutes.

Table 21-4

			Composition of Seawater			
Element	Form of occurrence	Grams per kilogram of seawater		Element	Form of occurrence	Grams per kilogram of seawater
Chlorine	Cl^-	19.4		Bromine	Br^-	0.0673
Sodium	Na^+	10.8		*Carbon	HCO_3^-, CO_3^{2-}	0.0281
Sulfur	SO_4^{2-}	2.71		Strontium	Sr^{2+}	0.0079
Magnesium	Mg^{2+}	1.29		Boron	H_3BO_3	0.0045
Calcium	Ca^{2+}	0.412		Silicon	H_4SiO_4	0.0030
Potassium	K^+	0.399		Fluorine	F^-	0.0013
70 other elements have been found in smaller amounts.				*Concentrations are subject to wide local variation.		

SUMMARY

1. When ionic compounds dissolve, the ions dissociate. 21:1

2. Polar solvents tend to dissolve polar solutes; nonpolar solvents tend to dissolve nonpolar solutes. 21:1-21:2

3. Two liquids that are mutually soluble in all proportions are completely miscible. 21:3

4. A solution is said to reach solution equilibrium when the rates of particles leaving and returning to the solution are equal. When solution equilibrium is reached, the solution is said to be saturated with the solute. 21:4

5. The rate of solution is affected by the surface area of crystal exposed and the kinetic energy of solute and solvent. 21:5

6. Enthalpy of solution is the energy change that occurs when one substance is dissolved in another. Most solids have positive enthalpies of solution. Gases have negative enthalpies of solution. 21:6

7. Henry's law: The mass of a gas that will dissolve in a liquid at a given temperature varies directly with the partial pressure of that gas. 21:7

8. Molarity, molality, and mole fraction are common concentration units. 21:8-21:10

VOCABULARY

solvent **Intro**
solute **Intro**
dissociation **21:1**
solvation **21:1**
hydration **21:2**
miscibility **21:3**

solution equilibrium **21:4**
saturated solution **21:4**
unsaturated solution **21:4**
supersaturated solution **21:4**
mole fraction **21:10**

PROBLEMS

1. a. not soluble
   b. not soluble
   c. miscible
   d. not soluble
   e. not soluble
   f. miscible
2. a. slightly soluble
   b. soluble
   c. soluble
   d. not soluble
   e. soluble
3. 0.909M
4. 4.36M
5. 13.9M
6. 0.721m
7. 2.18m
8. 0.259m
9. 0.0680 $C_{10}H_8$;
   0.932 $C_4H_{10}O$
10. 0.107 C_9H_7N;
    0.893 C_2H_6O
11. 0.0292 $C_5H_{10}O_5$;
    0.0280 CH_6ON_4;
    0.944 H_2O
12. 1.80 × 10² g
    Sc(NO₃)₃
13. 22.3 g Er₂(SO₄)₃
14. 18.2 g VBr₃
15. 6.51 g DyCl₃
16. 16.3 g IrCl₄
17. 4.28 g YBr₃
18. 5.81 g Li₂SO₄
19. 1.20 g KHC₂O₄
20. 34.4 g
    UO₂(NO₃)₂·6H₂O
21. 25.6 g HSO₃F

1. Predict the solubility of the first substance in the second on the basis of comparative polarities.
   a. RbF in ethanol
   b. CuS in water
   c. ethanol in water
   d. NCl_3 in C_6H_6
   e. gasoline in water
   f. benzene in hexane

2. Predict the solubility of the following in water on the basis of comparative polarities.
   a. CuF_2 **b.** $ScCl_3$ **c.** Rb_2S **d.** ThS_2 **e.** CsI

Calculate the molarity of the following solutions.

3. 31.1 g $Al_2(SO_4)_3$ in 1.00 × 10³ cm³ solution
4. 48.4 g $CaCl_2$ in 1.00 × 10² cm³ solution
5. 313.5 g $LiClO_3$ in 2.50 × 10² cm³ solution

Calculate the molality of the following solutions.

6. 98.0 g RbBr in 824 g water
7. 85.2 g $SnBr_2$ in 1.40 × 10² g water
8. 10.0 g $AgClO_3$ in 201 g water

Calculate the mole fraction for each component in the following solutions.

9. 75.6 g of $C_{10}H_8$ in 6.00 × 10² g $C_4H_{10}O$
10. 67.4 g of C_9H_7N in 2.00 × 10² g C_2H_6O
11. 5.48 g of $C_5H_{10}O_5$ and 3.15 g of CH_6ON_4 in 21.2 g H_2O

Compute the masses of solute needed to make the following solutions.

12. 1.000 dm³ of 0.780M Sc(NO₃)₃
13. 2.00 × 10² cm³ of 0.179M Er₂(SO₄)₃
14. 1.00 × 10² cm³ of 0.626M VBr₃
15. 2.50 × 10² cm³ of 0.0965M DyCl₃
16. 5.00 × 10² cm³ of 0.0978M IrCl₄
17. 1.00 dm³ of 0.0130M YBr₃
18. 1.00 × 10² cm³ of 0.528M Li₂SO₄
19. 2.00 × 10² cm³ of 0.0469M KHC₂O₄
20. 2.50 × 10² cm³ of 0.274M UO₂(NO₃)₂·6H₂O
21. 5.00 × 10² cm³ of 0.512M HSO₃F

Compute the mass of solute that will yield the following solutions.

22. $Fe_2(C_2O_4)_3$ to be added to 1.00×10^3 g of water for a $0.851m$ solution

23. $VOBr_3$ to be added to 1.00×10^3 g water for a $0.534m$ solution

24. $C_7H_4O_2Br_2$ to be added to 2.00×10^2 g of C_2H_6O so that the mole fraction of the solvent is 0.510

25. $C_{14}H_{16}N_2$ to be added to 1.00×10^3 g of $C_4H_{10}O$ so that the mole fraction of the solute is 0.363

26. $LiMnO_4$ to be added to 5.00×10^2 g of water for a $0.614m$ solution

27. Iodine crystals are relatively insoluble in water. However, they do dissolve in carbon tetrachloride. Explain why.

28. Using Table A-7 of the Appendix, select a reagent that will precipitate one of the metal ions in each of the following mixtures.

a. $AgNO_3$ and $NaNO_3$

b. $FeCl_3$ and $NaCl$

c. $BaCl_2$ and KNO_3

d. KCl and $CuSO_4$

29. A chemist has a 5.00 g mixture of silver and potassium nitrates. To isolate the silver, HCl is added. The dry AgCl precipitate has a mass of 3.50 g. What was the mass of $AgNO_3$ in the original mixture?

30. What is the relationship between ΔH and solubility for solids and gases?

31. How does molarity differ from molality? Explain using the equations for each.

Answers (right column):

22. 3.20×10^2 g $Fe_2(C_2O_4)_3$
23. 164 g $VOBr_3$
24. 1170 g $C_7H_4O_2Br_2$
25. 1630 g $C_{14}H_{16}N_2$
26. 38.7 g $LiMnO_4$
27. Both iodine and CCl_4 are nonpolar substances. Water is polar.
30. Most solids having positive enthalpies of solution are more soluble in hot water than cold. Gases with negative enthalpies of solution are more soluble in cold water.

31. $M = \dfrac{\text{moles}}{dm^3 \text{ of soln}}$ considers the volume of the solution

$m = \dfrac{\text{moles}}{\text{kg solvent}}$ considers the mass of the solvent only

28. a. $Cl^- \rightarrow AgCl(cr)$
b. $OH^- \rightarrow Fe(OH)_3(cr)$
c. $SO_4{}^{2-} \rightarrow BaSO_4(cr)$
d. $OH^- \rightarrow Cu(OH)_2(cr)$

29. 4.13 g $AgNO_3$

REVIEW

1. Compute the enthalpy change for the reaction:
$$Cu(cr) + 2H_2SO_4(aq) \rightarrow CuSO_4(cr) + SO_2(g) + 2H_2O(l)$$

2. Compute the free energy change for the reaction:
$$P_4O_{10}(cr) + 6H_2O(l) \rightarrow 4H_3PO_4(l)$$
if $\Delta H_{rxn} = -454.3$ kJ and $\Delta S_{rxn} = 3.76$ J/K at 25°C.

3. What is meant by the expression "standard states?"

4. Define the quantities "q" and "w."

Answers (right column):

1. $\Delta H = 177$ kJ
2. $\Delta G = -455$ kJ
3. Standard states: A reference set of conditions used in thermodynamic calculations.
4. $q =$ heat absorbed by the system.
$w =$ work done on the system.

ONE MORE STEP

1. Obtain an unknown substance from your instructor and attempt to identify it experimentally by determining its solubility curve.

2. Try to make a supersaturated solution of $Na_2S_2O_3$.

3. Measure the enthalpy of solution of anhydrous sodium phosphate at several different concentrations. See if you can determine how the molar enthalpy of solution varies with temperature.

See Teacher Guide for answers.

READINGS

Treptow, Richard S. "LeChatelier's Principle Applied to the Temperature Dependance of Solubility," *Journal of Chemical Education*, Vol. 61, No. 6(June 1984), pp. 499-502.

The vapor pressure of a substance in solution is dependent on the number of particles in the solution. Vapor pressure is a colligative property. Changes in vapor pressure are used on a large scale at a petroleum refinery. The distillation process involves separating the components of a mixture by the differences in their vapor pressures. What are the other colligative properties? What are some other applications of colligative behavior?

COLLIGATIVE AND COLLOIDAL PROPERTIES

GOALS:
• You will gain an understanding of the properties of solutions that depend upon the number of particles in solution.
• You will calculate boiling and freezing points for solutions of known concentrations and vice versa.
• You will differentiate between solutions and colloids.

Chapter 22 introduces colligative properties (vapor pressure, melting point, freezing point, and osmotic pressure) qualitatively and quantitatively. Molality, covered in Chapter 21, is used in calculations. These properties are discussed along with a study of colloids.

DEMONSTRATION: Prepare three 250 cm^3 side-arm vacuum flasks each connected to a U-tube which is half filled with colored H_2O. Add 50 cm^3 of H_2O to each flask. To the second flask, add 10 g of sugar. To the third flask, add 3.3 g of NaCl. Observe the levels of the H_2O manometer and comment on the vapor pressure lowering effects of the sugar and salt.

When a solute is dissolved in a solvent, there is a change in certain properties of the solvent. On the other hand, when particles too large to dissolve are dispersed throughout a liquid, the solvent's properties remain unchanged. In this chapter, we want to investigate those properties of solvents that are changed by solutes. We also want to look at the behavior of those particles that are too large to dissolve and have no effect on the liquid. Throughout the first six sections of this chapter, we will be dealing with an ideal solution. In Chapter 18 we were able to define an ideal gas. Unfortunately, we cannot define an ideal solution completely at this point. For the time being, we will just say that the particles of solute in an ideal solution have no effect on each other.

22:1 RAOULT'S LAW

Colligative properties are determined by the number of particles in solution rather than by the type of particle in solution. The properties so affected are vapor pressure, freezing point, boiling point, and the rate of diffusion through a membrane. Consider a solute dissolved in a liquid solvent. Some of the solute particles take up space on the liquid surface normally occupied by solvent particles. These solute particles decrease the opportunity for solvent particles to escape (evaporate) from the liquid surface. Thus, if the solute is nonvolatile, the vapor pressure of a solution is always less than that of the pure solvent at the same temperature. The lowering of the vapor pressure of the solvent varies directly as the mole fraction of dissolved solute. *Any nonvolatile solute at a specific concentration lowers the vapor pressure of a solvent by an amount that is characteristic of that solvent.* The characteristics of the solute are not involved.

Colligative properties depend on the number of particles in solution.

Colligative properties
1. vapor pressure
2. freezing point depression
3. boiling point elevation
4. rate of diffusion through a membrane

All ionic and molecular solids having low vapor pressures are said to be nonvolatile.

Ionic compounds and molecular compounds with high melting points are typical nonvolatile solutes. To determine the vapor pressure of a solution, we must correct the vapor pressure of the pure solvent for the presence of the solute. The equation used for correcting the vapor pressure is

$$\text{vapor pressure} \atop \text{(solution)} = \text{vapor pressure} \atop \text{(solvent)} \times \text{mole fraction} \atop \text{(solvent)}$$

This expression is a mathematical statement of **Raoult's law,** named for Francis Raoult, a French chemist. He first stated the principle that *the vapor pressure of a solution varies directly as the mole fraction of solvent.* Raoult's law describes an ideal solution. We can now define an ideal solution as one in which all intermolecular attractions are the same. In other words, solute-solute, solvent-solvent, and solute-solvent attractions are all essentially the same.

> An ideal solution: All intermolecular attractions are the same.

In the case of a volatile solute, Raoult's law is often inadequate to predict the behavior of the solution. However, there are many solutions whose behavior approaches the ideal closely enough to be treated as such. Each volatile component of an ideal solution has a vapor pressure that can be determined by Raoult's law.

EXAMPLE: Raoult's Law

Consider a solution composed of 1.00 mole of benzene, C_6H_6, and 1.00 mole of toluene, $C_6H_5CH_3$. The mole fraction of each volatile component in the solution is 0.500. Thus, the number of benzene molecules in the solution equals the number of toluene molecules. At 25°C, benzene has a vapor pressure of 12.7 kPa, and toluene has a vapor pressure of 3.79 kPa. What is the vapor pressure of the resulting solution?

Solving Process:

According to Dalton's law, the vapor pressure is the sum of the individual pressure of benzene and toluene. The vapor pressure of benzene in the solution is

$$(0.500)(12.7 \text{ kPa}) = 6.35 \text{ kPa}$$

The vapor pressure of toluene in the solution is

$$(0.500)(3.79 \text{ kPa}) = 1.90 \text{ kPa}$$

Thus, the vapor pressure of the resulting solution is 8.25 kPa (6.35 kPa + 1.90 kPa).

> The ratio of molecules in the liquid will not always be the same ratio for the vapor.
>
> liquid ratio 1:1
> vapor ratio 3.34:1

Note especially that the vapor phase is much richer in the more volatile component (benzene) than is the liquid phase. The vapors of the two substances are in the same volume and at the same temperature. Thus, the ratio of their pressures must be equal to the ratio of the number of vapor molecules of each. This ratio is 6.35/1.90 or 3.34/1.

PROBLEMS

1. Find the vapor pressure of a water solution in which the mole fraction of $HgCl_2$ (a nonvolatile solute) is 0.163 at 25°C. Use the vapor pressure of water table in Chapter 18 page 350.

2. Find the total vapor pressure of a solution of ethanal (mole fraction 0.300, vapor pressure at 18°C = 86.3 kPa) in methanol at 18°C. (Vapor pressure of methanol at 18°C = 11.6 kPa.)

1. 2.7 kPa
2. 34.0 kPa

22:2 FRACTIONAL DISTILLATION

We take advantage of the difference in vapor pressures of two components of a solution in the process of fractional distillation. Recall from Chapter 3 that distillation is a physical process of separating substances with different boiling points. If we plot the boiling point of mixtures of benzene and toluene, we obtain a graph as shown in the lower curve of Figure 22-1a. The boiling point of each mixture is, of course, the temperature at which the sum of the two vapor pressures equals 101.325 kPa. At each of these points, however, the vapor phase would be richer in the more volatile component. We have calculated the composition of the vapor in equilibrium with the liquid at each of these points, and plotted the data on the same graph (upper curve of Figure 22-1a).

Fractional distillation depends upon vapor pressure difference.

FIGURE 22-1. The lower curve in (a) represents the boiling point and composition of a benzene-toluene mixture of varying proportions. The upper curve represents the vapor concentrations. The stepwise line in (b) indicates how a benzene-toluene mixture can be separated into its components by fractional distillation.

a
MOLE FRACTION OF BENZENE

b
MOLE FRACTION OF BENZENE

Look at Figure 22-1b. Consider boiling a solution of benzene and toluene in which the mole fraction of benzene is 0.3. It will boil at the temperature represented by point A. The vapor in equilibrium with that solution will have the composition represented by point B, which is at the same temperature. It is richer in benzene than the original solution because benzene is more volatile than toluene. If we condense this vapor,

A fractionating tower works on the principle of condensing and revaporizing the already vaporized substance many times as it flows through the tower.

we will obtain a solution that will boil at point C. It will produce a vapor of composition D. This process can be continued until nearly pure benzene is obtained as vapor, and almost pure toluene remains behind. It is possible to construct a distillation apparatus in which separate distillations for each step are not necessary. The structure of the apparatus is such that each step takes place in a separate section of the equipment. In the laboratory, a fractional distillation apparatus is often used in separating volatile liquids. In industry, a fractionating tower is used for the same purpose on a commercial scale. Petroleum is separated into useful products by fractional distillation.

Table 22-1

Petroleum Distillation Fractions	
Name	**Boiling point range (°C)**
Gasoline	60-280
Jet fuel	190-450
Kerosene	350-550
Diesel fuel	430-700
Fuel oil	550-800
Lubricating oil	600-1000

FIGURE 22-2. The packing material in this distillation column (a) increases the surface area of the column. Thus, this column has the separating capabilities of one many times its height. A fractionating tower is used in industry to separate petroleum into its components (b).

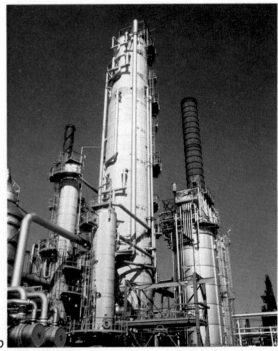

a

b

22:3   BOILING POINT AND FREEZING POINT

The presence of nonvolatile solute particles at the surface causes the boiling point of a solution to be raised. The boiling point of a liquid is the temperature at which the vapor pressure of the liquid equals the atmospheric pressure. In a solution, then, a higher temperature is needed to put enough solvent particles into the vapor phase to equal atmospheric pressure. The boiling point of a solution is, therefore, higher than that of the pure solvent.

How does the addition of a nonvolatile solute affect the freezing point of a solution? The freezing point is the temperature at which the vapor pressure of the solid and liquid are equal. Since the addition of solute particles lowers the vapor pressure, the vapor pressures of the solid and liquid will be equal at a lower temperature. Solutions, then, will freeze at a lower temperature than the pure solvent alone.

> The boiling point of a liquid is the temperature at which the vapor pressure of the liquid equals the atmospheric pressure.
>
> The boiling point of a solution is higher than the boiling point of the pure solvent.
>
> The freezing point of a liquid is the temperature at which the vapor pressures of the solid and liquid are equal.
> The freezing point of a solution is lower than the freezing point of the pure solvent.

FIGURE 22-3. The addition of solute particles lowers the vapor pressure of a solvent and causes it to freeze at a lower temperature and boil at a temperature higher than normal.

In summary, *the addition of a nonvolatile solute to a liquid causes both a boiling point elevation and a freezing point depression.* Both boiling point elevation and freezing point depression occur because the vapor pressure of the solvent is lowered by the solute. These changes depend only on the concentration of the solute particles, and not upon the chemical composition of the solute. We will now consider some general quantitative statements that can be made about these changes.

> BP elevation and FP depression depend on concentration of the solute particles.

22:4 CALCULATING FREEZING AND BOILING POINTS

Molal boiling point elevation for H_2O = 0.512 C°.

It has been found experimentally that 1 mole of nonvolatile solute particles will raise the boiling temperature of 1 kg of water 0.512 C°. The same concentration of solute will lower the freezing point of 1 kg of water 1.86 C°. These two figures are the molal boiling point constant and molal freezing point constant for water. The corresponding constants for some other common solvents are given in Table A-8 of the Appendix. A 1m solution of sugar in water contains 1 mol of solute particles per 1 kg of water. However, a 1m solution of salt contains 2 mole of solute particles (1 mol of Na^+ and 1 mol of Cl^- ions). A 1m solution of calcium chloride contains 3 mol of solute particles per 1 kg of water (1 mol of Ca^{2+} and 2 mol of Cl^- ions). The 1m sugar solution freezes 1.86 C° below the freezing point of pure water. However, the 1m salt solution freezes about 2(1.86 C°) below the freezing point of pure water. The 1m solution of calcium chloride freezes approximately 3(1.86 C°) below the freezing point of pure water. The multiple lowering of the freezing point and elevation of the boiling point by ionic substances supports the theory of dissociation.

Molal freezing point depression for H_2O = 1.86 C°.

Recall that C° represents a difference in two temperatures.

SUGGESTION: Students should not be required to memorize these constants.

Actual boiling point or freezing point depends greatly on ionization.

EXAMPLE: Freezing Point Depression and Boiling Point Elevation

If 85.0 grams of sugar are dissolved in 392 grams of water, what will be the boiling point and freezing point of the resulting solution? The molecular formula of sugar is $C_{12}H_{22}O_{11}$.

Solving Process:

(a) Determine the number of moles of solute. The mass of one mole of $C_{12}H_{22}O_{11}$ equals 342 g.

Since there are 85.0 g of sugar present, the number of moles of sugar in 392 g of water is found by

$$\frac{85.0 \text{ g } C_{12}H_{22}O_{11}}{} \left| \frac{1 \text{ mol } C_{12}H_{22}O_{11}}{342 \text{ g } C_{12}H_{22}O_{11}} \right. = 0.249 \text{ mol of } C_{12}H_{22}O_{11}$$

(b) Convert this quantity to mol/1000 g of water. The result is the molality of the solution.

$m = \dfrac{\text{moles of solute}}{\text{kilogram of solvent}}$

$$\frac{0.249 \text{ mol } C_{12}H_{22}O_{11}}{392 \text{ g water}} \left| \frac{1000 \text{ g water}}{1 \text{ kg water}} \right. = 0.635m \text{ solution}$$

(c) Determine the boiling point elevation. The boiling point is raised 0.512 C° for each mole of sugar added to 1000 g of water. Therefore, the boiling point is

The 100°C and 0°C points are exact since the Celsius scale is defined by these points.

$$100°C + (0.635m)(0.512 \text{ C°}/m) = (100 + 0.325)°C = 100.325°C$$

(d) Determine the freezing point depression. The freezing point is low-

ered 1.86 C° for each mole of sugar added to 1000 g of water. Therefore, the freezing point is

$$0°C - (0.635m)(1.86 \text{ C°}/m) = (0 - 1.18)°C = -1.18°C$$

Let us review what we have done. To determine the change in the
freezing point, we multiplied the freezing point constant by the molality.
We used a similar process for determining the boiling point elevation. To
aid in remembering this process, we can write two equations representing
the mathematical steps we have performed.

$$\Delta T_{FP} = (m)(K_{FP})$$
$$\Delta T_{BP} = (m)(K_{BP})$$

We may use these equations in solving boiling and freezing point problems. They may also be used in solving molecular mass problems as will
be seen in the next section.

EXAMPLE: Freezing Point Depression and Boiling Point Elevation

If 26.4 grams of nickel(II) bromide are dissolved in 224 grams of water,
what will be the boiling point and freezing point of the resulting solutions?
(Assume 100% dissociation and no interaction between ions.)

Solving Process:

(a) Determine the number of moles of solute. The formula mass of one
mole of $NiBr_2$ is 58.7 g + 2(79.9 g) = 219 g. The number of moles of
$NiBr_2$ is

$$\frac{26.4 \text{ g } \cancel{NiBr_2}}{} \left| \frac{1 \text{ mol } NiBr_2}{219 \text{ g } \cancel{NiBr_2}} \right. = 0.121 \text{ mol } NiBr_2$$

(b) Determine the molality of the solution. Since the mass of water is 224
g, the molality equals

$$\frac{0.121 \text{ mol}}{224 \text{ g } \cancel{water}} \left| \frac{1000 \text{ g } \cancel{water}}{1 \text{ kg water}} \right. = 0.540m \text{ } NiBr_2$$

However, the molality in total particles is three times this number
3(0.540) or 1.62m because

$$NiBr_2(cr) \rightarrow Ni^{2+}(aq) + 2Br^-(aq)$$

(c) Determine the boiling point.

$$\text{Boiling point} = 100°C + \Delta T_{BP} = 100°C + (m)(K_{BP}) \qquad \Delta T_{BP} = m \cdot K_{BP}$$
$$= 100°C + (1.62m)(0.512 \text{ C°}) = 100.829°C$$

(d) Determine the freezing point.

$$\text{Freezing point} = 0°C - \Delta T_{FP} = 0°C - (m)(K_{FP}) \qquad \Delta T_{FP} = m \cdot K_{FP}$$
$$= 0°C - (1.62m)(1.86 \text{ C°}) = -3.01°C$$

See the Appendix for molal freezing and boiling point constants.

3. FP = −1.88°C
    BP = 100.517°C
4. FP = −6.45°C
    BP = 101.78°C
5. FP = −5.19°C
    BP = 101.43°C
6. FP = −9.63°C
    BP = 102.65°C
7. FP = −5.2°C
    BP = 219°C

PROBLEMS

Compute the boiling and freezing points of the following solutions.

   3. 25.5 g $C_7H_{11}NO_7S$ *(4-nitro-2-toluenesulfonic acid dihydrate)* in 1.00 $\times$ 10^2 g H_2O *(nonionizing solute)*.

   4. 1.00 $\times$ 10^2 g $C_{10}H_8O_6S_2$ *(1,5-naphthalenedisulfonic acid)* in 1.00 $\times$ 10^2 g H_2O *(nonionizing solute)*

   5. 21.6 g $NiSO_4$ in 1.00 $\times$ 10^2 g H_2O *(assume 100% ionization)*

   6. 77.0 g $Mg(ClO_4)_2$ in 2.00 $\times$ 10^2 g H_2O *(assume 100% ionization)*

   7. 41.3 g $C_{15}H_9NO_4$ *(2-methyl-1-nitroanthraquinone)* in 1.00 $\times$ 10^2 g $C_6H_5NO_2$ *(nitrobenzene)*

FIGURE 22-4. This drawing shows an apparatus used in molecular mass determinations based on freezing point depression.

Stirrer

Thermometer

Stirrer

Freezing tube

Solution

Freezing mixture

22:5   EXPERIMENTAL DETERMINATION OF MOLECULAR MASS

Molecular mass of a solute may be determined by using boiling point elevation or freezing point depression. A known mass of the solute is added to known mass of a solvent. The resulting shift in the boiling or freezing point is then measured.

EXAMPLE: Molecular Mass Determination

99.0 grams of nonionizing solute are dissolved in 669 grams of water, and the freezing point of the resulting solution is −0.960°C. What is the molecular mass of the solute?

Solving Process:

(a) Determine the molality of the solution.

$$\Delta T_{FP} = (m)(K_{FP}) \qquad m = \frac{\Delta T_{FP}}{K_{FP}}$$

$$m = \frac{0.960\ \mathcal{C}}{} \ \left|\ \frac{1m}{1.86\ \mathcal{C}} \right. = 0.516\ \text{mol/kg}$$

(b) Calculate the molecular mass.

$$\frac{99.0\ \text{g solute}}{669\ \text{g water}} \ \left|\ \frac{1000\ \text{g}}{1\ \text{kg}} \right.\ \left|\ \frac{1\ \text{kg}}{0.516\ \text{mol}} \right. = 287\ \text{g/mol}$$

<table>
<tr><td>molality</td><td>convert to kilograms</td><td>convert to moles</td><td></td></tr>
</table>

See the Appendix for molal freezing and boiling point constants.

8. 40.3 g/mol

PROBLEMS

Calculate the molecular mass of the nonionic solutes. Use Table A-8 of the Appendix if necessary.

   8. 8.02 grams of solute in 861 grams of water lower the freezing point to −0.430°C.

9. 64.3 grams of solute in 3.90×10^2 grams of water raise the boiling point to 100.680°C.

10. 20.8 grams of solute in 128 grams of acetic acid lower the freezing point to 13.5°C.

11. 10.4 grams of solute in 164 grams of phenol lower the freezing point to 36.3°C.

12. 2.53 grams of solute in 63.5 grams of nitrobenzene lower the freezing point to 3.40°C.

9. 124 g/mol
10. 210 g/mol
11. 7.0×10^1 g/mol
12. 120 g/mol

22:6 OSMOTIC PRESSURE

There is another colligative property that is of great importance in living systems. Consider Figure 22-5. Two liquids are separated by a thin film called a membrane. One liquid is a pure solvent and the other liquid is a solution of the same solvent. The membrane separating the liquids is a special kind of membrane called a **semipermeable membrane.** Semipermeable membranes will allow small particles (ions and molecules) to pass through, but will stop large molecules. As a result of an unequal passing of particles, a pressure difference builds up between the two sides of the membrane. This pressure is called the **osmotic pressure** of the solution. Osmotic processes are very important in the human body. Absorption of the products of digestion and the operation of the kidney as a waste remover are two osmotic processes vital to life.

Osmosis: Diffusion through a semipermeable membrane.

Osmotic pressure (Π): Pressure required to stop the net transfer of solvent across a semipermeable membrane.

Tube

Piston

Solute dissolved in water

Water

Semipermeable membrane

FIGURE 22-5. Osmotic pressure can be measured as the force applied to the piston to oppose the osmotic flow through the membrane.

Since osmotic pressure is a colligative property, it can be expressed in an equation such as

$$\Pi = (m)(K_{osm})$$

where Π is the osmotic pressure. However, the constant for osmosis

DEMONSTRATION: Osmotic pressure can be shown by using a carrot or potato in a beaker of H_2O. Bore a large hole in the top, add 10 cm^3 of saturated sugar solution. Then stopper the hole with a 1-hole rubber stopper fitted with a 30 cm length of glass tubing. The water will go up the tube slowly. Allow at least 1 day before observing the results.

(K_{osm}) is highly temperature dependent. As a result, osmotic pressure is expressed in the form

$$\Pi = MRT$$

$\Pi = MRT$

In this equation, M is the molarity of the solution, R is the ideal gas constant, and T is the kelvin temperature.

EXAMPLE: Osmotic Pressure

What osmotic pressure is exerted by a solution that is 1.82M at 18°C?
Solving Process:

$$\Pi = MRT$$

Since the units of R are dm³·kPa/mol·K, we will express our molarity as 1.82 mol/1.00 dm³.

$$\Pi = \frac{1.82 \text{ mol}}{1.00 \text{ dm}^3} \mid \frac{8.31 \text{ dm}^3 \cdot \text{kPa}}{\text{mol} \cdot \text{K}} \mid \frac{291 \text{ K}}{} = 4.40 \times 10^3 \text{ kPa}$$

13. 5.15 kPa
14. 1.50 × 10⁴ g/mol
15. 60.8 kPa
16. 4890 g/mol

PROBLEMS

13. 18.6 g of a solute with molecular mass 8940 g are dissolved in enough water to make 1.00 dm³ of solution at 25°C. What is the osmotic pressure of the solution?

14. 96.0 g of a solute are dissolved in enough water to make 1.00 dm³ of solution at 25°C. The osmotic pressure of the resulting solution is 15.8 kPa. What is the molecular mass of the solute?

15. 69.7 g of a solute with molecular mass 2790 g are dissolved in enough water to make 1.00 dm³ of solution at 20.0°C. What is the osmotic pressure of the solution?

16. 2.00 × 10² g of a solute are dissolved in enough water to make 1.00 dm³ of solution at 21.0°C. The osmotic pressure of the resulting solution is 1.00 × 10² kPa. What is the molecular mass of the solute?

22:7 NONIDEAL SOLUTIONS

Chemists generally make the assumption that ionic compounds are completely dissociated in water solution. However, data obtained from colligative property experiments seem to contradict the assumption. The same indication comes from measurements of the solubility of certain compounds. The reasons for the deviation of these solutions from ideal behavior is the attractive force between oppositely charged ions. All real solutions deviate slightly from Raoult's law. However, except for this section, we have assumed that all solutions are ideal. In other words, we assume they obey Raoult's law.

Let us look at a specific case of deviation from Raoult's law. One mole of sodium chloride should produce 1 mole each of sodium ions and

Nonideal activity is due to ion interaction.

chloride ions. Therefore, you would expect a $2m$ solution of NaCl would lower the freezing point of the water by $4(1.86 \text{ C}°)$ or $7.44 \text{ C}°$. Salt actually lowers the freezing point only about three-quarters of this amount. This difference between theory and experiment is explained by assuming that the solute is completely dissociated into ions and the fact that these ions interact. A more detailed explanation of ion interaction in solution is given by the Debye-Hückel theory (page 501).

The actual ion effectiveness in freezing point depression and boiling point elevation is known as the **activity** of the ion. In dealing with a nonideal solution, chemists use activities in place of concentrations. As the solution becomes more concentrated, each ion individually becomes less effective through interaction with its neighboring ions.

When ions interact in solution, their effective concentration is reduced.

It is necessary to know the ion activity because, in solutions with appreciable concentrations of solute, the electrostatic interaction between oppositely charged ions reduces their effect upon the colligative properties.

22:8 COLLOIDS AND PHASES

In 1861, Thomas Graham, an English chemist, tested the passage of different substances through a parchment membrane. He found that one group of substances passed readily through the membrane, and another group did not pass through it at all. He called the first group **crystalloids** and the second group colloids. The name colloid means gluelike, and glue was one of the substances which did not pass readily through the membrane. Graham thought the ability or inability to pass through the membrane was due to elementary particle size. It was later discovered that any substance could be used to produce a colloid. Included were some of those substances Graham had classified as crystalloids. **Colloids** are now defined as mixtures composed of two phases of matter, the dispersed phase and the continuous phase. They are an intermediate class between suspensions and solutions. Colloid particles (dispersed phase) are larger than the single atoms, ions, or molecules of solutions. They are smaller than the particles of suspensions, which can be seen through a microscope and which settle out of suspension on standing. Colloids include materials labeled as emulsions, aerosols, foams, and gels.

Colloids are mixtures of two phases of matter.
1. dispersed phase
2. continuous phase

Colloidal particles are intermediate in size between solutions and suspensions.

FIGURE 22-6. Smoke particles are too small to settle out on standing. Milk is a colloid that can be separated into its components using a centrifuge.

22:9 COLLOIDAL SIZE

FIGURE 22-7. Gels and foams are classified as colloids.

Colloidal particles are too small to be seen with an ordinary microscope. In 1912, Richard Zsigmondy, a German professor of chemistry, designed the ultramicroscope. Using the ultramicroscope, it is possible to ''see'' colloidal particles. If a finely ground substance is placed in water, one of three things will happen. First, it may form a true solution that is simply a dispersion of atoms, molecules, or ions of the substance into a solvent. The particles in a true solution do not exceed 1 nm in size.

Second, the particles may remain larger than 100 nm. These particles are large enough to be seen with a microscope. They are strongly affected by gravity and gradually fall to the bottom of the container. Since the particles are temporarily suspended and settle out upon standing, this mixture is called a **suspension.**

Particles from 1 to 100 nm in size usually remain dispersed throughout the medium. Such a mixture is called a colloid. Colloids represent a transition between solutions and suspensions. However, they are considered heterogeneous, with the medium as the continuous phase and the dispersed substance as a separate phase.

Table 22-2

Comparison of Solutions, Suspensions, and Colloids		
Type	**Particle size**	**Permanence**
Solution	<1 nm	permanent
Suspension	>100 nm	settle out
Colloid	<100 nm but > 1 nm	permanent

Some extremely large molecules may be dispersed colloidally, for example proteins and polymers.
SUGGESTION: The table may be used to derive experimental methods of differentiating the three kinds of mixtures.

Actually, it is not enough to refer to colloids as being composed of particles in the above size range. Substances show unusual properties even when only one of the three dimensions of the particles is in the colloidal range. Thus, a long narrow particle whose thickness and width is < 100 nm but whose length is > 100 nm could act as a colloid. A thin sheet whose thickness < 100 nm but whose width and length is > 100 nm

Table 22-3

Properties of Solutions, Colloids, and Suspensions		
Solutions	**Colloids**	**Suspensions**
Do not settle out	Do not settle out	Settle out on standing
Pass unchanged through ordinary filter paper	Pass unchanged through ordinary filter paper	Separated by ordinary filter paper
Pass unchanged through membrane	Separated by a membrane	Separated by a membrane
Do not scatter light	Scatter light	Scatter light
Affect colligative properties	Do not affect colligative properties	Do not affect colligative properties

could also act as a colloid. **Colloid chemistry** is defined as the study of the properties of matter whose particles are colloidal in size in at least one dimension.

22:10 PROPERTIES OF COLLOIDS

If a beam of light is allowed to pass through a true solution, some of the light will be absorbed, and some will be transmitted. The particles in solution are not large enough to scatter the light. However, if light is passed through a colloid, the light is scattered by the larger, colloidal particles. The beam becomes visible from the side. This effect, called the **Tyndall effect,** is used in Zsigmondy's ultramicroscope. You may have seen this effect in the beam of a searchlight in the night air (suspended water droplets in air). You may also have observed it as the sunbeam coming through a hole in the blinds (suspended dust particles in the air).

DEMONSTRATION: Place 1 g of sodium thiosulfate into a 150 cm³ beaker that is full of H_2O. Dissolve the $Na_2S_2O_3$. Cover an overhead projector with cardboard. Cut a hole in the cardboard, slightly smaller than the beaker, and set the beaker over the hole. Turn on the projector, and turn off the room lights. Add 1 cm³ of conc. HCl to the beaker and stir. The colloidal sulfur will have the effect of a sunset. See Teacher Guide for more information.

Tyndall effect: The scattering of light by colloid particles.

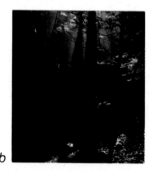
a   b

FIGURE 22-8. A light beam passes through a solution, but a colloid scatters the light (a). The Tyndall effect is seen as light passes through fog (b).

Colloids have another interesting property. If you look through an ultramicroscope, you would notice that the colloidal particles are in continuous random motion. This motion is called **Brownian motion.** This motion is due to their constant bombardment by the smaller molecules of the medium. The motion is the result of the collision of many molecules with the particle. It is as if a large crust of bread in a pond is moved back and forth as first one fish and then another hits the bread from opposite sides. Brownian motion is named in honor of Robert Brown, a biologist. Brown first noticed it while observing the motion of particles in a suspension of pollen grains in water.

As noted in Chapter 17, particles on the surface of a liquid are subject to unbalanced forces. Atoms, ions, or molecules at the surface of solids are also subject to unbalanced forces. As a result, solid and liquid surfaces tend to attract and hold substances with which they come into contact. This phenomenon is called **adsorption.** The stationary phase in chromatography operates through adsorption. Colloidal particles, because of their small size, have an extremely large ratio of surface to mass. A cube with a volume of 1 cm³ has a surface area of 6 cm². If that cube is cut into 1000 smaller cubes of equal size, the surface area of that same amount of matter is now 60 cm². If we subdivide these cubes until they measure 10

Brownian motion is the constant random movement of colloidal particles.

Adsorption occurs when solid or liquid surfaces attract and hold substances.

FIGURE 22-9. This gas mask filters poisonous gases by selective adsorption onto the activated charcoal.

SUGGESTION: The electrophoretic separation of amino acids is a good demonstration of a practical application of electrophoresis.

FIGURE 22-10. An electrophoresis apparatus is used in separating mixtures containing charged particles. Negative particles move toward the anode. Positive particles move toward the cathode.

Speed of migration can be increased by using high voltages.

Colloidal particles are excellent adsorbing materials.

Electrophoresis is the migration of charged colloidal particles within an electric field.

nm on edge, the surface area has risen to 6 000 000 000 cm^2! Such a large surface area makes colloidal particles excellent adsorbing materials, or adsorbents. Dispersed particles have the property of adsorbing charge on the surface.

If a colloid is subjected to an electric field, a migration of the particles can be observed. The positive particles are attracted to the cathode. The negative particles are attracted to the anode. This migration, called **electrophoresis,** is evidence that colloid particles are charged. The separation of amino acids and peptides obtained in protein analysis is accomplished rapidly using electrophoresis. The process is also common in nucleic acid research.

BIOGRAPHY   Thomas Graham (1805-1869)

Thomas Graham, known as the "father of colloid chemistry," was strongly opposed in his scientific pursuits early in life. Graham's father was insistent that his son be a clergyman and withdrew funds for his education when he persisted in the study of science.

He formulated the law that today bears his name. It relates the relative rates of diffusion of dissimilar gases. The study of diffusion and effusion of gases led Graham to investigate the passage of materials through membranes. When he discovered that some substances would diffuse through a membrane and others would not, he attempted to classify all materials as either crystalloids or colloids. The process of separating materials by passing them through a membrane is called dialysis. It is used today in both industrial and research laboratories.

TECHNOLOGY AND CHEMISTRY

22:11 Explosives

When someone mentions explosives, most of us immediately think of weapons of war. However, large quantities of explosives are used by industry. Mining and quarrying are two industries using explosives.

RDX   Tetryl   TNT   Nitroglycerin

Explosives are substances that react quite rapidly and produce large quantities of energy and large volumes of gases. These products exert a considerable force on their surroundings. One way of classifying explosives is by their sensitivity. The sensitivity of an explosive is the ease with which it may be detonated, or set off.

Explosives of moderate sensitivity often require more sensitive explosives called primers or detonators to set them off. Moderately sensitive explosives, on the other hand, may act as boosters to set off a low sensitivity explosive. A typical series might be a primer of mercury(II) fulminate, $Hg(OCN)_2$, a booster of tetryl, $(NO_2)_3C_6H_2CH_3NNO_2$, and a main charge of TNT, $CH_3C_6H_2(NO_2)_3$. Such an explosive might be used to crack rock near a water table when drilling a water well.

Another way of classifying explosives is based on brisance, which is the rate at which the explosion occurs. Most industrial applications call for a moderate brisance to obtain a shattering effect. A 40% TNT/60% $C_3H_6N_6O_6$ (RDX) mixture provides a very high brisance for military shells.

The most common industrial explosive is a mixture of 94% ammonium nitrate pellets and 6% fuel oil. This mixture has moderate brisance and low sensitivity. Thus, it requires a booster. Dynamite is another popular industrial explosive. Dynamite consists of 20–60% nitroglycerine, some sodium nitrate as an oxidizer, and a mixture of sawdust, starch, and other carbon-containing substances to absorb the oily nitroglycerine. Dynamite sensitivity is fairly high, so it needs only a detonator, but not a booster. It is useful for removing stumps, digging ditches, and similar localized jobs.

SUMMARY

1. The vapor pressure of a solution is the sum of the vapor pressures of its components. The vapor pressure of a component of a solution is its normal vapor pressure multiplied by its mole fraction in the solution. **22:1**

   Solutes affect the vapor pressure, boiling point, freezing point, and osmotic pressure of a solvent. **22:1**

3. Many substances can be separated by taking advantage of the difference in their vapor pressures. The process used is called fractional distillation. **22:2**

4. Changes in boiling and freezing points may be calculated from the relations $\Delta T_{FP} = (m)(K_{FP})$ and $\Delta T_{BP} = (m)(K_{BP})$ **22:3-22:5**

5. Osmotic pressure can be computed from $\Pi = MRT$ **22:6**

6. Ideal solutions obey Raoult's law. **22:1, 22:7**

7. A colloid is composed of two phases: the dispersed phase and the continuous phase. **22:8**

8. Colloid particles range between 1 and 100 nm in at least one dimension. **22:9**

9. Colloids possess some unusual properties. They can scatter light (Tyndall effect), undergo constant random motion (Brownian motion), and act as excellent adsorbing materials. **22:10**

VOCABULARY

colligative properties **22:1**
Raoult's Law **22:1**
semipermeable membrane **22:6**
osmotic pressure **22:6**
activity **22:7**
crystalloids **22:8**
colloids **22:8**

suspension **22:9**
colloid chemistry **22:9**
Tyndall effect **22:10**
Brownian motion **22:10**
adsorption **22:10**
electrophoresis **22:10**

See Teacher Guide for detailed solutions and answers.
1. vapor pressure
   freezing point
   boiling point
   osmosis
4. lowers vapor pressure

5. particle size is smaller
6. 17.7 kPa

7. 15.1 kPa

PROBLEMS

1. What are colligative properties?

2. What is the relationship between Raoult's law and ideal solutions?

3. Define a nonvolatile solute.

4. How does the addition of a nonvolatile solute cause the freezing point of the solvent to be depressed?

5. How does a colloid differ from a suspension?

6. What is the vapor pressure of a solution composed of 133 grams of citric acid, $C_6H_8O_7$, (nonvolatile solute) in 1.00×10^2 grams of water at 60.0°C?

7. What is the vapor pressure at 24°C of a solution of 8.27 grams of benzene, C_6H_6, (vapor pressure = 12.1 kPa) and 3.87 grams of chloroform, $CHCl_3$, (vapor pressure = 25.2 kPa)?

Calculate the boiling point and the freezing point of the following solutions of molecular substances.

8. 97.5 grams of $C_{12}H_{22}O_{11}$ *(sucrose)* in 185 grams of water

9. 14.0 grams of $C_{10}H_8$ *(naphthalene)* in 25.0 grams of C_6H_6

10. 5.00×10^2 grams of $C_{20}H_{27}NO_{11} \cdot 3H_2O$ *(amygdalin trihydrate)* in 5.00×10^2 grams of water

11. 2.50×10^2 grams of $C_7H_4BrNO_4$ *(3-bromo-2-nitrobenzoic acid)* in 5.00×10^2 grams C_6H_6

12. 60.0 grams of C_9H_{18} *(propylcyclohexane)* in 1.00×10^2 grams of acetic acid

13. What is the molecular mass of a nonionic solute, if 5.60 grams of it in 104 grams of water lower the freezing point to $-0.603°C$?

14. Find the osmotic pressure exerted by 8.10 grams of solute of molecular mass 1310 grams in 1.00 dm^3 of water at 22°C.

8. BP = 100.788°C, FP = $-2.86°C$

9. BP = 91.2°C, FP = $-16°C$

10. BP = 101.00°C, FP = $-3.65°C$

11. BP = 85.2°C, FP = $-4.5°C$

12. BP = 133 °C, FP = $-1.96°C$

13. 166 g/mol

14. 15.2 kPa

REVIEW

1. What is the molality of a solution made from 1.00×10^2 grams of water and 20.0 grams of $Fe_2(C_2O_4)_3$?

2. How would you prepare a 0.560m solution of Li_2S from 2.50×10^2 cm^3 of water?

3. What is the mole fraction of acetone, $(CH_3)_2CO$, in a solution of 50.0 grams of acetone and 50.0 grams of water?

1. 0.532m

2. dissolve 6.44 g Li_2S in 250 g H_2O

3. 0.237 mole fraction acetone

ONE MORE STEP

1. Try to separate a solution of two liquids by distillation, with and without a fractionating column. See your instructor about technique and possible mixtures to use.

2. An ultracentrifuge can be used to separate colloids. Prepare a report to the class on the use of this apparatus in characterizing colloids.

3. Find out what methods are now being used industrially to remove dust from stack gases and reduce air pollution.

4. Find three examples of protective colloids.

5. Describe the structure of protoplasm in terms of solutions, liquid crystals, and colloids.

See Teacher Guide for answers.

READINGS

Gomer, Robert, "Surface Diffusion," *Scientific American*, Vol. 247, No. 2(August 1982), pp. 98-109.

Lavenda, Bernard H., "Brownian Motion," *Scientific American*, Vol. 252, No. 2(February 1985), pp. 70-85.

Sarquis, Jerry, "Colloidal Systems," *Journal of Chemical Education*, Vol. 57, No. 8(August 1980), pp. 602-605.

Tanaka, Toyoichi, "Gels," *Scientific American*, Vol. 244, No. 1(January 1980), pp. 124-138.

The light in the test tube is produced during a chemical reaction. In this case, the energy produced by the reaction is in the form of visible light. This reaction differs from a combustion reaction in that it is not exothermic. The light produced is referred to as cold light. The reaction is highly specific and a catalyst is required for it to occur. What is the funtion of a catalyst? How is a reaction changed by a catalyst? What conditions govern the rate of a reaction? Why might scientists be interested in the large scale production of cold light?

REACTION RATE AND CHEMICAL EQUILIBRIUM

Chapter 23 begins with the study of reaction rates and the factors that affect the rate of a chemical reaction. The quantitative study of equilibrium is then presented.

DEMONSTRATION: Clock Reaction. This demonstration can be used to introduce the study of reaction rate, reaction mechanisms, and the rate determining step. It is dramatic for students to see two solutions mixed and then turn blue-black after 6-7 seconds. The system then remains at equilibrium. For preparation details see the Teacher Guide.

GOALS:
- You will determine the factors that affect the rate of reaction.
- You will determine the reaction mechanism for simple reactions.
- You will determine equilibrium constants for specific reactions and explain the effect of LeChatelier's principle.

In studying the properties of matter, chemists wish to find out both the physical and the chemical characteristics of a substance. They want to be able to describe the behavior of a given substance with many other substances. In other words, does it react? We have found that the change in free energy for a reaction can be used to answer that question. Of great importance, especially to the industrial chemist, is the answer to the question: How fast does it react?

Josiah Willard Gibbs discovered the relationship between entropy and enthalpy called the free energy. The amount of free energy after a spontaneous reaction is less than before the reaction.

Consider the reaction

$$2TiO \rightarrow 2Ti + O_2 \qquad \Delta G° = +495 \text{ kJ}$$

Since the free energy change is positive, the reaction does not take place. Titanium(II) oxide does not spontaneously decompose at room temperature. It is said to be **thermodynamically stable.**

As we have studied, when ΔG is negative, a reaction will proceed spontaneously. However, some spontaneous reactions take place so slowly that hundreds of years may pass before any observable change occurs. For example, the ΔG for combustion of glucose, a common sugar, is

$$C_6H_{12}O_6(cr) + 6O_2(g) \rightarrow 6CO_2(g) + 6H_2O(l) \qquad \Delta G = -2870 \text{ kJ}$$

However, at room temperature, the reaction proceeds so slowly that we can never detect a change. Thus, sugar is said to be kinetically stable. To predict whether a given spontaneous reaction will be economically useful, we must know the rate at which the reaction occurs as well as at what point equilibrium is established. Note that a compound is stable in terms of its tendency to decompose if the ΔG for that reaction is positive. A system may have $\Delta G < 0$ and still be stable if the rate of change is imperceptible.

The free energy change is the maximum work that can be obtained from a system.

A thermodynamically stable substance does not decompose spontaneously (ΔG is positive).

The free energy decreases (ΔG is negative) in a spontaneous reaction because the system is changing to a more stable state.

Consider what happens when we add an ice cube to a beaker of water. The temperature of the water drops. Energy is absorbed as the ice cube gets smaller and solid ice is converted into liquid water. We may represent this process by an equation.

$$solid + energy \rightarrow liquid$$

If we use a thermos bottle instead of a beaker and our ice cube is large enough, the temperature of the water will drop to 0°C. After the temperature reaches 0°C, we observe no further melting of the ice. If we now add a piece of metal that has been chilled to -20°C, we may be surprised to find that the ice cube grows larger! The process can go either way. At 0°C an equilibrium exists.

$$solid + energy \rightleftharpoons liquid$$

The relative amounts of solid and liquid can be changed by adding or removing a small amount of energy without changing the temperature. We say that the water-ice mixture is in equilibrium. Many chemical reactions also result in an equilibrium mixture.

23:1 REVERSIBLE REACTIONS

A chemist studies the structure of matter and the properties that result from this structure. Some of these properties are the chemical reactions which substances undergo. Actually, the study of chemical reactions is the study of the breaking and forming of chemical bonds. The formation of chemical bonds is a complex subject. So far we have discussed only the simplest chemical reactions, those that go to completion. A reaction goes to completion when all of one of the reactants is used completely and the reaction stops. Reactions of this kind go from reactants to products. Not all reactions go to completion. Consider the following reaction.

$$H_2(g) + I_2(g) \rightarrow 2HI(g)$$

The arrow means the reaction is read from left to right, but this equation is only partially correct. The bond between the hydrogen and iodine in the hydrogen iodide molecule is a weak bond. Therefore, hydrogen iodide breaks easily into hydrogen gas and iodine vapor. The following equation represents this reaction.

$$H_2(g) + I_2(g) \leftarrow 2HI(g)$$

Notice the direction in which the arrow points. This reaction is read from right to left. We now combine the two equations.

$$H_2(g) + I_2(g) \rightleftharpoons 2HI(g) \quad \text{(reversible reaction)}$$

The first reaction is said to go from left to right. The second reaction is said to go from right to left. The combined equation represents a **reversible reaction.**

SUGGESTION: Remind students that chemical equations are algebraic and subject to the same laws as other algebraic equations.

BACKGROUND: Note that the use of the word reversible is different from the use in Section 19:10 concerning work.

Not all reactions go to completion.

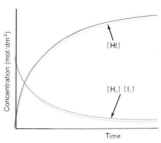

FIGURE 23-1. The rate for the reaction $H_2 + I_2 \rightleftharpoons 2HI$ can be expressed as the rate of appearance of the product, HI, or the rate at which the reactants, H_2 and I_2, disappear.

23:2 REACTION RATE

Suppose the product of a reversible reaction decomposes faster than the reactants form the product. Then there will always be more reactant than product. Here is an example. HI decomposes to H_2 and I_2 more rapidly than H_2 unites with I_2 to form HI. There will always be more hydrogen and iodine than hydrogen iodide. Consider a flask containing hydrogen, iodine, and hydrogen iodide. The hydrogen iodide is decomposing rapidly, more rapidly than H_2 and I_2 can combine to produce it. The rate of disappearance of hydrogen iodide is defined to be the reaction rate. Notice this reaction is the reverse reaction read from right to left.

$$H_2(g) + I_2(g) \leftarrow 2HI(g) \qquad \text{(rate of disappearance of HI)}$$

The rate of appearance of hydrogen iodide is defined as the rate of the reaction from left to right.

$$H_2(g) + I_2(g) \rightarrow 2HI(g) \qquad \text{(rate of appearance of HI)}$$

Reaction rate is usually defined in terms of the rate of disappearance of one of the reactants. It can also be defined as the rate of appearance of one of the products. The usual units for reaction rates are $mol/dm^3/s$. What we are actually measuring is the rate of change of concentration in a constant volume process. If we know the two reaction rates, we can predict whether product or reactant will be in the higher concentration at equilibrium. We will now consider some factors that affect reaction rates.

Reaction rate is the rate of disappearance of reactant or rate of appearance of product.

23:3 NATURE OF REACTANTS

The nature of the reactants involved in a reaction will determine the kind of reaction that occurs. Reactions with bond rearrangement or electron transfer take longer than reactions without these changes. Ionic reactions (such as double displacement and neutralization reactions) occur almost instantaneously. They are rapid because ions of one charge are attracted by those of opposite charge and ions collide frequently.

In a double displacement reaction between ions, no electron transfer is involved. Reactions between neutral molecules are slower than ionic reactions because electron transfer and bond rearrangement must occur. As pointed out in Chapter 15, most molecular collisions are elastic. The molecules simply rebound and move away unchanged. However, some collisions do have enough energy to cause changes in the electron clouds of the colliding molecules. When the change occurs, the colliding molecules may form an **activated complex.** The energy required to form the activated complex is known as the **activation energy.** If the activation energy is high, few collisions have enough energy to form the activated

Reaction rate depends upon the nature of the reactants.

Ionic reactions involve no electron transfer and are rapid.

The activated complex forms when molecules collide with enough energy to change their electron clouds.

The activation energy is the energy required to form the activated complex.

FIGURE 23-2. Activation energy is that energy which must be attained in order for a collision between the reactants to result in the formation of an activated complex.

complex. As a result, the reaction may be so slow that it cannot be detected. Consider the following reaction.

$$CH_3CH_2Br + OH^- \rightarrow CH_3CH_2OH + Br^-.$$

The activated complex is $CH_3CH_2(OH)Br^-$. From Figure 23-2 we can see that the activation energy is 89.5 kJ per mole of CH_3CH_2Br. We can also see that the enthalpy change for the reaction is -77.2 kJ. We can now see why some substances are kinetically stable even though many of their reactions may have negative free energy changes. These reactions have very high activation energies. Consequently, unless very strong reaction conditions are used, the reactions do not take place.

FIGURE 23-3. The Hindenberg explosion was a reaction between hydrogen in the ship and oxygen in the air. It is believed that lightning or some other electric spark caused the reaction.

For example, hydrogen and oxygen can be kept in the same container at room temperature for years without reacting to form water. Although the molecules collide, the activation energy will not be reached. If, however, the mixture is heated to 800°C, or a flame or spark is introduced, a violent reaction occurs. The heat, flame, or spark furnishes the activation energy.

23:4 CONCENTRATION

Another factor affecting reaction rate is concentration. Concentration refers to the quantity of matter that exists in a unit volume. For instance, in Chapter 5 we discussed the concentration in mol/dm^3 of solution. We referred to this concentration as the molarity of the solution. For a reaction to take place, the particles must collide. If the number of particles per unit volume is increased, the chance of their colliding is also increased. Reconsider the equation

$$H_2(g) + I_2(g) \rightarrow 2HI(g)$$

If we keep the concentration of the hydrogen molecules the same, we would expect doubling the concentration of iodine to double the number of collisions between iodine and hydrogen molecules. In turn, the reaction rate would double. Actual experiment confirms that the rate of reaction varies directly as the concentration of iodine. Written in equation form, it is

$$rate_1 = k_1[I_2]$$

where the brackets around the I_2 ([ ]) mean "mol/dm^3."

What if the concentration of iodine remains constant, and the concentration of hydrogen is allowed to vary? We can say that the number of collisions and, therefore, the reaction rate, varies directly as the concentration of hydrogen molecules. We write

$$rate_2 = k_2[H_2]$$

If we allow the concentration of both iodine and hydrogen to vary, what will happen? If we double the concentration of hydrogen and also double the concentration of iodine, there will be four times as many molecules. What will the reaction rate be? There will be four times as many molecules per unit volume and four times as many collisions. The reaction rate is found to be quadrupled. We conclude, then, that *the reaction rate varies directly as the product of the concentrations of the reactants (hydrogen and iodine).* We write

$$rate = k[H_2][I_2]$$

In this case, the constant k depends upon the size, speed, and kind of molecule involved in the reaction. Each reaction has only one value of k for a given temperature; this k is called the **specific rate constant** of the

DEMONSTRATION: Burn sulfur or charcoal in a bottle of air and then in a bottle of oxygen gas. The concentration of O_2 is increased, and so is the rate of the reaction. CAUTION: Use adequate ventilation; SO_2 is toxic.

Reaction rate depends upon concentration (molarity) of the reactants.

SUGGESTION: Concentration has been discussed in Chapters 5 and 21. Review these discussions and spend extra time on the discussion of concentration in this chapter. It is important that students have a good grasp of the concept of concentration before proceeding further.

[ ] indicates mol/dm^3

BACKGROUND: The dependence of the rate on the increased number of particles in the activation energy range is given by the Arrhenius equation:
$$k = Ae^{-E_a/RT}$$
where k = specific rate constant
A = a constant for a particular reaction
e = base of natural logarithms
E_a = activation energy
R = gas constant
T = absolute temperature
The slope of a plot of $\ln k$ vs. $1/T$ is used to determine E_a.

Specific rate constant k, has one value for a given temperature.

reaction. It should be pointed out here that the actual mechanism of this reaction involves the breaking of the I—I bond before collision. However, it can be demonstrated mathematically that the same rate expression results. The rate expression for the reaction $H_2O_2 + 2HI \rightarrow 2H_2O + I_2$ is written

$$rate = k[H_2O_2][HI]$$

Even though two HI molecules appear in the equation, only one appears in the rate expression. The only way to be sure of the rate expression is to use experimental data, as will be illustrated in section 23:7.

FIGURE 23-4. An increase in the concentration (number of particles) of the reactants increases the number of effective collisions to form products.

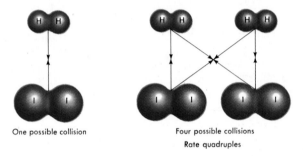

One possible collision

Four possible collisions
Rate quadruples

An increase in the pressure of a gas has the effect of increasing the concentration, and thus the reaction rate (at constant temperature).

A heterogenous reaction involves two or more phases.
DEMONSTRATION: Attempt to light a pile of lycopodium powder or corn starch. Then dust the powder or starch into the flame. **CAUTION:** *there will be a flare up of the burner flame. This flame is better seen in a darkened room.*
Increasing the surface available will increase the reaction rate.

An increase in the pressure on a gas results in a decrease in the volume occupied by the molecules (temperature constant). Since there are more molecules per unit volume, there has been an increase in concentration. Increasing the pressure on a gas, then, will also increase reaction rate.

Chemical reactions that take place at the interface between two phases are called **heterogeneous reactions.** An example of a heterogeneous reaction is zinc (a solid) reacting with sulfuric acid (a liquid). The reaction takes place on the surface of the zinc that is the interface between the two phases. If more surface is exposed, the reaction will take place more rapidly. Because of the unusual properties of surface molecules, their bonds are more easily broken. They react more readily than molecules within a solid. Increasing the surface area increases the number of surface molecules in the same space (increases concentration). Increasing surface area, then, increases the rate of a reaction.

23:5 TEMPERATURE

Reaction rate is also determined by the frequency of collision between molecules and increases as the frequency of collision increases. According to the kinetic theory, the speed (kinetic energy) of molecules increases as the temperature increases. Increased kinetic energy means that more collisions will occur and the reaction rate will increase. However, the increase in reaction rate depends less on the increase in the number of collisions than it does on another factor. This other factor is the

Reaction rate depends upon the temperature of the reactants.

increase in the number of molecules that have the activation energy. Note from the graph in Figure 23-5 that molecules must collide with a kinetic energy sufficient to react. Otherwise a collision will not lead to reaction. On the graph, the area under the curve indicates the number of molecules present. At temperature T_1 few molecules have attained activation energy. At temperature T_2, $(T_2 > T_1)$ many more molecules have reached the activation energy. The same number of molecules is present at this higher temperature. However, the fraction of molecules that have attained the activation energy is greater at the higher temperature T_2.

Figure 23-6 is a graph that shows the energy changes involved in the reaction of hydrogen with oxygen. This graph can be thought of as a map of the potential energy possessed by the atoms and molecules taking part in a reaction. The gases, H_2 and O_2, are considered to have no potential energy (0 kJ). As two molecules approach, the kinetic energy of motion is transformed into the potential energy of repulsion of electron clouds. As more and more kinetic energy is transformed into potential energy, the line of the graph, which represents potential energy, rises. If the molecules have enough kinetic energy to approach close enough to react chemically, they form an activated complex. From here, the activated complex must come apart in either direction. The activated complex may fall back on the left side and break into H_2 and O_2 molecules, or it may come apart to produce products (fall down on the right side). The chance of falling either way is equal. If the activated complex does react, energy will be released and a molecule of water will be formed. The effect of raising the temperature is to produce more activated complexes through

FIGURE 23-5. A ten degree increase in temperature from T_1 to T_2 will often double or triple the number of molecules that have sufficient energy to react.

When molecules collide very energetically, they form an activated complex.

DEMONSTRATION: Add an Alka-Seltzer® tablet to each of 3 flasks. One has ice H_2O, one has H_2O at room temperature, and one has H_2O that has been heated. Stopper each flask with a one-hole rubber stopper that has been fitted with a glass tube and a plastic bag. The rate of expansion of the bags can easily demonstrate the effect of temperature on the rate of a reaction.

FIGURE 23-6. For the water reaction, the energy of the reactants rises as they collide and their kinetic energy is converted to potential energy.

Increased temperature increases the number of activated complexes formed.

SUGGESTION: Point out to the students that catalysis is a complex subject and that in many instances, the reaction mechanism is still unknown.

Catalysts increase reaction rate, but appear to be unaffected throughout the reaction.

DEMONSTRATION: In advance: (A) dissolve 25 g potassium sodium tartrate in 300 cm^3 H$_2$O in a 600 cm^3 beaker. (B) prepare 100 cm^3 of 3 to 6% H$_2$O$_2$ (aq) (20 cm^3 30% H$_2$O$_2$/ 100 cm^3). **CAUTION:** *causes burns, handle carefully.* (C) dissolve 2 g of CoCl$_2$ in 30 cm^3 of H$_2$O. Heat solution *A* to 80°C and add *B*. The reaction is very slow. Place the beaker on a tray, and add the CoCl$_2$ catalyst *C*. **CAUTION:** *the beaker usually overflows.*

A heterogeneous (contact) catalyst works by adsorbing one of the reactants.

Adsorption is the adherence of one substance to the surface of another.

A homogeneous catalyst exists in the same phase as reactants.

collisions. Thus, with the increase in number of activated complexes, the number that will react will also increase.

An increase in temperature will increase the rate of any reaction. More activated complexes are formed because the number of collisions having the required activation energy increases.

23:6 CATALYSIS

A substance that increases a reaction rate without being permanently changed is called a catalyst. **Catalysis** is the process of increasing rates of reaction by the presence of a catalyst. The catalyst appears to be chemically unaffected by the reaction. It changes the reaction mechanism in such a way that the activation energy required is less than in the uncatalyzed reaction. We will discuss two kinds of catalysts: the heterogeneous (or contact) catalyst, and the homogeneous catalyst.

The reaction of sulfur dioxide gas with oxygen gas

$$2SO_2(g) + O_2(g) \rightarrow 2SO_3(g)$$

is extremely slow at room temperature. If these two gases are brought into contact in the presence of solid vanadium(V) oxide (V_2O_5), the reaction is rapid. Vanadium(V) oxide is called the catalyst in this reaction. Notice that vanadium(V) oxide is a solid and the reactants are gases. The V_2O_5 lowers the required activation energy by providing a surface on which the activated complex can form.

A reaction in which the reactants and catalysts are not in the same phase is a heterogeneous reaction. The catalyst is called a **heterogeneous catalyst.** This kind of catalyst has a surface on which the substances can react. Platinum and other finely divided metals and metallic oxides are common examples of this kind of catalyst. Most heterogeneous catalysts work by adsorbing one of the reactants. **Adsorption** is the adherence of one substance to the surface of another. It might be correct to think of the contact catalyst as taking part in the reaction. In the process of adsorbing a molecule, such as O_2, the catalytic surface attracts the O_2 molecule. This attraction weakens the O—O bond to the point where the other reactant can break the O—O bond. The reaction then proceeds. Catalytic converters on automobile exhaust systems employ a contact catalyst.

A **homogeneous catalyst** exists in the same phase as the reactants. This kind of catalyst does enter into the reaction, but is returned unchanged in a final step of the reaction mechanism. It forms an intermediate compound or compounds that react more readily than the uncatalyzed reactants. They react more readily because they require less activation energy. As an example of homogeneous catalysis, consider the hydrolysis of sucrose (cane sugar). The reaction is

$$C_{12}H_{22}O_{11}(aq) + H_2O(l) \rightarrow C_6H_{12}O_6(aq) + C_6H_{12}O_6(aq)$$
    Sucrose   Glucose   Fructose

a

b

c

FIGURE 23-7. This crystalline catalyst is being tested for use in automobile pollution control (a). The honeycomb shape of this catalyst provides more surface area for a reaction to occur (b). The catalytic convertor allows for more complete combustion thereby reducing the amounts of pollutants released in exhaust (c).

The reaction is normally very slow. If, however, the solution is made acidic, the presence of the acid causes the reaction to proceed readily. In the reaction, all substances are in aqueous solution (the same phase). Thus, the reaction is a homogeneous one, and the acid is a homogeneous catalyst. The acid lowers the required activation energy by attacking the oxygen atom linking the two parts of the sucrose molecule.

Catalysts are used a great deal in industry, as well as in the chemical laboratory. Other substances, called **inhibitors,** are also used to affect reaction rates. These substances do not "slow up" a reaction. Rather they "tie up" a reactant or catalytic substance in a complex, so that it will not react. Preservatives used in foods and medical preparations are included to avoid spoilage. These substances are examples of inhibitors.

Inhibitors stop reactions by tying up a reactant.

SUGGESTION: Emphasize that most reactions occur in a series of steps called the reaction mechanism. Often several different mechanisms are possible for the same overall reaction. Where a catalyst is involved, the mechanism for the catalyzed reaction is always different from the mechanism for the uncatalyzed one.

23:7   REACTION MECHANISM

Most reactions occur in a series of steps. Each step normally involves the collision of only two particles. Steps involving three or more particles are unlikely. There is little chance of three or more particles colliding with the proper position and energy to cause a reaction.

If a reaction consists of several steps such as the following

$$A \rightarrow B$$
$$B \rightarrow C$$
$$C \rightarrow \textit{final product}$$

Reaction rate depends on the rate determining (slowest) step.

Most reactions occur in a series of steps called the reaction mechanism.

one of the steps will be slower than all the others. This step is called the **rate determining step.** The other faster steps will not affect the rate. The series of reaction steps that must occur for a reaction to go to completion is called the **reaction mechanism.**

At a given temperature, the rate of a reaction varies directly as the product of the concentrations of the reactants in the slowest step. For the reaction $H_2(g) + I_2(g) \rightarrow 2HI(g)$, the rate expression was rate = $k[H_2][I_2]$. For the general reaction $A + B \rightarrow C$, the rate expression would be rate = $k[A][B]$. Hydrogen iodide decomposes into hydrogen and iodine. The equation is $2HI(g) \rightarrow H_2(g) + I_2(g)$. This reaction might be written $HI + HI \rightarrow H_2 + I_2$. The rate expression (if it is a one-step reaction) would be rate = $k[HI][HI]$, or rate = $k[HI]^2$.

The coefficient in the equation becomes the exponent in the rate expression for a single step reaction.

For a single step reaction, the exponents of concentration factors are the order of the expression.

How do we know if a reaction is a single-step? The only way to obtain accurate rate information is experimentally. As a result, the observation of reaction rates has given scientists an insight into the mechanisms of reactions. The reaction

$$C_2H_4Br_2(l) + 3I^-(aq) \rightarrow C_2H_4(l) + 2Br^-(aq) + I_3^-(aq)$$

has been shown to obey the rate expression rate = $k[C_2H_4Br_2][I^-]$. The exponents of the concentration factors are spoken of as the order of the expression. Thus, the reaction is first order with respect to $C_2H_4Br_2$ and first order with respect to I^-. Adding the exponents for all concentrations in the expression gives the overall order. The reaction then is second order. However, the reaction should be third order in I^- if it is a single-step reaction.

Reactants must collide with the proper activation energy and collision geometry (orientation) in order to form products.

In that case, four particles ($C_2H_4Br_2$ and $3I^-$) would have to collide all at once in the right orientation to react. This collision is highly unlikely. Therefore, the rate data tell us that we need to consider multiple-step mechanisms. The rate determining step, according to the data, involves only one I^- with the $C_2H_4Br_2$. There are a large number of possible mechanisms that would agree with the observed rate expression. Consider just one.

The reaction mechanism is the series of steps that occur during a reaction.

$$C_2H_4Br_2 + I^- \rightarrow C_2H_4Br^- + IBr \quad \text{(slow)}$$
$$C_2H_4Br^- \rightarrow C_2H_4 + Br^- \quad \text{(fast)}$$
$$IBr + I^- \rightarrow Br^- + I_2 \quad \text{(fast)}$$
$$I_2 + I^- \rightarrow I_3^- \quad \text{(fast)}$$

See if you can devise other mechanisms for this reaction that will agree with the rate data.

EXAMPLE: Rate Law

What is the rate expression for the following reaction?

$$H_2O_2 + 2HI \rightarrow 2H_2O + I_2$$

Trial	$[H_2O_2]$	[HI]	Rate
1	0.1M	0.1M	0.0076 mol/dm^3/s
2	0.1M	0.2M	0.0152 mol/dm^3/s
3	0.2M	0.1M	0.0152 mol/dm^3/s

Solving Process:
(a) By comparing trials 1 and 2, we can see that doubling the [HI] doubles the rate. Thus, there is a direct relationship: rate $\propto$ [HI].
(b) By comparing trials 1 and 3, we see that doubling the $[H_2O_2]$ also
doubles the rate and we again have a direct relationship: rate $\propto$
$[H_2O_2]$.
(c) The rate law is, then, $rate = k[H_2O_2][HI]$.

PROBLEMS

1. Assume that NO(g) and H_2(g) react according to the rate law: $rate = k[NO]^2[H_2]$. How does the rate change if

a. the concentration of H_2 is doubled?
b. the volume of the enclosing vessel is suddenly halved?
c. the temperature is decreased?

1. **a.** doubled
   b. eight times faster
   c. slows down

2. For the reaction H_2(g) + I_2(g) $\rightarrow$ 2HI(g), the following data were
obtained.

2. **a.** Rate = $k[H_2][I_2]$
       $k = 0.20(dm^3)^2$/mol·s
   b. 0.050 mol/s

Experiment	Initial $[H_2]$	Initial $[I_2]$	Initial rate of formation of HI
1	1.0M	1.0M	0.20 mol/dm^3/s
2	1.0M	2.0M	0.40 mol/dm^3/s
3	2.0M	2.0M	0.80 mol/dm^3/s

a. Write the rate law for this reaction, and calculate the value of the
rate constant.
b. What would be the initial rate of formation of HI if the initial
concentrations of H_2 and I_2 were each 0.50M?

3. The reaction $CH_3COCH_3 + I_2 \rightarrow CH_3COCH_2I + HI$ is run under
carefully controlled conditions in the presence of an excess of acid.
Write the rate law for the reaction using the following data.

3. Rate = $k[CH_3COCH_3]$

4. There are several possible mechanisms that will agree with the rate law expression. See Teacher Guide.

$I_2 + H^+ \rightarrow HI + I^+$
catalyzed step
$HI \rightarrow H^+ + I^-$
catalyst regenerated
$CH_3COCH_3 + I^- \rightarrow$
$CH_3COCH_2^- + HI$
slowest step
$CH_3COCH_2^- + I^+ \rightarrow$
CH_3COCH_2I

Initial concentration		Initial rate
$[CH_3COCH_3]$	$[I_2]$	
0.100M	0.100M	1.16×10^{-7} mol/dm^3/s
0.0500M	0.100M	5.79×10^{-8} mol/dm^3/s
0.0500M	0.500M	5.78×10^{-8} mol/dm^3/s

4. It has been determined that the reaction in Problem 3 is also first order with respect to the acid catalyst. Propose a mechanism for the slow step consistent with the data.

23:8   EQUILIBRIUM CONSTANT

We have seen that the reaction of H_2 and I_2 to form HI is an equilibrium reaction. As the reaction proceeds, the reaction rate of the hydrogen and iodine reaction decreases. As H_2 and I_2 are used, fewer collisions between H_2 and I_2 molecules occur per unit time. The reverse reaction, the collision of two HI molecules to form H_2 and I_2, does not occur initially because the concentration of HI is zero.

However, as the concentration of HI increases, the reverse reaction, the decomposition of hydrogen iodide, steadily increases. Equilibrium is attained when the rates of the two opposing reactions are equal. The rates of the forward and reverse reactions of the hydrogen iodide reaction are written

At equilibrium, opposing reaction rates are equal.

$$\text{rate of forward reaction} = k_f[I_2][H_2]$$
$$\text{rate of reverse reaction} = k_r[HI]^2$$

At equilibrium, the two rates are equal, and

$$k_f[I_2][H_2] = k_r[HI]^2$$

Dividing both sides by $k_r[I_2][H_2]$

$$\frac{k_f[I_2][H_2]}{k_r[I_2][H_2]} = \frac{k_r[HI]^2}{k_r[I_2][H_2]}$$

we obtain

$$\frac{k_f}{k_r} = \frac{[HI]^2}{[I_2][H_2]}$$

Since both k_f and k_r are constants, the ratio k_f/k_r is a constant. This new constant is called the equilibrium constant (K_{eq}).

$$K_{eq} = \frac{[HI]^2}{[I_2][H_2]}$$

FIGURE 23-8. Equilibrium is established when the rates of the forward and reverse reactions are equal.

(Note that the equilibrium constant K_{eq} is capitalized to distinguish it from the specific rate constant k.)

Must we know the rate expressions for the forward and reverse reactions for every equilibrium condition? Guldberg and Waage, two Norwegian chemists, worked on the problem in 1867. They found that the numerator of the equilibrium expression contained the products, and the denominator the reactants. They also found that the exponents in the equilibrium expression were the same as coefficients from the chemical equation. Thus, it is possible to determine the equilibrium constant without knowing the reaction mechanism.

For the general equation $mA + nB \rightarrow sP + rQ$, the equilibrium constant is

$$K_{eq} = \frac{[P]^s[Q]^r}{[A]^m[B]^n}$$

This K_{eq} establishes a relationship between the concentrations of the reactants and products of a reaction. If K_{eq} is very small (much less than 1), equilibrium will be established before much product is formed.

If K_{eq} is large (much greater than 1), the reaction will approach completion. For example, a K_{eq} of 1×10^{-8} would mean that equilibrium will be established before much product is formed. A K_{eq} of 1×10^8 would mean that equilibrium will be established only after a great deal of product is formed. An industrial chemist would want to use a reaction with a large K_{eq} in order to obtain large amounts of product.

Consider the following example of the reaction between carbon dioxide and hydrogen.

$$CO_2(g) + H_2(g) \rightleftharpoons CO(g) + H_2O(g)$$

At 1120°C, a measurement at equilibrium shows that the concentration of each substance is 0.01M, except H_2O, which is 0.02M. Substitution of the observed concentrations into the equilibrium expression results in a calculation of $K_{eq} = 2$.

$$K_{eq} = \frac{[CO][H_2O]}{[CO_2][H_2]} = \frac{[0.01][0.02]}{[0.01][0.01]} = 2$$

Thus, the products are favored. On the other hand, consider the reaction: $PCl_5(g) \rightleftharpoons PCl_3(g) + Cl_2(g)$. Measurement of its equilibrium constant at 200°C indicates a K_{eq} of 0.457. In this case, the reactant is favored.

For any reaction, K_{eq} remains constant only if the temperature remains constant. Each reaction has a unique K_{eq} for every temperature. Above we noted that the K_{eq} for $CO_2 + H_2 \rightleftharpoons CO + H_2O$ is 2 at 1120°C. At 500°C the same reaction has a $K_{eq} = 5.5$.

The concentrations of solids and pure liquids are constants that can be determined from their densities. The concentrations of gases and solutes, on the other hand, must be obtained for the specific conditions under consideration.

An equilibrium constant is the ratio of the rate expression of the forward reaction to the rate expression of the reverse reaction:

$$K_{eq} = \frac{k_f}{k_r}$$

The law of mass action states that the exponents in the equilibrium constant are the coefficients from the chemical equation.

If K_{eq} is small (much less than 1) very little product is formed.

If K_{eq} is large (much greater than 1) the reaction is nearly complete.

The K_{eq} is unique for any reaction at a given temperature.

EXAMPLE: Equilibrium Constants

What is the equilibrium constant for the following reaction if the final concentrations are $CH_3COOH = 0.302M$, $CH_3CH_2OH = 0.428M$, $H_2O = 0.654M$, and $CH_3CH_2OOCCH_3 = 0.655M$?

$$CH_3COOH + CH_3CH_2OH \rightleftarrows CH_3CH_2OOCCH_3 + H_2O$$

Solving Process:

$$K_{eq} = \frac{[CH_3CH_2OOCCH_3][H_2O]}{[CH_3COOH][CH_3CH_2OH]} = \frac{[0.655][0.654]}{[0.302][0.428]} = 3.31$$

EXAMPLE: Equilibrium Concentration

What is the equilibrium concentration of SO_3 in the following reaction if the concentration of SO_2 and O_2 are each $0.0500M$ and $K_{eq} = 85.0$? The equation for the reaction is

$$2SO_2 + O_2 \rightleftarrows 2SO_3$$

Solving Process:

$$K_{eq} = \frac{[SO_3]^2}{[SO_2]^2[O_2]}$$

$$85.0 = \frac{[x]^2}{[0.0500]^2[0.0500]}$$

$$x^2 = 0.0106$$

$$x = 0.103M$$

PROBLEMS

5. a. $K_{eq} = \frac{[CO_2][NH_3]^2}{[NH_2COONH_4]}$

   b. $K_{eq} = \frac{[Cl_2]^2[H_2O]^2}{[HCl]^4[O_2]}$

   c. $K_{eq} = \frac{[NH_3][H_2S]}{[NH_4HS]}$

   d. $K_{eq} = \frac{[CuSO_4][H_2O]^5}{[CuSO_4 \cdot 5H_2O]}$

6. $1.69 \times 10^{-3}M$

7. 1.3

5. Write equilibrium expressions for the following reactions.
   a. $NH_2COONH_4 \rightleftarrows CO_2 + 2NH_3$
   b. $4HCl + O_2 \rightleftarrows 2Cl_2 + 2H_2O$
   c. $NH_4HS \rightleftarrows NH_3 + H_2S$
   d. $CuSO_4 \cdot 5H_2O \rightleftarrows CuSO_4 + 5H_2O$

6. At a given temperature, the K_{eq} for the gas phase reaction, $2HI(g) \rightleftarrows H_2(g) + I_2(g)$, is 1.40×10^{-2}. If the concentrations of both H_2 and I_2 at equilibrium are $2.00 \times 10^{-4}M$, find [HI].

7. At a given temperature, the reaction (all gases) $CO + H_2O \rightleftarrows H_2 + CO_2$ produces the following concentrations: $CO = 0.200M$; $H_2O = 0.500M$; $H_2 = 0.32M$; $CO_2 = 0.42M$. Find the K_{eq} at that temperature.

8. If the temperature in the reaction in Problem 7 is changed, the K_{eq} becomes 2.40. By removing some H_2 and CO_2 and adding H_2O all concentrations except CO are adjusted to the values given in Problem 7. What is the new CO concentration?

9. Hydrogen sulfide decomposes according to the equation: $2H_2S(g) \rightleftharpoons 2H_2(g) + S_2(g)$. At 1065°C, measurement of an equilibrium mixture of these three gases shows the following concentrations: $H_2S = 7.06 \times 10^{-3}M$, $H_2 = 2.22 \times 10^{-3}M$, and $S_2 = 1.11 \times 10^{-3}M$. What is the value of K_{eq} for this equation?

10. At 60.2°C, the equilibrium constant for the reaction, $N_2O_4(g) \rightleftharpoons 2NO_2(g)$, is 8.75×10^{-2}. At this temperature, a vessel contains N_2O_4 at a concentration of $1.72 \times 10^{-2}M$ at equilibrium. What concentration of NO_2 does it contain?

8. 0.11 M
9. 1.10×10^{-4}
10. 3.88×10^{-2} M

23:9 LE CHATELIER'S PRINCIPLE

The conditions affecting equilibrium are temperature, pressure, and concentration of reactants and products. If a system is in equilibrium and a condition is changed, then the equilibrium will shift toward restoring the original conditions. As you learned in Chapter 17, this statement is called Le Chatelier's principle. Le Chatelier first described the effect of stress (change of conditions) upon systems at equilibrium. His principle holds for reaction equilibrium as well. If stress is put on a reversible reaction at equilibrium, the equilibrium will shift in such a way to relieve the stress. Let us see how it applies.

Le Chatelier's principle: A system at equilibrium that undergoes a change will shift toward restoring the original conditions.

The reaction for the preparation of ammonia by the Haber process is

$$N_2(g) + 3H_2(g) \rightleftharpoons 2NH_3(g) + heat$$

Energy can be treated as a reactant or product in a reaction.

Let us consider the effect of changes in concentration, pressure, and temperature on the equilibrium.

If the concentration of either of the reactants is increased, the number of collisions between reactant particles will increase. The result is an increase of the reaction rate toward the right. As the amount of NH_3 increases, the rate of the reverse reaction will also increase. However, the net result to the system as a whole is to shift the equilibrium toward the right. That is, more product is produced.

As the [H_2] is increased, the [N_2] decreases and the [NH_3] increases. Thus the value of the equilibrium constant K_{eq} remains the same.

If the pressure is increased, the same effect is noted. That is, more product is formed. Consider the situation if the pressure is doubled. The concentrations of nitrogen, hydrogen, and ammonia are all doubled. The equilibrium expression for this reaction shows the concentration of ammonia is squared.

Increasing the concentration of reactant will produce a greater concentration of product.

Increased pressure on a reaction system with a gas phase has the same effect as increased concentration of any gas(es).

$$K_{eq} = \frac{[NH_3]^2}{[N_2][H_2]^3}$$

The reverse reaction must then speed up by a factor of 4. On the other hand, the concentration of hydrogen is cubed. Further, it is multiplied by the concentration of nitrogen. Doubling the pressure should increase the rate of the forward reaction by $2^3 \times 2$, or 16 times! The net result is clearly an increase in product.

In the reaction $H_2(g) + Cl_2(g) \rightleftarrows 2HCl(g)$, all substances are again gases. Pressure would not shift the equilibrium, as the rate in each direction would be affected the same way. Pressure, of course, has an effect only on the gases in a reaction. A reaction taking place in solution would be unaffected by pressure.

Both the forward and reverse reactions at equilibrium are speeded by an increase in temperature. However, their rates are increased by different amounts. Also, the value of the equilibrium constant itself is changed by a change in temperature. One easy way to predict the shift in an equilibrium subjected to a temperature change is to consider energy as a reactant or product.

This observation applies only to ideal gases.

Pressure changes concentration, not K_{eq}.

Temperature change causes a change in K_{eq}.

a   b

FIGURE 23-9. The Haber process is used in the production of ammonia (a). The graph shows that by controlling the pressure and temperature of the reaction system, the yield of ammonia can be increased (b).

In the Haber process energy is produced when hydrogen and nitrogen react.

$$N_2(g) + 3H_2(g) \rightleftarrows 2NH_3(g) + energy$$

If energy is considered to be a product, the addition of energy (a product) will increase the concentration of the product. The equilibrium will be shifted to the left. In the Haber process, the reverse action (the decomposition of ammonia) is favored by the addition of energy.

In industry, a desired chemical (such as ammonia) can sometimes be obtained by a reversible reaction. However, equilibrium is often attained before enough product is produced to make the process economical. In such circumstances, the equilibrium can be shifted to give a higher yield of product. The chemist determines what conditions will tend to produce

FIGURE 23-10. The Haber process is used at this ammonia factory to produce large quantities of the substance.

the highest yield. The conditions that produce the highest yield are called the **optimum conditions.**

In the Haber process, there are five optimum conditions. First, a high concentration of hydrogen and nitrogen should be maintained. Second, ammonia should be removed as it is formed. Third, a temperature is used that is high enough to maintain a reasonable rate but low enough not to favor the reverse reaction. Fourth, a catalyst should be used to lower the required activation energy. Fifth, a high pressure should be maintained throughout the process. Each condition increases the yield by shifting the equilibrium to favor the product.

Optimum conditions are those which produce the highest yield of product.

The optimum conditions for the Haber process are
1. high concentration of H_2 and N_2
2. removal of NH_3
3. precise temperature control
4. use of a contact catalyst
5. high pressure
Each increases the yield through a shift of equilibrium to favor the products.

23:10 EQUILIBRIA AND GAS PHASE REACTIONS

Consider a system of gases in chemical equilibrium. The components of the system are in the same container, so they are all at the same temperature. If we solve the ideal gas equation for n/V:

$$PV = nRT$$

$$\frac{n}{V} = \frac{P}{RT}$$

The number of particles in a given volume n/V is the same as the concentration. Since R is a constant and T is the same for all components, then their pressures P must be in the same ratio as their concentrations nV:

$$\frac{n}{V} = \frac{P}{RT} \qquad \frac{n'}{V'} = \frac{P'}{RT}$$

therefore,

$$\frac{n/V}{n'/V'} = \frac{P}{P'}$$

Equilibrium constant expressions for gas phase reactions, K_p, are written in terms of partial pressures.

As a consequence, equilibrium constant expressions for gas phase reactions (K_p) can be written in terms of the partial pressures of the substances involved.

$$N_2 + 3H_2 \rightleftarrows 2NH_3$$

$$K_p = \frac{(ppNH_3)^2}{(ppN_2)(ppH_2)^3}$$

23:11   FREE ENERGY AND EQUILIBRIUM

We saw in Chapter 20 that reactions with $\Delta G < 0$ would occur spontaneously, and those with $\Delta G > 0$ would not occur. In this chapter, we have seen that reactions with very small K_{eq} do not occur to an appreciable extent. We also found that those with very large K_{eq} go almost to completion. As you might expect, there is a connection between free energy and the equilibrium constant. We will not derive the relationship here, as it involves complex mathematics. Simply stated, free energy and equilibria are related by the expression

$$\Delta G = -RT(\ln K_{eq})$$

$R = 0.008\ 31$ kJ/mol·K.

SUGGESTION: Refer students to Appendix B if they have difficulty with logarithms.

In the expression, R is the universal gas constant, T is the absolute temperature, and $\ln$ is the base of natural logarithms. Expressed in terms of common logarithms, the equation becomes

$$\Delta G = -2.30RT(\log K_{eq})$$

EXAMPLE: Free Energy Change

The equilibrium constant for the reaction of CO_2 and H_2 to form CO and H_2O at 1120°C is 2. What is ΔG for this reaction? Use $\Delta G = -2.30RT(\log K_{eq})$, $R = 0.008\ 31$ kJ/mol·K, and the log tables.

Solving Process:

$$\begin{aligned}
\Delta G &= -2.30RT(\log K_{eq}) \\
&= (-2.30)(0.008\ 31)(1393)(\log 2) \\
&= (-2.30)(0.008\ 31)(1393)(0.301) \\
&= -8.01 \text{ kJ}
\end{aligned}$$

EXAMPLE: Equilibrium Constant

The free energy change for the reaction $2Cu_2O + 2NO \rightleftarrows 4CuO + N_2$ is -389 kJ at 25°C. What is K_{eq} for this reaction?

Solving Process:
Solving the equation relating free energy to equilibrium for K_{eq}, we find that

$$log\ K_{eq} = \frac{\Delta G}{-2.30\ RT}$$

$$log\ K_{eq} = \frac{-389}{(-2.30)(0.008\ 31)(298)} = 68.297$$

using log tables, this value converts to

$$K_{eq} = 1.98 \times 10^{68}$$

The equilibrium constant is such a large number that we can safely assume that all the reactant is converted to product.

PROBLEMS

11. Calculate K_{eq} at 25.0°C for the reaction $CO + H_2 \rightleftarrows H_2CO$ if $\Delta G = +28.95$ kJ.

12. At 627°C, K_{eq} for the reaction $2SO_3 \rightleftarrows 2SO_2 + O_2$ is 3.16×10^{-4}. Compute ΔG for this reaction.

13. For the decomposition of PCl_5 at 200.0°C, the equilibrium constant is 0.457. What is the free energy change for this reaction?

11. 8.26×10^{-6}
12. 60.2 kJ/mol
13. 3.07 kJ/mol

BIOGRAPHY

Henry Louis Le Chatelier (1850-1936)

Henry Le Chatelier began his professional career as a mining engineer before turning to teaching chemistry. It was his experience as an engineer, however, that dictated his scientific investigations.

His greatest contribution to science was the equilibrium principle. Commonly known as Le Chatelier's principle, it states that if a system in stable equilibrium is subjected to a stress, then the equilibrium will shift to relieve the stress.

In other fields, he developed the platinum-rhodium thermocouple for measuring high temperatures. He also designed a special microscope to study metals and developed new abrasives to polish the surface of a metal to be examined.

TECHNOLOGY AND CHEMISTRY

23:12 Cryogenics

Cryogenics is the study of matter at extremely low temperatures, usually below 80 K. The term is derived from the Greek word *kryo,* meaning icy cold. The reduction of the temperature of a substance involves slowing the particles (lowering the kinetic energy of the system). As the particles of a substance slow down, the system not only decreases in temperature but also in disorder, or entropy. The decreased entropy leads to interesting phenomena at temperature close to absolute zero. It also allows scientists to study matter at temperatures where disorder is relatively low.

The third law of thermodynamics states that the entropy of a perfect crystal is zero at absolute zero. As a material is cooled toward absolute zero, some of its particles will reach the lowest possible energy level while most of the particles are still in energy levels above the minimum. Recall the kinetic energy distribution curves for a substance at T_1, Figure 17-1. It is these minimum energy particles that exhibit such unusual properties.

Liquid helium can be produced by the usual method of compression, cooling, and Joule-Thomson expansion. Liquid helium boils at 4.2 K. By reducing the pressure over liquid helium, the more energetic particles are removed from the liquid, and the temperature again drops. Helium can be cooled to approximately 1 K in this manner. Helium does not freeze unless the pressure is quite high, for example, about 2.5 MPa at 1 K.

At a temperature of 2.18 K, helium undergoes a liquid-liquid phase transition from helium I, the high temperature form, to helium II, the lower temperature form. Helium II has some strange properties. It behaves as though it has a zero viscosity, allowing it to flow through incredibly small spaces, and creep up and over the sides of its container. This property is called superfluidity. Helium II also conducts well, its thermal conductivity being over 1000 times better than that of normal metals. These properties are attributed to the atoms that have reached the minimum energy level.

Some metals develop a property called superconductivity at temperatures in the cryogenic range. Superconductors behave as though they have no electrical resistance. Scientists are investigating the use of superconducting metals to carry extremely heavy currents used in particle accelerators.

According to the third law of thermodynamics, absolute zero can never be reached. However, by making use of magnetic fields and the magnetic properties of atoms, it is possible to cool some materials to about 0.01 K. By working with the magnetic fields of nuclei, temperatures lower than 0.0001 K have been achieved.

SUMMARY

1. A reversible reaction is a reaction in which products may reform reactants. 23:1

2. Reaction rate is the rate of disappearance of one of the reactants of a reaction or the rate of appearance of one of the products. **23:2**

3. Four factors influence reaction rate: nature of reactants, concentration, temperature, and catalysis. **23:3-23:6**

4. More reactive materials require less activation energy. Therefore, they react more rapidly. **23:3**

5. Concentration is the quantity of matter present in a unit volume. The symbol [ ] means concentration in units of moles per cubic decimeter. **23:4**

6. Increasing the concentration of a reactant increases the rate of reaction by increasing the number of collisions. Increasing the pressure of a gas or the surface area of a heterogeneous reactant has the same effect on the reaction rate. **23:4**

7. Increasing the temperature increases the rate of reaction. Collisions are more frequent and more of the collisions involve sufficient energy to form the activated complex. **23:5**

8. A catalyst is a substance that causes an increase in reaction rate without being permanently changed. **23:6**

9. A reaction in which the reactants and catalyst are not in the same phase is a heterogeneous reaction. The catalyst used is called a heterogeneous catalyst. A homogeneous catalyst is one that is in the same phase as the reactants. **23:6**

10. Most reactions take place in a series of steps called the reaction mechanism. **23:7**

11. Analysis of rate data can give chemists an insight into reaction mechanisms. **23:7**

12. At a given temperature, the rate of a single-step reaction varies directly as the product of the concentrations of the reactants. **23:7**

13. The equilibrium constant, K_{eq}, is the ratio of the forward rate constant, k_f, to the reverse rate constant, k_r. **23:8**

14. Le Chatelier's principle states that if an equilibrium system is subjected to stress, then the equilibrium will shift to relieve the stress. **23:9**

15. Equilibrium constants for gas phase reactions can be expressed in terms of the partial pressures of the reactants and products. **23:10**

16. The free energy change for a reaction is related to its equilibrium constant by the expression $\Delta G = -2.30RT(\log K_{eq})$. **23:11**

VOCABULARY

thermodynamically stable **Intro**
reversible reaction **23:1**
reaction rate **23:2**
activated complex **23:3**
activation energy **23:3**
specific rate constant **23:4**
heterogeneous reactions **23:4**
catalysis **23:6**

heterogeneous catalyst **23:6**
adsorption **23:6**
homogeneous catalyst **23:6**
inhibitors **23:6**
rate determining step **23:7**
reaction mechanism **23:7**
optimum conditions **23:9**

1. a. $K_{eq} = \dfrac{[(NH_4)_2SO_4]}{[NH_3]^2[H_2SO_4]}$

b. 0.333

c. increases

d. shifts right

e. changes

2. $H_2(g) + Cl_2(g) \rightarrow 2HCl(g)$ (Cl_2 is more active than Br_2)

3. reaction rate increases

4. A match cannot raise the temperature of a log to its kindling temperature.

6. reaction rate doubles

7. rate increases

8. 275 kJ/mol

9. 1.33×10^{-14}

10. $K_{eq} = 4.10 \times 10^{52}$

11. $\Delta G = -32\,900$ J/mol $= -32.9$ kJ/mol

12. $K_{eq} = 1.63 \times 10^{88}$

13. $\Delta G = -6.48$ kJ/mol

14. $K_p = 1180$

PROBLEMS

1. Given $2NH_3(g) + H_2SO_4(g) \rightleftarrows (NH_4)_2SO_4(g)$.
   a. What is the equilibrium expression?
   b. If the concentrations in mol/dm^3 after the reaction of NH_3, H_2SO_4, and $(NH_4)_2SO_4$ are 2.00, 3.00, and 4.00, respectively, what is K_{eq}?
   c. If $[NH_3]$ is increased, what happens to $[(NH_4)_2SO_4]$?
   d. If pressure is added, what happens to the equilibrium?
   e. If heat is added, what happens to the value of K_{eq}?

2. Which of the following reactions would you expect to have the faster rate? (Assume the mechanism is to be the same.)
   $$H_2(g) + Cl_2(g) \rightarrow 2HCl(g) \text{ or } H_2(g) + Br_2(g) \rightarrow 2HBr(g)$$

3. The following reaction goes to completion. What effect would an increase in temperature have on its rate? $2NO(g) + H_2(g) \rightarrow N_2O(g) + H_2O(g) + 364\,000$ J

4. Why must a fire in a fireplace be started with paper and kindling? Why not light the logs directly?

5. On the same set of axes, show an energy diagram of a reaction, both catalyzed and uncatalyzed.

6. Assume the reaction in Problem 3 to be a single-step reaction. What would be the effect on the reaction rate if the hydrogen gas concentration were doubled?

7. How would an increase in pressure affect the rate of a reaction in which the products occupied less volume than the reactants?

8. The equilibrium constant for the reaction $2H_2O \rightleftarrows 2H_2 + O_2$ at 2.000×10^3 K is 6.45×10^{-8}. What is the free energy change for the reaction at that temperature?

9. The free energy change for the reaction $2CO_2 \rightleftarrows 2CO + O_2$ at $1.000 \times 10^{3}°C$ is 338 kJ. What is the equilibrium constant for the reaction at that temperature?

10. For the reaction $S + O_2 \rightleftarrows SO_2$ at 25°C, $\Delta G = -3.00 \times 10^2$ kJ. What is the equilibrium constant for the reaction at that temperature?

11. For the reaction $N_2 + 3H_2 \rightleftarrows 2NH_3$ at 25°C, $K_{eq} = 6.00 \times 10^5$. What is ΔG for the reaction at that temperature?

12. For the reaction $3C_2H_2 \rightleftarrows C_6H_6$ at 25°C, $\Delta G = -503$ kJ. What is the equilibrium constant for the reaction at that temperature?

13. For the reaction $2CaSO_4 + H_2O \rightleftarrows (CaSO_4)_2 \cdot H_2O$ at 25°C, $K_{eq} = 13.69$. What is ΔG for the reaction at that temperature?

14. A quantity of CH_3OH is heated to 1.000×10^3 K in a closed container. The equilibrium $CH_3OH \rightleftarrows HCHO + H_2$ is established with the following partial pressures:

$$ppH_2 = 176 \text{ kPa}$$
$$ppHCHO = 176 \text{ kPa}$$
$$ppCH_3OH = 26.3 \text{ kPa}$$

What is K_p for the reaction at 1.000×10^3 K?

REVIEW

1. Describe the process of solvation.

2. Would you expect water and butter to be miscible? Explain.

3. Describe three procedures that can be used to speed the solvation of a solute in a solvent.

4. Henry's law states that the mass of a gas that will dissolve in a liquid varies directly as the pressure of the gas. What statement can be made about the volume of a gas that will dissolve in a liquid as the pressure is changed?

5. What is the molarity of a solution that contains 16.0 g HIO_3 in 1.00×10^2 cm^3 of solution?

6. What effect does a nonvolatile solute have on the boiling point of a solvent?

7. Why does a $1.00m$ solution of NaCl have a freezing point slightly above the predicted $-3.72°C$?

8. What is the vapor pressure at 25°C of a solution of 98.1 g $C_{12}H_{22}O_{11}$ in 1.00×10^2 g water?

9. If 4.23 g of an unknown in 45.0 g water lower the freezing point to $-1.58°C$, what is the molecular mass of the unknown?

10. What osmotic pressure would be exerted by 4.70 g of a substance of molecular mass 6870 g dissolved in sufficient water to make 5.00×10^2 cm^3 of solution at 15°C?

1. the surrounding of solute particles by solvent particles
2. no, water is highly polar; butter is non-polar
3. crush solute, heat, stir
4. the volume of gas that will dissolve in a given quantity of liquid remains the same as pressure increases.
5. 0.909M
6. increases the boiling point
7. activity of the ions is slightly less than their concentrations
8. 3.0 kPa
9. 111 g
10. 3.27 kPa

ONE MORE STEP

1. If K_{eq} for 2A + B $\rightleftarrows$ 2C is 8, set up the expression used to calculate the concentration of C at equilibrium if the starting conditions were one-half mole each of A and B in a 10 dm^3 container.

2. Thermodynamic quantities ΔH, ΔS, and ΔG apply to the activated complex as well as the products and reactants. Investigate the relationship between the energy of activation and these thermodynamic quantities.

3. Prepare a class report on the step-by-step mechanism of a multistep reaction. Be sure to include information on the slowest step.

4. Find out what the mathematical relationship is between K_c (concentration) and K_p.

5. Enzymes in living systems are catalysts. Investigate their mechanisms.

6. To what extent does free energy depend upon temperature?

See Teacher Guide for answers

READINGS

Consumano, James A., "Designer Catalysts," *Science 85*, Vol. 6, No. 9(November, 1985), pp. 120-122.

Hegedus, L. Louis, and James J. Gumbleton, "Catalysts, Computers, and Cars: A Growing Symbiosis," *ChemTech*, Vol. 10, No. 10(October 1980), pp. 630-642

Sinfelt, John H., "Bimetallic Catalysts," *Scientific American*, Vol. 253, No. 3(September 1985), pp. 90-98

You may have thought salt to be only the compound sodium chloride. However, the term salt represents a large class of chemical compounds. Vast amounts of salt are obtained by mining and recovery processes. Salts can also be obtained from neutralization reactions by reacting an acid with a base. What are some industrial and biological applications of neutralization reactions? How do acids, bases, and salts differ?

ACIDS, BASES, AND SALTS

24

Chapter 24 begins with definitions of acids and bases by an introduction to three acid-base theories. It also includes a discussion of acid-base behavior, nomenclature, and some properties of salts.

DEMONSTRATION: Conductivity apparatus can be used to show relative ion concentration. Prepare solutions of 6.0M, 1.0M, 0.10M, and 0.01M HCl and CH$_3$COOH. The acetic acid will not conduct. The HCl will conduct down to 0.10M. See Teacher Guide for further information and discussion ideas. **CAUTION:** *Both acids are corrosive.*

GOALS:
• You will differentiate among three acid-base theories.
• You will compare and contrast properties of acids, bases, and salts.
• You will name acids, bases, and salts given the formula and write the formula given the name.
• You will calculate ionization constant, [H$_3$O$^+$] and percent of ionization.

Many foods have distinctive tastes. Some are bitter. Other foods are sour or salty. It is now known that a lemon or a grapefruit has a sour taste because it contains a compound called an acid. Soaps that contain lye, a base, taste bitter. Salty foods taste salty because they contain a salt, sodium chloride. The presence of these compounds, called acids, bases, and salts, gives many of our foods their distinctive flavors.

Acids taste sour (lemon). Bases taste bitter (soap).

It was discovered long ago that these substances, when dissolved in water, conduct an electric current. Because they conduct a current, they are called **electrolytes.** The definitions of acids, bases, and salts have undergone several modifications in the history of chemistry. As knowledge about chemistry expanded, definitions of these words were also expanded to cover larger groups of compounds. The first part of this chapter traces the development of the definitions of these terms.

Acids, bases, and salts are electrolytes.

Solutions of electrolytes conduct a current.

24:1 ARRHENIUS THEORY

In 1887, the Swedish chemist Svante Arrhenius published a paper concerning acids and bases. He knew that solutions containing acids or bases conducted an electric current. Arrhenius tried to explain why. He concluded that these substances released charged particles when dissolved. He called these charged particles ions (wanderers). He concluded that *acids were substances that separated (ionized) in water solution to produce hydrogen ions* (H$^+$, or free protons). He also believed that *bases were substances that ionized to produce hydroxide ions (OH$^-$) in water solution.*

BACKGROUND: The Arrhenius theory is the traditional approach. However, it still is adequate for most introductory chemistry.

The three classes of electrolytes are acids, bases, and salts. Their solutions conduct an electric current because they form ions.

Arrhenius theory: An acid produces H$^+$ in water solution; a base produces OH$^-$ in water solution.

$$HCl(g) \rightarrow H^+(aq) + Cl^-(aq)$$
$$NaOH(cr) \rightarrow Na^+(aq) + OH^-(aq)$$

Brønsted-Lowry theory: An acid is a proton donor; a base is a proton acceptor.

Free protons are hydrated by water molecules to form H_3O^+, the hydronium ion.

The conjugate base is the remaining particle of the acid after a proton is released.

The conjugate acid of a base is formed when the base accepts a proton.

FIGURE 24-2. The reaction between two water molecules produces the hydronium ion, which is an acid, and the hydroxide ion, which is a base.

24:2 BRØNSTED-LOWRY THEORY

As the knowledge of catalysts and nonaqueous solutions increased, it became necessary to redefine the terms acid and base. In 1923, an English scientist, T. M. Lowry, and a Danish scientist, J. N. Brønsted, independently proposed a new definition. They stated that *in a chemical reaction, any substance that donates a proton is an acid* and *any substance that accepts a proton is a base.* For example, when hydrogen chloride gas is dissolved in water, ions are formed.

$$HCl(g) + H_2O(l) \rightarrow H_3O^+(aq) + Cl^-(aq)$$
$$\text{acid} \qquad \text{base}$$

In this reaction, hydrogen chloride is an acid, and water is a base. Notice that the hydrogen ion (H^+) from the acid has combined with a water molecule to form the polyatomic ion H_3O^+, which is called the **hydronium** (hi DROH nee uhm) **ion.** There is strong evidence that the hydrogen ion is never found free as H^+. The bare proton is so strongly attracted by the electrons of surrounding water molecules that H_3O^+ forms immediately. Consider the opposite reaction.

$$H_3O^+(aq) + Cl^-(aq) \rightarrow HCl(g) + H_2O(l)$$
$$\text{acid} \qquad \text{base}$$

In this reaction, the H_3O^+ ion is an acid. It acts as an acid because it donates a proton to the chloride ion, which is a base. The hydronium ion is said to be the conjugate acid of the base, water. The chloride ion is called the conjugate base of the acid, hydrochloric acid. In general, any acid-base reaction is described as:

acid + base → conjugate base + conjugate acid

The **conjugate base** of an acid is the particle that remains after a proton has been released by the acid. The **conjugate acid** of a base is formed when the base acquires a proton from the acid. Table 24-1 contains a list of some bases and their conjugate acids.

Consider what happens when ammonia gas is added to water.

$$NH_3(g) + H_2O(l) \rightarrow NH_4^+(aq) + OH^-(aq)$$
$$\text{base} \quad + \quad \text{acid} \quad \rightarrow \quad \text{conjugate} \quad + \quad \text{conjugate}$$
$$\text{acid} \qquad\qquad \text{base}$$

H_2O

H_2O

OH^-

$$CH_3Cl + AlCl_3 \rightarrow CH_3^+ + AlCl_4^-$$

If benzene is also present in the mixture, the CH_3^+ ion attacks the π electrons of the ring compound.

$$CH_3^+ + C_6H_6 \rightarrow C_6H_6CH_3^+$$

This second step is the rate determining step. In the third step of the reaction mechanism, the $AlCl_4^-$ ion reacts with the organic ion.

$$C_6H_6CH_3^+ + AlCl_4^- \rightarrow C_6H_5CH_3 + HCl + AlCl_3$$

In this reaction $AlCl_3$ acts as a catalyst, returning unchanged at the last step.

Table 24-2

Summary of Acid-Base Theories		
Theory	**Acid Definition**	**Base Definition**
Arrhenius Theory	Any substance that releases H^+ ion in water solution	Any substance that releases OH^- ions in water solution
Brønsted-Lowry Theory	Any substance that donates a proton	Any substance that accepts a proton
Lewis Theory	Any substance that can accept an electron pair	Any substance that can donate an electron pair

Each succeeding theory is more inclusive.

A substance that is an acid or base under the Arrhenius theory is also an acid or base under the Lewis and the Brønsted-Lowry theories.

PROBLEMS

2. Classify the following substances as Lewis acids or Lewis bases.
   a. Cl^-
   b. CO_3^{2-}
   c. Na^+
   d. Br^-

Write equations for the following reactions:

3. $Ag^+ + NH_3 \rightarrow$ (coordination number = 2)
4. $Cu^{2+} + NH_3 \rightarrow$ (coordination number = 4)
5. $Co^{3+} + NH_3 \rightarrow$ (coordination number = 6)
6. $Fe^{3+} + CN^- \rightarrow$ (coordination number = 6)
7. $Zn^{2+} + OH^- \rightarrow$ (coordination number = 4)

2. a. base
   b. base
   c. acid
   d. base
3. $Ag^+ + 2NH_3 \rightarrow Ag(NH_3)_2^+$
4. $Cu^{2+} + 4NH_3 \rightarrow Cu(NH_3)_4^{2+}$
5. $Co^{3+} + 6NH_3 \rightarrow Co(NH_3)_6^{3+}$
6. $Fe^{3+} + 6CN^- \rightarrow Fe(CN)_6^{3-}$
7. $Zn^{2+} + 4OH^- \rightarrow Zn(OH)_4^{2-}$

24:4 NAMING BINARY ACIDS

Binary acids are acids containing only two elements. If you look at Table 24-3, you will notice that the prefix is always *hydro-* and the suffix is always *-ic*.

To name a binary acid, we determine what stem to use by finding what element is combined with hydrogen. For instance, chlorine will have the stem *-chlor-*, and fluorine the stem *-fluor-*. To this stem, the prefix *hydro-* and the suffix *-ic* are added. There are a few exceptions to the rule that binary acids begin with *hydro-* and end with *-ic*. One example is hydrocyanic acid, HCN, which really is ternary (Section 24:5). These exceptions must be learned separately, but HCN is the only one we will mention.

Binary acids contain only 2 elements.

The names of binary acids begin with *hydro-* and end in *-ic*.

Table 24-3

Naming Binary Acids				
Binary Compound + Water	**Prefix**	**Stem**	**Suffix**	**Name**
Hydrogen chloride gas dissolved in water	Hydro-	-chlor-	-ic	Hydrochloric acid
Hydrogen iodide gas dissolved in water	Hydro-	-iod-	-ic	Hydroiodic acid
Hydrogen sulfide gas dissolved in water	Hydro-	-sulfur-	-ic	Hydrosulfuric acid

PROBLEM

8. Name the following binary acids.
   a. HBr (aq)
   b. HF (aq)

8. a. hydrobromic
   b. hydrofluoric

24:5 NAMING TERNARY ACIDS AND BASES

Ternary acids are acids that contain three elements. The ternary acids we will be working with have oxygen as the third element. We find the stem by determining what element is combined with oxygen and hydrogen in the acid molecule. We determine the prefix (if there is one) and the suffix by the number of oxygen atoms in each molecule.

Generally, the most common form of the acid is given the suffix *-ic*. No prefix is used. Examples of common ternary acids are sulfur*ic* (H_2SO_4), chlor*ic* ($HClO_3$), and nitr*ic* (HNO_3).

If a second acid is formed containing the same three elements, but having fewer oxygen atoms, this acid is given the suffix *-ous*. There is no

Ternary acids contain 3 elements.

The stem for naming ternary acids is derived from the element that is combined with hydrogen and oxygen in the acid molecule.

The name of a ternary acid indicates the number of oxygen atoms in each molecule.

prefix. Examples of these acids are sulfur*ous* (H_2SO_3), chlor*ous* ($HClO_2$), and nitr*ous* (HNO_2).

If a third acid containing still fewer oxygen atoms is formed, it is given the prefix *hypo-* and the suffix *-ous*. An example is *hypochlorous* acid ($HClO$).

Acids containing more oxygen than the common form are named by adding the prefix *per-* to the common name, for example, is *per*chloric acid ($HClO_4$). See the examples in Table 24-4.

SUGGESTION: You may wish to mention peroxy-acids and condensed acids at this point.

Table 24-4

Naming Ternary Acids					
Compound	Number of Oxygen Atoms	Prefix	Stem	Suffix	Name of Acid
H_2SO_4	4	no prefix	sulfur-	-ic	sulfuric
H_2SO_3	3	no prefix	sulfur-	-ous	sulfurous
$HClO_4$	4	per-	-chlor-	-ic	perchloric
$HCLO_3$	3	no prefix	chlor-	-ic	chloric
$HClO_2$	2	no prefix	chlor-	-ous	chlorous
$HClO$	1	hypo-	-chlor-	-ous	hypochlorous

It is not possible, without previous knowledge, to know which form of an acid is most common. If the name of one form is known, the other ternary acids containing the same elements can be named. Bromine forms only two acids with hydrogen and oxygen: $HBrO$ and $HBrO_3$. Instead of being named bromous and bromic acids, they are named hypobromous and bromic acids. The exception occurs because they contain the same number of oxygen atoms as hypochlorous and chloric acids. The pattern of the chlorine acids is followed for the bromine acids because both elements are in the same group in the periodic table. The same pattern is followed in naming the ternary acids of the other halogens. As you can see, it is useful to memorize the names of common acids.

Arrhenius bases are composed of metallic, or positively charged, ions and the negatively charged hydroxide ion. These bases are named by adding the word *hydroxide* to the name of the positive ion. Examples are sodium hydroxide, $NaOH$, and calcium hydroxide, $Ca(OH)_2$.

Acids
per-STEM-*ic* more oxygen
STEM-*ic* most common
STEM-*ous* less oxygen
hypo-STEM-*ous* still less oxygen

SUGGESTION: Emphasize that the number of oxygen atoms in the *-ic* acid must be memorized. This number cannot be predicted. However, once the *-ic* acid is known, the others may be predicted although they may not exist.

Bases are named by using the name of the metallic ion and the word hydroxide.

PROBLEMS

9. Name the following acids.
  a. H_3BO_3 **c.** H_3PO_4 **e.** HIO_3
  b. HNO_2 **d.** H_3AsO_3

10. Write formulas for the following acids.
  a. carbonic acid   **c.** arsenic acid   **e.** hypoiodous
  b. nitric acid   **d.** selenic acid

9. a. boric acid
   b. nitrous acid
   c. phosphoric acid
   d. arsenious acid
   e. iodic acid
10. a. H_2CO_3
    b. HNO_3
    c. H_3AsO_4
    d. H_2SeO_4
    e. HIO

24:6 ACIDIC AND BASIC ANHYDRIDES

Anhydride means without water.

An acid anhydride will form an acid with water. A basic anhydride will form a base when dissolved in water.

When sulfur dioxide is dissolved in water, sulfurous acid is formed. Any oxygen-containing substance that will produce an acid when dissolved in water is called an **acidic anhydride.**

$$SO_2(g) + H_2O(l) \rightarrow H_2SO_3(aq)$$

$$\underset{\text{anhydride}}{\underset{\text{acid}}{}} \quad + \quad \text{water} \quad \rightarrow \quad \text{acid}$$

When sulfur-containing fuels such as coal and petroleum are burned, SO_2 is introduced into the atmosphere. Then, when water vapor condenses and rain falls, the SO_2 reacts with the water to produce sulfurous acid.

If sodium oxide is added to water, sodium hydroxide, a base, is formed. Any oxygen-containing substance that will produce a base when dissolved in water is called a **basic anhydride,** for example

FIGURE 24-3. Acid rain is produced when sulfur and nitrogen oxides in the air dissolve in water (a). The action of CO_2 in water (carbonic acid) causes the formations in this cavern (b). The deterioration of stone is the result of acid rain (c).

$$Na_2O(cr) + H_2O(l) \rightarrow 2NaOH(aq)$$

basic   +   water $\rightarrow$ base
anhydride

Anhydrous means without water, so anhydrides may be classified as acids or bases without water.

Organic acids may also form anhydrides. An example is acetic anhydride. It is formed by removing a water molecule from two acetic acid molecules.

$$CH_3-\overset{\overset{O}{\|}}{C}-O-H + H-O-\overset{\overset{O}{\|}}{C}-CH_3 \rightarrow CH_3-\overset{\overset{O}{\|}}{C}-O-\overset{\overset{O}{\|}}{C}-CH_3 + H_2O$$

Note that an acid anhydride reacts with a basic anhydride to produce a salt. This reaction is a neutralization reaction but no water is produced.

PROBLEMS

11. Predict the acidic or basic nature of the following anhydrides.
  a. Li_2O **c.** CO_2 **e.** SeO_2
  b. MgO **d.** K_2O

12. Write formulas for the anhydrides of the following.
  a. $Ba(OH)_2$ **c.** H_6TeO_6 **e.** $Zn(OH)_2$
  b. HIO_4 **d.** $Al(OH)_3$

11. a. basic
    b. basic
    c. acidic
    d. basic
    e. acidic
12. a. BaO
    b. I_2O_7
    c. TeO_3
    d. Al_2O_3
    e. ZnO

24:7 ACID-BASE BEHAVIOR

Consider a compound having the formula HO*X*. If the element *X* is highly electronegative, it will have a strong attraction for the electrons it is sharing with the oxygen. As these electrons are pulled toward *X*, the oxygen, in turn, will pull strongly on the electrons it is sharing with the hydrogen. The hydrogen ion, or proton, would then be lost easily. In this case, HO*X* is behaving as an acid.

If the element *X* has a low electronegativity, the oxygen will tend to pull the shared electrons away from *X*. The hydrogen will remain joined to the oxygen. Since in this case the formation of the hydroxide ion, OH^-, is likely, HO*X* is behaving as a base.

We know that nonmetals have high electronegativities and metals have low electronegativities. We can conclude, then, that nonmetals will tend to form acids, and metals will tend to form bases.

Some substances can react as either an acid or a base. If one of these substances is in the presence of a proton donor, then it reacts as a base. In the presence of a proton acceptor, it acts as an acid. Such a substance is said to be **amphoteric.** Water is the most common amphoteric substance.

Metals tend to form bases; nonmetals tend to form acids.

Amphoteric: A substance which can act as either an acid or a base.

$$HCl + H_2O \rightarrow H_3O^+ + Cl^-$$

proton   base
donor

$$NH_3 + H_2O \rightarrow NH_4^+ + OH^-$$

proton   acid
acceptor

24:8 DEFINITION OF A SALT

DEMONSTRATION: Slowly mix equal volumes of 6*M* HCl and 6*M* NaOH (a few cm³ of each is sufficient). Evaporate the solution to dryness. Ask students how they might identify the product. **CAUTION:** *HCl and NaOH are corrosive/caustic. Exothermic reaction.*

An acid-base neutralization reaction produces a salt.

An Arrhenius acid is composed of positive hydrogen ions combined with negative nonmetallic ions. Metallic bases are composed of negative hydroxide ions combined with positive metallic ions. An Arrhenius acid reacts with an Arrhenius base to form a salt and water. The water is formed from the hydrogen ion of the acid and the hydroxide ion of the base. If the water is evaporated, the negative ions of the acid will unite with the positive ions of the base to form a new compound called a salt. Such a reaction should result in removal of all hydrogen and hydroxide ions from solution. The resulting solution should be neither an acid nor a base. We say that the solution is **neutral** (neither acidic nor basic). The reaction of an acid and a base is called a **neutralization reaction.** A **salt** is a crystalline compound composed of the negative ion of an acid and the positive ion of a base. For example, if equivalent amounts of chloric acid and sodium hydroxide react, sodium chlorate and water are formed.

$$HClO_3(aq) + NaOH(aq) \rightarrow H_2O(l) + NaClO_3(aq)$$
$$\text{acid} \quad + \quad \text{base} \quad \rightarrow \quad \text{water} \quad + \quad \text{salt}$$

Salts may also result from the reactions of acidic or basic anhydrides with a corresponding base, acid, or anhydride.

$$Na_2O + H_2SO_4 \rightarrow Na_2SO_4 + H_2O \quad \text{(basic anhydride + acid)}$$
$$2NaOH + SO_3 \rightarrow Na_2SO_4 + H_2O \quad \text{(base + acid anhydride)}$$
$$Na_2O + SO_3 \rightarrow Na_2SO_4 \quad \text{(basic anhydride + acid anhydride)}$$

Although a salt is formed by neutralization, solutions of some salts in water are not neutral. It is possible to obtain salts that are acidic or basic. For example, if sodium hydroxide reacts with sulfuric acid in a 1:1 mole ratio the product, sodium hydrogen sulfate, is called an acidic salt.

$$H_2SO_4(aq) + NaOH(aq) \rightarrow H_2O(l) + NaHSO_4(aq)$$

It still contains an ionizable hydrogen atom. In a similar manner, partially neutralized bases form basic salts. Acidic or basic salts such as $NaHSO_4$ and $Cu_2(OH)_2CO_3$ are not neutral in solution.

You may have already noted that there is a relationship between the name of an acid and the name of the salt it forms. Binary acids (prefix *hydro-*, and suffix *-ic*) form salts ending in *-ide*. As an example, hydrochloric acid forms chloride salts. Ternary acids form salts in which *-ic* acids form *-ate* salts; *-ous* acids form *-ite* salts. Prefixes from the acid names remain in the salt names.

In naming acidic and basic salts, each ion is named separately. Hydrogen is generally named immediately before the negative ions and hydroxide immediately after the positive ions. Thus, $NaHC_2O_4$ is sodium hydrogen oxalate and $Pb_2(OH)_2CO_3$ is lead(II) hydroxide carbonate.

Table 24-5

Acid and Ion Names		
Acid		**Ion**
$HMnO_4$ permanganic acid	$\rightarrow$	MnO_4 permanganate
H_2SO_4 sulfuric acid	$\rightarrow$	$SO_4{}^{2-}$ sulfate
HNO_2 nitrous acid	$\rightarrow$	$NO_2{}^-$ nitrite
$HClO$ hypochlorous acid	$\rightarrow$	ClO^- hypochlorite
H_2CO_3 carbonic acid	$\rightarrow$	$HCO_3{}^-$ hydrogen carbonate

SUGGESTION: Review the various kinds of neutralization reactions now discussed.
acid + base
acid + basic anhydride
acid anhydride + base
acid anhydride + basic
                    anhydride

PROBLEMS

13. Name the following compounds.

    a. $NaHSO_4$ **d.** $NaHS$
    b. $KHC_4H_4O_6$ **e.** $Al(OH)SiO_3$
    c. NaH_2PO_4

14. Write formulas for the following compounds.

    a. sodium hydrogen carbonate
    b. sodium monohydrogen phosphate
    c. ammonium hydrogen sulfide
    d. potassium hydrogen sulfate
    e. tin(II) hydroxide nitrate

13. a. sodium hydrogen sulfate
    b. potassium hydrogen tartrate
    c. sodium dihydrogen phosphate
    d. sodium hydrogen sulfide
    e. aluminum hydroxide silicate
14. a. $NaHCO_3$
    b. Na_2HPO_4
    c. NH_4HS
    d. $KHSO_4$
    e. $Sn(OH)NO_3$

24:9   STRENGTHS OF ACIDS AND BASES

Not all acids and bases are completely ionized in water solution. An acid (such as hydrochloric) that is considered to ionize completely into positive and negative ions is called a **strong acid.** A base (such as sodium hydroxide) that is completely dissociated into positive and negative ions is called a **strong base.**

Some acids and bases ionize only slightly in solution. The most important base of this kind is ammonia. In water solution, this base ionizes only partially into $NH_4{}^+$ and OH^-. The major portion of the ammonia molecules remain unreacted. Such a base is called a weak base. Acetic acid ionizes only slightly in water solution. It is called a weak acid. A **weak acid** or a **weak base** is one that ionizes only slightly in solution.

Strong acids are completely ionized in water solution.

Strong bases, in water, are completely dissociated into + and − ions.

Weak acids and bases ionize only slightly in water solution.

Table 24-6

Relative Strengths of Some Acids and Bases		
Compound	**Formula**	**Relative Strength**
Hydrochloric acid	HCl	strong acid
Phosphorous acid	H_3PO_3	
Phosphoric acid	H_3PO_4	
Hydrofluoric acid	HF	
Hydroselenic acid	H_2Se	
Acetic acid	CH_3COOH	
Carbonic acid	H_2CO_3	
Hydrosulfuric acid	H_2S	
		neutral solution
Hypochlorite ion	ClO^-	
Cyanide ion	CN^-	
Ammonia	NH_3	
Carbonate ion	$CO_3{}^{2-}$	
Aluminum hydroxide	$Al(OH)_3$	
Phosphate ion	$PO_4{}^{3-}$	
Silicate ion	$SiO_3{}^{2-}$	
Hydroxide ion	OH^-	strong base

24:10   NET IONIC EQUATIONS

For reactions taking place in water, it is customary for chemists to write equations in the ionic form. In this method, only those ions taking part in the reaction are written. Other ions present in the solution but not involved in the reaction are known as **spectator ions** and are not included in the equation.

Spectator ions are not involved in the reaction, and are not written in the net ionic equation.

In writing net ionic equations, dissolved salts are considered in their ionic form. We list other substances as molecules or atoms. The following rule must be observed when writing net ionic equations. *Substances occurring in a reaction in molecular form are written as molecules. Those substances occurring as ions are written as ions.*

Some substances are written as molecules; others as ions.

Weak acids and bases are written in molecular form while strong acids and bases should be written in the ionized form. An acid may contain more than one ionizable hydrogen atom. Such an acid is called a **polyprotic acid.** Below are listed some "thumb rules" for deciding whether to use ions or molecules in writing net ionic equations. These rules are not applicable in all cases but work well in most reactions. If your equation must be exact, you should use a handbook. The handbook will help you determine whether substances are to be written as ions or molecules.

Polyprotic acids have more than one ionizable hydrogen atom.

Rule 1. *Binary acids:* HCl, HBr, and HI are strong; all others (including HCN) are weak. Strong acids are written in ionic form.

Rule 2. *Ternary acids:* If the number of oxygen atoms in the molecule exceeds the number of hydrogen atoms by two or more, the acid is strong.

Strong electrolytes are written in ionic form.

Weak: $HClO$, H_3AsO_4, H_2CO_3, H_4SiO_4, HNO_2
Strong: $HClO_3$, $HClO_4$, H_2SO_4, HNO_3, H_2SeO_4

Weak electrolytes are written in molecular form.

Rule 3. *Polyprotic acids:* In the second and subsequent ionizations the acids are always weak, whether or not the original acid is strong or weak.

It is often convenient to consider both protons of sulfuric acid as strong.

Rule 4. *Bases:* Hydroxides of the Groups IA and IIA elements (except beryllium) are strong. All others including ammonia, hydroxylamine, and organic bases are weak.

Rule 5. *Salts:* Salts are written in ionic form if soluble, and in molecular form if insoluble. Use the solubility rules in Table A-7.

Soluble salts are written in ionic form; insoluble salts are written in molecular form.

$$\text{Ionic: } K^+ + Cl^-, \ Zn^{2+} + 2NO_3^-$$
$$\text{Molecular: } AgBr, \ BaSO_4$$

Rule 6. *Oxides:* Oxides are always written in molecular form.

Rule 7. *Gases:* Gases are always written in molecular form.

EXAMPLE: Net Ionic Equations

Convert the following balanced equation to a net ionic equation.

$$H_2SiO_3 + 2NaOH \rightarrow Na_2SiO_3 + 2H_2O$$

Solving Process:

According to Rule 2, since there are three oxygens and two hydrogens in silicic acid, it must be weak. Rule 4 tells us that NaOH is strong. The sodium silicate salt is soluble and we apply Rule 5. Water is an oxide and Rule 6 applies. Using these rules the ionic equation is written as

$$H_2SiO_3 + 2Na^+ + 2OH^- \rightarrow 2Na^+ + SiO_3^{2-} + 2H_2O$$

To make the equation a net ionic equation, we remove (by subtracting from both sides) those species that appear on each side. For our reaction, two sodium ions appear on each side and are removed. The net ionic equation is then:

$$H_2SiO_3 + 2OH^- \rightarrow SiO_3^{2-} + 2H_2O$$

EXAMPLE: Net Ionic Equations

Convert the following balanced equation to a net ionic equation.

$$2HCl + Ba(OH)_2 \rightarrow BaCl_2 + 2H_2O$$

Solving Process:

Rule 1: HCl is a strong acid.
Rule 4: $Ba(OH)_2$ is a strong base.
Rule 5: $BaCl_2$ is soluble.
Rule 6: H_2O is molecular.

Ionic equation: $2H^+ + 2Cl^- + Ba^{2+} + 2OH^- \rightarrow Ba^{2+} + 2Cl^- + 2H_2O$
Net ionic equation: $2H^+ + 2OH^- \rightarrow 2H_2O$

Note that the net ionic equation should be further simplified by dividing through by 2 in order to put it in its lowest terms.

Final form: $H^+ + OH^- \rightarrow H_2O$

PROBLEMS

See Teacher Guide.

Reduce the following balanced equations to net ionic form.

15. $4HCl(aq) + 2Cr(NO_3)_2(aq) + 2HgCl_2(aq) \rightarrow$
$2CrCl_3(aq) + Hg_2Cl_2(cr) + 4HNO_3(aq)$

16. $2Mn(NO_3)_2(aq) + 5NaBiO_3(cr) + 14HNO_3(aq) \rightarrow$
$2NaMnO_4(aq) + 5Bi(NO_3)_3(aq) + 7H_2O(l) + 3NaNO_3(aq)$

17. $2AgNO_3(aq) + H_2SO_4(aq) \rightarrow Ag_2SO_4(cr) + 2HNO_3(aq)$

18. $H_4SiO_4(aq) + 4NaOH(aq) \rightarrow Na_4SiO_4(aq) + 4H_2O(l)$

19. $2CuSO_4(aq) + 2NH_4CNS(aq) + H_2SO_3(aq) + H_2O(l) \rightarrow$
$2CuCNS(cr) + (NH_4)_2SO_4(aq) + 2H_2SO_4(aq)$

24:11 IONIZATION CONSTANT

Acetic acid is a weak acid and ionizes only slightly. The equation of the ionization of acetic acid at equilibrium is

$$CH_3COOH(l) + H_2O(l) \rightleftarrows CH_3COO^-(aq) + H_3O^+(aq)$$

The equilibrium constant for this reaction is

$$K_{eq} = \frac{[\text{products}]}{[\text{reactants}]}$$

$$K_{eq} = \frac{[CH_3COO^-][H_3O^+]}{[CH_3COOH][H_2O]}$$

The CH_3COO^- and H_3O^+ ion concentrations are small, and the concentration of CH_3COOH is almost unaffected by the ionization. When acetic acid ionizes, hydrogen ions attach to a water molecule and form the hydronium ion (H_3O^+). However, acetic acid is a weak acid and ionizes only slightly. Thus, few hydrogen ions are formed. The concentration of water remains nearly constant (55.6 mol/dm^3—Section 25:2). Thus, we can multiply the concentration of water by the equilibrium constant and obtain the equation:

Ionization constant:
$K_{eq}[H_2O] = 55.6 \, K_{eq}$

$$K_{eq}[H_2O] = \frac{[CH_3COO^-][H_3O^+]}{[CH_3COOH]}$$

Because $[H_2O]$ is constant, the product of the equilibrium constant and the concentration of water ($K_{eq}[H_2O]$) produces a new constant. This new constant is called the **ionization constant,** and is given the symbol K_a. For any weak acid ($HA + H_2O \rightleftarrows H_3O^+ + A^-$), the ionization constant is

Ionization constant (K_a) is a special case of an equilibrium constant.
SUGGESTION: Make it clear to students that the ionization constant is simply a special case of the equilibrium constant.

$$K_a = \frac{[H_3O^+][A^-]}{[HA]}$$

In a similar way we can write ionization constant expressions for weak bases (K_b). Ammonia is a weak base that reacts with water as follows:

$$NH_3 + H_2O \rightleftarrows NH_4^+ + OH^-$$

The ionization constant expression for ammonia is

$$K_b = \frac{[NH_4^+][OH^-]}{[NH_3]}$$

EXAMPLE: Ionization of a Weak Acid

What is the hydronium ion concentration of a 0.100M solution of formic acid (HCOOH)? Formic acid has an ionization constant of 1.78×10^{-4}.

Solving Process:

$$HCOOH(l) + H_2O(l) \rightleftarrows H_3O^+(aq) + HCOO^-(aq)$$

$$K_a = \frac{[H_3O^+][HCOO^-]}{[HCOOH]} = 1.78 \times 10^{-4}$$

Let x represent $[H_3O^+]$ and $[HCOO^-]$. (The balanced equation shows that $[H_3O^+]$ is equal to $[HCOO^-]$ in this example.) If we let $x = [H_3O^+]$ or $[HCOO^-]$, then the concentration of formic acid [HCOOH] is $(0.100 - x)$. Because x is so small when compared with the concentration of formic acid, $(0.100 - x)$ is approximately equal to 0.100M. Therefore,

$$1.78 \times 10^{-4} = \frac{x^2}{0.100}$$
$$\text{and } x^2 = (0.100)(1.78 \times 10^{-4}) = 1.78 \times 10^{-5}$$
$$x = 4.22 \times 10^{-3}M$$

If x is sufficiently large compared to the acid concentration, a quadratic equation must be used to solve the problem.

EXAMPLE: H_3O^+ Concentration for a Weak Acid

SUGGESTION: Problems requiring the use of the quadratic equation can be considered optional at this level. However, if you use them be sure to review the mathematical process for students.

What is the hydronium ion concentration in a 0.100M solution of $HClO_2$? $K_a HClO_2 = 1.10 \times 10^{-2}$

Solving Process:

$$HClO_2 + H_2O \rightleftarrows H_3O^3 + ClO_2^-$$

$$K_a = \frac{[H_3O^+][ClO_2^-]}{[HClO_2]} = 1.10 \times 10^{-2}$$

Let $\quad x = [H_3O^+] = [ClO_2^-]$ and $(0.100 - x) = [HClO_2]$

Because K_a is 10^{-2} and [HClO$_2$] is 10^{-1}, the difference is not 3 orders of magnitude. Thus, $(0.1 - x)$ is needed.

$$ax^2 + bx + c = 0$$

$$x = \frac{-b \pm \sqrt{b^2 - 4ac}}{2a}$$

In this equation:
$a = 1$
$b = 1.10 \times 10^{-2}$
$c = 1.10 \times 10^{-3}$

A good "rule of thumb" is to neglect x in $(0.1 - x)$ when it is added to or subtracted from a number that differs from the K value by three powers of ten or more. The use of the quadratic equation will not result in a significantly different answer.

$$1.10 \times 10^{-2} = \frac{x^2}{(0.100 - x)}$$

$$x^2 = (0.100 - x)(1.10 \times 10^{-2})$$

$$x^2 = (1.10 \times 10^{-3}) - (1.10 \times 10^{-2})x$$

$$x^2 + (1.10 \times 10^{-2})x - (1.10 \times 10^{-3}) = 0$$

$$x = \frac{-(1.10 \times 10^{-2}) \pm \sqrt{(1.10 \times 10^{-2})^2 + 4(1.10 \times 10^{-3})}}{2}$$

$$x = \frac{-(1.10 \times 10^{-2}) \pm \sqrt{(1.21 \times 10^{-4}) + (4.40 \times 10^{-3})}}{2}$$

$$x = \frac{-(1.10 \times 10^{-2}) \pm \sqrt{4.52 \times 10^{-3}}}{2}$$

$$x = \frac{-(1.10 \times 10^{-2}) \pm (6.72 \times 10^{-2})}{2}$$

$$x = \frac{-7.82 \times 10^{-2}}{2}, \quad \frac{5.62 \times 10^{-2}}{2}$$

$$x = -3.91 \times 10^{-2}, 2.81 \times 10^{-2}$$

A negative concentration is impossible. Thus,

$$x = [H_3O^+] = 2.81 \times 10^{-2}M$$

PROBLEMS

20. $2.51 \times 10^{-5}M$

21. 3.03×10^{-6}

20. What is the hydronium ion concentration in 0.0200M HClO? $K_a = 3.16 \times 10^{-8}$.

21. What is K_b for N_2H_4 (hydrazine) if a 0.500M solution has the following concentrations at equilibrium? $[N_2H_4] = 0.499M$, $[OH^-] = 1.23 \times 10^{-3}$, $[N_2H_5^+] = 1.23 \times 10^{-3}$

24:12   PERCENT OF IONIZATION

When a weak acid or base is dissolved in water, it ionizes only slightly. It is often desirable in such cases to know just how much of a substance is ionized. This amount is usually expressed in terms of percent, and is called the **percent of ionization.** For example, at room temperature, we found the hydronium ion concentration of 0.100M formic acid, HCOOH, to be $4.22 \times 10^{-3}M$. We know that

$$HCOOH + H_2O \rightleftarrows H_3O^+ + HCOO^-$$

Percent ionization can be calculated from the ratio obtained by comparing the concentration of an ion in solution to the concentration of the solute before it ionized.

Thus, we can find the percent ionization of formic acid by dividing either $[H_3O^+]$ or $[HCOO^-]$ by $[HCOOH]$. Either $[H_3O^+]$ or $[HCOO^-]$ will show the correct ratio of dissociated ions because the two concentrations are equal.

EXAMPLE: Percent of Ionization

Find the percent of ionization of a 0.100M solution of formic acid if the hydronium ion concentration is $4.22 \times 10^{-3}M$.

Solving Process:

$$\text{Percent of ionization} = \frac{[amount\ ionized]}{[original\ acid]} \times 100$$

$$= \frac{4.22 \times 10^{-3}}{0.100} \times 100 = 4.22\%$$

PROBLEMS

22. The ionization constant of acetic acid, CH_3COOH, is 1.76×10^{-5}. Find the percent of ionization of 0.200M acetic acid.

23. A solution of 1.00M HA in water ionizes 2.00%. Find K_a.

22. 0.940%
23. $K_a = 4.08 \times 10^{-4}$

24:13   COMMON ION EFFECT

There are times when a chemist may wish to change the concentration of a specific ion in a solution. Such changes are often made by adding a new substance to the solution.

Acetic acid ionizes in a water solution to form both acetate and hydronium ions. What will happen if we add some sodium acetate to the solution?

Sodium acetate is a soluble salt and dissociates completely into acetate (CH_3COO^-) and sodium ions.

$$NaCH_3COO(cr) \rightarrow Na^+(aq) + CH_3COO^-(aq)$$

Acetic acid ionizes into acetate and hydronium ions.

$$H_2O(l) + CH_3OOCH_3(l) \rightleftarrows H_3O^+(aq) + CH_3COO^-(aq)$$

K_a for acetic acid is

$$\frac{[CH_3COO^-][H_3O^+]}{[CH_3COOH]} = 1.76 \times 10^{-5}$$

K_a is a constant, and does not change unless the temperature changes. If sodium acetate is added to an acetic acid solution, acetate ion concentration is increased and a shift in the equilibrium occurs. Because there are more particles of CH_3COO^-, there will be more collisions between CH_3COO^- and H_3O^+. Thus, the rate of reaction will increase toward acetic acid. Some of the excess acetate ions unite with hydronium ions to

An increase in acetate ion concentration will cause a decrease in hydrogen ion concentration.

The K_a remains the same if a common ion is added.

form molecular acetic acid and water. This reaction results in the removal of hydronium ions from solution (thus decreasing hydronium ion concentration). The acetic acid concentration increases slightly. A new equilibrium is established with more acetate ions and fewer hydronium ions. K_a remains unchanged.

The acetate ion is common to both acetic acid and sodium acetate. The effect of the acetate ion on the acetic acid and solution is called the **common ion effect.** The addition of a common ion increases the concentration of one of the products of the ionization. Thus, the equilibrium shifts toward the opposite side in accordance with Le Chatelier's principle. By adding acetate ions (sodium acetate), we have placed a stress on the system (a surplus of acetate ions). The system shifts to relieve the stress by reacting hydronium ions with acetate ions. In the process, acetate and hydronium ions are consumed and acetic acid molecules are produced.

The common ion effect is a good example of Le Chatelier's principle.

A common ion causes equilibrium to shift toward the opposite side of the equation.

EXAMPLE: Common Ion Effect

What would be the hydronium ion concentration in a solution 0.100M in HOCN, cyanic acid, and 0.0500M in NaOCN, sodium cyanate? $K_a = 3.47 \times 10^{-4}$.

Solving Process:
First, write the equation for the equilibrium system.

$$HOCN + H_2O \rightleftharpoons H_3O^+ + OCN^-$$

Then write the expression for the ionization constant.

$$K_a = \frac{[H_3O^+][OCN^-]}{[HOCN]}$$

The hydronium ion is the quantity we seek, so we will let x represent that concentration. If x hydronium ions are produced, then x acid molecules ionized and x cyanate ions were produced from the acid. However, cyanate ions were also produced from the soluble sodium salt. Since sodium cyanate is soluble, we assume it dissociates completely. In that case, the salt contributes a concentration of 0.05M to the cyanate ion concentration. The total cyanate ion concentration would be 0.05 + x. If x acid molecules ionized and we started with 0.100, then at equilibrium the molecular acid concentration must be 0.100 − x.

$$3.47 \times 10^{-4} = \frac{(x)(x + 0.05)}{(0.100 - x)}$$

$$(3.47 \times 10^{-4})(0.100 - x) = (x)(x + 0.05)$$

$$(3.47 \times 10^{-5}) - (3.47 \times 10^{-4})x = x^2 + 0.05x$$

$$x^2 + (5.03 \times 10^{-2})x - (3.47 \times 10^{-5}) = 0$$

$ax^2 + bx + c = 0$

$$x = \frac{-b \pm \sqrt{b^2 - 4ac}}{2a}$$

$$x = \frac{-5.03 \times 10^{-2} \pm \sqrt{(5.03 \times 10^{-2})^2 + 4(3.47 \times 10^{-5})(1)}}{2}$$

$$x = \frac{-5.03 \times 10^{-2} \pm \sqrt{(2.53 \times 10^{-3}) + (1.39 \times 10^{-4})}}{2}$$

$$x = \frac{-5.03 \times 10^{-2} \pm \sqrt{2.67 \times 10^{-3}}}{2}$$

$$x = \frac{-5.03 \times 10^{-2} \pm 5.17 \times 10^{-2}}{2}, \quad \frac{1.36 \times 10^{-3}}{2}, \quad \frac{1.4 \times 10^{-3}}{2}$$

$$x = [H_3O^+] = 6.80 \times 10^{-4}M, \ 7.0 \times 10^{-4}M$$

PROBLEMS

24. What is the hydronium ion concentration in a solution $0.150M$ in HNO_2 and $0.0300M$ in $NaNO_2$? Refer to Table A-9 for the K_a.

25. What is the hydronium ion concentration in a solution of $0.403M$ in HBr and $0.000195M$ in NaBrO? $K_a = 2.40 \times 10^{-9}$.

26. Given a solution of the weak acid H_2CO_3, how could the hydronium ion concentration of this solution be reduced? How could the carbonate ion concentration of this same solution be reduced?

For Problem 25 ignore x in $[0.403 - x]$
24. $2.30 \times 10^{-3}M$
25. $4.96 \times 10^{-6}M$
26. add NaHCO$_3$; add H$_3$O$^+$

24:14 POLYPROTIC ACIDS

An acid containing more than one ionizable hydrogen atom is called a **polyprotic acid.** Sulfuric acid is an example of a polyprotic acid. In sulfuric acid, the hydrogen atoms leave the molecule one at a time. Sulfuric acid is a strong acid because the first hydrogen atom ionizes completely. The remaining hydrogen sulfate ion ionizes only slightly, and is considered a weak acid. The reaction can be represented as follows.

Polyprotic acids have more than one ionizable hydrogen atom.

$$H_2SO_4(l) + H_2O(l) \rightarrow H_3O^+(aq) + HSO_4^-(aq) \quad \begin{array}{l}\text{ionizes readily}\\ \text{(strong acid)}\end{array}$$

$$HSO_4^-(aq) + H_2O(l) \rightleftarrows H_3O^+(aq) + SO_4^{-2}(aq) \quad \begin{array}{l}\text{ionizes slightly}\\ \text{(weak acid)}\end{array}$$

The first ionization of a polyprotic acid leaves behind a negative ion. Therefore, the attraction for hydrogen is increased. Because of this attraction, each successive ionization is more difficult and occurs to a lesser extent. Phosphoric acid is a triprotic acid (an acid containing three ionizable hydrogen atoms); it ionizes as follows.

The second ionization of a polyprotic acid contributes few hydrogen ions.

$$H_3PO_4(cr) + H_2O(l) \rightleftarrows H_3O^+(aq) + H_2PO_4^-(aq) \quad K_a = 7.11 \times 10^{-3}$$

$$H_2PO_4^-(aq) + H_2O(l) \rightleftarrows H_3O^+(aq) + HPO_4^{2-}(aq) \quad K_a = 7.99 \times 10^{-8}$$

$$HPO_4^{2-}(aq) + H_2O(l) \rightleftarrows H_3O^+(aq) + PO_4^{3-}(aq) \quad K_a = 4.80 \times 10^{-13}$$

Calculations involving diprotic acids are complex. There are three unknown quantities: hydronium ion, protonated anion, and anion. There is a large difference between the extent of first and second ionizations. Thus, it is usually possible to ignore the hydronium ion contributed by the second ionization.

PROBLEM

27. Calculate the ratio of the first ionization constant to the second ionization constant for each of the polyprotic acids listed in Table A-9 of the Appendix. Do you see any pattern?

BIOGRAPHY   Gilbert Newton Lewis (1875-1946)

Following his education at the University of Nebraska and Harvard, Gilbert Newton Lewis began his professional career in an unusual way—as an employee of the Philippine government. Here he assumed the positions of Supervisor of Weights and Measures and chemist in the Bureau of Science.

Lewis was the first chemist to introduce the idea of the electron-pair bond. In so doing, he redefined the nature of acids and bases as being electron pair donors and acceptors. His theory also led to a clearer understanding of the concept of oxidation state.

In addition to these accomplishments, Lewis was the first to isolate heavy hydrogen. His theory of excited electron states in organic compounds helped explain the phenomena of color, fluorescence, and phosphorescence.

TECHNOLOGY AND CHEMISTRY

24:15   ACID RAIN

The nonmetallic oxides produced by the burning of fossil fuels are all acidic anhydrides. Thus, when these gases contact water vapor or water droplets in the atmosphere, they react to produce these acids:

$$SO_2 + H_2O \rightarrow H_2SO_3 \qquad \textit{sulfurous acid}$$
$$SO_3 + H_2O \rightarrow H_2SO_4 \qquad \textit{sulfuric acid}$$
$$2NO_2 + H_2O \rightarrow HNO_2 + HNO_3 \quad \textit{nitrous and nitric acids}$$
$$CO_2 + H_2O \rightarrow H_2CO_3 \qquad \textit{carbonic acid}$$

Rain formed from these water droplets is acidic. Acid rain has a number of harmful effects. One effect is the increase in the rate of deterioration of stone. Buildings constructed of stone are affected over time. The art work and carvings that decorate buildings and public areas are damaged. The fine detail on statuary is destroyed. Acid rain dissolves some compounds, such as carbonates, in the stone while the remaining substances become a powdery coating. In addition, the acid rain eats into the stone leaving tiny cracks. When water fills these cracks and freezes, its expansion causes cracking and breaking of the stone.

Acid rain also has adverse effects on living organisms. Acid rain has increased the acidity of many lakes in the northeastern United States and Canada to such an extent that fish can no longer live in them. Acid rain also tends to dissolve vital minerals in the soil. These minerals are then washed away in run-off. Crops grown in these depleted soils give poor yields, if they grow at all. When the acidic run-off reaches waterways it further interferes with fish growth and development.

Correcting these problems by treating statues with preservatives and lakes with basic compounds such as lime is not really the answer. Removing the offending oxides from exhausts and using alternate energy sources are much preferred courses of action.

SUMMARY

1. There are three common acid-base theories: the Arrhenius theory, the Brønsted-Lowry theory, and the Lewis theory. **24:1-24:3**

2. Binary acids contain two elements. Ternary acids contain three elements. **24:4-24:5**

3. Metallic oxides tend to form basic anhydrides, while nonmetallic oxides tend to form acidic anhydrides. **24:6**

4. A salt is a crystalline compound composed of the negative ion of an acid and the positive ion of a base. **24:8**

5. A strong acid ionizes completely in a water solution. A weak acid ionizes only slightly in a water solution. **24:9**

6. In net ionic equations, only the reacting species are shown. Spectator ions do not appear. **24:10**

7. The ionization of a weak acid or base is an equilibrium process. **24:11**

8. Percent ionization is the amount ionized divided by the original amount and the quotient multiplied by 100. **24:12**

9. A common ion represses the ionization of a weak electrolyte. **24:13**

10. Polyprotic acids contain more than one ionizable hydrogen atom. Each successive ionization occurs to a lesser extent. **24:14**

VOCABULARY

electrolytes **Intro**	anhydrous **24:6**	weak acid **24:9**
hydronium ion **24:2**	amphoteric **24:7**	weak base **24:9**
conjugate base **24:2**	neutral **24:8**	spectator ions **24:10**
conjugate acid **24:2**	neutralization	polyprotic acid **24:10**
binary acids **24:4**	reaction **24:8**	ionization constant **24:11**
ternary acids **24:5**	salt **24:8**	percent of ionization **24:12**
acidic anhydride **24:6**	strong acid **24:9**	common ion effect **24:13**
basic anhydride **24:6**	strong base **24:9**	

The left margin contains answers:

2. a. $:\overset{..}{\underset{..}{Cl}}:\overset{..}{\underset{..}{Al}}:\overset{..}{\underset{..}{Cl}}:$ with $:\overset{..}{\underset{..}{Cl}}:$ above
   acid

   b. $:\overset{..}{\underset{..}{O}}:\overset{..}{\underset{..}{S}}::O$ with $\overset{..}{O}$ above
   acid

   c. H$:$P$:$H with H below
   base

   d. $:\overset{..}{\underset{..}{Xe}}:$
   base

   e. Zn^{2+}
   acid

3. a. hydrobromic
   b. hydroselenic
   c. iodic
   d. selenious
   e. hyponitrous

4. a. H_3PO_3
   b. H_3PO_2
   c. H_2Te
   d. HIO_4
   e. HIO_3
   f. HCl

5. a. NaOH
   b. $Ca(OH)_2$
   c. HNO_3
   d. RbOH
   e. H_2TeO_3
   f. CsOH

6. a. Sc_2O_3
   b. Cs_2O
   c. I_2O_5
   d. Ga_2O_3
   e. CdO
   f. K_2O

8. a. sodium phosphate, Na_3PO_4
   b. potassium borate, K_3BO_3
   c. chromium(III) perchlorate, $Cr(ClO_4)_3$
   d. cadmium bromide, $CdBr_2$
   e. lithium silicate, Li_4SiO_4

PROBLEMS

1. For each of the following reactions label the acid, base, conjugate acid, and conjugate base.

   a. $NH_3(g) + H_3O^+(aq) \rightarrow NH_4^+(aq) + H_2O(l)$
   b. $CH_3OH(l) + NH_2^-(aq) \rightarrow CH_3O^-(aq) + NH_3(g)$
   c. $OH^-(aq) + H_3O^+(aq) \rightarrow H_2O(l) + H_2O(l)$
   d. $NH_2^-(aq) + H_2O(l) \rightarrow NH_3(g) + OH^-(aq)$
   e. $H_2O(l) + HClO_4(aq) \rightarrow H_3O^+(aq) + ClO_4^-(aq)$

	Acid	Base	Conjugate Acid	Conjugate Base
a.	H_3O^+	NH_3	NH_4^+	H_2O
b.	CH_3OH	NH_2^-	NH_3	CH_3O^-
c.	H_3O^+	OH^-	H_2O	H_2O
d.	H_2O	NH_2^-	NH_3	OH^-
e.	$HClO_4$	H_2O	H_3O^+	ClO_4^-

2. Draw electron-dot formulas for each of the following substances. Decide if the substance would be a Lewis acid or base.

   a. $AlCl_3$ b. SO_3 c. PH_3 d. Xe   e. Zn^{2+}

3. Name the following acids.

   a. HBr(aq)
   b. H_2Se(aq)
   c. HIO_3(aq)
   d. H_2SeO_3 (H_2SO_3 is sulfurous acid)
   e. $H_2N_2O_2$ (HNO_3 is nitric acid and HNO_2 is nitrous acid)

4. Write formulas for the following acids.

   a. phosphorous acid
   b. hypophosphorous acid
   c. hydrotelluric acid
   d. periodic acid
   e. iodic acid
   f. hydrochloric acid

5. Write formulas for the acids or bases formed from the following anhydrides.

   a. Na_2O b. CaO   c. N_2O_5 d. Rb_2O e. TeO_2 f. Cs_2O

6. Write formulas for the anhydrides of the following.

   a. $Sc(OH)_3$ b. CsOH   c. HIO_3 d. $Ga(OH)_3$ e. $Cd(OH)_2$ f. KOH

7. Reduce the following complete equations to net ionic form.

   a. $6Cr(NO_3)_2 + 3CuSO_4 \rightarrow 3Cu + 4Cr(NO_3)_3 + Cr_2(SO_4)_3$
   b. $3H_2SO_4 + MnO_2 + 2KBr \rightarrow MnSO_4 + Br_2 + 2KHSO_4 + 2H_2O$
   c. $H_2SO_4 \rightarrow H_2O + SO_3$
   d. $P_4O_{10} + 6H_2O \rightarrow 4H_3PO_4$
   e. $4CuCNS + 7KIO_3 + 14HCl \rightarrow 4HCN + 4CuSO_4 + 7ICl + 7KCl + 5H_2O$

8. Give the name and formula of the salts obtained from complete neutralization reactions between the following acid-base pairs.

   a. sodium hydroxide and phosphoric acid
   b. potassium hydroxide and boric acid (H_3BO_3)
   c. chromium(III) hydroxide and perchloric acid
   d. cadmium hydroxide and hydrobromic acid
   e. lithium hydroxide and silicic acid (H_4SiO_4)

9. How does a Lewis acid differ from an Arrhenius acid?

10. Show the steps in the reaction whereby benzene reacts with ethyl chloride to give ethylbenzene in the presence of $AlCl_3$.

11. Why do metals tend to form bases rather than acids in water solution?

12. Why is H_2CO_3 considered a weak acid while H_2SO_4 is a strong acid?

13. In writing net ionic equations, why are insoluble salts shown in molecular form?

14. What is the common ion effect?

15. Why is the K_a smaller for each succeeding ionization of phosphoric acid?

16. What is the hydronium ion concentration in a 0.100M solution of $KHSO_4$? (See Table A-9 of the Appendix for K_a value.)

17. What is the percentage of ionization of the HSO_4^- ion in Problem 16?

18. What is the benzoate ion concentration in a 0.0178M solution of benzoic acid, C_6H_5COOH?

19. What would be the hydrogen ion concentration in a 0.884M solution of oxalic acid, $HOOCCOOH$?

16. $2.92 \times 10^{-2}M$
17. 29.2%
18. $1.07 \times 10^{-3}M$
19. 0.201M

REVIEW

1. What is meant by a reversible reaction?

2. In what units is the concentration measured when writing rate expressions?

3. What two effects does an increase in temperature have on reaction rate?

4. Describe the difference between homogeneous reactions and heterogeneous reactions.

5. What is the relationship between the specific rate constants for a reversible reaction and the equilibrium constant for the same reaction?

6. What effect would an increase in pressure have on the following equilibrium?

$$CH_3N_2CH_3(g) \rightleftarrows C_2H_6(g) + N_2(g)$$

7. Would you expect methane gas, CH_4, to dissolve in water?

8. Differentiate among unsaturated, saturated, and supersaturated solutions.

9. What is the difference between concentrated and dilute solutions?

10. When NH_4NO_3 is dissolved in water, the solution gets cold. Is the enthalpy of solution of NH_4NO_3 in water positive or negative?

11. What is the hydronium ion concentration in a 0.250M solution of C_6H_5OH with $K_a = 1.02 \times 10^{-10}$? $C_6H_5OH + H_2O \rightleftarrows H_3O^+ + C_6H_5O^-$

12. If the ΔG for a certain reaction is -55.6 kJ at 25°C, what is the K_{eq} for the reaction?

1. A reaction whose products will react to produce the original reactants.
2. molarity
3. more collisions/more activated complexes
4. homogeneous—all reactants in the same phase; heterogeneous—reactants in two or more phases
5. $\dfrac{k_f}{k_r} = K_{eq}$
6. shift left
7. No, it is nonpolar; water is polar.
8.
9. number of ions per unit volume
10. positive
11. $5.05 \times 10^{-6}M$
12. 5.78×10^9

ONE MORE STEP

1. What is meant by the "leveling effect" of water on very strong acids and very strong bases?

2. Find the names of the following acids. Why are they named as they are? H_2SO_5, $H_2S_2O_7$, $H_2S_2O_8$, $HNCO$, $HSCN$

3. Inorganic acids are compounds containing ionizable hydrogen atoms. Inorganic bases are compounds containing hydroxide ions. What are the comparable compounds in organic chemistry?

See Teacher Guide.

READINGS

"Salt-Free Salt," Science '85, Vol. 6, No. 2(March 1985), pp. 8-12.

Have you ever used an antacid to calm an upset stomach? When an excess of acid is released in the stomach, the pH is lowered causing physical discomfort. Antacids provide a buffering effect on stomach contents that raises the pH to the normal level. What is pH? How are buffer systems used to maintain a constant pH? Do you know of any other common buffering systems?

SOLUTIONS OF ELECTROLYTES

Chapter 25 includes a quantitative discussion of K_{sp}, K_W, and pH. Hydrolysis and buffers are presented as practical concepts. Indicators and titration calculations conclude the chapter.

DEMONSTRATION: Place 50 cm³ of 0.5M Pb(NO₃)₂ in a 250 cm³ Erlenmeyer flask. Add 100 cm³ of 0.5M Na₂SO₄. Allow the white PbSO₄ to settle ($K_{sp} = 1.9 \times 10^{-8}$). To the white solid, add 100 cm³ of 0.5M (NH₄)₂S or Na₂S. The black solid produced is PbS ($K_{sp} = 8.4 \times 10^{-28}$). **CAUTION:** *Pb²⁺ is poisonous. Na₂SO₄, (NH₄)₂S, and Na₂S are caustic.* This demonstration will help students realize that an insoluble precipitate is still very slightly soluble. As the equilibrium is disturbed, a majority of the Pb²⁺ ions from the PbSO₄ will be changed to PbS. See Teacher Guide.

GOALS:

- You will gain an understanding of the interaction of salts with water and with acid-base solutions.
- You will solve problems dealing with solubility, common ion, and solubility product.
- You will gain an understanding of pH and learn a number of methods for determining pH.

Thus far in our investigation of electrolytes we have dealt mainly with acids and bases. Solutions of salts also involve equilibria. It is possible, through a reaction called hydrolysis, for an apparently neutral salt to dissolve in water and produce an acidic or basic solution. In this chapter we will investigate further the interaction between electrolytes and water.

25:1 SOLUBILITY PRODUCT CONSTANT

Silver bromide is an ionic compound that is only slightly soluble in water. When an ionic compound is in a solution so concentrated that the solid is in equilibrium with its ions, the solution is saturated. The equilibrium equation for a saturated solution of silver bromide is

$$AgBr(cr) \rightleftarrows Ag^+(aq) + Br^-(aq)$$

The equilibrium constant (K_{eq}) for this equilibrium system is

$$K_{eq} = \frac{[Ag^+][Br^-]}{[AgBr]}$$

However, because we are dealing with a solid substance, the AgBr concentration is constant. Both sides of the equation can be multiplied by [AgBr], giving a new expression.

$$K_{eq}[AgBr] = \frac{[Ag^+][Br^-][AgBr]}{[AgBr]}$$

$$K_{eq}[AgBr] = [Ag^+][Br^-]$$

The ions in a saturated solution are in equilibrium with the undissolved solid.

The concentration of a solid such as AgBr is a constant because the equilibrium between the solid and liquid is established at the surface of the solid. The number of ions per square centimeter of solid surface is dependent on the crystal strucure which does not vary.

The solubility product constant is derived from a special case of equilibrium.

The term $K_{eq}[AgBr]$ is a constant. This new constant is called the **solubility product constant** K_{sp}.

$$K_{sp} = [Ag^+][Br^-]$$

At room temperature, K_{sp} of silver bromide is 7.70×10^{-13}. Consider some silver bromide dissolved in water and allowed to stand until the solution is at equilibrium. The product of the silver and bromide ion concentrations will then be 7.70×10^{-13}.

$$[Ag^+][Br^-] = 7.70 \times 10^{-13}$$

We can now determine the concentration of each ion using the following equation.

$$AgBr(cr) \rightleftarrows Ag^+(aq) + Br^-(aq)$$

For every silver ion there is one bromide ion.

$$[Ag^+] = [Br^-]$$

or $$[Ag^+][Ag^+] = 7.70 \times 10^{-13}$$

therefore, $$[Ag^+]^2 = 7.70 \times 10^{-13}$$

$$[Ag^+] = 8.78 \times 10^{-7} M$$

In a saturated solution containing only silver bromide and water, the concentration of silver ions is 8.78×10^{-7} mol/dm^3. The concentration of bromide ions is also 8.78×10^{-7} mol/dm^3.

Suppose, however, that some potassium bromide solution is added. What will happen? KBr dissociates completely to K^+ and Br^- ions. The

FIGURE 25-1. The addition of the common ion Br$^-$ to the AgBr equilibrium system decreases the Ag$^+$ concentration as more AgBr precipitates.

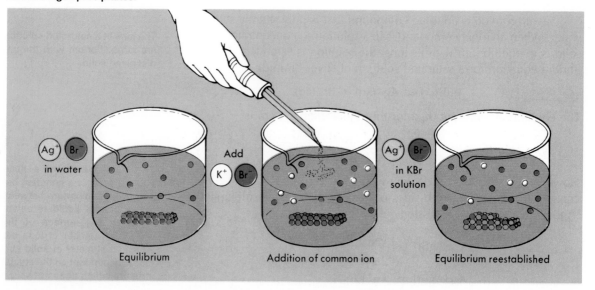

Ag$^+$ Br$^-$ in water	Add K$^+$ Br$^-$	Ag$^+$ Br$^-$ in KBr solution
Equilibrium	Addition of common ion	Equilibrium reestablished

increased number of bromide ions collide more frequently with silver ions. The equilibrium is thus shifted toward the solid silver bromide. When equilibrium is again established, the concentration of silver ion, $[Ag^+]$, has decreased. At the same time, the concentration of bromide ion, $[Br^-]$, has increased. Solid silver bromide has precipitated out, and the K_{sp}, 7.70×10^{-13}, has been reestablished. This reaction is an example of the common ion effect. The addition of a common ion removes silver ion from solution, and causes the equilibrium to shift toward the solid silver bromide. We could also say the addition of a common ion decreases the solubility of a substance in solution.

The addition of a common ion to a saturated solution causes precipitation of the solute.

The solubility of a substance is decreased by the addition of a common ion.

A solubility shift is predicted by the application of Le Chatelier's principle.

EXAMPLE: Common Ion

What will be the silver ion concentration in a saturated solution of silver bromide if 0.100 mol KBr is added to 1 dm^3 of the solution? Assume no increase in volume of the solution.

BACKGROUND: Students often need review on comparing (>, <) numbers expressed in scientific notation.

Solving Process:
Potassium bromide is a soluble salt. Thus, it will contribute a bromide ion concentration of 0.100M. The total bromide ion concentration will consist of 0.100M from the KBr plus some unknown amount from the AgBr. We will designate the amount of bromide ion from the AgBr as y. If the AgBr produces a bromide ion concentration of y, then it must also produce a silver ion concentration of y (AgBr → Ag^+ + Br^-). Substituting these values in the solubility product expression gives us

$$7.70 \times 10^{-13} = y(0.100 + y)$$

We know that y will be small compared to 0.100 since silver bromide is almost insoluble. Thus, 0.100 + y is essentially equal to 0.100.

$$7.70 \times 10^{-13} = 0.100y$$

$$y = 7.70 \times 10^{-12}M$$

EXAMPLE: Predicting Precipitation

Suppose 5.00×10^2 cm^3 of 0.200M NaCl are added to 5.00×10^2 cm^3 of 0.0100M $AgNO_3$. If the K_{sp} of AgCl is 1.56×10^{-10}, will any precipitate form?

Solving Process:
The total volume of solution will be 1.000×10^3 cm^3 since 5.00×10^2 cm^3 of each solution is used. Therefore, the concentrations of both the NaCl solution and the $AgNO_3$ solution will be halved.

$$[NaCl] = \tfrac{1}{2} \times 0.0200M = 0.0100M$$

$$[AgNO_3] = \tfrac{1}{2} \times 0.0100M = 0.00500M$$

Since both NaCl and AgNO$_3$ dissociate completely

$$K_{sp} = [Ag^+][Cl^-]$$

$$= (0.00500)(0.0100) = 0.000\ 0500 = 5.00 \times 10^{-5}$$

However, the ion product cannot exceed the K_{sp}, 1.56×10^{-10}. Therefore, AgCl will precipitate out of solution until

$$[Ag^+][Cl^-] = 1.56 \times 10^{-10}.$$

EXAMPLE: Ion Concentration

The solubility product constant is the product of the molar concentrations of the ions in a saturated solution each raised to the power of their coefficients from the balanced chemical equation.

What is the iodate concentration in a saturated solution of copper(II) iodate? The K_{sp} of Cu(IO$_3$)$_2$ is 1.40×10^{-7}.

$$Cu(IO_3)_2 \rightleftarrows Cu^{2+} + 2IO_3^-$$

Solving Process:
For every copper ion there are two iodate ions. If $[Cu^{2+}] = x$, then $[IO_3^-] = 2x$.

$$K_{sp} = [Cu^{2+}][IO_3^-]^2$$

$$1.40 \times 10^{-7} = x(2x)^2$$

$$1.40 \times 10^{-7} = x(4x^2)$$

$$1.40 \times 10^{-7} = 4x^3$$

$$x^3 = 3.50 \times 10^{-8}$$

$$[Cu^{2+}] = x = 3.27 \times 10^{-3}M$$

$$[IO_3]^- = 2x = 6.54 \times 10^{-3}M$$

PROBLEMS

1. a. $K_{sp} = [Pb^{2+}][I^-]^2$
   b. $K_{sp} = [Cu^{2+}]^3[PO_4^{3-}]^2$
2. $1.22 \times 10^{-8}M$
3. $K_{sp} = 4.00 \times 10^{-15}$
4. $3.42 \times 10^{-8}M$
5. $K_{sp} = 7.09 \times 10^{-9}$

1. Write the solubility product expression for each of the following.
   a. PbI$_2$(cr) $\rightleftarrows$ Pb^{2+}(aq) + 2I$^-$(aq)
   b. Cu$_3$(PO$_4$)$_2$(cr) $\rightleftarrows$ 3Cu^{2+}(aq) + 2PO$_4^{3-}$(aq)
2. The solubility product constant of silver iodide is 1.50×10^{-16}. What is [Ag$^+$] in a solution at equilibrium?
3. If [D$^+$] is $2.00 \times 10^{-5}M$ at equilibrium, what is the K_{sp} for D$_2$A?
4. What is the concentration of Be^{2+} in a saturated solution of Be(OH)$_2$? $K_{sp} = 1.60 \times 10^{-22}$
5. A saturated solution of PbI$_2$ has a lead ion concentration of $1.21 \times 10^{-3}M$. What is K_{sp} for PbI$_2$?

25:2 IONIZATION OF WATER

Conductivity experiments have shown that water ionizes according to the equation

$$H_2O(l) + H_2O(l) \rightleftharpoons H_3O^+(aq) + OH^-(aq)$$

Even though it does conduct a current, pure water is a poor conductor. An electric current is carried in a solution by the ions in the solution. Since pure water is a poor conductor of electricity, it must contain few ions. Thus, pure water must ionize only slightly. In pure water, the concentration of H_3O^+ is equal to the concentration of OH^-. Each molecule of H_2O that ionizes produces one ion each of H_3O^+ and OH^-.

Since water ionizes, it should be possible to find an equilibrium constant for this reaction.

$$K_{eq} = \frac{[H_3O^+][OH^-]}{[H_2O][H_2O]}$$

Conductivity experiments have indicated that pure water contains 1×10^{-7} mole of H_3O^+ (and the same amount of OH^-) per cubic decimeter. Therefore:

$$K_{eq} = \frac{(1.00 \times 10^{-7})(1.00 \times 10^{-7})}{[H_2O]^2}$$

We can find K_{eq} if we can arrive at some value for $[H_2O]$. Since water ionizes so slightly, we can approximate $[H_2O]$ in pure water by assuming that no ionization occurs. We assume that pure water contains only molecular H_2O.

One mole of water has mass 18.0 g (16.0 + 2.0). One dm^3 of pure water has mass 1000 g. The concentration of water in pure water is

$$[H_2O] = \frac{1 \text{ mol}}{18.0 \text{ g}} \left| \frac{1000 \text{ g}}{1 \text{ dm}^3} \right. = 55.6 \text{ mol/dm}^3$$

We can now find K_{eq} for water.

$$K_{eq} = \frac{(1.00 \times 10^{-7})(1.00 \times 10^{-7})}{(55.6)^2}$$

Because the value 55.6 mol/dm^3 is relatively constant, we can multiply both sides of the equation by $(55.6)^2$ and get a new constant

$$K_{eq}(55.6)^2 = [H_3O^+][OH^-] = 1.00 \times 10^{-14}$$

We will call this new constant $K_{eq}(55.6)^2$ the **ion product constant of water,** K_w.

$$K_w = [H_3O^+][OH^-] = 1.00 \times 10^{-14}$$

K_w is a constant for all dilute aqueous solutions. Although the concentrations of H_3O^+ and OH^- may change when substances are added to water, the product of $[H_3O^+]$ and $[OH^-]$ remains the same.

EXAMPLE: Concentration of Hydroxide Ion in Solution

What is the $[OH^-]$ in a water solution with $[H_3O^+] = 1.00 \times 10^{-5}$?

Pure water ionizes only slightly.

BACKGROUND: In one experiment which consisted of 2 wires 1 cm apart and 1 cm beneath the surface, triple distilled water carried 3.5 milliamps at 115 volts. For comparison, a 0.1M HCl solution under the same conditions carried a 120 milliamp current.

In pure water,
$[H_3O^+] = [OH^-]$
$\qquad = 1.00 \times 10^{-7}M$

Pure water is assumed to be molecular when calculating the K_{eq}.

These figures apply to water at room temperature. The K_w at other temperatures is slightly different.

K_w is the ion product constant of water.

If an acid is added to water, the $[H_3O^+]$ increases and the $[OH^-]$ decreases.

If a base if added to water, the $[OH^-]$ increases and $[H_3O^+]$ decreases.

Solving Process:

If an acid, HA, is added to water,

$$HA + H_2O \rightarrow H_3O^+ + A^-$$

an excess of hydronium ion is produced. Collisions between H_3O^+ and OH^- also increase.

$$H_3O^+ + OH^- \rightarrow H_2O + H_2O$$

As the $[H_3O^+]$ increases, the $[OH^-]$ decreases, and K_w remains 1.00×10^{-14}. If the $[H_3O^+]$ is increased to 1.00×10^{-5} by the addition of acid, the $[OH^-]$ must decrease.

$$[H_3O^+][OH^-] = 1.00 \times 10^{-14}$$

$$\text{and } [OH^-] = \frac{1.00 \times 10^{-14}}{[H_3O^+]}$$

$$[OH^-] = \frac{1.00 \times 10^{-14}}{1.00 \times 10^{-5}} = 1.00 \times 10^{-9}$$

If a base is added to water, the equilibrium shifts in the opposite direction, and the solution becomes more basic.

$$OH^-(aq) + H_3O^+(aq) \rightarrow H_2O(l) + H_2O(l)$$

H_3O^+ is removed from solution, and the ion product constant remains 1.00×10^{-14}.

PROBLEMS

6. $[OH^-] = 1.47 \times 10^{-5} M$
7. $[H_3O^+] = 1.76 \times 10^{-12} M$

6. What is the hydroxide ion concentration in a solution with hydronium ion concentration $6.80 \times 10^{-10} M$?

7. What is the hydronium ion concentration in a solution with hydroxide ion concentration $5.67 \times 10^{-3} M$?

25:3   pH SCALE

The ionization of water is so slight that it is almost never considered in the actual production or use of acids and bases. Why, then, was it introduced? Knowledge of the ion product constant for water has enabled chemists to develop a simple acidity scale, called the pH scale. The scale can be used to indicate the basicity as well as the acidity of any water solution. The **pH scale** is a measure of hydronium ion concentration.

The pH scale is a simplified way of stating the concentration of H_3O^+ ions in solution.

Hydrogen ion concentration is measured by pH.

The concentration of H_3O^+ is expressed in powers of 10, from 10^{-14} to 10^0. This method is a convenient way to indicate the $[H_3O^+]$. We could simplify this expression even further by writing only the exponent. For instance, 10^{-7} would be written as -7. However, the negative sign is undesirable. If $[H_3O^+] = 10^{-7}$, the log of $[H_3O^+] = -7$. If, however, we take the negative log of $[H_3O^+]$, we get the desired $+7$. The negative log of $[H_3O^+]$ is the pH. Thus, the pH equals 7.

EXAMPLE: pH Determination

The hydrogen ion concentration of a solution is $1.00 \times 10^{-9}M$. What is the pH of the solution?

Solving Process:

$$pH = -\log[H_3O^+]$$
$$[H_3O^+] = 1.00 \times 10^{-9}$$

Therefore:

$$= -\log(1.00 \times 10^{-9})$$
$$= -(\log 1.00 + \log 10^{-9}) = -[0 + (-9)] = 9$$

Note that a pH of 9 indicates a basic solution ($[H_3O^+] < [OH^-]$).

SUGGESTION: Students should form the habit of deciding whether the solution will be acidic or basic before they work the problem. Then they should check to see whether their answer is in the correct range (>7 or <7).

EXAMPLE: pH Determination

One-tenth mole of HCl is added to enough water to make 1 dm³ of solution. What is the pH of the solution? (Assume that the HCl is 100% ionized.)

Solving Process:

$$[H_3O^+] = 0.1M = 1 \times 10^{-1} \text{ mol/dm}^3$$
$$pH = -\log[H_3O^+] = -\log(1 \times 10^{-1})$$
$$pH = -(\log 1 + \log 10^{-1}) = -[0 + (-1)] = 1$$

Note that as the hydronium ion concentration increases and a neutral solution is made more acidic, the pH goes from 7 toward 0. If the pH of a solution falls between 7 and 14, the solution is basic. Table 25-1 indicates the pH of several common solutions. Note for those solutions that exist in the body, the maintenance of the pH shown is vital to life.

Suppose we wished to know the pH of a solution that was basic or about which we knew only the hydroxide ion concentration. We can use the ion product constant of water to find the relationship between pH and hydroxide ion concentration. If we take the logarithm of both sides of the ion product of water, we get

$$\log([H_3O^+][OH^-]) = \log 1.00 \times 10^{-14}$$
$$\log[H_3O^+] + \log[OH^-] = -14$$

Multiplying both sides of the equation by -1

$$-\log[H_3O^+] + (-\log[OH^-]) = 14$$

The pH of a neutral solution equals 7.
Acidic solution: pH < 7
Basic solution: pH > 7

If we now designate $-\log[OH^-]$ as pOH, and substitute

$$pH + pOH = 14$$

Table 25-1

pH of Some Common Substances	
Substance	**pH**
0.1M HCl	1
Stomach contents	2
Vinegar	2.9
Soda pop	3
Grapes	4
Beer	4.5
Pumpkin pulp	5
Bread	5.5
Intestinal contents	6.5
Urine	6.6
Bile	6.9
Saliva	7
Blood	7.4
Eggs	7.8
0.1M NH$_3$(aq)	11.1
0.1M NaOH	13

Acid — Increasing acidity

Neutral

Base — Increasing basicity

EXAMPLE: pH of Solution

Find the pH of a solution with OH^- concentration $1.00 \times 10^{-9}M$.
Solving Process:

$$[H_3O^+] = 10^{-14}/[OH^-] = 10^{-14}/10^{-9} = 10^{-5}$$
$$pH = -\log[H_3O^+]$$
$$= -\log(1.00 \times 10^{-5})$$
$$= -(\log 1.00 + \log 10^{-5}) = -[0 + (-5)] = 5$$

EXAMPLE: pH of Solution

Find the pH of a solution with H_3O^+ concentration $4.37 \times 10^{-4}M$.
Solving Process:

$$pH = -\log[H_3O^+] = -\log(4.37 \times 10^{-4})$$
$$= -(\log 4.37 + \log 10^{-4}) = -[0.640 + (-4)] = 3.36$$

EXAMPLE: H$_3$O$^+$ Concentration

Find the concentration of H_3O^+ if the pH of a solution is 8.000.

Solving Process:

$$pH = -\log[H_3O^+]$$
$$8.000 = -\log[H_3O^+]$$
$$-8.000 = \log[H_3O^+]$$
$$\text{antilog} -8.000 = [H_3O^+]$$
$$1.00 \times 10^{-8}M = [H_3O^+]$$

EXAMPLE: H_3O^+ Concentration

Find the concentration of H_3O^+ if the pOH of a solution is 11.700.

Solving Process:

$$pH = 14.000 - pOH = 14.000 - 11.700 = 2.300$$
$$pH = -\log[H_3O^+]$$
$$-2.300 = \log[H_3O^+]$$
$$0.700 - 3 = \log[H_3O^+]$$
$$5.01 \times 10^{-3}M = [H_3O^+]$$

PROBLEMS

8. Find the pH of solutions with the following H_3O^+ concentrations
   a. $1.00 \times 10^{-3}M$
   b. $1.00 \times 10^{-6}M$
   c. $6.59 \times 10^{-10}M$
   d. $7.01 \times 10^{-6}M$
   e. $9.47 \times 10^{-8}M$
   f. $6.89 \times 10^{-14}M$

9. Find the H_3O^+ concentration of the following solutions.
   a. pH = 3.000
   b. pH = 10.000
   c. pH = 6.607
   d. pH = 2.523
   e. pH = 6.149
   f. pH = 7.662

SUGGESTION: Encourage the use of calculators to determine the log/pH.

8. a. 3.00   d. 5.15
   b. 6.00   e. 7.02
   c. 9.18   f. 13.2

9. a. $1.00 \times 10^{-3}M$
   b. $1.00 \times 10^{-10}M$
   c. $2.47 \times 10^{-7}M$
   d. $3.00 \times 10^{-3}M$
   e. $7.10 \times 10^{-7}M$
   f. $2.18 \times 10^{-8}M$

25:4 HYDROLYSIS

A salt is composed of positive ions from a base and negative ions from an acid. When a salt dissolves in water, it releases ions having an equal number of positive and negative charges. Thus, a solution of a salt should be neither acidic nor basic. Some salts do form neutral solutions, but others react with water (hydrolyze) to form acidic or basic solutions. There are four kinds of salt solutions we will discuss.

Hydrolysis is the reaction of a salt with water to produce an acidic or basic solution.

If potassium chloride is dissolved in water, a neutral solution results. Each ion from the salt K^+ and Cl^-, is hydrated with no apparent reaction (except hydration). Water ionizes very slightly to form H_3O^+ and OH^- ions. The solution will, therefore, contain ions from the salt and ions from the water. In solution, the positive potassium ion could unite with the negative chloride ion or the negative hydroxide ion. However, potassium chloride is a salt that ionizes completely in water. Potassium hydroxide is a strong base that also ionizes completely. The same reasoning applies to

A neutral solution results when the salt produced from a strong acid and strong base is dissolved in water.

Cl^- and H_3O^+. No reaction occurs. The four ions remain in solution as ions, and the solution is neutral. The ions produced by the salt of a strong acid and strong base do not react with water, and the $[H_3O^+]$ remains equal to the $[OH^-]$. Such a solution has a pH of 7. No hydrolysis occurs.

In hydrolysis, the H_3O^+ and OH^- ions are produced in solution and do not actually come from the dissolved salt but from ionized water molecules which form as the salt dissolves and upsets the equilibrium between the water ions.

If we test a solution of aluminum chloride, a salt, we will find that the solution is acidic, not neutral as expected. With the exception of the metals of Groups IA and IIA, metallic hydroxides are all weak bases and in fact have low solubilities. The positive ions of such metals are strongly hydrated and give up a proton readily from the associated water molecule. When $AlCl_3$ is dissolved in water, the Al^{3+} become hydrated.

$$AlCl_3(cr) + 6H_2O(l) \rightarrow Al(H_2O)_6^{3+}(aq) + 3Cl^-(aq)$$

The hydrated aluminum ions then undergo hydrolysis. The reaction is

$$Al(H_2O)_6^{3+}(aq) + H_2O(l) \rightleftarrows Al(OH)(H_2O)_5^{2+}(aq) + H_3O^+(aq)$$

An acidic solution results when the salt produced from a strong acid and a weak base is dissolved in water.

Since HCl is a strong acid, the H_3O^+ ions do not combine with the Cl^- ions, and the solution is acidic.

A basic solution results when the salt produced from a weak acid and a strong base is dissolved in water.

If we test a water solution of sodium carbonate, a salt, we will find the solution to be basic.

$$CO_3^{2-}(aq) + H_2O(l) \rightleftarrows HCO_3^-(aq) + OH^-(aq)$$

A mixture of a weak acid and a weak base does not always produce a neutral solution. A neutral solution occurs only when both ions hydrolyze to approximately the same degree. This problem does not arise with a solution of strong acid and base because both ionize completely.

This reaction produces a large excess of hydroxide ions. Hydrogen carbonate ion, HCO_3^-, is an exceedingly weak acid, so that the reverse reaction proceeds only to a very slight extent.

$$HCO_3^-(aq) + H_2O(l) \rightleftarrows H_3O^+(aq) + CO_3^{2-}(aq)$$

Since more OH^- ions form than H_3O^+ ions, the solution becomes basic.

The salt produced from a weak acid and a weak base may form an acidic, basic, or neutral solution.

Hydrolysis is the reaction of a salt with water to produce an acidic or basic solution.

If the salt ammonium acetate is dissolved in water, ammonia and acetic acid are formed. Ammonia is a weak, slightly ionized base. Acetic acid is a weak, slightly ionized acid. Both H_3O^+ and OH^- ions are removed from solution. This reaction results in a neutral solution because acetic acid and ammonia are of the same degree of weakness. For other salts of two weak ions, you must know their relative degrees of weakness in order to predict the acidity of the solution. For example, a solution of NH_4CN would be basic. The acid, HCN, is far weaker than the base NH_3. On the other hand, a solution of NH_4IO_3 would be acidic since HIO_3 is stronger as an acid than NH_3 is as a base. Remember that the action of a salt with water to form an acidic or basic solution is called **hydrolysis.**

PROBLEM

10. a. acidic
    b. acidic
    c. acidic
    d. acidic
    e. basic
    f. basic

10. Using the rules in Section 24:10, predict the acidic, basic, or neutral character of the solutions of the following salts.

a. $CrBr_3$	**c.** $NiSO_4$	**e.** $MgC_4H_4O_6$
b. NH_4ClO_4	**d.** GaI_3	**f.** K_2CO_3

25:5 BUFFERS

Many of the fluids in your body must be maintained within a very narrow pH range if you are to remain healthy. There are also many instances in laboratory and industrial chemistry when the maintenance of a certain pH is important. In both cases, the end is accomplished in the same way: the creation of a buffer system. A **buffer system** is a solution that can absorb moderate amounts of acid or base without a significant change in its pH.

A buffer system can absorb acids or bases without significant change in pH.

Consider the reaction of ammonia in water.

$$NH_3(g) + H_2O(l) \rightleftarrows NH_4^+(aq) + OH^-(aq)$$

If we look at the reverse reaction in this equilibrium, we can see that ammonium ions will react with a base. What happens when we dissolve ammonium ions (from ammonium chloride, for example) in water?

$$NH_4^+(aq) + H_2O(l) \rightleftarrows NH_3(aq) + H_3O^+(aq)$$

From this reverse reaction, we can see that ammonia molecules will react with acids. If we had a solution with sufficient quantities of each of these substances, ammonium ions and ammonia molecules, we would have our desired buffer solution. The ammonia molecules would react with any added acid, and the ammonium ions would react with any added base. Buffer solutions are prepared by using a weak acid or a weak base with one of its salts. Stated in general terms, the reactions would appear as follows.

DEMONSTRATION: Effect of buffer on reactivity—prepare 200 cm^3 of 1.0M acetic acid. Use 100 cm^3 of this acid to prepare buffer by adding 16.4 g $NaCH_3COO$ to it. This results in a 2.0M $NaCH_3COO$ and 1.0M CH_3COOH solution. To two 100 cm^3 graduated cylinders add 3 g $CaCO_3$ to each. Pour the 1.0M CH_3COOH into one of the cylinders and simultaneously pour the buffered solution into the second cylinder. Observe the difference in the rate of CO_2 production.

For a weak acid:

$$HA + OH^- \rightarrow H_2O + A^-$$

$$A^- + H_3O^+ \rightarrow HA + H_2O$$

The weak acid, HA, will react with added base. The negative ion from the salt, A^-, will react with added acid.

For a weak base:

$$MOH + H_3O^+ \rightarrow M^+ + 2H_2O$$

$$M^+ + OH^- \rightarrow MOH$$

The weak base, MOH, will react with added acid. The positive ion from the salt, M^+, will react with added base.

Buffers are most efficient at neutralizing added acids or bases when the concentrations of weak acid (or base) and salt are equal. By choosing the correct weak acid (or base) we can prepare a buffer solution of almost any pH value. Note that there is a common ion between the weak electrolyte and its salt. The behavior of a buffer solution can always be predicted on the basis of Le Chatelier's principle and our knowledge of the common ion effect.

Le Chatelier's principle can be used to predict the behavior of a buffer solution.

Blood is buffered principally by the hydrogen carbonate ion, HCO_3^-.

Blood is buffered principally by HCO_3^- ion.

$$HCO_3^- + H_3O^+ \rightleftarrows H_2CO_3 + H_2O$$
$$HCO_3^- + OH^- \rightarrow H_2O + CO_3^{2-}$$

When the H_2CO_3 reaches the lungs, it decomposes to form

$$H_2CO_3 \rightleftarrows H_2O + CO_2$$

CO_2 is then exhaled. There is also buffering by the dihydrogen phosphate ion, $H_2PO_4^-$.

The buffering of the blood is upset when hyperventilation occurs.

Athletes sometimes upset the buffering of their blood through a process called hyperventilation. In the excitement of a contest, they breathe more rapidly and deeply than they need to. When hyperventilation occurs, a person expels more CO_2 than necessary, upsetting the carbonic acid equilibrium. According to Le Chatelier's principle, as the CO_2 is exhaled, more H_2CO_3 decomposes to replace the CO_2. As the H_2CO_3 is used, the equilibrium between carbonic acid and the hydrogen carbonate ion

$$HCO_3^- + H_3O^+ \rightleftarrows H_2CO_3 + H_2O$$

is upset and HCO_3^- is consumed in replacing the H_2CO_3.

Eventually, the HCO_3^- concentration drops to the point at which it is insufficient to maintain the blood pH at a safe level. Since using HCO_3^- also consumes H_3O^+, the blood pH is raised (becomes more basic). One response of the body to this condition is a constriction of the cerebral blood vessels. As the blood flow to the brain is reduced, the individual becomes dizzy and can lapse into unconsciousness. At that point, the body's reflex mechanisms usually restore normal breathing.

Hyperventilation can be stopped by rebreathing the exhalations from a paper bag. The partial pressure of CO_2 is greater in the re-inhaled air, allowing less to escape from the blood. Gradually the blood pH returns to normal.

25:6 INDICATORS

SUGGESTION: Natural indicators can be made from blueberry juice, red cabbage, carrots, and beets. Have your students determine the pH range over which they change color.

The chemist uses the pH meter to determine rapidly the degree of acidity of a solution.

Indicators are used to determine pH through color change.

In the laboratory, how do chemists know whether they are using an acidic, basic, or neutral solution? They could taste the solution to determine whether it is bitter or sour. However, this method is inexact as well as dangerous because most solutions are toxic or corrosive. They could experiment to determine what reactions the solution undergoes, but the experiment might take too much time. The chemist generally uses a **pH meter** to determine the degree of acidity in a solution. This electronic device indicates the pH of a solution directly when its electrodes are immersed in the solution. We will investigate the operation of the pH meter in Chapter 27.

There are times when a pH meter may not be available, or its use may not be convenient. At those times, substances called indicators are used. **Indicators** are weak organic bases and acids whose colors differ from the

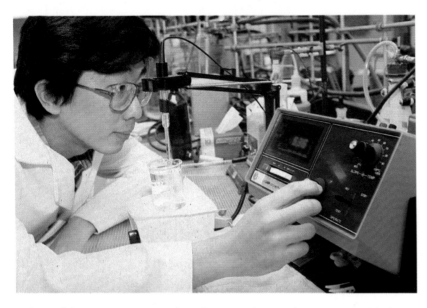

FIGURE 25-2. A pH meter provides a more accurate determination of the pH of a solution. Electrodes are immersed in the test solution and the pH is given by a digital readout.

colors of their conjugate acids or bases. When indicators are added to a test solution, the color that results is related to the pH of the solution. A number of indicators and their color changes are listed in Table A-11 of the Appendix.

There are, however, limitations to the use of indicators. Solutions in which they are to be used successfully must be colorless. Otherwise, the color of the solution may mask the color changes of the indicator. Another important limitation is the ability of the human eye to distinguish a slight color change. For any given indicator, we can notice a color change over only a very narrow range of the pH scale. To test for pH over a wide range of the pH scale, many indicators must be used. However, given a definite pH, any change in $[H_3O^+]$ or $[OH^-]$ can be detected by the use of one properly chosen indicator.

The ability of the human eye to distinguish color changes is the limiting factor in precision measurement of pH with indicators.

Indicators are useful only in colorless solutions, and over narrow pH ranges.

25:7 TITRATION

Analytical chemists often need to find the concentration of a solution. **Titration** is an analytical method in which a standard solution is used to determine the concentration of another solution. A **standard solution** is one for which the concentration is known.

If an acid is added to a base, a neutralization reaction occurs. The acid unites with the base to form a salt and water.

Titration is a quantitative process in which a standard solution is used to determine the concentration of another solution.

A standard solution is one for which the concentration is known.

$$acid \ + \ base \ \xrightarrow{\text{neutralization reaction}} \ salt \ + \ water$$

For example, acetic acid can be neutralized by sodium hydroxide to form

a   b   c

FIGURE 25-3. A pH meter is attached to a chart recorder (a). The burets used in titrations are graduated (b). The volume is measured by reading the level at the bottom of the meniscus. The chart recorder provides a graph of pH versus volume of titrating solution (c).

The endpoint occurs when an amount of standard solution has been added that just completely reacts with titrated solution.

The endpoint can be determined with a pH meter (graph) or an indicator (color change).

As pH meters have become more common, the use of indicators has declined.

Titration is a form of volumetric analysis.

BACKGROUND: See Teacher Guide for a suggested presentation of normality if you desire to teach this concentration unit.

sodium acetate and water. By adding an indicator, we can see at exactly what point complete neutralization occurs.

To carry out a titration, a buret is filled with a standard solution. A small amount of indicator is added to a measured amount of the solution of unknown concentration to be titrated. The buret is opened and the standard solution is allowed to flow (with stirring) into the solution to be titrated. Eventually a color change occurs. The color change indicates the endpoint of the reaction. At that point (the endpoint) an amount of standard solution has been added that just completely reacts with the solution titrated.

The endpoint may also be detected using a pH meter. If the pH meter is connected to a chart recorder, a graph of pH versus cm^3 of titrating solution added is obtained. The endpoint corresponds to the middle of that portion of the graph showing a very large change in pH with the addition of a small amount of titrating solution. The upper graph shown in Figure 25-4 is for the titration of a strong acid by a strong base. Weak electrolytes show a slightly different shape, shifted toward the pH of the stronger reactant.

The moles of standard solution can be calculated by multiplying the volume of standard solution used by its molarity.

$$\underset{\text{standard solution}}{moles} = \underset{\text{standard solution}}{volume} \times \underset{\text{standard solution}}{molarity}$$

The moles in the titrated solution of unknown concentration are then found using the coefficients in the balanced equation. Then, dividing the moles of the titrated solution by the volume of that solution gives us the concentration of the titrated solution.

$$\underset{\text{titrated solution}}{molarity\ (M)} = \frac{\underset{\text{titrated solution}}{moles}}{\underset{\text{titrated solution}}{volume}}$$

FIGURE 25-4. The graph in (a) represents the titration of a strong acid and strong base. The graph in (b) shows the titration of a weak acid and strong base. The graph in (c) shows the titration of a strong acid and weak base.

Let us use an example to show how titration works. Suppose you wanted to find the molarity of vinegar. Such a solution is acidic because vinegar is dilute acetic acid derived from the fermentation of fruit juice. Let us use a standard NaOH solution that we know to be 0.500*M*. (You could prepare this solution quite easily.) We will use phenolphthalein as an indicator.

A buret used for titration is a carefully calibrated glass tube designed to deliver measured volumes.

Two burets, including the tip, are filled with solution, one with acid and one with base, and the initial volumes recorded. A precise amount (20-25 cm³) of the vinegar solution is allowed to run into a beaker that contains a few drops of phenolphthalein. The phenolphthalein is colorless in acid solution.

While stirring constantly, the basic solution is allowed to run slowly into the beaker. You can tell when the acid is exactly neutralized. How? One drop of NaOH and then vinegar solution should alternately change the color. The volume used of each is recorded.

Solution turns pink

EXAMPLE: Titration

Suppose we used 15.0 cm^3 of 0.500M NaOH and 25.0 cm^3 of vinegar solution of unknown concentration. What is the molarity of the vinegar solution?

Solving Process:

(a) The balanced equation for the neutralization is

Acid + Base → Salt + Water

$$NaOH(aq) + CH_3COOH(aq) \rightarrow NaCH_3COO(aq) + H_2O(l)$$

(b) Since the concentration of the base is given, determine the moles of NaOH.

1000 cm^3 = 1 dm^3

$$\frac{15.0 \, \text{cm}^3 \, \text{soln}}{} \left| \frac{0.500 \text{ mol NaOH}}{1.00 \, \text{dm}^3 \, \text{soln}} \right| \frac{1 \, \text{dm}^3}{1000 \, \text{cm}^3} = 0.007 \, 50 \text{ mol NaOH}$$

(c) Since the coefficients from the equation are all 1's, the moles of NaOH that react are equal to the moles of CH$_3$COOH that react

At endpoint moles H$^+$ = moles OH$^-$

$$0.007 \, 50 \text{ mol NaOH} = 0.007 \, 50 \text{ mol CH}_3\text{COOH}$$

(d) Determine the molarity of the acid.

$$\frac{0.007 \, 50 \text{ mol CH}_3\text{COOH}}{25.0 \, \text{cm}^3 \, \text{soln}} \left| \frac{1000 \, \text{cm}^3}{1 \, \text{dm}^3} \right. = 0.300M \text{ CH}_3\text{COOH}$$

EXAMPLE: Neutralization

How many cm^3 of 0.200M KOH will exactly neutralize 15.0 cm^3 of 0.400M H$_2$SO$_4$?

Solving Process:

(a) $2KOH(aq) + H_2SO_4(aq) \rightarrow K_2SO_4(aq) + 2H_2O(l)$

(b) The number of moles of H$_2$SO$_4$ is

$$\frac{15.0 \, \text{cm}^3 \, \text{soln}}{} \left| \frac{0.400 \text{ mol H}_2\text{SO}_4}{1.00 \, \text{dm}^3 \, \text{soln}} \right| \frac{1 \, \text{dm}^3}{1000 \, \text{cm}^3} = 0.006 \, 00 \text{ mol H}_2\text{SO}_4$$

(c) Since 2 moles KOH are required for 1 mole H$_2$SO$_4$, 0.0120 (2 × 0.006 00) moles of KOH will be required.

(d) Therefore

$$\frac{0.0120 \text{ mol KOH}}{} \left| \frac{1.00 \, \text{dm}^3 \, \text{soln}}{0.200 \, \text{mol KOH}} \right| \frac{1000 \text{ cm}^3}{1 \, \text{dm}^3} = 60.0 \text{ cm}^3 \text{ KOH soln}$$

PROBLEMS

11. 24.0 cm^3 NaOH
12. 0.411M LiOH

11. How many cm^3 of 0.0947M NaOH are needed to neutralize 21.4 cm^3 of 0.106M HCl?

12. If 26.4 cm^3 of LiOH solution are required to neutralize 21.7 cm^3 of 0.500M HBr, what is the concentration of the base solution?

In the beginning, the brilliant ideas of Svante August Arrhenius were rejected by his colleagues. His theory of electrolytic dissociation or ionization nearly caused his dismissal as a student at the University of Stockholm. Arrhenius was barely allowed to receive his doctorate degree. The significance of his work was not considered important by his advisors.

However, through perseverance and help, he was finally able to promote his ideas. Ironically, Arrhenius was granted the Nobel Prize for the theory that had once been viewed as an unsatisfactory doctoral thesis.

Throughout his life, Arrhenius continued to investigate and publish his conclusions on the electrolytic behavior of solutions. He was also interested in other phases of science, namely astronomy and biochemistry.

TECHNOLOGY AND CHEMISTRY

25:8   Ion Activity and the Debye-Hückel Theory

Solutions of ions depart considerably from the behavior of ideal solutions. Recall from Chapter 21 that a general definition of an ideal solution is one in which the ions have no effect on each other. Weak force interactions between neutral molecules in a solution decrease as the sixth power of the distance between the molecules.

$$F \propto \frac{1}{d^6}$$

We assume that ionic compounds are completely dissociated in solution. The electrostatic interaction between ions varies as the reciprocal of the square of the distance between them as shown by the relationship

$$F \propto \frac{1}{d^2}$$

Ionic forces are obviously much longer range forces than weak forces.

Peter Debye and Eric Hückel developed a model to explain the behavior of ions in solution. The model could be used to predict the properties of many solutions. If electrical interactions alone are considered, then a solution might soon develop a high degree of order, similar to a crystal, where each positive ion is surrounded by negative ions. (Recall the model for sodium chloride on page 306.) However, in solution the ions are free to move and the normal thermal motion of the ions tends to distribute them in a random way. The properties of the solution, then, are a consequence of two opposing processes: electrostatically induced order and thermally induced disorder. An increase in order results in behavior that moves away from that of an ideal solution. The opposing process decreases order and the solution approaches ideal behavior.

In dealing with solutions, chemists use the concept of ionic strength, which considers the total ion effectiveness of a solution. Ionic strength is represented as I in the following relationship

$$I = \tfrac{1}{2}\Sigma m_i z_i^2$$

I is the sum (Σ) of the products of the molality (m_i) and the charge (z_i) squared for each ion in the solution. Since each ion behaves in a less than ideal manner, chemists call its actual behavior level the activity (a) of the ion. Activity is also referred to as the effective concentration of an ion. The ratio of the activity to the concentration (molality) is called the activity coefficient (γ) of the ion.

$$\gamma = \frac{a}{m}$$

The value for an activity coefficient is less than one. It approaches one as the concentration of the ions in solution decreases. The higher the ionic strength of a solution, the stronger the interionic forces and the less ideal the solution will behave. The activity coefficients of the ions in solution are related to the ionic strength by

$$\log \gamma = -0.509|z^+ z^-|(I)^{1/2}$$

γ is the geometric mean of the activity coefficients for the positive and negative ions. The charges on the ions are represented by z^+ and z^-. I is the ionic strength. Activity coefficients are difficult to calculate from experimental data. The activity of an ion depends not only on its own concentration but on the concentrations of all other ions that may be present in the solution. A more refined value can be obtained if additional factors are introduced to take into account the sizes of the ions, and thus the ease with which they move in the solution.

SUMMARY

1. The solubility product constant K_{sp}, and the ion product constant for water K_w, are special cases of the equilibrium constant. **25:1-25:2**

2. The pH of a solution is equal to $-\log [H_3O^+]$. Acids have a pH below 7. Bases have a pH above 7. Neutral solutions have a pH equal to 7. **25:3**

3. Hydrolysis is the reaction of a salt with water to form an acidic or basic solution. **25:4**

4. Buffer solutions are capable of absorbing moderate amounts of acid and/or base without a significant change in their pH value. **25:5**

5. Indicators are weak acids and bases used to indicate the pH of a solution. **25:6**

6. Acids and bases react with each other to form a salt and water. This type of reaction is called a neutralization reaction. **25:7**

7. Titration is a laboratory process used to find the concentration of a substance in solution. **25:7**

VOCABULARY

solubility product constant **25:1**
ion product constant of water **25:2**
pH scale **25:3**
hydrolysis **25:4**
buffer system **25:5**

pH meter **25:6**
indicators **25:6**
titration **25:7**
standard solution **25:7**

PROBLEMS

1. What volume of 0.196M LiOH is required to neutralize 27.3 cm^3 of 0.413M HBr? LiOH + HBr $\rightarrow$ LiBr + H$_2$O

2. If 75.0 cm^3 of 0.823M HClO$_4$ require 95.5 cm^3 of Ba(OH)$_2$ to reach the endpoint, what is the concentration of the Ba(OH)$_2$ solution? Ba(OH)$_2$ + 2HClO$_4$ $\rightarrow$ Ba(ClO$_4$)$_2$ + 2H$_2$O

3. A chemist wishes to precipitate as much Ag$^+$ as possible in the form of AgCl from a saturated solution of AgCl. How can the equilibrium between the precipitate and soluble ions be altered to allow more silver to precipitate?

4. What is the value for the ion product constant for water?

5. How does the pOH scale differ from the pH scale?

6. Define hydrolysis.

7. Why does the salt of a weak acid form a basic solution when added to water?

8. The salt of a strong acid and a strong base produces a neutral water solution. Will the salt of a weak acid and weak base also produce a neutral solution? Explain.

9. What is the relationship between common ion effect and buffer solutions?

10. How does rebreathing exhaled air help a person who is hyperventilating?

11. The solubility product of MnS is 1.40 $\times$ 10^{-15}. What concentration of sulfide ion is needed in a 0.100M solution of Mn(NO$_3$)$_2$ to just precipitate MnS?

1. 57.5 cm^3
2. 0.323M
3. Increase the Cl$^-$ concentration by adding a source of Cl$^-$ ions.
4. 1 $\times$ 10^{-14}
5. Reverse of each other
6. reaction of salt with H$_2$0 to form acid or base solution
7. more OH$^-$ ions form than H$_3$0$^+$
8. may form acid, base, or neutral solution
9. buffers are made from solutions with common ions
11. 1.40 $\times$ 10^{-14}M

12. $3.61 \times 10^{-5}M$
13. $7.41 \times 10^{-7}M$
14. 10.5
15. 10
16. 6.83
17. a. neutral
   b. basic
   c. acidic
   d. acidic
   e. neutral
18. 8.48
19. 0.0678M
20. 2.20M
21. 0.140M

12. What is the hydronium ion concentration in a solution in which the hydroxide ion concentration is $2.77 \times 10^{-10}M$?

13. Find the hydroxide ion concentration of a solution with pOH $= 6.13$.

14. The K_{sp} of magnesium hydroxide is 1.20×10^{-11}. What is the pH of a saturated solution at equilibrium?

15. What is the pH of 0.0001M NaOH?

16. What is the pH of a 0.300M solution of HCN in which the CN^- concentration has been adjusted to 0.00100M?

17. Predict whether each of the following salts in solution would form an acidic, a basic, or a neutral solution. Write the ionic equation for each.

   a. NaCl   **b.** K_2CO_3 **c.** $AlBr_3$ **d.** $HgCl_2$ **e.** $Ca(NO_3)_2$

18. What is the pH of a solution which is 0.0100M in HCN and 0.00150M in NaCN?

19. What is the concentration of a solution of NaOH if $21.2cm^3$ of a 0.0800M solution of HCl is needed to neutralize 25.0 cm^3 of the base?

20. If 86.2 cm^3 of 0.765M sodium hydroxide neutralize 30.0 cm^3 of hydrochloric acid solution, what is the concentration of the acid?

21. If 40.8 cm^3 of 0.106M sulfuric acid neutralize 61.8 cm^3 of potassium hydroxide solution, what is the concentration of the base?

REVIEW

1. 0.184M
2. 0.369M
3. 0.101
4. 4.04 kPa
5. BP $= 100.60°C$
   FP $= -2.18°C$
6. 90.2 g
7. 35.2 kPa
8. $R = k[PCl_3][Cl_2]$
9. $K_{eq} = \dfrac{[CO_3{}^{2-}]}{[HCO_3{}^-][OH^-]}$

1. What is the molarity of 1.00 dm^3 of a solution containing 46.6 g $Hg(CN)_2$?

2. What is the molality of 0.944 g K_3AsO_4 dissolved in 10.0 g water?

3. What is the mole fraction of solute if 1.00×10^2 g $Rb_2C_4H_4O_6$ dissolve in 50.0 g H_2O?

4. What is the vapor pressure, at 30°C, of a solution of 39.5 g $C_6H_{12}O_6$ in 1.00×10^2 g H_2O?

5. What are the freezing and boiling points of a solution of 42.2 g $C_6H_{12}O_6$ in 2.00×10^2 g H_2O?

6. What is the molecular mass of a substance if 22.2 g of it dissolved in 2.50×10^2 g H_2O lower the freezing point of the solution to $-1.83°C$?

7. What would be the osmotic pressure of a solution of 7.10 g of a substance of molecular mass 1.000×10^3 in sufficient water to make 5.00×10^2 cm^3 of solution? $T = 25°C$

8. Write the rate expression for the following reaction assuming it is a single-step reaction.

$$PCl_3 + Cl_2 \rightarrow PCl_5$$

9. Write the equilibrium constant expression for the following reaction.

$$HCO_3{}^- + OH^- \rightleftharpoons H_2O + CO_3{}^{2-}$$

10. Find the equilibrium constant for a reaction having $\Delta G = -8170$ J, $T = 25°C$.

11. From the following equation, label the acid, base, conjugate acid, and conjugate base.

$$BH_3 + LiH \rightarrow BH_4^- + Li^+$$

12. Is Tl^+ a Lewis acid or base?

10. 26.9

		conjugate	
acid	base	base	acid
11. BH_3	+ LiH $\rightarrow$	BH_4^-	+ Li^+

12. Both

ONE MORE STEP

1. Investigate the concept of hard and soft acids and bases.
2. What is the pH of a 0.100M solution of sodium acetate?
3. If NaCl is added slowly to a solution that is 1.00M in Ag^+ and 1.00M in Pb^{2+}, which salt will precipitate first?
4. In Problem 3, what will be the concentration of the metal ion whose salt precipitates first when the second salt starts to precipitate?
5. Look up the structural formula for a particular indicator and draw its structure in both the acidic and basic forms.

See Teacher Guide

2. 8.88
3. AgCl
4. $3.88 \times 10^{-8}M$

READINGS

Ember, Lois R., "Acid Pollutants: Hitchhikers Ride the Wind," *Chemical and Engineering News*, Vol. 59, No. 37(September 14, 1981), pp. 20-31.

Plants make their food by a process called photosynthesis. In a photosynthesis reaction, light energy is absorbed as carbon dioxide and water combine to form glucose and oxygen. This reaction involves electron transfer. What are reactions involving electron transfer called? In what ways are these reactions useful?

OXIDATION-REDUCTION

26

Chapter 26 involves the concept of redox reactions and using equations to represent the transfer of electrons between particles. Methods for balancing redox reactions are also presented.

DEMONSTRATION Place 20 g of copper(II) chloride dihydrate in a 250 cm³ beaker and dissolve in 175 cm³ of H_2O. Loosely crumple a 10 cm × 10 cm piece of aluminum foil and place it in the solution. **CAUTION:** *The reaction is exothermic; provide for adequate ventilation or use a fume hood.* Ask students if an aluminum tank could be used to transport a $CuCl_2$ solution. Use this demonstration to introduce new vocabulary. Discuss how redox relates to chemical spills and hazardous waste storage.

In one method of classifying chemical reactions there are basically two different types. In the first type, ions or molecules react with no apparent change in the electronic structure of the particles. In the second type, ions or atoms undergo changes of electronic structure. Electrons may be transferred from one particle to another or the sharing of the electrons may be changed. The second type of reaction, involving electron changes, is called an **oxidation-reduction reaction.** It is these "redox" reactions that we will now discuss. We will use the terms oxidation-reduction and redox interchangeably. Before we explain what oxidation-reduction reactions are, we will briefly contrast them with displacement reactions.

GOALS:
- You will gain an understanding of oxidation-reduction reactions.
- You will assign oxidation numbers to elements in compounds using a set of commonly agreed upon rules.
- You will balance oxidation-reduction equations.

In oxidation-reduction reactions, a particle's electronic structure undergoes change.

Oxidation-reduction reactions are known as "redox" reactions.

Table 26-1

Two Reaction Types
Double displacement
$BaCl_2(aq) + Na_2SO_4(aq) \rightarrow BaSO_4(cr) + 2NaCl(aq)$
$Ba^{2+} \rightarrow Ba^{2+}$
$Cl^- \rightarrow Cl^-$
$Na^+ \rightarrow Na^+$
$SO_4{}^{2-} \rightarrow SO_4{}^{2-}$
No change in charges
Redox
$16H^+(aq) + 2MnO_4{}^-(aq) + 5C_2O_4{}^{2-}(aq) \rightarrow 2Mn^{2+}(aq) + 8H_2O(l) + 10CO_2(g)$
$MnO_4{}^- \rightarrow Mn^{2+}$ $(Mn^{7+} \rightarrow Mn^{2+})$
$C_2O_4{}^{2-} \rightarrow CO_2$ $(C^{3+} \rightarrow C^{4+})$
Changes in charges

In the $BaSO_4$ reaction in Table 26-1, the substances are all ionic. Since there is no change in the charges of these ions during the reaction, there are no electron changes. This reaction is not an oxidation-reduction reaction. The production of a precipitate ($BaSO_4$) is nearly always a result of a non-redox reaction. Most acid-base reactions are also the non-redox type.

Since nearly every other kind of reaction is an oxidation-reduction reaction, redox reactions are important in the chemical laboratory. They are also important in life processes and in industry.

26:1 OXIDATION

The term oxidation was first applied to the combining of oxygen with other elements. There are many known instances of this behavior. Iron rusts and carbon burns. In rusting, oxygen combines slowly with iron to form Fe_2O_3. In burning, oxygen unites rapidly with carbon to form CO_2. Observation of these reactions gave rise to the terms "slow" and "rapid" oxidation.

FIGURE 26-1. The oxidation process is shown in the rusting of the oil rig (a) and the corrosion of the bronze statue (b).

Chemists recognize, however, that other nonmetallic elements unite with substances in a manner similar to that of oxygen. Hydrogen, antimony, and sodium all burn in chlorine, and iron will burn in fluorine. Since these reactions are similar, chemists formed a more general definition of oxidation. Electrons are removed from each free element by the reactants O_2 or Cl_2. Thus, **oxidation** is defined as the process by which electrons are apparently removed from an atom or ion.

Table 26-2

Oxidation Reactions				
Oxidation reaction	**Free element**	**Oxidizing agent**	**Electrons transferred**	**Oxidation product**
$4Fe(cr) + 3O_2(g) \rightarrow 2Fe_2O_3(cr)$	Fe	O_2	$12e^{-}$ *	Fe_2O_3
$C(cr) + O_2(g) \rightarrow CO_2(g)$	C	O_2	$4e^{-}$	CO_2
$H_2(g) + Cl_2(g) \rightarrow 2HCl(g)$	H	Cl_2	$2e^{-}$	HCl
$2Sb(cr) + 3Cl_2(g) \rightarrow 2SbCl_3(cr)$	Sb	Cl_2	$6e^{-}$	$SbCl_3$
$2Na(cr) + Cl_2(g) \rightarrow 2NaCl(cr)$	Na	Cl_2	$2e^{-}$	NaCl

*12 moles of electrons are removed from 4 moles of Fe to form 2 moles of $Fe_2O_3(Fe^{3+})$.

26:2   REDUCTION

A reduction reaction was originally limited to the type of reaction in which ores were "reduced" from their oxides. Iron(III) oxide was reduced to iron by carbon monoxide. Copper(II) oxide can be reduced to copper by hydrogen. In these reactions, oxygen is removed, and the free element is produced. The free element can be produced in other ways. An iron nail dropped into a copper(II) sulfate solution causes a reaction that produces free copper. An electric current passing through molten sodium chloride produces free sodium. The similarity between oxidation and reduction reactions led chemists to formulate a more generalized definition of reduction. By definition, **reduction** is the process by which electrons are apparently added to atoms or ions.

Oxides were said to be "reduced" by the removal of oxygen.

All of these processes are reductions.

Reduction is defined as the process by which electrons are added to atoms or ions.

FIGURE 26-2. A blast furnace is used in the reduction of iron ore compounds to elemental iron.

Table 26-3

Reduction Reactions				
Reduction reaction	Material reduced	Reducing agent	Electrons transferred	Reduction product
$Fe_2O_3(cr) + 3CO(g) \rightarrow 2Fe(cr) + 3CO_2(g)$	Fe^{3+}	CO	$6e^-$	Fe
$CuO(cr) + H_2(g) \rightarrow Cu(cr) + H_2O(g)$	Cu^{2+}	H_2	$2e^-$	Cu
$2Na^+Cl^-(l) \xrightarrow{\text{electric current}} 2Na(cr) + Cl_2(g)$	Na^+	e^-	$2e^-$	Na
$3Cu^{2+}(aq) + 2Fe(cr) \rightarrow 2Fe^{3+}(aq) + 3Cu(cr)$	Cu^{2+}	Fe	$2e^-$	Cu

Tables 26-2 and 26-3 are merely examples of some redox reactions. Not all redox reactions produce or require free elements.

Oxidation and reduction occur at the same time in a reaction. The number of electrons lost must equal the number gained.

26:3   OXIDIZING AND REDUCING AGENTS

In an oxidation-reduction reaction, electrons are transferred. All the electrons exchanged in an oxidation-reduction reaction must be accounted for. It seems reasonable, then, that oxidation and reduction must occur at the same time in a reaction. Electrons are lost and gained at the same time and the number lost must equal the number gained.

a   b   c

FIGURE 26-3. When iron nails are added to a copper(II) sulfate solution, copper begins to form. Note the color of the solution changes as the copper forms.

A reducing agent gives up electrons.

An oxidizing agent gains electrons.

The substance in the reaction that gives up electrons is called the **reducing agent.** The reducing agent contains the atoms that are oxidized (the atoms that lose electrons). Zinc is a good example of a reducing agent. It can be oxidized to the zinc ion, Zn^{2+}. The substance in the reaction that gains electrons is called the **oxidizing agent.** It contains the atoms that are reduced (the atoms which gain electrons). Dichromate ion, $Cr_2O_7^{2-}$, is a good example of an oxidizing agent. It can be reduced to the chromium(III) ion, Cr^{3+}. The reaction between Zn and $Cr_2O_7^{2-}$ in acid solution is

$$3Zn(cr) + \underset{\substack{\text{reducing} \\ \text{agent}}}{Cr_2O_7^{2-}(aq)} + 14\,H^+(aq) \rightleftharpoons 3Zn^{2+}(aq) + 2Cr^{3+}(aq) + 7H_2O(l)$$

reducing   oxidizing
agent   agent

To summarize, oxidation is the loss of electrons and reduction is the gain of electrons. The oxidizing agent is the substance containing the element reduced. The reducing agent contains the element oxidized. In the reaction

$$16H^+(aq) + 2MnO_4^-(aq) + C_2O_4^{2-}(aq) \rightarrow 2Mn^{2+}(aq) + 8H_2O(l) + 10CO_2(g)$$

manganese is reduced, so MnO_4^- is the oxidizing agent. Carbon is oxidized, so $C_2O_4^{2-}$ is the reducing agent.

If a substance gives up electrons readily, it is said to be a strong reducing agent. Its oxidized form, however, is normally a poor oxidizing agent. If a substance gains electrons readily, it is said to be a strong oxidizing agent. Its reduced form is a weak reducing agent.

26:4 OXIDATION NUMBERS

How is it possible to determine whether an oxidation-reduction reaction has taken place? We do so by determining whether any electron shifts have taken place during the reaction. To indicate electron changes, we look at the oxidation numbers of the atoms in the reaction. The oxidation number is the charge an atom appears to have when we assign electrons to it, in accordance with certain rules. Any change of oxidation numbers in the course of a reaction indicates an oxidation-reduction reaction has taken place.

For example, suppose iron, as a reactant in a reaction, has an oxidation number of 2+. If iron appears as a product with an oxidation number other than 2+, say 3+, or 0, then a redox reaction has taken place.

SUGGESTION: It is helpful to review electron dot diagrams before studying this section.

26:5 ASSIGNING OXIDATION NUMBERS

We have already seen in Chapters 4 and 10 how to predict oxidation numbers. Oxidation numbers are assigned according to the apparent charge of the element. To determine the apparent charge, you may find it helpful to consult the electron dot structure for the substance. However, the electron dot structure you draw will not give you the complete answer; it only helps you to visualize an atom, ion, or molecule.

Suppose you want to know the oxidation number of the sodium atom. The electron dot symbol is Na•, showing that the atom is not charged. The number of electrons is equal to the number of protons. The apparent charge of the sodium atom is 0, and its oxidation number is 0.

The sodium ion, however, is indicated in this manner: Na^+, showing that there is one more proton than electron. Since its apparent charge is 1+, its oxidation number is 1+.

The oxidation-number is the charge an atom appears to have when assigned a certain number of electrons.

A change in oxidation number of an atom or ion indicates a redox reaction.

Sometimes a distinction is made between oxidation state and oxidation number. For instance, in MnO_2, O is in the 2− oxidation state but O_2 (O_2^{4-}) in the compound has an oxidation number of 4−. However, this distinction is not always made. Instead, we may use the term oxidation number for a group of atoms meaning the algebraic sum of the oxidation numbers of the atoms in the group.

An ion's apparent charge is its oxidation number.

Free elements are assigned an oxidation number of zero.

Consider free chlorine, Cl_2, whose electronic structure is

$$:\overset{..}{\underset{..}{Cl}}:\overset{..}{\underset{..}{Cl}}:$$

Since each chlorine atom has the same electronegativity, the two chlorine atoms share the electrons equally. Thus, each is assigned seven electrons in the outer level, giving a net charge of 0 for each. Free chlorine (Cl_2), then, is assigned oxidation number 0.

Chlorine in hydrogen chloride

$$H:\overset{..}{\underset{..}{Cl}}:$$

has an oxidation number different from 0. The chlorine atom is more electronegative than the hydrogen atom. All the electrons shared are therefore arbitrarily assigned to the chlorine atom. Thus, the chlorine atom will have 18 electrons and 17 protons, and a resulting apparent charge of $1-$. Its oxidation number is $1-$. Hydrogen has had its electron assigned to chlorine, and will have one less electron than proton. The hydrogen atom's apparent charge will be $1+$ and its oxidation state will be $1+$.

Shared electrons are assigned to the more electronegative element.

Another name for the apparent charge is the formal charge.

Consider a possible electronic structure for sulfuric acid, H_2SO_4.

$$H:\overset{..}{\underset{..}{O}}:\overset{\overset{..}{O}:}{\underset{:\overset{..}{O}:}{S}}:\overset{..}{\underset{..}{O}}:H$$

BACKGROUND: Explain that oxidation numbers are used as an aid in understanding atomic structure. Point out, however, that oxidation numbers do not necessarily indicate the actual relationships existing between atoms and electrons in compounds.

It can be seen that the oxygen atoms share electrons with both sulfur and hydrogen atoms. Since oxygen is more electronegative than sulfur, the shared electrons are arbitrarily assigned to each oxygen atom. Thus, the sulfur atom is assigned six fewer electrons than it has protons. The sulfur atom, with a resulting apparent charge of $6+$, is assigned an oxidation number of $6+$. Each hydrogen atom, less electronegative than the oxygen atoms, will also have its electron assigned to oxygen. The hydrogen oxidation number in this compound is $1+$. Each oxygen atom has assigned to it all the shared electrons from either the sulfur or hydrogen atoms, or both. This assignment gives each oxygen atom a $2-$ oxidation number (ten electrons, eight protons). The total of the oxidation numbers of all the atoms in a compound must be zero. In H_2SO_4, one sulfur atom has an oxidation number $6+$, four oxygen atoms have the oxidation number $2-$, and two hydrogen atoms have $1+$. The apparent charge of the compound is zero.

The algebraic sum of the oxidation numbers of a compound is zero.

In sulfur dichloride, SCl_2, sulfur has a different oxidation state. Consider a possible electronic structure

$$\overset{:\overset{..}{Cl}:}{:\overset{..}{\underset{..}{S}}:\overset{..}{\underset{..}{Cl}}:}$$

The sulfur atom shares only four electrons with chlorine. Chlorine is more electronegative than sulfur. Thus the shared electrons are assigned to the chlorine. This gives sulfur an oxidation state of $2+$ (14 electrons, 16 protons). Each chlorine then has an oxidation state of 1− (18 electrons, 17 protons).

The oxidation number of an atom may change from compound to compound. Therefore, an electronic structure must be made for each new compound. The oxidation number can be determined from this electronic structure. Drawing electron dot structures takes time. Fortunately, there is an easier way.

26:6   RULES FOR ASSIGNING OXIDATION NUMBERS

The following general rules have been made to enable you to determine oxidation numbers more easily.

Rule 1. *The oxidation number of any free element is 0.* This statement is true for all atomic and molecular structures: monatomic, diatomic, or polyatomic.

Rule 2. *The oxidation number of a monatomic ion* (Na^+, Ca^{2+}, Al^{3+}, Cl^-) *is equal to the charge on the ion.* Some atoms have several different possible oxidation numbers. For example, iron can be either 2+ or 3+; tin, 2+ or 4+.

Rule 3. *The oxidation number of each hydrogen atom in most compounds is 1+.* There are some exceptions. In compounds such as lithium hydride (LiH), hydrogen, being the more electronegative atom, has an oxidation number of 1−.

Rule 4. *The oxidation number of each oxygen atom in most compounds is 2−* (H_2O). In peroxides, each oxygen is assigned 1− (Na_2O_2, H_2O_2).

Rule 5. *The sum of the oxidation numbers of all the atoms in a particle must equal the apparent charge of that particle.*

Rule 6. *In compounds, the elements of Group IA (1), Group IIA (2), and aluminum have positive oxidation numbers of 1+, 2+, and 3+, respectively.*

CAREER: Geologists use oxidation numbers to determine what conditions were present in past geologic periods. Fe^{3+} indicates shoreline deposition while Fe^{2+} indicates the sediment was deposited in deeper water.

EXAMPLE: Oxidation Numbers

What are the oxidation numbers of the elements in Na_2SO_4?

Solving Process:
According to rule 6, the oxidation number of sodium is 1+. According to rule 4, the oxidation number of oxygen is 2−. According to rule 5, the total of all oxidation numbers in the formula unit is 0. Letting x = oxidation number of sulfur, we have

$$2(1+) + x + 4(2-) = 0$$
$$x = 6+$$

EXAMPLE: Oxidation Numbers

What are the oxidation numbers of the elements in NO_3^-?

Solving Process:

According to rule 4, the oxidation number of oxygen is $2-$. According to rule 5, the total of the oxidation numbers in the ion is $1-$. Letting $x =$ the oxidation number of nitrogen, we have

$$x + 3(2-) = 1-$$
$$x = 5+$$

PROBLEM

1. a. 4+   f. 6+
   b. 7+   g. 6+
   c. 5+   h. 2-
   d. 4+   i. 2+
   e. 4+   j. 0

1. In the following, give the oxidation number for the indicated atoms.

   a. S in Na_2SO_3
   b. Mn in $KMnO_4$
   c. N in $Ca(NO_3)_2$
   d. C in Na_2CO_3
   e. N in NO_2

   f. S in HSO_4^-
   g. S in $H_2S_2O_7$
   h. S in Al_2S_3
   i. Mn in $MnCl_2$
   j. C in $C_{12}H_{22}O_{11}$

26:7   IDENTIFYING OXIDATION-REDUCTION REACTIONS

Oxidation numbers can be used to determine whether oxidation and reduction (electron transfer) occur in a specific reaction. Even the simplest reaction may be a redox reaction. Let us see how it is possible to determine whether a reaction is actually a redox reaction.

The direct combination of sodium and chlorine to produce sodium chloride is a simple example.

$$2Na(cr) + Cl_2(g) \rightarrow 2NaCl(cr)$$

As a reactant, each sodium atom has an oxidation number of 0. In the product, the oxidation number of each sodium atom is $1+$. Similarly, each chlorine atom as a reactant has an oxidation number of 0. As a product, each chlorine atom has an oxidation number of $1-$. Since a change of oxidation number has occurred, an oxidation-reduction reaction has taken place.

$$2Na(cr) + Cl_2(g) \rightarrow 2Na^+Cl^-(cr)$$

The change in oxidation number can result only from a shift of electrons between atoms. This shift of electrons alters the apparent charge (the oxidation numbers).

A reaction in which the oxidation number of any element changes is an oxidation-reduction (redox) reaction.

A gain of electrons means the substance is reduced. It also means that the oxidation number is algebraically lowered. In contrast, a loss of electrons is oxidation. When an atom is oxidized, its oxidation number increases.

The equation for a reaction can be used to determine whether the reaction is a redox reaction. It can also be used to find the substance oxidized, the substance reduced, and the oxidizing and reducing agents. Since the oxidation number of sodium in the equation

$$2Na(cr) + Cl_2(g) \rightarrow 2NaCl(cr)$$

changed from 0 to 1+, sodium is oxidized. Sodium is also the reducing agent. A reducing agent always loses electrons and is, therefore, always oxidized as it reduces the other substance.

EXAMPLE: Redox

For the following reaction, tell what is oxidized, what is reduced, and identify the oxidizing and reducing agents.

$$16H^+(aq) + 2MnO_4^-(aq) + 5C_2O_4^{2-}(aq) \rightarrow 2Mn^{2+}(aq) + 8H_2O(l) + 10CO_2(g)$$

Solving Process:
Manganese is reduced ($7+ \rightarrow 2+$) and carbon is oxidized ($3+ \rightarrow 4+$). The permanganate ion (MnO_4^-) is the oxidizing agent because it contains manganese, and manganese is reduced. The oxalate ion ($C_2O_4^{2-}$) is the reducing agent; it contains carbon, which is oxidized.

PROBLEMS

Some of the following unbalanced reactions are oxidation-reduction reactions, and some are not. In each case: (a) Is the reaction redox? (b) If yes, name the element reduced, the element oxidized, the oxidizing agent, and the reducing agent.

2. $BaCl_2(aq) + Na_2SO_4(aq) \rightarrow NaCl(aq) + BaSO_4(cr)$ reduced = X
oxidized = O
3. $H_2(g) + N_2(g) \rightarrow NH_3(g)$
4. $C(cr) + H_2O(g) \rightarrow CO(g) + H_2(g)$
5. $AgNO_3(aq) + FeCl_3(aq) \rightarrow AgCl(cr) + Fe(NO_3)_3(aq)$
6. $H_2CO_3(aq) \rightarrow H_2O(l) + CO_2(g)$
7. $MgSO_4(aq) + Ca(OH)_2(aq) \rightarrow Mg(OH)_2(aq) + CaSO_4(cr)$
8. $H_2O_2(aq) + PbS(cr) \rightarrow PbSO_4(cr) + H_2O(l)$
9. $KCl(cr) + H_2SO_4(aq) \rightarrow KHSO_4(aq) + HCl(g)$
10. $HNO_3(aq) + H_3PO_3(aq) \rightarrow NO(g) + H_3PO_4(aq) + H_2O(l)$
11. $HNO_3(aq) + I_2(cr) \rightarrow HIO_3(aq) + NO_2(g) + H_2O(l)$
12. $Na_2S(aq) + AgNO_3(aq) \rightarrow Ag_2S(cr) + NaNO_3(aq)$
13. $H^+(aq) + NO_3^-(aq) + Fe^{2+}(aq) \rightarrow H_2O(l) + NO(g) + Fe^{3+}(aq)$
14. $FeBr_2(aq) + Br_2(l) \rightarrow FeBr_3(aq)$
15. $S_2O_3^{2-}(aq) + I_2(cr) \rightarrow S_4O_6^{2-}(aq) + I^-(aq)$
16. $H_2O_2(aq) + MnO_4^-(aq) \rightarrow O_2(g) + Mn^{2+}(aq)$

A mnemonic device: LEO goes GER. *L*ose *E*lectrons *O*xidize; *G*ain *E*lectrons *R*educe.

Oxidation number change can help determine:
1. whether a reaction is redox
2. reducing and oxidizing agents in the reaction
3. elements that are oxidized or reduced

SUGGESTION: The student is not asked to balance these unbalanced redox equations. However, you may wish to have them do so to compare methods.

2. no

4. yes
C oxidized, reducing agent
H is reduced
H₂0 is oxidizing agent

	reducing agent	oxidizing agent
3.	hydrogen	nitrogen
4.	carbon	H₂0
8.	PbS	H₂O₂
10.	H₃PO₃	HNO₃
11.	I₂	HNO₃
13.	Fe²⁺	NO₃⁻
14.	FeBr₂	Br₂
15.	S₂O₃²⁻	I₂
16.	H₂O₂	MnO₄⁻

26:8   HALF-REACTION METHOD

Balancing some oxidation reduction equations can be difficult and lengthy by the trial and error method that we have been using. Let us look at an easier way.

The half-reaction method of balancing redox equations involves separating the reaction into two half-reactions. One of these half-reactions represents the oxidation that is taking place, and the other half-reaction represents the reduction. The number of electrons gained in the process of reduction must equal the number of electrons lost in oxidation. You may add half-reaction equations involving equal numbers of electrons to obtain a balanced redox equation. A most important fact must be kept in mind while writing half-reactions: *Always write the formulas of molecules and ions as they actually occur.* For example, in the reaction involving nitric acid and phosphorous acid

$$HNO_3(aq) + H_3PO_3(aq) \rightarrow NO(g) + H_3PO_4(aq) + H_2O(l)$$

there are no actual N^{5+}, N^{2+}, P^{3+}, or P^{5+} ions. The substances must be represented in the form in which they actually occur using the rules of Section 24:10. In this reaction, the actual ions and molecules are NO_3^-, NO, H_3PO_3, and H_3PO_4. We make one exception to this rule. We will represent H_3O^+ by H^+ to simplify balancing. You should always keep in mind that H^+ represents H_3O^+.

Each half-reaction and redox reaction can be balanced three ways: by electrons, by total charge, and by atoms. Any two of these three ways are sufficient to give an equation overall balance. The third method may be used as a check. In the following illustrations, we will use electrons and atoms to obtain the balanced equation. Then we will look for charge balance as a check.

26:9   NITRIC ACID-PHOSPHOROUS ACID REACTION

Consider the nitric acid-phosphorous acid reaction.

$$HNO_3(aq) + H_3PO_3(aq) \rightarrow NO(g) + H_3PO_4(aq) + H_2O(l)$$

(a) Write the skeleton half-reaction for the reduction process.

$$NO_3^- \rightarrow NO$$

Nitrogen is reduced from oxidation number 5+ to 2+, and therefore, each nitrogen atom gains three electrons. Incorporating the electrons in the skeleton equation, we have balanced the half-reaction with respect to electrons.

$$NO_3^- + 3e^- \rightarrow NO$$

(b) Now we must balance the half-reaction with respect to atoms. Note that one nitrogen atom appears on each side of the equation, and the equation is balanced with respect to nitrogen. For oxygen however, there are three atoms on the left and only one on the right. It is, therefore, necessary to add two oxygen atoms to the right side of the half-reaction. From the information about the reaction taking place, we know that no oxygen is generated. However, there must be some species present that contain oxygen. Here is a second important rule for balancing redox reactions: In aqueous solutions, H^+, H_2O, and OH^- are available. The nature of the reactants determines which participate in the reaction. In the reaction we are now considering, two acids are involved, and the available substances are H^+ and H_2O. (If a basic substance is present, the substances available are OH^- and H_2O.) The two oxygen atoms to be added to the right-hand side of the reduction half-reaction must be present in the form of water. The equation becomes

Remember H^+ stands for H_3O^+ in solution.

In aqueous solutions, either H^+ and H_2O, or OH^- and H_2O are available.

$$NO_3^- + 3e^- \rightarrow NO + 2H_2O$$

The half-reaction is now balanced with nitrogen and oxygen atoms. However, with the introduction of hydrogen on the right side, four hydrogen atoms must be placed on the left. In the acidic solution, hydrogen is largely in the form of hydrogen ions. Hydrogen must be added to the equation in ionic form.

Balance the total number of atoms.

In acid solution, hydrogen is in the form of hydrogen ions.

$$NO_3^- + 3e^- + 4H^+ \rightarrow NO + 2H_2O$$

The half-reaction is now balanced with respect to electrons and to atoms. Let us check the balance by total charge. On the left we have one nitrate ion with a $1-$ charge, three electrons with $1-$ charges and four hydrogen ions with $1+$ charges. The sum of these charges shows a net left-hand charge of 0. On the right, nitrogen(II) oxide and water are both neutral molecules and the total charge is 0. The half-reaction is then balanced with respect to total charge.

Balance the total charge.

(c) Repeat the same procedure with the oxidation half-reaction.

$$H_3PO_3 \rightarrow H_3PO_4$$

We calculate that the phosphorous atom changes in oxidation state from $3+$ in H_3PO_3 to $5+$ in H_3PO_4 as a result of losing two electrons. The half-reaction balanced with respect to electrons is then

Balance the number of electrons.

$$H_3PO_3 \rightarrow H_3PO_4 + 2e^-$$

(d) The half-reaction is already balanced with respect to hydrogen and phosphorus. Adding one oxygen atom to the left side of the equation should balance it with respect to atoms. The oxygen must be added in the form of water, making the half-reaction

Balance the number of atoms.

$$H_3PO_3 + H_2O \rightarrow H_3PO_4 + 2e^-$$

Now the hydrogen is out of balance, and two hydrogen atoms must be added to the right side in form H^+.

Balance the charges.

$$H_3PO_3 + H_2O \rightarrow H_3PO_4 + 2e^- + 2H^+$$

In checking charges, we see that each side is neutral.

Balance the electrons in the two half-reactions and add.

(e) The two half-reactions are now balanced, but we have shown three electrons gained and only two electrons lost. You know that the number of electrons lost must equal the number of electrons gained. Before adding the two half-reactions, it is necessary to have the same number of electrons in each half-reaction. In balancing oxidation-reduction reactions, you must find the least common multiple of the number of electrons lost and gained. In the example with which we are working, the least common multiple of electrons is 3×2 or 6. The reduction half-reaction must then be adjusted so that six electrons are gained by the substance being reduced. Similarly the oxidation half-reaction is adjusted so that six electrons are lost by the substance being oxidized. By multiplying the reduction half-reaction by 2 and the oxidation half-reaction by 3, we get

$$2(NO_3^- + 3e^- + 4H^+ \rightarrow NO + 2H_2O)$$

$$3(H_3PO_3 + H_2O \rightarrow H_3PO_4 + 2e^- + 2H^+)$$

$$2NO_3^- + 6e^- + 8H^+ \rightarrow 2NO + 4H_2O$$

$$3H_3PO_3 + 3H_2O \rightarrow 3H_3PO_4 + 6e^- + 6H^+$$

Adding the two equations, we get

$$2NO_3^- + 6e^- + 8H^+ + 3H_3PO_3 + 3H_2O \rightarrow 2NO + 4H_2O + 3H_3PO_4 + 6e^- + 6H^+$$

Add two equations and simplify.

Note that electrons, hydrogen ions, and water molecules appear on both sides of the equation. By subtracting those quantities that appear on both sides of the equation, the equation may be simplified.

$$2NO_3^-(aq) + 2H^+(aq) + 3H_3PO_3(aq) \rightarrow 2NO(g) + H_2O(l) + 3H_3PO_4(aq)$$

If any electrons remain on either side, you have made a mistake. You will note that this equation is balanced with respect to electrons, atoms, and total charge.

26:10   SILVER-NITRIC ACID REACTION

Silver will react with nitric acid to produce silver nitrate, nitrogen(II) oxide, and water. Write and balance the equation for this reaction.

$$Ag(cr) + HNO_3(aq) \rightarrow AgNO_3(aq) + NO(g) + H_2O(l) \quad (acidic)$$

The reduction half-reaction equation is the same as in the last reaction.

Reduction half-reaction

$$NO_3^- + 3e^- + 4H^+ \rightarrow NO + 2H_2O$$

The oxidation half-reaction is

$$Ag \rightarrow Ag^+ + e^-$$

Oxidation half-reaction

This equation is balanced with respect to electrons, atoms, and charge. The least common multiple of the electrons in both half-reactions is 3. So that $3e^-$ will appear on both sides of the equation, the oxidation half-reaction is multiplied by 3.

Balance the electrons.

$$3Ag \rightarrow 3Ag^+ + 3e^-$$

Add the two half-reactions and simplify.

$$NO_3^-(aq) + 4H^+(aq) + 3Ag(cr) \rightarrow NO(g) + 2H_2O(l) + 3Ag^+(aq)$$

Add the two half-reactions and simplify.

This equation is the complete redox equation. It is balanced with respect to electrons, atoms, and charge.

26:11 IODINE-HYPOCHLOROUS ACID REACTION

Suppose one or more of the substances appears as two or more atoms per formula unit of reactant. What happens then? Consider the following reaction.

$$I_2(cr) + HClO(aq) + H_2O(l) \rightarrow HIO_3(aq) + HCl(aq) \quad (acidic)$$

The oxidation number of iodine changes from 0 to 5+, and the oxidation number of chlorine changes from 1+ to 1−. However, iodine is a diatomic molecule, so both atoms are oxidized. If one atom must lose five electrons to go from 0 to 5+, two atoms must lose ten electrons. Each chlorine is reduced from 1+ to 1− and must gain two electrons for each atom. The balancing of the oxidation half-reaction then proceeds as follows.

Skeleton	$I_2 \rightarrow 2IO_3^-$
Electrons	$I_2 \rightarrow 2IO_3^- + 10e^-$
Oxygen	$I_2 + 6H_2O \rightarrow 2IO_3^- + 10e^-$
Hydrogen	$I_2 + 6H_2O \rightarrow 2IO_3^- + 10e^- + 12H^+$
Check charge	$0 = 0$

SUGGESTION: Encourage students to check the charge.

The reduction half-reaction proceeds as follows.

Skeleton	$HClO \rightarrow Cl^-$
Electrons	$HClO + 2e^- \rightarrow Cl^-$
Oxygen	$HClO + 2e^- \rightarrow Cl^- + H_2O$
Hydrogen	$HClO + 2e^- + H^+ \rightarrow Cl^- + H_2O$
Check charge	$1- = 1-$

To obtain the overall redox equation, proceed as follows.

Electron least common multiple = 10

The reduction half-reaction is multiplied by 5 to obtain the correct number of electrons.

$$I_2 + 6H_2O \rightarrow 2IO_3^- + 10e^- + 12H^+$$
$$5HClO + 10e^- + 5H^+ \rightarrow 5Cl^- + 5H_2O$$

The final reaction should be checked for both atomic balance and charge balance.

Adding and simplifying

$$I_2(cr) + 5HClO(aq) + H_2O(l) \rightarrow 2IO_3^-(aq) + 7H^+(aq) + 5Cl^-(aq)$$

26:12 REVIEW EXAMPLES

Consider the reduction of permanganate ion (MnO_4^-) to manganese(II) ion in acid solution. The reduction is accomplished with sulfur dioxide as the reducing agent, and sulfur is oxidized to sulfate ion. Balance the equation.

$$H^+(aq) + MnO_4^-(aq) + SO_2(g) \rightarrow Mn^{2+}(aq) + SO_4^{2-}(aq) \quad (acidic)$$

Taking the reduction half-reaction first, we obtain the following sequence of steps.

Skeleton	$MnO_4^- \rightarrow Mn^{2+}$
Electrons	$MnO_4^- + 5e^- \rightarrow Mn^{2+}$
Oxygen	$MnO_4^- + 5e^- \rightarrow Mn^{2+} + 4H_2O$
Hydrogen	$MnO_4^- + 5e^- + 8H^+ \rightarrow Mn^{2+} + 4H_2O$
Check charge	$2+ = 2+$

For the oxidation half-reaction

Skeleton	$SO_2 \rightarrow SO_4^{2-}$
Electrons	$SO_2 \rightarrow SO_4^{2-} + 2e^-$
Oxygen	$SO_2 + 2H_2O \rightarrow SO_4^{2-} + 2e^-$
Hydrogen	$SO_2 + 2H_2O \rightarrow SO_4^{2-} + 2e^- + 4H^+$
Check charge	$0 = 0$

For the complete equation the least common multiple for electrons = 10

Multiplying the equations appropriately

$$2MnO_4^- + 10e^- + 16H^+ \rightarrow 2Mn^{2+} + 8H_2O$$
$$5SO_2 + 10H_2O \rightarrow 5SO_4^{2-} + 10e^- + 20H^+$$

Adding and simplifying

$$2MnO_4^-(aq) + 5SO_2(g) + 2H_2O(l) \rightarrow 2Mn^{2+}(aq) + 5SO_4^{2-}(aq) + 4H^+(aq)$$

Consider the oxidation of oxalate ion to carbonate ion by permanganate ion, which in turn is reduced to manganese(IV) oxide. The reaction takes place in basic solution. Balance the reaction.

$$C_2O_4^{2-}(aq) + MnO_4^-(aq) + OH^-(aq) \rightarrow MnO_2(cr) + CO_3^{2-}(aq) + H_2O(l) \quad \text{(basic)}$$

The reduction half-reaction

Skeleton	$MnO_4^- \rightarrow MnO_2$
Electrons	$MnO_4^- + 3e^- \rightarrow MnO_2$
Oxygen	$2H_2O + MnO_4^- + 3e^- \rightarrow MnO_2 + 4OH^-$
Check charge	$4- = 4-$

In basic solution oxygen is balanced by adding OH^- instead of H_2O. H_2O is added to the opposite side to balance the hydrogen in the OH^-. Because of the 2:1 hydrogen-oxygen ratio, it is necessary to add twice as many hydroxide ions as needed oxygen atoms.

The oxidation half-reaction

Skeleton	$C_2O_4^{2-} \rightarrow 2CO_3^{2-}$
Electrons	$C_2O_4^{2-} \rightarrow 2CO_3^{2-} + 2e^-$
Oxygen	$4OH^- + C_2O_4^{2-} \rightarrow 2CO_3^{2-} + 2H_2O + 2e^-$
Check charge	$6- = 6-$

For the overall redox reaction the least common multiple of electrons is 6. Multiply the manganese half-reaction by 2 and the oxalate half-reaction by 3.

$$4H_2O + 6e^- + 2MnO_4^- \rightarrow 2MnO_2 + 8OH^-$$

$$12OH^- + 3C_2O_4^{2-} \rightarrow 6CO_3^{2-} + 6e^- + 6H_2O$$

Add the half-reactions and simplify. The result is the overall redox reaction.

$$2MnO_4^-(aq) + 4OH^-(aq) + 3C_2O_4^{2-}(aq) \rightarrow 2MnO_2(cr) + 6CO_3^{2-}(aq) + 2H_2O(l)$$

PROBLEMS

Balance the following equations. All reactions occur in acid solution unless indicated.

17. $MnO_4^-(aq) + H_2SO_3(aq) + H^+(aq) \rightarrow Mn^{2+}(aq) + HSO_4^-(aq) + H_2O(l)$

Detailed answers to problems are given in the Teacher Guide.

18. $Cr_2O_7^{2-}(aq) + H^+(aq) + I^-(aq) \rightarrow Cr^{3+}(aq) + I_2(cr) + H_2O(l)$

19. $NH_3(g) + O_2(g) \rightarrow NO(g) + H_2O(g)$ *(basic)*

20. $As_2O_3(cr) + H^+(aq) + NO_3^-(aq) + H_2O(l) \rightarrow H_3AsO_4(aq) + NO(g)$

21. $I_2(cr) + H_2SO_3(aq) + H_2O(l) \rightarrow I^-(aq) + HSO_4^-(aq) + H^+(aq)$

22. $H_3AsO_4(aq) + Zn(cr) \rightarrow AsH_3(g) + Zn^{2+}(aq)$

23. $MnO_4^{2-}(aq) + H^+(aq) \rightarrow MnO_4^-(aq) + MnO_2(cr)$

24. $MnO_4^-(aq) + SO_2(g) \rightarrow Mn^{2+}(aq) + SO_4^{2-}(aq) + H^+(aq)$

25. $NO_2(g) + OH^-(aq) \rightarrow NO_2^-(aq) + NO_3^-(aq)$ *(basic)*

26. $HgS(cr) + Cl^-(aq) + NO_3^-(aq) \rightarrow HgCl_4^{2-}(aq) + S(cr) + NO(g)$

BIOGRAPHY   Jane Haldimond Marcet (1769-1845)

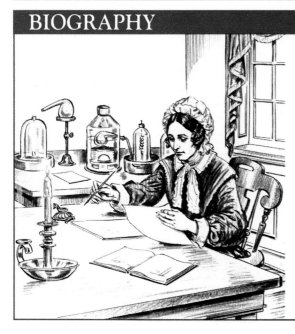

Although not a research chemist, Jane Marcet nonetheless had a profound effect on the chemists of her day and those that followed. Her book, Conversations in Chemistry, *was first published early in the 1800's and was continually revised to reflect the new scientific breakthroughs through sixteen editions. At the time of the American Civil War, nearly 200 000 copies had been sold in England and the United States.*

The book, written in dialogue form, provided experiments to illustrate chemical concepts and an approach that today would be labeled as discovery. Marcet's work provided the chemical foundation for a young bookbindery clerk named Michael Faraday. Later, as a famous scientist, Faraday referred to Conversations in Chemistry *as an "anchor in chemical knowledge."*

TECHNOLOGY AND CHEMISTRY

26:13 Extractive Metallurgy

Metallurgy is the science of extracting metals from their ores, refining the metals, and treating the metals by heat and/or pressure to achieve desired properties. Gold and metals in the platinum group are usually found free in nature. Some small quantities of silver and copper are also found free. All other ores are metal compounds. Most are oxides and sulfides, although some occur as carbonates, sulfates, silicates, and phosphates.

Oxide and sulfide ores are commercially most important. Sulfide ores are generally roasted as a first step. Roasting is heating the sulfide ore in the presence of air to convert it to sulfur dioxide and an oxide of the metal.

$$2PbS + 3O_2 \rightarrow 2PbO + 2SO_2$$

The reduction of an oxide to the free metal can be accomplished in several ways. One method is to use a more active metal to displace the desired metal from its oxide. Chromium is produced by this method.

$$Cr_2O_3 + 2Al \rightarrow Al_2O_3 + 2Cr$$

Another method is to use a gas that is a good reducing agent. Carbon monoxide is used to reduce iron in iron(III) oxide to iron metal.

$$3CO + Fe_2O_3 \rightarrow 3CO_2 + 2Fe$$

Oxides may also be reduced by electricity. The electrode supplying the electrons is then the reducing agent as in the production of aluminum.

$$Al^{3+} + 3e^- \rightarrow Al$$

Reactive metals require special treatment. Zirconium, which occurs in the mineral zircon (zirconium silicate), is converted to zirconium carbide with coke (carbon). The carbide is then changed to zirconium tetrachloride with chlorine gas.

$$ZrSiO_4 + 4C \rightarrow ZrC + SiO + 3CO$$
$$ZrC + 4Cl_2 \rightarrow ZrCl_4 + CCl_4$$

Zirconium ores are always contaminated with hafnium which is removed in a water-organic process. The zirconium leaves the hafnium separation process as zirconyl chloride, $ZrOCl_2$, which is converted to the basic sulfate and then to the hydroxide.

$$ZrCl_4 + H_2O \rightarrow ZrOCl_2 + 2HCl$$
$$ZrOCl_2 + H_2SO_4 \rightarrow 2HCl + ZrOSO_4$$
$$ZrOSO_4 + 2NH_3 + 3H_2O \rightarrow Zr(OH)_4 + (NH_4)_2SO_4$$

The hydroxide is heated to produce the oxide, and then the oxide is treated with coke and chlorine to produce the tetrachloride again.

$$Zr(OH)_4 \rightarrow ZrO_2 + 2H_2O$$
$$ZrO_2 + 2C + 2Cl_2 \rightarrow ZrCl_4 + 2CO$$

Zirconium is then displaced by magnesium. As you might expect, zirconium is expensive.

$$ZrCl_4 + 2Mg \rightarrow Zr + 2MgCl_2$$

SUMMARY

1. An oxidation-reduction reaction involves an apparent transfer of electrons from one particle to another. **Intro.-26:3**

2. Oxidation is the process by which electrons are apparently removed from an atom or group of atoms. **26:1**

3. Reduction is the process by which electrons are apparently added to atoms or groups of atoms. **26:2**

4. Any substance in a reaction which loses electrons is a reducing agent. Any substance in a reaction which gains electrons is an oxidizing agent. **26:3**

5. If a substance gives up electrons readily, it is a strong reducing agent. Its oxidized form is usually a poor oxidizing agent. If a substance acquires electrons readily, it is a strong oxidizing agent. Its reduced form is usually a poor reducing agent. **26:3**

6. Oxidation number is the charge an atom appears to have when we assign a certain number of electrons to that atom. **26:4**

7. Six rules for assigning oxidation numbers: **26:5-26:6**
    a. The oxidation number of any free element is 0.
    b. The oxidation number of any single-atom ion is equal to the charge on that ion.
    c. The oxidation number of hydrogen is usually 1+.
    d. The oxidation number of oxygen in most compounds is 2−.
    e. The sum of the oxidation numbers of all the atoms in a particle must equal the apparent charge of that particle.
    f. In compounds, elements of Group IA(1) and Group IIA(2) and aluminum have oxidation numbers of 1+, 2+, and 3+ respectively.
8. In all chemical reactions, charge, number and kind of atoms, and number of electrons are conserved. Knowing these quantities, you can balance a redox equation. **26:7-26:12**
9. Redox reactions are more easily balanced by splitting the equation into half-reactions. **26:8**

VOCABULARY

oxidation-reduction reaction **Intro**   reducing agent **26:3**
oxidation **26:1**   oxidizing agent **26:3**
reduction **26:2**

PROBLEMS

Detailed discussions and answers to problems are given in the Teacher Guide.

1. Reactions in which electrons are transferred.
2. Oxidizing agents contain the element reduced. Reducing agents contain the element oxidized.
3. a. 5+
   b. 5+
   c. 4+
   d. 1+
   e. 4+
   f. 5+

Students can refer to Section 24:10 for a review of net ionic equations.

14. oxidation = e^- loss
    reduction = e^- gain
15. 11.9 g
16. 10.0 cm³

1. Define redox reaction.
2. Distinguish between oxidizing and reducing agents.
3. Give the oxidation number for the indicated atoms:
    a. $AlPO_4$
    b. $(NH_4)_3AsO_4$
    c. $(NH_4)_2SiF_6$
    d. $Ba(ClO)_2$
    e. $BaSiO_3$
    f. $Pb(IO_3)_2$

Balance the following ten equations after putting them in net ionic form.

4. $Cu(cr) + HNO_3(aq) \rightarrow Cu(NO_3)_2(aq) + NO(g) + H_2O(l)$
5. $Fe(NO_3)_2(aq) + HNO_3(aq) \rightarrow Fe(NO_3)_3(aq) + NO(g) + H_2O(l)$
6. $Zn(cr) + HNO_3(aq) \rightarrow Zn(NO_3)_2(aq) + NO_2(g) + H_2O(l)$
7. $Sb(cr) + H_2SO_4(aq) \rightarrow Sb_2(SO_4)_3(aq) + SO_2(g) + H_2O(l)$
8. $H_2S(g) + H_2SO_3(aq) \rightarrow S(cr) + H_2O(l)$
9. $HCl(aq) + HNO_3(aq) \rightarrow HClO(aq) + NO(g)$
10. $Ag(cr) + HClO_3(aq) + HCl(aq) \rightarrow AgCl(cr) + H_2O(l)$
11. $KI(aq) + O_2(g) + HI(aq) \rightarrow KI_3(aq) + H_2O(l)$
12. $HNO_3(aq) + H_2SO_4(aq) + Hg(l) \rightarrow Hg_2SO_4(cr) + NO(g) + H_2O(l)$
13. $CO(g) + I_2O_5(g) \rightarrow CO_2(g) + I_2(g)$
14. In terms of this chapter, how do oxidation and reduction differ?
15. How many grams of K_2SO_3 can be oxidized to K_2SO_4 by 7.90 g of $KMnO_4$ which will be reduced to MnO_2?
16. How many cm³ of $0.200M$ $KClO_3$ will be required to react completely with 20.0 cm³ of $0.100M$ Cr_2O_3 to produce K_2CrO_4 and Cl^-?

REVIEW

1. The solubility product for $Cd_3(PO_4)_2$ is 2.50×10^{-33}. What is the concentration of Cd^{2+} in a saturated solution of $Cd_3(PO_4)_2$?

2. What effect does an increase in pressure have on the rate of a reaction involving gases?

3. Which step in a reaction mechanism determines the overall reaction rate?

4. What substance is produced from the anhydride SrO and water?

5. Reduce the following equation to net ionic form.
$$NaH_2PO_4 + HCl \rightarrow NaCl + H_3PO_4$$

6. If a solution of $0.100M$ propanoic acid (CH_3CH_2COOH) has a H_3O^+ concentration of $1.16 \times 10^{-3}M$, what is K_a for the acid?

7. What is the percent ionization in Problem 6?

8. What is the H_3O^+ concentration in a solution which is $0.100M$ in HF and $0.0100M$ in NaF?

9. At equilibrium, $[H^+]$ is 0.200, $[CHCl_2COO^-]$ is 0.200, and $[CHCl_2COOH]$ is 1.20. What is the K_{eq} for the reaction? $CHCl_2COOH \rightleftharpoons CHCl_2COO^- + H^+$

10. In the reaction in Problem 9, what is the percent ionization?

11. In Problem 9 if enough $CHCl_2COO^-$ were added as a common ion to make the concentration of $CHCl_2COO^-$ exactly $0.400M$, what would be the concentration of $CHCl_2COOH$?

1. 3.54×10^{-7} M
2. Increases rate
3. slowest step
4. $Sr(OH)_2$
6. 1.36×10^{-5} M
7. 1.16%
8. 3.53×10^{-3} M
9. $K_{eq} = 3.33 \times 10^{-2}$
10. 14.3%
11. $1.29M$

ONE MORE STEP

1. Assuming maximum appropriate values for oxidation numbers, write formulas for hypothetical binary compounds of the following pairs of elements.

   a. Ba and N
   b. Cr and O
   c. Ca and P
   d. Sr and H
   e. Fr and C
   f. Li and O
   g. Fe and S
   h. Sc and F
   i. Ti and Cl

2. Draw the electron dot diagram for the thiosulfate ion and assign oxidation numbers to each atom. What is unusual about this ion?

3. Nitrogen exhibits nine oxidation numbers (including zero). Try to write a formula for a compound representing each state.

4. Using a chemical handbook investigate the compound Fe_3O_4. What color is it? What are the oxidation numbers of the elements composing it? What are its properties?   4. Black; (O) = 2−, one Fe = 2+, two Fe = 3+; magnetic

5. The reduction of ores to metals is still an important industrial process even though the word reduction has been broadened in meaning. Investigate the reduction of ilmenite and one other ore to the metals they contain. Ilmenite contains titanium. The other ore you select should be a substance containing some metal other than titanium.

1. a. Ba_3N_2 f. Li_2O
   b. CrO_3 g. Fe_2S_3
   c. Ca_3P_2 h. ScF_3
   d. SrH_2 i. $TiCl_4$
   e. Fr_4C

2. :Ö:S:Ö:
     :Ö:

   sulfur has two different oxidation states

3. 3− NH_3
   2− N_2H_4
   1− NH_2OH
   0 N_2
   1+ N_2O
   2+ NO
   3+ N_2O_3
   4+ NO_2
   5+ N_2O_5

READINGS

Conkling, John A., "Chemistry of Fireworks," *Chemical and Engineering News*, Vol. 59, No. 26 (June 29, 1981), pp. 24-32.

By passing an electric current through a silver salt solution, silver can be plated out on this dish. Thus, objects are produced having the beauty and luster of silver at a much lower cost than solid silver. The same dish made of pure silver would be quite expensive. This process is used in plating many metals for ornamental and protective purposes. What factors affect the amount of metal that can be plated during a given time period? What properties must a metal possess in order to make it suitable for plating? What are some other applications of electrochemistry?

ELECTRO-CHEMISTRY

27

Chapter 27 uses the topics discussed in Chapters 25 and 26 to develop an understanding of electrochemistry.

DEMONSTRATION: On an overhead projector, place 4 drops of phenolphthalein into a solution of KI (2 g in 100 cm^3 H$_2$O) in a petri dish. Connect two pieces of Cu wire (electrodes) to a 3-6 V power supply and dip the electrodes into the KI soln. Note the formation of I$_2$ (anode) and H$_2$ and OH$^-$ (cathode). See Teacher Guide for more detail. This demonstration can be used to introduce the vocabulary in Chapter 27.

You press the button of your pocket flashlight and light (a form of radiant energy) is produced. You know already that the light results from the passage of an electric current through the flashlight bulb. Where does the electricity come from? The obvious answer is the battery. What then, is a flashlight battery? How does it function?

GOALS:
• You will gain an understanding of how electricity can produce chemical changes and how chemical changes can produce an electric current.
• You will determine the cell potential given different electrodes.
• You will use Faraday's laws to determine the amount of element deposited by a given current for a given length of time.

BACKGROUND: A battery is a cell in which a spontaneous redox reaction takes place. The battery produces a current because the electrons involved in the redox reaction are forced to travel through a wire or external circuit.

Light bulb

Switch

Electrodes

Electric outlet

Apparatus for testing conductivity

FIGURE 27-1. If a conductor is placed in the beaker, the bulb will light when the apparatus is plugged into the wall. The bulb will not light if a nonconductor is placed in the beaker.

SUGGESTION: Use a battery eliminator type of power supply. Remove the special plug and solder two alligator clips to the wire ends. A small lantern bulb and socket can also be connected in the circuit. You now have a low voltage power supply for chemical reactions.

Metals conduct electricity.

If we plug the apparatus in Figure 27-1 into an electric outlet, the bulb does not light because the circuit is not complete. Whenever we complete the circuit with a conducting substance, the bulb does light. In the circuit shown, a conducting substance in the beaker would complete the circuit. We now have an easy way of observing which substances are conductors of electricity. If we touch the two electrodes to a piece of copper or other metal, the bulb lights. Metals are conductors of electricity. Copper is one of the best conductors; for this reason it is used in

Ag, Cu, and Al are the three most common metal conductors used in electric applications.

Ionic or ionizable materials in solution and metals conduct electricity because these substances contain charged particles which are free to move in an electric field.

Current can be produced by two dissimilar metals immersed in a salt solution.

A salt bridge is a solution containing ions in a U-tube.

FIGURE 27-2. Current flows in (a) and (c). In (b) the circuit is not complete, thus no current flows.

electric equipment. If we touch the electrodes to a piece of glass or a sulfur crystal, the bulb does not light. Most nonmetallic solids, including salts, are nonconductors. If we immerse the electrodes in pure water, benzene, alcohol, sugar solution, or other solution of a nonionizing substance, the bulb does not light. These liquids are all nonconductors. However, if we add a small amount of sodium chloride (or any other salt), a small amount of hydrochloric acid, or sodium hydroxide, the bulb lights. These solutions are conductors of electricity. What materials conduct electricity in solution? Why do they conduct electricity?

Let us take pieces of two dissimilar metals and connect them to the terminals of a galvanometer. A **galvanometer** is an instrument for measuring electric current. The two pieces of metal are kept from making contact with each other and put into a salt solution. The galvanometer needle registers a flow of current. How is the current produced? If we place the two metal plates into separate beakers containing salt solutions, as shown in Figure 27-2, no current flows. When we add the salt bridge to the system as shown, a current is produced. The **salt bridge** is a U-tube containing an ionic substance in solution. What is the function of the salt bridge? It connects the two separate solutions without mixing them. Can the solutions be mixed and still be used to produce a current? In this chapter, we shall answer these and other related questions.

27:1 CONDUCTIVITY AND POTENTIAL DIFFERENCE

Metals, in general, are excellent conductors of electricity. This statement is true whether the metal is in the solid state or the liquid state. Mercury, a liquid at room temperature, is used in scientific apparatus because of its excellent electric conductivity. In Chapter 12, we found that the outer electrons of metal atoms are free to move if excited to the conduction band. If the potential energy of the electrons in the metal is raised, these electrons will flow to a point where their potential energy is lower. The flow or movement of electrons through a conductor is an **electric current.**

A difference in electric potential can be brought about in a number of ways. One way is to use a generator. Suppose we connect the two ends of a long wire to a generator. Electrons are added at one end of the wire and removed at the other end. When a potential energy difference is created at the ends of the wire, current flows. Energy is required to create a potential difference and work is done on the system when a current is made to flow through a wire.

Metals are excellent conductors of electricity because their electrons are free to move when a small potential difference is created. In nonconducting substances, the outer electrons are tightly held. The forbidden zone represents a large energy gap. Very large potential differences are required to move electrons in these substances which we call insulators. However, even the best insulators break down and conduct a current if the potential difference is high enough.

Electric potential difference is measured in units called **volts.** The voltage (potential difference) produced by a generator or battery can be thought of as electric pressure. In fact, it is often easier to consider a generator or battery as an electron pump. The rate of electron flow, or current, is measured in **amperes** in SI (see Table A-1 of the Appendix for its definition).

Metallic conduction occurs by movement of free electrons to the conduction band.

An electric current is the movement of electrons through a conductor.

FIGURE 27-3. Electricity travels through wires when a potential difference exists between the two ends.

Work is done when electricity flows through a wire.

27:2 ELECTROLYTIC CONDUCTION

Solid acids, bases, and salts (for example, oxalic acid, sodium hydroxide, and sodium chloride) are nonconductors. When any one of these substances is dissolved in water, the resulting solution is a conductor. Those substances that are conductors in solution are known as electrolytes. Any substance that produces ions in solution is an electrolyte. Salts are ionic even in the solid state; but a salt must dissolve or melt in order for the ions to separate from each other and become free to move. Acids and bases may be either ionic or molecular substances. However, when they dissolve in water, ions are formed. Electrolytic conduction is

Electrolytes are substances whose solutions conduct electricity.

Molten salts and solutions of acids, bases, and salts will conduct electricity.

Electron flow

Anion

Beaker

Cation

Electrolytic solution

FIGURE 27-4. Anions in solution move toward the anode. Cations move toward the cathode.

Individual ions may move only a few hundred nanometers. It is the general trend of this motion which allows current to flow through a liquid.

Negative ions (anions) are attracted to the anode. Positive ions (cations) are attracted to the cathode.

At the cathode, positive ions are reduced by gaining electrons.

SUGGESTION: It may be helpful to warn students that reduction does not always take place at the positive or negative pole. In fact, it is probably desirable to avoid this means of labeling and to speak only of anode and cathode.

possible because ions move freely in aqueous solution. If we connect the conductivity device to a direct current, one of the electrodes will be negative and the other electrode will be positive. It is customary to call the negative electrode the cathode and the positive electrode the anode. If we immerse the electrodes in an ionic solution, positive ions in the solution will be attracted to the cathode. For this reason, positive ions are called **cations.** Negative ions will be attracted toward the anode. Consequently, they are called **anions.** The movement of ions through a solution results in an electric current just as the movement of electrons in a metal results in a current.

27:3   ELECTRODE REACTIONS

What happens to a moving ion when it reaches the electrode to which it is attracted? We will consider molten sodium chloride, a system that contains only two kinds of ions and no other particles. We will use electrodes that are inert, that is, electrodes that do not react chemically with sodium or chloride ions. The positive sodium ions, or cations, are attracted to the cathode. The cathode is made negative by the action of a generator which, in effect, pumps electrons into it. The electrons in the cathode are in a state of high potential energy. The sodium ion has a positive charge. It has an attraction for electrons. An electron in a sodium atom would have a lower potential energy than an electron on the cathode. Thus, electrons move from the cathode (high potential energy) to the sodium ions (lower potential energy). At the cathode, the sodium ions will be converted into sodium atoms by the addition of an electron. This change is a chemical reaction and can be shown by an equation.

$$Na^+ + e^- \rightarrow Na$$

Note that this chemical change represents a gain of electrons. We found in Chapter 26 that electron gain is called reduction. The chemical change that occurs at the cathode is always reduction. In this case, the sodium ion is reduced to sodium metal.

Now consider what happens at the anode. The anode has a positive charge and negative ions are attracted to it. The anode is positive because the generator is, in effect, pumping electrons out of it. Thus, electrons in the anode may be said to exist in a state of low potential energy. Since the chloride ion has a negative charge, its outer electrons are in a state of higher potential. When chloride ions reach the electron-deficient anode, they give up electrons to it. Electrons move from a state of higher potential energy to a state of lower potential energy. We can show the chemical change that occurs at the anode by the following.

$$2Cl^- \rightarrow Cl_2 + 2e^-$$

Note that in this reaction chloride ions lose electrons to become chlorine atoms that then combine to form Cl_2 molecules. The $Cl_2(g)$ bubbles off at the anode. This reaction results in a loss of electrons. The name applied to a change in which electrons are lost is oxidation. The anode reaction is always oxidation.

At the anode, negative ions are oxidized by losing electrons.

We have shown the oxidation and reduction processes by separate equations because they take place at different points. However, these processes do not occur independently. The generator does not produce the electrons; it moves the electrons from one place to another. The electrons that the generator adds to the cathode are taken from the anode. The reduction process cannot occur without the oxidation process going on at the same time. The role of the generator is to raise the potential energy of the electrons on the cathode.

Chemical change at the anode is oxidation.

These electrode reactions are called half-reactions. The anode reaction involves a loss of electrons and the cathode reaction involves a gain of electrons. Therefore, the electrons must balance when we add the two half-reactions. The overall reaction for the electrolysis of sodium chloride is

In a cell, oxidation and reduction occur as separate half-reactions at the same time.

$$2Na^+(l) + 2Cl^-(l) \rightarrow 2Na(l) + Cl_2(g)$$

The process by which an electric current produces a chemical change is called electrolysis. Electrolysis of molten sodium chloride is the commercial process used to produce metallic sodium. Chlorine gas is produced at the same time as a by-product.

Electrolysis is the use of an electric current to produce a chemical change.

FIGURE 27-5. A Downs cell is used in the industrial production of sodium.

27:4 ELECTROLYSIS OF A SALT SOLUTION

Another important commercial process involves the electrolysis of a concentrated sodium chloride solution. In this process, the anode reaction is exactly the same as that which occurs when molten sodium chloride is used. Chlorine gas is produced at the anode. The reaction at the cathode, however, will be different. Around the cathode, sodium ions and water molecules are present. An electron has a lower potential energy on a water molecule than on a sodium atom. Thus, electrons at the cathode are transferred to water molecules instead of sodium ions. When a water molecule acquires an extra electron, the electron is accepted by a hydrogen ion (a proton) that becomes a hydrogen atom. This change leaves a hydroxide ion. The hydrogen atoms produced combine to form H_2 molecules, and hydrogen gas bubbles from the solution at the cathode. The solution surrounding the cathode acquires a high concentration of sodium ions and hydroxide ions. If this solution is drained off and evaporated, the product is solid sodium hydroxide. Commercial sodium hydroxide is usually produced by this process. Chlorine gas is also produced.

The half-reactions are

$$2Cl^- \rightarrow Cl_2 + 2e^-$$

$$2H_2O + 2e^- \rightarrow 2OH^- + H_2$$

The equation for the overall reaction may be written

$$2NaCl(aq) + 2H_2O(l) \rightarrow 2NaOH(aq) + H_2(g) + Cl_2(g)$$

It should be noted that sodium metal, chlorine gas, hydrogen gas, and sodium hydroxide are all produced from rock salt. Rock salt is a very cheap raw material. The most costly part of this operation is the electric power required.

In the processes we have just described, two kinds of electric conduction are involved. In the generator and the cables leading to the electrodes, conduction takes place by the movement of electrons through a metal. This conduction is known as **electron conduction** or **metallic conduction.** The electric path in electrolysis is completed through the liquid between the electrodes. This part of the conduction process takes place by the migration of ions and is called **electrolytic conduction.** Both kinds of conduction involve the movement of electric charge. For electrolytic conduction it is necessary that ions be present and that they be free to move. Ions move freely in solution or as molten salts. Solid salts do not conduct electricity. Note that all electrolytic operations involve both oxidation and reduction.

27:5 VOLTAIC CELLS

The processes that we have described are examples in which electric energy is used to cause chemical changes. These processes take place in devices called electrolytic cells. When you use a pocket flashlight, however, you are using a chemical process to produce electricity. In other

FIGURE 27-6. A voltaic cell can also be referred to as a galvanic cell.

words, you are converting chemical potential energy into electric energy. A device that makes such a conversion is known as a **voltaic cell.** An example of a simple voltaic cell is shown in Figure 27-6. In this cell, there are two compartments separated by a porous barrier or salt bridge that prevents the two solutions from mixing by diffusion. However, the barrier permits the migration of ions from one side of the cell to the other. The cathode in the left hand compartment consists of a strip of copper immersed in a copper(II) sulfate solution. Note that there is no external source of electrons (no generator). The anode, in the right hand compartment, consists of a strip of zinc immersed in a zinc sulfate solution. If the two electrodes are connected through a precision voltmeter, an electric current flows and the voltmeter reads 1.10 volts. Electrons flow from the zinc anode through the voltmeter to the copper cathode. Chemical changes occur at the electrodes. Zinc is a more active metal than copper because its outer electrons have a higher potential energy than outer electrons in copper atoms. In other words, zinc has a greater tendency to give up electrons than copper. Electrons move from the zinc with its higher potential energy through the voltmeter to the copper with its lower potential energy. The anode half-reaction that occurs at the zinc electrode is

$$Zn \rightarrow Zn^{2+} + 2e^-$$

Since this change involves loss of electrons it is an oxidation reaction. Zinc metal is oxidized at the anode (the zinc bar in the zinc half-cell, in Figure 27-6). The copper cathode in the copper half-cell acquires excess electrons. It has a negative charge and copper ions move to it. The potential energy of electrons on the copper electrode is higher than the potential energy the electrons would have on the copper ions in the solution. The cathode transfers electrons to the copper ions and copper metal plates out on the cathode. The cathode reaction is

$$Cu^{2+} + 2e^- \rightarrow Cu$$

A voltaic cell converts chemical energy into electric energy.

Reactions take place at separate electrodes. Electrons travel through the external circuit.

Electrons flow from the anode to the cathode in the external circuit.

In the zinc-copper cell, zinc metal is oxidized at the anode and copper ion is reduced at the cathode.

FIGURE 27-7. Redox reactions can occur without the production of electricity. In this reaction, heat is released as copper ions are reduced.

Note that copper atoms are deposited on the surface of the zinc.

This process involves a gain of electrons and is a reduction reaction. Note that the operation of the cell involves both oxidation and reduction, but the two changes do not occur at the same electrode. Rather, the electrons travel through the external circuit (in this case, the voltmeter) and do electrical work.

Note that these changes can occur without producing an electric current. Consider a piece of zinc placed in a copper sulfate solution. Zinc metal is converted to Zn^{2+} ions, and Cu^{2+} ions are converted to copper metal. Energy is also produced but is released in the form of heat that is not available for practical use. No current is produced because the electrons are transferred directly from Zn atoms to Cu^{2+} ions.

BACKGROUND: This experiment indicates that if a useful current is to be produced, the two half-reactions must be separated.

27:6 STRUCTURE OF VOLTAIC CELLS

A voltaic cell is a device used to produce electric energy from an oxidation-reduction reaction. The main feature of the voltaic cell is the porous barrier or salt bridge that separates the two solutions and keeps them from mixing freely, Figure 27-8. If this barrier is not porous enough to allow ions to migrate through it, the cell will not operate. The anode compartment acquires an excess of positive zinc ions. In order to maintain neutrality, it must have negative ions to balance the positive zinc ions. At the same time, the cathode compartment uses copper ions. In order to maintain neutrality, it must lose negative ions. Sulfate ions move through the porous barrier from the cathode compartment to the anode compartment. In that way electric neutrality is maintained in the two compartments. The cell continues to operate as long as there is a potential energy difference between the half-cells. The two compartments in the cell are called half-cells because the reactions that occur in them are half-reactions.

For a voltaic cell to operate, free movement of ions between the anode and cathode compartments is necessary.

The two compartments in the cell are called half-cells and their reactions are called half-reactions.

Note: The porous barrier completes the circuit. It also permits the free passage of ions. This movement prevents the accumulation of an excess of ions of one sign in a half-cell.

FIGURE 27-8. The porous barrier between the two cells keeps the solutions from mixing. Without the barrier, the cell would not operate.

The two most commonly used voltaic cells are the dry cell and the lead storage cell. A flashlight battery is an example of a dry cell. An automobile battery is a lead storage cell.

Chemists have a shorthand method of representing cell reactions. The oxidation half-cell is written first. The reduced and oxidized species are separated by a vertical line. The zinc half-cell from the zinc-copper cell would be written

$$Zn \,|\, Zn^{2+}$$

The reduction half-cell is written in the reverse order.

$$Cu^{2+} \,|\, Cu$$

The two half-cells are separated by two vertical lines representing the salt bridge. The entire zinc-copper cell is thus shown as

$$Zn \,|\, Zn^{2+} \,\|\, Cu^{2+} \,|\, Cu$$

When using the shorthand method of representing cells place the anode on the left.

anode ‖ cathode

a

Graphite (cathode)

Paste of MnO_2, NH_4Cl and graphite powder

Porous spacer

Zinc shell (anode)

b

Cathode

Anode

Cell connector

Cell spacer

PbO_2 Pb

Cell with electrolyte

FIGURE 27-9. A dry cell (a) and an automobile battery (b) are both voltaic cells. The auto battery contains an electrolyte (H_2SO_4) in solution. The dry cell has an electrolyte in paste form.

27:7 REDOX POTENTIALS

There is no way in which the potential energy of a single half-cell can be measured. However, the difference in potential between two half-cells in a voltaic cell can be measured by means of a voltmeter. This potential difference is a measure of the relative tendency of two substances to take on electrons. For example, consider the zinc-copper cell that gives a voltmeter reading of 1.10 volts. If we arbitrarily assign a potential of zero to the copper half-cell, we will say the zinc half-cell has a potential of -1.10 volts. The negative sign indicates that zinc ions are less likely to take on electrons than the copper ions. On the other hand, if we assign a

BACKGROUND: The situation here is similar to measuring heat content as discussed in Section 20:4. The analogy used was "How high is a hill?" The height must be measured from some arbitrarily chosen point.

H₂

Salt bridge

H₂ bubbles

Platinum electrode

H⁺   H⁺

Acid solution (1 molar)

Arbitrary standard

FIGURE 27-10. The apparatus shown is used in the reduction of hydrogen. The hydrogen reduction reaction is assigned a potential of zero for comparison purposes.

The hydrogen (reference) half-cell is assigned zero potential.

potential of zero to the zinc half-cell, we will say that the copper half-cell has a potential of +1.10 volts. In principle, any half-cell could be used for the reference half-cell. That is, any half-cell could be the one assigned zero potential. In practice, the zero potential is assigned to the hydrogen half-cell. The half-reaction is

$$2H^+(aq) + 2e^- \rightleftharpoons H_2(g)$$

The hydrogen half-cell consists of a sheet of platinum whose surface has been specially treated. The platinum is immersed in a one molar ($1M$) ideal solution of H^+ ions. Hydrogen gas, from a cylinder, is bubbled into the solution around the platinum at a pressure of 101.325 kPa. The H_2 molecules are adsorbed on the platinum surface and form the electrode. The hydrogen half-cell is an ideal that can only be approached in practice.

DEMONSTRATION: Place a clean penny in a petri dish on the overhead projector. Add AgNO₃ solution to the petri dish and observe the reaction. Refer to Table 27-1 to show students how they can use it to predict the products of the reaction.

Potentials vary with temperature, pressure, and concentration.

Half-cell potential tables are useful for predicting direction of chemical reactions.

27:8   STANDARD ELECTRODE POTENTIALS

If we use the hydrogen half-cell with the zinc half-cell, our voltmeter reads −0.76 volts. We assign this potential to the zinc half-cell. If we use the hydrogen half-cell with the copper half-cell, the voltmeter reads +0.34 volts. This potential is assigned to the copper half-cell. In this way, potentials can be experimentally determined for almost all oxidation-reduction half-reactions. Some of these half-cell potentials are given in Table 27-1. Potentials are dependent on temperature, pressure, and concentration. The values given in the table are for a temperature of 25°C, a pressure of 101.325 kPa, and a $1M$ ionic concentration. A table of half-cell potentials is of great practical importance. It enables us to predict the direction for a large number of chemical reactions, the maximum voltage that can be produced by a particular voltaic cell, and the products of an electrolytic cell.

Table 27-1

Standard Reduction Potentials (at 25°C, 101.325 kPa, 1M)			
Half-Reaction	**E° (Volts)**	**Half-Reaction**	**E° (Volts)**
$Li^+ + e^- \rightarrow Li$	−3.05	$AgCl + e^- \rightarrow Ag + Cl^-$	0.22
$K^+ + e^- \rightarrow K$	−2.93	$Hg_2Cl_2 + 2e^- \rightarrow 2Hg + 2Cl^-$	0.27
$Cs^+ + e^- \rightarrow Cs$	−2.92	$UO_2^{2+} + 4H^+ + 2e^- \rightarrow U^{4+} + 2H_2O$	0.33
$Ba^{2+} + 2e^- \rightarrow Ba$	−2.90	$Cu^{2+} + 2e^- \rightarrow Cu$	0.34
$Ca^{2+} + 2e^- \rightarrow Ca$	−2.87	$Fe(CN)_6^{3-} + e^- \rightarrow Fe(CN)_6^{4-}$	0.36
$Na^+ + e^- \rightarrow Na$	−2.71	$Cu^+ + e^- \rightarrow Cu$	0.52
$Am^{3+} + 3e^- \rightarrow Am$	−2.38	$I_2 + 2e^- \rightarrow 2I^-$	0.53
$Mg^{2+} + 2e^- \rightarrow Mg$	−2.36	$Hg_2SO_4 + 2e^- \rightarrow 2Hg + SO_4^{2-}$	0.62
$Ce^{3+} + 3e^- \rightarrow Ce$	−2.34	$2HgCl_2 + 2e^- \rightarrow Hg_2Cl_2 + 2Cl^-$	0.63
$H_2 + 2e^- \rightarrow 2H^-$	−2.25	$O_2 + 2H^+ + 2e^- \rightarrow H_2O_2$	0.68
$Pu^{3+} + 3e^- \rightarrow Pu$	−2.03	$Fe^{3+} + e^- \rightarrow Fe^{2+}$	0.77
$Be^{2+} + 2e^- \rightarrow Be$	−1.85	$Hg_2^{2+} + 2e^- \rightarrow 2Hg$	0.79
$Al^{3+} + 3e^- \rightarrow Al$	−1.66	$Ag^+ + e^- \rightarrow Ag$	0.80
$SiF_6^{2-} + 4e^- \rightarrow Si + 6F^-$	−1.20	$NO_3^- + 2H^+ + e^- \rightarrow NO_2 + H_2O$	0.80
$Mn^{2+} + 2e^- \rightarrow Mn$	−1.18	$O_2 + 4H^+(10^{-7}M) + 4e^- \rightarrow 2H_2O$	0.82
$OCN^- + H_2O + 2e^- \rightarrow CN^- + 2OH^-$	−0.97	$Hg^{2+} + 2e^- \rightarrow Hg$	0.85
$Cr^{2+} + 2e^- \rightarrow Cr$	−0.91	$ClO^- + H_2O + 2e^- \rightarrow Cl^- + 2OH^-$	0.90
$2H_2O + 2e^- \rightarrow H_2 + 2OH^-$	−0.83	$2Hg^{2+} + 2e^- \rightarrow Hg_2^{2+}$	0.92
$Zn^{2+} + 2e^- \rightarrow Zn$	−0.76	$NO_3^- + 3H^+ + 2e^- \rightarrow HNO_2 + H_2O$	0.94
$U^{4+} + e^- \rightarrow U^{3+}$	−0.61	$NO_3^- + 4H^+ + 3e^- \rightarrow NO(g) + 2H_2O$	0.96
$Ga^{3+} + 3e^- \rightarrow Ga$	−0.56	$Pd^{2+} + 2e^- \rightarrow Pd$	0.99
$H_3PO_3 + 2H^+ + 2e^- \rightarrow H_3PO_2 + H_2O$	−0.50	$Br_2 + 2e^- \rightarrow 2Br^-$	1.07
$2CO_2 + 2H^+ + 2e^- \rightarrow H_2C_2O_4$	−0.49	$MnO_2 + 4H^+ + 2e^- \rightarrow Mn^{2+} + 2H_2O$	1.23
$NO_2^- + H_2O + e^- \rightarrow NO + 2OH^-$	−0.46	$O_2 + 4H^+ + 4e^- \rightarrow 2H_2O$	1.23
$Fe^{2+} + 2e^- \rightarrow Fe$	−0.44	$2HNO_2 + 4H^+ + 4e^- \rightarrow N_2O + 3H_2O$	1.27
$Eu^{3+} + 3e^- \rightarrow Eu$	−0.43	$Cr_2O_7^{2-} + 14H^+ + 6e^- \rightarrow 2Cr^{3+} + 7H_2O$	1.33
$Cr^{3+} + e^- \rightarrow Cr^{2+}$	−0.41	$Cl_2 + 2e^- \rightarrow 2Cl^-$	1.36
$2H^+(10^{-7}M) + 2e^- \rightarrow H_2$	−0.41	$Au^{3+} + 2e^- \rightarrow Au^+$	1.42
$Cd^{2+} + 2e^- \rightarrow Cd$	−0.40	$PbO_2 + 4H^+ + 2e^- \rightarrow Pb^{2+} + 2H_2O$	1.46
$PbSO_4 + 2e^- \rightarrow Pb + SO_4^{2-}$	−0.36	$2ClO_3^- + 12H^+ + 10e^- \rightarrow Cl_2 + 6H_2O$	1.47
$Co^{2+} + 2e^- \rightarrow Co$	−0.28	$HClO + H^+ + 2e^- \rightarrow Cl^- + H_2O$	1.49
$Ni^{2+} + 2e^- \rightarrow Ni$	−0.25	$Au^{3+} + 3e^- \rightarrow Au$	1.50
$Sn^{2+} + 2e^- \rightarrow Sn$	−0.14	$MnO_4^- + 8H^+ + 5e^- \rightarrow Mn^{2+} + 4H_2O$	1.51
$Pb^{2+} + 2e^- \rightarrow Pb$	−0.13	$MnO_4^- + 4H^+ + 3e^- \rightarrow MnO_2 + 2H_2O$	1.70
$AgCN + e^- \rightarrow Ag + CN^-$	−0.02	$H_2O_2 + 2H^+ + 2e^- \rightarrow 2H_2O$	1.78
$2H^+ + 2e^- \rightarrow H_2$	0.00	$Co^{3+} + e^- \rightarrow Co^{2+}$	1.81
$UO_2^{2+} + e^- \rightarrow UO_2^+$	0.06	$S_2O_8^{2-} + 2e^- \rightarrow 2SO_4^{2-}$	2.01
$S + 2H^+ + 2e^- \rightarrow H_2S$	0.14	$O_3 + 2H^+ + 2e^- \rightarrow O_2 + H_2O$	2.07
$Sn^{4+} + 2e^- \rightarrow Sn^{2+}$	0.15	$F_2 + 2e^- \rightarrow 2F^-$	2.87
$Cu^{2+} + e^- \rightarrow Cu^+$	0.15	$F_2 + 2H^+ + 2e^- \rightarrow 2HF$	3.03
$SO_4^{2-} + 4H^+ + 2e^- \rightarrow SO_2(aq) + 2H_2O$	0.17		

Weak Oxidizing Agents/Strong Reducing Agents

Strong Oxidizing Agents/Weak Reducing Agents

SUGGESTION: Work with various combinations of half-reactions here so that use of the reduction potential table becomes a habit.

Electrons flow from donor (anode) to acceptor (cathode).

In Table 27-1, the substance on the left side of the arrow in each case is an oxidizing agent. It is an electron acceptor. The oxidizing agent with the highest positive potential is the strongest oxidizing agent. The oxidizing agents in this table are arranged in the order of increasing strength from top to bottom. Think of this series of substances as a list arranged in order of ability to attract electrons in competition with other oxidizing agents. The substance on the right side of the arrow in each case is a reducing agent. The strongest reducing agent is at the top of the table and the strength of the reducing agents decreases toward the bottom of the table. Let us see how this table can be used to predict the course of a particular reaction. Remember that electrons must flow from an electron donor (reducing agent) to an electron acceptor (oxidizing agent).

The half-reactions in Table 27-1 are all written as reductions. If we reverse a reaction and write it as an oxidation, the voltage remains the same in magnitude, but of opposite sign. For example.

$$Li^+ + e^- \rightarrow Li \qquad -3.05 \text{ volts}$$

but

$$Li \rightarrow Li^+ + e^- \qquad +3.05 \text{ volts}$$

As an example, consider what will happen if a strip of copper is immersed in a silver nitrate solution. A possible reaction could be written as

$$Cu(cr) + 2Ag^+(aq) \rightarrow 2Ag(cr) + Cu^{2+}(aq)$$

If this reaction is to occur, copper must give up electrons to silver ions. A glance at Table 27-1 shows that silver ions have a greater attraction for electrons than copper ions. This reaction may be done in the laboratory by immersing a coil of copper wire in a silver nitrate solution.

SUGGESTION: Perform this experiment in the laboratory as a demonstration.

FIGURE 27-11. Copper atoms are oxidized in a silver nitrate solution (a). No reaction occurs between copper and the zinc sulfate solution in (b).

When silver ions are converted to silver atoms, a beautiful feathery deposit of metallic silver appears on the copper coil.

Assume we immerse a strip of copper in a solution containing zinc ions. If a reaction is to occur, copper atoms must give up electrons to zinc ions. Table 27-1 shows that copper has a greater attraction for electrons than zinc. Thus, we can predict that copper atoms cannot give electrons to zinc ions. No reaction will occur.

PROBLEMS

Using Table 27-1, predict if the following reactions will occur spontaneously as written.

1. $Al^{3+}(aq) + Ni(cr) \rightarrow Ni^{2+}(aq) + Al(cr)$
2. $Ag^+(aq) + Co(cr) \rightarrow Co^{2+}(aq) + Ag(cr)$
3. $Sn^{2+}(aq) + Pb^{2+}(aq) \rightarrow Sn^{4+}(aq) + Pb(cr)$
4. $Au^{3+}(aq) + Fe(cr) \rightarrow Au(cr) + Fe^{2+}(aq)$

1. −1.41 V no reaction
2. +1.08 V rxn occurs
3. −0.28 V no reaction
4. +1.94 V rxn occurs

27:9 CELL POTENTIAL

Suppose we wish to find what voltage we could obtain from a cell using $Mg|Mg^{2+}$ and $Cu|Cu^{2+}$. We will assume that Mg will be oxidized and Cu^{2+} will be reduced. From Table 27-1, we see that

$$Mg^{2+} + 2e^- \rightarrow Mg \quad -2.36 \text{ volts}$$

Thus, the oxidation reaction is

$$Mg \rightarrow Mg^{2+} + 2e^- \quad +2.36 \text{ volts}$$

The reduction reaction is

$$Cu^{2+} + 2e^- \rightarrow Cu \quad +0.34 \text{ volts}$$

The sum of the two potentials is +2.70 volts. This quantity is the voltage of the cell if the ion concentration in each compartment is one molar, and the temperature is 25°C. The direction of electron flow in the external circuit can be determined from the fact that the magnesium ion is losing electrons. Magnesium (the anode) gives up electrons that flow through the external circuit to the copper electrode. There the reduction reaction occurs. Would it be possible to construct a cell in which copper metal is used as the anode and magnesium ion is reduced at the cathode? Remember, a negative voltage indicates that the reverse reaction occurs.

Note that the reduction potentials in Table 27-1 are expressed in volts. This voltage indicates how strong a tendency each half-reaction has to gain electrons. Lithium with a voltage of −3.05 has a weak tendency to gain an electron and fluorine at the bottom of the table has a strong tendency to gain an electron.

Magnesium has a higher potential than copper.

If a reaction yields a negative voltage, the reverse action yields a positive voltage.

The standard reduction potential indicates a tendency of the half-reaction to gain electrons. The greater the voltage, the greater the tendency to gain electrons.

EXAMPLE: Cell Voltage

What voltage should be produced by the following cell?

$$Fe|Fe^{2+}||Br_2|Br^-$$

Solving Process:
The table of standard reduction potentials lists the voltage for the two half-reactions as

$$Fe^{2+} + 2e^- \rightarrow Fe \qquad -0.44 \text{ V}$$

$$Br_2 + 2e^- \rightarrow 2Br^- \qquad 1.07 \text{ V}$$

Since we have iron being oxidized to iron(II) ions, the voltage for that half-cell would be +0.44 V. The sum of the two half-cell voltages gives us the cell potential.

$$0.44 + 1.07 = 1.51 \text{ V}$$

PROBLEM

5. a. 0.32 volts
   b. 2.25 volts
   c. 2.00 V
   d. 1.04 V
   e. 0.46 V
   f. 1.49 V

5. Predict the voltages produced by the following cells. Use Table 27-1.

  a. $Zn|Zn^{2+}||Fe^{2+}|Fe$

  b. $Mn|Mn^{2+}||Br_2|Br^-$

  c. $H_2C_2O_4|CO_2||MnO_4^-|Mn^{2+}$

  d. $Ni|Ni^{2+}||Hg_2^{2+}|Hg$

  e. $Cu|Cu^{2+}||Ag^+|Ag$

  f. $Pb|Pb^{2+}||Cl_2|Cl^-$

27:10   PRODUCTS OF ELECTROLYSIS

In Section 27:4 we saw that there could be competition for reaction at the electrodes in an electrolytic cell. In the case examined there, the competition was between sodium ions and water molecules.

Reduction tables can be used to predict electrolysis products.

In order to predict which reactions will actually occur at an electrode, we use the table of reduction potentials. The energy required to cause an electrode reaction to occur varies directly with the negative voltage of that reaction. The reaction that requires the least amount of energy is associated with the least negative (most positive) voltage. Since most electrolysis reactions take place in water solution, we need to know the voltage required to oxidize and reduce water. In investigating the voltages involved in these reactions, we must remember that water dissociates slightly into H^+ and OH^-. In a neutral solution, both of these ions are found in a concentration of $10^{-7}M$. The reactions of interest to us are reduction of water:

$$2H_2O + 2e^- \rightleftarrows H_2 + 2OH^- \qquad -0.414 \text{ volts } (10^{-7}M \text{ OH}^-)$$

oxidation of water:

$$2H_2O \rightleftarrows 4e^- + 4H^+ + O_2 \qquad -0.82 \text{ volts } (10^{-7}M \text{ H}^+)$$

The voltage required to reduce water = -0.414 volts.

The voltage required to oxidize water = -0.82 volts.

EXAMPLE: Predicting Products of Electrolysis

Predict the products of the electrolysis of a solution of potassium iodide in water.

Solving Process:

The possible reduction reactions are

$$K^+ + e^- \rightarrow K \qquad -2.93 \text{ V}$$

$$2H_2O + 2e^- \rightarrow H_2 + 2OH^- \qquad -0.414 \text{ V}$$

The least negative value is the reduction of water, so the product at the cathode is hydrogen gas. The possible oxidations are

$$2I^- \rightarrow I_2 + 2e^- \qquad -0.53 \text{ V}$$

$$2H_2O \rightarrow 4e^- + 4H^+ + O_2 \qquad -0.82 \text{ V}$$

The least negative value is the oxidation of iodide ion, so the product at the anode is iodine.

The "least negative value" is the greater value on the number line.

PROBLEM

6. Predict the products of the electrolysis of the following aqueous $1M$ solutions.

    a. Na_2SO_4 **c.** CoF_2 **e.** LiBr

    b. $CuCl_2$ **d.** $Pb(NO_3)_2$ **f.** NaCl

6. a. H_2 and O_2
   b. Cu and O_2
   c. Co and O_2
   d. Pb and O_2
   e. H_2 and O_2
   f. H_2 and Cl_2

27:11 EFFECT OF CONDITIONS ON CELLS AND ENERGY

In the latter part of the nineteenth century, H. W. Nernst, a German chemist, worked with voltaic cells. He found the relationship between the voltage of a cell and the conditions under which it was operating. The voltage of a cell under standard conditions is called $E°$. The values in Table 27-1 are $E°$ values for $1M$ solutions at 25°C and 101.325 kPa pressure. If we now call the voltage of a cell at other than standard conditions E, we can use the relationship worked out by Nernst.

The $E°$ values in Table 27-1 are at 25°C, a pressure of 101.325 kPa, and an ionic concentration of $1M$.

$$E = E° - \frac{RT}{nF} \ln \frac{(concentration\ of\ products)}{(concentration\ of\ reactants)}$$

Let us look at each of the factors in the equation. The value of R is the universal gas constant that we developed in the ideal gas equation (Section 19:3). However, in applying R to electric measurements it must be expressed in convenient units. These units will be different from the $dm^3 \cdot kPa/mol \cdot K$ used in gas calculations. Conversion to $J/mol \cdot K$ gives a value of 8.31. The value of T is the absolute temperature in K. The value of n is the number of electrons transferred in the balanced equation representing the change taking place in the cell. The value of F is a conversion factor from volts to joules per mole and is equal to 96 500. The symbol ln stands for the natural logarithm that we can replace with (2.30 log) to use common logarithms. If we combine the constants (R/F) 2.30 with the standard temperature, 298 K, we obtain 0.0592. We may then write the Nernst equation in a simpler form.

The Nernst equation can be used to find the voltage at concentrations other than standard.

$$E = E° - \frac{0.0592}{n} \log \frac{(concentration\ of\ products)}{(concentration\ of\ reactants)}$$
at standard temperature

SUGGESTION: Refer students to Appendix B if they experience difficulty with logarithms.

Let us now apply this equation to a sample problem.

EXAMPLE: Nonstandard Concentrations

What would be the voltage of a cell using $Ni|Ni^{2+}$ (2.50M) for one half-cell and $Ag|Ag^+$ (0.100M) for the other half-cell? Assume the pressure and temperature to be at standard values.

Solving Process:

Determine the balanced redox equation for the cell.

(a) Determine the equation for the total cell reaction. In a comparison between Ni^{2+} and Ag^+, silver has the greater tendency to gain electrons. On that basis, nickel is oxidized and silver is reduced.

$$Ni(cr) + 2Ag^+(aq) \rightarrow Ni^{2+}(aq) + 2Ag(cr)$$

(b) Determine the values to be substituted into the Nernst equation.

$E = E° - \frac{0.0592}{n} \log \frac{[products]}{[reactants]}$

$$E = E° - \frac{0.0592}{n} \log \frac{[Ni^{2+}]}{[Ag^+]^2}$$

Solids having a constant concentration do not appear in the equation.

From Table 27-1, $E° = \overset{Ni\ oxidation}{+0.25\ volts} + \overset{Ag^+\ reduction}{0.80\ volts} = 1.05\ volts$

$n = 2$ (the number of electrons transferred)

$$E = 1.05\ V - \frac{0.0592}{2} \log \frac{[2.50]}{[0.100][0.100]}$$

$= 1.05 - 0.0296(\log 250)$
$= 1.05 - 0.0296(2.40)$
$= 1.05 - 0.07 = 0.98\ volts$

Note that the concentration of silver ion is squared in the expression. The concentrations of reactants and products are handled in the Nernst equation exactly as they are in an equilibrium constant expression.

PROBLEMS

7. What voltage could you expect (ideally) from the following cell at 25°C?

$Pb|Pb^{2+}(0.485M)\|Sn^{4+}(0.652M)|Sn^{2+}(0.346M)$

8. What voltage could you expect (ideally) from the following cell at 25°C?

$Ni|Ni^{2+}(1.00M)\|Cu^{2+}(0.0100M)|Cu$

9. What voltage could you expect (ideally) from the following cell at 25°C?

$Fe|Fe^{2+}(0.720M)\|Ag^{+}(0.785M)|Ag$

7. 0.30 V
8. 0.56 V
9. 1.24 V

27:12   pH METER

The Nernst equation can be applied to half-cells as well as to an entire cell. Consider the hydrogen half-cell at normal temperature and pressure.

$$2H^+ + 2e^- \rightarrow H_2$$

$$E = E° - 0.0592 \log \frac{1}{[H^+]}$$

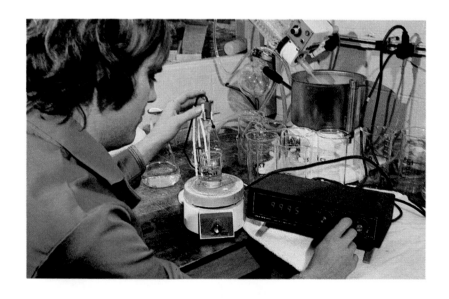

FIGURE 27-12. A pH meter is an analytical instrument used to measure electrically the hydrogen ion concentration of a solution. The voltage difference between the electrodes is measured in pH units.

Using the relationship $\log 1/x = -\log x$, we can rearrange the above equation.

$$E = E° + 0.0592 \log [H^+]$$

We know that $E°$ for the hydrogen half-cell is 0.00 volts. We also know that $-\log [H^+] = pH$. Substituting these values we get

$$E = -0.0592 \; pH$$

E is a linear function of pH.

Thus E is a linear function of pH. By combining a reference electrode with a hydrogen electrode, we can measure the pH of a solution electrically. The reference electrode usually chosen is the saturated calomel* electrode because it has a known constant voltage. The meter measuring the voltage between the reference and hydrogen ion electrodes is calibrated to read directly in pH units. This calibration then saves the chemist the trouble of converting from volts to pH units.

The pH meter makes use of a hydrogen ion electrode and a reference electrode.

27:13   ENERGY AND ELECTRIC CELLS

In Chapter 23 we saw that the free energy change for a reaction was related to the equilibrium constant for the reaction. The relationship was $\Delta G° = -2.30RT \log K$. Perhaps you have already noticed the similarity between this expression and the Nernst equation. The Nernst equation may be written as

$$E = E° - \frac{2.30RT}{nF} \log K$$

The value of F is a conversion factor from volts to joules per mole and is equal to 96 500.

At equilibrium, there is no net change, so E would equal zero. Solving the equation for $(2.30RT) \log K$ and substituting 0 for E, we obtain

$$2.30RT \log K = nFE°$$

Substituting the equivalent expression in the free energy equation we get

$$\Delta G° = -nFE°$$

Recall $\Delta G = \Delta H - T\Delta S$

These relationships are important to a chemist. Once the cell voltages have been measured, they can be used to derive a great deal of other information. If the voltage is known, the free energy change for the reaction may be calculated. With other information, enthalpy and entropy changes can be found. Measurement of voltages may also be used to determine the equilibrium constant for reactions. We have seen that free energy, standard cell potentials, and equilibrium constants are related. Any of these factors can be used as a predictor of reaction spontaneity. A reaction tends to be spontaneous if K_{eq} is considerably larger than 1, $E° > 0$, and $\Delta G < 0$.

Voltages can be used to determine K_{eq}.

*Calomel is Hg_2Cl_2.

PROBLEMS

10. What is the free energy change for the following reaction at standard conditions?

$$2U^{3+} + Hg^{2+} \rightarrow 2U^{4+} + Hg$$

11. What is the free energy change for the following reaction at standard conditions?

$$Zn + 2Hg^{2+} \rightarrow Zn^{2+} + Hg_2^{2+}$$

10. −282 kJ
11. −324 kJ

Recall F = 96 500 C

27:14 QUANTITATIVE ASPECTS OF ELECTROCHEMISTRY

The equations for the electrode half-reactions can be balanced like any other chemical equation. They have the same quantitative significance. Consider the equation for the formation of sodium metal in the electrolysis of molten sodium chloride. It indicates that 1 mole of electrons is required to produce 1 mole of sodium atoms. However, other than in chemical reactions, electricity is not measured in moles. The more common unit for electricity is the coulomb. One coulomb (C) is the quantity of electricity produced by a current of one ampere flowing for one second. 96 500 coulombs is the equivalent of 1 mole of electrons. This quantity is a convenient unit for electrochemical calculations.

96 500 coulombs = 1 mole of electrons

One mole of sodium is 23 grams. To produce 23 grams of sodium by an electrolytic reaction, one mole of electrons must be used. One mole of electrons equals 96 500 coulombs. Since 1 coulomb is equal to a current of one ampere flowing for one second, 1 coulomb is equal to 1 ampere·second. The number of coulombs used in a reaction can be obtained by multiplying the number of amperes by the number of seconds. We could produce 23 grams of sodium by using a current of 10 amperes for 9650 seconds. Any combination of amperes and seconds that gives a product of 96 500 A·s will yield 23 g of sodium (one mole).

In the anode reaction for the electrolysis of sodium chloride, one chlorine molecule requires the release of two electrons. Thus, one mole of chlorine gas will require two moles of electrons.

The principles that we have just discussed are expressed in more concise form as Faraday's laws. They were proposed by Michael Faraday.

Since the amount of electricity produced is equal to the current in amperes multiplied by the time in seconds, we may say:

coulombs = amperes × seconds

DEMONSTRATION: Plate copper metal on an electrode made from a pencil with the wood cut back. See the Teacher Guide for details. After Cu has been plated, the cell can be reconnected to demonstrate an electrochemical cell producing a voltage.

One coulomb is the quantity of electricity produced by 1 ampere flowing for 1 second.

1 C = 1 A·s

Further, we can write the following expression.

$$moles\ of\ electrons = \frac{ampere}{}\ \bigg|\ \frac{second}{}\ \bigg|\ \frac{1\ coulomb}{1\ ampere·second}\ \bigg|\ \frac{1\ mole\ e^-}{96\ 500\ coulomb}$$

From a balanced equation we obtain the relationship between the formula mass of a substance and the moles of electrons.

$$\frac{mass\ of\ substance}{per\ mole\ of\ electrons} = \frac{formula\ mass\ of\ substance}{moles\ of\ electrons\ transferred}$$

Combining the two expressions, we get the mathematical statement of Faraday's laws.

$$mass\ of\ substance = \frac{coulombs}{}\ \bigg|\ \frac{1\ mole\ e^-}{96\ 500\ coulombs}\ \bigg|\ \frac{formula\ mass}{mole\ e^-}$$

Note that the coefficient of the substance in the equation must be taken into account.

EXAMPLE: Faraday's Law Calculation

What mass of copper will be deposited by a current of 7.89 amperes flowing for a period of 1200 seconds?

Solving Process:
The cathode reaction is

$$Cu^{2+}(aq) + 2e^- \rightarrow Cu(cr)$$

$Cu^{2+} + 2e^- \rightarrow Cu$
2 moles of electrons will reduce
1 mole of Cu^{2+} to Cu.

and therefore 2 moles of e^- plate out 63.5 g Cu(cr). By combining the expressions, we obtain

$$\frac{7.89\ A}{}\ \bigg|\ \frac{1200\ s}{}\ \bigg|\ \frac{1\ C}{A·s}\ \bigg|\ \frac{1\ mole\ e^-}{96\ 500\ C}\ \bigg|\ \frac{1\ mol\ Cu}{2\ mole\ e^-}\ \bigg|\ \frac{63.5\ g\ Cu}{1\ mol\ Cu} = 3.1\ g\ Cu$$

EXAMPLE: Faraday's Law Calculation

What mass of Cr^{3+} ion is produced by a current of 0.713 ampere flowing for 12 800 seconds? The equation for the total reaction is

$$14H_3O^+(aq) + 6Fe^{2+}(aq) + Cr_2O_7{}^{2-}(aq) \rightarrow 6Fe^{3+}(aq) + 2Cr^{3+}(aq) + 21H_2O(l)$$

Solving Process:

Cr in $Cr_2O_7{}^{2-}$ has an oxidation number of 6+.

You must verify that the moles of electrons involved in the equation as written are equal to six ($Cr_2O_7{}^{2-} \rightarrow 2Cr^{3+}$). Then by substituting in the Faraday's Law equation the following expression is obtained.

$$\frac{0.713\ A}{}\ \bigg|\ \frac{12\ 800\ s}{}\ \bigg|\ \frac{1\ C}{A·s}\ \bigg|\ \frac{1\ mole\ e^-}{96\ 500\ C}\ \bigg|\ \frac{2\ mol\ Cr^{3+}}{6\ mole\ e^-}\ \bigg|\ \frac{52.0\ g\ Cr^{3+}}{1\ mol\ Cr^{3+}} = 1.64\ g\ Cr^{3+}$$

PROBLEMS

12. How many grams of silver will be deposited by a current of 1.00 A flowing for 9650 s?

13. A current of 5.00 A flows through a cell for 10.0 min. How many grams of silver could be deposited during this time? Write the cathode reaction.

14. What current must be used to plate 1.75 mole of copper on an electrode in 6.24 min?

15. What period of time, in hours, was required if a current of 5.00 A was passed through a salt (sodium chloride) solution and 1.00 mole of chlorine was produced?

16. How many minutes would be necessary to deposit 0.375 g of calcium from a cell with a current of 3.93 A?

12. 10.8 g Ag
13. 3.36 g Ag, $Ag^+ + e^- \rightarrow Ag$
14. 902 A
15. 10.7 h (643 min)
16. 7.65 min

27:15 ELECTROANALYSIS

An immediate application of electrochemistry is its use in quantitative analysis. For example, suppose that it is necessary for you to determine the percentage of copper in a given water soluble copper compound. A sample of the compound of known mass could be dissolved in water and inert electrodes inserted. The mass of the cathode should be measured before the current is applied. As the current is passed through the cell, metallic copper plates onto the electrode of known mass. When the action is complete and current no longer flows, all the copper is plated. The mass of the electrode is again measured. The difference in mass (due to the copper) is compared to the mass of the sample to find the percentage of copper in the sample. Electroanalysis is a useful tool of the chemist.

Platinum is usually used.

EXAMPLE: Electroanalysis

What is the percentage of nickel in an alloy with the following analysis:

Mass of alloy sample = 6.73 g
Mass of cathode before depositing Ni = 19.142 g
Mass of cathode after depositing Ni = 19.634 g

Solving Process:
(a) Find the mass of nickel deposited.

$$19.634 - 19.142 = 0.492 \text{ g Ni}$$

(b) Find the percentage of nickel in this alloy.

$$\frac{0.492 \text{ g}}{6.73 \text{ g}} \times 100 = 7.31\% \text{ Ni}$$

$$\% = \frac{mass\ difference}{mass\ of\ sample} \times 100$$

Brass is an alloy of Cu and Zn.

17. 79.9% Cu

PROBLEM

17. A chemist must analyze a sample of brass with mass 2.60 g for copper content. Brass is an alloy of copper and zinc. It is usually contaminated with tin, lead, and iron. The zinc and iron do not interfere with the electroanalysis. The alloy is dissolved in nitric acid, and the tin present is precipitated as SnO_2. The solution is then treated with sulfuric acid, precipitating the lead as $PbSO_4$. The resulting solution is prepared for electrolysis to determine the copper content. The mass of the cathode of the electrolysis apparatus is measured and found to be 26.041 grams. The electrolysis is run, the cathode is dried, and its mass is again measured. Its new mass is 28.118 g. What is the percentage of copper in the alloy?

BIOGRAPHY

Michael Faraday (1791-1867)

The son of an English blacksmith, Michael Faraday was apprenticed early in life to a bookbinder. As a result he could devote only his spare time to his pursuits in science. Largely self-educated, his real boost into the scientific world came through the sponsorship of Sir Humphrey Davy, an English chemist and physicist. Faraday's greatest work involved passing a current through different solutions and finding that it caused an electrolysis reaction. The relationship between the amount of current used and the amount of product formed was expressed in the form of two laws now known as Faraday's laws. He also discovered that an electric current creates a magnetic field.

In other areas, he discovered benzene and several organic chlorides. He also did research on the physics of polarized light and the diffusion and liquefaction of gases.

TECHNOLOGY AND CHEMISTRY

27:16   Corrosion

The chemical reactions of metals with their environment is called corrosion. Corrosion results in the deterioration of the metal in forming metal compounds. The cost of trying to prevent and correct this deterioration runs to many billions of dollars each year.

Water and oxygen are the chief reactants, but many other substances are involved. The pale green coating that copper and brass acquire (see

Figure 26-1) involves carbon dioxide as well as oxygen and water. Dirt, salts used in treating icy streets, and other metals all increase the rate of corrosion. As in other chemical reactions, an increase in temperature increases the rate of corrosion.

Many corrosion processes, including rusting, are electrochemical processes. Consider an iron surface on which a piece of soot (carbon) has fallen, followed by a drop of water. Some carbon dioxide from the air dissolves in the water to form carbonic acid.

$$CO_2 + H_2O \rightarrow H_2CO_3$$

$$H_2CO_3 + H_2O \rightarrow H_3O^+ + HCO_3^-$$

The essential components of a voltaic cell are present—two electrodes (carbon and iron), and an electrolyte (a solution of H_3O^+ and HCO_3^-). The iron, being more active, acts as the anode. The carbon acts as the cathode.

$$Fe \rightarrow Fe^{2+} + 2e^- \qquad O_2 + 2H_2O + 4e^- \rightarrow 4OH^-$$

The Fe^{2+} ions can be oxidized by the air to Fe^{3+} ions, before or after combining with the OH^- ions. The $Fe(OH)_3$ formed soon becomes rust, $Fe_2O_3 \cdot xH_2O$, a hydrated iron(III) oxide.

Corrosion can be prevented in several ways. Some metals form a self-protecting layer of oxidized metal on the surface. This layer is impervious and protects the interior of the metal from further attack. Aluminum, nickel, and chromium are typical metals which exhibit this behavior. Metallurgists are learning how to create these types of layers on other metals. Coating or alloying corrosion-prone metals with self-protective metals is one way of fighting corrosion.

Metals may be coated with nonmetallic materials also. Grease, paint, and porcelain enamel have all been used to protect metals from corrosion. Another protective measure takes advantage of the electrochemical nature of corrosion. The metal to be protected is connected electrically to a more active metal. The connection may be a direct contact or by wire. When two metals in electric contact are subjected to an oxidizing agent, the more active metal is oxidized, while the less active metal remains unchanged. Zinc and magnesium are frequently used for this purpose in the shipping industry. Blocks of these more active metals are attached to the less active steel hull (see Figure 11-17). Underground pipes are also protected in this way.

SUMMARY

1. An electric current is carried through a metal by the movement of electrons. An electric current is carried through a solution or molten salt by the movement of positive and negative ions. 27:1

2. When two points with a potential difference are connected by a conductor, an electric current will flow. An electric current is the flow of electricity through a conductor. It passes from the point of higher potential to the point of lower potential. 27:1

3. Current is measured with an ammeter or galvanometer and is expressed in amperes (A). 27:1

4. Voltage is the measure of potential difference. Voltage is measured with a volt-meter and is expressed in volts (V). 27:1

5. Electrolyte solutions are electrically neutral, but contain ions which are free to move, as do molten ionic compounds. Cations are positive ions; anions are negative ions. 27:2

6. When ions migrating through an electrolytic cell reach an electrode, they undergo oxidation or reduction reactions. 27:3-27:4

7. A voltaic cell is a cell which produces an electric current and is composed of two dissimilar metals and an electrolyte. 27:5-27:6

8. Any oxidation-reduction reaction can (theoretically) be set up in such a way that current will be produced. 27:5

9. An oxidation-reduction reaction is a reversible reaction. Therefore, any change in temperature, pressure, or concentration will affect the flow of electric current. 27:8

10. The reduction potential of electrode reactions measures the relative strength of oxidizing and reducing agents. 27:8

11. The standard electrode potential series is a group of half-reactions arranged in order of their reduction potential. The hydrogen half-cell is the standard reference cell and is assigned a voltage of 0.0000 V at standard conditions. 27:8

12. The table of standard electrode potentials can be used to predict the direction of reaction, the electromotive force of cells, and the products of electrolysis. 27:8-27:10

13. A reaction in a voltaic cell will occur spontaneously if the voltage for the overall reaction is positive. 27:9

14. An electrolytic cell is a cell in which the electrons are forced to flow in a direction opposite to their normal flow. This flow-reversing process is called electrolysis. 27:10

15. In both electrolytic and voltaic cells, oxidation occurs at the anode and reduction occurs at the cathode. 27:3-27:5, 27:10

16. The Nernst equation relates the voltage of a cell to the conditions under which the cell is operating. 27:11

$$E = E° - \frac{2.30RT}{nF} \log K$$

17. The relationship between hydrogen ion concentration and the voltage of the hydrogen half-cell can be used as the basis for the electrical measurement of pH. 27:12

18. The voltage generated by a cell and the free energy change of the reaction occurring in the cell are related by the following equation. 27:13

$$\Delta G = -nFE°$$

19. One coulomb is the quantity of electricity produced by a current of 1 ampere flowing for 1 second. 96 500 coulombs = 1 mole of electrons. 27:14

20. The mass of matter reacting in a cell is determined by formula mass and the amount of electricity which passes through the cell. 27:14-27:15

VOCABULARY

galvanometer Intro
salt bridge Intro
electric current 27:1
volts 27:1
amperes 27:1
cations 27:2

anions 27:2
electronic conduction 27:4
metallic conduction 27:4
electrolytic conduction 27:4
voltaic cell 27:5

PROBLEMS

1. Which of the following reactions will proceed spontaneously?

   a. $Na + Cl_2 \rightarrow$?   **c.** $Cu + H_2 \rightarrow$?   **e.** $Zn + Pb^{2+} \rightarrow$?
   b. $Fe^{2+} + Cu \rightarrow$?   **d.** $Cu^{2+} + Ag^+ \rightarrow$?   **f.** $Fe + Pb^{2+} \rightarrow$?

   1. a. yes   d. no
      b. no   e. yes
      c. no   f. yes

2. Explain how to determine whether a given electrode is an anode or a cathode.

   2. oxidation occurs at anode, reduction at cathode

3. How can an insulator be made to conduct a current?

4. Why does an ionic solid inhibit the flow of electric current?

5. How does electrolysis differ from electrolytic conduction?

6. If a particular metal is considered more active than another, what does that statement tell you concerning its electronic structure?

7. From each of the following pairs, select the better reducing agent.

   a. Cd, Fe   **c.** Pb, Zn
   b. Ca, Mg   **d.** Br^-, Cu

   7. a. Fe
      b. Ca
      c. Zn
      d. Cu

8. From each of the following pairs, select the better oxidizing agent.

   a. Ca^{2+}, Li^+ **c.** Cl_2, Hg^{2+}
   b. Fe^{3+}, Hg_2^{2+} **d.** Cu^+, Cu^{2+}

   8. a. Ca^{2+}
      b. Hg_2^{2+}
      c. Cl_2
      d. Cu^+

9. How do electronic and electrolytic conduction differ?

10. What maximum voltage could you expect from a cell that consisted of $Al|Al^{3+}$ and $Ag|Ag^+$ half cells? Write the electrode reactions and the overall reaction.

    10. 2.46 V

11. What reaction would you expect at the electrodes of a Hooker cell (a device for the electrolysis of sodium chloride solution)?

    12. 6.22 dm^3

12. The electrolysis of 10.0 grams of water would produce what volume in dm^3 of O_2 at STP? Give each electrode reaction.

13. 3.80 V
14. 1.16 V
15. −110 kJ
16. $K = 9.83 \times 10^{19}$
17. $E° = 0.31$ V
18. 35.0% Ni
19. 1.34 h (80.4 min)
20. a. $Ag^+ + e^- \rightarrow Ag$
    b. 40.3 g

13. What voltage could you expect from the following cell at 25°C?
    $Mg|Mg^{2+}(0.170M)\|Cl_2|Cl^-(0.100M)$

14. What voltage would be obtained at 25°C from the following cell?
    $Cd|Cd^{2+}(0.500M)\|Fe^{3+}(0.100M)|Fe^{2+}(0.200M)$

15. Using the standard reduction potential table compute the free energy change for the reaction: $Sn^{4+} + Fe \rightarrow Fe^{2+} + Sn^{2+}$

16. Find the equilibrium constant for the reaction in Problem 15, at standard conditions.

17. What voltage would you expect to realize from a cell employing a reaction with a free energy change of −30 kJ if the balanced equation shows one electron being transferred?

18. A platinum electrode has a mass of 7.601 g before being plated with nickel, and 9.186 g after the nickel is deposited. If the nickel was obtained from an alloy sample with mass 4.525 g, what percentage of the alloy is nickel?

19. How long, in hours, must a current of 20.0 A be passed through a sodium chloride solution to produce 40.0 g of NaOH?

20. A silver ion solution is subjected to a current of 5.00 A for 2.00 h.
    a. Give the cathode reaction.
    b. How much silver would be plated out?

REVIEW

1. loss of electrons
2. gains of electrons
3. a. 6+
   b. 4+
   c. 7+
   d. 5+

5. proton acceptor
6. hydrotelluric acid
7. hypochlorous acid
8. metallic
9. 2.50×10^{-7}
10. 0.158%
11. $H_4IO_6^-$
12. $2.77 \times 10^{-9}M$
13. 5.44

1. What is the modern definition of oxidation?

2. What does an oxidizing agent do?

3. Show oxidation numbers for the indicated atoms in the following compounds.
   a. U in UF_6
   b. Si in $Al_2(SiF_6)_3$
   c. Cl in $Pb(ClO_4)_2$ (lead is 2+)
   d. As in $Fe_3(AsO_4)_2$ (iron is 2+)

4. Balance by half-reactions:
   $$Fe^{2+} + Cr_2O_7^{2-} \rightarrow Fe^{3+} + Cr^{3+} \text{ (in acid solution)}$$

5. Define a Brønsted base.

6. What is the name of $H_2Te(aq)$?

7. What is the name of HClO?

8. What kind of elements tend to form bases?

9. What is the ionization constant for the dihydrogen pyrophosphate ion, $H_2P_2O_7^{2-}$, if a 0.100M solution of the ion has a hydronium ion concentration of $1.58 \times 10^{-4}M$?

10. What is the percentage ionization in Problem 9?

11. Which ion would you expect to produce a more acidic solution, $H_4IO_6^-$ or $H_3IO_6^{2-}$?

12. What is the hydroxide ion concentration in a solution with hydronium ion concentration of $3.61 \times 10^{-6}M$?

13. What is the pH of the solution in Problem 12?

ONE MORE STEP

1. Trace the development of the search for an understanding of electricity from the first experience with static electricity to our present-day knowledge. You can find this information most easily in a history of science or in an encyclopedia.

2. Use the Nernst equation to compute the voltage of a cell in which one half-cell is made with Zn and $1.00M$ Zn^{2+} and the other half-cell is Zn and $0.100M$ Zn^{2+} at standard conditions.

3. Compute the voltage of a cell in which one half-cell is the hydrogen half-cell with hydrogen at a pressure of 203 kPa and the other half-cell is Zn and Zn^{2+} at $1.00M$. All other conditions are standard.

4. Some batteries carry a warning against recharging. See if you can discover what danger is involved and the reactions which produce that danger.

5. Investigate fuel cells as a source of electricity from chemical reactions.

2. 0.0296 V
3. 0.75 V

READINGS

Alkire, R. C., "Electrochemical Engineering," *Journal of Chemical Education,* Vol. 60, No. 4(1983), pp. 274-276.

Dickie, R. A., and A. G. Smith, "How Paint Arrests Rust," *Chemtech,* Vol. 10, No. 1(January 1980), pp. 31-35.

Douglas, D. L., and J. R. Birk, "Batteries for Energy Storage," *Chemtech,* Vol. 13, Nos. 1 and 2(January and February 1983), pp. 58-64 and 120-129.

Faulkner, Larry R., "Chemical Microstructures on Electrodes," *Chemical and Engineering News,* Vol. 62, No. 9(February 27, 1984), pp. 28-45.

The nucleus of an atom may become a major energy resource. Much research concerning the nucleus centers around controlling the energy produced in nuclear reactions. One such reaction involves combining low molecular mass nuclei to produce tremendous amounts of energy. This fusion process requires extremely high temperatures. Lasers are being used to excite the nucleus to a temperature where fusion can occur. The computer photograph showing a fusion explosion allows scientists to monitor the course of the reaction. What is a fusion reaction? What problems must be overcome before fusion reactions can be a practical energy source?

Chapter 28 introduces the basic aspects of nuclear chemistry: elementary particles, particle accelerators, radioactivity, half-life, and nuclear reactions. Fission and fusion are presented in relation to their development and control.

NUCLEAR CHEMISTRY

28

DEMONSTRATION: Use a Geiger counter to show the presence of radioactive particles as background radiation and from a radioactive source such as uranyl nitrate. Discuss what causes the "click" students hear. You may use a cloud chamber if a counter is not available. The tracks show up best under a strong light. See the Teacher Guide for preparation details concerning a cloud chamber.

In 1896, Henri Becquerel, a French physicist, found that matter containing uranium exposes sealed photographic film. This fact led Becquerel's assistant Marie Curie and her husband, Pierre, to an important discovery. They found that rays are given off by the elements uranium and radium.

Uranium and radium can be found in nature in an ore called pitchblende. This ore is mined in Canada, Colorado, and Germany. If some of this ore is placed near, but not touching a charged electroscope, the leaves become discharged. Substances that have this effect are called radioactive substances. **Radioactivity** is the phenomenon of rays being produced spontaneously by unstable atomic nuclei.

BACKGROUND: The air surrounding the radioactive source becomes ionized by the emitted rays. The air also becomes a conductor which discharges the electroscope leaves.

28:1 NUCLEAR STRUCTURE

The rays produced by radioactive materials are a mixture of particles and quanta. The particles and quanta are given off by the nuclei of radioactive atoms during spontaneous nuclear decay. We say the decay is spontaneous because we have no control over it. The amount of energy released in a nuclear change is very large. It is so large that it cannot be a result of an ordinary chemical change.

Albert Einstein was the first to explain the origin of this energy (Chapter 1). From his theory, we see that mass and energy are equivalent. This statement can be expressed in the equation

$$E = mc^2$$

E is the energy (in joules) released

m is the mass (in kilograms) of matter involved

c is a constant, the speed of light (in meters per second)

The energy-mass change in normal chemical reactions is too small to be measured. However, we are familiar with the nuclear changes that

Radioactive materials produce particles and energy.

Nuclear decay is spontaneous.

Ordinary chemical reactions do not produce nearly as much energy as nuclear reactions produce.

Actually more accurately expressed: $\Delta E = (\Delta m)c^2$

FIGURE 28-1. A radioactive substance will discharge the leaves of an electroscope.

Ordinary forces are not strong enough to hold a nucleus together.

Nucleons (protons and neutrons) have a property which corresponds to electron spin.

FIGURE 28-2. Uranium ore is mined in both underground and surface mines.

Leptons and hadrons are the two classes of subatomic particles.

Every particle has a mirror-image anti-particle (electron-positron).

involve a mass-energy interconversion. The large amount of energy released in splitting the nuclei of uranium or plutonium is measurable. For example, if 1 mol ^{235}U dissolves in hydrochloric acid, $U(cr) + 4HCl(aq) \rightarrow UCl_4(aq) + 2H_2(g)$, 764kJ are produced. On the other hand, if 1 mol ^{235}U undergoes nuclear fission (Section 28:11), 1.90×10^{10} kJ are produced!

The nucleus of the uranium-238 atom contains 92 protons and 146 neutrons. These particles are bound tightly in the nucleus. Acting alone, electrostatic attraction would allow the uncharged neutrons to float away. Since protons all have the same positive charge, electrostatic forces should cause them to fly apart. Gravitational force, which keeps us at the surface of the earth, is not strong enough to hold the nucleus together. What force, then, holds the nucleus together? The **nuclear force** that holds protons and neutrons together is effective for very short distances only (about 10^{-15} m). This distance is about the same as the diameter of the nucleus. Ideas explaining nuclear structure differ, but scientists agree on certain facts.

(1) **Nucleons** (protons and neutrons) have a property that corresponds to the spin of electrons.

(2) Electrons do not exist in the nucleus, yet they can be emitted from the nucleus.

28:2 SUBATOMIC PARTICLES

Nuclear scientists divide subatomic particles into two broad classes, leptons and hadrons. Current theory holds that **leptons** ("light" particles) are truly elementary particles. The electron is the best known lepton.

For every particle, a mirror-image particle called an **antiparticle** exists, or is believed to exist. Thus, there is an antielectron, called a positron, which is like an electron in every way except that it has a positive charge. Positrons are not common. They exist only until they collide with an electron. Such a collision is very likely in our world. When the collision occurs, both particles are destroyed and two quanta of energy are produced. It is interesting to note that there is at least one particle that is its own antiparticle. This particle is the neutral pion.

There are several other leptons. In order to account for the emission of electrons from the nucleus, a neutral particle called a **neutrino** was postulated. The neutrino has been identified and found to be essentially massless. The muon and the tau, both much more massive than the electron, make up the rest of the lepton family. A neutrino has been discovered for the muon and one is predicted for the tau. There are antiparticles for all these particles.

The **hadrons** are subdivided into two groups, the mesons and the baryons. Protons and neutrons are baryons, as are a number of short-lived particles. There are several kinds of mesons.

Mesons and baryons are made of smaller particles called **quarks.** There are six kinds of quarks: "up," "down," "charmed," "strange," "top," and "bottom." The names convey nothing about the properties of the quarks. They are just labels to identify different particles. Each quark comes in three "colors," red, blue, and green. Again, the color label refers only to a distinguishing property, not an appearance. Each kind of quark, of course, has an antimatter counterpart, an antiquark.

Baryons are composed of three quarks, each of a different color. **Mesons** are composed of a quark and an antiquark of complementary color.

It is believed that quarks are held together by exchanging "particles" called **gluons.** The exchange of gluons between quarks is analogous to the exchange of photons by atoms. In a similar manner, the nucleons are held together in the nucleus by the exchange of pions. There are believed to be eight (or maybe nine) gluons, each of which is characterized by possessing one color and one anticolor.

The entire field of nuclear structure and the relationships of subatomic particles is a field of intense study. Much of the study is done using particle accelerators.

28:3 ACCELERATORS

Nuclear scientists use both linear and circular devices to accelerate particles. Both types operate using the charges on the particles. When the particle has achieved a very high speed (and thus a very high energy), it is aimed at a target material. The interaction that results as a consequence of the collision helps scientists understand the structure of the nucleus.

In a linear accelerator a particle is introduced using a device similar to the mass spectrometer ion-beam generator, Figure 28-3, page 558. The charged particle in motion will be affected by an electromagnetic wave. A radio wave is used to "push," or accelerate, the particle down the "pipe" forming the core of the accelerator. The wave, however, is traveling at the

BACKGROUND: Elementary particles:
Leptons (light particles)
Mesons (middle particles)
Baryons (heavier particles)

There are two groups of hadrons-mesons and baryons.

Mesons and baryons are made of smaller particles called quarks.

Baryons are composed of three different colored quarks.

Mesons are composed of a quark and antiquark of complementary colors.

The exchange of gluons between quarks holds them together.

Accelerators make use of magnetic fields and electromagnetic waves to accelerate charged particles.

a

b

FIGURE 28-3. The linear accelerator at Stanford University is 2 miles long (a). The drift tube arrangement in the interior of the accelerator is shown (b).

speed of light. Since the particle is not traveling as fast, the wave tends to overtake the particle. If that were to happen, the particle would then decelerate. Therefore, there are uncharged tubes in the pipe called **"drift tubes."** The particle drifts through the tube until the next accelerating part of the radio wave is in the correct position.

Careful design of the drift tubes as well as control of the radio wave frequency is important to assure maximum acceleration. The exit of the particle from the drift tube and the arrival of the accelerating part of the wave must coincide.

In a circular accelerator, the pipe through which the particles move is in the shape of a circle, or slightly modified circle, Figure 28-4. Particles

FIGURE 28-4. The synchrotron is a circular accelerator. Magnets are used to control the path and acceleration of the particles.

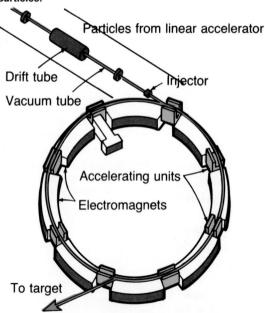

Particles from linear accelerator

Drift tube

Injector

Vacuum tube

Accelerating units

Electromagnets

To target

are accelerated by electric fields in several locations around the ring. The path of the particles is confined to the ring by huge magnets surrounding the ring. As the particles are accelerated, the magnetic field must be increased to keep the particles in the ring. Careful synchronization of acceleration and increasing magnetic fields is important. Hence, the device is called a **synchrotron.**

Recently, some experiments have involved two rings whose beams collide head-on. An accelerator is used to produce a stream of particles that is stored in one ring. The accelerator can then generate a second stream to collide with those already in the storage ring.

28:4 RADIOACTIVITY

If the structure of a nucleus is not stable, the nucleus will eject a particle or a quantum of energy in order to reach a more stable arrangement. Some nuclei are unstable as found in nature. Other nuclei can be made artificially radioactive by bombardment in an accelerator.

Three forms of radiation can come from naturally radioactive nuclei. Two forms are made of particles. The third is made of quanta. The particles are alpha (α) and beta (β) particles. The rays are gamma (γ) rays. An **alpha particle** is a helium nucleus. It consists of two protons and two neutrons. A **beta particle** is an electron (β^- or $_{-1}^{0}e$). **Gamma rays** are very high energy X rays. The symbol for gamma radiation is γ. Nuclei that emit rays or particles are said to decay.

Scientists use a shorthand method of representing information about a particle. Each "corner" of a symbol for an element (or particle) is used to show some property of the particle. Let's look at the example in Figure 28-5. We already know that the upper right-hand corner is used to show the electric charge on an ion. The lower right-hand corner is used to show the number of atoms in a formula unit. The upper left-hand corner is used for the mass number, or number of nucleons, in an atom or particle. In the lower left-hand corner, the charge on a particle or the nucleus of an atom is shown. Thus, an electron, which has a negligible mass and a 1− charge, is represented as $_{-1}^{0}e$. A typical sulfur nucleus or atom is represented as $_{16}^{32}S$. An alpha particle is $_{2}^{4}He$.

Scientists have created many radioactive nuclides that do not exist in nature. These substances are generated by bombarding stable nuclei with accelerated particles or exposing stable nuclei to neutrons in a nuclear reactor, Section 28:9. These artificially radioactive nuclides can decay by α, β, and γ rays as well as several other methods such as positron emission and K-capture.

Most antiparticles have been formed and observed during the bombardment of normal nuclei in particle accelerators. They may also be formed in other ways. Other artificially radioactive nuclides decay by capturing one of the two $1s$ electrons outside the nucleus. The first energy level ($n = 1$) is sometimes called the K level. For this reason, this radioactive process is called K-capture.

Three types of natural radiation are

1. alpha particles ($_{2}^{4}He$)
2. beta particles ($_{-1}^{0}e$)
3. gamma rays (γ)

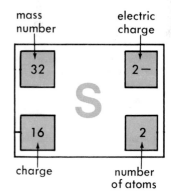

FIGURE 28-5. The diagram shows how the shorthand form for representing sulfur as $_{16}^{32}S$ is derived.

One way radioactive nuclides decay is by positron emission.

K-capture is the process in which the nucleus captures an electron from the first energy level outside the nucleus.

One rad equals 10 microjoules of energy per gram of living tissue.

One rem is the amount of damage done in a human by one rad of x rays.

Background radiation is about 100-150 (millirem)/yr.

Gamma rays are the most penetrating.

28:5   BIOLOGICAL EFFECTS OF RADIATION

All radiation, particles and electromagnetic waves, has an effect on living organisms. If the radiation has enough energy, it can penetrate living cells and disrupt their operation. The disruption is particularly dangerous if a nucleic acid molecule (Chapter 30) is affected.

Radiation is measured in units called Radiation Absorbed Dose (rad). One **rad** is equivalent to the transfer of 10 microjoules of energy to a gram of living tissue. The damage done biologically is better indicated by the unit Roentgen Equivalent Man (rem). A **rem** is equal to a rad multiplied by a factor called the Relative Biological Equivalent (RBE). A rem can also be defined as the damage done in a human by one rad of X rays.

We are always subject to some radiation from rocks containing radioactive elements, cosmic rays, and radioactive atoms naturally present in foods and water. These sources subject the average person to about 100 mrem/year. In addition, about 2 mrem/year have been added by testing nuclear weapons and operating nuclear plants.

The radiation from radioactive sources varies in its effect on humans. All three radiations, α, β, and γ, occur in a range of energies. However, we may make the following general observations. Alpha particles are the least penetrating; a thin cotton garment will stop them. Gamma rays are the most penetrating. But, if an alpha particle gets inside the body, for example by respiring or eating contaminated material, it will do the most damage. Remember that an alpha particle has a large mass and charge compared to the other radiation types.

Radiation exposure must sometimes be balanced against other factors in a value judgment. For example, an X ray of a leg would produce about 20 mrem. However, if your leg is broken, you may very well decide to have your leg X-rayed. The danger of being crippled as a result of an incorrectly set bone outweighs the slight additional radiation exposure.

FIGURE 28-6. A dosimeter detects exposure to radiation. The film badge dosimeter shown here is worn by an X-ray technician. When the film is developed it will indicate the amount of radiation the technician received during the work day.

28:6 HALF-LIFE

The rate at which many radioactive nuclides decay has been determined experimentally. The number of atoms that disintegrate in a unit of time varies directly as the number of atoms present. The length of time it takes for one-half of the atoms to disintegrate has been chosen as a standard for comparison purposes. This time interval is called **half-life.** For example, the half-life of $^{131}_{56}$Ba is 12 days. If we start with a given number n of atoms of $^{131}_{56}$Ba, then at the end of 12 days, $n/2$ atoms will have changed into another element or isotope. At that time, we will have $n/2$ Ba atoms left. At the end of the next 12 days, half of the remaining atoms will have disintegrated and we will have $n/4$ Ba atoms left. In 12 more days, half of these atoms will have disintegrated and $n/8$ atoms of $^{131}_{56}$Ba will remain. How many atoms will remain at the end of another 12 days?

These half-life figures are determined experimentally for a large number of atoms of an individual nuclide. They predict the behavior of large numbers of atoms. At present, it is not possible to predict the exact instant when an individual atom will decay.

Half-life is the length of time required for one-half of the atoms of a radioactive sample to decay.

Experimentally determined half-life figures are based on a large number of atoms.

Table 28-1

Half-Life and Decay Mode of Selected Nuclides					
Nuclide	Half-Life	Decay Mode	Nuclide	Half-Life	Decay Mode
$^{3}_{1}$H	12.3 years	β^-	$^{129}_{55}$Cs	32.1 hours	K-capture and γ
$^{6}_{2}$He	0.802 seconds	β^-	$^{149}_{61}$Pm	53.1 hours	β^- and γ
$^{14}_{6}$C	5730 years	β^-	$^{145}_{64}$Gd	25 minutes	β^+ and γ
$^{19}_{8}$O	29.1 seconds	β^- and γ	$^{183}_{76}$Os	12.0 hours	K-capture and γ
$^{20}_{9}$F	11.6 seconds	β^- and γ	$^{212}_{82}$Pb	10.6 hours	β^- and γ
$^{26}_{14}$Si	2.1 seconds	β^+ and γ	$^{194}_{84}$Po	0.5 seconds	α
$^{39}_{17}$Cl	55.5 minutes	β^- and γ	$^{210}_{84}$Po	138 days	α
$^{49}_{21}$Sc	57.5 minutes	β^- and γ	$^{226}_{88}$Fr	1602 years	α and γ
$^{60}_{26}$Fe	3×10^5 years	β^-	$^{227}_{92}$U	1.3 minutes	α and γ
$^{71}_{30}$Zn	2.4 minutes	β^- and γ	$^{235}_{92}$U	7.1×10^8 years	α and γ
$^{84}_{34}$Se	3.2 minutes	β^-	$^{238}_{92}$U	4.51×10^9 years	α and γ
$^{87}_{37}$Rb	4.8×10^{10} years	β^-	$^{236}_{94}$Pu	2.85 years	α and γ
$^{91}_{42}$Mo	15.5 minutes	β^+ and γ	$^{242}_{94}$Pu	3.79×10^5 years	α
$^{100}_{46}$Pd	4.0 days	K-capture and γ	$^{244}_{100}$Fm	0.0033 seconds	Spontaneous fission

EXAMPLE: Half-life

If you start with 2.97×10^{22} atoms of $^{91}_{42}$Mo, how many atoms will remain after 62 minutes? The half-life of $^{91}_{42}$Mo is 15.5 min.

SUGGESTION: The facts given in this chart can be used to practice writing nuclear equations.

Solving Process:
Divide 62 by 15.5 to find the number of half-lives.

$$\frac{62}{15.5} = 4 \text{ half-lives}$$

The $^{91}_{42}$Mo will go through four half-life decay cycles in 62 minutes.

$$(\tfrac{1}{2})^4 = \tfrac{1}{16} = 0.0625$$

One-sixteenth of the atoms will remain. Multiplying $\tfrac{1}{16}$ by the number of atoms you started with gives

$$2.97 \times 10^{22} \, (\tfrac{1}{16}) = 1.86 \times 10^{21}$$

Thus, after 62 minutes, 1.86×10^{21} atoms of $^{91}_{42}$Mo remain.

PROBLEMS

1. 321 h
2. 2.27×10^{26} atoms
3. Half-life is the length of time required for one-half of the atoms of a radioactive sample to decay.

1. If you start with 5.32×10^9 atoms of $^{129}_{55}$Cs, how much time will pass before the amount is reduced to 5.20×10^6 atoms?
2. If you start with 5.80×10^{28} atoms of $^{242}_{94}$Pu, how many will remain in 3.03×10^6 years?
3. Define half-life.

28:7   STABILITY OF NUCLIDES

Not all isotopes of an element are equally stable. For example, the half-lives of three uranium isotopes are quite different, as shown in Table 28-1. It is possible, however, to estimate which nuclides will be most stable by applying three rules.

These are comparative rules, not absolute rules.

Rule 1. *The greater the binding energy per nucleon the more stable the nucleus.* The binding energy is the energy needed to separate the nucleus into individual protons and neutrons.

Consider the oxygen-16 nuclide. It contains eight protons, eight electrons, and eight neutrons. We can think of it as eight hydrogen atoms

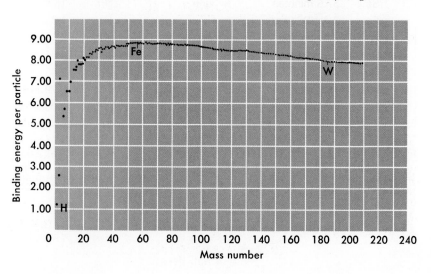

FIGURE 28-7. For heavy elements, the binding energy per particle decreases as mass increases. For lighter elements, the binding energy decreases as mass decreases.

and eight neutrons. Each hydrogen atom has a mass of 1.007 825 2 u. Each neutron has a mass of 1.008 665 2 u. Thus, the total mass of an oxygen-16 atom should be 16.131 923 2 u. However, the actual mass of the oxygen-16 atom is 15.994 915 0 u. The difference between the calculated mass and the actual mass is called the **mass defect.**

mass of 8 $^1_1$H atoms + mass of 8 ^1_0n = mass (expected) of $^{16}_8$O atom

$$8(1.007\ 825\ 2\ u) + 8(1.008\ 665\ 2\ u) = 16.131\ 923\ 2\ u$$
$$\text{actual mass of } ^{16}_8\text{O atom} = \underline{15.994\ 915\ 0\ u}$$
$$\text{mass defect} = 0.137\ 008\ 2\ u$$

For an oxygen-16 atom, the mass defect is 0.137 008 2 u. This mass has been converted to energy and released in the formation of the nucleus. Thus, it is also the energy that must be put back into the nucleus to separate the nucleons.

We can convert this mass defect of 0.137 008 2 u into its energy equivalent using the equation

$$E = mc^2$$

$$E = \frac{0.137\ 008\ 2\ \cancel{u}}{} \left| \frac{1.660\ 40 \times 10^{-27}\ \text{kg}}{1\ \cancel{u}} \right| \frac{(2.997\ 93 \times 10^8\ \text{m})^2}{(\text{s})^2}$$

$$= 2.044\ 57 \times 10^{-11}\ \frac{\text{kg·m}^{2*}}{\text{s}^2}$$

$$= 2.044\ 57 \times 10^{-11}\ \text{J}$$

This energy ($E = 2.044\ 57 \times 10^{-11}$ J) is called the **binding energy.** If we divide the total binding energy by the total number of nucleons in the oxygen atom, we obtain the binding energy per nucleon.

> Binding energy is the energy needed to separate the nucleus into individual particles.

Total nucleons = 8 protons + 8 neutrons = 16 nucleons

$$\text{Energy per nucleon} = \frac{2.044\ 57 \times 10^{-11}\ \text{J}}{1.6 \times 10^1\ \text{nucleons}}$$

$$= 1.277\ 85 \times 10^{-12}\ \frac{\text{J}}{\text{nucleon}}$$

The greater the binding energy per nucleon, the greater the stability of the nucleus. In Figure 28-7, the binding energy per nucleon is graphed against the mass number of known nuclides. Note that energy will be released in two reaction types involving the nucleus. It is released when two small nuclei join to form a medium-sized nucleus. It is also released when one large nucleus splits to form two medium-sized nuclei. In both cases the medium-sized nuclei have greater binding energies per nucleon than the nuclei from which they were produced.

> The greater the binding energy, the greater the stability of the nucleus.

*Recall that one joule is the energy required to maintain a force of one newton through a distance of one meter. A newton is equivalent to kg·m/s². Thus,

$$1\ \text{J} = (\text{kg·m/s}^2)(\text{m}) = \text{kg·m}^2/\text{s}^2$$

BACKGROUND: Two kinds of nuclear change lead to greater binding energy: the break-up of large nuclei (fission) and combination of light nuclei (fusion).

FIGURE 28-8. Stable nuclei are represented by the shaded area. The nuclei in region *A* emit neutrons or beta particles. The nuclei in region *B* emit alpha particles. Those in *C* emit positrons or capture electrons.

Light nuclei with a 1:1 neutron-proton ratio are stable.

Rule 2. *Nuclei of low atomic numbers with a 1:1 neutron-proton ratio are very stable.* In Figure 28-8, the ratio of neutrons to protons is plotted for the known stable nuclei. For low atomic numbers, the ratio has a value very close to one. However, as the atomic number increases, the value of the neutron-proton ratio steadily increases. The closer the value of the neutron-proton ratio of a nuclide is to the shaded area in this figure, the more stable it is.

Stable nuclei tend to contain an even number of both protons and neutrons.

Rule 3. *The most stable nuclei tend to contain an even number of both protons and neutrons.* Of the known stable nuclei, 57.8% have an even number of protons and an even number of neutrons. Those nuclei with an even number of one kind of nucleon but an odd number of the other are slightly less stable. Thus, 19.8% of stable nuclei have an even number of neutrons but an odd number of protons; and 20.9% of stable nuclei have an even number of protons and an odd number of neutrons. Only 1.5% of stable nuclei have both an odd number of neutrons and an odd number of protons.

Stability of a nuclide depends upon
1. the binding energy per particle.
2. the neutron-proton ratio.
3. an even number of both protons and neutrons.

In Figure 28-8, nuclei falling within the regions *A, B,* and *C* are all unstable. Those nuclei lying in region *A* have excess neutrons and become more stable either by emitting neutrons or, more commonly, beta particles. Nuclei falling within the *B* region are too large for stability and are usually alpha emitters. A nucleus in the *C* region has excess protons and can become stable by positron emission or by *K*-electron capture. Either the loss of a positron (β^+) or the capture of an electron (β^-) results in a new atom. This atom has the same mass number as the original atom but has an atomic number whose value is one unit lower. When a nucleus in the *B* region emits an alpha particle, its composition moves parallel to the 1:1 ratio line toward the *A* region. Note that in the heavy-element radioactivity series, several alpha emissions are always followed by beta emission. The beta emission moves the nucleus back into the *B* region.

Spontaneous fission is also observed in this region.

Binding energy may be increased by several kinds of nuclear reactions
  1. α-particle emission
  2. *K*-electron capture
  3. β^+ emission
  4. β^- emission
  5. neutron emission

28:8 TRANSMUTATIONS

Nuclear reactions can result in the change of one element into another. If a reaction changes the number of protons in the nucleus, an atom with a different atomic number is obtained. This change is called transmutation. The most common isotope of natural uranium is $^{238}_{92}U$. Uranium-238 decays by emitting an alpha particle. The resulting nuclide contains two fewer protons and two fewer neutrons than uranium-238. Thus, it has an atomic number of 90 and a mass number of 234. This new nuclide is a thorium atom, $^{234}_{90}Th$. By a natural process, uranium will transmute to thorium-234.

A nuclear transmutation reaction occurs when an atom with a different atomic number is produced.

$$^{238}_{92}U \rightarrow {}^{234}_{90}Th + {}^4_2He \text{ (natural)}$$

Thorium-234 decays by emitting a beta particle. Since the mass of an electron is negligible, the new nuclide also has the mass number 234, but has one more positive charge than before. Thus, its atomic number is 91. The new atom is $^{234}_{91}Pa$.

Some elements undergo natural transmutation.

FIGURE 28-9. The nuclear decay of uranium-238 takes place in a series of steps. Note that each new product has a different half-life.

$$^{234}_{92}\text{Th} \rightarrow \,^{0}_{-1}\text{e} + \,^{234}_{91}\text{Pa}$$

The series of disintegrations that begins with $^{238}_{92}\text{U}$ ends with $^{206}_{82}\text{Pb}$, which is a stable nuclide as shown in Figure 28-9.

The earliest artificial transmutation was performed by Lord Rutherford in 1911. Rutherford bombarded nitrogen-14 with alpha particles. He obtained $^{17}_{8}\text{O}$ and protons as products. This transmutation can be represented in equation form.

$$^{14}_{7}\text{N} + \,^{4}_{2}\text{He} \rightarrow \,^{17}_{8}\text{O} + \,^{1}_{1}\text{H} \; \textit{(artificial)}$$

Equations representing nuclear changes are completed by keeping in mind two rules.

Rule 1. *Mass number is conserved in a nuclear change.* In other words, the sum of the mass numbers before the change must equal the sum of the mass numbers after the change.

Rule 2. *Electric charge is conserved in a nuclear change.* The total electric charges before and after a change must be equal. This electric charge refers to the charges on subatomic particles and nuclei.

SUGGESTION: Students should be able to write and balance nuclear equations. Take the time necessary to allow them to acquire this skill.

In a nuclear equation mass number and electric charge are conserved.

EXAMPLE: Nuclear Equation

Complete the following nuclear equation.

$$^{18}_{9}\text{F} \rightarrow \,^{0}_{+1}\text{e} + \;?$$

Solving Process:

(a) Find the mass number of the unknown product. We know that the mass number is conserved in a nuclear reaction.

mass no. of $_{+1}^{0}\text{e}$ + mass no. of ? = 18

mass no. of ? = 18 − mass no. of $_{+1}^{0}\text{e}$

= 18 − 0 = 18

(b) Find the charge of the unknown product. We know that electric charge is conserved in a nuclear equation.

charge of $_{+1}^{0}\text{e}$ + charge of ? = 9

charge of ? = 9 − charge of $_{+1}^{0}\text{e}$

= 9 − 1 = 8+

Use the periodic table to determine the identity of an element.

(c) Determine the identity of the unknown product and complete the nuclear equation. Turn to the periodic table and find which nuclide has an 8+ charge. This nuclide is oxygen. The symbol for an oxygen atom with a mass number of 18 is $^{18}_{8}\text{O}$. Thus, the completed nuclear equation is

$$^{18}_{9}\text{F} \rightarrow \,^{0}_{+1}\text{e} + \,^{18}_{8}\text{O}$$

EXAMPLE: Nuclear Equation

Complete the following nuclear equation.

$$^{83}_{37}Rb + ? \rightarrow ^{83}_{36}Kr$$

Solving Process:

(a) Find the mass of the unknown reactant.

$$83 - 83 = 0$$

(b) Find the charge of the unknown reactant.

$$36 - 37 = -1$$

(c) Determine the identity of the unknown reactant and complete the nuclear equation. The unknown reactant has a charge of -1 and a mass of zero. The only particle that fits this description is an electron. The symbol for an electron is $_{-1}^{0}e$. Thus the completed nuclear equation is

$$^{83}_{37}Rb + _{-1}^{0}e \rightarrow ^{83}_{36}Kr$$

PROBLEMS

Complete the following equations.

4. $^{27}_{12}Mg$ decays by beta-minus emission
5. $^{49}_{24}Cr$ decays by beta-plus emission
6. $^{76}_{36}Kr$ decays by K-capture
7. $^{213}_{88}Ra$ decays by alpha emission
8. $^{231}_{90}Th$ decays by alpha emission

4. $^{27}_{12}Mg \rightarrow _{-1}^{0}e + ^{27}_{13}Al$
5. $^{49}_{24}Cr \rightarrow _{+1}^{0}e + ^{49}_{23}V$
6. $^{76}_{36}Kr + _{-1}^{0}e \rightarrow ^{76}_{35}Br$
7. $^{213}_{88}Ra \rightarrow ^{4}_{2}He + ^{209}_{86}Rn$
8. $^{231}_{90}Th \rightarrow ^{4}_{2}He + ^{227}_{88}Ra$

28:9 SYNTHETIC ELEMENTS

Elements with atomic numbers greater than 92 are called the transuranium elements. All of the synthesized transuranium elements have been produced by converting a lighter element into a heavier one. Such a change requires an increase in the number of protons in the nucleus. One of the processes of synthetic transmutation occurs as follows. A nuclear reactor produces a high concentration of neutrons that are "packed" into the nucleus of the element plutonium-239. As the mass number builds, a beta particle is emitted. When beta emission occurs, a neutron is converted into a proton with no significant loss of mass. This process produces an element with an atomic number greater than the original element. The process can be written

$$^{239}_{94}Pu + _{0}^{1}n \rightarrow ^{240}_{94}Pu$$

$$^{240}_{94}Pu + _{0}^{1}n \rightarrow ^{241}_{94}Pu$$

$$^{241}_{94}Pu \rightarrow ^{241}_{95}Am + _{-1}^{0}e$$

Transuranium elements have atomic numbers > 92.

Some transuranium elements have been produced in nuclear reactors by bombarding plutonium-239 with neutrons.

BACKGROUND: Glenn T. Seaborg, who received credit for discovery of several transuranium elements, actually applied for and received a patent for elements he has produced. He assigned rights to these patents to the United States Government.

Americium-241 in turn can be used as a target to produce another element with a higher atomic number. Fermium-256 ($^{256}_{100}$Fm) is the element with the highest atomic number reached in this manner.

A second method of synthesizing transuranium elements makes use of nuclear explosions that produce vast amounts of neutrons. Some neutrons are captured by uranium atoms. Successive electron emissions produce new elements. Fermium-256 is the element with the highest atomic number produced in this way also.

Other transuranium elements have been produced by bombarding target elements with other elements.

Elements with atomic numbers greater than 100 have been produced using other elements to bombard target elements. Mendelevium-256 was created by bombarding einsteinium-254 with alpha particles.

$$^{254}_{99}\text{Es} + ^{4}_{2}\text{He} \rightarrow ^{256}_{101}\text{Md} + 2^{1}_{0}n$$

Nobelium, atomic number 102, was created by using carbon ions and curium. The production of lawrencium, atomic number 103, made use of boron and californium. One way element 104 can be produced is the bombardment of plutonium by neon. Element 105 can be produced by the bombardment of californium with nitrogen. A heavy-ion accelerator in California is being prepared to accelerate particles as heavy as bromine nuclei.

$$^{12}_{6}\text{C} + ^{244}_{96}\text{Cm} \rightarrow ^{254}_{102}\text{No} + 2^{1}_{0}n$$

$$^{11}_{5}\text{B} + ^{251}_{98}\text{Cf} \rightarrow ^{259}_{103}\text{Lr} + 3^{1}_{0}n$$

$$^{12}_{6}\text{C} + ^{249}_{98}\text{Cf} \rightarrow ^{257}_{104}\text{Unq} + 4^{1}_{0}n$$

$$^{15}_{7}\text{N} + ^{249}_{98}\text{Cf} \rightarrow ^{260}_{105}\text{Unp} + 4^{1}_{0}n$$

$$^{209}_{83}\text{Bi} + ^{58}_{26}\text{Fe} \rightarrow ^{267}_{109}\text{Une}$$

Eventually, it may be possible to produce synthetic elements with atomic numbers up to 126.

It is highly possible that elements with even greater atomic numbers can be produced. The elements produced thus far are characterized by low yields and extremely short half-lives. Only a few atoms of elements 103–109 were first prepared, and these had half-lives of seconds. Nuclear scientists believe that elements with atomic numbers as high as 126 might be produced.

28:10   USES OF RADIOACTIVE NUCLIDES

Radioactive nuclides can be used as tracers.

BACKGROUND: Some nonradioactive nuclides can also be used as tracers.

Since readioactive elements are easily detected by their radiation, they can be used as "tracers." Tracers have a number of practical applications in chemistry. In quantitative analysis, a small amount of a radioactive nuclide of the element sought is introduced into the sample. The proportion of the unstable nuclide recovered in the analytical process is measured. That ratio along with the actual total amount of substance recovered can be used to compute the original quantity of unknown.

Radioactive nuclides have also been used extensively to study the mechanisms of reactions. For example, the detection of the step-by-step process of photosynthesis is greatly assisted by the use of radioactive nuclides.

Naturally occurring radioactive nuclides can be used for dating certain objects. Using the half-life of a nuclide sample we can date when organisms died, up to about 20 000 years ago. By the same technique, we can date the time of formation of rocks as far back as the origin of the earth.

Suppose we want to know what part of the human body utilizes a certain substance in our diet. Using a radioactive nuclide of an element in the substance, we would prepare some of the substance. We would have to use a very low level radiation if we were working with human beings. After a person eats or drinks the substance, we would examine the person's body with radiation detectors. The detectors would be set to observe only radiation from the nuclide being used in the diagnosis. The part of the body activating the detectors is where the substance is concentrated.

Half-life may be used to date objects.

Because of the low original concentration of $^{14}_{6}C$, the method is sensitive only for about four half-lives (23 000 years).

Radioactive nuclides (tracers) can be detected using a radiation detector.

28:11 FISSION

If a very heavy nucleus becomes too unstable, it breaks into two approximately equal parts. At the same time a large amount of energy is released. This process is called **fission.** A nucleus can be made unstable by bombardment with a number of particles, including neutrons.

The heaviest elements are the only ones that exhibit the phenomenon of fission. When a heavy nucleus breaks up, two heavy fragments plus one or more neutrons are emitted. One atom splits due to bombardment by a neutron. In the process of splitting, the atom gives off a neutron. In

Fission is the breakup of a heavy nucleus into two approximately equal parts.

Fission reactions release very large amounts of energy.

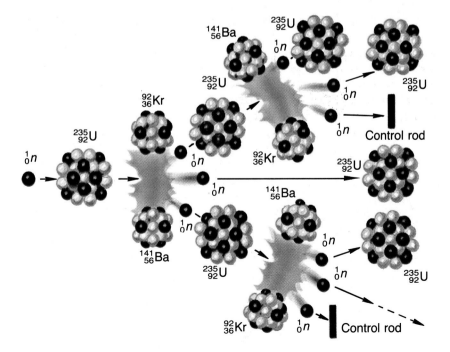

FIGURE 28-10. The fission process in a reactor consists of a chain of fission reactions. Control rods are used to break the chain and slow or stop the reaction.

SUGGESTION: Point out that mass-energy interconversion involves a nuclear reaction and that the popular term "atomic bomb" is inaccurate. Such a bomb should be called a nuclear bomb.

Water and graphite are good moderators, causing neutrons to slow down as a result of collisions.

In a nuclear reactor, the rate of the reaction is regulated with control rods.

FIGURE 28-11. The diagram shows the parts of a pressurized water fission reactor. Reactors of this design are most common. Note that the cooling towers are not shown.

turn the neutron can cause a second atom to split. This process continues until a very large number of the atoms present have reacted. Thus, the emitted neutrons produce a chain reaction. Since a large energy change is involved in the fission process, a chain reaction can serve as an energy source for various purposes. A **nuclear reactor** is a device for controlling nuclear fission. Reactors can be designed to produce heat for electric power generation plants, or for propulsion units in ships and submarines. In nuclear reactors, the rate of the chain reaction is controlled very carefully. An uncontrolled nuclear chain reaction results in an explosion similar to a nuclear bomb, often incorrectly called an atomic bomb.

In a nuclear reactor, a fissionable element is used as fuel. Not all isotopes will fission under appropriate conditions. The chief fuels are $^{235}_{92}U$ and $^{239}_{94}Pu$ (itself a product of a reactor). It is also possible to convert $^{232}_{90}Th$ to $^{233}_{92}U$ in a reactor and use the uranium isotope as a fuel. The neutrons being produced during fission are traveling too fast to initiate efficiently the fission process in other atoms. As a result, most reactors contain a material called a **moderator** that causes the neutrons to slow down through collisions. Water and graphite are good moderators.

The reaction rate is controlled by rods composed of good neutron-absorbing materials such as boron, cadmium, or gadolinium. By inserting the rod (or withdrawing it somewhat), the reaction rate can be carefully adjusted to the desired level. The energy produced by the fissioning atoms

PRESSURIZED WATER REACTOR (PWR)

Containment structure   Steam   Steam line

Steam generator

Control rods

Pressure vessel

Core

Pump

Pump

Turbine generator

To cooling towers

Condenser cooling water

is in the form of kinetic energy of the particles produced. As these particles collide with the materials in the reactor, their kinetic energy is gradually transferred to these other materials and the temperature of the whole system increases. It is necessary, then, to have a coolant to keep the reactor from overheating. Several substances have been tried as coolants, with water being the most popular. Liquid metals, such as Na, Na-K alloys, and gases such as He have been tried. The energy gained by the coolant is used to perform useful work, such as running an electric generator.

The whole reactor system is encased in protective materials because of the intense radioactivity. The **containment vessel** keeps radioactive materials from escaping into the environment. It also shields personnel in the plant from the radiation produced in the reactor.

The demand for energy in the United States has surpassed our ability to produce new sources. Worldwide resources of fossil fuels such as petroleum and coal may last only a few decades. We have begun to utilize fission reactors as a source of electric power. However, they represent only a fraction of the total power production facilities in operation. Fission reactors do not represent an unlimited source of energy. However, they do offer a source of energy for the immediate future. As with other energy sources, there are problems associated with nuclear power. For example, what is to be done with the highly radioactive waste material? Can we be sure that strict safety measures will be maintained at reactor sites? European countries are aggressively pursuing nuclear power as a means of satisfying energy demands. The future of fission power reactors will have to be carefully considered by all people.

FIGURE 28-12. Water, used as a coolant within the reactor, is channeled to cooling towers to prevent thermal pollution.

Water is the most widely used coolant preventing a reactor core from overheating.

The containment vessel encases the whole reactor system to prevent the escape of radioactive materials.

BACKGROUND: Nuclear reactor workers are permitted to receive up to 5 rem/yr of radiation. 100 rem/h results in radiation poisoning. 300-500 rem/h can result in death in 50% of the cases. Background radiation is about 0.1 rem/yr.

In fusion reactions, two or more smaller nuclei combine to form a larger nucleus.

Fusion reactions release much larger amounts of energy per particle than fission reactions.

28:12 FUSION

The peak of the binding energy curve in Figure 28-7 occurs near the element iron, atomic number 26. We can see how both fission and the emission of small particles by atoms of high atomic number lead to more stable atoms. Note also that stability could be gained by the combination of the smallest nuclei into larger ones. A nuclear reaction in which two or more small nuclei combine to form one larger nucleus is called a **fusion reaction.** Note also that the slope of the binding energy curve is greater on the low atomic number side than it is on the high side. We should therefore expect fusion reactions to produce much greater amounts of energy per particle than fission reactions. This prediction is supported by observation.

Scientists have harnessed the fission reaction in a controlled process on a small scale for limited power production. If we could harness the fusion reaction for power production, we would have a solution to energy problems for some time to come. Some of the difficult problems associated with fission reactions as a power source would also be eliminated. The availability of "fuel" for nuclear fusion reactions is much greater than for fission reactions. Also, fusion reactions useful for power production do not produce radioactive waste.

The most likely reactions for fusion generators are the following.

$$_1^2H + {_1^2}H \rightarrow {_2^3}He + {_0^1}n$$

$$_1^2H + {_1^2}H \rightarrow {_1^3}H + {_1^1}H$$

$$_1^2H + {_1^3}H \rightarrow {_2^4}He + {_0^1}n$$

The last of these reactions is the most promising from the standpoint of power production. However, it does have drawbacks. Tritium ($_1^3H$) is a radioactive nuclide that occurs naturally in only tiny amounts. It can be produced by exposing lithium-6 to neutrons.

$$_3^6Li + {_0^1}n \rightarrow {_2^4}He + {_1^3}H$$

A disadvantage is that the reactor itself will become radioactive as it is exposed to these radiations.

On the other hand, the reactions involving only deuterium ($_1^2H$) are free of radioactivity. Also, the supply of deuterium could provide the earth with energy for as long as 10^{12} years. Extraction of deuterium from water supplies would require only a small fraction of the power output of a fusion reactor.

Present research could produce practical fusion installations within your lifetime. If certain technical problems are solved, these reactors could appear in the near future. Let us look at some of these problems.

Isotopes of hydrogen
Tritium $_1^3H$
Deuterium $_1^2H$

Supplies of naturally-occuring deuterium are estimated to be large enough to fuel fusion reactors for 10^{12} years.

28:13   FUSION REACTORS

In order for two atomic nuclei to undergo fusion, they must come almost into contact. Recall that the nuclear force extends only about a distance equal to the diameter of the nucleus. However, since all nuclei are positively charged, they tend to repel each other strongly. In order for

FIGURE 28-13. The magnetic field coils of a fusion reactor are shown in this interior view (a). Note that the fusion reactor (b) is much smaller than a fission reactor.

a

b

fusion reactions to occur, the reactants must be held in the temperature range of 10^8 to 10^{9}°C for a suitable time. The energy requirements to achieve these temperatures are quite high. The length of time required depends upon how closely packed the particles are during that time. At these high temperatures, matter is in the form of plasma. One major problem in designing a fusion reactor is containing the fuel at that temperature. Containers made from usual materials cannot be used. The plasma would lose energy to them so rapidly that fusion temperatures would never be reached. Since plasmas are charged particles, they are affected by magnetic fields. By properly shaping a magnetic field, a plasma may be contained. As fusion occurs and the temperature rises, the pressure of a plasma causes it to expand. With charged particles in the plasma moving around at tremendous velocities, the plasma itself generates electric currents. Both of these effects make leakage from the magnetic ''bottle'' a difficult problem to solve. All of these problems are topics of present research. Who can predict what role developments in this fascinating field will play in shaping our future!

Matter must be in the form of plasma (10^8°C) for a fusion reaction to occur.

Fusion reactions can be contained in ''magnetic bottles.''

BIOGRAPHY   Shirley Ann Jackson (1946-   )

Shirley Jackson has a history of being first at a number of accomplishments. She was first in her high school graduating class and eventually became the first black woman to earn a doctorate degree at Massachusetts Institute of Technology. Following graduation from MIT, she did research at the Fermi National Accelerator Laboratory and at CERN in Geneva, Switzerland.

Although her interest was high energy physics, Dr. Jackson now works with microscopic solid state physics in the development of miniature physical systems such as electronic chips and microtransistors. Although she is currently employed by Bell Laboratories, she retains her tie to MIT through membership on the board of trustees.

TECHNOLOGY AND CHEMISTRY

28:14   Stellar Nucleosynthesis

In addition to the moon, stars, and planets we see in the sky, there are great clouds of gas and dust. About 75% of the matter in the universe is hydrogen and almost 25% is helium. All other elements make about 1% of the matter in the universe.

Let us consider why there are such massive amounts of these two light elements present in the universe. When a star forms, a cloud of hydrogen, helium, and dust contracts through the mutual gravitational attraction the particles have for one another. As these particles fall inward, they pick up speed and their temperatures are thus increased. Eventually, the core of the star is hot enough (10^7 K) to start the fusion reaction among hydrogen atoms to make helium. This process consists of a series of steps.

$$^1_1H + ^1_1H \rightarrow ^2_1H + ^0_1e + \gamma \qquad ^2_1H + ^1_1H \rightarrow ^3_2He \qquad ^3_2He + ^3_2He \rightarrow ^4_2He + 2^1_1H$$

As the hydrogen fuel is exhausted, the star continues to collapse. This collapse increases the density of the star and raises the temperature (10^8 K) to a range where helium fusion reactions begin.

$$^4_2He + ^4_2He \rightarrow ^8_4Be \; unstable \qquad ^8_4Be + ^4_2He \rightarrow ^{12}_6C \qquad ^{12}_6C + ^4_2He \rightarrow ^{16}_8O$$

Similar processes can continue in massive stars until iron nuclei are formed. Nuclei beyond iron consume energy when formed instead of producing it. As a consequence, the star starts a rapid collapse as the core turns to iron and the nuclear "fires" go out. The collapse of such a large amount of matter (at least four times the mass of the sun) produces an incredible amount of energy. The collapse finally ends in a catastrophic explosion of the entire star. In the process of the explosion, so much energy is available that all natural elements, including those above iron, are formed. The exploding star is called a supernova. All the naturally occurring elements above iron in the universe have been produced in supernova explosions.

The length of time required for a star to pass through these stages varies with the star's mass. Small stars burn their fuels slowly and last a long time, as long as 2×10^{10} years. On the other hand, super-massive stars burn quickly, lasting perhaps only 3×10^6 years.

SUMMARY

1. Radioactivity is the phenomenon of particle or quantum emission due to nuclear disintegration. **Intro.**

2. Radioactive decay is spontaneous; that is, it cannot be controlled. **28:1**

3. Subatomic particles are divided into elementary particles called leptons and complex particles called hadrons. **28:2**

4. Hadrons are believed to be made of particles called quarks. **28:2**

5. Quarks and hadrons are thought to be held together by exchanging gluons and pions respectively. **28:2**

6. Linear accelerators and synchrotrons are devices used by nuclear scientists to investigate nuclear structure by bombarding nuclei with high energy particles. **28:3**

7. Naturally radioactive nuclides emit three kinds of radiation: alpha (helium nuclei), beta (electrons), and gamma (quanta of energy). 28:4

8. Many subatomic particles in addition to electrons and nucleons have been discovered. Some of these are classified as antimatter. 28:4

9. All radiation has an effect on living organisms. Our environment and the food and water we consume emit small amounts of naturally occurring radiation. 28:5

10. Radiation is measured in rads. Damage done to living tissue is measured in rems. 28:5

11. Each radioactive nuclide emits a characteristic radiation. Therefore, radioactive nuclides are extremely useful in the laboratory and in industry. 28:6, 28:10-28:13

12. The half-life of a radioactive substance is the time it takes for one-half of the atoms of a sample of the substance to disintegrate. 28:6

13. Three relationships can be used to predict the stability of nuclides. 28:7
    (a) the binding energy per particle
    (b) the neutron-proton ratio
    (c) an even number of both protons and neutrons

14. The calculated mass defect of an atom indicates the transformation of mass into binding energy. 28:7

15. Binding energy is the energy needed to separate the nucleus into individual protons and neutrons. 28:7

16. The changing of one element into another is called transmutation. 28:8

17. In completing nuclear equations, both mass number and electric charge must be conserved. 28:8-28:9

18. New elements may be synthesized by combining particles or nuclei with other nuclei. 28:8-28:9

19. Fission is the splitting of a large, unstable nucleus into two smaller, approximately equal parts. 28:11

20. A nuclear reactor is a device for containing and controlling a fission reaction. 28:11

21. Fusion is the combining of two or more small nuclei into one larger nucleus. 28:12

VOCABULARY

radioactivity Intro	mesons 28:2	half-life 28:6
nuclear force 28:1	gluons 28:2	mass defect 28:7
nucleons 28:1	drift tubes 28:3	binding energy 28:7
leptons 28:2	synchrotron 28:3	fission 28:11
antiparticle 28:2	alpha particle 28:4	nuclear reactor 28:11
neutrino 28:2	beta particle 28:4	moderator 28:11
hadrons 28:2	gamma rays 28:4	containment vessel 28:11
quarks 28:2	rad 28:5	fusion reaction 28:12
baryons 28:2	rem 28:5	

PROBLEMS

2. binding energy, n/p ratio
3. chemical and medical tracers, dating, γ production
4. Fusion: joining of small nuclei to form one large nucleus. Fission: splitting a large nucleus into smaller nuclei.

5.
a. $^3_1H \rightarrow ^3_2He + ^0_{-1}e$
b. $^{61}_{30}Zn \rightarrow ^{61}_{29}Cu + ^0_{+1}e$
c. $^9_3Li \rightarrow ^9_4Be + ^0_{-1}e$
d. $^{240}_{96}Cm \rightarrow ^{236}_{94}Pu \rightarrow ^4_2He$
e. $^{199}_{84}Po + ^0_{-1}e \rightarrow ^{199}_{83}Bi$

6. 12 min

7.
a. $^{242}_{94}Pu \rightarrow ^4_2He + ^{238}_{92}U$
b. $^{30}_{13}Al \rightarrow ^0_{-1}e + ^{30}_{14}Si$
c. $^{55}_{26}Fe + ^0_{-1}e \rightarrow ^{55}_{25}Mn$
d. $^{93}_{44}Ru \rightarrow ^0_{+1}e + ^{93}_{43}Tc$

8.
a. $^{257}_{102}No \rightarrow ^{253}_{100}Fm + ^4_2He$
b. $^{80}_{38}Sr + ^0_{-1}e \rightarrow ^{80}_{37}Rb$
c. $^{140}_{62}Sm \rightarrow ^{140}_{61}Pm + ^0_{+1}e$
d. $^{211}_{82}Pb \rightarrow ^{211}_{83}Bi + ^0_{-1}e$

1. it is reduced
2. If mixed, they will not conduct.
3. not spontaneously
4. 0.15 V
5. 0.412 g Sn

6. Cu and O_2
7. 3.10 V
8. 0.276 V per e^- transferred

9. gain of electrons
10. 5+

1. What are the differences among the three types of natural radiation?
2. What are the tests for stability of an isotope?
3. What are some uses for radioactive nuclides?
4. What are the differences between fusion and fission?
5. Complete the following equations.
   a. $^3_1H \rightarrow ? + ^0_{-1}e$
   b. $^{61}_{30}Zn \rightarrow ? + ^0_{+1}e$
   c. $^9_3Li \rightarrow ^9_4Be + ?$
   d. $^{240}_{96}Cm \rightarrow ? + ^4_2He$
   e. $^{199}_{84}Po + ^0_{-1}e \rightarrow ?$ (K-capture)
6. How long will it take 6.00×10^{20} atoms of $^{71}_{30}Zn$ to disintegrate to 1.88×10^{19} atoms?
7. Write a balanced nuclear equation for each of these changes.
   a. alpha emission for plutonium-242
   b. beta emission from aluminum-30
   c. electron capture by iron-55
   d. positron emission by ruthenium-93
8. Write the symbols, including atomic number and mass number, for the radioactive nuclides that would give each of these products.
   a. fermium-253 by alpha emission
   b. rubidium-80 by electron capture
   c. promethium-140 by positron emission
   d. bismuth-211 by beta emission

REVIEW

1. What happens to a positive ion when it reaches the cathode?
2. Why is it necessary to separate the half-cells when constructing a voltaic cell?
3. Will Ni react with Zn^{2+}? (Use the table of standard reduction potentials.)
4. What voltage would you expect from a cell using $Co|Co^{2+}$ and $Pb|Pb^{2+}$ half-cells?
5. How many grams of Sn would be deposited from a Sn^{2+} solution by a current of 0.506 amperes flowing for 22.0 minutes?
6. What will be the products of the electrolysis of a water solution of $CuBr_2$?
7. What voltage could you expect from the following cell at 25°C?
   $$Pb|Pb^{2+}(0.282M)\|F_2|F^-(0.0400M)$$
8. What voltage could you expect to obtain from a reaction with a free energy change of -26.6 kJ?
9. What is the modern definition of reduction?
10. What is the oxidation number of Br in $AgBrO_3$?

11. What is the oxidation number of Hg in $Hg(ClO_3)_2$? (Chlorine is 5+.)

12. How may an oxidation-reduction reaction be identified?

13. Balance: $MnO_4^- + Cl^- \rightarrow Cl_2 + Mn^{2+}$ (*in acid solution*).

14. Balance: $MnO_4^- + I^- \rightarrow I_2 + MnO_2$ (*in basic solution*).

11. 2+

12. at least one element changes oxidation number

13. $16H^+ + 2MnO_4^- + 10Cl^- \rightarrow 2Mn^{2+} + 8H_2O + 5Cl_2$

14. $4H_2O + 2MnO_4^- + 6I^- \rightarrow 2MnO_2 + 8OH^- + 3I_2$

ONE MORE STEP

1. Using a Geiger counter or similar device and a radioactive source, determine (a) the change in radiation intensity with change in distance between source and detector, and (b) the shielding effect of paper, masonry, and metal.

2. Determine the difference between "weak" and "strong" interactions between nuclear particles.

3. Prepare a report on the differences and similarities of various accelerators: the cyclotron, the betatron, the synchrotron, and so on.

4. What progress has been made toward large-scale production of energy by nuclear fusion?

5. Investigate the use of $^{14}_{6}C$ for dating the age of once-living objects.

6. Investigate the dating of minerals by the use of naturally occurring radioactive nuclides.

7. Investigate the use of lasers to produce the temperatures necessary for fusion.

READINGS

Agnew, Harold M., "Gas-cooled Nuclear Power Reactors," *Scientific American,* Vol. 244, No. 6(June 1981), pp. 55-63.

Boslough, John, "Worlds within the Atom," *National Geographic,* Vol. 167, No. 5(May 1985), pp. 634-663.

Fritsch, Harold, *Quarks: The Stuff of Matter,* New York: Basic Books, 1983.

Greiner, Walter, and Horst Stocker, "Hot Nuclear Matter," *Scientific American,* Vol. 252, No. 1(January 1985), pp. 76-87.

Jelinski, Lynn W., "Modern NMR Spectroscopy," *Chemical and Engineering News,* Vol. 62, No. 45(November 5, 1984), pp. 26-47.

Landa, Edward R., "The First Nuclear Industry," *Scientific American,* Vol. 247, No. 5(November 1982), pp. 180-193.

LoSecco, J. M., et al., "The Search for Proton Decay," *Scientific American,* Vol. 252, No. 6(June 1985), pp. 54-62.

O'Sullivan, Dermot A., "Pebble-Bed Nuclear Reactor Readied for Power Generation," *Chemical and Engineering News,* Vol. 62, No. 10(March 5, 1984), pp. 20-21.

Quigg, Chris, "Elementary Forces and Particles," *Scientific American,* Vol. 252, No. 4(April 1985), pp. 84-95.

Weinberg, Steven, "The Decay of the Proton," *Scientific American,* Vol. 244, No. 6(June 1981), pp. 64-75.

Zurer, Pamela S., "Archeological Chemistry," *Chemical and Engineering News,* Vol. 61, No. 8(February 21, 1983), pp. 26-44.

Many of today's most common products are derived from organic sources. The manufacturing process for ribbon involves a knowledge of organic chemistry. The ribbon fiber is produced from organic compounds. The permanent press characteristics of this synthetic material depends on bonding and structure. The energy used to run the spinning machines probably comes from an organic source. What is organic chemistry? What are the characteristics of organic compounds? How are these compounds classified?

CLASSES OF
ORGANIC
COMPOUNDS

Chapter 29 is an introduction to organic chemistry. Nomenclature and the characteristics of hydrocarbons and functional derivatives are presented.

DEMONSTRATION: Esters that smell like pineapple, banana, and wintergreen can easily be prepared and placed on filter paper. As they are passed around the room, ask students what would happen to the price and abundance of flavorings, odors, and perfumes if we depended upon natural oils (esters) only. See the Teacher Guide for preparation details and discussion ideas.

GOALS:
• You will classify hydrocarbons according to bonding families.
• You will name and write structural formulas for simple hydrocarbons and substituted hydrocarbons.
• You will differentiate among formulas and properties of substituted hydrocarbon families.

Early chemists observed that there were two types of substances—those from living matter and those from nonliving matter. These two types became known as organic substances and inorganic substances. It was found that all organic substances had some similar properties. Most organic compounds were found to decompose easily when heated. Most inorganic substances were observed to change very little, if any, when heated. Also, organic substances were thought to be produced only by living organisms.

Later chemists began to study organic substances in greater detail. They learned that nearly all organic compounds are made of chains and rings of carbon atoms. Chemists then learned to synthesize some simple organic compounds directly from inorganic substances! This amazing discovery marked the beginning of modern organic chemistry. Today, we define **organic chemistry** as the chemistry of carbon compounds.

29:1 CLASSIFICATION OF HYDROCARBONS

One of the largest classifications of organic compounds is the group known as the hydrocarbons. These compounds are composed only of carbon and hydrogen. Almost all other organic compounds can be considered as derivatives of the simple hydrocarbons. If the carbon atoms are linked in chains, the compounds are called **aliphatic** (al ih FAT ihk) compounds. If the atoms are linked in rings, the compounds are called **cyclic** compounds.

Hydrocarbons are composed of hydrogen and carbon.

Aliphatic compounds have carbon atoms linked in chains.

The chain compounds may be further classified on the basis of the individual carbon-carbon bonds. A chain compound in which all carbon-carbon bonds are single bonds is called an **alkane** (AL kayn). This type of compound is also called a **saturated hydrocarbon** because each carbon-carbon bond is a single bond. Thus, additional atoms can be bonded to the original atoms in the compound only by breaking the compound into two or more fragments.

In saturated hydrocarbons each carbon-carbon bond is a single bond.

Table 29-1

29:2   ALKANES

This series of compounds is also called the paraffin series.

The alkane series is the least complex set of hydrocarbons. The first four members of the alkane series and their formulas are methane, CH_4; ethane, C_2H_6; propane, C_3H_8; and butane, C_4H_{10}. After butane, the members of the alkane series are named using the Greek or Latin prefix for the number of carbon atoms. The word ending characteristic of this family is -ane.

Alkanes are saturated hydrocarbons.

Each alkane differs from the next by a —CH_2— group. You can think of this series as being formed by removing a hydrogen atom from one of the carbon atoms, adding a —CH_2— group, and replacing the hydrogen. For example:

Members of the alkane series differ by —CH_2—.

$$H-\underset{\underset{H}{|}}{\overset{\overset{H}{|}}{C}}-H + -\underset{\underset{H}{|}}{\overset{\overset{H}{|}}{C}} - \rightarrow H-\underset{\underset{H}{|}}{\overset{\overset{H}{|}}{C}}-\underset{\underset{H}{|}}{\overset{\overset{H}{|}}{C}}-H$$

$$CH_4 \quad + \quad CH_2 \quad \rightarrow \quad C_2H_6$$

BACKGROUND: These are conventionalized diagrams. The bonds in the actual molecules are arranged around the carbon atoms in such a way that the four bonds formed by each carbon are as far apart as possible. This results in a tetrahedral distribution of bonds.

Note that this equation does not represent the actual preparation of an alkane.

A series of compounds whose structures differ from each other by a specific structural unit is called a **homologous** (hoh MAHL uh guhs) series. In the case of the alkanes, the specific structural unit is —CH_2—. A general formula can be written for all of the members of a homologous series such as the alkanes. For the alkanes, the formula is C_nH_{2n+2}, where n is the number of carbon atoms in the compound.

Each member of a homologous series differs from each other member by a specific structural unit.

General formula for alkanes: C_nH_{2n+2}.

The simplest alkane is methane. Methane contains one carbon atom and four hydrogen atoms. The structural formula for methane is shown at the right. The structural formulas of the next three compounds in the alkane series are

$$H-\underset{\underset{H}{|}}{\overset{\overset{H}{|}}{C}}-H$$

methane

ethane

propane

butane

If one hydrogen atom, together with its associated electron, is removed from a hydrocarbon molecule, a radical is left.

A hydrocarbon radical is a hydrocarbon molecule from which a hydrogen atom has been removed.

methane   methyl radical

propane   propyl radical

Radicals are named by substituting the ending *-yl* for the normal *-ane* ending of the parent compound.

Radicals are named by substituting the *-yl* ending for the normal *-ane* ending.

There are general trends in physical and chemical properties within homologous series. For instance, as the molecular mass of the compounds in a series increases, the boiling point increases as shown in Table 29-2. Alkanes are soluble in nonpolar solvents.

Table 29-2

Alkanes					
Name of Alkane	Formula	Melting Point, °C	Boiling Point, °C	Name and Formula of Radical	
Methane	CH_4	−183	−162	Methyl	CH_3-
Ethane	C_2H_6	−172	−89	Ethyl	C_2H_5-
Propane	C_3H_8	−188	−42	Propyl	C_3H_7-
Butane	C_4H_{10}	−138	−1	Butyl	C_4H_9-
Pentane	C_5H_{12}	−130	36	Pentyl	$C_5H_{11}-$
Hexane	C_6H_{14}	−95	69	Hexyl	$C_6H_{13}-$
Heptane	C_7H_{16}	−91	98	Heptyl	$C_7H_{15}-$
Octane	C_8H_{18}	−57	126	Octyl	$C_8H_{17}-$
Nonane	C_9H_{20}	−54	151	Nonyl	$C_9H_{19}-$
Decane	$C_{10}H_{22}$	−30	174	Decyl	$C_{10}H_{21}-$
—					
Dodecane	$C_{12}H_{26}$	−10	215	Dodecyl	$C_{12}H_{25}-$
—					
Hexadecane	$C_{16}H_{34}$	+19	288	Hexadecyl	$C_{16}H_{33}-$
Heptadecane	$C_{17}H_{36}$	+23	303	Heptadecyl	$C_{17}H_{35}-$

29:3 NAMING BRANCHED ALKANES

For convenience in naming organic compounds, carbon atoms in a structural formula are given position numbers. In an unbranched chain molecule, the numbering of carbon atoms can begin at either end of the chain as shown on the left for butane.

Not all alkanes have unbranched chains of carbon atoms. In naming branched alkanes, we must first find the longest chain of carbon atoms. This chain is used as the basis of the compound name and is called the parent chain. The parent chain does not necessarily occur in a straight line. Look at the following structure.

Carbon atoms in a structural formula of an organic compound are given position numbers.

Alkanes are named on the basis of the longest continuous chain of carbon atoms (parent chain).

The parent chain does not necessarily occur in a straight line.

The longest chain contains six carbon atoms. Thus, the parent chain is hexane (C_6H_{14}). The carbon atoms of the longest chain are given position numbers beginning at the end of the parent chain closer to the branch.

The CH_3— group that is attached to the main chain is called a **branch** or **substituent.** The branch is named as a radical. We indicate, by number, the position of the carbon atom of the parent chain to which the branch (radical) is attached. In our example, the branch is attached to the third carbon. The branch is a methyl radical. The parent chain is hexane. The name of this compound is 3-methylhexane. The name is written with a hyphen between the substituent position number and the substituent name. The substituent and the parent are written as one word. Numbering of the carbon atoms of the parent alkane chain always begins at the end that will give the lowest position numbers to the substituents.

How do we name an alkane that has more than one branch? Consider the following example:

Substituents or branch chains are attached to the main chain of carbon atoms.

Carbons of parent chain are numbered to give the lowest position numbers to branches.

The parent chain is hexane. Both an ethyl group and a methyl group are attached to the parent chain. They are attached to the third carbon. The name of this alkane is 3-ethyl-3-methylhexane. Note that the radicals appear in the name in alphabetical order. Why is the name of this compound not 4-ethyl-4-methylhexane?

If there are two or more substituent groups that are alike, it is convenient to use prefixes such as *di-, tri-,* and *tetra-* instead of writing each substituent separately. A comma is placed between the position numbers of the substituents that are alike. For example, the name of the following compound is 2,3-dimethylhexane. Why is the name not 4,5-dimethylhexane?

A prefix is used to indicate two or more identical substituent groups.

Note that the number of positions and the number of groups must *agree.*

PROBLEMS

1. c

1. What is the correct name for this compound?

    a. 2-ethyl-3-methylbutane
    b. 2-methyl-3-ethylbutane
    c. 2,3-dimethylpentane
    d. 2-methylhexane

2. a. 2,2-dimethylbutane
  b. hexane
  c. 3-methylpentane
  d. 3-ethyl-2-methylhexane

2. Name the following.

3. a. CH_3—$\overset{\displaystyle CH_3}{\underset{\displaystyle |}{CH}}$—$CH_3$

3. Write structural formulas for the following.
    a. methylpropane   **c.** 3-ethyl-2-methylhexane
    b. 2,3,4-trimethyloctane   **d.** 4-propyloctane

29:4 ISOMERS OF ALKANES

Isomers have the same formula but different molecular structures.

    Note that only one structural diagram can be drawn for methane, ethane, or propane. There are, however, two possible structures for butane as shown on page 585.

Each of these two structures of butane is an isomer of butane. It is important for you at this point to review the information on isomers in Chapter 13. Most organic compounds have isomers. There is no known way of predicting exactly how many isomers most compounds can form. Pentane (C_5H_{12}), the next member of the alkane family, has three isomers. Hexane (C_6H_{14}) has five isomers. Heptane (C_7H_{16}) has nine. Isomers are named according to the longest chain and not according to the total number of carbon atoms in the molecule. The second structure of butane is named 2-methylpropane.

Our work will be easier if we modify the structural formulas to a condensed form. There can be only one bond between carbon and hydrogen atoms. In the condensed form of a structural formula, carbon atoms are still written separately. However, the hydrogen atoms that are attached to a carbon atom are grouped with that carbon atom. Thus, the isomers of pentane may be written as

butane

2-methylpropane

$$CH_3-CH_2-CH_2-CH_2-CH_3$$

pentane

$$CH_3-CH_2-\overset{\displaystyle CH_3}{\overset{\displaystyle |}{CH}}-CH_3$$

2-methylbutane

$$CH_3-\overset{\displaystyle CH_3}{\underset{\displaystyle CH_3}{\overset{\displaystyle |}{\underset{\displaystyle |}{C}}}}-CH_3$$

2,2-dimethylpropane

pentane

2-methylbutane

2,2-dimethylpropane

FIGURE 29-1. Note from the models for the isomers of pentane that the C—C bonds are not at 90° or 180° as shown by the structural formulas.

PROBLEMS

4. Name the following.

a. $CH_3-\overset{\displaystyle CH_3}{\overset{\displaystyle |}{CH}}-\overset{\displaystyle CH_3}{\overset{\displaystyle |}{CH}}-CH_2-CH_3$

b. $CH_3-CH_2-CH_2-CH_2-CH_2-CH_2-CH_2-CH_3$

c. $CH_3-CH_2-CH_2-CH_2-\overset{\displaystyle CH_3}{\overset{\displaystyle |}{CH}}-\overset{\displaystyle CH_3}{\underset{\displaystyle CH_3}{\overset{\displaystyle |}{\underset{\displaystyle |}{C}}}}-CH_3$

d. $CH_3-\overset{\displaystyle CH_3}{\overset{\displaystyle |}{CH}}-\overset{\displaystyle CH_3}{\overset{\displaystyle |}{CH}}-\overset{\displaystyle CH_3}{\overset{\displaystyle |}{CH}}-CH_2-CH_3$

4. a. 2,3-dimethylpentane
   b. octane
   c. 2,2,3-trimethylheptane
   d. 2,3,4-trimethylhexane

e. 2,2-dimethylbutane

$$CH_3-\overset{\overset{\displaystyle CH_3}{|}}{\underset{\underset{\displaystyle CH_3}{|}}{C}}-CH_2-CH_3$$

e.

5. b.
$$CH_3-\overset{\overset{\displaystyle CH_3}{|}}{\underset{\underset{\displaystyle CH_3}{|}}{C}}-\overset{\overset{\displaystyle CH_3}{|}}{\underset{\underset{\displaystyle CH_3}{|}}{C}}-CH_3$$

5. Draw structural formulas (condensed form) for the following.

   a. 2-methylheptane

   b. tetramethylbutane

   c. 2,2,4-trimethylpentane

   d. 3-ethyl-2-methylpentane

   e. 3-ethylhexane

6. Hint: there are 5 isomers.

6. Draw structural formulas for all the isomers of hexane.

7. Name each isomer in Problem 6.

29:5 OPTICAL ACTIVITY

$$H-\overset{\overset{\displaystyle CH_2CH_2CH_3}{|}}{\underset{\underset{\displaystyle CH_2CH_3}{|}}{C}}-CH_3$$
3-methylhexane

$$CH_3-\overset{\overset{\displaystyle CH_2CH_2CH_3}{|}}{\underset{\underset{\displaystyle CH_2CH_3}{|}}{C}}-H$$
3-methylhexane

Optical isomers are mirror images of each other.

Asymmetric molecules of the same substance are optically active.

Another kind of isomerism concerns organic molecules of the same compound that are assymmetrical with respect to each other. They are mirror images. An **asymmetric carbon** atom is one attached to four different particles. As an example of asymmetrical objects, look at your hands. We think of our hands as being identical. Yet there is no way we can rotate our left hand in order to make it look exactly like our right hand. The left hand is a mirror image of the right hand. They have an asymmetrical relationship. So do the molecules of 3-methylhexane shown on the left. It is impossible to rotate the one to look exactly like the other. The two isomers are called **stereoisomers.** Stereoisomers have the same physical properties except in their behavior toward light. Asymmetrical molecules are said to be **optically active.** They have the property of rotating the plane in which polarized light is vibrating.

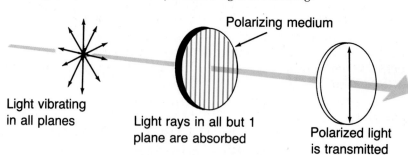

Polarizing medium

Light vibrating in all planes

Light rays in all but 1 plane are absorbed

Polarized light is transmitted

FIGURE 29-2. When light enters a polarizer, only those waves vibrating in one plane can pass through it.

Polarized light vibrates in only one plane.

The electromagnetic waves in a beam of light vibrate in all directions, not just up and down or sideways. However, it is possible, using the proper kind of filter, to obtain light in which all the vibrations are taking place in the same plane. Such light is called **polarized light.**

   An optically active substance will rotate the plane of polarized light when the light is passed through the substance. The amount of rotation is a characteristic of the substance through which the light is passing. This

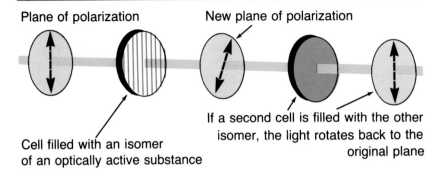

Plane of polarization

New plane of polarization

Cell filled with an isomer
of an optically active substance

If a second cell is filled with the other
isomer, the light rotates back to the
original plane

FIGURE 29-3. The polarimeter measures the rotation of polarized light as it passes through a solution containing an optically active substance.

property is a useful analytical tool when an instrument called a **polarimeter** is used. It measures the amount of rotation of polarized light passing through a solution of unknown substance. The technique is most useful in measuring unknown concentrations of solutions.

The sugars dextrose and levulose were named for their optical activity. Dextrose rotates light to the right and levulose rotates light to the left. In the example using 3-methylhexane, one form would rotate plane polarized light in one direction. The other form would rotate it in the other direction.

A polarimeter measures the amount that a compound rotates polarized light.

A dextrorotatory substance (Latin: *dexter*, right) rotates light to the right. A levorotatory substance (Latin: *laevus*, left) rotates light to the left.

29:6 NUCLEAR MAGNETIC RESONANCE

Chemists use a property of the atomic nucleus to distinguish among certain kinds of isomers. The technique is particularly useful for identifying structural, positional, and functional isomers. In Section 8:11 we found that nucleons have the property of spin. We know that a charged particle in motion creates a magnetic field. A spinning proton, then, should have a magnetic field, but a spinning neutron should not. It can be shown that both particles have a magnetic field! Just as electrons pair in orbitals, like nucleons also pair. If two neutrons pair, their spins will be opposite and their magnetic fields will cancel each other. However, for nuclei with unpaired nucleons, the nucleus as a whole should possess a magnetic field.

If a nucleus with a magnetic field is placed in an external magnetic field, two energy states are possible for the nucleus. The two fields are either aligned or opposed. The opposed fields represent a higher energy

Spinning protons and neutrons have magnetic fields.

Nuclei with unpaired nucleons possess a magnetic field.

The magnetic field of a nucleus when placed in an external magnetic field will be either aligned or opposed.

FIGURE 29-4. NMR spectroscopy can be used to identify a sample of organic isomers. The height of the peaks and the points at which they occur are characteristic of the structure of the molecule.

state. The energy required to "flip" the nucleus from one state to the other is affected by nearby atoms in the molecule. The energy can be measured by a process called **nuclear magnetic resonance (NMR) spectroscopy.**

About two-thirds of the naturally occurring nuclei have magnetic fields. The hydrogen atom, with its single proton as a nucleus, has been by far the most widely studied through NMR spectroscopy. An NMR spectrum of an organic molecule will show several energy peaks. These peaks correspond to hydrogen atoms (protons) in different locations in the molecule. Each hydrogen atom with a different arrangement of the other atoms around it will give a separate peak.

29:7 CYCLOALKANES

We have studied two forms of saturated hydrocarbons: straight-chain forms (alkanes) and branched-chain forms (also alkanes). There is a third form of saturated hydrocarbons; these cyclic forms are called cycloalkanes. Cycloalkanes contain only single bonds and have the general formula C_nH_{2n}. Cycloalkanes occur in petroleum in such forms as cyclopropane, cyclopentane, and cyclohexane.

Cycloalkanes are single-bond ring compounds.

General formula for cycloalkanes: C_nH_{2n}

In a structural formula for an organic molecule, a carbon atom is represented by the intersection of each pair of straight lines. All other bonds of the carbon atoms are to hydrogen atoms.

The formation of a ring causes bond strain in all cycloalkanes except cyclohexane.

cyclopropane   cyclopentane   cyclohexane

A strained bond results when the molecular geometry shows the bonding electrons to be closer than the normal 109.5°.

These diagrams are somewhat unwieldy. Organic chemists use stylized drawings to represent cyclic compounds. In the symbols for cyclic compounds, a carbon atom is understood to be at the point where each pair of straight lines meets. Each carbon atom is understood to be bonded to enough hydrogen atoms to produce a total of four bonds. Standard symbols can be used to represent the first five cycloalkanes.

In cyclobutane, the internal angle is 100°.

cyclopropane   cyclobutane   cyclopentane   cyclohexane   cycloheptane

In naming cycloalkanes, the ring carbons are numbered so as to give the substituents the lowest set of numbers. Some derivative compounds of the cycloalkanes are shown on page 589.

Recall that the normal bond angles around a single-bonded carbon atom are 109.5°. The interior angle of an equilateral triangle is 60°. Thus, the C—C—C bond angle in cyclopropane is 60°. Bonding electrons forced that close exert a strong repelling force on each other. These bonds are called "strained" bonds and lead to a less stable molecule than a similar chain hydrocarbon. Other cycloalkanes also exhibit strained bonds.

Cyclohexane is an industrially important cycloalkane. It is produced from benzene (Section 13:7) and is used as a raw material in making one type of nylon.

methylcyclopropane

1,3-dimethylcyclohexane

ethylcyclopentane

29:8 ALKENES

Some hydrocarbons contain multiple bonds between carbon atoms. These hydrocarbons may combine with other elements or compounds by adding on at the multiple bond. When addition occurs, the carbon chain remains unbroken. Thus, hydrocarbons that contain multiple bonds are called **unsaturated hydrocarbons.**

Unsaturated hydrocarbons containing double bonds between carbon atoms are called **alkenes** (AL keens) or olefins (OH leh fihns). Alkenes are another homologous series of hydrocarbons. The names of these compounds end in -ene. The -ene ending tells you that there is double bonding between carbon atoms.

The alkenes constitute a homologous series with the general formula C_nH_{2n}. The first five members of the alkene series are ethene, C_2H_4; propene, C_3H_6; butene, C_4H_8; pentene, C_5H_{10}; and hexene, C_6H_{12}. As with the alkanes, there are general trends in the physical and chemical properties of alkenes as the molecular mass increases.

Since the carbon atoms in an alkene are held together by two pairs of electrons, they are closer than two carbon atoms held by a single bond. The double bond is stronger than a single bond. Since the second pair of electrons (the pi bond) is further from the two nuclei than the sigma bond, the double bond is not twice as strong as a single bond. In addition, the greater π bond-nuclei distance makes a double bond more reactive than a single bond. The less tightly held π electrons are more easily attacked by a reactant. The arrangement of the π electron cloud off the axis (Figure 13-13) prevents free rotation of the atoms on either end of the bond. This rigidity allows for the possibility of geometric isomers.

29:9 NAMING ALKENES

With the introduction of double bonds, a new way of forming positional isomers is introduced. Butene in a straight chain can still have two isomers. These isomers are shown on page 590.

Compounds with double bonds, which exist in isomeric form, are named by using a position number for the double bond. The number

Unsaturated hydrocarbons contain multiple bonds.

carbon-carbon double bond

Alkenes contain double bonds.

General formula for alkenes: C_nH_{2n}.

Double bond is stronger than a single bond.

DEMONSTRATION: Show the presence and reactivity of a double bond by adding a few cm^3 of bromine water to some cyclohexane, and then cyclohexene in separate test tubes. Use fume hood. Repeat adding $Br_2(aq)$ to warm cottonseed oil. **CAUTION:** *Hydrocarbons are flammable. $Br_2(aq)$ is corrosive and poisonous.*
DEMONSTRATION: You can test for unsaturated bonds in bacon by placing 3–4 pieces of very crisp bacon in a flask that has been filled with Br_2 vapor. Shake well. In the stoppered flask, the color of Br_2 disappears. The glycerol part of fat molecules is converted into an unsaturated substance called acrolein. **CAUTION:** *Br_2 is corrosive and poisonous.*

$$\ce{H}\diagdown\underset{\ce{H}}{\overset{1}{C}}=\underset{\underset{\ce{H}}{|}}{\overset{\ce{H}}{\overset{2}{C}}}-\underset{\underset{\ce{H}}{|}}{\overset{\ce{H}}{\overset{3}{C}}}-\underset{\underset{\ce{H}}{|}}{\overset{\ce{H}}{\overset{4}{C}}}-\ce{H}$$

1-butene

$$\ce{H}-\underset{\underset{\ce{H}}{|}}{\overset{\overset{\ce{H}}{|}}{\overset{1}{C}}}-\underset{\underset{\ce{H}}{|}}{\overset{\ce{H}}{\overset{2}{C}}}=\underset{\ce{H}}{\overset{3}{C}}-\underset{\underset{\ce{H}}{|}}{\overset{\ce{H}}{\overset{4}{C}}}-\ce{H}$$

2-butene

Alkene isomers differ in the location of their double bonds.

Compounds are named according to the longest chain with a double bond.

The lowest possible positional number is assigned to the first double-bonded carbon atom.

Geometric isomerism may result from double bonds.

cyclohexene

Double bonds are also found in cyclic compounds.

A molecule whose name ends in -diene, contains two double bonds.

comes from the carbon atom on which the double bond begins, and is always placed before the name of the parent compound.

Alkenes are numbered so that the lowest position number is assigned to the first carbon atom to which the double bond is attached. The parent compound is named from the longest continuous chain containing a double bond. Thus, the name of the following alkene is 3-propyl-1-heptene.

$$\overset{1}{C}H_2$$
$$\|$$
$$\overset{2}{C}H$$
$$\overset{7}{C}H_3-\overset{6}{C}H_2-\overset{5}{C}H_2-\overset{4}{C}H_2-\overset{3}{C}H-CH_2-CH_2-CH_3$$

3-propyl-1-heptene

The double bond also makes possible another kind of isomerism: geometric isomerism. This type of isomerism was discussed in Chapter 13.

Two alkenes are commercially important, ethene (common name *ethylene*) and propene (common name *propylene*). In fact, ethene is the number one organic chemical in industry. Over 10 million tons per year are produced! It is obtained chiefly as one product of the refining of petroleum (Section 30:6). It is used to produce plastics, antifreeze, synthetic fibers, and solvents. Propene is also a by-product of petroleum refining and is used to manufacture plastics and synthetic fibers. Double bonds may also be found in cyclic compounds. A typical cycloalkene is cyclohexene shown on the left.

A single molecule may contain more than one double bond. In that case the -ene ending must be preceded by a prefix indicating the number of double bonds in the molecule. Thus, the compound CH_2=CH—CH=CH_2 is named 1,3-butadiene. 1,3-butadiene is produced from petroleum in large quantities to be used in the production of synthetic rubber.

1,3-cyclohexadiene

Alkynes contain triple bonds.

$$H-C\equiv C-H$$

ethyne (acetylene)

$$H-C\equiv C-\underset{\underset{H}{|}}{\overset{\overset{H}{|}}{C}}-H$$

propyne

29:10 ALKYNES

A third homologous series of hydrocarbons consists of molecules containing triple bonds between carbon atoms.

$$H\!:\!C\!:\!:\!:\!C\!:\!H$$

carbon-carbon triple bond

Compounds with triple-bonded carbon atoms are called **alkynes** (AL kyns). Alkynes constitute a homologous series with the general formula C_nH_{2n-2}. They are important raw materials for industries producing synthetic materials such as plastics and fibers. Chemically, alkynes are very reactive. The alkynes are named just as the alkenes, except the ending *-yne* replaces *-ene*. *Acetylene* is the common name for ethyne, the first member of this series. Acetylene is commercially the most important member of the alkyne family. The first three members of the alkyne family are ethyne, C_2H_2; propyne, C_3H_4; and butyne, C_4H_6.

In naming alkynes, the numbering system for location of the triple bond and the substituent groups follows much the same pattern as was used for naming the alkenes. For example, the name of the following compound is 4,4-dimethyl-2-pentyne.

$$\overset{1}{C}H_3 - \overset{2}{C} \equiv \overset{3}{C} - \overset{4}{\underset{\underset{CH_3}{|}}{\overset{\overset{CH_3}{|}}{C}}} - \overset{5}{C}H_3$$

4,4-dimethyl-2-pentyne

29:11 AROMATIC HYDROCARBONS

To an organic chemist, one of the most important organic compounds is benzene, a cyclic hydrocarbon. Its structural resonance forms can be written

The benzene ring is diagrammed as

benzene

In this structural representation, it is assumed that there is a carbon atom at each corner with one hydrogen atom attached. Note from Chapter 13 that the benzene ring has a conjugated system of double and single bonds in a continuous loop. Therefore, it possesses great stability. This diagram should not be confused with the symbol for cyclohexane. Cyclohexane is an alkane composed of only single bonds.

Thousands of compounds are derived from benzene. The study of benzene derivatives constitutes a whole branch of organic chemistry. Most of these compounds have rather distinctive odors. Thus, they are called **aromatic compounds.** Aromatic compounds are normally named as derivatives of benzene. Aromatic compounds occur in small quantities in some petroleum reserves. They occur to a large extent in coal tar obtained from the distillation of coal. Some compounds consist of a fused

SUGGESTION: Explain to students that it is not necessary for a compound to have a distinctive odor for it to be an aromatic compound. It is only necessary for the compound to include a benzene ring.

2-butyne

General formula for alkynes: C_nH_{2n-2}.

Alkynes are very reactive chemically.

The lowest possible position number is assigned to the first triple-bonded carbon atom.

BACKGROUND: Compounds with two or more triple bonds are not alkynes. They belong to groups called alkadiynes, alkatriynes, etc. The second triple bond does not have much effect on the first unless they are relatively close in the chain.

The actual molecule is considered a resonance hybrid of these two structures.

The benzene ring contains a conjugated system of bonds.

cyclohexane

Aromatic compounds are generally derived from benzene.

naphthalene

Naphthalene, $C_{10}H_8$, has a fused ring structure.

Anthracene, $C_{14}H_{10}$, forms when three benzene rings fuse together.

system of several rings. These compounds have properties similar to benzene. An example of a fused ring compound is naphthalene. The symbol for this fused ring system is shown on the left.

Chemists have found a number of compounds that exhibit behavior similar to benzene-containing compounds, but that do not contain a benzene ring. All of these aromatic compounds, both with and without benzene rings, have a common structural feature. This feature is a cyclic conjugated π electron system containing $(4n + 2)$ π electrons. The symbol n stands for any whole number. For benzene, with six π electrons, $n = 1$. For naphthalene, with 10 π electrons, $n = 2$. Examples of non-benzenoid aromatic species are

$n = 0$

cyclopentadienyl anion

$n = 1$

cyclopropenyl cation

$n = 3$

annulene

phenyl radical

The radical formed from a benzene ring is the phenyl radical.

The radical formed by removing a hydrogen atom from a benzene ring is called the phenyl radical. The symbol for the phenyl radical is shown on the left.

Some examples of benzene compounds are

CH₃ — methylbenzene (toluene)

CH₂—CH₃ — ethylbenzene

CH=CH₂ — phenylethene (styrene)

CH₃—CH—CH₃ — 2-phenylpropane (cumene)

CH₃ / CH₃ — 1,4-dimethylbenzene (p-xylene)

Do not confuse the phenyl radical with the benzyl radical which is

—CH₂—

Aromatic compounds are economically important to many chemical industries such as rubber, plastics, fibers, explosives, paint, and petroleum.

Benzene, toluene, and xylene are synthesized from petroleum. Ethylbenzene and cumene are made from benzene, while styrene is made from ethylbenzene. All of these compounds are important to our economy. Benzene is used in making plastics and fibers. Toluene is used to improve the quality of gasoline, as well as in the production of explosives and other chemicals. The explosive TNT is 2,4,6-trinitrotoluene. Ethylbenzene is converted almost entirely to styrene. Styrene is a vital component of synthetic rubber, plastics, and paints. The compound p-xylene is a raw material for polyester fibers. Cumene is used in making plastics. Other xylenes, 1,2- and 1,3-dimethylbenzenes, are used in producing chemicals, plastics, and in enriching gasoline. A very large part of our synthetic materials industry is based upon aromatic compounds containing a benzene ring.

Substitutions in a hydrocarbon generally increase the reactivity.

29:12 HALOGEN DERIVATIVES

Atoms other than carbon and hydrogen can be substituted for part of a hydrocarbon molecule. When this substitution occurs, the chemical reactivity of the hydrocarbon is generally increased. The nonhydrocarbon part of the molecule is called a functional group. Most of the chemical reactivity of the substituted hydrocarbon is due to the functional group.

One family of substituted hydrocarbon molecules has a halogen atom substituted for a hydrogen atom. For example, if we substitute a bromine atom for a hydrogen atom on methane, we obtain CH_3Br. The name of this compound is bromomethane. It is also possible to replace more than one hydrogen atom by halogen atoms. In the compound $CHCl_3$, three chlorine atoms have been substituted for three of the hydrogen atoms in a methane molecule. The name of this compound is trichloromethane. You may know this compound by its common name, *chloroform*. Chloroform has been widely used as a solvent. It was once used as an anesthetic. In the compound CCl_4, four chlorine atoms have been substituted for the four hydrogen atoms in a methane molecule. The common name of this tetrachloromethane compound is carbon tetrachloride. These compounds are named as derivatives of the hydrocarbons.

In large chains, we number the carbon atoms to avoid any confusion in naming the compounds. Suppose we have a chain that contains both a double bond and a halogen. In this case, begin the numbering at the end closer to the double bond. Thus, the name of the following compound is 1,4-dichloro-1-butene.

In aromatic compounds, it is necessary to indicate the relative positions of the various substituent groups on the ring. If two or more substituents are attached to the benzene ring, it is necessary to assign position numbers to the carbon atoms of the ring. The atoms in the benzene ring are numbered to give the smallest position numbers to the substituents. For example, the name of the compound shown on the right is 1,3-dibromobenzene, not 1,5-dibromobenzene.

There are four 1-positions possible in each molecule of naphthalene. The 1-position that gives the lowest numbers to substituents is always used. The 1-position is next to the atom without a hydrogen atom attached. The numbering system for naphthalene is as follows.

tetrachloromethane

trichloromethane

bromomethane

A halogen derivative has a halogen atom substituted for a hydrogen atom.

Substituted hydrocarbons are named with lowest possible position numbers for the substituents.

Note that the double bond has precedence over the halogen.

1,3-dibromobenzene

naphthalene

2-chloronaphthalene

1,3-dibromonaphthalene

Several more examples that illustrate the naming of substituted hydrocarbons are

1-bromopropane

2-bromopropane

bromobenzene

1,3-dichlorobenzene

1,2-dichloroethane
(ethylene dichloride)

chloroethene
(vinyl chloride)

4-chloro-2-pentene

1-iodonaphthalene

Well-known halogen-substituted hydrocarbons are ethyl chloride, often used as a local anesthetic, and iodoform, often used as an antiseptic.

1,2-dichloroethane (common name *ethylene dichloride*) is manufactured in large quantities from ethene. In turn, it is converted to chloroethene (common name *vinyl chloride*). The vinyl chloride is used to make a plastic, polyvinyl chloride (PVC). PVC has numerous applications, such as water and waste piping.

29:13 ORGANIC OXYGEN COMPOUNDS

Many alcohols are important in industry as solvents and reagents.

Hundreds of thousands of organic compounds contain oxygen as well as hydrogen and carbon. Many of these compounds are familiar household items. Many more are important solvents and reactants in industry. Table 29-3 lists the names of the principal classes of oxygen-

Table 29-3

Organic Compounds Containing Oxygen*			
Class	General Formula	Ending	Example
Alcohol	R—O—H	-ol	CH_3OH methanol
Ether	R—O—R'	-oxy-	$CH_3OCH_2CH_3$ methoxyethane
Aldehyde	$R-\overset{\overset{O}{\|\|}}{C}-H$	-al	CH_3CH_2CHO propanal
Ketone	$R-\overset{\overset{O}{\|\|}}{C}-R'$	-one	$CH_3COCH_2CH_3$ butanone
Acid	$R-\overset{\overset{O}{\|\|}}{C}-O-H$	-oic acid	$CH_3CH_2CH_2CH_2COOH$ pentanoic acid
Ester	$R-\overset{\overset{O}{\|\|}}{C}-O-R'$	-yl -oate	$CH_3CH_2CH_2OOCCH_3$ propyl ethanoate

*R— and R'— each represent a hydrocarbon radical. The two radicals may be the same, or they may be different.

containing compounds. It also gives the general formula of the family. The symbol R— represents any hydrocarbon radical. Thus, R—OH is the general formula for alcohols. If R— represents CH_3—, the alcohol has the formula CH_3OH. The endings in the third column indicate the method of naming compounds of each class. For example, alcohols have the ending -*ol*. The alcohol CH_3OH is methanol.

29:14   ALCOHOLS AND ETHERS

Alcohols contain the hydroxyl group, —OH. Yet alcohols are neither acidic nor basic. The hydrogen atom is displaced only by active metals. Methanol, CH_3OH, is manufactured from CO and H_2 and is used extensively in producing plastics and fibers. Ethanol, CH_3CH_2OH, is produced from ethene and is one of the most important solvents as well as a raw material for other chemical products. 2-propanol, $CH_3CHOHCH_3$, is produced from propene and is converted to acetone, an important solvent. 2-propanol with 30% water added is "rubbing alcohol."

Alcohol molecules contain a hydroxyl functional group. R-OH represents an alcohol molecule.

Alcohols contain the hydroxyl group, R-OH, but they are neither acidic or basic.

The lower molecular mass alcohols are soluble in water through hydrogen bonding with the water. Alcohols with four or more carbon atoms, however, have such a large nonpolar part of the molecule that they are not soluble in water, a polar solvent.

Lower molecular mass alcohols are water soluble due to hydrogen bonding with the water.

It is possible to have more than one hydroxyl group in a single molecule.

$$CH_2—CH_2$$
$$|\quad\ \ |$$
$$OH\quad OH$$

1,2-ethanediol
(ethylene glycol)

This compound is called 1,2-ethanediol. Its common name is *ethylene glycol* and as such it is sold in large amounts as automobile cooling system antifreeze.

A single molecule, having two hydroxyl groups, has a name ending in -*diol.*

When hydroxyl groups are attached to the benzene ring, the resulting compounds tend to be slightly acidic. The simplest of these compounds is phenol

Phenol is formed when a hydroxyl group attaches to a benzene ring.

phenol

Phenol is produced from cumene and is used to make plastics, drugs, and fibers. Since aromatic hydroxyl compounds differ somewhat in properties from most alcohols, they are classed as **phenols.**

Ethoxyethane (diethyl ether) was used for many years as an anesthetic. The cyclic ether, ethylene oxide,

Phenol is used extensively in sore throat sprays. However, it is poisonous in large concentrations.

$$CH_2——CH_2$$
$$\diagdown_O\diagup$$

ethylene oxide

The general formula of an ether is R—O—R'

is synthesized from ethene. In addition to being converted to ethylene glycol, it is also used in making fibers, films, and detergents. Propylene oxide,

$$CH_3-CH\underset{\diagdown O \diagup}{-\!\!-\!\!-}CH_2$$

propylene oxide

produced from propene, is used in making plastics, cellophane, and hydraulic fluids.

29:15 ALDEHYDES AND KETONES

The general formula of an aldehyde is
$$R-\overset{\displaystyle O}{\overset{\|}{C}}-H$$

Methanal, better known as *formaldehyde,* is manufactured from methanol and is used to make plastics and adhesives. There are no other aldehydes of great industrial significance. Both aldehydes and ketones are characterized by the carbonyl group, C=O. The most important ketone is propanone, or acetone. Acetone is made from 2-propanol and used in plastics, solvents, and making other chemicals.

The general formula of a ketone is
$$R-\overset{\displaystyle O}{\overset{\|}{C}}-R'$$

$$CH_3-\overset{\displaystyle O}{\overset{\|}{C}}-CH_3$$

propanone
(acetone)

29:16 ACIDS AND ESTERS

Organic acids contain the carboxylic acid group, R—COOH.

Most organic acids are characterized by the carboxylic acid group, —COOH, and are weak acids. However, the strength of these acids is strongly influenced by other atoms in the molecule. Since the strength of the acid depends upon the breaking of the O—H bond by having the hydrogen ion removed by a water molecule, anything that would weaken that bond results in a stronger acid. The effect of one functional group on another functional group is called an **inductive effect.** If a chlorine atom bonds to a carboxylic acid molecule, the acid becomes stronger. Chlorine, with its high electronegativity, tends to attract electrons to itself from other parts of the molecule. The chlorine draws electrons away from the

The strength of carboxylic acid can be increased through the inductive effect.

Organic acids in foods
cranberries — benzoic acid
grapes — tartaric acid
citrus fruits — citric acid
sour milk — lactic acid
rhubarb — oxalic acid
green apples — malic acid

Table 29-4

Ionization Constants of Some Organic Acids		
Name	Formula	Ionization Constant
Acetic acid	CH_3COOH	1.74×10^{-5}
Chloroacetic acid	$ClCH_2COOH$	1.38×10^{-3}
Dichloroacetic acid	$Cl_2CHCOOH$	5.01×10^{-2}
Trichloroacetic acid	Cl_3CCOOH	2.29×10^{-1}

acid group. As an example, consider the K_a values for the acids in Table 29-4.

You have used ethanoic acid *(acetic acid)* in the laboratory. This acid is produced in large quantities from methanol and carbon monoxide. Vinegar is a 5% solution of acetic acid made by fermenting fruit or grain. Acetic acid is also used in the manufacture of fibers and plastics. Hexanedioic acid *(adipic acid)* is synthesized from cyclohexane in making nylon. What is its structure?

$HOOC(CH_2)_4COOH$, adipic acid

The compound, p-xylene is used to make the dicarboxylic acid, terephthalic acid.

COOH

terephthalic acid

Fibers, films, and bottles made of polyester all contain terephthalic acid.

It is possible to have anhydrides of organic acids just as for inorganic acids. Thus, acetic anhydride can be made from acetic acid and is used to produce rayon and plastics.

Anhydrides of organic acids also exist.

$$CH_3-\overset{\overset{\displaystyle O}{\|}}{C}-O-H + H-O-\overset{\overset{\displaystyle O}{\|}}{C}-CH_3 \rightarrow CH_3-\overset{\overset{\displaystyle O}{\|}}{C}-O-\overset{\overset{\displaystyle O}{\|}}{C}-CH_3 + H_2O$$
acetic acid / acetic anhydride / water

Esters can be considered as having been made from an acid and an alcohol. For example, consider the reaction between ethanol and ethanoic acid.

Esters can be considered as having been made from an acid and an alcohol.

Esters have the general formula $R-\overset{\overset{\displaystyle O}{\|}}{C}-O-R'$

$$CH_3CH_2-O-H + H-O-C\overset{\displaystyle O}{\underset{\displaystyle CH_3}{\diagup}} \rightarrow CH_3CH_2-O-C\overset{\displaystyle O}{\underset{\displaystyle CH_3}{\diagup}} + H_2O$$
ethanol / acetic acid / ethyl acetate / water

When they react, they produce water and ethyl acetate. The $^{18}_{8}O$ nuclide can be used to determine the path of oxygen in the reaction. For example, assume we have some ethanol that contains $^{18}_{8}O$ atoms. This ethanol is then reacted with acetic acid containing the common $^{16}_{8}O$. The products are separated after the reaction and separately analyzed by mass spectrometer. We find the $^{18}_{8}O$ in the ethyl acetate. We now know that the oxygen in the ester came from the alcohol, not from the acid.

Ethenyl ethanoate *(vinyl acetate)*, $CH_3COOCH=CH_2$, is an ester produced from ethyne and ethanoic acid. It is used to make adhesives and paints.

$C_3H_7COOC_2H_5$ is ethyl butyrate and has a pineapple odor.

Methyl salicylate has a wintergreen odor.

$\overset{\overset{\displaystyle O}{\|}}{C}-O-CH_3$

OH

29:17   ORGANIC NITROGEN COMPOUNDS

An amine contains nitrogen bonded to alkyl groups and/or hydrogen.

$$H—\underset{\underset{H}{|}}{N}—H \qquad H—\underset{\underset{H}{|}}{N}—R$$

ammonia   primary amine

$$R—\underset{\underset{H}{|}}{N}—R' \qquad R—\underset{\underset{R''}{|}}{N}—R'$$

secondary amine   tertiary amine

Amines are bases since the N atom possesses an unshared pair of electrons.

Many organic compounds of biological importance contain nitrogen. Because nitrogen has more than one oxidation state, it can combine with organic radicals in a number of ways.

Amines are organic compounds in which a nitrogen atom is bound to alkyl groups and hydrogen atoms. Amines are derivatives of ammonia. If only one hydrogen atom of ammonia is replaced by an alkyl group, the compound is a primary amine. If two hydrogen atoms are replaced, the compound is a secondary amine. If all three are replaced, the compound is a tertiary amine. In general, chemists use the symbol R— to represent an alkyl group. General formulas for amines are shown on the left.

Amines are usually named as derivatives of ammonia. For example, the name of the following compound is diethylamine.

$$CH_3—CH_2—\underset{\underset{H}{|}}{N}—CH_2—CH_3$$

diethylamine

Amines may also be named as amino-substituted hydrocarbons. The carbon chain is numbered to give the amine group the lowest number. For example, the name of the following compound is 1,4-diaminobutane.

$$\overset{1}{H_2N}—\overset{2}{CH_2}—\overset{3}{CH_2}—\overset{4}{CH_2}—CH_2—NH_2$$

1,4-diaminobutane

Amides are characterized by a carbonyl group and an amine group.

SUGGESTION: Use structural models to demonstrate how Wöhler rearranged the atoms of NH_4OCN to form urea, $(NH_2)_2CO$, by heating. He demonstrated that a "vital force" was not necessary to produce an organic compound.

$$NH_4OCN \rightarrow H_2NCONH_2$$

ammonium cyanate → urea

Amides are characterized by a carbonyl group and an amine group. An amine-like compound of importance in both industry and living systems is urea, $H_2N—CO—NH_2$. Some organisms secrete their nitrogenous wastes in the form of urea. Commercially, urea is formed from ammonia and carbon dioxide. It is used as a fertilizer, a raw material for plastics production, and a livestock feed supplement.

Other important classes of nitrogen-containing compounds are listed in Table 29-5. G— is used in place of R— with amino acids. Some amino

Table 29-5

Organic Compounds Containing Nitrogen		
Class	General Formula	Example
Amines	$R—NH_2$	$CH_3CH_2NH_2$ ethanamine
Amides	$R—\overset{\overset{O}{\|\|}}{C}—NH_2$	CH_3CONH_2 ethanamide
Amino acids	$G—\overset{\overset{NH_2}{\|}}{CH}—COOH$	$CH_3CH(NH_2)COOH$ alanine (2-aminopropanoic acid)
Nitriles	$R—C\equiv N$	$CH_3CH_2CH_2CN$ butanenitrile
Nitro compounds	$R—NO_2$	$C_6H_5NO_2$ nitrobenzene

acids have other elements in addition to C and H so the symbol G— is used. For example, G— for aspartic acid represents $HOOC—CH_2—$. G— for methionine represents $CH_3—S—CH_2—CH_2—$.

Nitriles are characterized by a carbon-nitrogen triple bond. One important nitrile is propenenitrile (acrylonitrile). It is manufactured from propene, ammonia, and oxygen and is used in fibers, plastics, and synthetic rubber.

BIOGRAPHY   Maria Goeppert Mayer (1906-1972)

Maria Goeppert Mayer was the seventh generation of university professors in her family. She was the second woman to win a Nobel Prize in physics. Goeppert Mayer received her doctorate degree at the age of 24, in spite of the fact that she had to prepare by herself to take the German University exams. At that time, the only school that prepared women for the University had closed.

Goeppert Mayer worked with the major physicists and chemists of her time, including Max Born. She was interested primarily in researching quantum theory, electrodynamics, spectroscopy, and crystal physics. She conceptualized a shell model for the atomic nucleus. She believed the relative stability of the nucleus could be explained by considering single particle orbits in various shells in the nucleus. For this proposal, she won the Nobel Prize in 1963.

At the time of her death, Goeppert Mayer was a faculty member at the University of California in San Diego.

TECHNOLOGY AND CHEMISTRY

29:18   Synfuels

The limited supply of petroleum as a resource has led government and industry to investigate other hydrocarbon sources for use as fuels and raw materials for the chemical industry. Synfuels or synthetic fuels are derived from organic sources that are more difficult to convert or environmentally less acceptable than traditional fuels. Some of the sources being investigated are renewable: grains, sugars, and wood. The production of methanol and ethanol from these sources promises to be a major factor in increasing the supply of hydrocarbons for both fuels and industrial use in the immediate future.

Other sources are nonrenewable but important because they are found in large quantities. Tar sands, found mostly in Canada, contain hydrocarbon mixtures similar to the heaviest and thickest fractions of petroleum. Tar sands are chemically treated at extraction plants. Naphthalene is added and the mixture is moved to settling tanks. The sand is removed and the thick bitumen mixed with naphthalene is skimmed off the top. The bitumen-naphthalene mixture is separated by distillation. A thermal cracking process yields synthetic crude oil, coke, and some fuel gas.

Oil shales, found all over the world, also contain petroleum-like materials. Bitumen and kerogen can be thermally decomposed to yield oil, gas, and carbon. Major concentrations of oil shales are found in the United States. Note that the conversion of tar sands and oil shales to useable fuels requires a number of costly processes. However if the price of crude oil remains high, these processes will become more economically feasible.

Coal is one of the most abundant raw materials in the world. Though coal is mostly carbon, it also contains small quantities of hydrogen, sulfur, and nitrogen. The most efficient fuels have a high hydrogen content. Therefore, the conversion of coal to a more useable fuel would involve the addition of hydrogen. There are two basic approaches in using coal to produce synthetic fuels. In one process, the coal is reacted with hydrogen in the presence of a catalyst to produce a liquid fuel directly. The general equation is

$$nC + (n + 1)H_2 \rightarrow C_nH_{2n+2}$$

Note that the product has the general formula for members of the alkane series. An alternative method is to gasify the coal as the first step. In this process the coal is reacted with steam.

$$C + H_2O \rightarrow CO + H_2$$

The carbon monoxide and hydrogen produced can then be combined in the presence of a catalyst to form methane.

$$CO + 3H_2 \rightarrow CH_4 + H_2O$$

Methane can then be used directly as a fuel or be converted by an additional process to a liquid hydrocarbon fuel such as gasoline. By varying the catalyst used and the reaction conditions, carbon monoxide and hydrogen can react in another way to produce methanol.

$$CO + 2H_2 \rightarrow CH_3OH$$

Methanol can then be used as a reactant to produce a synthetic fuel or other chemical product.

The basic chemistry of these processes was researched decades ago. Most of the work concerning synfuels was done in Germany. Widespread utilization of these processes depends upon the development of efficient, economical technologies. The descriptions given here are greatly simplified. Specific temperatures and pressures must be maintained during each step. Many side reactions occur, producing unwanted by-products. Catalysts are contaminated in some reactions and must be replaced continuously. Impurities in the reactants produce polluting products. Some, but not all of these problems have been overcome.

SUMMARY

1. Unsaturated hydrocarbons contain one or more double or triple bonds. Saturated hydrocarbons are hydrocarbons that contain only single bonds between carbon atoms 29:1

2. Straight-chain (aliphatic) carbon compounds are formed of carbon chains in which the atoms are covalently bound together. Cyclic carbon compounds are formed when the carbon atoms of a chain are bonded in a ring. 29:1, 29:7

3. Hydrocarbons are carbon compounds that contain only carbon and hydrogen.
   (a) Alkanes are saturated hydrocarbons with chainlike molecules. 29:2
   (b) Cycloalkanes are saturated hydrocarbons with ringlike molecules. 29:7
   (c) Alkenes are hydrocarbons that contain a double bond between carbon atoms. 29:8
   (d) Alkynes are hydrocarbons that contain a triple bond between carbon atoms. 29:10
   (e) Aromatic hydrocarbons are hydrocarbons that contain a benzene ring or $(4n + 2)$ delocalized π electrons. 29:11

4. A hydrocarbon radical is a hydrocarbon that has lost one hydrogen atom with its associated electron. It acts as a substituent to a carbon chain or ring. 29:11

5. A functional group is a nonhydrocarbon part of an organic molecule. 29:12

6. The principal classes of oxygen containing compounds are alcohols, ethers, aldehydes, ketones, acids, and esters. 29:13-29:16

7. The principal classes of nitrogen-containing compounds are amines, amides, amino acids, nitriles, and nitro compounds. 29:17

VOCABULARY

organic chemistry Intro
aliphatic 29:1
cyclic 29:1
alkane 29:1
saturated hydrocarbon 29:1
homologous 29:2
radicals 29:2
branch 29:3
substituent 29:3
asymmetric carbon 29:5
stereoisomers 29:5
optically active 29:5
polarized light 29:5

polarimeter 29:5
nuclear magnetic resonance
    spectroscopy (NMR) 29:6
unsaturated hydrocarbons 29:8
alkenes 29:8
alkynes 29:10
aromatic compounds 29:11
alcohols 29:14
phenols 29:14
inductive effect 29:16
amines 29:17
amides 29:17

PROBLEMS

1. What is a homologous series?
2. Write the general formula for alkenes.
3. Write a formula for
   a. 6 carbon alkene   **b.** 8 carbon alkane   **c.** 10 carbon alkyne
4. Write the general formula for an alkyl radical.
5. What reasons can you cite to explain why the boiling point of alkanes increases as a function of their molecular mass?
6. Write structural formulas for octane and nonane.
7. What is the chemical formula for the heptyl radical?
8. Use position numbers to label the asymmetric carbon atom in the following.

a.
$$CH_2-CH-CH-CH_3$$
with CH_3 above third carbon, Cl below first and second carbons

b.
$$CH_3-CH_2-CH-CH_3$$
with Cl below third carbon

9. What is a substituent group?
10. What rules are followed in labeling the positions of substituent groups in naming hydrocarbons?
11. Using the general formula for alkenes, write the formula for octene, heptene, and decene.
12. Which of the following compounds, octane, pentene, or heptyne, would you predict to be most reactive? Why?
13. Write the formula for TNT, 2,4,6,-trinitrotoluene.
14. Write the formula for 1,3-xylene.
15. Write the general formula for an alkyne.
16. Classify each of the following as a(n) amine, amide, nitrile, or amino acid.

a. benzene ring—C(=O)—NH$_2$ **c.** benzene ring—C≡N

b. benzene ring—NH$_2$ **d.** benzene ring—CH$_2$CHC(=O)OH with NH$_2$

17. Classify each of the following as a(n) alcohol, ether, aldehyde, or ketone.

a. benzene ring—CH$_2$CH$_2$OH   **c.** benzene ring—C(H)=O

b. cyclohexane—OH   **d.** benzene ring—C(=O)—CH$_3$

18. Classify each of the following as a(n) ester, carboxylic acid, alcohol, or ether.

a. $\langle\bigcirc\rangle$—O—CH_3

b. CH_2—CH—CH_2
          | | |
          OH   OH   OH

c.

COOH
COOH

(benzene ring with COOH groups)

d. CH_3—O—$\underset{\underset{CH_3}{|}}{\overset{\overset{CH_3}{|}}{C}}$—$CH_3$

19. Diagram the nine isomers of heptane.

20. Name the following.

a. CH_3—CH—CH_2—CH—CH_2—CH—CH_2—CH_3
          | | |
          CH_3 CH_2 (CH$_3$ top)
                          |
                          CH_3

b. CH_3—CH=CH—CH_2—CH_3

c. CH_2—CH_3
         |
        (benzene ring)—CH_2—CH_3

d. CH_3 CH_3
(cyclohexane ring with two CH$_3$ at top and one CH$_3$ at bottom)
                    CH_3

e. CH_3
CH≡C—$\overset{\overset{CH_3}{|}}{\underset{\underset{CH_3}{|}}{C}}$—$CH_3$

21. Draw the structural formula (condensed form) for the following.
   a. 3-ethylhexane
   b. 1,2,3,4,5,6-hexamethylcyclohexane
   c. 2-methylpropene
   d. 1-hexyne
   e. 2-methylnaphthalene

22. What is the molecular mass of the 40-carbon saturated hydrocarbon?

23. Name the following compounds.
   a. CH_3—CH_2—CH_2—OH

   b. CH_3—$\overset{\overset{OH}{|}}{\underset{\underset{CH_3}{|}}{C}}$—$CH_3$

   c. CH_3—CH_2—CH_2—CH_2—CH_2—O—CH_2—CH_2—CH_2—CH_2—CH_2—CH_3

   d. CH_3—CH_2—CH_2—$\overset{\overset{O}{||}}{C}$—H

   e. CH_3—$\overset{\overset{O}{||}}{C}$—$CH_2$—$CH_2$—$CH_2$—$CH_3$

18. a. ether
    b. alcohol
    c. carboxylic acid
    d. ether
20. a. 2,6-dimethyl-
       4-ethyloctane
    b. 2-pentene
    c. 1,2-diethylben-
       zene
    d. 1,1,4-trimethylcy-
       clohexane
    e. 3,3-dimethyl-1-
       butyne
22. 562 U
23. a. 1-propanol
    b. 2-methyl-2-propa-
       nol
    c. 1-pentoxyhexane
    d. butanal
    e. 2-hexanone

f. butanoic acid
g. hexyl propanoate
h. 1-propanamine
   (1-aminopropane)

f. $CH_3-CH_2-CH_2-\overset{\overset{O}{\|}}{C}-OH$

g. $CH_3-CH_2-CH_2-CH_2-CH_2-CH_2-O-\overset{\overset{O}{\|}}{C}-CH_2-CH_3$

h. $CH_3-CH_2-CH_2-\underset{\underset{H}{|}}{N}-H$

24. Draw condensed structural formulas for the following compounds.

a. 1-butanol
b. 2-methyl-1-propanol
c. 1-propoxybutane
d. ethanal
e. 3-pentanone

f. propyl methanoate
g. trimethylamine
h. propanoic acid
i. propanamide
j. nitromethane

25. the effect of one functional group on another

25. What is the inductive effect?

26. element with high electronegativity increases acidity

26. How does the addition of functional groups affect the acidity of a carboxylic acid?

27. position and electronegativity of Cl substituent

27. How do you account for the difference in K_a's for the following acids?

$$CH_3CH_2CHClCOOH \qquad\qquad ClCH_2CH_2CH_2COOH$$
(2-chlorobutanoic acid)   (4-chlorobutanoic acid)
$$K_a = 1.39 \times 10^{-3} \qquad\qquad K_a = 2.96 \times 10^{-5}$$

29. a. 2-methylpropanal
    b. 2-methylbutanal
    c. methanoic acid
       (formic acid)
    d. ethanedioic acid
       (oxalic acid)
    e. methylamine
    f. chloromethane

28. Write condensed structural formulas for the following compounds.

a. cyclopentanone
b. 3-pentene-2-one
c. butyl butanoate
d. ethyl chloroethanoate

e. ethanenitrile
f. 2-amino-3-phenylpropanal
g. 1,2-dibromo-1-phenylethane
h. hexadecane

29. Name the following compounds.

a.
$$CH_3-\underset{\underset{CH_3}{|}}{\overset{\overset{CH_3}{|}}{CH}}-CHO$$

b. $CH_3-\underset{\underset{CH_3}{|}}{CH}-CH_2-CHO$

c. HCOOH
d. HOOC—COOH
e. CH_3NH_2
f. $CH_3—Cl$

30. Write structural formulas for the following.

a. 1-phenylpropene
b. 1,2,4-trimethylbenzene
c. iodobenzene

d. 1-bromopentane
e. 3-methyl-3-pentanol
f. 4-methylphenol

REVIEW

1. What is the current theory for the source of the nuclear force?
2. How do the different particles emitted by naturally radioactive materials differ in charge and mass?

3. Why is binding energy per particle an indication of nuclear stability?

4. Describe the mechanism of a fission chain reaction.

5. How would you recommend attempting to produce element 110?

6. Predict the voltage to be expected at 25°C from a cell constructed as follows: $Co|Co^{2-}(0.100M)\|Cu^{2+}(2.00M)|Cu$.

7. If a voltaic cell produces a potential difference of 1.00 volt, what is the equilibrium constant for the reaction taking place in the cell? What is the free energy change for the reaction? Assume one electron is transferred in the balanced equation.

8. A piece of metal alloy with mass 0.8128 grams is to be analyzed for its nickel content. The metal is dissolved in acid and any ions likely to interfere are removed by appropriate chemical treatment. The resulting solution is then subjected to electrolysis using a platinum cathode. The cathode has mass 12.3247 g before the electrolysis and 12.6731 g after the electrolysis. What is the percentage of nickel in the alloy?

9. The half life of an Ir isotope is 74.2 days. How long will it take 6.30×10^{11} atoms of that nuclide to disintegrate to 2.46×10^9 atoms?

10. Complete: $^{240}_{92}U \rightarrow \;_{-1}^{0}e + ?$

6. 0.66 V
7. −96.5 kJ
8. 42.86%
9. 594 days
10. $^{240}_{93}Np$

ONE MORE STEP

1. Investigate the industrial production methods and uses for the five organic chemicals produced in greatest volume in the United States.

2. Silicones are chemicals containing silicon as well as organic radicals. Find out how they are made, what they are used for, and what properties they have that lend themselves to these uses.

3. Make a list of the names of the first thirty alkanes. Use reference books suggested by your instructor.

4. Find out how many isomers there are of nonane and decane.

See Teacher Guide

4. nonane = 35 isomers
decane = 75 isomers

READINGS

Flavin, Christopher, "Petroleum: Too Valuable to Burn?" *SciQuest*, Vol. 53, No. 9(November 1980), pp. 18-21.

The complex motion of an athlete can be broken down into a series of simpler movements. A photograph such as the one shown allows the athlete to analyze each step. The human body can be considered a complex chemical factory where thousands of reactions occur simultaneously. However, like the motion of the athlete, these processes can be broken down and classified to make their study easier. How are organic reactions classifed? What are the four classes of biomolecules?

ORGANIC REACTIONS AND BIOCHEMISTRY

30

Chapter 30 begins with the study of five common types of organic reactions. The industrial and biological aspects of organic chemistry are covered in the last part of the chapter.

DEMONSTRATION: The preparation of nylon helps students understand and visualize organic reactions. Complete preparation instructions are in the Teacher Guide. A relatively strong strand of nylon can be produced using these instructions. **CAUTION:** *Perform this demonstration only in an area with good ventilation.*

GOALS:
• You will complete and balance equations dealing with five common types of organic reactions.
• You will determine the practical and biological significance of some organic compounds.

There are thousands of kinds of organic reactions. However, just as in inorganic chemistry, by studying a few common types of reactions we can understand a great deal of the behavior of organic molecules.

30:1 OXIDATION

Hydrocarbons undergo oxidation in the presence of excess oxygen to form CO_2 and H_2O. However, at the high temperature necessary for oxidation of hydrocarbons, many different reactions take place at the same time. Hydrocarbon chains break into fragments. Carbon atoms change from one oxidation state to another. Oxygen atoms attach to the hydrocarbon fragments. Oxidation is complete when the only products are carbon dioxide and water.

The complete combustion of hydrocarbon products yields CO_2 and H_2O.

Some hydrocarbons have very large enthalpies of combustion. Thus, they are used commercially as fuels. Natural gas (methane) and bottled gas (butane containing some propane and ethane) are used in the home for heating and cooking. Acetylene is used in cutting and welding torches.

Fuels used commercially are hydrocarbons that have a very large enthalpy of combustion.

The enthalpies of combustion for a number of common organic fuels are given in Table 30-1, page 608. The values are in units of kJ/mol. To find out which of several fuels would be the most economical, the price must be considered. If we know the price of the fuel per kilogram, we can convert the data as follows:

$$\frac{kJ}{mol} \left| \frac{1 \text{ mol}}{x \text{ g}} \right| \frac{1000 \text{ g}}{1 \text{ kg}} \left| \frac{1 \text{ kg}}{y \text{ dollars}} \right. = kJ \text{ per dollar}$$

If a gaseous fuel is being purchased, the sales unit may be a unit of volume. Then the temperature and pressure at which the volume is quoted must be known. From this information, the actual amount of matter may be computed from the ideal gas equation.

Table 30-1

Enthalpies of Combustion of Common Organic Fuels			
Fuel	Enthalpy of Combustion (kJ/mol)	Fuel	Enthalpy of Combustion (kJ/mol)
Benzene	3273	Propane	2202
Cyclohexane	3924	Butane	2879
Ethyne	1305	Ethanol	1371
Methane	882	Heptane	4811
Ethane	1541	2,2,4-Trimethylpentane	5456

PROBLEM

1. $2C_6H_{14} + 19O_2 \rightarrow 12CO_2 + 14H_2O$

1. Complete and balance. (Assume complete oxidation.)
   $C_6H_{14} + O_2 \rightarrow$

30:2 SUBSTITUTION REACTIONS

Organic chemists use the term substitution to describe the replacement of one functional group by another.

In substitution reactions, a hydrogen atom is replaced with a functional group.

   A reaction in which a hydrogen atom of a hydrocarbon is replaced by a functional group is called a **substitution reaction**. Alkane molecules react with chlorine in the presence of sunlight to produce chlorosubstituted compounds. The product is a mixture of different isomers with very similar properties. Thus, this process is not a satisfactory way to prepare chlorine derivatives of alkanes. A number of aromatic compound substitution reactions can be controlled to produce specific products. For example, benzene reacts with nitric acid in the presence of concentrated sulfuric acid to form nitrobenzene.

BACKGROUND: Substitution and addition reactions are not always easily controlled. Many such reactions yield a number of unwanted products in addition to the desired product. The amount of desired product formed compared to the amount that could have been formed is called the "yield" of the reaction.

Alcohols react with hydrogen halides to form alkyl halides.

Alkyl groups and halogen atoms can also be substituted easily onto a benzene ring.
   In a second type of substitution reaction, one functional group replaces another. Alcohols undergo substitution reactions with hydrogen halides to form alkyl halides. For example, 2-propanol reacts with hydrogen iodide to form 2-iodopropane.

Alkyl halides, in turn, react with ammonia to produce amines. For example, bromoethane reacts with ammonia to produce ethylamine.

$$CH_3-CH_2-Br(l) + NH_3(aq) \rightarrow CH_3-CH_2-NH_2(aq) + HBr(aq)$$

bromoethane   ammonia   ethylamine   hydrogen bromide

Alkyl halides react with ammonia, NH_3, to produce amines.

PROBLEM

2. Complete and balance this substitution reaction.
$HOH + (CH_3)_3CI \rightarrow$

2. $HOH + (CH_3)_3CI \rightarrow HI + (CH_3)_3COH$

30:3 ADDITION REACTIONS

Each carbon atom contributes two electrons to a double bond. Suppose one bond is broken and the other remains intact. Each carbon atom then has one electron available to bond with some other atom. A number of substances will cause one bond of a double bond to break by adding on at the double bond. This type of reaction is called an **addition reaction.** An example is the addition of bromine to the double bond of ethene. The product of this reaction is 1,2-dibromoethane.

In addition reactions of alkenes, two species are added by breaking one bond of the double bond.

$$H_2C=CH_2(g) + Br_2(l) \rightarrow BrH_2C-CH_2Br(l)$$

ethene   bromine   1,2-dibromoethane

Atoms of many substances can be added at the double bond of an alkene. Common addition agents are the halogens (except fluorine), the hydrogen halides, and sulfuric acid. The double bonds in the benzene ring of aromatic compounds are so stabilized that addition reactions do not occur readily.

Addition reactions in more complex alkenes often lead to rearrangement of the molecule.

FIGURE 30-1. A bromine solution is used in testing compounds for the presence of unsaturated bonds. Bromine loses its color in the presence of an unsaturated hydrocarbon, but will not react with a saturated hydrocarbon.

3. $CH_3CH_2CH{=}CH_2 + Br_2 \rightarrow$
   $CH_3CH_2BrHC{-}CH_2Br$

3. Complete and balance this addition reaction.
$CH_3CH_2CH{=}CH_2 + Br_2 \rightarrow$

30:4   ELIMINATION REACTIONS

In elimination reactions, one product has a double bond.

We have seen that under certain circumstances, atoms can be "added on to" a double bond. It is also possible to remove certain atoms from a molecule to create a double bond. Such a reaction is known as an **elimination reaction.** In the most common elimination reactions, a water molecule is removed from an alcohol. A hydrogen atom is removed from one carbon atom, and a hydroxyl group is removed from the next carbon atom. For example, propene can be made from 1-propanol by the removal of water. Sulfuric acid is used as the dehydrating agent.

HCl and HNO_2 are other substances which are often eliminated.

$$H{-}\overset{\displaystyle H}{\underset{\displaystyle H}{\overset{|}{\underset{|}{C}}}}{-}\overset{\displaystyle H}{\underset{\displaystyle H}{\overset{|}{\underset{|}{C}}}}{-}\overset{\displaystyle H}{\underset{\displaystyle OH}{\overset{|}{\underset{|}{C}}}}{-}H(l) \xrightarrow{H_2SO_4} H{-}\overset{\displaystyle H}{\underset{\displaystyle H}{\overset{|}{\underset{|}{C}}}}{-}\overset{\displaystyle H}{\overset{|}{C}}{=}\overset{\displaystyle H}{\overset{|}{C}}{-}H(g) + H_2O(l)$$

1-propanol   propene   water

4. $CH_3CH_2CH_2CH_2OH \rightarrow$
   $CH_3CH_2CH{=}CH_2 + H_2O$

4. Complete and balance this elimination reaction.
$CH_3CH_2CH_2CH_2OH \xrightarrow{H_2SO_4}$

30:5   ESTERIFICATION AND SAPONIFICATION REACTIONS

The reaction of an alcohol and an organic acid produces an ester.

When an alcohol reacts with either an organic acid or an organic acid anhydride, an ester is formed. This type of reaction is called **esterification.** For example, in the reaction between acetic acid and methanol, methyl acetate and water are formed. Methyl acetate is an ester.

$$CH_3{-}\overset{\displaystyle O}{\overset{\|}{C}}{-}OH(l) + CH_3{-}OH(l) \rightarrow CH_3{-}\overset{\displaystyle O}{\overset{\|}{C}}{-}OCH_3(l) + H_2O(l)$$

acetic acid   methanol   methyl acetate   water

Esters are split into alcohols and salts of carboxylic acids in saponification reactions.

DEMONSTRATION: It is easy to prepare soap. See Teacher Guide for details.

An ester can be split into an alcohol and a carboxylic acid by hydrolysis. The hydrolysis reaction is the reverse of the reaction shown above. However, if a metallic base is used for the hydrolysis instead of water, the metallic salt of the carboxylic acid is obtained, not the acid. This process is called **saponification.** Saponification is the process used in making soaps. Since ancient times, soaps have been made from vegetable and animal oils and fats cooked in bases (KOH, NaOH). Soap is a metallic salt of a fatty acid. The natural fat or oil is an ester. In the following saponification reaction, the natural fat is a glyceride ester. The products of the reaction are soap and glycerol (the alcohol of the glyceride).

A soap is a metallic salt of a fatty acid.

Fats are esters of glycerol.

$$CH_2-O-\overset{\overset{\displaystyle O}{\|}}{C}-(CH_2)_{16}-CH_3\,{}^*$$

$$CH-O-\overset{\overset{\displaystyle O}{\|}}{C}-(CH_2)_{16}-CH_3 \;+\; 3NaOH \rightarrow \underset{\underset{\displaystyle OH\;\;OH\;\;OH}{\big|\;\;\;\big|\;\;\;\big|}}{CH_2-CH-CH_2} \;+\; 3[CH_3-(CH_2)_{16}-COO^-Na^+]$$

$$CH_2-O-\overset{\overset{\displaystyle O}{\|}}{C}-(CH_2)_{16}-CH_3$$

fat (a glyceride ester)   base   glycerol   soap

BACKGROUND: Fats and fatty acids will be discussed in Section 30:12.

PROBLEM

5. Complete and balance this esterification reaction.
$$CH_3CH_2OH + CH_3CH_2CH_2COOH \rightarrow$$

5. $CH_3CH_2OH + CH_3CH_2CH_2COOH \rightarrow CH_3CH_2CH_2\overset{\overset{\displaystyle O}{\|}}{C}-O-CH_2CH_3 + H_2O$

30:6 PETROLEUM

The chief source of organic compounds is the naturally occurring mixture called petroleum. Other important sources are coal tar, natural gas, and fermentation of natural materials. Petroleum is a mixture of hydrocarbons containing small amounts of nitrogen, oxygen, and sulfur compounds. The hydrocarbons are mainly alkanes and cycloalkanes. The initial treatment of petroleum in a refinery is a fractional distillation. This treatment separates the mixture into portions having different boiling ranges. The chief fractions are petroleum ether (20°C-60°C), ligroin (60°C-100°C), gasoline (40-205°C), kerosene (175-325°C), gas oil (>275°C), and lubricating oil. The remainder is asphalt.

Petroleum is the chief source of natural organic compounds.

Petroleum can be separated into portions with different boiling ranges by fractional distillation.

The products from the distillation cannot be marketed as is. They must be refined to remove undesirable substances, particularly sulfur compounds. Additives are blended with gasoline and other products to improve their performance. Many by-products of gasoline production are used as raw materials for the production of plastics, synthetic fibers, and rubber.

The yield of gasoline can be improved in a number of ways. In one process, smaller molecules from the lower boiling fractions are joined to form larger molecules. In another process, the larger molecules of the higher boiling fractions are cracked, or broken, into smaller molecules.

Cracking involves splitting large molecules of a higher boiling fraction into smaller molecules.

Gasolines are rated on a scale known as **octane rating.** The basis for this scale is the property of some fuels to cause "knocking" in engines. The knocking occurs when some of the fuel explodes suddenly instead of burning evenly. High octane gasolines contain more ring compounds and highly branched hydrocarbons than low octane gasolines.

The octane rating describes how evenly gasoline burns.

*A fat is an amorphous material, one that does not have a fixed melting point.

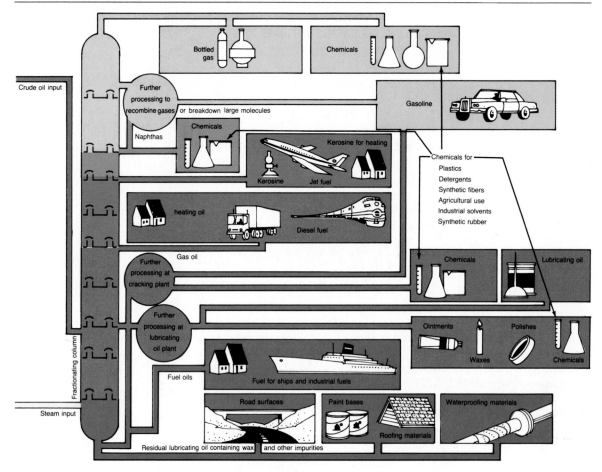

FIGURE 30-2. The products of petroleum fractionation and some of their uses are shown. Note from the diagram it should be obvious why the supply of petroleum is critical to the chemical industry.

PROBLEM

6. Name five fractions obtained by distilling petroleum.

6. asphalt, lubricating oil, gas oil, kerosene, gasoline, ligroin, petroleum ether

30:7   SYNTHETIC RUBBER

The producers of synthetic substitutes for rubber have built a thriving industry based on organic chemistry. No one synthetic material can as yet replace natural rubber. However, there are many synthetics that can perform a particular job as well as or better than natural rubber. The production of synthetic rubber depends primarily upon a chemical reaction called addition polymerization. In this reaction, a molecule called a monomer, which contains a double or triple bond, adds to other similar molecules. Chains (or cross-linked chains) of very large molecular size and mass are formed. For example, consider the reaction between two molecules of ethene.

Synthetic rubber is a result of polymerization.

In addition polymerization, a molecule called a monomer adds to other monomers.

Polymerization is the joining together of molecules which contain double or triple bonds.

$$CH_2{=}CH_2(l) + CH_2{=}CH_2(l) \rightarrow {-}CH_2{-}CH_2{-}CH_2{-}CH_2{-}(amor)$$

This process can continue almost indefinitely. The bonds at the end of a chain cross-link to other chains. Gigantic molecules are formed. Such molecules are called **polymers.** In this case, the polymer is named polyethene or polyethylene.

Natural rubber is a polymer of 2-methylbutadiene. The 2-methylbutadiene molecule is the monomer of natural rubber. Many types of synthetic rubber can be made from verious monomers. Often they are made by polymerizing two or more substances containing double bonds.

The largest selling synthetic rubber is a copolymer of 1,3-butadiene and styrene. It is used chiefly in the production of automobile tires.

30:8 PLASTICS

The production of plastics has created another important organic chemical industry. Plastics can be produced by polymerization. Some common plastics made by **addition polymerization** are polyethylene, polypropylene, polyvinyl acetate, polystyrene, and acrylics.

Plastics can also be made by a similar process in which both the polymer and another product, usually water, result. In this type of reaction, the molecules actually condense. This type of reaction is called a **condensation polymerization** reaction. Other plastics such as cellophane and celluloid can be made by the chemical treatment of cellulose.

Structural diagrams for monomers and polymer units of some polymerization and condensation plastics are shown below.

BACKGROUND: Much of the early research in synthetics was done in Germany in the period prior to and during World War II.

DEMONSTRATION: The effect of cross-linking on a polymer can be demonstrated by using safe, polyvinyl alcohol. The cross linker is sodium borate, borax. The product is fun to experiment with in the laboratory. Some students call it slime. See the Teacher Guide for preparation details.

An interesting exception is thiokol in which NaCl is the second product.

Plastics may be made by condensation reactions.

Addition polymerization plastics:

phenylethene
or
styrene

polystyrene
(amor)

Condensation polymerization plastics:

phenol

methanal
or
formaldehyde

phenol-formaldehyde
(amor)

30:9 SYNTHETIC FIBERS

Rayon is reconstituted cellulose.

Cellulose is a natural polymer of glucose, $C_6H_{12}O_6$.

One of the earliest synthetic fibers produced is rayon. Rayon is simply reconstituted cellulose, which is the principal structural element of plants. Cellulose is a natural polymer of glucose, $C_6H_{12}O_6$.

Cellulose in the form of purified wood pulp is soaked in a sodium hydroxide solution. The cellulose is converted to sodium cellulose whose structure is unknown. The sodium cellulose is then treated with carbon disulfide, CS_2, forming sodium cellulose xanthate, which is soluble in sodium hydroxide solution. This solution, called "viscose," is squeezed through a small hole into a solution of sulfuric acid. The xanthate reacts with the sulfuric acid to regenerate the cellulose fiber.

Nylon is the name for a group of polyamide fibers.

Nylon is a name for a whole group of polyamide fibers. Nylon 66, made from adipic acid (hexanedioic acid) and hexamethylenediamine (1,6-diaminohexane), is the most common form. The amino group

FIGURE 30-3. Most synthetic fibers are produced in continuous filaments. The properties of the fiber depend on the spinning process used to give the filament its shape.

of the amine and the carboxyl group of the acid form an amide by condensation.

$$H-\underset{\underset{H}{|}}{N}-(CH_2)_6-\underset{\underset{H}{|}}{N}-H + H-O-\underset{\overset{O}{\|}}{C}-(CH_2)_4-\underset{\overset{O}{\|}}{C}-O-H \rightarrow \cdots -\underset{\underset{H}{|}}{N}-\underset{\overset{O}{\|}}{C}- \cdots + H_2O$$

Since each reactant has a functional group on each end, a polymer can be formed. The polymer is melted and forced through a small hole into a stream of cool air where the polymer solidifies to a fiber.

PROBLEM

7. What natural material is imitated by rayon?

7. cellulose

30:10 PROTEINS

Approximately one half of your non-water mass consists of substances called proteins. These substances compose some structural parts of the body such as cartilage and tendons. However, more than three fourths of the protein in your body is used within the cells as catalysts! Biological catalysts are called enzymes. When we think of the word fuel, we think of burning a substance to obtain energy. Organisms, composed of cells, require energy. "Burning" fuels would destroy the cells. Thus, enzymes are present in the cells to enable reactions to occur at temperatures that are not injurious to the cells. **Proteins** are polymers made of **amino acids.** There are about 20 common amino acids. These acids are listed in Table 30-2, page 616.

In Section 29:17 we found that carboxylic acids reacted with amines to form amides.

Biological catalysts are called enzymes. These compounds are classified as proteins.

Enzymes are present in cells to enable reactions to occur at temperatures which do not injure cells.

$$-\underset{\overset{O}{\|}}{C}-\underset{\underset{H}{|}}{N}-.$$

Amino acids are linked through the same condensation process. However, biochemists call the amide link a **peptide bond.** The new molecule formed from two amino acids is called a **dipeptide.** Three amino acids form a **tripeptide.** Many amino acids condense to a polypeptide. If a **polypeptide** has a biological function, it is called a protein.

Proteins differ from each other in several ways. The first difference, and the most important, is the sequence of the amino acids composing the protein. Another way they differ is the way the polymer chain is coiled, folded, and twisted. Finally, the type of bonding holding the polymer in a particular shape can vary. Proteins contain from about 30 to several thousand amino acids. The 20 acids can form an enormous number of different proteins.

Amino acids link because the carboxylic acid reacts with the amine to form a peptide bond.

Many amino acids condense to form a polypeptide.

Proteins differ in the order of amino acids, how the chain is coiled, folded, or twisted, and in the type of bonding holding the polymer in a particular shape.

Table 30-2

Amino Acids

Amino acids have the form

$$\begin{array}{c} COOH \\ | \\ H-C-NH_2 \\ | \\ G \end{array}$$

In the table, only the composition of G is represented.

Name	G	Symbol
Glycine	H—	Gly
Alanine	CH_3—	Ala
Valine	CH_3-CH- 	 CH_3	Val
Leucine	$CH_3-CH-CH_2-$ 	 CH_3	Leu
Isoleucine	CH_3-CH_2-CH- 	 CH_3	Ile
Tryptophan	(indole ring)—CH_2—	Trp
Lysine	$H_2N-CH_2-CH_2-CH_2-CH_2-$	Lys
Arginine	$H_2N-\overset{\parallel NH}{C}-NH-CH_2-CH_2-CH_2-$	Arg
Phenylalanine	(benzene ring)—CH_2—	Phe
Histidine	(imidazole ring)—CH_2—	His
Asparagine	$O=C-CH_2-$ 	 NH_2	Asn
Glutamine	$O=C-CH_2-CH_2-$ 	 NH_2	Gln
Serine	$HO-CH_2-$	Ser
Threonine	CH_3-CH- 	 OH	Thr
Aspartic acid	$HOOC-CH_2-$	Asp
Glutamic acid	$HOOC-CH_2-CH_2-$	Glu
Tyrosine	$HO-$(benzene ring)$-CH_2-$	Tyr
Methionine	$CH_3-S-CH_2-CH_2-$	Met
Cysteine	$HS-CH_2-$	Cys
Proline (an exception to the general formula)	$\begin{array}{c} H_2C————CH_2 \\ |\qquad\qquad| \\ H_2C\qquad CH-COOH \\ \backslash\quad / \\ N \\ | \\ H \end{array}$	Pro

Reactions utilizing catalysts, as any reaction, consume or produce energy. Some of the energy produced appears as heat in the cell. However, most of the energy must be converted to forms other than heat or the cell will die. In cells, this "excess" energy is used to produce a product whose synthesis requires the input of energy. This compound is usually adenosine-5'-phosphate, or ATP for short. When an enzymatic reaction requiring energy occurs, some ATP can be decomposed to provide that energy. The structure of ATP is

In cells, "excess energy" is used to produce ATP.

PROBLEMS

8. What synthetic fiber imitates a protein?

9. What is a peptide link?

8. nylon

9.

30:11 CARBOHYDRATES

Carbohydrates are also important to living systems. These compounds contain the elements carbon, hydrogen, and oxygen. Almost all carbohydrates are either simple sugars or condensation polymers of sugars. The most common simple sugar is glucose.

Carbohydrates are simple sugars or polymers of sugars.

glucose

Another common simple sugar is fructose.

fructose

A disaccharide forms when two simple sugars combine.

Combining two simple sugars produces a disaccharide. In this case, combining glucose and fructose produces common table sugar, sucrose.

sucrose

There are a number of biologically important polysaccharides formed from the monomer, glucose. The chief storage form for carbohydrates in plants is starch, while in animals it is glycogen. Cellulose (Section 30:9) is yet another polymer of glucose.

Chief storage form for carbohydrates is starch in plants, and glycogen in animals.

Glycogen, starch, and cellulose differ simply in the way the monomers are bonded to each other. The links in the chain and the manner in which the chains are cross-linked determine which substance is produced by the condensation polymerization.

Carbohydrates break down in the organism to produce H_2O, CO_2, and energy.

The process of breaking down carbohydrates to carbon dioxide and water is the chief energy source of an organism. Carbohydrate storage (starch/glycogen) is the energy reserve of the organism. The oxidation of glucose is the "burning" of the cell's "fuel." However, the enzymes in the cell permit this oxidation to take place under conditions that are healthy for the cell.

PROBLEM

10. energy source

10. What is the principal function of carbohydrates in the body?

30:12   LIPIDS

Proteins and carbohydrates tend to be soluble in water.

Lipids (fats) are more soluble in nonpolar solvents than in water.

Proteins and carbohydrates tend to be more soluble in water than in nonpolar solvents. **Lipids** are those compounds more soluble in nonpolar solvents than in water. Lipids can be divided into several different groups.

Fats are esters formed from glycerol and fatty acids (Section 30:5). Fatty acids are carboxylic acids with 12 to 20 carbon atoms in the chain. The number of carbons in the chain is an even number. The most abundant fatty acids are composed of 16-18 carbon atom chains. Some fatty acids are saturated while others have as many as four double bonds. In general, animal fats are saturated and plant oils are unsaturated. There are a number of other lipids derived from glycerol in addition to fats. Many of these other lipids are used to build cell membranes.

Animal fats are saturated and plant oils are unsaturated.

Steroids (lipids) have a tetracyclic ring system.

Another class of lipids consists of compounds called steroids. All steroids contain the tetracyclic ring system.

One steroid is cholesterol.

cholesterol

Cholesterol is found in bile and is an important constituent of cell membranes.

Some vitamins are lipids. **Vitamins** are substances used by cells to aid enzymatic reactions. The compounds chlorophyll and heme are also sometimes considered lipids. Chlorophyll is the green pigment used by plants in the process of converting carbon dioxide and water to carbohydrates. Heme is a component of hemoglobin. Hemoglobin is the red pigment utilized by humans and some other animals as an oxygen carrier.

Vitamins are lipids used by the cell to aid enzymatic reactions.

Chlorophyll is the green pigment used in plant photosynthesis.

Hemoglobin is the red pigment used as an oxygen carrier in animals.

PROBLEMS

11. Name three kinds of lipids that are structurally quite different.

12. How do animal fats differ from plant oils?

11. fats, steroids, vitamins
12. Animal fats are saturated and plant oils are unsaturated.

30:13   NUCLEIC ACIDS

Even though they are present in only small quantities, nucleic acids are an important group of biological polymers. They determine our genetic inheritance through the process of replication or duplicating themselves. Within a cell, nucleic acids control the synthesis of enzymes.

Nucleic acids are polymers of units called nucleotides. Each **nucleotide** is composed of three parts: a nitrogen base, a sugar, and a phosphate group. Only two sugars are found in nucleic acids, ribose and deoxyribose.

Nucleic acids are polymers of nucleotides.

Each nucleotide has three parts: nitrogen base, a sugar, and a phosphate group.

ribose   deoxyribose

DNA genetically transfers information to the next generation.

RNA is used to make enzymes.

These two sugars give rise to two nucleic acids, ribonucleic acid (RNA) and deoxyribonucleic acid (DNA). Of the five nitrogen bases found in nucleic acids, DNA contains adenine, cytosine, guanine, and thymine. RNA also contains adenine, cytosine, and guanine, but substitutes uracil for thymine.

adenine

cytosine

guanine

thymine

DNA is used in transferring genetic information from one generation to the next. Within a cell, the DNA is used to make several kinds of RNA. The RNA in turn is used to make enzymes. The process is quite a bit more complicated than what has been presented here, and not all of it is fully understood. Biochemical investigation is perhaps the most exciting area of emphasis in current research.

uracil

13. RNA contains uracil instead of thymine. DNA transfers information genetically to next generation. RNA is used to make enzymes.

PROBLEM

13. How do RNA and DNA differ in terms of structure? In terms of function?

BIOGRAPHY   Percy Lavon Julian (1899-1975)

Percy Lavon Julian was born in Montgomery, Alabama. He attended a public school for black students and then went to a small state teachers school. In 1917, he enrolled in DePauw University where he majored in chemistry. He graduated as class valedictorian and as a member of Phi Beta Kappa. After receiving his master's degree from Harvard, he was awarded a fellowship to study chemistry in Vienna, where he received his doctorate degree.

As an industrial chemist and director of research for a major company, his achievements included the extraction of soybean protein to produce an aero-foam for putting out fires. He did research on indoles, amino acids, and anti-fatigue drugs. He also synthesized progesterone, testosterone, and cortisone. In fact, Julian's synthesis put cortisone within the price range of the average arthritic patient for the first time.

TECHNOLOGY AND CHEMISTRY

30:14   Genetic Engineering

There are many substances produced commercially by the action of microorganisms. Yeasts produce ethanol from grain and bacteria produce cheese from milk. Bacteria are also used in the production of propanone (acetone). Citric acid can be obtained from molds.

Biochemists have now developed methods for "custom tailoring" organisms to produce pharmaceuticals and substances of industrial importance. The substances produced by a microorganism are determined by its nucleic acids. By modifying the DNA of a microorganism, the substances it produces can be controlled.

Most DNA is found in cell chromosomes. Some DNA, however, is found outside the chromosomes in the form of long, continuous loops called plasmids. Using appropriate enzymes, a plasmid may be split open by breaking a chemical bond. Part of a DNA molecule from another organism may then be inserted and the loop is then closed. When the recombinant DNA plasmid is reinserted in the microorganism, the new section of nucleic acid leads to the production of the desired substance.

There are many problems to be overcome before the process described above can take place. Intensive research is done to identify the DNA section that is coded to produce the desired substance. Once a suitable host microorganism is found, the correct position for inserting the

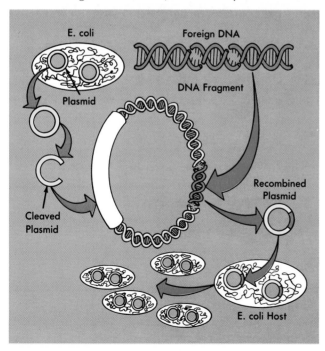

FIGURE 30-4. The model shows recombining the DNA of another organism to a cleaved plasmid.

new section in the plasmid must be located. All cells have defense mechanisms to reject foreign DNA. By chemically reducing the cell's defense mechanism, the host cell is "fooled" into accepting the new plasmid. Enzymatic reactions in cells must be controlled chemically if the desired product is to be obtained in economical quantities.

Figure 30-4 shows a model for gene-splicing using *Escherichia coli* bacteria *(E. coli)*. This microorganism is often used in recombinant DNA studies because of its comparatively simple genetic make-up. An enzyme is used to break the plasmid ring leaving, two "sticky ends." DNA from another microorganism is attached to the cleaved plasmid.

Biochemical production of insulin and interferon by recombinant DNA microorganisms is a reality. Many new products in the health science field are being developed. The gene-splicing process itself provides us with a better understanding of growth and development. Scientists are hoping recombinant DNA research will provide answers to such problems as birth defects and cancer.

SUMMARY

1. Hydrocarbons may undergo oxidation, addition, substitution, or elimination reactions. 30:1-30:4

2. The formation of an ester from an alcohol and an acid or acid anhydride is called esterification. 30:5

3. The splitting of an ester into the alcohol and the salt of the acid is called saponification. 30:5

4. Petroleum is the principal source of organic chemicals. It is composed mostly of hydrocarbons. 30:6

5. Addition polymerization is a reaction in which many carbon molecules containing a double bond add to each other to form a chain or cross-linked chains of very great molecular size and mass. 30:7-30:8

6. Condensation polymerization is a reaction in which hundreds of small molecules react to produce a large molecule (polymer) and many small molecules, such as water. 30:8

7. Synthetic rubber, plastics, and synthetic fibers are all made by addition and condensation polymerization reactions. 30:7-30:9

8. The principal classes of chemical compounds of biological interest are proteins, carbohydrates, lipids, and nucleic acids. 30:10-30:13

9. Proteins are polymers of amino acids. They act as structural parts of the organism and as catalysts called enzymes. 30:10

10. Carbohydrates are the materials utilized by cells to produce energy. They contain carbon, hydrogen, and oxygen. 30:11

11. Lipids are soluble in nonpolar solvents. Lipid materials exist in many different forms from fats to pigments. 30:12

12. Nucleic acids control the behavior of cells and transfer genetic information from one generation to the next. 30:13

VOCABULARY

substitution reaction 30:2
addition reaction 30:3
elimination reaction 30:4
esterification 30:5
saponification 30:5
octane rating 30:6
polymers 30:7
addition polymerization 30:8
condensation polymerization 30:8
proteins 30:10

amino acids 30:10
peptide bond 30:10
dipeptide 30:10
tripeptide 30:10
polypeptide 30:10
lipids 30:12
fats 30:12
vitamins 30:12
nucleic acids 30:13
nucleotide 30:13

PROBLEMS

1. Predict the product of the reaction between ethene and hydrogen iodide.
2. Predict the structure of the copolymer of ethene and phenylethene.
3. Complete and balance equations for the following.
   a. chlorine + propene
   b. preparation of pentyl ethanoate
   c. complete combustion of benzene
   d. elimination of water from 1-butanol
   e. saponification of glyceryl trioctadecanoate with NaOH
4. What is the difference between addition polymerization and condensation polymerization?
5. Draw the structural formula for the tripeptide formed from alanine, valine, and tryptophan, in that order. Assume the acid group of alanine reacts.
6. Draw the structural diagram for the polypeptide formed from glycine, cysteine, tyrosine, and lysine, in that order. Assume the acid group of glycine reacts.
7. Why can only 20 amino acids form so many different proteins?
8. What is the principal function of proteins in the body?
9. What compound is produced with excess energy in a cell?
10. What role do vitamins play in the cell?

Detailed answers to problems are given in the Teacher Guide.
1. CH_3—CH_2I
2. —CH—CH_2—CH_2—CH_2—(amor)

   (benzene ring structure)

8. catalysts and structural components
9. ATP
10. aid enzymatic reactions

REVIEW

1. Balance the following redox reaction (acidic).
$$Bi + NO_3^- + H^+ \rightarrow Bi^{3+} + NO + H_2O$$

2. What voltage should be generated by the following cell under standard conditions?
$$Co|Co^{2+}||HgCl_2|Hg_2Cl_2$$

3. What products would you expect from the electrolysis of a solution of iron(II) sulfate?

2. 0.91 V
3. H_2 and SO_2

4. 1.05 V
5. −187 kJ
6. 16.8 g
7. 16.9 g
8. $^{129}_{54}$Xe

4. What voltage would you expect from the following cell at standard temperature and pressure? (Assume [H$^+$] = 1.00M)

$$Cu|Cu^+||MnO_4{}^-|Mn^{2+}(0.0100M)$$

5. What is the free energy change for a reaction if it shows a potential difference in a cell of 1.94 volts and 1e$^-$ is transferred?

6. What mass of bromine will be produced by a current of 2.60 amperes flowing for 2.17 hours?

7. What is the amount of $^{100}_{46}$Pd left at the end of 16 days if 270 g existed originally and the half-life is 4 days?

8. Complete: $^{129}_{55}$Cs + $_{-1}^{0}$e → ?

9. Name the following compounds.

a. CH$_3$—CH—CH$_2$—CH$_3$
 (Br)

b. CH$_3$—CH=CH$_2$

c.

d.

10. Write the formulas for the following.
   a. 1-bromo-1-chloropropene
   b. ethene
   c. 3-chlorocyclopropene
   d. 1-bromo-1,2-diphenylpropane

ONE MORE STEP

See Teacher Guide

1. By reference work in the library, prepare a short report to your class on the mechanism of a well-known reaction in organic chemistry such as the Grignard or the Wurtz reaction.

2. Investigate the monomers which go into the production of Saran, Kodel, Acrilan, Dynel, and Mylar.

3. Find out what a Zwitterion is.

4. What is the difference between α-helix proteins and β-pleated proteins?

5. What is the biochemical role of nicotinamide adenine dinucleotide (NAD) in cell energy transfer?

6. The vitamin thiamine is converted in the cell to thiamin pyrophosphate. Find the structure of this molecule.

7. The citric acid cycle is the name for an important series of reactions in cells. Draw a series of equations describing the changes in the cycle.

8. Acidosis is a physiological condition brought on by the lack of cells' ability to transport glucose across the cell membrane. It is a symptom of diabetes mellitus. Find out how the condition obtained its name.
9. Folic acid is one of the B vitamins. Write its structure.

READINGS

Scientific American, Vol. 253, No. 4(October 1985), pp. 48-173. (devoted to biochemistry topics)

Bechgaard, Klaus, and Denis Jerome, "Organic Superconductors," *Scientific American,* Vol. 247, No. 1(July 1982), pp. 52-61.

Block, Eric, "The Chemistry of Garlic and Onions," *Scientific American,* Vol. 252, No. 3(March 1985), pp. 114-119.

Chain, Ernst, "Penicillin—the Crucial Experiment," *Chemtech,* Vol. 10, No. 8(August 1980), pp. 474-481.

Chiles, James R., "Plastic Has—Literally—Found Its Way Into Our Hearts," *Smithsonian,* Vol. 16, No. 8(November 1985), pp. 76-87.

Gardiner, William C., Jr., "The Chemistry of Flames," *Scientific American,* Vol. 246, No. 2(February 1982), pp. 110-124.

Graff, Gordon, "Synthetic Metals Near Reality," *High Technology,* Vol. 5, No. 11(November 1985), pp. 64-66.

Jansson, Robert, "Organic Electrosynthesis," *Chemical and Engineering News,* Vol. 62, No. 47(November 19, 1984), pp. 43-57.

Krassner, Michael B., "Brain Chemistry," *Chemical and Engineering News,* Vol. 61, No. 35(August 29, 1983), pp. 22-33.

Mussinan, Cynthia, "Analytical Chemistry and Flavor Creation," *Chemtech,* Vol. 10, No. 10(October 1980), pp. 618-622.

Putnam, Alan R., "Allelopathic Chemicals," *Chemical and Engineering News,* Vol. 61, No. 14(April 4, 1983), pp. 34-45.

Rawls, Rebecca L., "Oncogene Research Quickens in Search for Cancer's Cellular Origin," *Chemical and Engineering News,* Vol. 62, No. 50(December 10, 1984), pp. 11-15.

Zurer, Pamela S., "The Chemistry of Vision," *Chemical and Engineering News,* Vol. 61, No. 48(November 28, 1983), pp. 24-35.

Zurer, Pamela S., "Drugs in Sport," *Chemical and Engineering News,* Vol. 62, No. 18(April 30, 1984), pp. 69-78.

APPENDIX A

Table A-1

Definitions of Standards
1 ampere is the constant current which, if maintained in two straight parallel conductors of infinite length, of negligible circular cross-section, and placed 1 meter apart in a vacuum, would produce a force of 2×10^{-7} newton per meter of length between these conductors.
1 candela is the luminous intensity, in the perpendicular direction, of a surface of 1/600 000 m^2 of a blackbody at the temperature of freezing platinum at a pressure of 101 325 pascals.
1 cubic decimeter is equal to 1 liter.
1 kelvin is 1/273.16 of the thermodynamic temperature of the triple point of water.
1 meter is the distance light travels in 1/299 792 458 of a second.
1 mole is the amount of substance containing as many elementary entities as there are atoms in 0.012 kilogram of carbon-12.
1 second is equal to 9 192 631 770 periods of the natural electromagnetic oscillation during that transition of ground state $^2S_{1/2}$ of cesium-133 which is designated $(F = 4, M = 0) \leftrightarrow (F = 3, M = 0)$
Avogadro's number $= 6.02217 \times 10^{23}$
1 electronvolt $= 1.60219 \times 10^{-19}$ J
Faraday's constant $= 96\ 486.7$ C/mole e^-
Ideal gas constant $= 8.31430$ J/K $\cdot$ mol $= 8.31430$ $dm^3 \cdot$ kPa/mol $\cdot$ K
Ideal gas volume at STP $= 22.4136$ dm^3
Planck's constant $= 6.62620 \times 10^{-34}$ J/Hz
Speed of light $= 2.997\ 925 \times 10^8$ m/s

Table A-2

Symbols and Abbreviations		
α	= rays from radioactive materials, helium nuclei	
β	= rays from radioactive materials, electrons	
γ	= rays from radioactive materials, high-energy quanta	
Δ	= change in	
λ	= wavelength	
ν	= frequency	
Π	= osmotic pressure	
A	= ampere (*electric current*)	
°C	= Celsius degree (*temperature*)	
C	= coulomb (*quantity of electricity*)	
c	= speed of light	
cd	= candela (*luminous intensity*)	
C_p	= specific heat	
D	= density	
E	= energy, electromotive force	
F	= force, Faraday	
G	= free energy	
g	= gram (*mass*)	
H	= enthalpy	
Hz	= hertz (*frequency*)	
h	= Planck's constant	
h	= hour (*time*)	
J	= joule (*energy*)	
K	= kelvin (*temperature*)	
K_a	= ionization constant (acid)	
K_b	= ionization constant (base)	
K_{eq}	= equilibrium constant	

K_{sp}	= solubility product constant
kg	= kilogram
M	= molarity
m	= mass, molality
m	= meter (*length*)
mol	= mole (*amount*)
min	= minute (*time*)
N	= newton (*force*)
N_A	= Avogadro's number
n	= number of moles
P	= pressure, power
Pa	= pascal (*pressure*)
p	= momentum
q	= heat
R	= gas constant
S	= entropy
s	= second (*time*)
T	= temperature
U	= internal energy
u	= atomic mass unit
V	= volume
V	= volt (*electromotive force*)
v	= velocity
W	= watt (*power*)
w	= work
x	= mole fraction

Table A-3

Some Properties of the Elements

Element	Symbol	Atomic Number (Z)	Atomic Mass* (M)	Melting Point (°C)	Boiling Point (°C)	Density (g/cm³)	Atomic Radius (nm)	First Ionization Energy (kJ/mol)	Standard Reduction Potential (V) (for elements from or to oxidation state indicated)	Enthalpy of Fusion (kJ/mol)	Specific Heat (J/g·°C)	Enthalpy of Vaporization (kJ/mol)	Abundance in Earth's Crust (%)	Major Oxidation States
Actinium	Ac	89	[227.0278]	817	2470	10.07	0.188	666	(3+) −2.6	10.5	—	293	trace	3+
Aluminum	Al	13	26.98154	660	2467	2.70	0.143	578	(3+) −1.66	10.5	0.900	291	8.3	3+
Americium	Am	95	[243.0614]	1170	2600	13.67	0.184	579	(3+) −2.38	10.0	—	239	—	3+, 4+
Antimony	Sb	51	121.75	631	1587	6.697	0.136	834	—	20.0	0.207	195	2×10^{-4}	3+, 5+
Argon	Ar	18	39.948	−189.37	−185.9	0.00178403	0.191	1521	—	1.21	0.519	6.52	—	
Arsenic	As	33	74.9216	816 (3910 kPa)	615 (sublimes)	5.778	0.125	947	—	93.7	0.331	128 (sublimes)	1.8×10^{-4}	3+, 5+, 3−
Astatine	At	85	[209.9871]	302	337	—	0.14	917	(1−) +0.3	11.9	—	45.2	trace	
Barium	Ba	56	137.33	727	1850	3.62	0.217	503	(2+) −2.90	7.8	0.179	136	0.039	2+
Berkelium	Bk	97	[247.0703]	986	—	14.78	—	—	—	—	—	—	—	
Beryllium	Be	4	9.01218	1287	2500	1.848	0.111	900	(2+) −1.85	15	1.83	309	0.001	2+
Bismuth	Bi	83	208.9804	271	1564	9.808	0.155	703	—	10.5	0.122	172	2×10^{-5}	3+, 5+
Boron	B	5	10.811	2180	3650	2.35	0.083	801	—	23.6	1.03	505	0.001	3+
Bromine	Br	35	79.904	−7.25	59.5	3.19	0.111	1140	(1−) +1.065	10.6	0.349	30.0	5×10^{-5}	1−
Cadmium	Cd	48	112.41	321	765	8.65	0.149	868	(2+) −0.4026	6.4	0.232	100	5×10^{-5}	2+
Calcium	Ca	20	40.078	839	1494	1.55	0.197	590	(2+) −2.76	8.6	0.652	155	4.66	2+
Californium	Cf	98	[251.0796]	900	—	—	—	—	—	—	—	—	—	
Carbon	C	6	12.011	4100	4827	3.614	0.077	1087	—	105	0.716	326	0.018	4+
Cerium	Ce	58	140.12	804	3470	6.773	0.183	528	(3+) −2.335	5.2	0.194	398	0.0066	3+, 4+
Cesium	Cs	55	132.9054	28.5	705	1.90	0.265	376	(1+) −2.923	2.09	0.238	67	1×10^{-4}	1+
Chlorine	Cl	17	35.453	−101.00	−34.0	0.00298	0.099	1251	(1−) +1.3583	6.41	0.477	20.4	0.0126	1−
Chromium	Cr	24	51.9961	1900	2690	7.14	0.125	653	(2+) −0.557	21	0.448	342	0.0122	2+, 3+, 6+
Cobalt	Co	27	58.9332	1495	3100	8.90	0.125	758	(2+) −0.28	16.3	0.446	382	0.0029	2+, 3+
Copper	Cu	29	63.546	1083	2567	8.95	0.128	745	(2+) +0.3402, (1+) +0.522	13.0	0.386	307	0.0068	1+, 2+
Curium	Cm	96	[247.0703]	1340	—	13.51	—	—	—	—	—	—	—	3+
Dysprosium	Dy	66	162.50	1407	2600	8.559	0.177	572	(3+) −2.35	17.2	0.173	280	3×10^{-4}	3+
Einsteinium	Es	99	[252.0828]	860	—	—	—	—	—	—	—	—	—	
Erbium	Er	68	167.26	1497	2900	9.045	0.176	589	(3+) −2.30	17.2	0.168	280	2.4×10^{-4}	3+
Europium	Eu	63	151.96	826	1939	5.245	0.204	547	(3+) −2.41	10.5	0.156	176	1.2×10^{-4}	2+, 3+
Fermium	Fm	100	[257.0951]	—	—	—	—	—	—	—	—	—	—	
Fluorine	F	9	18.998403	−218.6	−188.14	0.001580	0.072	1681	(1−) +2.87	0.51	0.824	6.54	0.0544	1−
Francium	Fr	87	[223.0197]	27	677	—	0.27	—	—	—	—	—	—	1+
Gadolinium	Gd	64	157.25	1312	3000	7.886	0.180	592	(3+) −2.4	15.5	0.232	301	5.3×10^{-4}	3+
Gallium	Ga	31	69.723	29.78	2403	5.904	0.122	579	(3+) −0.560	5.59	0.374	270	7×10^{-4}	3+
Germanium	Ge	32	72.59	945	2850	5.323	0.123	762	(2+) +0.23	36.8	0.322	328	1.5×10^{-4}	2+, 4+

*[ ] indicates mass of longest-lived isotope

Element	Symbol	Atomic Number (Z)	Atomic Mass (M)*	Melting Point (°C)	Boiling Point (°C)	Density (g/cm³)	Atomic Radius (nm)	First Ionization Energy (kJ/mol)	Standard Reduction Potential (V) (for oxidation from or to oxidation state indicated)	Enthalpy of Fusion (kJ/mol)	Specific Heat (J/g·°C)	Enthalpy of Vaporization (kJ/mol)	Abundance in Earth's Crust (%)	Major Oxidation States
Gold	Au	79	196.9665	1064	2808	19.32	0.144	890	$(3+)+1.42$	12.8	0.128	343	5×10^{-7}	1+, 3+
Hafnium	Hf	72	178.49	2222	4450	13.3	0.156	675	$(4+)-1.70$	25.1	0.136	571	5×10^{-4}	4+
Helium	He	2	4.002602	−272.2 (2536 kPa)	−268.9	0.00017847	0.122	2372	—	0.0182	5.19	0.08	—	
Holmium	Ho	67	164.9304	1461	2600	8.78	0.177	581	$(3+)-2.32$	17.2	0.165	280	1.2×10^{-4}	3+
Hydrogen	H	1	1.00794	−259.19	−252.76	0.00008987	0.053	1312	$(1+)0.0000$	0.117	14.3	0.904	0.152	1+
Indium	In	49	114.82	157	2080	7.31	0.163	558	$(3+)-0.338$	3.26	0.235	232	1×10^{-5}	1+, 3+
Iodine	I	53	126.9045	113.6	185.2	4.94	0.128	1008	$(1-)+0.535$	15.5	0.285	41.0	5×10^{-5}	1−
Iridium	Ir	77	192.22	2443	4550	22.61	0.136	878	$(3+)+1.15$	26.4	0.130	612	1×10^{-7}	2+, 3+, 4+
Iron	Fe	26	55.847	1535	2750	7.874	0.124	759	$(2+)-0.409$	13.8	0.448	340	6.2	2+, 3+
Krypton	Kr	36	83.80	−157.20	−153.4	0.0037493	0.198	1351	—	1.63	0.247	9.05	1.4×10^{-8}	
Lanthanum	La	57	138.9055	920	3420	6.17	0.188	538	$(3+)-2.37$	8.5	0.199	402	0.0035	3+
Lawrencium	Lr	103	[260.1054]											3+
Lead	Pb	82	207.2	327.5	1751	11.342	0.175	716	$(2+)-0.126$	4.81	0.138	178	0.002	2+, 4+
Lithium	Li	3	6.941	180.54	1347	0.534	0.152	520	$(1+)-3.045$	2.93	3.48	148	0.005	1+
Lutetium	Lu	71	174.967	1652	3327	9.840	0.173	524	$(3+)-2.25$	19.2	0.137	414	5×10^{-5}	3+
Magnesium	Mg	12	24.305	649	1105	1.738	0.160	738	$(2+)-2.375$	8.9	1.01	127	2.76	2+
Manganese	Mn	25	54.9380	1244	2060	7.43	0.124	717	$(2+)-1.029$	13.4	0.480	221	0.106	2+, 4+, 6+, 7+
Mendelevium	Md	101	[258.0986]											2+, 3+
Mercury	Hg	80	200.59	−38.84	356.58	13.534	0.160	1007	$(2+)+0.851$	2.30	0.139	59.1	5×10^{-6}	1+, 2+
Molybdenum	Mo	42	95.94	1620	4650	10.28	0.136	685	$(3+)-0.2$	27.6	0.248	594	1.5×10^{-4}	2+, 3+, 4+, 5+, 6+
Neodymium	Nd	60	144.24	1024	3027	7.003	0.182	530	$(3+)-2.246$	7.13	0.201	289	0.0040	3+
Neon	Ne	10	20.179	−248.61	−246.06	0.00089994	0.160	2081	—	0.324	1.03	1.74	5×10^{-7}	
Neptunium	Np	93	237.0482	640	5235	20.45	0.131	737	$(3+)-1.86$	9.46	0.124	336	—	3+, 4+, 6+
Nickel	Ni	28	58.69	1455	2920	8.908	0.125	737	$(2+)-0.23$	17.2	0.443	375	0.0099	2+, 3+
Niobium	Nb	41	92.9064	2468	4758	8.57	0.143	664	$(3+)-1.1$	26.8	0.266	680	0.0020	3+, 4+, 5+
Nitrogen	N	7	14.0067	−210.0	−195.8	0.0012500	0.070	1402	—	0.721	1.04	5.58	0.0019	3−
Nobelium	No	102	[259.1009]											2+, 3+
Osmium	Os	76	190.2	3045	5025	22.57	0.134	839	$(2+)+0.85$	31.7	0.130	738	5×10^{-6}	2−, 3+, 4+, 6+, 8+
Oxygen	O	8	15.9994	−218.8	−182.96	0.001429	0.066	1314	—	0.445	0.916	6.81	45.5	2−
Palladium	Pd	46	106.42	1552	2940	11.99	0.138	805	$(2+)+0.83$	17.6	0.245	362	—	2+, 3+, 4+
Phosphorus	P	15	30.97376	44.1	281	1.823	0.115	1012	—	2.51	0.724	49.8	0.112	3+, 5+, 3−
Platinum	Pt	78	195.08	1769	4170	21.410	0.138	868	$(2+)+1.2$	19.7	0.134	469	1×10^{-6}	2+, 4+, 6+
Plutonium	Pu	94	[244.0642]	640	3230	19.86	0.157	560	$(3+)-2.02$	2.80	0.137	344	—	3+, 4+, 5+, 6+
Polonium	Po	84	[208.9824]	254	962	9.32	0.167	812	$(2+)+0.60$	12.6	0.126	103	trace	2+, 4+
Potassium	K	19	39.0983	63.2	766	0.856	0.227	419	$(1+)-2.924$	2.39	0.748	79.0	1.84	1+
Praseodymium	Pr	59	140.9077	935	3020	6.475	0.183	523	$(3+)-2.47$	11.3	0.197	331	8.0×10^{-4}	3+, 4+
Promethium	Pm	61	[144.9128]	1168	2460	7.22	0.181	536	$(3+)-2.42$	12.6	0.185	293	—	3+

*[ ] indicates mass of longest-lived isotope

Element	Symbol	Atomic Number (Z)	Atomic Mass (M)*	Melting Point (°C)	Boiling Point (°C)	Density (g/cm³)	Atomic Radius (nm)	First Ionization Energy (kJ/mol)	Standard Reduction Potential (V) (for elements from or to oxidation state indicated)	Enthalpy of Fusion (kJ/mol)	Specific Heat (J/g·°C)	Enthalpy of Vaporization (kJ/mol)	Abundance in Earth's Crust (%)	Major Oxidation States
Protactinium	Pa	91	231.0359	1552	4227	15.37	0.161	—	—	16.7	0.121	481	trace	4+, 5+
Radium	Ra	88	226.0254	700	1140	5.5	0.220	509	(2+) −2.92	8.37	0.120	146	1×10^{-11}	2+
Radon	Rn	86	[222.176]	−71	−62	0.00973	0.22	1037	—	3.25	0.0937	18.1	4×10^{-17}	
Rhenium	Re	75	186.207	3180	5650	21.02	0.137	760	—	34	0.138	704	1×10^{-7}	3+, 4+, 5+, 6+, 7+
Rhodium	Rh	45	102.9055	1960	3760	12.39	0.135	720	(3+) +0.8	21.6	0.245	494	1×10^{-7}	2+, 3+, 4+
Rubidium	Rb	37	85.4678	39	688	1.532	0.248	403	(1+) −2.924	2.20	0.359	76	0.0078	1+
Ruthenium	Ru	44	101.07	2282	4050	12.41	0.133	711	—	25.5	0.238	568	4×10^{-8}	3+, 4+, 5+, 8+
Samarium	Sm	62	150.36	1072	1800	7.536	0.180	543	(3+) −2.41	8.9	0.188	165	6×10^{-4}	2+, 3+
Scandium	Sc	21	44.95591	1539	2748	2.989	0.16	631	(3+) −2.08	15.8	0.524	333	0.0022	3+
Selenium	Se	34	78.96	217	685	4.39	0.114	941	(2−) −0.78	5.10	0.272	59.7	9×10^{-6}	2−, 4+, 6+
Silicon	Si	14	28.0855	1420	3280	2.336	0.117	787	—	50.6	0.705	383	27.2	4+, 4−
Silver	Ag	47	107.86821	961	2155	10.49	0.144	731	(1+) +0.7996	11.1	0.236	258	1×10^{-5}	1+
Sodium	Na	11	22.98977	97.81	881.4	0.968	0.192	496	(1+) −2.7109	2.64	1.23	99	2.27	1+
Strontium	Sr	38	87.62	768	1381	2.63	0.215	550	(2+) −2.89	8.2	0.296	158	0.0384	2+
Sulfur	S	16	32.066	112.8	444.7	2.07	0.104	1000	(2−) −0.508	1.23	0.736	10.5	0.034	2−, 4+, 6+
Tantalum	Ta	73	180.9479	2980	5534	16.65	0.136	761	—	24.7	0.140	758	2×10^{-4}	3+, 4+, 5+
Technetium	Tc	43	97.9072	2200	4567	11.50	0.143	702	—	23.0	0.243	585	—	4+, 5+, 6+, 7+
Tellurium	Te	52	127.60	452	989.8	6.25	0.178	869	(2−) −0.92	13.5	0.201	49.8	2×10^{-7}	2−, 2+, 4+, 6+
Terbium	Tb	65	158.9254	1356	2800	8.253	0.170	564	(3+) −2.39	16.3	0.182	293	1×10^{-4}	3+, 4+
Thallium	Tl	81	204.383	303.5	1457	11.85	0.180	589	(1+) −0.3363	4.31	0.129	166	7×10^{-5}	1+, 3+
Thorium	Th	90	232.0381	1750	4850	11.78	0.175	671	(4+) −1.90	16.11	0.123	514	0.0015	4+
Thulium	Tm	69	168.9342	1545	1727	9.318	0.141	596	(3+) −2.28	18.4	0.160	247	4.6×10^{-5}	3+
Tin	Sn	50	118.710	232	2623	7.265	0.145	709	(2+) −0.136	7.07	0.220	296	6×10^{-4}	2+, 4+
Titanium	Ti	22	47.88	1667	3285	4.50	0.137	658	(2+) −1.63	18.8	0.520	425	0.632	2+, 3+, 4+
Tungsten	W	74	183.85	3410	5500	19.3	—	770	—	35.2	0.134	824	1.5×10^{-4}	2+, 3+, 4+, 5+, 6+
Unnilennium	Une	109	[266]	—	—	—	—	—	—	—	—	—	—	
Unnilhexium	Unh	106	[263]	—	—	—	—	—	—	—	—	—	—	
Unniloctium	Uno	108	[265]	—	—	—	—	—	—	—	—	—	—	
Unnilpentium	Unp	105	[260]	—	—	—	—	—	—	—	—	—	—	
Unnilquadium	Unq	104	[257]	—	—	—	—	—	—	—	—	—	—	
Unnilseptium	Uns	107	[258]	—	—	—	—	—	—	—	—	—	—	
Uranium	U	92	238.0289	1130	3930	19.05	0.139	587	(3+) −1.80	12.6	0.116	417	2×10^{-4}	3+, 4+, 5+, 6+
Vanadium	V	23	50.9415	1915	3350	6.11	0.132	650	(2+) −1.18	17.5	0.484	459.7	0.0136	2+, 3+, 4+, 5+
Xenon	Xe	54	131.29	−111.80	−108.1	0.0058971	0.218	1170	—	3.10	0.158	12.7	—	
Ytterbium	Yb	70	173.04	824	1427	6.973	0.194	603	(3+) −2.27	3.35	0.132	159	3×10^{-4}	2+, 3+
Yttrium	Y	39	88.9059	1530	3264	4.469	0.181	616	(3+) −2.37	11.5	0.291	367	0.0033	3+
Zinc	Zn	30	65.39	419.5	907	7.14	0.133	906	(2+) −0.763	7.28	0.386	114	0.0076	2+
Zirconium	Zr	40	91.224	1857	4200	6.506	0.160	660	(4+) −1.53	19.2	0.278	567	0.0162	2+, 3+, 4+

*[ ] indicates mass of longest-lived isotope

Table A-4

Major Formal Oxidation States of Polyatomic Ions			
1−	**2−**	**3−**	**4−**
Azide, N_3^-	Chromate, CrO_4^{2-}	Arsenite, AsO_3^{3-}	Hexacyanoferrate(II),
Benzoate, $C_6H_5COO^-$	Dichromate, $Cr_2O_7^{2-}$	Citrate, $C_6H_5O_7^{3-}$	$Fe(CN)_6^{4-}$
Bromate, BrO_3^-	Hexachloroplatinate(IV),	Hexacyanoferrate(III),	Pyrophosphate, $P_4O_7^{4-}$
Chlorate, ClO_3^-	$PtCl_6^{2-}$	$Fe(CN)_6^{3-}$	
Formate, $HCOO^-$	Molybdate, MoO_4^{2-}		
Hypophosphite, $PH_2O_2^-$	Peroxide, O_2^{2-}		
Metaphosphate, PO_3^-	Peroxydisulfate, $S_2O_8^{2-}$		
Nitrite, NO_2^-	Sulfite, SO_3^{2-}		
Periodate, IO_4^-	Tellurate, TeO_4^{2-}		
Permanganate, MnO_4^-	Tetraborate, $B_4O_7^{2-}$		
Peroxyborate, BO_3^-	Thiosulfate, $S_2O_3^{2-}$		
Thiocyanate, SCN^-	Tungstate, WO_4^{2-}		
Vanadate, VO_3^-			

Table A-5

Specific Heat Capacities (in J/g·C°)					
Substance	**C_p**	**Substance**	**C_p**	**Substance**	**C_p**
AlF_3	0.987	CCl_3CCl_3	0.728	$Mg(OH)_2$	1.31
BeO	1.05	CH_3COCH_3	2.18	$MgSO_4$	0.929
CaC_2	1.00	CH_3CH_2OH	2.45	Na_2CO_3	1.14
$CaSO_4$	0.716	CH_3COOH	2.05	PCl_3	0.874
CCl_4	0.856	HI	0.235	SiC	0.686
C_6H_6	1.74	ICl	0.661	SiO_2	0.749
C_6H_{14}	2.26	K_2CO_3	0.904	$TiCl_4$	0.803
C_6H_5Br	0.989	$LiNO_3$	1.21	ZnS	0.469
$C_6H_5CH_3$	1.80	$MgCO_3$	0.837		

Table A-6

Thermodynamic Properties (at standard states)

$\Delta H_f°$ in kJ/mol $\Delta G_f°$ in kJ/mol   S° in J/mol·K
concentration of aqueous solutions is 1M

Substance	$\Delta H_f°$	$\Delta G_f°$	S°	Substance	$\Delta H_f°$	$\Delta G_f°$	S°
Ag	0	0	42.7	H_3PO_3	−972	—	—
AgCl	−127	−110	96.1	H_3PO_4	−1280	−1120	110
AgCN	−146	−164	83.7	H_2S	−20.1	−33.0	206
Al	0	0	28.3	$H_2SO_3(aq)$	−614	−538	232
Al_2O_3	−1670	−1580	51.0	$H_2SO_4(aq)$	−908	−742	17.2
$BaCl_2(aq)$	−873	−823	121	$HgCl_2$	−230	−177	—
$BaSO_4$	−1470	−1350	132	Hg_2Cl_2	−265	−211	196
Be	0	0	9.54	Hg_2SO_4	−742	−624	201
Be_3N_2	−568	−512	—	I_2	0	0	117
Bi	0	0	56.9	K	0	0	63.6
$BiCl_3$	−379	−319	190	KBr	−392	−379	96.4
Bi_2S_3	−183	−164	146	$KMnO_4$	−813	−714	172
Br_2	0	0	152	KOH	−426	—	—
CH_4	−74.8	−50.8	186	LiBr	−350	—	—
C_2H_2	+227	+209	201	LiOH	−487	−444	50.2
C_2H_4	+52.3	+68.1	219	Mn	0	0	32.0
C_2H_6	−84.7	−32.9	229	$MnCl_2(aq)$	−555	−491	38.9
C_4H_{10}	−125	−15.7	310	$Mn(NO_3)_2(aq)$	−636	−451	218
CH_2O	−117	−113	219	MnO_2	−521	−466	53.1
CO	−111	−137	198	MnS	−214	—	—
CO_2	−393.5	−394.4	214	N_2	0	0	192
CS_2	+87.9	+63.6	151	NH_3	−46.2	−16.6	193
Ca	0	0	41.6	NH_4Br	−270	−175	113
$Ca(OH)_2$	−987	−897	—	NO	+90.4	—	211
Cl_2	0	0	223	NO_2	−33.8	+51.8	240
$CoCO_3$	−723	−650	—	N_2O	+82.1	+104	220
CoO	−239	−213	43.9	Na	0	0	51.0
Cr_2O_3	−1130	−1050	81.2	NaBr	−360	—	—
CsCl(aq)	−415	−371	188	NaCl	−411	−384	72.4
$Cs_2SO_4(aq)$	−1400	−1310	283	$NaNO_3(aq)$	−447	—	—
CuI	−67.8	−69.5	96.7	NaOH	−427	—	—
CuS	−53.1	−53.7	66.5	$Na_2S(aq)$	−437	—	—
Cu_2S	−79.5	−86.2	121	Na_2SO_4	−1380	−1270	149
$CuSO_4$	−770	−662	113	O_2	0	0	205
F_2	0	0	203	P_4O_6	−1640	—	—
$FeCl_3$	−405	—	—	P_4O_{10}	−2980	−2700	229
FeO	−267	—	—	$PbBr_2$	−277	−260	162
Fe_2O_3	−822	−741	90.0	$PbCl_2$	−359	−314	136
Fe_3O_4	−1118	−1016	146	S	0	0	31.9
H	+218	—	115	SO_2	−297	−300	249
H_2	0	0	131	SO_3	−438	−368	95.6
HBr	−36.2	−53.2	198	SrO	−590	−560	54.4
HCl	−92.3	−95.3	187	Ti	0	0	30.3
HCl(aq)	−167	−131	56.5	TiO_2	—	−853	50.2
HCN(aq)	+151	+172	94.1	TlI	−50.2	−83.3	236
HF	−269	−271	174	UCl_4	−1050	−962	198
HI	+25.9	+1.30	206	UCl_5	−1100	−993	259
$H_2O(l)$	−286	−237	70.0	Zn	0	0	41.6
$H_2O(g)$	−242	−229	189	$ZnCl_2(aq)$	−487	−410	3.72
H_2O_2	—	−118	110	ZnO	−348	−318	43.6
H_3PO_2	−609	—	—	$ZnSO_4(aq)$	−1063	−892	−92.0

Table A-7

Solubility Rules
You will be working with water solutions, and it is helpful to have a few rules concerning what substances are soluble in water. The more common rules are listed below.
1. All common salts of the Group IA elements and ammonium ion are soluble.
2. All common acetates and nitrates are soluble.
3. All binary compounds of Group VIIA elements (other than F) with metals are soluble except those of silver, mercury(I), and lead.
4. All sulfates are soluble except those of barium, strontium, lead, calcium, silver, and mercury(I).
5. Except for those in Rule 1, carbonates, hydroxides, oxides, and phosphates are insoluble.

Table A-8

Molal Freezing and Boiling Point Constants (in C°/mol/1000 g solvent)

Substance	Freezing point (°C)	Molal freezing point constant	Boiling point (°C)	Molal boiling point constant
Acetic Acid	16.604	−3.90	117.9	3.07
Benzene	5.5	−4.90	80.1	2.53
Camphor	179.8	−37.7	204	5.95
Cyclohexane	6.55	−20.0	80.74	2.79
Nitrobenzene	5.7	−7.00	210.8	5.24
Phenol	43	−7.40	181.75	3.56
Water	0.00	−1.86	100.00	0.512

Table A-9

Ionization Constants

Substance	Ionization Constant	Substance	Ionization Constant	Substance	Ionization Constant
HCOOH	1.69×10^{-4}	HBO_3^{-2}	1.60×10^{-14}	HS^-	1.10×10^{-13}
CH_3COOH	1.76×10^{-5}	H_2CO_3	4.30×10^{-7}	HSO_4^-	1.20×10^{-2}
$CH_2ClCOOH$	1.40×10^{-3}	HCO_3^-	5.61×10^{-11}	H_2SO_3	1.54×10^{-2}
$CHCl_2COOH$	3.32×10^{-2}	HCN	4.93×10^{-10}	HSO_3^-	1.02×10^{-7}
CCl_3COOH	2.00×10^{-1}	HF	3.53×10^{-4}	$HSeO_4^-$	1.20×10^{-2}
HOOCCOOH	5.90×10^{-2}	HNO_2	4.60×10^{-4}	H_2SeO_3	3.50×10^{-2}
$HOOCCOO^-$	6.40×10^{-5}	H_3PO_4	7.52×10^{-3}	$HSeO_3^-$	4.80×10^{-9}
CH_3CH_2COOH	1.34×10^{-5}	$H_2PO_4^-$	6.23×10^{-8}	HBrO	2.06×10^{-9}
C_6H_5COOH	6.46×10^{-5}	HPO_4^{2-}	2.20×10^{-13}	HClO	2.95×10^{-5}
H_3AsO_4	6.31×10^{-3}	H_3PO_3	1.00×10^{-2}	HIO	2.30×10^{-11}
$H_2AsO_4^-$	1.05×10^{-7}	$H_2PO_3^-$	2.60×10^{-7}	NH_3	1.77×10^{-5}
H_3BO_3	7.30×10^{-10}	H_3PO_2	7.94×10^{-2}	H_2NNH_2	1.70×10^{-6}
$H_2BO_3^-$	1.80×10^{-13}	H_2S	1.32×10^{-7}	H_2NOH	1.07×10^{-8}

Table A-10

Solubility Product Constants (at 25°C)					
Substance	**K_{sp}**	**Substance**	**K_{sp}**	**Substance**	**K_{sp}**
AgBr	7.70×10^{-13}	BaSO$_4$	1.08×10^{-10}	Li$_2$CO$_3$	1.70×10^{-2}
AgBrO$_3$	5.77×10^{-5}	CaCO$_3$	8.70×10^{-9}	MgCO$_3$	2.60×10^{-5}
Ag$_2$CO$_3$	6.15×10^{-12}	CaSO$_4$	9.12×10^{-6}	MnCO$_3$	1.82×10^{-11}
AgCl	1.56×10^{-10}	CdS	3.60×10^{-29}	NiCO$_3$	6.61×10^{-9}
Ag$_2$CrO$_4$	9.00×10^{-12}	Cu(IO$_3$)$_2$	1.40×10^{-7}	PbCl$_2$	1.62×10^{-5}
Ag$_2$Cr$_2$O$_7$	2.00×10^{-7}	CuC$_2$O$_4$	2.87×10^{-8}	PbI$_2$	1.39×10^{-8}
AgI	1.50×10^{-16}	Cu(OH)$_2$	2.19×10^{-20}	Pb(IO$_3$)$_2$	2.60×10^{-13}
AgSCN	1.16×10^{-12}	CuS	6.31×10^{-36}	SrCO$_3$	1.60×10^{-9}
Al(OH)$_3$	1.26×10^{-33}	FeC$_2$O$_4$	2.10×10^{-7}	TlBr	3.39×10^{-6}
Al$_2$S$_3$	2.00×10^{-7}	Fe(OH)$_3$	3.98×10^{-38}	ZnCO$_3$	1.45×10^{-11}
BaCO$_3$	8.10×10^{-8}	FeS	3.70×10^{-19}	ZnS	1.20×10^{-23}
BaCrO$_4$	1.17×10^{-10}	Hg$_2$SO$_4$	7.41×10^{-7}		

Table A-11

Acid-Base Indicators			
Indicator	**Acid Color**	**Range**	**Base Color**
Methyl violet	yellow	0.0–1.6	blue
Cresol red	red	1.0–2.0	yellow
Orange IV	red	1.4–2.6	yellow
Phloxine B	colorless	2.1–4.1	pink
2,4-Dinitrophenol	colorless	2.8–4.0	yellow
Methyl orange	red	3.2–4.4	yellow.
α-Naphthyl red	red	4.0–5.6	yellow
Methyl red	red	4.8–6.0	yellow
4-Nitrophenol	colorless	5.4–6.6	yellow
Bromothymol blue	yellow	6.0–7.6	blue
Brilliant yellow	yellow	6.6–7.9	orange
Cresol red	yellow	7.0–8.8	red
2,6-Divanillylidenecyclohexanone	yellow	7.8–9.4	red
Phenolphthalein	colorless	8.3–10.0	dark pink
Ethyl bis(2,4-dinitrophenyl) acetate	colorless	8.4–9.6	blue
Thymolphthalein	colorless	9.4–10.6	blue
Alizarin yellow R	yellow	10.0–12.0	red
Malachite green hydrochloride	green-blue	10.2–12.5	colorless
Methyl blue	blue	10.6–13.4	pale violet
Orange G	yellow	11.5–14.0	pink
2,4,6-Trinitrotoluene	colorless	11.7–12.8	orange

APPENDIX B

LOGARITHMS

A logarithm or log is an exponent. We will work with exponents given in terms of base 10.

$$N = b^x$$

$$\text{number} = \text{base}^{\text{exponent or logarithm}}$$

$$100 = 10^{2.0000}$$

For the log 2.000, the part of the numeral to the left of the decimal point is the characteristic. The part to the right of the decimal point is the mantissa.

$$\text{Log } 100 = 2.000$$
characteristic   mantissa

EXAMPLE: How to Find a Logarithm

Find the log of 657.

(a) Write the number in scientific notation, 6.57×10^2
(b) Look in the table under the column (N). Find the first two digits, (65)
(c) Look to the right and find the mantissa that is in the vertical column under the third digit of the number (7). It is .8176
(d) From the scientific notation, write the power of ten as the characteristic, to the left of the decimal point.
(e) Write the four digits from the table as the mantissa to the right of the characteristic and the decimal point, 2.8176

$$\text{thus } 657 = 10^{2.8176} \text{ or log } 657 = 2.8176$$

When given a logarithm and asked to find the number it represents, we use the table to find the first three digits for the number. We use the characteristic to determine where to locate the decimal point with respect to these digits.

EXAMPLE: How to Find the Antilogarithm

Given the logarithm 2.8176, find the number it represents (antilog).

(a) In the log table, find the mantissa that is closest to .8176
(b) We find by looking under the column (N) that this mantissa corresponds to 65. The third digit is found at the top of the column in which the mantissa appears, 7. (657)
(c) Write the three digits (657) in scientific notation, 6.57×10^x
(d) The characteristic will be the power of ten.

$$\text{antilog } 2.8176 = 6.57 \times 10^2 \text{ or } 657$$

EXAMPLE: Logarithms of Numbers Less Than 1

Find the log 0.00657.

(a) Write the number in scientific notation, 6.57×10^{-3}
(b) Look in the table under the column N for the first two digits, 6.5, and to the right in the column under the third digit, 7, for the mantissa. Note that the mantissa is always a positive number, .8176
(c) From the scientific notation, we get the negative characteristic, -3.
(d) Add the negative characteristic and the positive mantissa $(-3.0000) + (+.8176) = -2.1824$. This value is more commonly represented as 7.8176-10. However, the negative logarithm -2.1824 is more useful in pH calculations.

EXAMPLE: Antilog of a Negative Logarithm

Find the antilog of -2.1824.

(a) We ask ourselves what number would we add to the next, lesser integer, $-3.$, to get the log -2.1824. It would be 0.8176.

$$\begin{array}{r} -3.0000 \\ \text{subtract} \quad -2.1824 \\ \hline 0.8176 \end{array}$$

We know that logarithm tables do not give mantissas for negative numbers. So, we have changed the -2.1824 into the sum of a negative characteristic and a positive mantissa. The characteristic is always the next negative number. The positive mantissa was determined by asking ourselves what positive number would we add to the negative characteristic to get -2.1824.

$$-2.1824 = -3. + 0.8176$$

(b) Antilog -2.1824 = antilog $-3. \times$ antilog 0.8176
We know the antilog of $-3.$ is 10^{-3}. From the table, we find that the antilog $0.8176 = 6.57$. Therefore the antilog of $-2.1824 = 6.57 \times 10^{-3}$.

Table B-1

					Logarithms of Numbers					
N	0	1	2	3	4	5	6	7	8	9
10	0000	0043	0086	0128	0170	0212	0253	0294	0334	0374
11	0414	0453	0492	0531	0569	0607	0645	0682	0719	0775
12	0792	0828	0864	0899	0934	0969	1004	1038	1072	1106
13	1139	1173	1206	1239	1271	1303	1335	1367	1399	1430
14	1461	1492	1523	1553	1584	1614	1644	1673	1703	1732
15	1761	1790	1818	1847	1875	1903	1931	1959	1987	2014
16	2041	2068	2095	2122	2148	2175	2201	2227	2253	2279
17	2304	2330	2355	2380	2405	2430	2455	2480	2504	2529
18	2553	2577	2601	2625	2648	2672	2695	2718	2742	2765
19	2788	2810	2833	2856	2878	2900	2923	2945	2967	2989
20	3010	3032	3054	3075	3096	3118	3139	3160	3181	3201
21	3222	3243	3263	3284	3304	3324	3345	3365	3385	3404
22	3424	3444	3464	3483	3502	3522	3541	3560	3579	3598
23	3617	3636	3655	3674	3692	3711	3729	3747	3766	3784
24	3802	3820	3838	3856	3874	3892	3909	3927	3945	3962
25	3979	3997	4014	4031	4048	4065	4082	4099	4116	4133
26	4150	4166	4183	4200	4216	4232	4249	4265	4281	4298
27	4314	4330	4346	4362	4378	4393	4409	4425	4440	4456
28	4472	4487	4502	4518	4533	4548	4564	4579	4594	4606
29	4624	4639	4654	4669	4683	4698	4713	4728	4742	4757
30	4771	4786	4800	4814	4829	4843	4857	4871	4886	4900
31	4914	4928	4942	4955	4969	4983	4997	5011	5024	5038
32	5051	5065	5079	5092	5105	5119	5132	5145	5159	5172
33	5185	5198	5211	5224	5237	5250	5263	5276	5289	5302
34	5315	5328	5340	5353	5366	5378	5391	5403	5416	5428
35	5441	5453	5465	5478	5490	5502	5514	5527	5539	5551
36	5563	5575	5587	5599	5611	5623	5635	5647	5658	5670
37	5682	5694	5705	5717	5729	5740	5752	5763	5775	5786
38	5798	5809	5821	5832	5843	5855	5866	5877	5888	5899
39	5911	5922	5933	5944	5955	5966	5977	5988	5999	6010
40	6021	6031	6042	6053	6064	6075	6085	6096	6107	6117
41	6128	6138	6149	6160	6170	6180	6191	6201	6212	6222
42	6232	6243	6253	6263	6274	6284	6294	6304	6314	6325
43	6335	6345	6355	6365	6375	6385	6395	6405	6415	6425
44	6435	6444	6454	6464	6474	6484	6493	6503	6513	6522
45	6532	6542	6551	6561	6571	6580	6590	6599	6609	6618
46	6628	6637	6646	6656	6665	6675	6684	6693	6702	6712
47	6721	6730	6739	6749	6758	6767	6776	6785	6794	6803
48	6812	6821	6830	6839	6848	6857	6866	6875	6884	6893
49	6902	6911	6920	6928	6937	6946	6955	6964	6972	6981
50	6990	6998	7007	7016	7024	7033	7042	7050	7059	7067
51	7076	7084	7093	7101	7110	7118	7126	7135	7143	7152
52	7160	7168	7177	7185	7193	7202	7210	7218	7226	7235
53	7243	7251	7259	7267	7275	7284	7292	7300	7308	7316
54	7324	7332	7340	7348	7356	7364	7372	7380	7388	7396

N	0	1	2	3	4	5	6	7	8	9
55	7404	7412	7419	7427	7435	7443	7451	7459	7466	7474
56	7482	7490	7497	7505	7513	7520	7528	7536	7543	7551
57	7559	7566	7574	7582	7589	7597	7604	7612	7619	7627
58	7634	7642	7649	7657	7664	7672	7679	7686	7694	7701
59	7709	7716	7723	7731	7738	7745	7752	7760	7767	7774
60	7782	7789	7796	7803	7810	7818	7825	7832	7839	7846
61	7853	7860	7868	7875	7882	7889	7896	7903	7910	7917
62	7924	7931	7938	7945	7952	7959	7966	7973	7980	7987
63	7993	8000	8007	8014	8021	8028	8035	8041	8048	8055
64	8062	8069	8075	8082	8089	8096	8102	8109	8116	8122
65	8129	8136	8142	8149	8156	8162	8169	8176	8182	8189
66	8195	8202	8209	8215	8222	8228	8235	8241	8248	8254
67	8261	8267	8274	8280	8287	8293	8299	8306	8312	8319
68	8325	8331	8338	8344	8351	8357	8363	8370	8376	8382
69	8388	8395	8401	8407	8414	8420	8426	8432	8439	8445
70	8451	8457	8463	8470	8476	8482	8488	8494	8500	8506
71	8513	8519	8525	8531	8537	8543	8549	8555	8561	8567
72	8573	8579	8585	8591	8597	8603	8609	8615	8621	8627
73	8633	8639	8645	8651	8657	8663	8669	8675	8681	8686
74	8692	8698	8704	8710	8716	8722	8727	8733	8739	8745
75	8751	8756	8762	8768	8774	8779	8785	8791	8797	8802
76	8808	8814	8820	8825	8831	8837	8842	8848	8854	8859
77	8865	8871	8876	8882	8887	8893	8899	8904	8910	8915
78	8921	8927	8932	8938	8943	8949	8954	8960	8965	8971
79	8976	8982	8987	8993	8998	9004	9009	9015	9020	9025
80	9031	9036	9042	9047	9053	9058	9063	9069	9074	9079
81	9085	9090	9096	9101	9106	9112	9117	9122	9128	9133
82	9138	9143	9149	9154	9159	9165	9170	9175	9180	9186
83	9191	9196	9201	9206	9212	9217	9222	9227	9232	9238
84	9243	9248	9253	9258	9263	9269	9274	9279	9284	9289
85	9294	9299	9304	9309	9315	9320	9325	9330	9335	9340
86	9345	9350	9355	9360	9365	9370	9375	9380	9385	9390
87	9395	9400	9405	9410	9415	9420	9425	9430	9435	9440
88	9445	9450	9455	9460	9465	9469	9474	9479	9484	9489
89	9494	9499	9504	9509	9513	9518	9523	9528	9533	9538
90	9542	9547	9552	9557	9562	9566	9571	9576	9581	9586
91	9590	9595	9600	9605	9609	9614	9619	9624	9628	9633
92	9638	9643	9647	9652	9657	9661	9666	9671	9675	9690
93	9685	9689	9694	9699	9703	9708	9713	9717	9722	9727
94	9731	9736	9741	9745	9750	9754	9759	9763	9768	9773
95	9777	9782	9786	9791	9795	9800	9805	9809	9814	9818
96	9823	9827	9832	9836	9841	9845	9850	9854	9859	9863
97	9868	9872	9877	9881	9886	9890	9894	9899	9903	9908
98	9912	9917	9921	9926	9930	9934	9939	9943	9948	9952
99	9956	9961	9965	9969	9974	9978	9983	9987	9991	9996

APPENDIX C

CALCULATOR OPERATION

There are two basic types of hand-held calculators: algebraic (e.g., Texas Instruments, Casio, Sharp) and reverse Polish notation (e.g., Hewlett-Packard). There are also two types of operations to be done on a calculator, monadic and dyadic.

Monadic operations involve only one number. Examples would be taking the log, the square root, or the reciprocal of a number. In both types of calculators, monadic operations are performed in the same way. Press the keys representing the value of the number and then press the operation key. For example, to get 47^2, press ④ ⑦ and (x²). (Answer: 2209) The answer appears in the read-out window. For some monadic operations you may have to press "Inverse" or "2nd function" key before the operation key. A typical example would be in finding an antilog. To find the antilog of -6.77, press the following keys: ⑥ (.) ⑦ ⑦ (±) or (CHS) then (INV) or (2nd F) and (LOG). (Answer: 1.69×10^{-7})

Dyadic operations involve two numbers. Addition, subtraction, multiplication, and division are typical dyadic operations. We will consider dyadic operations on the two types of calculators separately. On an algebraic calculator, the keys for one number are pressed, then the key for the operation, then the keys for the second number, and, finally, the equal key.

Consider these examples:

Problem	Keys	Answer
3 + 4	③ ⊕ ④ ⊜	12
7 − 6	⑦ ⊖ ⑥ ⊜	1
2 × 11	② ⊗ ① ① ⊜	22
18 ÷ 5	① ⑧ ⊘ ⑤ ⊜	3.6

Another frequently used dyadic operation is y^x.

4^3 ④ (yˣ) ③ ⊜   64

Consider the problem

30.6	101	298
	103	273

This problem can be represented as

$$(30.6 \times 101) \left(\frac{1}{103}\right) (298) \left(\frac{1}{273}\right)$$

The key strokes to solve the problem are

③ ⓪ (.) ⑥ ⊗ ① ⓪ ① ⊜
⊘ ① ⓪ ③ ⊜
⊗ ② ⑨ ⑧ ⊜
⊘ ② ⑦ ③ ⊜   (Answer: 32.8)

For problems involving more than two numbers, it is faster not to get intermediate answers as the chain of operations is carried out. Do *not* record an intermediate answer after each $=$ and then re-enter as a new factor.

Using a reverse Polish notation (RPN) calculator, the procedures are somewhat different. Keys are pressed for one number and then the "ENTER" key is pressed. The keys for the second number are pressed and then the key for the operation.

Problem	Keys	Answer
9 + 1	(9) (ENTER) (1) (+)	10
2 − 10	(2) (ENTER) (1) (0) (−)	−8
3 × 12	(3) (ENTER) (1) (2) (×)	36
13 ÷ 4	(1) (3) (ENTER) (4) (÷)	3.25

For the chain calculation

$$\frac{62.8 \mid 103 \mid 299}{106 \mid 276}$$

the key strokes would be

(6) (2) (.) (8) (ENTER) (1) (0) (3) (×)
(1) (0) (6) (÷) (2) (9) (9) (×)
(2) (7) (6) (÷)   (Answer: 66.1)

Note that the RPN calculator required 3 less strokes for this problem than the algebraic calculator. For some algebraic calculators the $=$ key does not need to be pressed between computations. In simple calculations, such as the one used here, the number of key strokes would be the same as for an RPN calculator. For more complex calculations, RPN calculators will require fewer key strokes than algebraic calculators.

APPENDIX D

CHEMISTRY RELATED CAREERS

Most professional careers require some background in chemistry. Many careers depend heavily on the study of chemistry. Some of the fields in which chemistry plays a prominent part are listed below. If you are considering a chemistry-related career, you should realize that there are many possibilities apart from laboratory work. For instance, within the field of chemistry, there are opportunities in sales, management, patent law, and technical writing. To pursue a professional career you will probably need at least a bachelor's degree in your field. Some careers will require graduate study to obtain a master's or doctor's degree. However, there are many opportunities for technologists and technicians. Technologists may have an associate's degree, while technicians may have an associate's degree or high school diploma. Both technologists and technicians work with the other professionals in the field carrying out routine procedures, gathering data, and furnishing additional insight to a project or program.

Pure Sciences

Astronomer	studies the structure, motion, and evolution of the universe.
Biologist	studies the basic principles of plant and animal life.
Chemist	performs quantitative and qualitative tests to determine the structure and properties of materials.
Geologist	studies the composition, structure, and history of the earth.
Meteorologist	studies the physics and chemistry of the atmosphere, and forecasts weather.
Oceanographer	studies the physics, chemistry, geology, and biology of the oceans.
Physicist	researches the interaction of matter and energy.

Chemists

Analytical chemist	develops and improves the procedures for analyzing the structure and properties of substances.
Biochemist	studies the chemical effects of foods, drugs, and hormones on body processes and living systems.
Inorganic chemist	researches those substances which are relatively free of carbon such as ores, metals, and glass.
Organic chemist	researches those substances in which carbon is a major constituent; may specialize in agriculture, food, textiles or a number of other fields.
Physical chemist	determines the physical properties of substances and other relationships involving energy and matter.

Applied Sciences

Agricultural Fields

Agronomist	develops new methods of raising field crops to insure more efficient production and better quality.
Forester	studies the growth, conservation, and harvesting of trees.

Horticulturist	researches the breeding, production, and processing of fruits, vegetables, and decorative plants.
Wood scientist	develops and improves methods of treating wood and wood by-products.

Engineering Fields

Biomedical engineer	may design artificial organs or develop more efficient hospital laboratory systems.
Ceramic engineer	processes non-metallic materials such as glass, tile, and porcelain into useful products.
Chemical engineer	designs, builds, and operates chemical production plants.
Environmental engineer	designs and maintains industrial structures with respect to the environment.
Metallurgical engineer	processes metallic materials into useful products.
Nuclear engineer	researches the development and control of nuclear energy.
Petroleum engineer	develops more efficient drilling and processing methods for oil and natural gas.

Technical Fields

Drafter, Surveyor	determines the measurements and specifications required for the development of a new product or structure.
Machinist	determines the tools, materials, and specifications required for the production of precision products.
Media technician	operates the light and sound equipment used in the production of films, radio and television broadcasts.
Photoengraver, Photographer	photographs and develops negatives for the design and production of publications.

Health Sciences

Dentist	examines and treats oral disease and abnormalities.
Dietician, Food Service	plans and prepares for the nutritional needs of individuals and groups.
Medical technologist	performs quantitative and qualitative tests to provide information for the treatment of disease.
Occupational and Physical Therapist	designs therapy programs to help patients overcome physical or emotional handicaps.
Pharmacologist, Pharmacist	researches the function, behavior, and preparation of drugs.
Veterinarian	diagnoses and treats diseases in animals.

This appendix contains just a small sample of chemistry-related careers. Additional information can be obtained from the American Chemical Society, the National Science Teachers Association, and the Manufacturing Chemists Association. *The Occupational Outlook Handbook, The Dictionary of Occupational Titles,* and college catalogues can provide more complete descriptions of many careers as well as the potential needs in each area.

There are many other occupations that require some knowledge of chemistry besides the occupations described. Some examples of specific occupational classifications follow. For further information, use the *Dictionary of Occupational Titles* (DOT) number as a reference guide.

DOT No.   Professional, Technical and Managerial Occupations

DOT No.	Occupation	DOT No.	Occupation
003.167-022	electrolysis and corrosion control engineer	022.161-014	colorist
		022.161-018	perfumer
005.061-030	sanitary engineer	022.261-014	malt specifications control assistant
006.061-014	ceramic engineer		
006.261-010	scientific glass blower	022.281-010	assayer
008.061-101	absorption and adsorption engineer	029.081-010	environmental analyst
		029.081-014	materials scientist
008.151-010	chemical sales engineer	029.261-014	pollution-control technician
008.167-010	technical director, chemical plant	029.281-010	criminalist (police chemist)
		029.381-010	cloth tester
010.061-014	mining engineer	040.061-014	animal nutritionist
010.061-018	petroleum engineer	040.061-022	dairy technologist
011.061.010	foundry metallurgist	040.061-030	forester
001.261-010	metallurgical technician	070.061-010	pathologist
011.281-014	spectroscopist	070.101-010	anesthesiologist
012.167-034	industrial health engineer	073.101-010	veterinarian
012.281-010	smoke tester	074.161-010	pharmacist
013.061-010	agricultural engineer	075.264-010	nurse practitioner
015.362-022	radioisotope production operator	077.061-010	research dietitian
		078.261-010	chemistry technologist
017.281-034	technical illustrator	091.227-010	chemistry teacher
019.061-014	materials engineer	131.267-026	technical writer
022.061-014	food chemist		
022.137-010	laboratory supervisor		

Representatives of Other Occupations Using Chemistry

DOT No.	Occupation	DOT No.	Occupation
262.357-010	sales representative, chemicals and drugs	558.382-050	polymerization kettle operator
		559.130-010	chemical processing supervisor
332.271-010	cosmetologist	582.587-010	chemical strength tester
364.361-010	dyer	709.687-022	chemical inspector
408.381-010	pest control worker	712.281-010	dental ceramicist
500.380-010	plater	737.684-018	fireworks maker
503.362-010	pickler	954.382-014	water treatment plant operator
550.485-010	chemical mixer	955.382-014	waste treatment operator
550.685-030	chemical preparer	971.261-010	etcher
558.362-010	catalytic converter operator		

GLOSSARY

absolute zero: The temperature at which all molecular motion should cease.

accuracy: The relationship between the graduations on a measuring device and the actual standard for the quantity being measured.

acid: A substance which produces hydrogen ions in water solution (Arrhenius). A proton donor (Brönsted). An electron-pair acceptor (Lewis).

acidic anhydride: An oxide formed by removal of water from an acid.

actinide: An element whose highest energy electron is in the 5f sublevel.

actinide series: Fourteen elements beginning with actinium in which the diagonal rule predicts the highest energy electrons to be in the 5f sublevel.

activated complex: The species formed when the reactants in a chemical reaction have collided with sufficient energy to meet the activation energy requirement.

activated molecules: Molecules which have sufficient energy to form the activated complex.

activation energy: The energy required to start a chemical reaction.

activity (ion): The effective concentration of a species.

addition polymerization: The formation of a polymer from monomers by an addition reaction.

addition reaction: The adding on of a substance to the double bond of an alkene or the triple bond of an alkyne.

adiabatic: A process taking place without interchange of energy with its surroundings.

adiabatic system: System in which there is no interchange of energy with the surroundings.

adsorption: The process of one substance being attracted and held to the surface of another.

alcohol: A class of organic compounds characterized by the presence of the hydroxyl group, —OH.

aldehyde: A class of organic compounds characterized by the presence of the carbonyl group ($>C=O$) on the end carbon of the chain (RCHO).

aliphatic: A subdivision of hydrocarbons characterized by open chains and nonaromatic rings.

alkali metal: An element from Group IA(1) of the periodic table.

alkaline earth metal: An element from Group IIA(2) of the periodic table.

alkane: An aliphatic compound having only single carbon-carbon bonds.

alkene: An aliphatic compound having a double carbon-carbon bond.

alkyne: An aliphatic compound having a triple carbon-carbon bond.

allotropes: Different forms of the same element.

alloy: A mixture of two or more metals.

alpha particle: Helium nucleus.

amide: Organic compound containing the —CO—NH— group.

amine: An organic compound derived from ammonia by replacement of one or more hydrogen atoms by organic radicals.

amino acid: An organic compound characterized by the presence of an amino group and a carboxylic acid group on the same carbon atom.

amorphous: A solid-appearing material without crystalline structure.

ampere: The unit of electric current equal to one coulomb per second.

amphoteric: A substance which can act as either an acid or a base.

amplitude: The displacement of a wave from the average position.

anhydride: A compound without water of hydration.

anion: A negative ion.

anode: The positive electrode (general). The electrode at which oxidation occurs (electrochemical).

antibonding orbital: In molecular orbital theory, an orbital of the molecule which represents a higher energy than the atomic orbitals from which it was formed.

antiparticles: Particles identical in all respects except charge and magnetic moment which are opposites.

aromatic: A group of organic ring compounds having $(4n + 2)$ pi electrons.

asymmetric: The property of not having symmetry.

assymetric carbon atom: A carbon atom bonded to four different groups.

atom: The smallest particle of an element which possesses the properties of that element.

atomic mass: The average mass of the atoms of an element.

atomic mass unit: One-twelfth the mass of the carbon-12 atom.

atomic number: The number of protons in the nucleus of an atom.

atomic radius: The radius of an atom without regard to surrounding atoms.

atomic theory: The body of knowledge concerning the existence of atoms and their characteristic structure.

Avogadro's number: The number of objects in a mole equal to 6.02×10^{23}.

Avogadro's principle: The statement that equal volumes of gases at the same temperature and pressure contain the same number of molecules.

balance: A device used to measure mass.

band: A group of extremely closely spaced energy levels occupied by free electrons in a metal crystal.

barometer: A manometer used to measure the atmospheric pressure.

baryon: A subatomic particle classified as a large hadron.

base: A substance which produces hydroxide ions in water solution (Arrhenius). A proton acceptor (Brønsted). An electron-pair donor (Lewis).

basic anhydride: An oxide formed by removal of water from a base.

beta particle: An electron ($-$) or positron ($+$).

bidentate: A ligand which attaches to the central ion in two locations.

binary: A compound containing two elements.

binary acid: Acid containing only hydrogen and one other element.

binary compound: Compound composed of only two elements.

binding energy: The energy required to split the nucleus into separate nucleons.

body-centered cubic: Unit cell which is a cubic cell with the addition of a particle in the center of the cube.

Bohr atom: The planetary atom.

boiling point: The temperature at which the vapor pressure of the liquid phase of a substance is equal to atmospheric pressure.

bond: The force holding atoms together in a compound.

bond angle: The angle between two bond axes extending from the same atom.

bond axis: The imaginary line connecting the nuclei of two bonded atoms.

bond character: The relative ionic or covalent character of a bond.

bond length: Internuclear distance between bonded atoms.

bond order: The number of electron pairs bonding two atoms as described by molecular orbital theory.

bond strength: The energy required to break a bond.

bonding orbital: In molecular orbital theory, a molecular orbital which is at a lower energy level than the atomic orbitals from which it was formed.

Boyle's law: The volume of a specific amount of gas varies inversely as the pressure if the temperature remains constant.

Brownian motion: The random motion of colloidal particles due to their bombardment by the molecules of the continuous phase.

buffer: A solution which can receive moderate amounts of either acid or base without significant change in its pH.

calorimeter: A device for measuring the change in enthalpy during a chemical change.

capillary rise: The tendency of a liquid to rise in a tube of small diameter due to the surface tension of the liquid.

carbide ion: A carbon atom which has gained four electrons.

carboxylic acid: A class of organic compounds characterized by the presence of the carboxyl group

$$\left(-C \overset{\displaystyle O}{\underset{\displaystyle OH}{\Big\langle}} \right)$$

catalysis: The speeding up of chemical reactions by the presence of a substance which remains unchanged after the reaction.

catalyst: A substance which speeds a chemical reaction without being permanently changed itself.

catenation: The joining in chains of carbon atoms.

cathode: The negative electrode (general). The electrode at which reduction occurs (electrochemical).

cathode rays: The beam of electrons in a gas discharge tube.

cation: A positive ion.

cell potential: The voltage obtained from a voltaic cell.

cellulose: A biological polymer of glucose.

Celsius scale: The temperature scale based on the freezing point, $0°$, and boiling point, $100°$, of water.

chain reaction: A reaction in which the product from each step acts as a reactant for the next step.

chalcogen: An element from Group VIA (16) of the periodic table.

Charles' law: The volume of a specific amount of gas varies directly as the absolute temperature if the pressure remains constant.

chemical change: A change in which one or more new substances with new properties are formed.

chemical formula: Shorthand representation of a substance.

chemical properties: The properties characteristic of a substance when it is involved in a chemical change.

chemical reaction: A chemical change.

chemical symbol: Shorthand representation of an element.

chemistry: The study and investigation of the structure and properties of matter.

chromatography: The separation of a mixture using a technique based upon differential adsorption.

closest-packing: A crystal structure particle arrangement in which the empty space between particles is minimized.

coefficient: A number placed before a formula in a balanced chemical equation to indicate the relative amount of the substance represented by the formula.

colligative properties: Properties of solutions which depend only on the number of particles present, without regard to type.

colloid: A dispersion of particles from 1 to 100 nm in at least one dimension, in a continuous medium.

colloid chemistry: Chemistry of substances with at least one dimension in the range 1–100 nm; chemistry of surfaces.

column chromatography: A chromatographic technique utilizing a column packed with adsorbent.

common ion effect: An equilibrium phenomenon in which an ion common to two or more substances in a solution shifts an equilibrium away from itself.

complex ion: A central positive ion surrounded by bonded ligands.

compound: Two or more elements combined by chemical bonds.

concentrated solution: A solution in which there is a high ratio between solute and solvent.

concentration: The ratio between the amount of solute and the amount of solvent or solution in which the solute is dissolved.

condensation polymer: A polymer formed by a reaction in which a small molecule, usually water, is produced as the monomers form the polymer.

condensed state: The solid or liquid form of a substance.

conduction band: The group of extremely closely spaced energy levels in a metal which free electrons can occupy.

conductivity: A property involving the transport of electrons or heat from one point to another.

conjugate acid: The particle obtained after a base has gained a proton.

conjugate base: The particle remaining after an acid has donated a proton.

conjugated system: A group of four or more adjacent atoms with unhybridized p orbital overlap forming an extended π bonding system in a molecule.

contact catalyst: A catalyst which functions by adsorbing one of the reactants on its surface.

containment vessel: Reinforced concrete and steel structure designed to contain any leakage from a nuclear reactor.

continuous phase: The dispersing medium in a colloid.

control rods: Neutron absorbing materials used to control the rate of reaction in a nuclear reactor.

coordinate covalent bond: A covalent bond in which both electrons of the shared pair were donated by the same atom.

coordination number: The number of ligands surrounding the central ion.

corrosion: The gradual electrochemical destruction of a metal by substances in their environment.

coulomb: A quantity of electricity equal to 1/96 500 of a mole of electrons.

covalent bond: A bond characterized by a shared pair of electrons.

covalent radius: The radius of an atom along the bond axis.

critical pressure: The pressure needed to liquefy a gas at a critical temperature.

critical temperature: The temperature above which no amount of pressure will liquefy a gas.

crystal: A solid in which the particles are arranged in a regular, repeating pattern.

crystallization: Separating a solid from a solution by evaporating the solvent, or by cooling.

crystalloid: Substance which can penetrate a semipermeable membrane.

cubic: Unit cell with one particle centered on each vertex of a cube.

cubic closest-packing: Face-centered cubic.

cyclic compounds: Compounds in which the atoms are bonded in a ring.

cycloalkanes: Aliphatic hydrocarbons with the carbon atoms bonded in rings.

Dalton's law: In a mixture of gases the total pressure of the mixture is the sum of the partial pressures of each component gas.

De Broglie's hypothesis: Particles may have the properties of waves.

decomposition: A reaction in which a compound breaks into two or more simpler substances.

defect: An imperfection in a crystal lattice.

degenerate: Having the same energy.

dehydrating agent: A substance which can absorb water from other substances.

deliquescence: The absorption of water from the air by a solid to form a liquid solution.

deliquescent: Property of a solid to absorb sufficient water from the air to form a liquid solution.

delocalized electrons: Electrons which are free to move through the π cloud of p orbitals as in benzene.

density: Mass per unit volume.

desiccant: A dehydrating agent.

diagonal rule: A system for predicting the order of filling energy sublevels with electrons.

diffusion: The spreading of gas molecules throughout a given volume.

dilute solution: A solution with a low ratio of solute to solvent.

dipeptide: Two amino acids joined by an amide link.

dipole: A polar molecule.

dipole-dipole force: An attraction between dipoles.

dipole-induced dipole force: An attraction between a dipole and a nonpolar molecule which has been induced to become a dipole.

dipole moment: The strength of a dipole expressed as charge multiplied by distance.

dislocation: A crystal defect.

dispersed phase: Colloidal particles distributed throughout the continuous phase.

dispersion force: The force between two particles due to the attraction of instantaneous separations of their charge centers.

dissociation: The separation of ions in solution.

distillation: The process of evaporating a liquid and condensing its vapor.

doping: Deliberate introduction of impurities into a crystal.

dot diagram: A pictorial representation of the location of outer level electrons in an atom, ion, or molecule.

double bond: A covalent bond in which two atoms share two pairs of electrons.

double displacement: A reaction in which the positive part of one compound combines with the negative part of another compound, and vice versa.

ductility: The property of a substance which enables it to be drawn into a fine wire.

dynamic equilibrium: An equilibrium in which two or more changes are taking place simultaneously, but at the same rate.

edge dislocation: A crystal defect in which a layer of atoms extends into the lattice between layers of unit cells.

efflorescence: The release of water molecules to the air by a hydrate.

effusion: The passage of gas molecules through small openings.

elastic: Collisions in which kinetic energy is conserved.

electrochemistry: The study of the integration of electric current and atoms, ions, and molecules.

electrode potential: The reduction potential in volts of a half-reaction compared to the potential of the hydrogen half-reaction at 0.0000 V.

electrolysis: A chemical change produced by an electric current.

electrolyte: A substance whose aqueous solution conducts electricity.

electrolytic cell: A cell in which an electrolysis reaction is taking place.

electrolytic conduction: Migration of ions in solution.

electromagnetic energy: Radiant energy; energy transferred by electromagnetic waves.

electron: A subatomic particle representing the unit of negative charge.

electron affinity: The attraction of an atom for an electron expressed as the energy needed to remove an electron from a negative ion to restore neutrality.

electron cloud: The space effectively occupied by an electron in an atom.

electron configuration: A description of the energy level and sublevel for all the electrons in an atom.

electron dot diagram: Representation of an atom in which the symbol stands for the nucleus and all inner level electrons while dots stand for outer level electrons.

electronegativity: The relative attraction of an atom for a shared pair of electrons.

electronic conduction: Flow of electrons in a metal.

electrophoresis: The migration of colloidal particles under the influence of an electric field.

element: A substance whose atoms have the same number of protons in the nucleus.

elimination reaction: An organic reaction in which a small molecule is removed from a larger molecule leaving a double bond in the larger molecule.

empirical formula: The formula giving the simplest ratio between the atoms of the elements present in a compound.

endergonic: Process having an increase in free energy.

endothermic: A change which takes place with the absorption of heat.

endpoint: The point in a titration where equivalent numbers of moles of reactants are present.

energy: A property of matter which may be converted to work under the proper circumstances.

energy level: A specific amount of energy or group of energies which may be possessed by electrons in an atom.

energy sublevel: A specific energy which may be possessed by an electron in an atom.

enthalpy: That part of the energy of a substance which is due to the motion of its particles.

enthalpy of formation: The amount of energy produced or consumed when a mole of a compound is formed from its elements.

enthalpy of fusion: The energy required to change 1 gram of a substance from solid to liquid.

enthalpy of reaction: The energy produced or consumed when a chemical change takes place in the amounts indicated by the equation involved.

enthalpy of solution: The amount of energy produced or consumed when a substance is dissolved in water.

enthalpy of vaporization: The energy needed to change 1 gram of a substance from liquid to gas.

entropy: The degree of disorder in a system.

enzyme: A biological catalyst.

equation: A shorthand representation of a chemical change using symbols and formulas.

equilibrium: A state in which no net change takes place in a system.

equilibrium constant: A mathematical expression giving the ratio of the product of the concentrations of the substances produced to the product of the concentration of the reactants for a reaction.

ester: A class of organic compounds characterized by the presence of the $-C$ $\overset{\displaystyle O}{\underset{\displaystyle O-}{}}$ group between two hydrocarbon radicals.

esterification reaction: The production of an ester by the reaction of an alcohol with an acid.

ether: A class of organic compounds characterized by the presence of $-O-$ between two hydrocarbon radicals.

evaporation: The process by which a molecule leaves the surface of a liquid or solid and enters the gaseous state.

excess reactant: Reactant remaining when all of some other reactant has been consumed.

exclusion principle: No two electrons in an atom may have the same set of quantum numbers.

exergonic: Process having a decrease in free energy.

exothermic: A change which produces heat.

extensive property: A property dependent on the amount of matter present.

face-centered cubic: Unit cell which is a cubic cell with the addition of a particle in the center of each face.

factor-label method: A problem-solving method in which units (labels) are treated as factors.

family: A vertical column of the periodic table.

fat: A biological ester of glycerol and a fatty acid.

first ionization energy: Energy required to remove the most loosely held electron from an atom.

fission: The splitting of a nucleus into two approximately equal parts.

fluid: A material which flows (liquid or gas).

forbidden zone: The energy gap between the outer level band and the conduction band in crystals.

formula: A combination of atomic symbols and numbers indicating the elements and their proportions in a compound.

formula mass: The sum of the atomic masses of the atoms in a formula.

formula unit: The amount of a substance represented by its formula.

fractional crystallization: The separation of a mixture into its components through differences in solubility.

fractional distillation: The separation of a mixture into its components through differences in boiling points.

fractionation: Separating a whole into its parts.

free electrons: Electrons not bound to one atom or associated with one bond.

free energy: The chemical reaction potential of a substance or system.

freezing point: The temperature at which the vapor pressures of the solid and liquid are equal.

frequency: The number of complete wave cycles per unit of time.

functional isomers: Organic compounds with the same formula, but with the nonhydrocarbon part of the molecule bonded in different ways.

fusion: The combining of two or more small nuclei into one larger nucleus.

fusion reaction: Nuclear reaction in which small nuclei are combined to make a larger nucleus.

galvanizing: Coating iron with a protective layer of zinc.

galvanometer: An instrument used to detect an electric current.

gamma ray: A quanta of energy of very high frequency and very small wavelength.

gas: A physical state characterized by random motion of the particles which are far apart compared to their diameters.

gas chromatography: A chromatographic method in which a carrier gas (inert) distributes the vapor being analyzed in a packed column.

geometric isomers: Compounds with the same formula but different arrangement of substituents around a double bond.

gluon: A theoretical massless particle exchanged by quarks.

glycogen: A biological polymer of glucose.

Graham's law: The ratio of the relative rates of diffusion of gases is equal to the square root of the inverse ratio of their molecular masses.

ground state: All electrons in the lowest possible energy sublevels.

group: The members of a vertical column in the periodic table.

hadrons: A class of heavy subatomic particles.

half-cell: The part of an electrochemical cell in which either the oxidation or reduction reaction is taking place.

half-life: The length of time necessary for one-half an amount of a radioactive nuclide to distintegrate.

half-reaction: The oxidation or reduction reaction in a chemical reaction.

halogen: An element from Group VIIA (17) of the periodic table.

heat: Energy transfer from a hotter object to a cooler object.

Henry's law: The mass of a gas which will dissolve in a specific amount of a liquid varies directly with the pressure.

hertz: Unit of frequency equal to one cycle per second.

Hess's law: The enthalpy change for an overall reaction is equal to the sum of the enthalpy changes for each step in the change.

heterogeneous: Composed of different parts not uniformly dispersed.

heterogeneous catalyst: Catalyst in a phase different from that of the reactants.

heterogeneous reaction: Reaction in which reactants are in different phases.

homogeneous: Uniform throughout.

homogeneous catalyst: Catalyst in the same phase as the reactants.

homologous series: A series of organic compounds which differ from each other by a specific structural unit.

hybrid orbitals: Equivalent orbitals formed from orbitals of different energies.

hybridization: The merging of two or more unlike orbitals to form an equal number of identical orbitals.

hydration: The adhering of water molecules to dissolved ions.

hydrate: A compound (crystalline) in which the ions are hydrated.

hydride ion: A hydrogen atom which has gained an electron.

hydrocarbons: Compounds composed solely of carbon and hydrogen.

hydrogen bonding: An exceptionally strong type of dipole-dipole interaction due to the strong positive center in molecules in which hydrogen is bonded to a highly electronegative element (N,O,F).

hydrogen ion: A hydrogen atom which has lost its electron.

hydrolysis: Reaction with water to form a weak acid or base.

hydronium ion: H_3O^+.

hygroscopic: Absorbing water from the air.

ideal gas: A model in which gas molecules are treated as though they were geometric points exerting no force on each other.

ideal gas equation: $PV = nRT$.

ideal solution: A solution obeying Raoult's law.

immiscible: Two liquids which will not dissolve in each other.

index of refraction: Measurement of bending of light waves as they pass from one medium to another at an acute angle.

indicator: A weak organic acid whose conjugate base differs in color. Used to indicate the pH of a solution.

inductive effect: The influence of one functional group on another.

inertia: The tendency of an object to resist any change in its velocity.

infrared spectroscopy: A spectroscopic method useful in investigating the bonding in molecules.

inhibitor: A substance which prevents a reaction from taking place by forming a complex to tie up one of the reactants.

inorganic compound: Compound not containing carbon or one of a very few carbon compounds.

insulator: A substance having a large forbidden zone and which does not conduct.

intensive properties: Those properties of a substance which are independent of the amount of matter present.

interface: The area of contact between two phases.

intermolecular force: Force holding molecules to each other.

internal energy: That energy of a system which is altered by the absorption or release of heat and by doing work or having work done on it.

internuclear distance: Distance between the nuclei of two atoms.

intramolecular force: Force holding atoms together in molecules.

ion: A particle with an electric charge.

ionic bond: The electrostatic attraction between ions of opposite charge.

ionic radius: The radius of an ion.

ionization constant: The equilibrium constant for the ionization of a weak electrolyte.

ionization energy: The energy required to remove an electron from an atom.

ion product constant for water: The product of the hydronium and hydroxide ion concentrations, equal to 10^{-14} at room temperature.

irreversible thermodynamic change: A change in volume or pressure in which some energy is lost to an entropy change.

isobaric: At constant pressure.

isomerism: Property of having more than one structure for the same formula.

isomers: Two compounds having the same formula but different structures.

isomorphism: Two or more compounds having the same crystalline structure.

isothermal: At constant temperature.

isotopes: Two or more atoms of an element having the same number of protons but different numbers of neutrons.

joule: The SI units of energy equal to 1 $kg \cdot m^2/s^2$.

Joule-Thomson effect: The cooling effect achieved by allowing a highly compressed gas to expand rapidly after passing through a small opening.

kelvin scale: The SI unit of temperature equal to 1/273.16 the thermodynamic temperature of the triple point of water.

ketone: A class of organic compounds characterized by the presence of the carbonyl group ($>C=O$) between hydrocarbon radicals.

kilogram: The SI unit of mass.

kinetic energy: Energy due to motion.

kinetic theory: The group of ideas treating the interaction of matter and the energy due to particle motion.

lanthanide: An element whose highest energy electron is the 4f sublevel.

lanthanide series: Fourteen elements beginning with lanthanum in which the diagonal rule predicts the highest energy electrons to be in the 4f sublevel.

law of conservation of energy: Energy is conserved in all changes except nuclear reactions.

law of conservation of mass: Mass is conserved in all changes except nuclear reactions.

law of conservation of mass and energy: The total amount of mass and energy in the universe is constant.

law of conservation of matter: In non-nuclear changes, energy cannot be created or destroyed.

law of definite proportions: The elements composing a compound are always present in the same proportions by mass.

law of multiple proportions: The masses of one element which combine with a specific mass of another element in a series of compounds. These masses are in the ratio of small whole numbers.

law of octaves: The same properties appear every eighth element when the elements are listed in order of their atomic masses.

Le Chatelier's principle: If a stress is placed on a system at equilibrium, the system will shift so as to offset the stress.

length: Distance between two points.

leptons: A class of light subatomic particles.

ligand: A negative ion or polar molecule attached to a central ion in a complex.

limiting reactant: The reactant which is used completely in a reaction.

linear accelerator: A device for imparting a high energy to atomic or subatomic particles traveling in a straight line.

lipid: A biological molecule which is soluble in nonpolar solvents.

liquefaction: Changing a gas to a liquid.

liquid: A state characterized by particles in such close proximity that their random motion appears to be a vibration about a moving point.

liquid crystal: A substance which has order in the arrangement of its particles in only one or two dimensions.

liter: A unit of volume equal to 1 dm^3.

London forces: *See dispersion forces.*

macromolecule: A crystal which consists of a single molecule with all component atoms bonded in a network fashion.

magnetohydrodynamics: The study of plasmas.

malleability: The property of a substance which allows it to be hammered into thin sheets.

manometer: A device for measuring gas pressure.

mass: The measure of the amount of matter.

mass defect: The difference between the mass of a nucleus and the sum of the masses of the particles from which it was formed.

mass-mass problem: Problem in which the given quantity is the mass of one substance and the required quantity is the mass of another substance.

mass number: The number of nucleons in an atom.

mass spectrometry: The separation of atoms or radicals on the basis of the varied effects of electric and magnetic fields on different masses.

matter: Anything which exhibits the property of inertia.

mean free path: The average distance a molecule travels between collisions.

melting point: The temperature at which the vapor pressures of the solid and liquid phases of a substance are equal.

meson: A subatomic particle classed as a hadron.

metal: An element which tends to lose electrons in chemical reactions.

metallic bond: A force holding metal atoms together and characterized by free electrons.

metallic conduction: Electronic conduction.

metalloid: An element which has properties characteristic of a metal and a nonmetal.

metastable: State of stability which will not change unless acted upon by an outside force, but not the most stable state of a system.

meter: *See Appendix A-1.*

miscible: Two liquids which are mutually soluble in all proportions.

mixture: A combination of two or more substances.

mobile phase: The fluid containing the mixture to be analyzed in chromatography.

moderator: A substance used to slow neutrons in a nuclear reactor.

molal boiling point constant: A value characteristic of a solvent indicating the rise in the boiling point of 1 kilogram of the solvent if it contains 1 mole of particles.

molal freezing point constant: A value characteristic of a solvent indicating the drop in the freezing point of 1 kilogram of the solvent if it contains 1 mole of particles.

molality: A unit of concentration equal to the number of moles of solute in 1 kilogram of solvent.

molar heat capacity: The amount of energy required to change the temperature of 1 mole of a substance by 1 Celsius degree.

molar volume: The volume occupied by 1 mole of gas at standard temperature and pressure and equal to $22.4 \ dm^3$.

molarity: A unit of concentration equal to the number of moles of solute in 1 dm^3 of solution.

mole: Avogadro's number of objects = 6.02×10^{23}.

mole fraction: A unit of concentration equal to the number of moles of solute in a mole of solution.

molecular formula: A formula indicating the actual number of each kind of atom contained in a molecule.

molecular mass: The mass of a molecule found by adding the atomic masses of the atoms comprising the molecule.

molecular orbital: Orbital belonging to two or more atoms in a molecule.

molecular orbital theory: A model of molecular structure based upon the formation of molecular orbitals from corresponding atomic orbitals.

molecule: A neutral particle in which two or more atoms are held together by covalent bonds.

momentum: The product of mass and velocity.

nematic substance: A liquid crystal with order in one dimension only.

net ionic equation: A chemical equation indicating only those substances taking part in the reaction and omitting spectator ions.

network crystal: Crystal in which each atom is covalently bonded to all its nearest neighbors, so that the entire crystal is one molecule.

neutral: Neither acidic nor basic (electrolytes). Neither positive nor negative (electricity).

neutralization: The combining of an acid and a base until the amounts present correspond to the proportions shown by the equation for their reaction.

neutralization reaction: Double displacement reaction between an acid and a base to produce a salt and water.

neutrino: Neutral particle associated with leptons.

neutron: A neutral particle found in the nucleus of an atom and having a mass of approximately one atomic mass unit.

Newtonian mechanics: Laws of mechanics used in the macroscopic world.

nitrile: A class of organic compounds characterized by the presence of the —CN group.

nitro: A class of organic compounds characterized by the presence of the $—NO_2$ group.

noble gas: Any element from Group VIIIA (18) of the periodic table.

noble gas configuration: Eight electrons in the outer level, except for helium with two electrons in the outer level.

nonmetal: An element which tends to gain electrons in chemical reactions.

nonvolatile: A substance which has a high boiling point, strong intermolecular forces, and a low vapor pressure at room temperature.

normal boiling point: Temperature at which the vapor pressure of the liquid is equal to 101.325 kPa.

nuclear force: Force holding nucleons together in the nucleus of the atom.

nuclear magnetic resonance spectroscopy: A spectroscopic method based on the energy required to reorient a nucleus with a magnetic field with respect to an external magnetic field.

nuclear reactor: Device engineered to contain a controlled nuclear reaction.

nucleic acid: Organic compound containing nitrogenous bases, sugars, and phosphate groups; compounds which transfer genetic information (DNA) or control cell metabolism (RNA).

nucleon: A particle found in the nucleus of an atom. A proton or neutron.

nucleotide: Combination of a nitrogenous base, a sugar, and a phosphate group.

nuclide: An element containing a specific number of protons and a specific number of neutrons.

octahedral: A molecular or ionic shape in which six particles are clustered about a central particle at the vertices of a regular octahedron.

octane rating: A system of rating gasoline based upon the proportions of heptane and 2,2,4-trimethylpentane in the mixture.

octet rule: The tendency of atoms to react in such a way that they acquire eight electrons in their outer level. He with 2 electrons also conforms.

ohm: The unit of electric resistance. One volt will force 1 ampere through 1 ohm.

olefin: Another name for an alkene.

optical isomers: Mirror image molecules which rotate a plane of polarized light in opposite directions.

optically active: A property of substances characterized by their ability to rotate a plane of polarized light.

optimum conditions: Conditions maximizing the shift of an equilibrium in a certain direction.

orbital: The space which can be occupied by 0, 1, or 2 electrons with the same energy level, energy sublevel, and spacial orientation.

organic: Related to carbon compounds.

organic chemistry: The study of the compounds of carbon.

organic compound: Compound containing carbon with a very few exceptions.

organic oxidation reaction: The combustion of an organic compound to produce carbon dioxide and water.

osmotic pressure: The pressure developed across a semipermeable membrane by differential diffusion through the membrane.

oxidation: The loss of electrons.

oxidation number: The charge on an atom if the electrons in a compound are assigned in an arbitrary manner according to established rules.

oxidation-reduction reaction: Chemical reaction in which electrons are transferred from one species to another.

oxidizing agent: A substance which tends to gain electrons.

packing: An adsorbent used in columns for column and gas chromatography.

pair repulsion: A model for molecular shape based upon the assumption that electron clouds will repel each other and be as far away from each other as possible.

paper chromatography: A chromatographic method based upon the movement of a solvent through paper by capillary action.

parent chain: The longest continuous chain of carbon atoms used for naming organic molecules.

partially miscible: Two liquids which are soluble in each other to a limited extent.

pascal: The SI unit of pressure equal to 1 N/m^2.

Pauli exclusion principle: No two electrons in an atom can have the same set of quantum numbers.

peptide bond: An amide link.

percent of ionization: The amount ionized divided by the original amount, all multiplied by 100.

percentage composition: The proportion of an element present in a compound found by dividing the mass of the element present by the mass of the whole compound and multiplying by 100.

period: Horizontal row of the periodic table.

periodic law: The properties of the elements are a periodic function of their atomic numbers.

periodic table: A pictorial arrangement of the elements based upon their electron configurations.

petroleum: A natural mixture of organic compounds found in liquid form.

pH: The negative logarithm of the hydronium ion concentration.

pH meter: Electronic device for the determination of pH values in solutions.

pH scale: Logarithmic scale expressing degree of acidity or basicity.

phase: A physically distinct section of matter set off from the surrounding matter by physical boundaries.

phase diagram: A graphical representation of the vapor pressures of the solid and liquid forms of a substance.

photoelectric effect: The ejection of electrons from a surface which is exposed to light.

photon: Quantum.

physical change: A change in which the substance or substances present after the change are the same chemically as those present before.

physical properties: The characteristics of a material as it is subjected to physical changes.

pi bond: A bond formed by the sideways overlap of *p* orbitals.

planetary model: Model of the atom in which the nucleus is likened to the sun and the electrons to planets in orbit around the sun.

plasma: A high temperature physical state characterized by the separation of atoms into electrons and nuclei.

pOH: The negative logarithm of the hydroxide ion concentration.

point mass: Ideal gas particle with mass but no dimensions.

polar covalent bond: Shared pair of electrons which are more strongly attracted to one atom than to the other.

polarimeter: A device for measuring the rotation of plane polarized light.

polarity: Unsymmetrical charge distribution.

polarized light: Light in which the field variations are all in the same plane.

polyatomic ion: A group of atoms bonded to each other covalently but possessing an overall charge.

polymer: A very large molecule made from simple units repeated many times.

polymerization: The reaction producing a polymer from monomers.

polymorphism: The property of existing in more than one crystalline form.

polyprotic acid: An acid with more than one ionizable hydrogen atom.

positional isomers: Two molecules having the same formula but differing in the position to which a substituent is attached to the parent chain.

positron: A subatomic particle identical to an electron except possessing a positive charge. The antiparticle of the electron.

potential difference: The difference in potential energy of electrons located at different points.

potential energy: Energy of an object due to its position.

precipitate: A solid produced from a reaction occurring in aqueous solution.

precision: The relative uncertainty in a measurement.

pressure: Force per unit area.

principal quantum number: The value of "n" in the Schrodinger equation.

probability: Mathematical expression of "chance" or "odds."

product: A substance produced as the result of a chemical change.

protein: A biological polymer of amino acids.

proton: A positive particle found in nuclei and having a mass of approximately 1 atomic mass unit.

quadridentate: A ligand which attaches to a central ion in four locations.

qualitative: Concerning the kinds of matter present.

quantitative: Concerning the amounts of materials present.

quantum: A discrete "packet" of energy (plural: quanta).

quantum number: A number describing a property of an electron in an atom.

quantum theory: The concept that energy is transferred in discrete units.

quark: A theoretical particle believed to be a constituent of a hadron.

rad: Radiation absorbed dose; 10 microjoules/gram of living tissue.

radiant energy: Energy in transit between two objects.

radical: A fragment of a molecule. It is neutral yet at least one atom is lacking its octet of electrons.

radioactivity: The spontaneous disintegration of nuclei.

Raoult's law: The vapor pressure of a solution of a nonvolatile solute is the product of the vapor pressure of the pure solvent and the mole fraction of the solvent.

rate determining step: Slowest step in a reaction mechanism.

reactant: A substance which undegoes a chemical change.

reaction mechanism: The actual step-by-step description of the interaction of atoms, ions, and molecules in a reaction.

reaction rate: The rate of disappearance of a reactant or the rate of appearance of a product.

real gas: Gas in nature with particles of finite volume and van der Waals forces between particles.

redox reaction: A reaction involving the transfer of electrons.

reducing agent: A substance which tends to donate electrons.

reduction: The gain of electrons.

refraction: The bending of a beam of light as it passes from one medium to another.

refractometer: A device for measuring the refraction of light.

relative error: Absolute error divided by the measurement.

rem: Roentgen equivalent man; damage done to human tissue by one rad of x rays.

resonance: The phenomenon in which several equally valid dot diagrams can be drawn for a substance. The actual substance is an average of all the possible arrangements.

reversible chemical change: A change in which the products can be changed back into the original reactants, under the proper conditions.

reversible thermodynamic change: An ideal change in which the difference in pressure causing the change is infinitesimal.

salt: A compound formed from a positive ion and a negative ion other than hydrogen.

salt bridge: An ionic solution used to complete an electrical circuit in a voltaic cell.

saponification reaction: The reaction of an ester with a strong base to form a soap and glycerol.

saturated: State of a gaseous phase which contains a vapor in equilibrium with its liquid state.

saturated hydrocarbon: A hydrocarbon in which all carbon-carbon bonds are single bonds.

saturated solution: A solution in which undissolved solute is in equilibrium with dissolved solute.

science: The systematic investigation of nature.

scientific notation: Expression of numbers in the form $M \times 10^n$ where $1.00 \leq M < 10$ and n is an integer.

screw dislocation: A crystal defect in which the unit cells are improperly aligned.

second: *See Appendix A-1.*

semiconductor: A device in which the electrons are involved in bonding, but which may be made to conduct under the proper conditions.

semipermeable membrane: Barrier allowing the passage of small ions and molecules but blocking passage of large particles.

shared pair: Two electrons in an orbital shared by two bonded atoms.

shielding effect: The decrease in the force between outer electrons and the nucleus due to the presence of other electrons between them.

SI units: The internationally accepted set of standards for measurement.

side chain: A hydrocarbon radical attached to the parent chain of an organic molecule.

sigma bond: A bond formed by the end-to-end overlap of atomic orbitals.

significant digits: Digits in the value of a measurement indicating the quantity to an accuracy justified by the measuring device and technique used to make the measurement.

silicates: Compounds containing silicon and oxygen.

single displacement: A reaction in which one element replaces another in a compound.

smectic substance: A liquid crystal having order in two dimensions.

solid: A physical state characterized by particles in such close proximity that their random motion appears to be vibration about a fixed point.

solubility: The quantity of a solute which will dissolve in a specific quantity of solvent at a specific temperature.

solubility product constant: The equilibrium constant for the dissolving of a slightly soluble salt.

solute: The substance present in lesser quantity in a solution.

solution: A homogeneous mixture composed of solute and solvent.

solution equilibrium: Solute is dissolving and crystallizing at the same rate.

solvation: The attaching of solvent particles to solute particles.

solvent: The substance present in the greater amount in a solution.

space lattice: The theoretical arrangement pattern of the unit cells in a crystal.

specific heat: The amount of energy required to raise the temperature of 1 gram of a substance by 1 Celsius degree.

specific rate constant: A constant used to determine the rate of a reaction from the concentration of the reactants.

spectator ion: An ion present in a solution but not taking part in the reaction.

spectrum: Unique set of wavelengths absorbed or radiated by a substance.

spin: A property of subatomic particles which corresponds most closely with our concept of rotation about an axis.

spontaneous: Occurring without outside influence.

square planar: An arrangement of particles in a complex ion in which the ligands are arranged in a plane with the central ion and form a square with the central ion in the center.

stability: The tendency (or lack of it) for a compound to disintegrate or decompose.

standard solution: A solution whose concentration is known with precision.

standard state: A reference set of conditions for thermodynamic measurements equal to 25°C, 101.325 kPa, and $1M$.

standard temperature and pressure: A set of reference conditions for dealing with gases equal to 0°C and 101.325 kPa.

starch: A biological polymer of glucose.

state: A physical property of a phase designating it as solid, liquid, gas, or plasma.

state function: Thermodynamic quantity which is determined solely by the conditions, not the method of arriving at those conditions.

stationary phase: The adsorbent in chromatography.

stereoisomers: Compounds which are mirror images of each other and contain an assymetric carbon.

stoichiometry: The solution of problems involving specific quantities of a substance or substances.

STP: Standard temperature and pressure (273 K and 101.325 kPa).

strong (acid or base): A completely ionized electrolyte.

structural isomers: Two compounds with the same formula but differing arrangements of the parent carbon chain.

subatomic particle: Particle smaller than an atom.

sublevel: Division of an energy level.

sublimation: The change directly from solid to gas.

substance: Matter of constant composition.

substituent: A hydrocarbon branch or nonhydrocarbon group attached to the parent chain or ring in organic compounds.

substitution reaction: A reaction in organic compounds in which a hydrogen atom or substituent is replaced by another substituent.

supercooled liquid: A liquid cooled below its normal freezing point without having changed state to the solid form. A metastable state.

supersaturated solution: A solution containing more solute than a saturated solution at the same temperature. A metastable state.

surface tension: The apparent "skin" effect on the surface of a liquid due to unbalanced forces on the surface particles.

suspension: A dispersion of particles larger than 100 nm throughout a continuous medium.

symmetry: The property of being balanced with respect to the relative positions of atoms or substituents on opposite sides of an imaginary center or axis.

synchrotron: A device for accelerating subatomic particles in a circular path.

synthesis: Formation of a compound from two or more simpler substances.

synthetic element: An element not occurring in nature produced by means of nuclear reactions.

technology: The application of scientific principles for practical use.

temperature: A measure of the average kinetic energy of molecules.

ternary: A compound formed from three elements.

ternary acid: Acid containing hydrogen and two other elements.

tetrahedral: An arrangement in which four particles surround a central particle at angles of 109.5° to each other.

thermodynamic stability: Stability of a substance due to a positive change in free energy for the decomposition of the substance.

thermodynamics: The study of the interaction of energy and matter.

thermometer: A device for measuring temperature.

thin layer chromatography: A method of chromatography utilizing an adsorbent spread over a flat surface in a thin layer.

time: The interval between two occurrences.

titration: A laboratory technique for measuring the relative strength of solutions.

tracer: A nuclide used to follow a reaction or process.

transistor: An electronic device whose operation is based upon the behavior of certain crystals with deliberate built-in defects.

transition element: An element whose highest energy electron is in a *d* sublevel.

transmutation: The change of one element into another.

transuranium element: An element with $Z > 92$.

triad: Group of three elements.

tridentate: A ligand which attaches to the central ion in three locations.

tripeptide: Three amino acids joined by amide links.

triple bond: A covalent bond in which two atoms share three pairs of electrons.

triple point: The temperature and pressure at which all three phases of a substance are in equilibrium.

Tyndall effect: The scattering of light by colloids.

ultraviolet spectroscopy: A spectroscopic technique using light of wavelength slightly less than visible light and lending evidence to the electronic structure of atoms and molecules.

uncertainty principle: The impossibility of measuring exactly both the position and the momentum of an object at the same time.

unit cell: The simplest unit of repetition in a crystal lattice.

unsaturated compound: Compound containing one or more multiple bonds.

unsaturated hydrocarbon: Hydrocarbon containing one or more multiple bonds.

unsaturated molecule: An organic molecule containing at least one double or triple bond.

unsaturated solution: A solution containing less solute than a saturated solution at the same temperature.

unshared pair: Two electrons in an orbital belonging to a single atom.

van der Waals forces: Weak forces of attraction between molecules.

van der Waals radii: The radius of an atom in the direction of adjacent nonbonded atoms.

vapor: Gaseous state of a substance which is liquid or solid at room temperature and pressure.

vapor equilibrium: The state in which evaporation and condensation are taking place at the same rate.

vapor pressure: The pressure generated by a vapor in equilibrium with its liquid.

velocity: Speed expressed as a vector quantity.

viscosity: The resistance of a fluid to flow.

visible spectroscopy: A spectroscopic method useful in investigating the behavior of electrons in atoms.

vitamin: A group of lipids which are necessary for some enzymatic reactions to take place.

volatile: A substance with a low boiling point, weak intermolecular forces, and a high vapor pressure at room temperature.

volt: The unit of electric potential difference.

voltaic cell: An electrochemical cell in which a chemical reaction generates an electric current.

wave: A periodic disturbance in a medium.

wave equation: A mathematical expression treating the electron as a wave and providing the amplitude of the wave at specific points in space with reference to the nucleus as the origin.

wavelength: The distance between corresponding crests or troughs in a wave.

wave-particle duality of nature: The property of particles behaving as waves as well as particles and the property of waves behaving as particles as well as waves.

weak (acids and bases):   An electrolyte which is only slightly ionized.

weak forces: Attractive forces between molecules and consisting of dipole-dipole, dipole-induced dipole, and dispersion forces.

weight: The gravitational attraction of the Earth or a celestial body for an object.

work: A force moving through a distance.

INDEX

International Atomic Masses

Element	Symbol	Atomic number	Atomic mass	Element	Symbol	Atomic number	Atomic mass
Actinium	Ac	89	227.0278*	Neon	Ne	10	20.179
Aluminum	Al	13	26.98154	Neptunium	Np	93	237.0482
Americium	Am	95	243.0614*	Nickel	Ni	28	58.69
Antimony	Sb	51	121.75	Niobium	Nb	41	92.9064
Argon	Ar	18	39.948	Nitrogen	N	7	14.0067
Arsenic	As	33	74.9216	Nobelium	No	102	259.1009*
Astatine	At	85	209.9871*	Osmium	Os	76	190.2
Barium	Ba	56	137.33	Oxygen	O	8	15.9994
Berkelium	Bk	97	247.0703*	Palladium	Pd	46	106.42
Beryllium	Be	4	9.01218	Phosphorus	P	15	30.97376
Bismuth	Bi	83	208.9804	Platinum	Pt	78	195.08
Boron	B	5	10.811	Plutonium	Pu	94	244.0642*
Bromine	Br	35	79.904	Polonium	Po	84	208.9824*
Cadmium	Cd	48	112.41	Potassium	K	19	39.0983
Calcium	Ca	20	40.078	Praseodymium	Pr	59	140.9077
Californium	Cf	98	251.0796*	Promethium	Pm	61	144.9128*
Carbon	C	6	12.011	Protactinium	Pa	91	231.0359*
Cerium	Ce	58	140.12	Radium	Ra	88	226.0254
Cesium	Cs	55	132.9054	Radon	Rn	86	222.0176*
Chlorine	Cl	17	35.453	Rhenium	Re	75	186.207
Chromium	Cr	24	51.9961	Rhodium	Rh	45	102.9055
Cobalt	Co	27	58.9332	Rubidium	Rb	37	85.4678
Copper	Cu	29	63.546	Ruthenium	Ru	44	101.07
Curium	Cm	96	247.0703*	Samarium	Sm	62	150.36
Dysprosium	Dy	66	162.50	Scandium	Sc	21	44.95591
Einsteinium	Es	99	252.0828*	Selenium	Se	34	78.96
Erbium	Er	68	167.26	Silicon	Si	14	28.0855
Europium	Eu	63	151.96	Silver	Ag	47	107.8682
Fermium	Fm	100	257.0951*	Sodium	Na	11	22.98977
Fluorine	F	9	18.998403	Strontium	Sr	38	87.62
Francium	Fr	87	223.0197*	Sulfur	S	16	32.066
Gadolinium	Gd	64	157.25	Tantalum	Ta	73	180.9479
Gallium	Ga	31	69.723	Technetium	Tc	43	97.9072*
Germanium	Ge	32	72.59	Tellurium	Te	52	127.60
Gold	Au	79	196.9665	Terbium	Tb	65	158.9254
Hafnium	Hf	72	178.49	Thallium	Tl	81	204.383
Helium	He	2	4.002602	Thorium	Th	90	232.0381
Holmium	Ho	67	164.9304	Thulium	Tm	69	168.9342
Hydrogen	H	1	1.00794	Tin	Sn	50	118.710
Indium	In	49	114.82	Titanium	Ti	22	47.88
Iodine	I	53	126.9045	Tungsten	W	74	183.85
Iridium	Ir	77	192.22	Unnilennium†	Une	109	266*
Iron	Fe	26	55.847	Unnilhexium†	Unh	106	263*
Krypton	Kr	36	83.80	Unniloctium†	Uno	108	265*
Lanthanum	La	57	138.9055	Unnilpentium†	Unp	105	262*
Lawrencium	Lr	103	260.1054*	Unnilquadium†	Unq	104	261*
Lead	Pb	82	207.2	Unnilseptium†	Uns	107	262*
Lithium	Li	3	6.941	Uranium	U	92	238.0289
Lutetium	Lu	71	174.967	Vanadium	V	23	50.9415
Magnesium	Mg	12	24.305	Xenon	Xe	54	131.29
Manganese	Mn	25	54.9380	Ytterbium	Yb	70	173.04
Mendelevium	Md	101	258.0986*	Yttrium	Y	39	88.9059
Mercury	Hg	80	200.59	Zinc	Zn	30	65.39
Molybdenum	Mo	42	95.94	Zirconium	Zr	40	91.224
Neodymium	Nd	60	144.24				

*The mass of the isotope with the longest known half-life.

†Names for elements 104-109 have been approved for temporary use by the IUPAC. The USSR has proposed Kurchatovium (Ku) for element 104, and Bohrium (Bh) for element 105. The United States has proposed Rutherfordium (Rf) for element 104, and Hahnium (Ha) for element 105.